Horizons

Algebra 1
Teacher's Guide

Author:
Shelly Chittam, M.S.

Managing Editor:
Alan Christopherson, M.S.

Editors:
Laura Messner, B.A.
Rachelle Wiersma, M.A.

Graphic Design & Illustration:
Shelly Chittam, M.S.
Alan Christopherson, M.S.

Alpha Omega Publications • Rock Rapids, IA

804 N. 2nd Ave. E.
Rock Rapids, IA 51246-1759

Printed in the United States of America

ISBN 978-0-7403-2554-0

Horizons

Algebra 1

Teacher's Guide

Contents

Course Introduction

Purpose

This Algebra 1 course has a two-fold purpose. First, students have a thorough review of pre-algebra concepts that are vital for success in upper-level math courses. These concepts include order of operations, signed numbers, roots, exponents, and algebraic properties and notation. Emphasis is placed on practical application of the concepts.

The second purpose of the course is to increase the student's understanding and mastery of algebra, including some advanced algebraic concepts, in preparation for upper-level math courses. After completing this course of study, students should be well prepared for high school level courses in Algebra 2, Geometry, and Trigonometry.

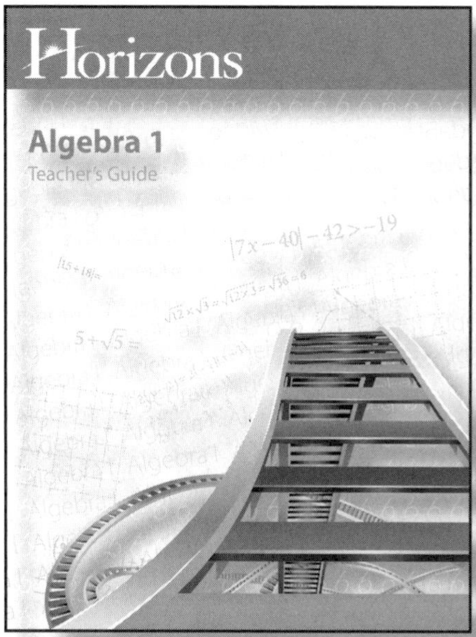

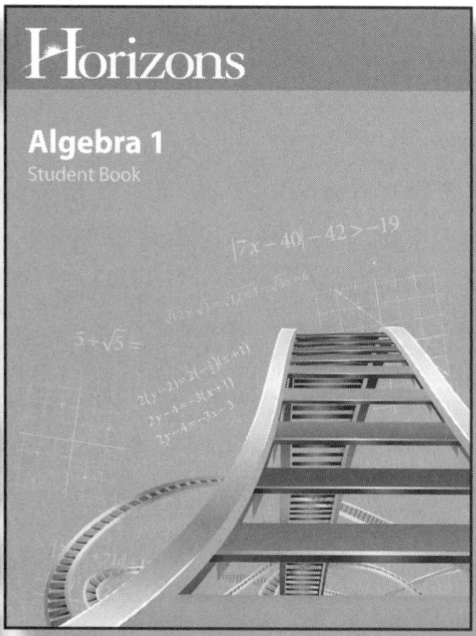

Materials

Materials available for this course include the Teacher's Guide, the Student Book, and the Tests and Resources Book. The students will have to supply notebook paper, as well as a scientific calculator, colored pencils, a ruler, and graph paper. Often the Student Book will not have sufficient space for working out all of the steps to the problems. Notebook paper should be used for these situations. Graph paper should have no more than five squares per inch, although quad-rule paper is recommended. The Tests and Resources Book was designed to be a consumable. It has perforated pages for easy tear out. It is recommended that the Student Book remain intact to serve as a resource when students wish to review previously covered concepts.

Layout

Each Lesson in the Student Text has a teaching box in the upper left side of the first page and a Classwork section in the upper right side of the first page. The teaching box is intended for use by both the teacher and the students as an aid to understanding the lesson. New concepts are presented here in detail so students who miss a lesson in class should be able to catch up any missed work with minimal outside help. The Classwork section is intended for the class to do together, with individual students explaining the problems for the class.

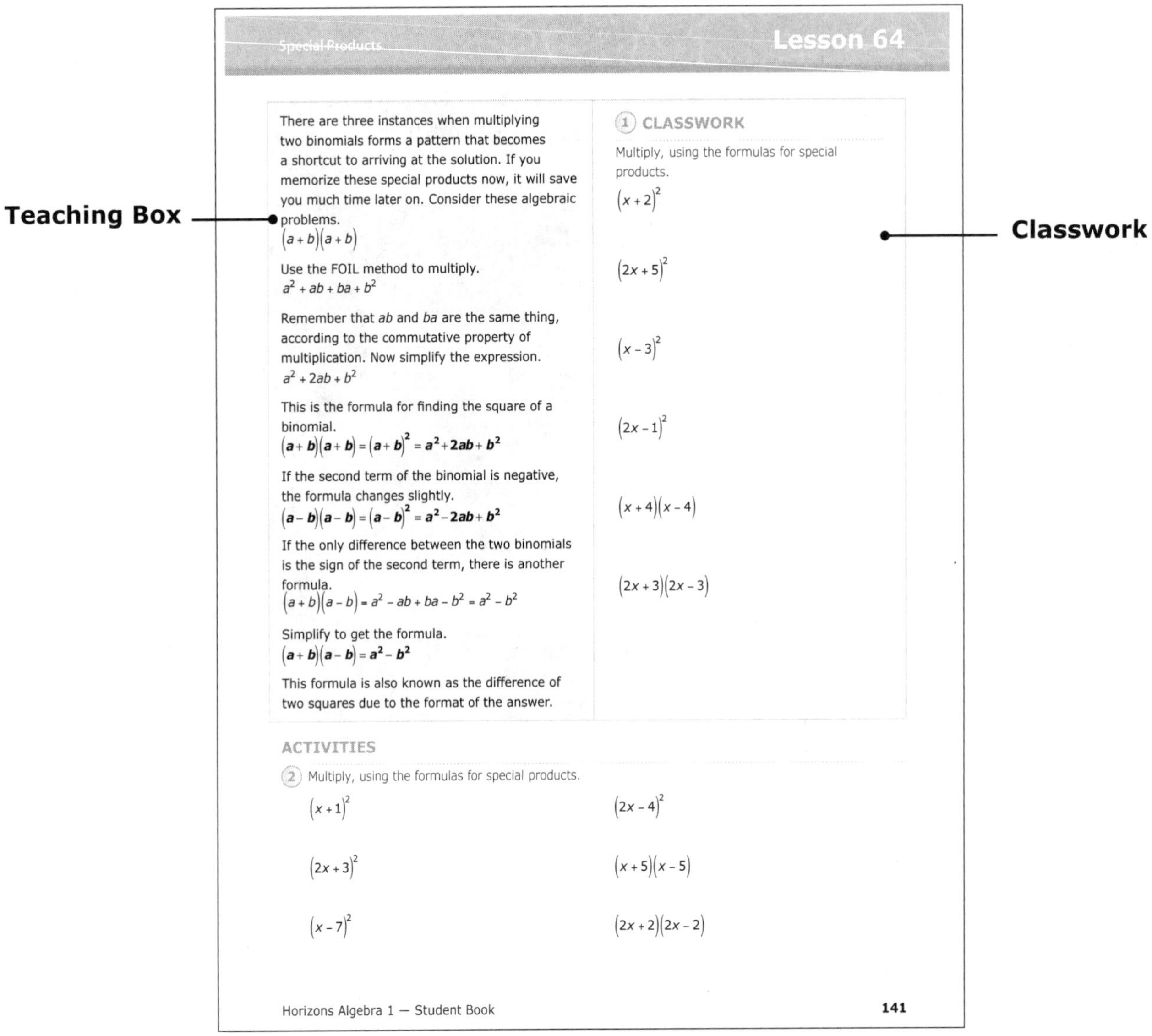

Special Products **Lesson 64**

There are three instances when multiplying two binomials forms a pattern that becomes a shortcut to arriving at the solution. If you memorize these special products now, it will save you much time later on. Consider these algebraic problems.

$(a+b)(a+b)$

Use the FOIL method to multiply.

$a^2 + ab + ba + b^2$

Remember that *ab* and *ba* are the same thing, according to the commutative property of multiplication. Now simplify the expression.

$a^2 + 2ab + b^2$

This is the formula for finding the square of a binomial.

$(\mathbf{a}+\mathbf{b})(\mathbf{a}+\mathbf{b}) = (\mathbf{a}+\mathbf{b})^2 = \mathbf{a}^2 + \mathbf{2ab} + \mathbf{b}^2$

If the second term of the binomial is negative, the formula changes slightly.

$(\mathbf{a}-\mathbf{b})(\mathbf{a}-\mathbf{b}) = (\mathbf{a}-\mathbf{b})^2 = \mathbf{a}^2 - \mathbf{2ab} + \mathbf{b}^2$

If the only difference between the two binomials is the sign of the second term, there is another formula.

$(a+b)(a-b) = a^2 - ab + ba - b^2 = a^2 - b^2$

Simplify to get the formula.

$(\mathbf{a}+\mathbf{b})(\mathbf{a}-\mathbf{b}) = \mathbf{a}^2 - \mathbf{b}^2$

This formula is also known as the difference of two squares due to the format of the answer.

(1) CLASSWORK

Multiply, using the formulas for special products.

$(x+2)^2$

$(2x+5)^2$

$(x-3)^2$

$(2x-1)^2$

$(x+4)(x-4)$

$(2x+3)(2x-3)$

ACTIVITIES

(2) Multiply, using the formulas for special products.

$(x+1)^2$ $\quad$ $(2x-4)^2$

$(2x+3)^2$ $\quad$ $(x+5)(x-5)$

$(x-7)^2$ $\quad$ $(2x+2)(2x-2)$

Horizons Algebra 1 — Student Book **141**

Layout continued:

Following the Classwork section is the Activities section. The first problem set in each Activities section is for reinforcement of the concept taught in that lesson. The remaining Activities sections are for review of previously taught concepts. The Activities sections are part of the assignment for each lesson.

(3) Multiply. Use the formulas for special products when possible.

$(x+9)^2$	$(2x+3)(x^2+7x-2)$
$(x+1)(x^2+x+3)$	$(4x-3)^2$
$(3x+2)(3x-2)$	$(x+11)(x-11)$
$(x-3)(x^2-4x-3)$	$(2x+9)(3x^2+2x-6)$
$(x+5)(x^2-7x-4)$	$(3x-1)(4x^2+2x-3)$
$(x-1)^2$	$(4x+5)^2$
$(x^2+5x+6)(x^2-2x-3)$	$(5x^2-2x-7)(3x^2+4x+8)$

Activities

(4) Solve.

A swimming pool is 3 feet deep on the shallow end. The floor of the pool is level for a distance of 10 feet from the entrance steps, then slopes downward at an even rate until it is 8 feet deep at a distance of 15 feet from the entrance steps. What is the slope of the pool in the first 10 feet?

What is the slope of the floor where the pool is getting deeper?

142 Horizons Algebra 1 — Student Book

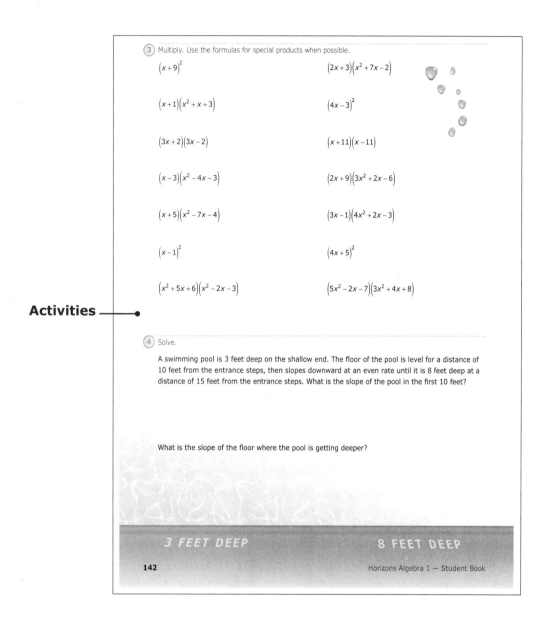

Lesson Plans

Each Lesson Plan lists all concepts taught and reviewed for that individual lesson. The Learning Objectives always relate to the new material taught in that lesson. Each Lesson Plan contains Teaching Tips to aid the teacher in presenting the new material. As often as possible, new material is introduced following a review of related, previously-taught material. The Lesson Plans give detailed helps for the teacher, including sample problems, illustrations, and visual aids. The solution keys for the student activities are also part of each lesson plan.

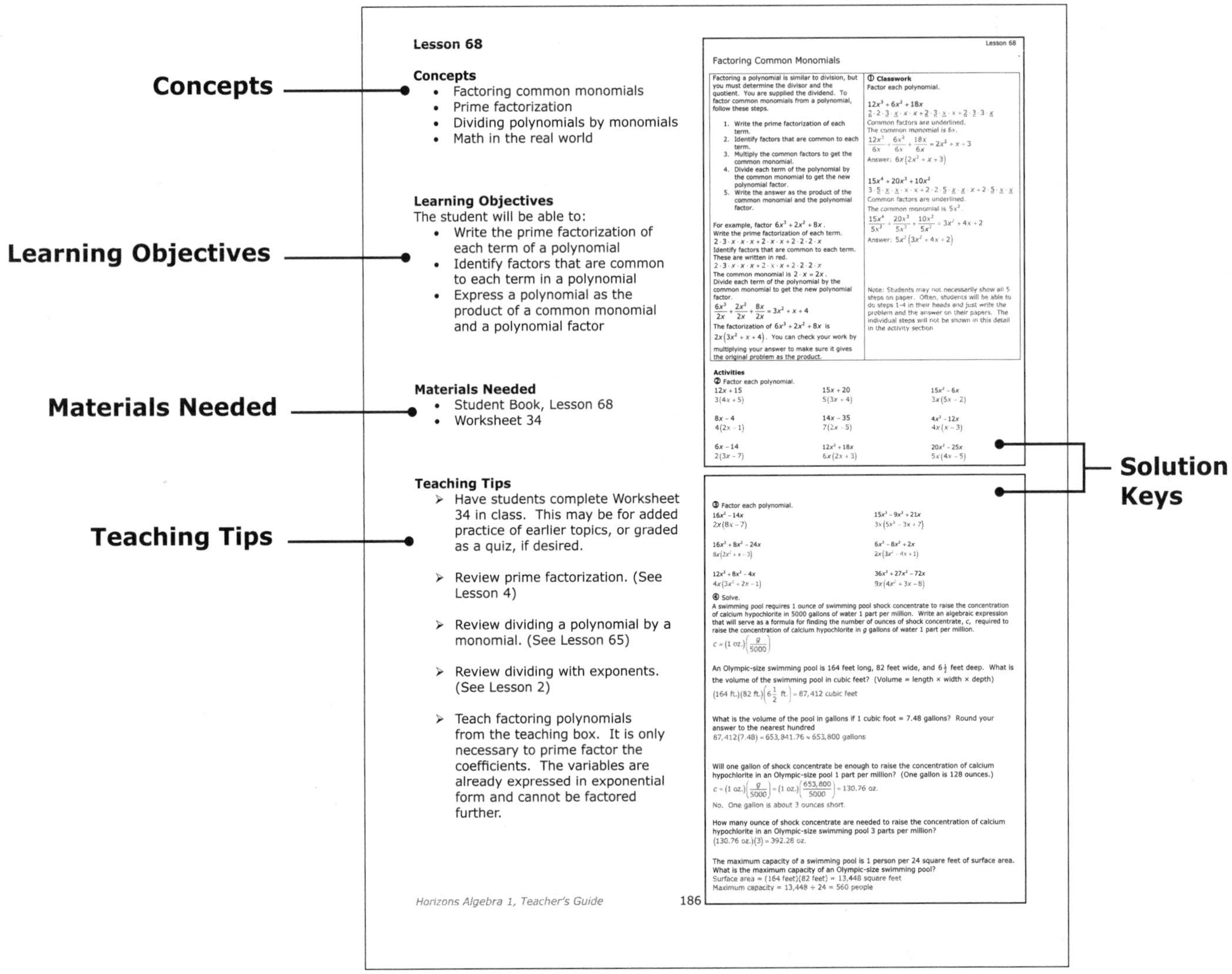

Lesson 68

Concepts
- Factoring common monomials
- Prime factorization
- Dividing polynomials by monomials
- Math in the real world

Learning Objectives
The student will be able to:
- Write the prime factorization of each term of a polynomial
- Identify factors that are common to each term in a polynomial
- Express a polynomial as the product of a common monomial and a polynomial factor

Materials Needed
- Student Book, Lesson 68
- Worksheet 34

Teaching Tips
- Have students complete Worksheet 34 in class. This may be for added practice of earlier topics, or graded as a quiz, if desired.
- Review prime factorization. (See Lesson 4)
- Review dividing a polynomial by a monomial. (See Lesson 65)
- Review dividing with exponents. (See Lesson 2)
- Teach factoring polynomials from the teaching box. It is only necessary to prime factor the coefficients. The variables are already expressed in exponential form and cannot be factored further.

Horizons Algebra 1, Teacher's Guide 186

Lesson 68

Factoring Common Monomials

Factoring a polynomial is similar to division, but you must determine the divisor and the quotient. You are supplied the dividend. To factor common monomials from a polynomial, follow these steps.

1. Write the prime factorization of each term.
2. Identify factors that are common to each term.
3. Multiply the common factors to get the common monomial.
4. Divide each term of the polynomial by the common monomial to get the new polynomial factor.
5. Write the answer as the product of the common monomial and the polynomial factor.

For example, factor $6x^3 + 2x^2 + 8x$.
Write the prime factorization of each term.
$2 \cdot 3 \cdot x \cdot x \cdot x + 2 \cdot x \cdot x + 2 \cdot 2 \cdot 2 \cdot x$
Identify factors that are common to each term. These are written in red.
$2 \cdot 3 \cdot x \cdot x \cdot x + 2 \cdot x \cdot x + 2 \cdot 2 \cdot 2 \cdot x$
The common monomial is $2 \cdot x = 2x$.
Divide each term of the polynomial by the common monomial to get the new polynomial factor.
$\frac{6x^3}{2x} + \frac{2x^2}{2x} + \frac{8x}{2x} = 3x^2 + x + 4$
The factorization of $6x^3 + 2x^2 + 8x$ is $2x(3x^2 + x + 4)$. You can check your work by multiplying your answer to make sure it gives the original problem as the product.

① **Classwork**
Factor each polynomial.

$12x^3 + 6x^2 + 18x$
$2 \cdot 2 \cdot 3 \cdot x \cdot x \cdot x + 2 \cdot 3 \cdot x \cdot x + 2 \cdot 3 \cdot 3 \cdot x$
Common factors are underlined.
The common monomial is $6x$.
$\frac{12x^3}{6x} + \frac{6x^2}{6x} + \frac{18x}{6x} = 2x^2 + x + 3$
Answer: $6x(2x^2 + x + 3)$

$15x^4 + 20x^3 + 10x^2$
$3 \cdot 5 \cdot x \cdot x \cdot x \cdot x + 2 \cdot 2 \cdot 5 \cdot x \cdot x \cdot x + 2 \cdot 5 \cdot x \cdot x$
Common factors are underlined.
The common monomial is $5x^2$.
$\frac{15x^4}{5x^2} + \frac{20x^3}{5x^2} + \frac{10x^2}{5x^2} = 3x^2 + 4x + 2$
Answer: $5x^2(3x^2 + 4x + 2)$

Note: Students may not necessarily show all 5 steps on paper. Often, students will be able to do steps 1-4 in their heads and just write the problem and the answer on their papers. The individual steps will not be shown in this detail in the activity section

Activities
② Factor each polynomial.

$12x + 15$ $3(4x + 5)$	$15x + 20$ $5(3x + 4)$	$15x^2 - 6x$ $3x(5x - 2)$
$8x - 4$ $4(2x - 1)$	$14x - 35$ $7(2x - 5)$	$4x^2 - 12x$ $4x(x - 3)$
$6x - 14$ $2(3x - 7)$	$12x^2 + 18x$ $6x(2x + 3)$	$20x^2 - 25x$ $5x(4x - 5)$

③ Factor each polynomial.

$16x^2 - 14x$ $2x(8x - 7)$	$15x^3 - 9x^2 + 21x$ $3x(5x^2 - 3x + 7)$
$16x^3 + 8x^2 - 24x$ $8x(2x^2 + x - 3)$	$6x^3 - 8x^2 + 2x$ $2x(3x^2 - 4x + 1)$
$12x^3 + 8x^2 - 4x$ $4x(3x^2 + 2x - 1)$	$36x^3 + 27x^2 - 72x$ $9x(4x^2 + 3x - 8)$

④ Solve.

A swimming pool requires 1 ounce of swimming pool shock concentrate to raise the concentration of calcium hypochlorite in 5000 gallons of water 1 part per million. Write an algebraic expression that will serve as a formula for finding the number of ounces of shock concentrate, c, required to raise the concentration of calcium hypochlorite in g gallons of water 1 part per million.
$c = (1 \text{ oz.})\left(\frac{g}{5000}\right)$

An Olympic-size swimming pool is 164 feet long, 82 feet wide, and $6\frac{1}{2}$ feet deep. What is the volume of the swimming pool in cubic feet? (Volume = length × width × depth)
$(164 \text{ ft.})(82 \text{ ft.})\left(6\frac{1}{2} \text{ ft.}\right) = 87{,}412$ cubic feet

What is the volume of the pool in gallons if 1 cubic foot = 7.48 gallons? Round your answer to the nearest hundred
$87{,}412(7.48) = 653{,}841.76 \approx 653{,}800$ gallons

Will one gallon of shock concentrate be enough to raise the concentration of calcium hypochlorite in an Olympic-size pool 1 part per million? (One gallon is 128 ounces.)
$c = (1 \text{ oz.})\left(\frac{g}{5000}\right) = (1 \text{ oz.})\left(\frac{653{,}800}{5000}\right) = 130.76$ oz.
No. One gallon is about 3 ounces short.

How many ounce of shock concentrate are needed to raise the concentration of calcium hypochlorite in an Olympic-size swimming pool 3 parts per million?
$(130.76 \text{ oz.})(3) = 392.28$ oz.

The maximum capacity of a swimming pool is 1 person per 24 square feet of surface area. What is the maximum capacity of an Olympic-size swimming pool?
Surface area = (164 feet)(82 feet) = 13,448 square feet
Maximum capacity = 13,448 ÷ 24 = 560 people

Lesson Plans continued:

Some Lesson Plans will include a Worksheet. These are found in the Tests and Resources Book. Some Worksheets are for additional practice of a new concept while others are for review or a quiz grade. The Lesson Plan will indicate which case applies for each Worksheet. Those intended for additional practice will appear in the Assignments section at the end of the Lesson Plan.

Worksheet
(In *Tests & Resources*)

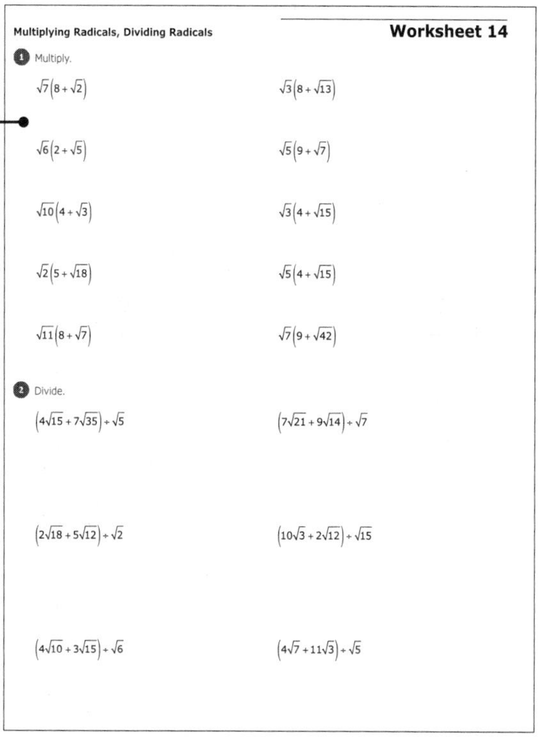

Multiplying Radicals, Dividing Radicals **Worksheet 14**

1 Multiply.

$\sqrt{7}(8+\sqrt{2})$ $\sqrt{3}(8+\sqrt{13})$

$\sqrt{6}(2+\sqrt{5})$ $\sqrt{5}(9+\sqrt{7})$

$\sqrt{10}(4+\sqrt{3})$ $\sqrt{3}(4+\sqrt{15})$

$\sqrt{2}(5+\sqrt{18})$ $\sqrt{5}(4+\sqrt{15})$

$\sqrt{11}(8+\sqrt{7})$ $\sqrt{7}(9+\sqrt{42})$

2 Divide.

$(4\sqrt{15}+7\sqrt{35})\div\sqrt{5}$ $(7\sqrt{21}+9\sqrt{14})\div\sqrt{7}$

$(2\sqrt{18}+5\sqrt{12})\div\sqrt{2}$ $(10\sqrt{3}+2\sqrt{12})\div\sqrt{15}$

$(4\sqrt{10}+3\sqrt{15})\div\sqrt{6}$ $(4\sqrt{7}+11\sqrt{3})\div\sqrt{5}$

Worksheet Solution
(In *Teacher's Guide*)

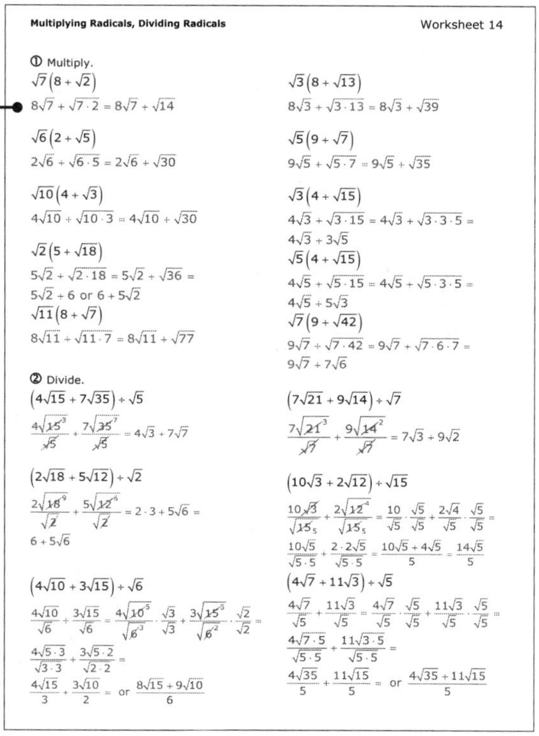

Multiplying Radicals, Dividing Radicals Worksheet 14

① Multiply.

$\sqrt{7}(8+\sqrt{2})$
$8\sqrt{7}+\sqrt{7\cdot 2}=8\sqrt{7}+\sqrt{14}$

$\sqrt{3}(8+\sqrt{13})$
$8\sqrt{3}+\sqrt{3\cdot 13}=8\sqrt{3}+\sqrt{39}$

$\sqrt{6}(2+\sqrt{5})$
$2\sqrt{6}+\sqrt{6\cdot 5}=2\sqrt{6}+\sqrt{30}$

$\sqrt{5}(9+\sqrt{7})$
$9\sqrt{5}+\sqrt{5\cdot 7}=9\sqrt{5}+\sqrt{35}$

$\sqrt{10}(4+\sqrt{3})$
$4\sqrt{10}+\sqrt{10\cdot 3}=4\sqrt{10}+\sqrt{30}$

$\sqrt{3}(4+\sqrt{15})$
$4\sqrt{3}+\sqrt{3\cdot 15}=4\sqrt{3}+\sqrt{3\cdot 3\cdot 5}=$
$4\sqrt{3}+3\sqrt{5}$

$\sqrt{2}(5+\sqrt{18})$
$5\sqrt{2}+\sqrt{2\cdot 18}=5\sqrt{2}+\sqrt{36}=$
$5\sqrt{2}+6$ or $6+5\sqrt{2}$

$\sqrt{5}(4+\sqrt{15})$
$4\sqrt{5}+\sqrt{5\cdot 15}=4\sqrt{5}+\sqrt{5\cdot 3\cdot 5}=$
$4\sqrt{5}+5\sqrt{3}$

$\sqrt{11}(8+\sqrt{7})$
$8\sqrt{11}+\sqrt{11\cdot 7}=8\sqrt{11}+\sqrt{77}$

$\sqrt{7}(9+\sqrt{42})$
$9\sqrt{7}+\sqrt{7\cdot 42}=9\sqrt{7}+\sqrt{7\cdot 6\cdot 7}=$
$9\sqrt{7}+7\sqrt{6}$

② Divide.

$(4\sqrt{15}+7\sqrt{35})\div\sqrt{5}$
$\frac{4\sqrt{15}^{3}}{\sqrt{5}}+\frac{7\sqrt{35}^{7}}{\sqrt{5}}=4\sqrt{3}+7\sqrt{7}$

$(7\sqrt{21}+9\sqrt{14})\div\sqrt{7}$
$\frac{7\sqrt{21}^{3}}{\sqrt{7}}+\frac{9\sqrt{14}^{2}}{\sqrt{7}}=7\sqrt{3}+9\sqrt{2}$

$(2\sqrt{18}+5\sqrt{12})\div\sqrt{2}$
$\frac{2\sqrt{18}^{9}}{\sqrt{2}}+\frac{5\sqrt{12}^{6}}{\sqrt{2}}=2\cdot 3+5\sqrt{6}=$
$6+5\sqrt{6}$

$(10\sqrt{3}+2\sqrt{12})\div\sqrt{15}$
$\frac{10\sqrt{3}}{\sqrt{15}_{5}}+\frac{2\sqrt{12}^{4}}{\sqrt{15}_{5}}=\frac{10}{\sqrt{5}}\cdot\frac{\sqrt{5}}{\sqrt{5}}+\frac{2\sqrt{4}}{\sqrt{5}}\cdot\frac{\sqrt{5}}{\sqrt{5}}=$
$\frac{10\sqrt{5}}{\sqrt{5\cdot 5}}+\frac{2\cdot 2\sqrt{5}}{\sqrt{5\cdot 5}}=\frac{10\sqrt{5}+4\sqrt{5}}{5}=\frac{14\sqrt{5}}{5}$

$(4\sqrt{10}+3\sqrt{15})\div\sqrt{6}$
$\frac{4\sqrt{10}}{\sqrt{6}}+\frac{3\sqrt{15}}{\sqrt{6}}=\frac{4\sqrt{10}^{5}}{\sqrt{6}^{3}}\cdot\frac{\sqrt{3}}{\sqrt{3}}+\frac{3\sqrt{15}^{5}}{\sqrt{6}^{2}}\cdot\frac{\sqrt{2}}{\sqrt{2}}=$
$\frac{4\sqrt{5\cdot 3}}{\sqrt{3\cdot 3}}+\frac{3\sqrt{5\cdot 2}}{\sqrt{2\cdot 2}}=$
$\frac{4\sqrt{15}}{3}+\frac{3\sqrt{10}}{2}=$ or $\frac{8\sqrt{15}+9\sqrt{10}}{6}$

$(4\sqrt{7}+11\sqrt{3})\div\sqrt{5}$
$\frac{4\sqrt{7}}{\sqrt{5}}+\frac{11\sqrt{3}}{\sqrt{5}}=\frac{4\sqrt{7}}{\sqrt{5}}\cdot\frac{\sqrt{5}}{\sqrt{5}}+\frac{11\sqrt{3}}{\sqrt{5}}\cdot\frac{\sqrt{5}}{\sqrt{5}}=$
$\frac{4\sqrt{7\cdot 5}}{\sqrt{5\cdot 5}}+\frac{11\sqrt{3\cdot 5}}{\sqrt{5\cdot 5}}=$
$\frac{4\sqrt{35}}{5}+\frac{11\sqrt{15}}{5}=$ or $\frac{4\sqrt{35}+11\sqrt{15}}{5}$

Learning Styles

Students learn in different ways. Some students can master a concept by listening to instructions or watching someone else do it while others are very "hand-on" and must physically do something to learn a new concept. This book addresses the various learning styles by using a lecture-demonstration method to teach new concepts and review old concepts, and manipulatives are used where appropriate to aid in the understanding of new concepts.

Algebra Tiles

Algebra tiles are located in the Tests and Resources Book. Students should cut these out the first time the Lesson Plan calls for them and store them in a zip-top bag for future use. These manipulatives will assist both visual and kinesthetic learners in mastering algebraic concepts. Details on their use are given in the Lesson Plans where needed.

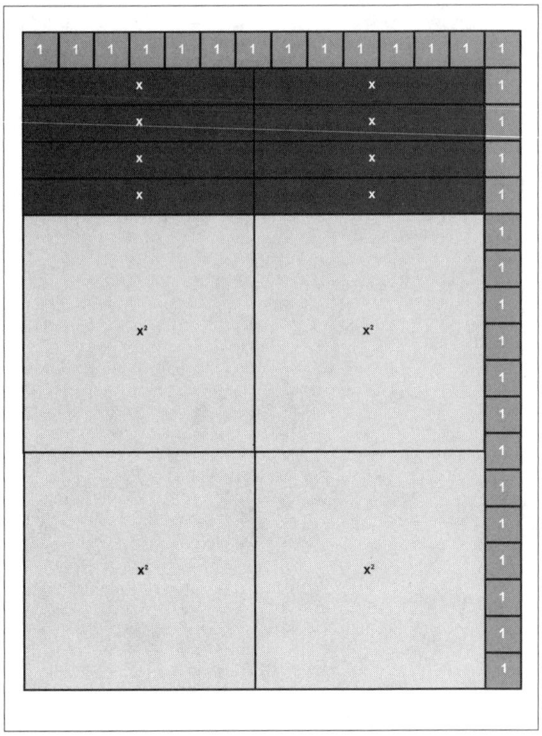

Exploring Math through . . .

At the beginning of each set of 10 lessons the students will read about a sport or hobby that uses math. The word problems that appear in the section will be based on the featured sport or hobby. Each of the 16 sections of material in this course utilizes a different sport or hobby. None of these activities require a high school education to participate in but all involve extensive mathematics in one way or another.

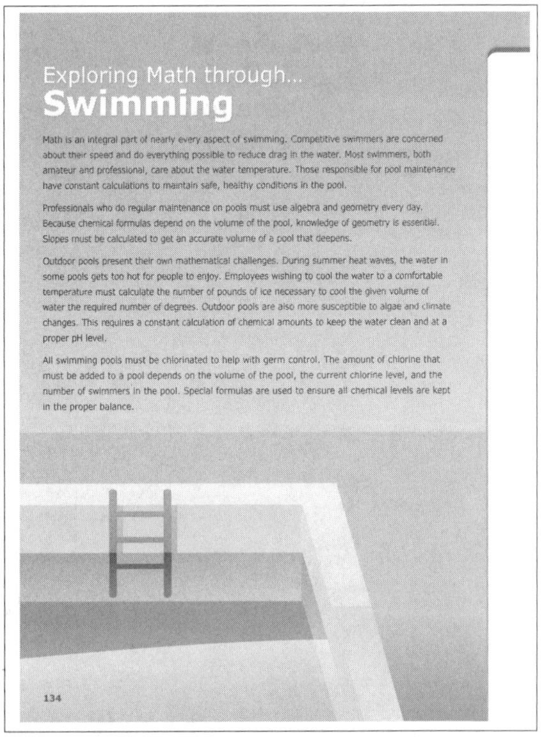

Exploring Math through...
Swimming

Math is an integral part of nearly every aspect of swimming. Competitive swimmers are concerned about their speed and do everything possible to reduce drag in the water. Most swimmers, both amateur and professional, care about the water temperature. Those responsible for pool maintenance have constant calculations to maintain safe, healthy conditions in the pool.

Professionals who do regular maintenance on pools must use algebra and geometry every day. Because chemical formulas depend on the volume of the pool, knowledge of geometry is essential. Slopes must be calculated to get an accurate volume of a pool that deepens.

Outdoor pools present their own mathematical challenges. During summer heat waves, the water in some pools gets too hot for people to enjoy. Employees wishing to cool the water to a comfortable temperature must calculate the number of pounds of ice necessary to cool the given volume of water the required number of degrees. Outdoor pools are also more susceptible to algae and climate changes. This requires a constant calculation of chemical amounts to keep the water clean and at a proper pH level.

All swimming pools must be chlorinated to help with germ control. The amount of chlorine that must be added to a pool depends on the volume of the pool, the current chlorine level, and the number of swimmers in the pool. Special formulas are used to ensure all chemical levels are kept in the proper balance.

134

College Test Prep

As your students progress through their high school years, they will take a number of standardized tests that measure their skills in math, grammar, writing, vocabulary, and reading comprehension. Most colleges use the scores on these tests to determine whether or not to grant students admission to their colleges. Many scholarships are also based on the test scores, so it is important that students do as well as they can.

At the close of each set of 10 lessons, the students will be given a section of multiple choice questions. These questions are the same style and format as questions that are likely to appear on the math sections of standardized tests. They are also the same difficulty level as the Algebra 1 questions that appear on the tests.

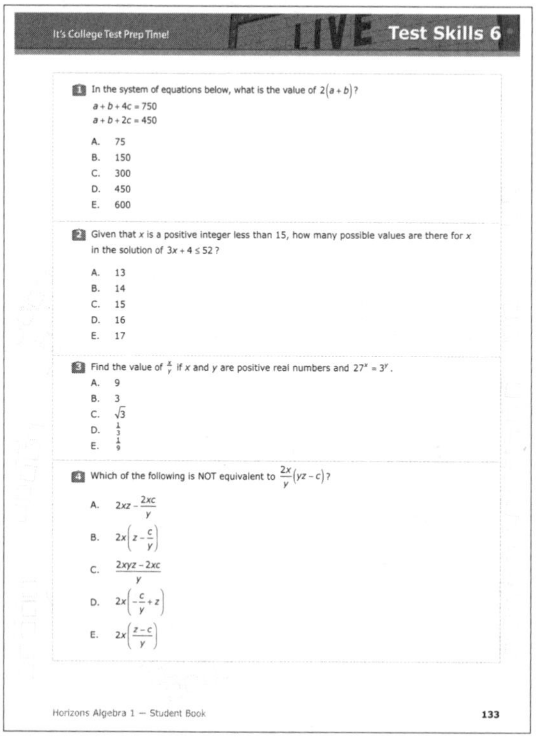

It's College Test Prep Time! **Test Skills 6**

1. In the system of equations below, what is the value of $2(a+b)$?
   $a+b+4c=750$
   $a+b+2c=450$
   A. 75
   B. 150
   C. 300
   D. 450
   E. 600

2. Given that x is a positive integer less than 15, how many possible values are there for x in the solution of $3x+4 \le 52$?
   A. 13
   B. 14
   C. 15
   D. 16
   E. 17

3. Find the value of $\frac{x}{y}$ if x and y are positive real numbers and $27^x = 3^y$.
   A. 9
   B. 3
   C. $\sqrt{3}$
   D. $\frac{1}{3}$
   E. $\frac{1}{9}$

4. Which of the following is NOT equivalent to $\frac{2x}{y}(yz-c)$?
   A. $2xz - \frac{2xc}{y}$
   B. $2x\left(z-\frac{c}{y}\right)$
   C. $\frac{2xyz-2xc}{y}$
   D. $2x\left(-\frac{c}{y}+z\right)$
   E. $2x\left(\frac{z-c}{y}\right)$

Horizons Algebra 1 — Student Book 133

Evaluation

This course has 16 tests, 4 exams, and 80 worksheets. One test follows each set of 10 lessons, and one exam follows every 40 lessons. Exam 4 is also a final exam. You have the option of administering the first two pages as a fourth quarter exam, or all six pages as a cumulative final exam. Many of the worksheets are used as quizzes at the teacher's discretion. Worksheets that are appropriate for quizzes are identified in the corresponding Lesson Plans.

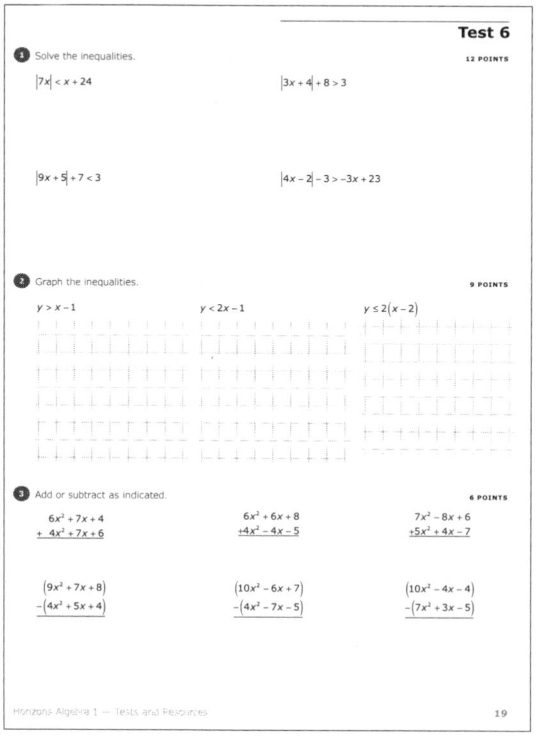

Test 6

1. Solve the inequalities. **12 POINTS**

   $|7x| < x+24$ $\quad$ $|3x+4|+8>3$

   $|9x+5|+7<3$ $\quad$ $|4x-2|-3>-3x+23$

2. Graph the inequalities. **9 POINTS**

   $y > x-1$ $\quad$ $y < 2x-1$ $\quad$ $y \le 2(x-2)$

3. Add or subtract as indicated. **6 POINTS**

   $(6x^2+7x+4) + (4x^2+7x+6)$ $\quad$ $(6x^2+6x+8) + (4x^2-4x-5)$ $\quad$ $(7x^2-8x+6) + (5x^2+4x-7)$

   $(9x^2+7x+8) - (4x^2+5x+4)$ $\quad$ $(10x^2-6x+7) - (4x^2-7x-5)$ $\quad$ $(10x^2-4x-4) - (7x^2+3x-5)$

Horizons Algebra 1 — Tests and Resources 19

Readiness Evaluation

Why Evaluate Readiness?

Teaching could be defined as the process of starting with what a student knows and guiding him to added knowledge with new material. While this may not be a dictionary definition of teaching, it is descriptive of the processes involved. Determining a student's readiness for Algebra 1 is the first step to successful teaching.

Types of Readiness

True readiness has little to do with chronological age. Emotional maturity and mental preparation are the main components of academic readiness. The teacher who is dealing directly with the student is best able to determine a child's emotional maturity. All emotionally immature students may need special student training in their problem areas. A child's mental *preparation* can be more easily discerned with a simple diagnostic evaluation. Observing the child's attitude of confidence or insecurity while taking the evaluation may help determine emotional readiness.

Determining Readiness

The Algebra 1 *Readiness Evaluation* on the following pages helps the teacher to determine if student(s) are ready to begin studying math at the Algebra 1 level. Complete this evaluation the first or second day of school.

The evaluation should take 45-60 minutes. It would be helpful to evaluate all of the students to determine what each student knows. However, you may want to evaluate only those student(s) whom you sense have not had a thorough preparation for this course. It is especially important to evaluate any student who is using this curriculum for the first time. The student(s) should be able to complete the test on his own with the teacher making sure he understands the directions for each individual activity.

The answer key follows the test. Count each individual answer as a separate point. The total for the test is 60 points. The student(s) should achieve a score of 42 or more points to be ready to begin Algebra 1. Be sure to note the areas of weakness of each student, even those who have scored over 42 points. Students who score under 42 points may need to repeat a previous math level or do some refresher work in their areas of weakness. For possible review of the identified areas of weakness, refer to the chart *Appearance of Concepts* in the *Horizons Pre-Algebra Teacher's Guide*. It will locate lessons where the concepts were taught.

Horizons Algebra 1 Readiness Evaluation

Name: ______________________________

① Solve, using the rules for signed numbers. **10 points**

(+38) + (+7) =

(-6) + (+44) =

(-3) − (-34) =

(-18) − (+82) =

(8)(12) =

(5)(-7) =

(-9)(6) =

(-4)(-20) =

(-11)(8)(-1) =

(-5)(-12)(-1) =

② Solve, using the rules of absolute values. **6 points**

$|-2| + |-75| =$

$|-3| + |56| =$

$|75| - |-9| =$

$-|12| + |-4| =$

$-|-21| - |-18| =$

$-|16 - 2| + |6 - 9| =$

③ Solve, following the order of operations. **9 points**

$5 + 3 \times 8 =$

$8 \div (2 + 6) + 1 =$

$3 - (7 + 2) + 9 =$

$8^2 - 3^2 \times 4 =$

$4 \times 3^2 - 6 \times 4 =$

$3^2 - 4^2 \div 8 - 7 =$

$5^2 \times (4 - 6^2 \div 9) =$

$2 \times (3^2 + 1) - 5 \times 2 =$

$5 + (1 - 2^2) + 8 =$

④ Simplify the roots. **8 points**

$\sqrt{36} =$

$\sqrt{27} =$

$\sqrt{18} =$

$\sqrt[3]{8} =$

$\sqrt[3]{64} =$

$\sqrt{11} + 4\sqrt{11} =$

$6\sqrt[3]{5} - 2\sqrt[3]{5} =$

$(\sqrt{8})(\sqrt{2}) =$

⑤ Solve. **6 points**

$x + 6 + 5 = 18$

$x + 3x + 3 + 7 = 26$

$5x - 2x + 11 - 4 - 1 = 24$

$-5x < 15$

$2x + 7 > x - 3$

$7x + 9 < 3x + 1$

⑥ Translate the following words into a mathematical expression. Do not solve. **10 points**

The product of 7 and a number.

The ratio of a number to 8.

A number increased by 29.

The total of a number and 13 is 51.

8 fewer than a number equals 3.

A number times 6 yields 42.

The sum of 16 and a number is 79.

6 less than a number is 19.

A number increased by a factor of 4 gives 32.

51 more than a number is 88.

⑦ Add, subtract, multiply, or divide as indicated. **8 points**

$\frac{1}{7}+\frac{4}{7}=$ $\frac{2}{5}\times\frac{1}{5}=$

$\frac{1}{3}+\frac{1}{6}=$ $\frac{5}{8}\times\frac{4}{5}=$

$\frac{4}{5}-\frac{3}{5}=$ $\frac{3}{8}\div\frac{1}{8}=$

$\frac{9}{10}-\frac{3}{4}=$ $\frac{5}{8}\div\frac{3}{4}=$

⑧ Graph the equations. **3 points**

$y=x-3$ $y=-4x+1$ $y\geq 2(x+1)$

Horizons Algebra 1 Readiness Evaluation Answer Key

① Solve, using the rules for signed numbers. **10 points**

(+38) + (+7) = 38 + 7 = 45
(-6) + (+44) =44 – 6 = 38
(-3) – (-34) = (-3) + (+34) = 34 - 3 = 31
(-18) – (+82) = (-18) + (-82) = -100
(8)(12) = 96
(5)(-7) = -35
(-9)(6) = -54
(-4)(-20) = 80
(-11)(8)(-1) = (-88)(-1) = 88
(-5)(-12)(-1) = (60)(-1) = -60

② Solve, using the rules of absolute values. **6 points**

$|-2| + |-75| = 2 + 75 = 77$

$|-3| + |56| = 3 + 56 = 59$

$|75| - |-9| = 75 - 9 = 66$

$-|12| + |-4| = (-12) + (+4) = -(12 - 4) = -8$

$-|-21| - |-18| = (-21) - (+18) = (-21) + (-18) = -39$

$-|16 - 2| + |6 - 9| = (-14) + (+3) = -(14 - 3) = -11$

③ Solve, following the order of operations. **9 points**

$5 + 3 \times 8 = 5 + 24 = 29$

$8 \div (2 + 6) + 1 = 8 \div 8 + 1 = 1 + 1 = 2$

$3 - (7 + 2) + 9 = 3 - 9 + 9 = -6 + 9 = 3$

$8^2 - 3^2 \times 4 = 64 - 9 \times 4 = 64 - 36 = 28$

$4 \times 3^2 - 6 \times 4 = 4 \times 9 - 6 \times 4 = 36 - 24 = 12$

$3^2 - 4^2 \div 8 - 7 = 9 - 16 \div 8 - 7 = 9 - 2 - 7 = 7 - 7 = 0$

$5^2 \times (4 - 6^2 \div 9) = 5^2 \times (4 - 36 \div 9) = 5^2 \times (4 - 4) = 25 \times 0 = 0$

$2 \times (3^2 + 1) - 5 \times 2 = 2 \times (9 + 1) - 5 \times 2 = 2 \times 10 - 5 \times 2 = 20 - 10 = 10$

$5 + (1 - 2^2) + 8 = 5 + (1 - 4) + 8 = 5 + (-3) + 8 = 5 - 3 + 8 = 2 + 8 = 10$

④ Simplify the roots. **8 points**

$\sqrt{36} = 6$

$\sqrt{27} = \sqrt{3 \times 3 \times 3} = 3\sqrt{3}$

$\sqrt{18} = \sqrt{2 \times 3 \times 3} = 3\sqrt{2}$

$\sqrt[3]{8} = \sqrt[3]{2 \times 2 \times 2} = 2$

$\sqrt[3]{64} = \sqrt[3]{4 \times 4 \times 4} = 4$

$\sqrt{11} + 4\sqrt{11} = 5\sqrt{11}$

$6\sqrt[3]{5} - 2\sqrt[3]{5} = 4\sqrt[3]{5}$

$(\sqrt{8})(\sqrt{2}) = \sqrt{8 \times 2} = \sqrt{16} = 4$

⑤ Solve. **6 points**

$x + 6 + 5 = 18$
$x + 11 = 18$
$x = 7$

$x + 3x + 3 + 7 = 26$
$4x + 10 = 26$
$4x = 16$
$x = 4$

$5x - 2x + 11 - 4 - 1 = 24$
$3x + 6 = 24$
$3x = 18$
$x = 6$

$-5x < 15$
$-x < 3$
$x > -3$

$2x + 7 > x - 3$
$x > -10$

$7x + 9 < 3x + 1$
$4x < -8$
$x < -2$

⑥ Translate the following words into a mathematical expression. Do not solve. **10 points**

The product of 7 and a number.	$7x$
The ratio of a number to 8.	$\frac{x}{8}$
A number increased by 29.	$x + 29$
The total of a number and 13 is 51.	$x + 13 = 51$
8 fewer than a number equals 3.	$x - 8 = 3$
A number times 6 yields 42.	$6x = 42$
The sum of 16 and a number is 79.	$16 + x = 79$
6 less than a number is 19.	$x - 6 = 19$
A number increased by a factor of 4 gives 32.	$4x = 32$
51 more than a number is 88.	$x + 51 = 88$

⑦ Add, subtract, multiply, or divide as indicated. **8 points**

$$\frac{1}{7}+\frac{4}{7}=\frac{1+4}{7}=\frac{5}{7}$$

$$\frac{1}{3}+\frac{1}{6}=\frac{1\times2}{3\times2}+\frac{1}{6}=\frac{2}{6}+\frac{1}{6}=\frac{3}{6}=\frac{1}{2}$$

$$\frac{4}{5}-\frac{3}{5}=\frac{4-3}{5}=\frac{1}{5}$$

$$\frac{9}{10}-\frac{3}{4}=\frac{9\times2}{10\times2}-\frac{3\times5}{4\times5}=\frac{18}{20}-\frac{15}{20}=\frac{3}{20}$$

$$\frac{2}{5}\times\frac{1}{5}=\frac{2\times1}{5\times5}=\frac{2}{25}$$

$$\frac{{}^{1}\cancel{5}}{{}_{2}\cancel{8}}\times\frac{\cancel{4}^{1}}{\cancel{5}_{1}}=\frac{1}{2}$$

$$\frac{3}{8}\div\frac{1}{8}=\frac{3}{{}_{1}\cancel{8}}\times\frac{\cancel{8}^{1}}{1}=\frac{3}{1}=3$$

$$\frac{5}{8}\div\frac{3}{4}=\frac{5}{{}_{2}\cancel{8}}\times\frac{\cancel{4}^{1}}{3}=\frac{5\times1}{2\times3}=\frac{5}{6}$$

⑧ Graph the equations. **3 points**

$y = x - 3$

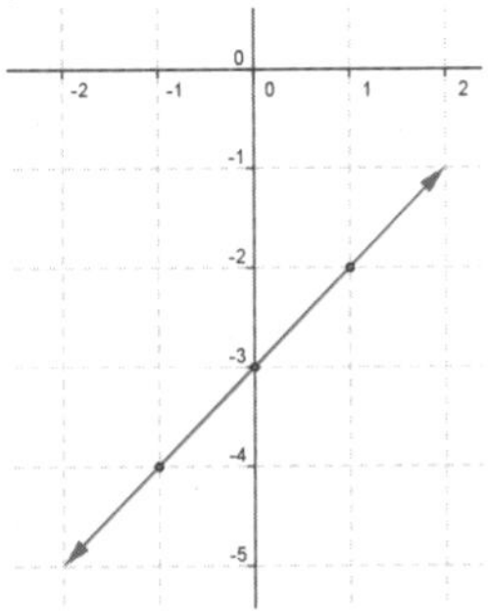

$y = -4x + 1$

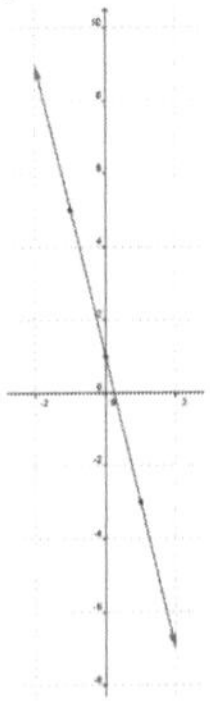

$y \geq 2(x + 1)$

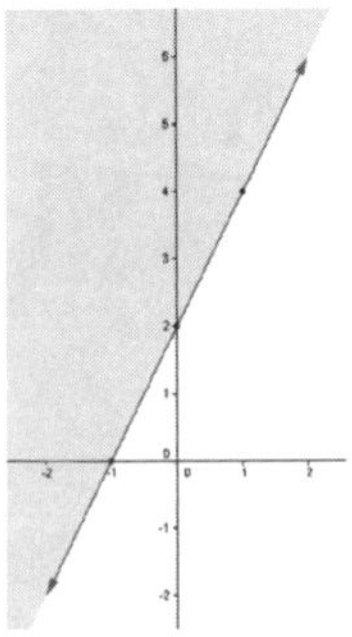

Preparing a Lesson

GENERAL INFORMATION

There is some room on the teacher lessons for you to write your own notes. The more you personalize your teacher's guide in this way, the more useful it will be to you. You will notice that there are 160 student lessons in the curriculum. This allows for the inevitable interruptions to the school year like holidays, test days, inclement weather days, and those unexpected interruptions. It also allows the teacher the opportunity to spend more time teaching any concept that gives the student(s) difficulty. Or, you might wish to spend a day doing some of the fun activities mentioned in the Teaching Tips. If you find that the student(s) need extra drill, use the worksheets.

STUDENT'S LESSONS
Organization

The lessons are designed to be completed in forty-five to sixty minutes a day. If extra manipulatives or worksheets are utilized, you will need to allow more time for teaching. Each lesson consists of a major concept and practice of previously taught concepts. If the student(s) finds the presence of four or five different activities in one lesson a little overwhelming at the beginning, start guiding the student(s) through each activity. By the end of two weeks, the student(s) should be able to work more independently as she adjusts to the format. Mastery of a new concept is not necessary the first time it is presented. Complete understanding of a new concept will come as the concept is approached from different views using different methods at different intervals.

Tests

Tests are in the *Tests and Resources* book. The test structure is such that the student(s) will have had sufficient practice with a concept to have learned it before being tested. Therefore, no concept is tested until the initial presentation has been completed. For example, Test 2 covers concepts completed in Lessons 8-17. Lessons 18-20 may include the introduction of some new material which will not be covered in Test 2. The Lesson Plans state which Lessons are covered on each Test in the Assignment section of every tenth Lesson. Tests may be administered after every tenth lesson as a separate class day or as part of the following lesson. For example, Test 1 may be administered at the beginning of the class period for Lesson 11 or as a separate day if you wish to give students the entire class period to complete the test. Lessons 149-160 are review for Exam 4 with no new material introduced, so you have the option of combining review lessons to allow enough days in the school year to complete the full curriculum and still allow a full class period for tests. There are a total of 180 Lessons, Tests, and Exams.

TEACHER'S LESSONS
Organization

Each lesson is organized into the following sections: **Concepts**, **Learning Objectives**, **Materials Needed**, and **Teaching Tips**. To be a master teacher you will need to prepare each lesson well in advance.

Concepts

Concepts are listed at the beginning of each lesson. New concepts are listed first followed by concepts that are practiced from previous lessons. The concepts are developed in a progression that is designed to give the student(s) a solid foundation in the math skills while providing enough variety to hold the student's interest.

Learning Objectives

The Learning Objectives list criteria for the student's performance. They state what the student should be able to do at the completion of the lesson. You will find objectives helpful in determining the student's progress, the need for remedial work, and readiness for more advanced information. Objectives are stated in terms of measurable student performance. The teacher then has a fixed level of performance to be attained before the student(s) is ready to progress to the next level.

Materials Needed

Materials Needed lists the things you'll need to find before you teach each lesson. Sometimes you will also find instructions on how to make your own materials. This section also lists the worksheets. There is approximately one worksheet for every two lessons. If worksheets are suggested in a particular lesson you will find them listed. Each worksheet has a worksheet number. The *Teacher's Guide* identifies where these resource worksheets are essential to the lessons. The worksheets will be handy for many purposes. You might use them for extra work for student(s) who demonstrate extra aptitude or ability or as remedial work for the student(s) who demonstrate a lack of aptitude or ability. You may also make your own worksheets and note where you would use them in the materials section on the teacher's lesson.

Teaching Tips

The Teaching Tips are related to the Activities in the lesson. Some Teaching Tips require the teacher to make a manipulative needed to complete the activity. Teaching Tips are activities that the teacher can do to enhance the teaching process. You will find them useful for helping the student who needs additional practice to master the concepts or for the student who needs to be challenged by extra work.

In the Teaching Tips the teacher will find directions for teaching each lesson. All activities are designed to be teacher directed both in the student lesson and in the teacher's guide. You will need to use your own judgment concerning how much time is necessary to carry out the activities. Each activity is important to the overall scope of the lesson and must be completed.

Please do not put off looking at the activities in the lesson until you are actually teaching. Taking time to preview what you will be teaching is essential. Choose the manipulatives that fit your program best.

Each lesson in the Student Book starts with a **Teaching Box** that discusses the new material being introduced in the lesson. Sample problems are often included in this section. Some students will be able to read and comprehend the information on their own. Other students need to be guided through this section for complete understanding. Next to the Teaching Box is the **Classwork** section. The Classwork section gives the student(s) an opportunity to perform guided practice on the new concept. Following the Teaching Box and Classwork section of each lesson are the numbered **Activities** problems for the lesson. Number 2 of the **Activities** section always applies the skills learned in the Teaching Box. The remaining activities review previously taught concepts.

ANSWER KEYS

The reduced page answer keys in the *Teacher's Guide* provide solutions to the activities. It is suggested that you give the student(s) a grade for tests and quizzes only. Daily work is to be a learning experience for the student, so do not put unnecessary pressure on him/her. You should correct every paper. At the beginning of each class period, the teacher should quickly check for completion of each student paper, without checking each problem for accuracy. The teacher may then either give the answers to the Activities, or have individual students work the problems on the board. Students should check their own papers and make corrections as needed. It is important to allow students the opportunity to ask questions about the previous day's assignment. This will save much time over the teacher grading all of the homework, and allow the students to have immediate follow-up and reinforcement of concepts missed.

WORKSHEETS

Worksheets are in the *Tests and Resources* book. These worksheets have been developed for reinforcement and drill. There is a complete listing of worksheets and where they might best be used on pages of the introduction. Answer keys to the worksheets are provided in the same manner as for the student lessons.

Horizons

Algebra 1 Scope and Sequence

1. **Integers and Real Numbers**
   Kinds of numbers
   Number line
   Absolute value
   Adding real numbers
   Subtracting real numbers
   Multiplying real numbers
   Dividing real numbers
   Exponents and powers
   Order of operations
   Factoring and prime numbers
   Greatest common factor and least common multiple
   Roots and radicals
   Distributive property

2. **Algebra**
   Variables in algebra
   Equations and inequalities
   Translating words into mathematical symbols
   Evaluating algebraic expressions
   Combining like terms
   Removing parentheses
   Using formulas
   Solving word problems
   Functions

3. **Solving Linear Equations**
   Properties of equality
   Solving equations using addition and subtraction
   *Solving equations using multiplication and division
   *Solving multi-step equations
   *Solving equations with variables on both sides
   *Solving decimal equations
   *Absolute value equations
   *Clearing equations of fractions
   Coin and interest problems
   Motion problems
   *Mixture problems
   Formulas
   Ratios and rates
   Percents

4. **Graphing Linear Equations and Functions**
   Coordinate plane
   Graphing linear equations
   Slope
   Slope-intercept form
   *Graphing horizontal and vertical lines
   *Graphing lines using intercepts
   *Point-slope form
   *Finding the equation of a line given two points
   *Direct variation
   *Functions and relations

5. **Writing Linear Equations**
   Slope-intercept form
   *Point-slope form
   *Writing linear equations given two points
   *Standard form
   *Perpendicular lines

6. **Solving and Graphing Linear Inequalities**
   Solving inequalities using addition or subtraction
   Solving inequalities using multiplication or division
   *Adding and subtracting inequalities
   *Multiplying and dividing inequalities
   *Conjunctions
   *Disjunctions
   *Absolute value inequalities
   *Solving multi-step inequalities
   *Solving compound inequalities involving "and" or "or"
   *Solving absolute value equations
   Graphing inequalities in two variables

7. **Systems of Linear Equations and Inequalities**
   *Graphing linear systems
   Solving linear systems
   *Solving linear systems by linear combinations
   Linear systems and problem solving
   *Special types of linear systems – no solution or infinite solutions
   *Systems of linear inequalities

8. **Exponents and Exponential Functions**
   Multiplication properties of exponents
   Zero and negative exponents
   *Graphs of exponential functions
   *Division properties of exponents
   *Rational exponents
   Scientific notation
   *Exponential growth functions
   *Exponential decay functions

9. Quadratic Equations and Functions
*Zero product property
*Solving quadratic equations by factoring
*Solving equations by taking roots
*Completing the square
*Completing the square with leading coefficients
*The quadratic formula
*Solving quadratic equations
*Quadratic functions of the form $f(x) = ax^2$
*Quadratic functions of the form $f(x) = ax^2 + k$
*Quadratic functions of the form $f(x) = a(x - h)^2 + k$
*Zeros of a function
*Applications of quadratic functions
*Word problems with quadratic equations
Simplifying radicals
*Graphing quadratic functions
*Solving quadratic functions by graphing
*Solving quadratic functions by the quadratic formula
*Using the discriminant
*Graphing quadratic inequalities

10. Polynomials and Factoring
Classifying and evaluating polynomials
Adding and subtracting polynomials
Multiplying by a monomial
Multiplying binomials
Multiplying polynomials
*Special products
Dividing by a monomial
Dividing polynomials
*Solving quadratic equations in factored form
Factoring common monomials
*Factoring the difference of two squares
*Factoring perfect square trinomials
*Factoring trinomials of the form $x^2 + bx + c$
*Factoring trinomials of the form $ax^2 + bx + c$
*Factoring trinomials of the form $ax^2 + bxy + cy^2$
*Factoring completely
*Factoring special products
*Factoring cubic polynomials

11. Rational Expressions and Equations
*Simplifying rational expressions
*Multiplying rational expressions
*Dividing rational expressions
*Adding and subtracting rational expressions
*Adding rational expressions with different denominators
*Subtracting rational expressions with different denominators
*Complex rational expressions
Numerical denominators
*Polynomial denominators
Work problems
Investment problems
Motion problems
Literal equations
Proportions
*Direct and inverse variation

12. Radicals
Expressing square roots
Simplifying radicals
Multiplying radicals
*Dividing radicals and rationalizing denominators
Adding and subtracting radicals
*Multiplying and dividing radical expressions
*Radical equations
*Functions involving square roots
*Operations with radical expressions

13. Geometry
The Pythagorean Theorem
*Distance formula
*Midpoint formula

*New concepts

Where To Use Horizons *Algebra 1 Worksheets*

In the *Tests and Resources* book you will find eighty worksheets.
This chart shows where worksheets may be used for *Horizons Algebra 1*.

No.	Concept	Lessons Where Worksheets Are Used
1	Identify Numbers, Signed Numbers, Exponential Expressions	2
2	Order of Operations, Simplifying Exponents	3
3	Order of Operations, Simplifying Exponents	5
4	Prime Factorization, Absolute Value	7
5	Translating Words into Mathematical Statements, Roots	8
6	Translating Words into Mathematical Statements, Distributive Property	12
7	Evaluating Algebraic Expressions, Adding and Subtracting Polynomials	13
8	Evaluating Algebraic Expressions, Adding and Subtracting Polynomials	15
9	Multiplying and Dividing Monomials	18
10	Algebraic Equations, Extraneous Solutions	20
11	Algebraic Equations, Properties of Equality	22
12	Dividing Radicals	23
13	Dividing Radicals	25
14	Multiplying Radicals, Dividing Radicals	28
15	Graphing Linear Equations	30
16	Graphing Linear Equations	32
17	Point-slope Form, Slope-intercept Form	33
18	Slope, Slope-intercept Form	35
19	Slope and y-intercept	38
20	Point-slope Form, Standard Form	40
21	Slope-intercept Form, Point-slope Form, Standard Form	42
22	Perpendicular and Parallel Lines	43
23	Equations in Standard Form	45
24	Inequalities	48
25	Graphing Inequalities	50
26	Inequalities with Absolute Value	52
27	Solving Systems of Equations by Adding	53
28	Adding and Subtracting Polynomials, Systems of Equations	55
29	Systems of Equations	58
30	Multiplying Polynomials by Monomials	60
31	Solving Systems of Equations by Graphing	62
32	The FOIL Method, Multiplying Polynomials	63
33	The FOIL Method, Multiplying Polynomials	65
34	Special Products, Dividing Polynomials by Monomials	68
35	Factoring Polynomials with Special Products	70
36	Factoring Polynomials with Special Products	72
37	Factoring Polynomials	73
38	Factoring Polynomials	75
39	Factoring Special Products	78
40	Rational Expressions	80

Where To Use Horizons Algebra 1 Worksheets, continued:

No.	Concept	Lessons Where Worksheets Are Used
41	Rational Expressions	82
42	Adding Rational Expressions with Different Denominators	83
43	Multiplying and Dividing Rational Expressions	85
44	Adding Rational Expressions with Different Denominators	88
45	Complex Rational Expressions	89
46	Complex Rational Expressions, Quadratic Equations	92
47	Solving Quadratic Equations	93
48	Solving Quadratic Equations	95
49	The Quadratic Formula	98
50	Sketching the Graph of Parabolas	100
51	Graphing Parabolas, Completing the Square	102
52	Vertex of a Parabola, Zeros of a Function	103
53	Vertex of a Parabola, Zeros of a Function	105
54	Finding Zeros of Quadratic Functions	108
55	Using the Discriminant, Finding Parts of a Parabola	110
56	Parts of a Parabola, Graphing Inequalities	112
57	Money, Investment, and Motion Problems	113
58	Money, Investment, and Motion Problems	115
59	Mixture Problems	118
60	Consecutive Integers, Direct and Inverse Variation	120
61	Consecutive Integers, Direct and Inverse Variation	122
62	Graphing Inequalities on a Number Line	123
63	Graphing Inequalities on a Number Line	125
64	Conjunctions, Disjunctions	128
65	Systems of Inequalities	131
66	Systems of Inequalities	132
67	Graphs of Exponential Functions	133
68	Exponential Growth and Decay	135
69	Ratios and Proportions, Literal Equations	138
70	Factoring Polynomials, Solving Rational Expressions	140
71	Motion and Investment Problems	142
72	Pythagorean Theorem, Length of a Segment	143
73	Pythagorean Theorem, Length of a Segment	145
74	Distance Formula, Midpoint Formula	148
75	Equations of Parallel, Perpendicular, Horizontal, Vertical Lines	150
76	Systems of Equations	152
77	Solving Quadratic Equations	153
78	Quadratic Equations with Radicals	155
79	Slope, y-intercept, Standard Form Equations, Graphing	158
80	Limits of the Domain, Graphing Exponential Functions	160

Horizons Algebra 1 Appearance of Concepts

Lesson 1
Number terminology
Signed numbers
Word problems

Lesson 2
Exponents
Signed numbers
Addition
Subtraction
Multiplication
Division

Lesson 3
Order of operations
Exponents
Signed numbers
Word problems

Lesson 4
Factoring
Prime numbers
Exponents

Lesson 5
Absolute value
Signed numbers
Factoring
Prime numbers
Order of operations

Lesson 6
Greatest common factor
Least common multiple
Factoring
Exponents
Prime numbers

Lesson 7
Roots
Exponents
Absolute value
Signed numbers

Lesson 8
Algebraic expressions
Roots
Greatest common factor
Least common multiple
Word problems

Lesson 9
Algebraic expressions
Roots
Absolute value
Word problems

Lesson 10
Distributive property
Roots
Prime factorization
Exponents
Order of operations

Lesson 11
Algebraic expressions
Exponents
Absolute value
Word problems

Lesson 12
Adding polynomials
Signed numbers
Word problems

Lesson 13
Subtracting polynomials
Distributive property
Order of operations

Lesson 14
Multiplying monomials
Adding polynomials
Subtracting polynomials
Word problems

Lesson 15
Dividing monomials
Adding polynomials
Subtracting polynomials
Multiplying monomials

Lesson 16
Properties of equality
Algebraic equations
Greatest common factor

Lesson 17
Algebraic equations
Properties of equality
Adding polynomials
Subtracting polynomials
Multiplying monomials
Dividing monomials

Lesson 18
Algebraic equations
Fractions
Properties of equality
Least common multiple
Roots
Word problems

Horizons Algebra 1 Appearance of Concepts, continued:

Lesson 19
Algebraic equations
Decimals
Fractions
Word problems

Lesson 20
Algebraic equations
Absolute value
Multiplying monomials
Dividing monomials
Fractions
Decimals

Lesson 21
Algebraic equations
Fractions
Decimals
Absolute value
Word problems

Lesson 22
Radical expressions
Rationalizing the denominator
Absolute value
Word problems

Lesson 23
Dividing radicals
Rationalizing the denominator
Decimals
Fractions
Absolute value

Lesson 24
Multiplying radical expressions
Dividing radicals
Rationalizing the denominator
Fractions
Decimals
Algebraic equations
Word problems

Lesson 25
Dividing radical expressions
Absolute value
Fractions
Properties of equality

Lesson 26
Algebraic equations
Properties of equality
Exponents

Lesson 27
Scientific notation
Powers of 10
Adding polynomials
Subtracting polynomials
Absolute value
Radicals

Lesson 28
Rational exponents
Decimals
Fractions
Dividing radicals
Rationalizing the denominator
Word problems

Lesson 29
Coordinate plane
Graphing points
Rational exponents
Radicals

Lesson 30
Solving linear equations
Graphing linear equations
Coordinate plane
Coordinate points

Lesson 31
Slope
Linear equations
Coordinate points
Graphing linear equations

Lesson 32
y-intercept
Slope-intercept form
Slope
Graphing linear equations
Radicals
Extraneous solutions

Lesson 33
Point-slope form
Slope-intercept form
Graphing linear equations
Word problems

Horizons Algebra 1 Appearance of Concepts, continued:

Lesson 34
Horizontal and vertical lines
Writing linear equations
Graphing linear equations
Word problems

Lesson 35
Intercepts
Linear equations
Graphing linear equations
Word problems

Lesson 36
Perpendicular lines
Slope
Linear equations
Graphing intersecting lines

Lesson 37
Parallel lines
Slope
Slope-intercept form
Perpendicular lines
Graphing linear equations
Writing linear equations

Lesson 38
Standard form
Graphing linear equations
Slope-intercept form
Point-slope form
Slope

Lesson 39
Writing linear equations
Slope-intercept form
Slope
Point-slope form

Lesson 40
Writing linear equations
Point-slope form
Standard form
Absolute value
Radicals
Extraneous solutions

Lesson 41
Writing linear equations in standard form
Slope
Writing linear equations in point-slope form
Adding polynomials
Subtracting polynomials
Multiplying monomials
Dividing monomials
Word problems

Lesson 42
Perpendicular lines
Slope
Writing linear equations in point-slope form
Writing linear equations in standard form
Graphing linear equations

Lesson 43
Parallel lines
Slope
Point-slope form
Standard form
Graphing linear equations
Word problems

Lesson 44
Writing linear equations from graphs
Horizontal lines
Vertical lines
Slope
Parallel lines
Perpendicular lines
Word problems

Lesson 45
Inequalities
Absolute value
Extraneous solutions
Square roots
Word problems

Lesson 46
Inequalities
Algebraic equations with Fractions
Properties of equality

Lesson 47
Inequalities
Fractions
Decimals
Word problems

Horizons Algebra 1 Appearance of Concepts, continued:

Lesson 48
Inequalities
Absolute value
Multiplying monomials
Dividing monomials

Lesson 49
Inequalities
Absolute value
Word problems

Lesson 50
Graphing linear inequalities
Graphing linear equations
Parallel lines
Perpendicular lines
Slope
Word problems

Lesson 51
Systems of equations
Coordinate points
Order of operations
Word problems

Lesson 52
Adding polynomials
Subtracting polynomials
Systems of equations
Inequalities
Radicals
Absolute value

Lesson 53
Systems of equations
Adding linear equations
Standard form
Fractions
Word problems

Lesson 54
Systems of equations
Subtracting linear equations
Standard form
Slope-intercept form
Perpendicular lines
Parallel lines

Lesson 55
Systems of equations
Multiplying a polynomial by a constant
Adding linear equations
Subtracting linear equations
Order of operations
Inequalities

Lesson 56
Systems of equations
Dividing a polynomial by a constant
Adding linear equations
Subtracting linear equations
Word problems

Lesson 57
Systems of equations
Adding linear equations
Multiplying a polynomial by a constant
Word problems

Lesson 58
Systems of equations
Adding linear equations
Subtracting linear equations
Linear combinations
Word problems

Lesson 59
Systems of equations
Graphing linear equations
Word problems

Lesson 60
Multiplying a polynomial by a monomial
Absolute value
Radicals
Extraneous solutions
Fractions
Properties of equality

Lesson 61
Multiplying binomials
Multiplying a polynomial by a monomial
Systems of equations
Adding linear equations
Subtracting linear equations
Multiplying linear equations
Dividing linear equations

Horizons Algebra 1 Appearance of Concepts, continued:

Lesson 62
The FOIL method
Multiplying binomials
Absolute value
Extraneous solutions
Roots
Word problems

Lesson 63
Multiplying polynomials
Multiplying monomials
Linear equations
Fractions
Word problems

Lesson 64
Special products of binomials
The FOIL method
Multiplying polynomials
Word problems

Lesson 65
Dividing a polynomial by a monomial
Dividing a monomial by a monomial
Exponents

Lesson 66
Dividing a polynomial by a binomial
Order of operations
Exponents
Roots
Inequalities

Lesson 67
Multiplying polynomials
Dividing polynomials
Special products of binomials

Lesson 68
Factoring common monomials
Prime factorization
Dividing a polynomial by a monomial
Word problems

Lesson 69
Factoring the difference of two squares
Systems of equations
Word problems

Lesson 70
Factoring perfect square trinomials
Graphing linear equations
Graphing linear inequalities
Perpendicular lines
Parallel lines

Lesson 71
Factoring trinomials
Factoring common monomials
Factoring the difference of two squares
Factoring perfect square trinomials
Dividing radicals

Lesson 72
Factoring trinomials
Word problems

Lesson 73
Factoring trinomials
Simplifying roots
Word problems

Lesson 74
Factoring the difference of two squares
Factoring perfect square trinomials
Identifying perfect square trinomials

Lesson 75
Factoring completely
Adding fractions with roots
Subtracting fractions with roots
Multiplying fractions with roots
Dividing fractions with roots
Word problems

Lesson 76
Factoring cubic polynomials
Systems of equations
Absolute value
Extraneous solutions
Word problems

Lesson 77
Factoring by grouping
Factoring completely
Factoring the difference of two squares
Factoring perfect square trinomials

Lesson 78
Rational expressions
Exclusions
Fractions
Word problems

Lesson 79
Adding rational expressions
Subtracting rational expressions
Exclusions
Inequalities
Fractions

Lesson 80
Multiplying rational expressions
Exclusions
Factoring trinomials
Factoring completely
Factoring the difference of two squares
Factoring perfect square trinomials
Factoring by grouping

Lesson 81
Dividing rational expressions
Exclusions
Systems of equations

Lesson 82
Adding rational expressions
Subtracting rational expressions
Inequalities
Absolute value
Word problems

Lesson 83
Adding rational expressions
Common denominators of rational expressions
Exclusions
Factoring polynomials

Lesson 84
Subtracting rational expressions
Lowest common denominator
Exclusions
Word problems

Lesson 85
Multiplying rational expressions
Exclusions
Adding rational expressions
Subtracting rational expressions
Lowest common denominator

Lesson 86
Dividing rational expressions
Exclusions
Word problems

Lesson 87
Complex fractions
Systems of equations
Graphing

Lesson 88
Complex rational expressions
Equations with radicals
Equations with absolute value
Word problems

Lesson 89
Complex rational expressions
Lowest common denominator

Lesson 90
Quadratic equations
Dividing rational expressions
Multiplying rational expressions
Adding rational expressions
Subtracting rational expressions

Lesson 91
Quadratic equations
Solving quadratic equations by factoring
Complex rational expressions

Horizons Algebra 1 Appearance of Concepts, continued:

Lesson 92
Quadratic equations
Solving quadratic equations by taking roots
Solving quadratic equations by factoring
Word problems

Lesson 93
Quadratic equations
Solving quadratic equations by completing the square
Complex rational expressions

Lesson 94
Quadratic equations
Quadratic formula
Solving quadratic equations by factoring
Solving quadratic equations by taking roots

Lesson 95
Discriminant
Double roots
Word problems

Lesson 96
Quadratic equations
Discriminant
Systems of equations
Absolute value
Dividing polynomials

Lesson 97
Functions
Domain
Range
Graphing functions

Lesson 98
Quadratic functions
Parabolas
Conic sections
Word problems

Lesson 99
Parabolas
Vertex
Sketching parabolas

Lesson 100
Completing the square
Quadratic equations

Lesson 101
Quadratic functions
Parabolas
Completing the square

Lesson 102
Quadratic functions
Parabolas
Zeros of a function
Graphing parabolas
Trends in graphs

Lesson 103
Zeros of a function
Completing the square
Word problems

Lesson 104
Quadratic functions
Zeros of a function
Word problems

Lesson 105
Radicals in quadratic equations
Quadratic formula
Systems of equations

Lesson 106
Parabolas
Directrix
Focus
Axis of symmetry
Dividing polynomials

Lesson 107
Parabolas
Vertex
Focus
Directrix
Axis of symmetry
Graphing
Word problems

Lesson 108
Discriminant
Parabolas
Roots of quadratic equations
Factoring polynomials

Horizons Algebra 1 Appearance of Concepts, continued:

Lesson 109
Quadratic functions
Parts of a parabola
Discriminant
Roots of equations

Lesson 110
Graphing quadratic inequalities
Order of operations
Radicals
Word problems

Lesson 111
Money
Systems of equations
Graphing quadratic inequalities
Word problems

Lesson 112
Simple interest
Word problems

Lesson 113
Motion
Quadratic formula
Word problems

Lesson 114
Mixtures
Word problems

Lesson 115
Mixtures
Completing the square
Parabolic form
Word problems

Lesson 116
Ratios
Zeros of functions
Radicals
Word problems

Lesson 117
Consecutive integers
Word problems

Lesson 118
Functions
Relations
Word problems

Lesson 119
Direct variation
Quadratic equations
Parabolas
Dividing polynomials

Lesson 120
Inverse variation
Discriminant
Quadratic functions
Completing the square
Parabolas

Lesson 121
Inequalities on a number line
Word problems

Lesson 122
Compound inequalities
Inequalities on a number line

Lesson 123
Compound inequalities
Inequalities on a number line
Functions

Lesson 124
Conjunctions
Compound inequalities
Inequalities on a number line
Word problems

Lesson 125
Disjunctions
Conjunctions
Compound inequalities
Inequalities on a number line

Lesson 126
Inequalities
Absolute value
Inequalities on a number line

Lesson 127
Compound inequalities
Inequalities on a number line
Conjunctions
Disjunctions

Lesson 128
Systems of linear inequalities
Bounded solutions
Unbounded solutions
Inequalities

Horizons Algebra 1 Appearance of Concepts, continued:

Lesson 129
Systems of linear inequalities
Word problems

Lesson 130
Systems of linear inequalities
Direct variation
Inverse variation

Lesson 131
Exponential growth
Compound interest
Word problems

Lesson 132
Exponential decay
Quadratic equations
Factoring
Word problems

Lesson 133
Graphs of exponential functions
Adding polynomials
Subtracting polynomials
Word problems

Lesson 134
Ratios
Proportions
Word problems

Lesson 135
Literal equations
Pythagorean Theorem
Quadratic equations
Completing the square
Word problems

Lesson 136
Work problems
Fractions
Quadratic formula
Solving quadratic equations
Word problems

Lesson 137
Investment problems
Literal equations
Simple interest
Subtracting polynomials
Word problems

Lesson 138
Motion problems
Distance formula
Literal equations
Adding polynomials
Multiplying polynomials by monomials
Word problems

Lesson 139
Square roots without a calculator
Radicals

Lesson 140
Functions
Square roots
Domain
Range
Graphing functions

Lesson 141
Pythagorean Theorem
Hypotenuse
Square roots
Word problems

Lesson 142
Pythagorean Theorem
Literal equations
Systems of equations
Parabolas

Lesson 143
Length of a segment
Pythagorean Theorem
Word problems

Lesson 144
Distance formula
Length of a segment
Adding polynomials

Lesson 145
Middle of a segment
Subtracting polynomials
Multiplying a polynomial by a monomial
Dividing a polynomial by a monomial
Word problems

Lesson 146
Midpoint formula
Systems of equations
Slope
y-intercept
Graphing linear equations

Lesson 147
Literal equations
Pythagorean Theorem
Distance formula
Midpoint formula
Word problems

Lesson 148
Absolute value
Extraneous solutions
Radicals
Adding polynomials
Subtracting polynomials
Multiplying monomials
Dividing monomials
Multiplying polynomials

Lesson 149
Linear equations
Slope-intercept form
Point-slope form
Intercepts
Parallel lines
Perpendicular lines

Lesson 150
Linear inequalities
Absolute value
Graphing inequalities

Lesson 151
Systems of equations
Multiplying a polynomial by a monomial
Multiplying binomials
Multiplying polynomials
Dividing polynomials

Lesson 152
Factoring polynomials
Rational expressions

Lesson 153
Rational expressions
Complex fractions
Quadratic equations

Lesson 154
Parabolas
Vertex
Focus
Axis of symmetry
Directrix
Graphing parabolas

Lesson 155
Graphing quadratic inequalities
Quadratic equations with radicals
Roots of quadratic equations
Square roots without a calculator

Lesson 156
Investment problems
Motion problems
Mixture problems
Ratios and proportions
Consecutive integers
Word problems

Lesson 157
Exponential growth
Exponential decay
Ratios and proportions
Investment problems
Work problems
Distance problems
Word problems

Lesson 158
Slope
y-intercept
Graphing linear equations
Systems of equations
Direct variation
Inverse variation

Lesson 159
Inequalities on a number line
Conjunctions
Disjunctions
Inequalities with absolute value
Systems of linear inequalities

Lesson 160
Functions with square roots
Graphs of exponential functions
Dividing polynomials by binomials
Pythagorean Theorem
Distance formula
Midpoint formula

Lesson 1

Concepts

- Number terminology
- Signed number rules
- Four operations with signed numbers
- Math in the real world

Learning Objectives

The student will be able to:

- Define terms related to numbers
- Identify numbers as *natural*, *whole*, *integer*, *rational*, *irrational*, and *real*
- Apply the rules of signed numbers
- Add and subtract numbers with different signs
- Multiply and divide numbers with different signs

Materials Needed

- Student Book, Lesson 1
- Exploring Math through Football

Teaching Tips

- Administer the Readiness Test. This test is not to be graded as part of the course grade, but rather as an aid in determining individual student readiness for Algebra 1. Worksheets may be assigned as necessary to assist students who need further help.

- Emphasize that math is necessary for life, not just for those who pursue a career in a math-related field. Introduce the Exploring Math pages. These features will appear throughout the book at the beginning of every 10-lesson segment. Each word problem in the 10 lessons following an Exploring Math page will relate to the featured hobby or sport. Introduce Exploring Math through... Football.

Introduction to...

Exploring Math through...

Often students ask:

Who uses this stuff anyway?

I will NEVER be a math major. Why do I have to learn all this?

Will I ever have to use algebra in the real world?

Math is a school subject that is used daily by people in their work, homes, and play. Many people use math in their jobs, even if those jobs do not require a college degree in mathematics. There is a good chance you will use math on an algebra level when you get a job. Math is also an integral part of recreation. Almost every sport or hobby uses math in some way.

While you may find some of the topics in algebra challenging, they will help you learn more about math and God's carefully designed world. You do not know what plans God has for your life. You may be surprised in the directions God leads you and find that you use math in ways you never expected.

Throughout this book, you will read about several sports and hobbies that require the use of math. Whether or not God's plan for your life includes college, math will play a role in your future.

"For I know the plans I have for you," declares the LORD, "plans to prosper you and not to harm you, plans to give you hope and a future."
Jeremiah 29:11 NIV

Exploring Math through...
Football

Football statistics require a variety of math skills. Signed numbers are used in calculating yardage. Percents calculate player efficiency. This includes finding the percent of passes a quarterback completes, the percent of passes a receiver catches, and the percent of passes a quarterback throws to a particular section of the field. General math calculations are used in determining a player's running speed, keeping score, and deciding if a team should attempt two extra points rather than the standard one extra point after a touchdown.

Order of operations is vital in some football calculations. For example, in each football game, quarterbacks receive a grade known as the Passer Rating. This grade is based on the number of yards gained, touchdowns, interceptions, completions, and pass attempts. The Passer Rating of a college football quarterback is calculated using the formula NCAA QB Passer Rating = $[(8.4y) + (330t) - (200i) + (100c)] \div a$, where y is the number of passing yards, t is the number of touchdowns thrown, i is the number of interceptions thrown, c is the number of completed passes, and a is the number of pass attempts.

Geometry is also a part of football plays. Receivers may run routes that require them to turn a 45-degree angle. The defense must be able to calculate angles while they are running to intercept the receiver, or they will miss a tackle opportunity.

Lesson 1

Kinds of Numbers

Natural numbers are counting numbers. (1, 2, 3, . . .) **Whole numbers** are the natural numbers and zero. (0, 1, 2, . . .) **Integers** are the positive and negative whole numbers. (. . . -1, 0, 1, . . .)	**Rational numbers** are numbers that can be written as a fraction. $\left(\frac{1}{2}, \frac{4}{3}, \frac{7}{1}, 10.5\right)$ **Irrational numbers** are numbers that CANNOT be written as a fraction. $\left(\sqrt{2}, \pi\right)$ **Real numbers** are numbers in any of the above categories.

Signed Number Rules:
When adding two numbers with the same sign, add the numbers like normal, and keep the same sign in the answer.
(+2) + (+5) = (+7) and (-2) + (-5) = (-7)

When adding two numbers with opposite signs, ignore the signs (use the absolute values) and subtract the smaller number from the larger number. Keep the sign of the larger number as the sign in the answer.
(+5) + (-2) = (5 – 2) = 3. 5 is larger than 2 and 5 is positive in the problem, so the answer is positive.
(+5) + (-2) = (+3).

(-5) + (+2) = -(5 – 2) = -3. 5 is larger than 2 and 5 is negative in the problem, so the answer is negative.
(-5) + (+2) = (-3)

When subtracting signed numbers, change the sign of the second number and add.
$(+5)-(-2)=(+5)+(+2)=5+2=7$

When multiplying two numbers with the same sign, the answer is ALWAYS positive.
$(+5)\times(+4)=20 \quad (-5)\times(-4)=20$

When multiplying two numbers with different signs, the answer is ALWAYS negative.
$(+5)\times(-4)=-20 \quad (-5)\times(+4)=-20$

When multiplying more than two numbers, count the number of negatives. If there is an even number of negative terms, the answer is positive. If there is an odd number of negative terms, the answer is negative.

When dividing signed numbers, follow the rules for multiplying signed numbers.

① **Classwork**

Identify each number as *natural, whole, integer, rational, irrational,* or *real.* Some numbers may have more than one answer.

	7	-4	$\sqrt{2}$	0	$1\frac{1}{4}$	$\frac{1}{6}$	π	5.3
Natural	x							
Whole	x			x				
Integer	x	x		x				
Rational	x	x		x	x	x		x
Irrational			x				x	
Real	x	x	x	x	x	x	x	x

Solve, using the rules for signed numbers.

(+42) + (+61) = 42 + 61 = 103

(+42) + (-61) = -(61 – 42) = -19

(+42) – (-61) = 42 + 61 = 103

(-42) – (-61) = (-42) + (+61) = 61 – 42 = 19

(-3)(-4) = 12

(-3)(4) = -12

(-3)(4)(2) = (-12)(2) = -24

(-3)(-4)(2) = (12)(2) = 24

$(+12)\div(-3)=-4$

$(-12)\div(-3)=4$

Activities

② Identify each number as *natural, whole, integer, rational, irrational,* or *real.* Some numbers may have more than one answer.

	11	$-\sqrt{3}$	$6\frac{3}{4}$	-7	0	21.62	π	$\frac{5}{6}$	-0.09
Natural	x								
Whole	x				x				
Integer	x			x	x				
Rational	x		x	x	x	x		x	x
Irrational		x					x		
Real	x	x	x	x	x	x	x	x	x

③ Solve, using the rules for signed numbers. Write the problem vertically, if necessary.

(-6) + (+19) = 19 – 6 = 13

(-6) + (-19) = -(6 + 19) = -25

(+6) – (-19) = 6 + 19 = 25

(-6) – (-19) = 19 – 6 = 13

(+23) + (-74) = -(74 – 23) = -51

(-23) + (-74) = -(23 + 74) = -97

(-23) – (-74) = (-23) + (+74) = 74 – 23 = 51

(-23) – (+74) = -(23 + 74) = -97

(-5)(8) = -40

(-5)(-8) = 40

(-36) ÷ (-9) = 4

(36) ÷ (-9) = -4

(10)(-8) = -80

(-8)(-5)(2) = 80

(-81) ÷ (-9) = 9

(81) ÷ (-9) = -9

④ Solve.
In one drive of a football game, the quarterback passed the ball for a 38-yard gain, was sacked for a 7-yard loss, and rushed for a 3-yard gain. How many total yards did the offense move the ball on the drive?

(+38) + (-7) + (+3) = 38 – 7 + 3 = 31 + 3 = 34 yards

If the offense started on the 50-yard line, how many yards away from the goal line are they at the end of the drive?

50 – 34 = 16 yards

Teaching Tips, Cont.

- Define the terms in the teaching box of Lesson 1. Ask students to give other examples of each type of number. They may find it difficult to think of other examples of irrational numbers. Some students may give the square root of other numbers. This is correct UNLESS the student gives the square root of a perfect square.
- Teach the rules for signed numbers from the teaching box. Explain that there are really only two sets of rules to memorize — one set that applies to addition and subtraction, and one set that applies to multiplication and division.
- Complete the Classwork exercises. Have some students work the problems on the board for the class and explain their answers. If you are using the books as consumables, have students mark the correct answers in their books. Otherwise, have the students complete all work on notebook paper. Explain that the value of π is a decimal that never ends and never repeats. In math, it is acceptable to use the value 3.14 or $\frac{22}{7}$ for π when an exact answer is not required.
- The first 100 digits of pi:
3.1415926535897932384626433832795028841971693993751058209749445923078164062862089986280348253421170679....
(Neither you nor the students are expected to know or memorize this. Often, students will ask, just to see if you know!)

Assignment

- Complete Lesson 1, Activities 2-4.

Lesson 2

Concepts

- Exponents
- Adding and subtracting signed numbers
- Multiplying and dividing signed numbers

Learning Objectives

The student will be able to:

- Define *exponent* and *base*
- Use exponents to express products
- Write exponential notations in expanded form
- Solve exponential expressions

Materials Needed

- Student Book, Lesson 2
- Worksheet 1
- Calculator

Teaching Tips

> Many older calculators will calculate exponential numbers when you repeatedly press the [=] key. Try this on your calculator before class to make sure it works! Have a student press [2] [x] [2] [=] [=] [=] . . . and read the numbers as they appear. Write the numbers on the chalkboard so the class can see them as they are called out. The students should get 4, 8, 16, 32, etc. These numbers will be used later in the lesson. Note: This will not work on the new scientific calculators or those with multiple display lines.

Exponents and Powers

Exponents tell how many times a number is multiplied by itself. The number being multiplied is called the **base**. The exponent is written as a small number on the upper right side of the base. In the expression 4^3, the number 4 is the base and the number 3 is the exponent. $4^3 = 4 \times 4 \times 4 = 64$
The answer to an exponential expression is always a multiple of the base.

Rules for working with exponents
Any number (except zero) raised to the 0th power equals 1. $3^0 = 1$

Any number raised to the 1st power equals itself. $3^1 = 3$

When multiplying terms with equal bases, add the exponents. $3^2(3^3) = 3^5$

When dividing terms with equal bases, subtract the exponents. $3^3 \div 3^2 = 3^1$

When the product of two or more factors has an exponent, raise each individual factor to that exponent. $(2 \times 3)^4 = 2^4 \times 3^4$ Note that this is the same as 6^4.

When a number has a negative exponent, take the reciprocal of the number (the numerator and denominator switch places) and make the exponent positive. $3^{-2} = \frac{1}{3^2}$ and

$\left(\frac{2}{3}\right)^{-3} = \left(\frac{3}{2}\right)^3 = \frac{3^3}{2^3}$

① **Classwork**
Read and solve the following exponential expressions.

$2^2 = 2$ squared $= 2 \times 2 = 4$
$3^2 = 3$ squared $= 3 \times 3 = 9$
$2^3 = 2$ cubed $= 2 \times 2 \times 2 = 8$
$3^3 = 3$ cubed $= 3 \times 3 \times 3 = 27$
$4^2 = 4$ squared $= 4 \times 4 = 16$
$4^3 = 4$ cubed $= 4 \times 4 \times 4 = 64$

Simplify the expressions. You do not have to solve exponents greater than 3.

$13^0 = 1$

$22^1 = 22$

$6^4 \times 6^3 = 6^7$

$5^6 \div 5^4 = 5^2 = 25$

$(4 \times 5)^2 = 4^2 \times 5^2 = 16 \times 25 = 400$

$7^{-2} = \left(\frac{1}{7}\right)^2 = \frac{1^2}{7^2} = \frac{1}{49}$

$\left(\frac{2}{5}\right)^2 = \frac{2^2}{5^2} = \frac{4}{25}$

$\left(\frac{3}{2}\right)^{-3} = \left(\frac{2}{3}\right)^3 = \frac{2^3}{3^3} = \frac{8}{27}$

Activities
② Simplify the expressions. You do not have to solve exponents greater than 3.

$11^0 = 1$

$27^0 = 1$

$17^1 = 17$

$38^1 = 38$

$8^2 \times 8^4 = 8^6$

$9^3 \times 9^2 = 9^5$

$6^5 \div 6^3 = 6^2 = 36$

$10^5 \div 10^2 = 10^3 = 1{,}000$

$(3 \times 4)^2 = 3^2 \times 4^2 = 9 \times 16 = 144$

$(2 \times 4)^3 = 2^3 \times 4^3 = 8 \times 64 = 512$

$3^{-3} = \left(\frac{1}{3}\right)^3 = \frac{1^3}{3^3} = \frac{1}{27}$

$11^{-2} = \left(\frac{1}{11}\right)^2 = \frac{1^2}{11^2} = \frac{1}{121}$

$\left(\frac{1}{4}\right)^2 = \frac{1^2}{4^2} = \frac{1}{16}$

$\left(\frac{1}{4}\right)^3 = \frac{1^3}{4^3} = \frac{1}{64}$

$\left(\frac{2}{5}\right)^{-2} = \left(\frac{5}{2}\right)^2 = \frac{5^2}{2^2} = \frac{25}{4}$

$\left(\frac{5}{3}\right)^{-3} = \left(\frac{3}{5}\right)^3 = \frac{3^3}{5^3} = \frac{27}{125}$

③ Solve, following the rules of signed numbers.

(+242) + (+397) = 242 + 397 = 639

(-242) + (-397) = -(242 + 397) = -639

(-242) – (+397) = -(242 + 397) = -639

(+242) – (-397) = 242 + 397 = 639

(-29) – (-15) =
(-29) + (+15) = -(29 – 15) = -14

(+29) – (+15) =
(+29) +(-15) = 29 – 15 = 14

(-29) – (+15) = (-29) + (-15) = -44

14 + (-13) + 17 – (-12) =
14 – 13 + 17 + 12 = 30

$(+8) \times (+5) = 40$

$(+8) \times (-5) = -40$

$(-56) \div (+8) = -7$

$(-56) \div (-8) = 7$

$(-4)(5)(-2) = (-20)(-2) = 40$

$(-4)(-5)(-2) = (20)(-2) = -40$

$(72) \div (-9) = -8$

$(72) \div (9) = 8$

Identify Numbers, Signed Numbers, Exponential Expressions Worksheet 1

① Identify each number as *natural, whole, integer, rational, irrational,* or *real.* Some numbers may have more than one answer.

	$4\sqrt{11}$	-3	π	0	$1\frac{2}{3}$	$\frac{13}{7}$	65	$-\frac{1}{8}$	41.3
Natural							x		
Whole				x			x		
Integer		x		x			x		
Rational		x		x	x	x	x	x	x
Irrational	x		x						
Real	x	x	x	x	x	x	x	x	x

② Solve, using the rules for signed numbers.

(+48) + (+35) = 48 + 35 = 83

(-48) + (+35) = -(48 − 35) = -13

(-48) + (-35) = -(48 + 35) = -83

(+48) + (-35) = 48 − 35 = 13

(+48) − (-35) = 48 + 35 = 83

(-48) − (-35) = (-48) + (+35) = -(48 − 35) = -13

(11)(12) = 132

(11)(-12) = -132

(-132) ÷ (11) = -12

(-132)÷(-12) = 11

③ Write the following exponential expressions in expanded form and solve.

$3^4 = 3 \times 3 \times 3 \times 3 = 81$

$4^3 = 4 \times 4 \times 4 = 64$

$6^3 = 6 \times 6 \times 6 = 216$

$10^4 = 10 \times 10 \times 10 \times 10 = 10{,}000$

$11^2 = 11 \times 11 = 121$

Note regarding negative exponents in quotients:

Consider the problem $2^2 \div 2^4$. According to the rules of dividing exponents, this equals $2^{2-4} = 2^{-2}$. Written as a fraction, you have

$$\frac{1 \cdot \cancel{2} \cdot \cancel{2}}{1 \cdot \cancel{2} \cdot \cancel{2} \cdot 2 \cdot 2} = \frac{1}{2 \cdot 2} = \frac{1}{2^2} = \frac{1}{4}$$

Teaching Tips, Cont.

- Define *exponent* and *base* from the teaching box. Tell students that the base is the number on the bottom. (This concept will carry over in later years when they are learning logarithms with different bases.) It will also help to remember that the exponent is elevated.
- Demonstrate the proper form for writing numbers with exponents, using the numbers from the calculator as an example.
- Teach the rules for working with exponents from the teaching box.
- Emphasize that any number raised to the zero power is equal to 1. If students are still questioning the validity of this fact, show students that $2^1 \div 2^1$ can be solved by following the rules of exponents: $2^{1-1} = 2^0 = 1$. This problem is obviously equal to 1 because anything divided by itself equals 1. Following the rules of dividing exponents, the resulting term has a zero exponent.
- Complete the Classwork exercises. Have some students work the problems on the board for the class and explain their answers. All students should work the problems in their books. Worksheets that appear in the assignments section may be used at the teacher's discretion. These are designed for additional review of recent topics for students who need more practice prior to being quizzed or tested over the material.

Assignments

- Complete Lesson 2, Activities 2-3.
- Worksheet 1 (Optional).

Lesson 3

Concepts

- Order of operations
- Adding and subtracting signed numbers
- Multiplying and dividing signed numbers
- Math in the real world

Learning Objectives

The student will be able to:

- Memorize the correct sequence for the order of operations
- Apply the order of operations to mathematical expressions
- Calculate correctly the answer to mathematical expressions with multiple terms

Materials Needed

- Student Book, Lesson 3
- Worksheet 2

Teaching Tips

➢ Ask students what would happen in a football game if there were no rules. How would you know how many points to give a team for a field goal, touchdown, extra point(s), safety, etc? Elicit the idea that rules are necessary for the game to be played properly. Tie this in with the fact that God is a God of order, and the Bible teaches that all things should be done decently and in order. (1 Cor. 14:40)

Order of Operations

There is a specific order you must follow in working more complex math problems to get the correct answer. This is known as the **Order of Operations**. When simplifying mathematical expressions, first look for any **parentheses** and simplify inside each set of parentheses. Second, apply any **exponents** in the problem. Next, do all **multiplication** and **division** together in the order they appear in the expression from left to right. Finally, do all **addition** and **subtraction** together in the order they appear in the expression from left to right. You can remember the proper order of operations by remembering this sentence:
Please **E**xcuse **M**y **D**ear **A**unt **S**ally.
(**P**arentheses, **E**xponents, **M**ultiplication, **D**ivision, **A**ddition, and **S**ubtraction)

To solve the problem $6+2(1+3)^2$, first simplify the parentheses to get $6+2(4)^2$.
Next, take care of the exponent: $6+2(16)$ and then do all multiplication. (There is no division in this expression, or that would be done in this step, as well.) You should have $6+32$, which gives you $6+32=38$.

① **Classwork**
Simplify the expressions, following the proper order of operations.

$7-4+3(5-3)^3=$
$7-4+3(2)^3=$
$7-4+3(8)=$
$7-4+24=$
$3+24=27$

$(12-9)^2+20\div4=$
$(3)^2+20\div4=$
$9+20\div4=$
$9+5=14$

$3+2^3-2(24\div6)=$
$3+2^3-2(4)=$
$3+8-2(4)=$
$3+8-8=$
$11-8=3$

Activities
② Simplify each expression, following the proper order of operations.

$21-4\times3=21-12=9$

$18\div9\times3+2-1\times3=2\times3+2-1\times3=6+2-1\times3=6+2-3=8-3=5$

$(8-5)^2-10\div2=(3)^2-10\div2=9-10\div2=9-5=4$

$(3+4)-2^2+3\times4=7-2^2+3\times4=7-4+3\times4=7-4+12=3+12=15$

$(15-12)^3-5^2+2\times7=(3)^3-5^2+2\times7=27-25+2\times7=27-25+14=2+14=16$

$2^3\times3\div(7-1)-4=2^3\times3\div6-4=8\times3\div6-4=24\div6-4=4-4=0$

$(4^2-(13-8)+1)\div6=(4^2-5+1)\div6=(16-5+1)\div6=(11+1)\div6=12\div6=2$

$((6+2\times3)\div3)^2=((6+6)\div3)^2=(12\div3)^2=4^2=16$

③ Solve, following the rules of signed numbers.

(+57) + (+73) = 57 + 73 = 130

(+57) + (-73) = -(73 - 57) = -16

(-57) + (+73) = 73 - 57 = 16

(-57) + (-73) = -(57 + 73) = -130

(+242) - (+397) = (+242) + (-397) = -(397 - 242) = -155

(+242) + (-397) = -(397 - 242) = -155

(-242) + (+397) = 397 - 242 = 155

(-242) - (-397) = (-242) + (+397) = 397 - 242 = 155

(-3)(7)(2) = (-21)(2) = -42

(8)(-7)(1) = (-56)(1) = -56

(-9)(-7)(-1) = (63)(-1) = -63

(-7)(8)(2) = (-56)(2) = -112

(-4)(-9)(3) = (36)(3) = 108

(12)(5)(-2) = (60)(-2) = -120

(-11)(2)(-4) = (-22)(-4) = 88

(-9)(-4)(-3) = (36)(-3) = -108

④ Solve.

The Passer Rating of a college football quarterback is calculated using the formula NCAA QB Passer Rating = [(8.4*y*) + (330*t*) - (200*i*) + (100*c*)] ÷ *a*, where *y* is the number of passing yards, *t* is the number of touchdowns thrown, *i* is the number of interceptions thrown, *c* is the number of completed passes, and *a* is the number of pass attempts.

Calculate the passer rating of a quarterback that had 220 passing yards, 1 touchdown thrown, no interceptions, 13 completed passes, and 17 pass attempts in his last game. Round answers to the nearest hundredth.

Passer Rating = [(8.4)(220) + (330)(1) - (200)(0) + (100)(13)] ÷ 17
= (1848 + 330 - 0 + 1300) ÷ 17 = 3478 ÷ 17 = 204.59

Order of Operations, Simplifying Exponents Worksheet 2

① Simplify each expression, following the proper order of operations.

$8 + 28 \div 4 =$
$8 + 7 = 15$
$27 - 3 \times 8 =$
$27 - 24 = 3$
$16 - 4 \times 3 + 7 =$
$16 - 12 + 7 = 4 + 7 = 11$
$6 + 9 \times 7 \div 3 =$
$6 + 63 \div 3 = 6 + 21 = 27$
$30 \div 6 \times 6 + 7 - 3 \times 2 =$
$5 \times 6 + 7 - 3 \times 2 = 30 + 7 - 3 \times 2 = 30 + 7 - 6 = 37 - 6 = 31$
$24 \div (3 \times 4) + 5 - 4 \times 1 =$
$24 \div 12 + 5 - 4 \times 1 = 2 + 5 - 4 \times 1 = 2 + 5 - 4 = 7 - 4 = 3$
$(11 - 4) \times 4 - 11 =$
$7 \times 4 - 11 = 28 - 11 = 17$
$(12 - 7)^2 - 42 \div 7 =$
$(5)^2 - 42 \div 7 = 25 - 42 \div 7 = 25 - 6 = 19$
$(21 - 4) - 3^2 + 2 \times 4 =$
$17 - 3^2 + 2 \times 4 = 17 - 9 + 2 \times 4 = 17 - 9 + 8 = 8 + 8 = 16$
$(14 - 11)^3 - 4^2 - 2 \times 3 =$
$(3)^3 - 4^2 - 2 \times 3 = 27 - 16 - 2 \times 3 = 27 - 16 - 6 = 11 - 6 = 5$
$2^3 \times 4 \div (9 + 7) - 3^2 =$
$2^3 \times 4 \div 16 - 9 = 8 \times 4 \div 16 - 9 = 32 \div 16 - 9 = 2 - 9 = -7$
$(6^2 - (12 + 13) + 7) \div 6 =$
$(6^2 - 25 + 7) \div 6 = (36 - 25 + 7) \div 6 = (11 + 7) \div 6 = 18 \div 6 = 3$
$((8 + 4 \times 3) \div 5)^2 =$
$((8 + 12) \div 5)^2 = (20 \div 5)^2 = 4^2 = 16$

② Simplify the expressions. You do not have to solve exponents greater than 3.

$37^0 = 1$
$92^1 = 92$
$14^2 \times 14^6 = 14^8$
$12^9 \div 12^7 = 12^2 = 144$
$(63 \div 9)^2 = 7^2 = 49$
$4^{-3} = \left(\frac{1}{4}\right)^3 = \frac{1^3}{4^3} = \frac{1}{64}$
$\left(\frac{1}{11}\right)^2 = \frac{1^2}{11^2} = \frac{1}{121}$
$\left(\frac{3}{5}\right)^{-2} = \left(\frac{5}{3}\right)^2 = \frac{5^2}{3^2} = \frac{25}{9}$

Teaching Tips, Cont.

- Write the following problem on the board: 4 + 10 ÷ 2 =. Ask several students for the answer to the problem. (Students will most likely give 7 as the answer, but the real answer is 9.) For both answers, ask the student supplying the answer to tell how he/she arrived at the answer.
- Explain that without rules in math, we would have the same situation as a football game without rules. There would be no way to tell who was right and who was wrong when two different answers were given.
- Introduce the order of operations in the teaching box. Point out the mnemonic device for remembering the order of operations.
- Complete the Classwork exercises. Have some students work the problems on the board for the class and explain their answers. All students should work the problems in their books.

Assignments

- Complete Lesson 3, Activities 2-4.
- Worksheet 2 (Optional).

Lesson 4

Concepts

- Prime numbers
- Factoring
- Exponents

Learning Objectives

The student will be able to:

- Define *factor*, *prime*, and *composite*
- Find all natural number factors of a given number
- Express the prime factorization of a given number using exponents when appropriate

Materials Needed

- Student Book, Lesson 4
- Algebra tiles (cut from the *Tests and Resources* book)
- Zip-top sandwich bags - 1 per student

Teaching Tips

➢ Define *factor* from the teaching box. Ask a student to define *natural number*. (Refer to Lesson 1, if necessary.) You may wish to do the following activity repeated from the Horizons Pre-Algebra book.

➢ Have students take out 12 of the single unit squares from the algebra tiles. Ask them to arrange the squares to form a rectangle. The dimensions of the rectangle are factors. A 3 x 4 rectangle shows that 3 and 4 are factors of 12.

➢ This activity also works to arrange the squares in equal-sized groups. They should try groups of 1, 2, 3, etc. all the way up to 12. Which group sizes work? Which ones don't? The group sizes that work are the factors of 12.

Lesson 4

Factoring and Prime Numbers

A **factor** is a natural number that divides into another number with no remainder.
4 is a factor of 12 because $12 \div 4 = 3$.
From this example, we can see that 3 is also a factor of 12.
All the factors of 12 are 1, 2, 3, 4, 6, and 12.

Prime numbers are natural numbers whose only factors are 1 and itself. 3 is a prime number because its only factors are 1 and 3.

Composite numbers are all numbers greater than 1 that are not prime.

The numbers 0 and 1 are neither prime nor composite, and 2 is the only even prime number.

Prime factors of a number are the prime numbers that divide into the number with no remainder.
Prime factorization is the process of finding all the prime numbers that multiply together to get the original number.

There are two ways to find the prime factorization of a number. One is to continually divide by prime numbers until you get a quotient that is prime.

$24 \div 2 = 12$

$12 \div 2 = 6$

$6 \div 2 = 3$

The prime factors of 24 are 2, 2, 2, and 3.

The second way is to make a factor tree. Write the original number as the product of any two factors you think of. Continue factoring these factors until all factors are prime.

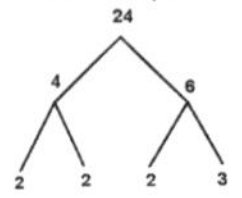

$24 = 2 \times 2 \times 2 \times 3 = 2^3 \times 3$

① **Classwork**

Find all the factors of each number. Use this information to identify each as either *prime* or *composite*.

7 1, 7 Prime

8 1, 2, 4, 8 Composite

9 1, 3, 9 Composite

10 1, 2, 5, 10 Composite

11 1, 11 Prime

Find the prime factorization of each number.

16

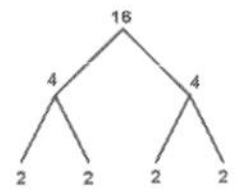

$16 = 2^4$

18

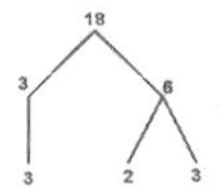

$18 = 2 \times 3^2$

28

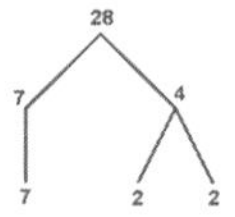

$28 = 2^2 \times 7$

45

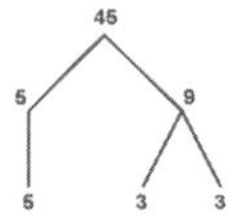

$45 = 3^2 \times 5$

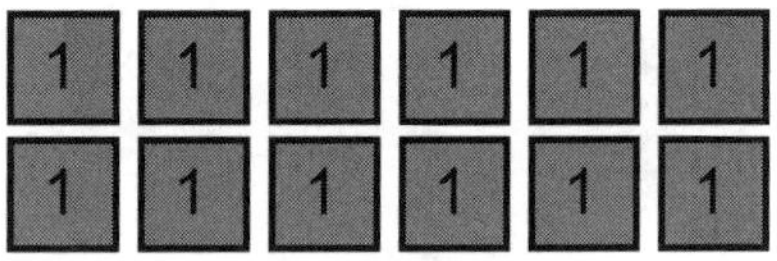

2 and 6 are factors

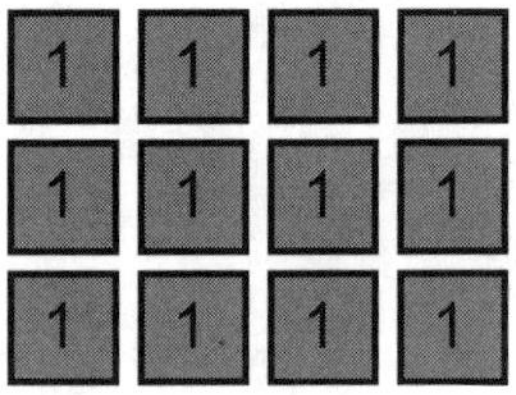

3 and 4 are factors

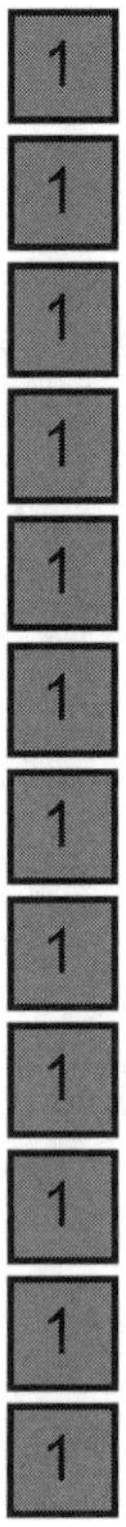

1 and 12 are factors

Activities

② Find the prime numbers in the list below by following the directions.

1. Cross out the number 1.
2. Circle the number 2. Cross out every other number after two (the multiples of 2).
3. Circle the number 3. Cross out every third number after three (the multiples of 3).
4. Circle the number 5. Cross out every fifth number after five (the multiples of 5).
5. Circle the number 7. Cross out every seventh number after seven (the multiples of 7).
6. Circle all remaining numbers. The circled numbers are the prime numbers less than 100.

1	(2)	(3)	4	(5)	6	(7)	8	9	10
(11)	12	(13)	14	15	16	(17)	18	(19)	20
21	22	(23)	24	25	26	27	28	(29)	30
(31)	32	33	34	35	36	(37)	38	39	40
(41)	42	(43)	44	45	46	(47)	48	49	50
51	52	(53)	54	55	56	57	58	(59)	60
(61)	62	63	64	65	66	(67)	68	69	70
(71)	72	(73)	74	75	76	77	78	(79)	80
81	82	(83)	84	85	86	87	88	(89)	90
91	92	93	94	95	96	(97)	98	99	100

Write the prime numbers less than 100.

2, 3, 5, 7, 11, 13, 17, 19, 23, 29, 31, 37, 41,

43, 47, 53, 59, 61, 67, 71, 73, 79, 83, 89, 97

③ Find the prime factorization of each number. Use exponents where appropriate.

12
$12 = 2 \times 2 \times 3$
$12 = 2^2 \times 3$

14
$14 = 2 \times 7$

15
$15 = 3 \times 5$

20
$20 = 2 \times 2 \times 5$
$20 = 2^2 \times 5$

21
$21 = 3 \times 7$

22
$22 = 2 \times 11$

24
$24 = 2 \times 2 \times 2 \times 3$
$24 = 2^3 \times 3$

25
$25 = 5 \times 5$
$25 = 5^2$

Teaching Tips, Cont.

- Define *prime factor* and *prime factorization* from the teaching box.
- Demonstrate the procedure for factorization by division. (See example below.) Emphasize that prime numbers must be used as the divisors when doing repeated division, but any factor may be used in a factor tree.
- Complete the Classwork exercises. Have some students work the problems on the board for the class and explain their answers. All students should work the problems in their books.

Assignment

- Complete Lesson 4, Activities 2-3.

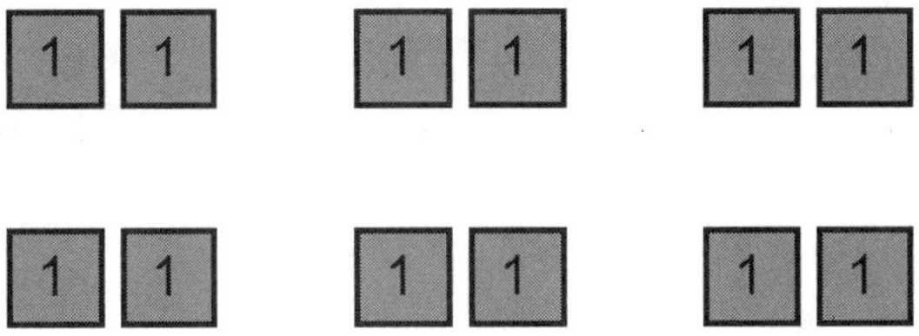

2 and 6 are factors

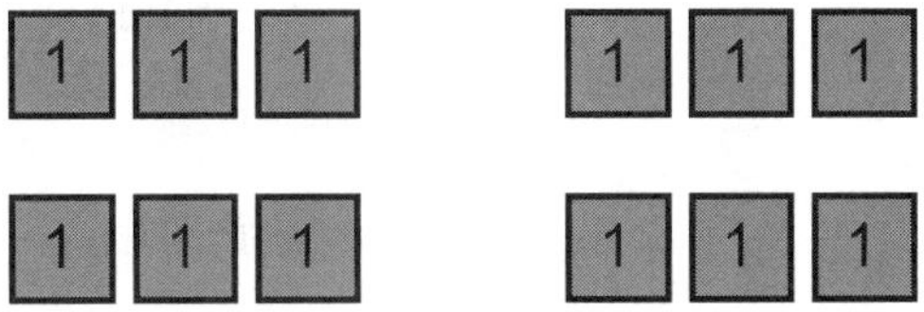

3 and 4 are factors

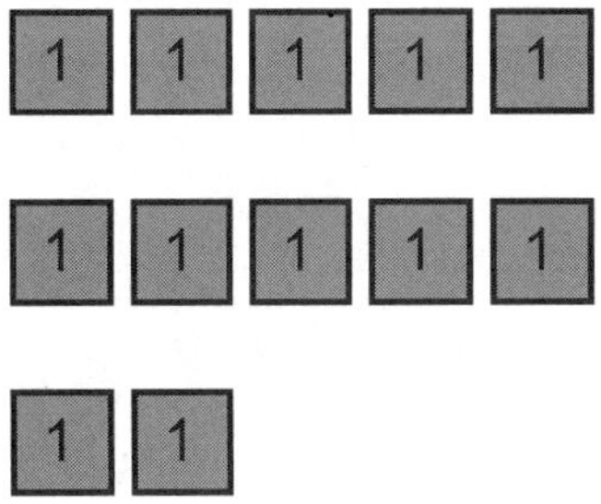

5 is not a factor

Note: Factorization by division can be done by dividing upside-down:

Step 1:
(2)|24
12

Step 2:
(2)|24
(2)|12
6

Step 3:
(2)|24
(2)|12
(2)| 6
(3)

Continue dividing the quotient by prime numbers until the quotient is prime. This method makes it easy to identify all of the prime factors.

Lesson 5

Concepts

- Absolute value
- Adding and subtracting signed numbers
- Multiplying and dividing signed numbers
- Prime factorization
- Order of operations

Learning Objectives

The student will be able to:

- Define *absolute value*
- Find the absolute value of positive and negative numbers
- Find the absolute value of mathematical expressions

Materials Needed

- Student Book, Lesson 5
- Worksheet 3

Teaching Tips

- Have students complete Worksheet 3 in class. This may be for added practice of earlier topics or graded as a quiz.
- Define *absolute value* from the teaching box. Emphasize that absolute value is a number's distance from zero on the number line. Distance is always positive.
- Explain that absolute value gives a number's distance from zero. Inverse operations get a number back to its starting point, no matter what that starting point is. Inverse operations are the foundation of math fact families.

Absolute Value

The **absolute value** of a number is the number's distance from zero on a number line. The absolute value of 5, written as $|5|$, is 5, because the number 5 is 5 units away from zero. The absolute value of −5, written as $|-5|$, is also 5, because −5 is 5 units away from zero.

① **Classwork**
Solve the following absolute value problems.

$|37| = 37$ $\quad -|8| = -8$

$|-19| = 19$ $\quad -|-47| = -47$

Activities

② Solve, using the rules of absolute values.

$|3| = 3$

$|49| = 49$

$|-25| = 25$

$|-79| = 79$

$-|11| = -11$

$-|-82| = -82$

$-|16| = -16$

$-|-43| = -43$

$|19 + 3| = 22$

$-|22 + 11| = -33$

$|15 + 18| = 33$

$|5 - 4| = 1$

$-|17 - 20| = -3$

$-|2 + 17| = -19$

$-|33 - 35| = -2$

$|16| + |4| = 16 + 4 = 20$

$|9| + |-15| = 9 + 15 = 24$

$|-27| + |-3| =$
$27 + 3 = 30$

$|-29| + |6| = 29 + 6 = 35$

$|5| - |-24| = 5 - 24 = -19$

$-|9| + |-13| =$
$-9 + 13 = 4$

$-|1| - |-28| =$
$-1 - 28 = -29$

$|26| - |35| = 26 - 35 = -9$

$-|-12| - |-15| =$
$-12 - 15 = -27$

$|19 + 18| + |23 - 17| =$
$37 + 6 = 43$

$-|24 - 16| + |15 - 17| =$
$-8 + 2 = -6$

$-|26 + 14| - |42 - 18| =$
$-40 - 24 = -64$

③ Solve, using the rules for adding signed numbers. Write the problem vertically, if necessary.

$(+7) + (+15) = 7 + 15 = 22$

$(-13) + (+4) = -(13 - 4) = -9$

$(-18) - (-6) =$
$(-18) + (+6) = -(18 - 6) = -12$

$(+17) + (-65) = 17 - 65 = -48$

$(+29) + (+19) = 29 + 19 = 48$

$(+34) - (-16) =$
$(+34) + (+16) = 34 + 16 = 50$

$(-27) + (+8) = -(27 - 8) = = -19$

$(-43) + (-12) = -(43 + 12) = -55$

$(+41) - (+14) = 41 - 14 = 27$

$(+19) + (-6) = 19 - 6 = 13$

$(-16) + (+27) = 27 - 16 = 11$

$(-7) - (-28) =$
$(-7) + (+28) = 28 - 7 = 21$

④ Find the prime factorization of each number. Use exponents where appropriate.

27
$27 = 3 \times 3 \times 3$
$27 = 3^3$

28
$28 = 2 \times 2 \times 7$
$28 = 2^2 \times 7$

30
$30 = 2 \times 3 \times 5$

32
$32 = 2 \times 2 \times 2 \times 2 \times 2$
$32 = 2^5$

33
$33 = 3 \times 11$

35
$35 = 5 \times 7$

⑤ Solve, following proper order of operations.

$5 + 12 \div 3 = 5 + 4 = 9$

$27 - 3 \times 5 = 27 - 15 = 12$

$13 - 2 \times 4 + 6 = 13 - 8 + 6 = 5 + 6 = 11$

$4 + 3^2 + 5 = 4 + 9 + 5 = 13 + 5 = 18$

$12 \div 6 \times 5 + 3 - 1 \times 7 = 2 \times 5 + 3 - 1 \times 7 = 10 + 3 - 1 \times 7 = 10 + 3 - 7 = 13 - 7 = 6$

$16 \div 2^2 + 5 - 3 \times 2 = 16 \div 4 + 5 - 3 \times 2 = 4 + 5 - 3 \times 2 = 4 + 5 - 6 = 9 - 6 = 3$

$(11 - 2)4 \div 6 - 5 = 9 \times 4 \div 6 - 5 = 36 \div 6 - 5 = 6 - 5 = 1$

$(7 - 3)^2 - 20 \div 4 = (4)^2 - 20 \div 4 = 16 - 20 \div 4 = 16 - 5 = 11$

$(4 + 3) - 2^2 + 6 \times 2 = 7 - 2^2 + 6 \times 2 = 7 - 4 + 6 \times 2 = 7 - 4 + 12 = 3 + 12 = 15$

$(11 - 8)^3 - 5^2 + 7 \times 2 = (3)^3 - 5^2 + 7 \times 2 = 27 - 25 + 7 \times 2 = 27 - 25 + 14 = 2 + 14 = 16$

$3^3 \div 9 + (5 + 1) - 4 = 3^3 \div 9 + 6 - 4 = 27 \div 9 + 6 - 4 = 3 + 6 - 4 = 9 - 4 = 5$

$(2 \times 8 - (21 - 16) + 1) \div 6 = (16 - 5 + 1) \div 6 = (11 + 1) \div 6 = 12 \div 6 = 2$

$((2 + 4 \times 3) \div 7)^2 = ((2 + 12) \div 7)^2 = (14 \div 7)^2 = 2^2 = 4$

Order of Operations, Simplifying Exponents Worksheet 3

① Simplify each expression, following the proper order of operations.

$6 + 9 \times 8 \div 12 =$
$6 + 72 \div 12 = 6 + 6 = 12$
$33 \div 3 \times 4 + 4 - 2 \times 7 =$
$11 \times 4 + 4 - 2 \times 7 = 44 + 4 - 2 \times 7 = 44 + 4 - 14 = 48 - 14 = 34$
$36 \div (3 \times 6) + 9 - 2 \times 4 =$
$36 \div 18 + 9 - 2 \times 4 = 2 + 9 - 2 \times 4 = 2 + 9 - 8 = 11 - 8 = 3$
$(25 - 20) \times 4 - 19 =$
$5 \times 4 - 19 = 20 - 19 = 1$
$(12 - 3)^2 - 20 \times 3 =$
$(9)^2 - 20 \times 3 = 81 - 20 \times 3 = 81 - 60 = 21$
$(13 + 8) - 4^2 + 3 \times 2 =$
$21 - 4^2 + 3 \times 2 = 21 - 16 + 3 \times 2 = 21 - 16 + 6 = 5 + 6 = 11$
$(9 - 7)^3 + 3^2 - 4 \times 2 =$
$(2)^3 + 3^2 - 4 \times 2 = 8 + 9 - 4 \times 2 = 8 + 9 - 8 = 17 - 8 = 9$
$3^3 \div 9 \times (11 - 7) - 6 =$
$3^3 \div 9 \times 4 - 6 = 27 \div 9 \times 4 - 6 = 3 \times 4 - 6 = 12 - 6 = 6$
$(8^2 - (15 + 19) + 9) \div 13 =$
$(8^2 - 34 + 9) \div 13 = (64 - 34 + 9) \div 13 = (30 + 9) \div 13 = 39 \div 13 = 3$
$((4 + 3 \times 7) \div 5)^2 =$
$((4 + 21) \div 5)^2 = (25 \div 5)^2 = 5^2 = 25$
$(9 + 18 \div 3 - 5)^2 \div 2 + 13 =$
$(9 + 6 - 5)^2 \div 2 + 13 = 10^2 \div 2 + 13 = 100 \div 2 + 13 = 50 + 13 = 63$
$1^3 + 2^3 - 3^2 \times 4^0 + 9 \div 3 =$
$1 + 8 - 9 \times 1 + 9 \div 3 = 1 + 8 - 9 + 3 = 9 - 9 + 3 = 0 + 3 = 3$

② Simplify the expressions. You do not have to solve exponents greater than 3.

$41^0 = 1$
$53^1 = 53$
$23^2 \times 23^6 = 23^8$
$9^{13} \div 9^{11} = 9^2 = 81$
$(54 \div 6)^2 = 9^2 = 81$

$7^{-4} = \left(\frac{1}{7}\right)^4 = \frac{1^4}{7^4} = \frac{1}{7^4}$
$\left(\frac{1}{12}\right)^2 = \frac{1^2}{12^2} = \frac{1}{144}$
$\left(\frac{2}{3}\right)^{-3} = \left(\frac{3}{2}\right)^3 = \frac{3^3}{2^3} = \frac{27}{8}$

Teaching Tips, Cont.

- To illustrate absolute value and inverse operations, ask the students the following questions: If John jogs 1 mile east, turns around, and jogs 1 mile west, how many miles has John jogged? (2) Changing direction does not affect the sign of the answer. Traveling east is like moving in the positive direction on the number line. Traveling west is like moving in the negative direction on the number line. If John starts at mile marker 8 and bicycles for 6 miles, at what mile marker will he end? (14) How many miles must he bicycle to return to mile marker 8? (6) This is using inverse operations.
  $8 + 6 = 14$ and $14 - 6 = 8$
- When working absolute value problems, always solve inside the absolute value sign first (the answer inside the absolute value sign is always positive), then apply any signs and operations outside the absolute value sign.
- Complete the Classwork exercises. Have some students work the problems on the board for the class. All students should work the problems in their books.

Assignment

- Complete Lesson 5, Activities 2-5.

Lesson 6

Concepts

- Greatest common factor
- Least common multiple
- Exponents
- Prime numbers

Learning Objectives

The student will be able to:

- Define *greatest common factor*
- Identify common factors of a given set of natural numbers
- Calculate the greatest common factor of a set of 2 or 3 natural numbers
- Define *least common multiple*
- Identify the highest order primes from a set of 2 or 3 natural numbers
- Calculate the least common multiple of a set of 2 or 3 natural numbers

Materials Needed

- Student Book, Lesson 6

Teaching Tips

➢ Review prime factoring from Lesson 4.

➢ Have students find the prime factorization of 8 and 12. ($2 \times 2 \times 2$ and $2 \times 2 \times 3$) Ask them to identify factors that appear in both sets (2×2).

➢ Define *greatest common factor* from the teaching box.

Lesson 6

Greatest Common Factor and Least Common Multiple

The **greatest common factor** of two or more numbers is the largest factor that is common to all the given numbers.

To find the greatest common factor, begin by finding the prime factorization of each number. For example, to find the greatest common factor of 12 and 18, find the prime factorization of each number.

$12 = 2 \times 2 \times 3$

$18 = 2 \times 3 \times 3$

Then, circle all prime number factors that are common to both numbers.

$12 = \textcircled{2} \times 2 \times \textcircled{3}$

$18 = \textcircled{2} \times 3 \times \textcircled{3}$

Finally, multiply the circled prime factors to find the greatest common factor.

$2 \times 3 = 6$

The greatest common factor of 12 and 18 is 6.

The **least common multiple** of two or more numbers is the smallest number that is a multiple of all the given numbers.

To find the least common multiple, begin by finding the prime factorization of each number. For example, to find the least common multiple of 12 and 18, find the prime factorization of each number and express it using exponents.

$12 = 2 \times 2 \times 3 = 2^2 \times 3$

$18 = 2 \times 3 \times 3 = 2 \times 3^2$

Then, for each prime number, draw a box around the value with the largest exponent.

$12 = 2 \times 2 \times 3 = \boxed{2^2} \times 3$

$18 = 2 \times 3 \times 3 = 2 \times \boxed{3^2}$

Multiply the boxed factors to find the least common multiple.

$2^2 \times 3^2 = 4 \times 9 = 36$

The least common multiple of 12 and 18 is 36.

You can also list the multiples of each number until you find a multiple in common.

12: 12, 24, **36**

18: 18, **36**

① **Classwork**

Find the greatest common factor of each set of numbers.

9 and 15

$9 = \textcircled{3} \times 3$

$15 = \textcircled{3} \times 5$

GCF is 3

15 and 24

$15 = \textcircled{3} \times 5$

$24 = 2 \times 2 \times 2 \times \textcircled{3}$

GCF is 3

6, 9, and 15

$6 = 2 \times \textcircled{3}$

$9 = \textcircled{3} \times 3$

$15 = \textcircled{3} \times 5$

GCF is 3

Find the least common multiple of each set of numbers.

3 and 5

$3 = 1 \times \boxed{3}$

$5 = 1 \times \boxed{5}$

LCM: $3 \times 5 = 15$

8 and 12

$8 = 2 \times 2 \times 2 = \boxed{2^3}$

$12 = 2 \times 2 \times 3 = 2^2 \times \boxed{3}$

LCM: $2^3 \times 3 = 8 \times 3 = 24$

6, 8, and 9

$6 = 2 \times 3$

$8 = 2 \times 2 \times 2 = \boxed{2^3}$

$9 = 3 \times 3 = \boxed{3^2}$

LCM: $2^3 \times 3^2 = 8 \times 9 = 72$

Activities

② Find the greatest common factor of each set of numbers.

9 and 12
$9 = 3 \times \textcircled{3}$
$12 = 2 \times 2 \times \textcircled{3}$
GCF is 3

12 and 16
$12 = \textcircled{2} \times \textcircled{2} \times 3$
$16 = \textcircled{2} \times \textcircled{2} \times 2 \times 2$
GCF is $2 \times 2 = 4$

15 and 35
$15 = 3 \times \textcircled{5}$
$35 = \textcircled{5} \times 7$
GCF is 5

16 and 18
$16 = \textcircled{2} \times 2 \times 2 \times 2$
$18 = \textcircled{2} \times 3 \times 3$
GCF is 2

16 and 20
$16 = \textcircled{2} \times \textcircled{2} \times 2 \times 2$
$20 = \textcircled{2} \times \textcircled{2} \times 5$
GCF is $2 \times 2 = 4$

20 and 24
$20 = \textcircled{2} \times \textcircled{2} \times 5$
$24 = \textcircled{2} \times \textcircled{2} \times 2 \times 3$
GCF is $2 \times 2 = 4$

12, 15, and 18
$12 = 2 \times 2 \times \textcircled{3}$
$15 = \textcircled{3} \times 5$
$18 = 2 \times \textcircled{3} \times 3$
GCF is 3

16, 24, and 32
$16 = \textcircled{2} \times \textcircled{2} \times \textcircled{2} \times 2$
$24 = \textcircled{2} \times \textcircled{2} \times \textcircled{2} \times 3$
$32 = \textcircled{2} \times \textcircled{2} \times \textcircled{2} \times 2 \times 2$
GCF is $2 \times 2 \times 2 = 8$

10, 18, and 30
$10 = \textcircled{2} \times 5$
$18 = \textcircled{2} \times 3 \times 3$
$30 = \textcircled{2} \times 3 \times 5$
GCF is 2

③ Find the least common multiple of each set of numbers.

6 and 9
$6 = \boxed{2} \times 3$
$9 = 3 \times 3 = \boxed{3^2}$
LCM: $2 \times 3^2 = 2 \times 9 = 18$

4 and 6
$4 = 2 \times 2 = \boxed{2^2}$
$6 = 2 \times \boxed{3}$
LCM: $2^2 \times 3 = 4 \times 3 = 12$

9 and 12
$9 = 3 \times 3 = \boxed{3^2}$
$12 = 2 \times 2 \times 3 = \boxed{2^2} \times 3$
LCM: $2^2 \times 3^2 = 4 \times 9 = 36$

9 and 15
$9 = 3 \times 3 = \boxed{3^2}$
$15 = 3 \times \boxed{5}$
LCM: $3^2 \times 5 = 9 \times 5 = 45$

12 and 15
$12 = 2 \times 2 \times 3 = \boxed{2^2} \times 3$
$15 = \boxed{3} \times \boxed{5}$
LCM: $2^2 \times 3 \times 5 = 60$

12 and 16
$12 = 2 \times 2 \times 3 = 2^2 \times \boxed{3}$
$16 = 2 \times 2 \times 2 \times 2 = \boxed{2^4}$
LCM: $3 \times 2^4 = 3 \times 16 = 48$

3, 4, and 5
$3 = 1 \times \boxed{3}$
$4 = 2 \times 2 = \boxed{2^2}$
$5 = 1 \times \boxed{5}$
LCM: $2^2 \times 3 \times 5 = 60$

10, 15, and 20
$10 = 2 \times \boxed{5}$
$15 = \boxed{3} \times 5$
$20 = 2 \times 2 \times 5 = \boxed{2^2} \times 5$
LCM:
$2^2 \times 3 \times 5 = 4 \times 3 \times 5 = 60$

9, 12, and 15
$9 = 3 \times 3 = \boxed{3^2}$
$12 = 2 \times 2 \times 3 = \boxed{2^2} \times 3$
$15 = 3 \times \boxed{5}$
LCM: $2^2 \times 3^2 \times 5 = 180$

Note: Circles have been used to mark the common factors for finding the greatest common factor, and squares have been used to mark the factors for the least common multiple. The visual of placing boxes around the exponential expressions and circles around individual prime numbers should help students remember what they are to do in each case. Your cupped palm (i.e. circle) is easily able to hold one thing at a time (individual prime numbers). A box is more practical for holding large or multiple items (exponential numbers). The individual *factors* (circled primes) are used to find the greatest common *factor*. The boxes with primes and *multiples* (exponents) are used to find the least common *multiple.*

Teaching Tips, Cont.

- Teach the procedure for finding the greatest common factor. Remind students to always circle the prime factors that appear as a factor in every number in the set. If a prime number appears more than once in every number in the set, circle it the same number of times that it appears in every number.
- Emphasize that the answer will always be less than or equal to the smallest number in the given set.
- Ask the students why the answer must be less than or equal to the smallest number in the set. (Factors are numbers that multiply together to produce a new number. You can't multiply a natural number by another natural number and end up with a smaller number than one of your factors.)
- Define *least common multiple* from the teaching box. Reinforce the difference between greatest common factor (which is always less than or equal to the smallest number in the set) and least common multiple (which is always greater than or equal to the largest number in the set).
- Hint: The *greatest* common factor can be *no greater than* the smallest given number, and the *least* common multiple must be *at least* as big as the biggest given number.
- Complete the Classwork exercises. Have some students work the problems on the board for the class. All students should work the problems in their books.

Assignment

- Complete Lesson 6, Activities 2-3.

Lesson 7

Concepts

- Roots
- Exponents
- Absolute value
- Addition and subtraction of signed numbers
- Multiplication and division of signed numbers

Learning Objectives

The student will be able to:

- Use proper terms relating to roots
- Calculate square roots and cube roots of numbers
- Simplify expressions using radicals
- Express exponential equations in radical form

Materials Needed

- Student Book, Lesson 7
- Worksheet 4

Teaching Tips

- Have students complete Worksheet 4 in class. This may be for added practice of earlier topics, or graded as a quiz, if desired.
- Define terms relating to roots in the teaching box. Show students the relationship between the base, exponent, and answer in an exponential equation, and the radicand (or argument), index, and answer in a radical expression.
- Review square numbers. Have students list all perfect squares less than 150. (1, 4, 9, 16, 25, 36, 49, 64, 81, 100, 121, 144)
- Explain that it is not necessary to prime factor the radicand, but rather look for perfect squares that are factors.

Root and Radicals

The opposite of raising a number to an exponent is taking the **root** of a number. The root is represented by the symbol $\sqrt{\ }$, called the **radical**. The number under the radical is called the **radicand** (or **argument**), and the number that indicates the root is called the **index** and corresponds to the exponent. For example, $2^3 = 8$. To express this as a root, write $\sqrt[3]{8} = 2$, where 8 is the radicand, 3 is the index, and 2 is the root. In this case, 2 is the cube root of 8.

To find the **square root** of a number, find a number that, when multiplied by itself, gives the radicand.

For example, $\sqrt{16} = \sqrt{4 \times 4} = 4$

For larger numbers, write the radicand as the product of perfect square factors and find the square roots.

$\sqrt{128} = \sqrt{8 \times 8 \times 2} = 8\sqrt{2}$

To add or subtract roots, the radicands and indexes must be equal. Add the numbers immediately to the left of the radical. If there is no number, treat it as a 1.

For example, $\sqrt{3} + \sqrt{3} = 2\sqrt{3}$ and $2\sqrt{5} + 4\sqrt{5} = 6\sqrt{5}$. If the radicands or indexes are not equal, the roots cannot be added or subtracted.

To multiply or divide roots with the same index, multiply or divide the radicands and write the answer under one radical. Multiply or divide the numbers outside the radical and write outside the radical in the answer. Simplify if necessary.

For example, $\sqrt{12} \times \sqrt{3} = \sqrt{12 \times 3} = \sqrt{36} = 6$

① **Classwork**

Rewrite the following expressions as roots.

$2^4 = 16 \quad 2 = \sqrt[4]{16}$

$3^2 = 9 \quad 3 = \sqrt{9}$

$5^2 = 25 \quad 5 = \sqrt{25}$

$5^3 = 125 \quad 5 = \sqrt[3]{125}$

$6^3 = 216 \quad 6 = \sqrt[3]{216}$

Solve the following roots.

$\sqrt{16} = \sqrt{4 \times 4} = 4$

$\sqrt[3]{27} = \sqrt[3]{3 \times 3 \times 3} = 3$

$\sqrt{32} = \sqrt{2 \times 4 \times 4} = 4\sqrt{2}$

$\sqrt[3]{16} = \sqrt[3]{2 \times 2 \times 2 \times 2} = 2\sqrt[3]{2}$

$\sqrt{2} + \sqrt{2} = 2\sqrt{2}$

$\sqrt{5} + 2\sqrt{5} = 3\sqrt{5}$

$\sqrt[3]{10} + 5\sqrt[3]{10} = 6\sqrt[3]{10}$

$6\sqrt{7} - 4\sqrt{7} = 2\sqrt{7}$

$5\sqrt[3]{5} - 4\sqrt[3]{5} = \sqrt[3]{5}$

$(\sqrt{10})(\sqrt{2}) =$

$\sqrt{10 \times 2} = \sqrt{20} = \sqrt{2 \times 2 \times 5} = 2\sqrt{5}$

$(3\sqrt{5})(2\sqrt{2}) = (3 \times 2)\sqrt{5 \times 2} = 6\sqrt{10}$

$\sqrt{27} \div \sqrt{3} = \sqrt{27 \div 3} = \sqrt{9} = \sqrt{3 \times 3} = 3$

$10\sqrt[3]{16} \div 5\sqrt[3]{4} = (10 \div 5)\sqrt[3]{16 \div 4} = 2\sqrt[3]{4}$

$3 \div \sqrt{3} = \sqrt{3 \times 3} \div \sqrt{3} = \sqrt{9 \div 3} = \sqrt{3}$

Activities

② Rewrite the following expressions as roots.

$2^6 = 64 \quad 2 = \sqrt[6]{64}$

$5^2 = 25 \quad 5 = \sqrt{25}$

$4^3 = 64 \quad 4 = \sqrt[3]{64}$

$8^2 = 64 \quad 8 = \sqrt{64}$

$3^4 = 81 \quad 3 = \sqrt[4]{81}$

$7^2 = 49 \quad 7 = \sqrt{49}$

③ Solve the following roots.

$\sqrt{36} = \sqrt{6 \times 6} = 6$

$\sqrt[3]{8} = \sqrt[3]{2 \times 2 \times 2} = 2$

$\sqrt{12} = \sqrt{2 \times 2 \times 3} = 2\sqrt{3}$

$\sqrt[3]{24} = \sqrt[3]{2 \times 2 \times 2 \times 3} = 2\sqrt[3]{3}$

$\sqrt{6} + \sqrt{6} = 2\sqrt{6}$

$3\sqrt{7} + 2\sqrt{7} = 5\sqrt{7}$

$2\sqrt[3]{15} + 5\sqrt[3]{15} = 7\sqrt[3]{15}$

$8\sqrt{10} - 3\sqrt{10} = 5\sqrt{10}$

$7\sqrt[3]{2} - 4\sqrt[3]{2} = 3\sqrt[3]{2}$

$(\sqrt{10})(\sqrt{5}) =$

$\sqrt{10 \times 5} = \sqrt{50} = \sqrt{2 \times 5 \times 5} = 5\sqrt{2}$

$(4\sqrt{3})(3\sqrt{2}) = (4 \times 3)\sqrt{3 \times 2} = 12\sqrt{6}$

$\sqrt{32} \div \sqrt{2} = \sqrt{32 \div 2} = \sqrt{16} = \sqrt{4 \times 4} = 4$

$15\sqrt[3]{16} \div 3\sqrt[3]{2} =$

$(15 \div 3)\sqrt[3]{16 \div 2} = 5\sqrt[3]{8} = 5\sqrt[3]{2 \times 2 \times 2}$

$= 5 \times 2 = 10$

$5 \div \sqrt{5} = \sqrt{5 \times 5} \div \sqrt{5} = \sqrt{25 \div 5} = \sqrt{5}$

④ Solve, using the rules of absolute values.

$|8| - |-17| = 8 - 17 = -9$

$-|24| + |-7| = -24 + 7 = -(24 - 7) = -17$

$-|51| - |-28| = -51 - (+28) = -51 + (-28)$
$= -(51 + 28) = -79$

$|73| - |57| = 73 - 57 = 16$

$-|-35| - |-18| = -35 - (+18) =$
$-35 + (-18) = -(35 + 18) = -53$

$|91 + 18| + |33 - 27| = 109 + 6 = 115$

$-|42 - 26| + |25 - 37| =$
$-16 + 12 = -(16 - 12) = -4$

$-|19 + 14| - |37 - 28| =$
$-33 - 9 = -(33 + 9) = -42$

⑤ Solve, using the rules for signed numbers. Write the problem vertically, if necessary.

$(-48) + (+53) = 53 - 48 = 5$

$(-39) + (-15) = -(39 + 15) = -54$

$(+93) - (-65) = 93 + 65 = 158$

$(-117) - (-68) =$
$(-117) + (+68) = -(117 - 68) = -49$

$(-13)(4) = -52$

$(-36) \div (-2) = 18$

$(+121) + (+31) = 121 + 31 = 152$

$(+95) + (-137) = -(137 - 95) = -42$

$(-93) - (+65) = -(93 + 65) = -158$

$(+117) - (+68) =$
$(117 - 68) = 49$

$(5)(-2)(13) = (-10)(13) = -130$

$(-108) \div (+9) = -12$

Prime Factorization, Absolute Value Worksheet 4

① Find the prime factorization of each number. Use exponents where appropriate.

12	25	32
$12 = 2 \times 2 \times 3$	$25 = 5 \times 5$	$32 = 2 \times 2 \times 2 \times 2 \times 2$
$12 = 2^2 \times 3$	$25 = 5^2$	$32 = 2^5$
18	**24**	**27**
$18 = 2 \times 3 \times 3$	$24 = 2 \times 2 \times 2 \times 3$	$27 = 3 \times 3 \times 3$
$18 = 2 \times 3^2$	$24 = 2^3 \times 3$	$27 = 3^3$

② Solve, using the rules of absolute values.

$|41| = 41$

$|-72| = 72$

$-|14| = -14$

$-|-29| = -29$

$|36 + 40| = 76$

$-|33 + 21| = -54$

$|-22 + 35| = 13$

$-|-18 + 5| = -13$

$|26 - 30| = 4$

$-|62 - 71| = -9$

$|-12 - 15| = 27$

Teaching Tips, Cont.

- Have students express each of the following numbers as the product of a perfect square and another factor:
  12 = (4 × 3), 18 = (9 × 2),
  20 = (4 × 5), 24 = (4 × 6).

- Show students that the process for finding any other root is the same as finding the square root, except the number of equal factors in the radicand must equal the number in the index. For example, the cube root of a number must have the same factor appearing three times in the radicand. The 4th root of a number must have the same factor appearing 4 times in the radicand. Encourage students to prime factor the radicand if they are having difficulty finding the root.

- Complete the Classwork exercises. Have some students work the problems on the board for the class. All students should work the problems in their books.

Assignment

- Complete Lesson 7, Activities 2-5.

Lesson 8

Concepts

- Polynomial expressions
- Constants
- Coefficients
- Monomials
- Binomials
- Trinomials
- Roots
- Greatest common factor
- Least common multiple
- Math in the real world

Learning Objectives

The student will be able to:

- Identify algebraic expressions as monomials, binomials, trinomials, and polynomials
- Define *constant*
- Define *coefficient*

Materials Needed

- Student Book, Lesson 8
- Worksheet 5

Teaching Tips

- ➢ Teach polynomials from the teaching box. Emphasize that plus and minus signs are the only symbols that separate terms. Items that are multiplied or divided are considered one term.

- ➢ Define *constant* and *coefficient* from the teaching box. Explain that although they are both numbers, a constant is never attached to a variable, and a coefficient is always attached to a variable.

Algebraic Expressions

A **polynomial** is an algebraic expression. If that expression contains two or more terms, the terms must be separated by a plus or minus sign. All variables must have a positive integer as an exponent, and no variable may appear in a denominator.

A **constant** is a term that has a number but no variable.

A **coefficient** is a number that is multiplied by a variable.

A **monomial** is an expression containing one term, such as x^2, $3x$, or 5. A constant is a monomial.

A **binomial** is a polynomial containing two terms, such as $3x + 5$ or $x^2 - 4x$.

A **trinomial** is a polynomial containing three terms, such as $x^2 - 4x + 3$.

Identify whether or not each expression is a polynomial. For each polynomial, identify it as a constant, monomial, binomial, or trinomial.

$x^2 + 2x - 1$
This is a polynomial and a trinomial.

$4x^{-2} - 3x + 7$
This is not a polynomial because there is a -2 as an exponent.

① **Classwork**
Identify whether or not each expression is a polynomial. For each polynomial, identify it as a constant, monomial, binomial, or trinomial.

$6x - 4$
This is a polynomial and a binomial.

17
This is a polynomial, a monomial, and a constant.

$4x^2 + \frac{5}{x} - 3$
This is not a polynomial because the x is in the denominator.

$3x^{-2} - 5$
This is not a polynomial because there is a negative exponent.

$3x^2 - 4x + 2$
This is a polynomial and a trinomial.

Activities

② Identify whether or not each expression is a polynomial. For each polynomial, identify it as a constant, monomial, binomial, or trinomial.

$9x - 4$	This is a polynomial and a binomial.
$7x^2 + \frac{3}{x} - 4$	This is not a polynomial because the x is in the denominator.
$8x^{-2} + 9$	This is not a polynomial because there is a negative exponent.
31	This is a polynomial, a monomial, and a constant.
$10x^2 - 13x + 6$	This is a polynomial and a trinomial.
-3x	This is a polynomial and a monomial.

③ Solve the following roots.

$\sqrt{25} = \sqrt{5 \times 5} = 5$

$\sqrt[3]{64} = \sqrt[3]{4 \times 4 \times 4} = 4$

$\sqrt{8} = \sqrt{2 \times 2 \times 2} = 2\sqrt{2}$

$\sqrt[3]{54} = \sqrt[3]{2 \times 3 \times 3 \times 3} = 3\sqrt[3]{2}$

$2\sqrt{7} + 5\sqrt{7} = 7\sqrt{7}$

$2\sqrt{13} + 6\sqrt{13} = 8\sqrt{13}$

$4\sqrt[3]{21} + 9\sqrt[3]{21} = 13\sqrt[3]{21}$

$14\sqrt{11} - 8\sqrt{11} = 6\sqrt{11}$

$17\sqrt[3]{14} - 6\sqrt[3]{14} = 11\sqrt[3]{14}$

$\left(\sqrt{15}\right)\left(\sqrt{3}\right) =$
$\sqrt{15 \times 3} = \sqrt{45} = \sqrt{3 \times 3 \times 5} = 3\sqrt{5}$

$\left(3\sqrt{7}\right)\left(4\sqrt{5}\right) = (3 \times 4)\sqrt{7 \times 5} = 12\sqrt{35}$

$\sqrt{72} \div \sqrt{6} =$
$\sqrt{72 \div 6} = \sqrt{12} = \sqrt{2 \times 2 \times 3} = 2\sqrt{3}$

$15\sqrt[3]{44} \div 5\sqrt[3]{11} = (15 \div 5)\sqrt[3]{44 \div 11} = 3\sqrt[3]{4}$

$8 \div \sqrt{8} =$
$\sqrt{8 \times 8} \div \sqrt{8} = \sqrt{64 \div 8} = \sqrt{8} = \sqrt{2 \times 2 \times 2} = 2\sqrt{2}$

④ Find the greatest common factor of each set of numbers.

16, 18, and 20
16 = ②×2 × 2 × 2
18 = ②×3 × 3
20 = ②×2 × 5
GCF is 2

16, 20, and 24
16 = ②×②×2 × 2
20 = ②×②×5
24 = ②×②×2 × 3
GCF is $2 \times 2 = 4$

10, 18, and 30
10 = ②×5
18 = ②×3 × 3
30 = ②×3 × 5
GCF is 2

⑤ Find the least common multiple of each set of numbers.

12, 15 and 16
$12 = 2 \times 2 \times 3 = 2^2 \times \boxed{3}$
$15 = 3 \times \boxed{5}$
$16 = 2 \times 2 \times 2 \times 2 = \boxed{2^4}$
LCM:
$3 \times 2^4 \times 5 = 3 \times 16 \times 5 = 240$

6, 8, and 9
$6 = 2 \times 3$
$8 = 2 \times 2 \times 2 = \boxed{2^3}$
$9 = 3 \times 3 = \boxed{3^2}$
LCM: $2^3 \times 3^2 = 8 \times 9 = 72$

9, 12, and 20
$9 = 3 \times 3 = \boxed{3^2}$
$12 = 2 \times 2 \times 3 = \boxed{2^2} \times 3$
$20 = 2 \times 2 \times 5 = 2^2 \times \boxed{5}$
LCM: $2^2 \times 3^2 \times 5 = 180$

⑥ Solve.

The Passer Rating of a college football quarterback is calculated using the formula NCAA QB Passer Rating = $[(8.4y) + (330t) - (200i) + (100c)] \div a$, where y is the number of passing yards, t is the number of touchdowns thrown, i is the number of interceptions thrown, c is the number of completed passes, and a is the number of pass attempts.

Calculate the passer rating of a quarterback that had 5691 passing yards, 39 touchdowns thrown, 10 interceptions, 436 completed passes, and 658 pass attempts in his college career. Round answers to the nearest hundredth.

Passer Rating = [(8.4)(5691) + (330)(39) − (200)(10) + (100)(436)] ÷ 658

= (47804.4 + 12870 − 2000 + 43600) ÷ 658 = 102274.4 ÷ 658 = 155.43

Translating Words into Mathematical Statements, Roots Worksheet 5

① Translate the following words into a mathematical expression.

The total of a number and 71	$x + 71$
18 fewer than a number	$x - 18$
A number times 12	$12x$
The sum of 62 and a number	$62 + x$
The quotient of a number and 11	$x \div 11$
25 less than a number	$x - 25$
A number increased by a factor of 6	$6x$
83 more than a number	$x + 83$
A number less than 90	$90 - x$
The product of 5 and a number	$5x$
The ratio of a number to 7	$x \div 7$
A number increased by 53	$x + 53$

② Solve the following roots.

$\sqrt{25} = 5$

$\sqrt{81} = 9$

$\sqrt{24} = \sqrt{2 \times 2 \times 6} = 2\sqrt{6}$

$\sqrt{27} = \sqrt{3 \times 3 \times 3} = 3\sqrt{3}$

$\sqrt{48} = \sqrt{4 \times 4 \times 3} = 4\sqrt{3}$

$\sqrt{44} = \sqrt{2 \times 2 \times 11} = 2\sqrt{11}$

$\sqrt[3]{8} = 2$

$\sqrt[3]{27} = 3$

$\sqrt[3]{40} = \sqrt[3]{2 \times 2 \times 2 \times 5} = 2\sqrt[3]{5}$

$\sqrt[3]{54} = \sqrt[3]{3 \times 3 \times 3 \times 2} = 3\sqrt[3]{2}$

$\sqrt[3]{16} = \sqrt[3]{2 \times 2 \times 2 \times 2} = 2\sqrt[3]{2}$

$\sqrt[3]{64} = \sqrt[3]{4 \times 4 \times 4} = 4$

$6\sqrt{13} + 2\sqrt{13} =$
$(6 + 2)\sqrt{13} = 8\sqrt{13}$

$\sqrt{22} + 4\sqrt{22} = (1 + 4)\sqrt{22} = 5\sqrt{22}$

$16\sqrt{10} - 9\sqrt{10} =$
$(16 - 9)\sqrt{10} = 7\sqrt{10}$

$(\sqrt{2})(\sqrt{5}) = \sqrt{2 \times 5} = \sqrt{10}$

$(2\sqrt{18})(3\sqrt{8}) =$
$(2 \times 3)(\sqrt{18} \times \sqrt{8}) = 6(3\sqrt{2} \times 2\sqrt{2}) =$
$6(3 \times 2)(\sqrt{4}) = 6 \times 6 \times 2 = 72$

$\sqrt[3]{40} \div \sqrt[3]{5} = \sqrt[3]{40 \div 5} = \sqrt[3]{8} = 2$

$15\sqrt{12} \div 3\sqrt{6} =$
$(15 \div 3)(\sqrt{12} \div \sqrt{6}) = 5\sqrt{2}$

$\sqrt{50} \div 5 = \sqrt{50} \div \sqrt{25} = \sqrt{2}$

Teaching Tips, Cont.

- Teach how to identify monomials, binomials, and trinomials based on the number of terms.
- Emphasize that all variables must have positive exponents, and no variable may appear in the denominator of a polynomial. If either of these situations occurs, the expression is not a polynomial.
- Complete the Classwork exercises. Have some students work the problems on the board for the class. All students should work the problems in their books.

Assignments

- Complete Lesson 8, Activities 2-6.
- Worksheet 5 (Optional).

Lesson 9

Concepts

- Writing expressions with one variable
- Roots
- Absolute value
- Math in the real world

Learning Objectives

The student will be able to:

- Define *variable* and *constant*
- Translate words into mathematical expressions
- Use variables to represent unknown values
- Identify like terms in mathematical expressions
- Combine like terms

Materials Needed

- Student Book, Lesson 9
- 2 or more of each of the following items: pencils, pieces of paper, books
- Algebra tiles

Teaching Tips

➢ Define *variable* and *constant* in the teaching box. Explain that a variable simply represents an unknown amount – the amount they are looking for in a problem.

➢ Teach the rules for translating words into mathematical expressions. Point out that while this is not an exhaustive list, these are the most common words found in word problems.

Lesson 9

Writing Algebraic Expressions

A **variable** is a letter used to represent an unknown numerical value. In algebra, *x* is the most common variable. In an expression or equation, a letter appearing in more than one location always represents the same amount. To write expressions with a variable, let *x* represent the unknown amount. Use the following rules to translate words into a numeric expression: **Addition**: more than, total, sum, increased by, added to, together **Subtraction**: less than, fewer than, difference, decreased by, reduced by **Multiplication**: times, of, multiplied by, product, increased by a factor of **Division**: per, a, ratio, quotient, percent, out of When simplifying expressions, combine like terms. **Like terms** have identical variables with identical exponents or are constants. **Constants** (numbers with no variables) are all like terms and may be combined following the order of operations. Variables that are like terms may be combined following the order of operations.	① **Classwork** Translate the following words into a mathematical expression. 9 more than a number $x + 9$ 6 less than a number $x - 6$ A number increased by a factor of 12 $12x$ A number increased by 3 $x + 3$ 23 decreased by a number $23 - x$ A number multiplied by 5 $5x$ Simplify by combining like terms. $x + 2x = 3x$ $4 + 3 + x = 7 + x$ or $x + 7$ $x + 3x + 2 + 6 = 4x + 8$ or $8 + 4x$

Activities

② Translate the following words into a mathematical expression.

The total of a number and 63 $x + 63$
17 fewer than a number $x - 17$
A number times 11 $11x$
The sum of 37 and a number $37 + x$
The quotient of a number and 10 $x \div 10$
8 less than a number $x - 8$
A number increased by a factor of 5 $5x$
71 more than a number $x + 71$
A number less than 104 $104 - x$
The product of 19 and a number $19x$
The ratio of a number to 8 $x \div 8$
A number increased by 44 $x + 44$

Using Algebra Tiles

When using algebra tiles, the red pieces always represent negative terms. All other colors represent positive terms. In this set, green pieces are constants, blue pieces are x-terms, and yellow pieces are x^2 terms. The colors and shapes will help the students identify like terms. A red piece may be combined with another color of the same size and shape. A red piece will always negate a corresponding green, blue, or yellow piece, and therefore remove both pieces. For example, if you have 5 green squares and 3 red squares, the three red squares cancel out 3 of the green squares, leaving 2 green squares. This is the representation of 5 - 3 = 2.

③ Solve the following roots.

$\sqrt{63} = \sqrt{3 \times 3 \times 7} = 3\sqrt{7}$

$\sqrt[3]{108} = \sqrt[3]{3 \times 3 \times 3 \times 4} = 3\sqrt[3]{4}$

$4\sqrt{13} + 3\sqrt{13} = 7\sqrt{13}$

$\sqrt{8} + \sqrt{50} = 2\sqrt{2} + 5\sqrt{2} = 7\sqrt{2}$

$\sqrt[3]{24} + 5\sqrt[3]{81} = 2\sqrt[3]{3} + 5\left(3\sqrt[3]{3}\right) = 17\sqrt[3]{3}$

$9\sqrt{10} - 2\sqrt{10} = 7\sqrt{10}$

④ Solve, using the rules of absolute values.

$|-21| + |-45| = 21 + 45 = 66$

$|-18| + |73| = 18 + 73 = 91$

$|46| - |-26| = 46 - 26 = 20$

$-|35| + |-17| =$
$-35 + 17 = -(35 - 17) = -18$

$-|52| - |-38| = -52 - (+38) =$
$-52 + (-38) = -(52 + 38) = -90$

$|94| - |68| = 94 - 68 = 26$

$-|-67| - |-52| = -67 - (+52) =$
$-67 + (-52) = -(67 + 52) = -119$

$|33 + 24| + |18 - 8| = 57 + 10 = 67$

$-|94 - 79| + |28 - 15| =$
$-15 + 13 = -(15 - 13) = -2$

$-|31 + 19| - |23 - 17| = -50 - (+6) =$
$-50 + (-6) = -(50 + 6) = -56$

⑤ Write an algebraic expression for each scenario. The first one has been done for you.

8.4 times the number of passing yards, *y* **8.4*y***

The number of touchdowns, *t*, increased by a factor of 330 330*t*

The number of interceptions, *i*, times 200 200*i*

The product of 100 and the number of completions, *c* 100*c*

The total points, *p*, scored in a football game is equal to the sum of the number of extra points, *e*, 6 times the number of touchdowns, *t*, and the product of 3 and the number of field goals, *f*.
$p = e + 6t + 3f$

$2x + 3$ is represented by

This visual makes is clear that the *x* terms cannot be combined with the constants.

$2x - x + 3 - 2$ is represented by

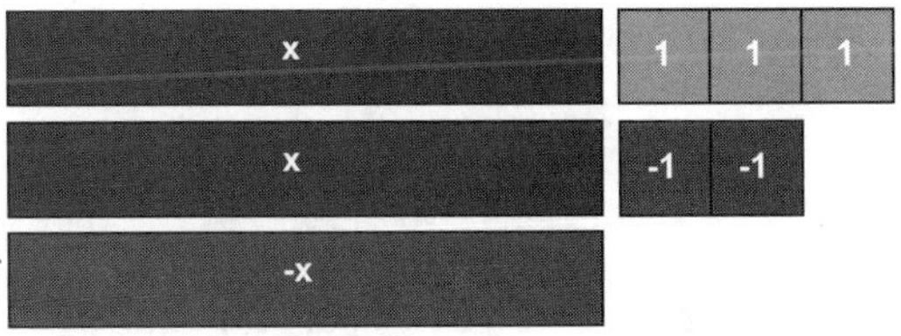

and simplifies to

or $x + 1$.

Teaching Tips, Cont.

- Explain to students that any letter may be used as a variable. When solving word problems, they may want to use the letter that corresponds with the first letter of the unknown. Point out that *l* and *s* are not good variable choices since they tend to look like 1s and 5s.

- Teach students to identify and combine like terms. Show the students two pencils. (Make sure they are identical pencils, if possible.) Ask them if these two items are alike. (Yes.) Ask the students what one pencil plus one pencil equals. (Two pencils.) Now show the students a pencil and a book. Ask the students what one pencil plus one book equals. (One pencil plus one book – they cannot be combined because they are not alike.) Continue this process with the pencils, paper, and books until the students grasp the concept. Then illustrate the same concept using variables. Emphasize that the base and exponent must match to combine variables as like terms.

- Illustrate combining like terms using the algebra tiles. See the illustrations at the left. Encourage students to use their algebra tiles as necessary to check their work in the Classwork and Activities exercises for this lesson.

- Complete the Classwork exercises. Have some students work the problems on the board for the class. All students should work the problems in their books.

Assignment

- Complete Lesson 9, Activities 2-5.

Lesson 10

Concepts

- Distributive property
- Roots
- Prime factorization
- Order of operations

Learning Objectives

The student will be able to:

- Explain the distributive property
- Use the distributive property to simplify expressions
- Analyze expressions to determine the best method of solving

Materials Needed

- Student Book, Lesson 10

Teaching Tips

- Review the order of operations from Lesson 3.
- Write the following problem on the board: 7(10 + 6) =. Have students solve it, following the order of operations. ($7 \times 16 = 112$).
- Show students that sometimes it is easier to "distribute" the 7 to each member inside the parentheses. $7 \times 10 + 7 \times 6 = 70 + 42 = 112$.

The Distributive Property

The **Distributive Property** allows another method of working with parenthetical expressions that are multiplied by a single factor.

In some cases, it is easier to multiply each term in the parentheses by the factor outside the parentheses and then simplify.

$2(15+13) = 2(15) + 2(13) = 30 + 26 = 56$

rather than $2(15+13) = 2(28) = 56$

① **Classwork**

Simplify the expressions, using the distributive property.

$4(10+9) = 40 + 36 = 76$

$5(12+7) = 60 + 35 = 95$

$9(20-3) = 180 - 27 = 153$

Something to Think About...
Two parentheses next to each other with no symbol between them means multiply.
(5)(4) = 20 (-5)(4) = -20

Commutative Property of Multiplication: You can change the order of the terms and still get the same product.
$2 \times 3 = 6$ and $3 \times 2 = 6$

Associative Property of Multiplication: You can group the terms in different ways and still get the same product.
$2 \times (3 \times 4) = 2 \times 12 = 24$ and
$(2 \times 3) \times 4 = 6 \times 4 = 24$

Identity Property of Multiplication: You can multiply any number by one and the product is always the number. $1 \times 4 = 4$ and $4 \times 1 = 4$

Activities

② Use the distributive property to simplify each expression.

$2(35+7) = 70 + 14 = 84$

$4(9+5) = 36 + 20 = 56$

$7(1+40) = 7 + 280 = 287$

$7(30+9) = 210 + 63 = 273$

$8(20+9) = 160 + 72 = 232$

$4(25+9+15) = 100 + 36 + 60 = 196$

③ Solve the following roots.

$\sqrt[3]{375} - 2\sqrt[3]{24} = (5\sqrt[3]{3}) - 2(2\sqrt[3]{3}) = \sqrt[3]{3}$

$(\sqrt{10})(\sqrt{5}) = \sqrt{10 \times 5} = \sqrt{50} = \sqrt{2 \times 5 \times 5} = 5\sqrt{2}$

$(4\sqrt{5})(3\sqrt{15}) = (4 \times 3)\sqrt{5 \times 15} = 12\sqrt{75} = 12\sqrt{3 \times 5 \times 5} = 60\sqrt{3}$

$\sqrt{27} \div 3 = \sqrt{27} \div \sqrt{9} = \sqrt{27 \div 9} = \sqrt{3}$

$12\sqrt[3]{54} \div 3\sqrt[3]{2} = (12 \div 3)\sqrt[3]{54 \div 2} = 4\sqrt[3]{27} = 4(3) = 12$

④ Find the prime factorization of each number. Use exponents where appropriate.

36 36 = 2 x 2 x 3 x 3 $36 = 2^2 \times 3^2$	38 38 = 2 x 19	39 39 = 3 x 13
40 40 = 2 x 2 x 2 x 5 $40 = 2^3 \times 5$	42 42 = 2 x 3 x 7	44 44 = 2 x 2 x 11 $44 = 2^2 \times 11$
45 45 = 3 x 3 x 5 $45 = 3^2 \times 5$	46 46 = 2 x 23	48 48 = 2 x 2 x 2 x 2 x 3 $48 = 2^4 \times 3$
49 49 = 7 x 7 $49 = 7^2$	50 50 = 2 x 5 x 5 $50 = 2 \times 5^2$	52 52 = 2 x 2 x 13 $52 = 2^2 \times 13$

⑤ Solve, following proper order of operations.

$(8+17)-3^3+4\times7=25-3^3+4\times7=25-27+4\times7=25-27+28=-2+28=26$

$(12-9)^3-6^2+6\times7=(3)^3-6^2+6\times7=27-36+6\times7=27-36+42=-9+42=33$

$4^3\div8+(25-17)-4=4^3\div8+8-4=64\div8+8-4=8+8-4=16-4=12$

$(2(2^3)-(32-27)+1)\div(27-21)=$
$(2(8)-5+1)\div6=(16-5+1)\div6=(11+1)\div6=12\div6=2$

$((4^2-10\div2+1)\div3\div2)^3=$

$((16-10\div2+1)\div3\div2)^3=((16-5+1)\div3\div2)^3=((11+1)\div3\div2)^3=(12\div3\div2)^3=$
$(4\div2)^3=2^3=8$

Teaching Tips, Cont.

- Teach the distributive property in the teaching box. Emphasize that the distributive property should not be used in place of the traditional order of operations in every case. There are times when solving inside the parentheses first will produce a problem that is easier to solve than using the distributive property. Every problem must be evaluated on a case-by-case basis.
- Complete the Classwork exercises. Have some students work the problems on the board for the class. All students should work the problems in their books.
- Review for Test 1 using worksheets 1-5. These worksheets were all assigned in previous lessons.

Assignments

- Complete Lesson 10, Activities 2-5.
- Study for Test 1 (Lessons 1-7).

Test 1

Testing Objectives

The student will be able to:

- Apply the rules of adding, subtracting, multiplying, and dividing signed numbers
- Simplify expressions with exponents
- Solve expressions with exponents less than or equal to 3
- Apply the order of operations to solve expressions
- Express the prime factorization of a number using exponents
- Solve expressions with absolute values
- Find the greatest common factor of a set of three numbers
- Find the least common multiple of a set of three numbers
- Add, subtract, multiply, divide, and simplify radical expressions

Materials Needed

- Test 1
- *It's College Test Prep Time!* from Student Book
- Exploring Math through … Soccer from Student Book

Teaching Tips

- Administer Test 1, allowing the students 30-40 minutes to complete the test.
- When all students are finished taking the test, introduce the College Test Prep Time from the student book. This page may be completed in class or assigned as homework.
- Have students read the Exploring Math feature for Lessons 11-20.

① Solve, using the rules for signed numbers. **8 points**

$(-438) + (+172) = -(438 - 172) = -266$

$(-15)(80) = -1200$

$(-351) - (-683) = 683 - 351 = 332$

$(108) \div (-18) = -6$

$(+378) + (-937) = -(937 - 378) = -559$

$(-25)(-12) = 300$

$(-249) - (+534) = -(249 + 534) = -783$

$(-132) \div (-11) = 12$

② Simplify the expressions. You do not have to solve exponents greater than 3. **12 points**

$46^0 = 1$

$16^5 \times 16^8 = 16^{13}$

$37^1 = 37$

$10^{16} \div 10^{13} = 10^3 = 1{,}000$

$14^3 \times 14^7 = 14^{10}$

$(2 \times 4)^3 = 2^3 \times 4^3 = 8 \times 64 = 512$

$11^9 \div 11^7 = 11^2 = 121$

$13^{-2} = \left(\frac{1}{13}\right)^2 = \frac{1^2}{13^2} = \frac{1}{169}$

$(15 \div 3)^2 = 15^2 \div 3^2 = 225 \div 9 = 25$

$\left(\frac{2}{3}\right)^3 = \frac{2^3}{3^3} = \frac{8}{27}$

$5^{-3} = \left(\frac{1}{5}\right)^3 = \frac{1^3}{5^3} = \frac{1}{125}$

$\left(\frac{5}{2}\right)^{-3} = \left(\frac{2}{5}\right)^3 = \frac{2^3}{5^3} = \frac{8}{125}$

③ Simplify each expression, following the proper order of operations. **8 points**

$45 - 5 \times 4 = 45 - 20 = 25$

$26 \div 13 \times 3 + 8 - 3 \times 4 = 2 \times 3 + 8 - 3 \times 4 = 6 + 8 - 3 \times 4 = 6 + 8 - 12 = 14 - 12 = 2$

$(14 - 11)^2 - 45 \div 9 = (3)^2 - 45 \div 9 = 9 - 45 \div 9 = 9 - 5 = 4$

$(9 + 16) - 5^2 + 4 \times 7 = 25 - 5^2 + 4 \times 7 = 25 - 25 + 4 \times 7 = 25 - 25 + 28 = 0 + 28 = 28$

$(25 - 21)^3 - 6^2 + 14 \div 7 = (4)^3 - 6^2 + 14 \div 7 = 64 - 36 + 14 \div 7 = 64 - 36 + 2 = 28 + 2 = 30$

$2^3 \times 5 \div (13 - 5) - 7 = 2^3 \times 5 \div 8 - 7 = 8 \times 5 \div 8 - 7 = 40 \div 8 - 7 = 5 - 7 = -2$

$(6^2 - (28 - 13) + 3) \div 6 = (6^2 - 15 + 3) \div 6 = (36 - 15 + 3) \div 6 = (21 + 3) \div 6 = 24 \div 6 = 4$

$((2 + 4 \times 7) \div 6)^3 = ((2 + 28) \div 6)^3 = (30 \div 6)^3 = 5^3 = 125$

④ Find the prime factorization of each number. Use exponents where appropriate. **4 points**

24: $24 = 2 \times 2 \times 2 \times 3$; $24 = 2^3 \times 3$

35: $35 = 5 \times 7$

36: $36 = 2 \times 2 \times 3 \times 3$; $36 = 2^2 \times 3^2$

40: $40 = 2 \times 2 \times 2 \times 5$; $40 = 2^3 \times 5$

⑤ Solve, using the rules of absolute values. **15 points**

$|101| = 101$

$|-253| = 253$

$-|141| = -141$

$-|-852| = -852$

$|129 + 33| = 162$

$-|212 + 121| = -333$

$|56 - 43| = 13$

$-|137 - 240| = -103$

$|216| + |34| = 216 + 34 = 250$

$|91| + |-105| = 91 + 105 = 196$

$|25| - |-54| = 25 - 54 = -29$

$-|39| + |-63| = -39 + 63 = 24$

$-|-132| - |-145| = -132 - 145 = -277$

$-|124 - 76| + |85 - 57| = -48 + 28 = -20$

$-|236 + 124| - |412 - 148| = -360 - 264 = -624$

⑥ Find the greatest common factor of each set of numbers. **3 points**

9, 15, and 18
$9 = 3 \times ③$
$15 = ③ \times 5$
$18 = 2 \times ③ \times 3$
GCF is 3

16, 24, and 40
$16 = ② \times ② \times ② \times 2$
$24 = ② \times ② \times ② \times 3$
$40 = ② \times ② \times ② \times 5$
GCF is $2 \times 2 \times 2 = 8$

10, 18, and 24
$10 = ② \times 5$
$18 = ② \times 3 \times 3$
$24 = ② \times 2 \times 2 \times 3$
GCF is 2

⑦ Find the least common multiple of each set of numbers. **3 points**

6, 8, and 10
$6 = 2 \times \boxed{3}$
$8 = 2 \times 2 \times 2 = \boxed{2^3}$
$10 = 2 \times \boxed{5}$
LCM: $2^3 \times 3 \times 5 = 120$

10, 15, and 24
$10 = 2 \times \boxed{5}$
$15 = \boxed{3} \times 5$
$24 = 2 \times 2 \times 2 \times 3 = \boxed{2^3} \times 3$
LCM: $2^3 \times 3 \times 5 = 120$

9, 15, and 24
$9 = 3 \times 3 = \boxed{3^2}$
$15 = 3 \times \boxed{5}$
$24 = 2 \times 2 \times 2 \times 3 = \boxed{2^3} \times 3$
LCM: $2^3 \times 3^2 \times 5 = 360$

⑧ Solve the following roots. **14 points**

$\sqrt{121} = \sqrt{11 \times 11} = 11$

$\sqrt[3]{64} = \sqrt[3]{4 \times 4 \times 4} = 4$

$\sqrt{24} = \sqrt{2 \times 2 \times 6} = 2\sqrt{6}$

$\sqrt[3]{54} = \sqrt[3]{2 \times 3 \times 3 \times 3} = 3\sqrt[3]{2}$

$\sqrt{15} + \sqrt{15} = 2\sqrt{15}$

$5\sqrt{29} + 9\sqrt{29} = 14\sqrt{29}$

$17\sqrt[3]{63} + 10\sqrt[3]{63} = 27\sqrt[3]{63}$

$28\sqrt{33} - 13\sqrt{33} = 15\sqrt{33}$

$72\sqrt[3]{18} - 47\sqrt[3]{18} = 25\sqrt[3]{18}$

$(\sqrt{18})(\sqrt{2}) = \sqrt{18 \times 2} = \sqrt{36} = \sqrt{6 \times 6} = 6$

$(5\sqrt{12})(4\sqrt{9}) = (5 \times 4)\sqrt{12 \times 9} = 20\sqrt{108} = 20\sqrt{2 \times 2 \times 3 \times 3 \times 3} = 120\sqrt{3}$

$\sqrt{72} \div \sqrt{2} = \sqrt{72 \div 2} = \sqrt{36} = \sqrt{6 \times 6} = 6$

$36\sqrt[3]{54} \div 9\sqrt[3]{2} = (36 \div 9)\sqrt[3]{54 \div 2} = 4\sqrt[3]{27} = 4\sqrt[3]{3 \times 3 \times 3} = 4 \times 3 = 12$

$10 \div \sqrt{5} = \sqrt{10 \times 10} \div \sqrt{5} = \sqrt{100 \div 5} = \sqrt{20} = \sqrt{2 \times 2 \times 5} = 2\sqrt{5}$

67 points

It's College Test Prep Time!

1. P = the set of positive integer factors of 16 1, 2, 4, 8, 16
   Q = the set of positive integer factors of 20 1, 2, 4, 5, 10, 20
   R = the set of positive integer factors of 24 1, 2, 3, 4, 6, 8, 12, 24

   P, Q, and R represent three sets of numbers, as defined above. Which set of numbers below belongs to all three sets?
   A. {1, 2, 4}
   B. {1, 2, 3, 4}
   C. {1, 2, 4, 16}
   D. {1, 2, 3, 4, 16}
   E. {1, 2, 3, 4, 16, 24}

2. Given $4(e-f)-5=3$, what is the value of $e-f$?
   A. $-\frac{1}{2}$
   B. 2 $4(e-f)=8;\ e-f=8\div4=2$
   C. 4
   D. 8
   E. 32

3. Given $(3+a)(7-b)=0$ and a is a natural number, what is the value of b?
   A. -7
   B. -3
   C. 0
   D. 3
   E. 7 A natural number is positive, making the first parentheses positive. The second parentheses MUST then equal zero.

4. If $13^7 \times 13^x = 13^{21}$, what is the value of x?
   A. 3
   B. 7
   C. 14 $13^{7+x}=13^{21};\ 7+x=21;\ x=14$
   D. 21
   E. 147

Exploring Math through... Soccer

Nearly every aspect of soccer involves math. When it comes to the actual calculations, much of it is higher-level math. For example, the goalie must have a good working knowledge of geometry and angles to be able to defend the goal. Players must calculate angles, speed, and forces when running and kicking the ball. Fortunately, for the soccer player, the mathematics of game play is mostly estimation.

While soccer play is a game of estimation, there are other parts that require specific mathematical calculations. There are precise rules for the measurements of the field, the size and shape of the ball, and even the timing of the game itself. Next time you look at a soccer ball, notice the different shapes. The soccer ball has 12 pentagons and 20 hexagons spaced evenly around the ball. Remember from pre-algebra that a solid figure made up of 12 pentagons is a dodecahedron, and a solid figure made up of 20 hexagons is an icosahedron. The soccer ball is a combination of two solid figures.

Assignments

- Complete *It's College Test Prep Time!*
- Read Exploring Math through ... Soccer

ing algebraic expressions
e variable
aluating algebraic expressions with multiple variables

- Simplifying exponential expressions
- Absolute value
- Math in the real world

Learning Objectives

The student will be able to:

- Evaluate algebraic expressions with one variable
- Evaluate algebraic expressions with multiple variables
- Evaluate algebraic expressions with powers of variables

Materials Needed

- Student Book, Lesson 11
- Soccer ball

Teaching Tips

- ➢ Teach evaluating algebraic expressions from the teaching box. Explain that this is simply a process of substitution.
- ➢ Remind students that a coefficient next to a variable means that the value of the variable is multiplied by the coefficient.
- ➢ Tell students that when the value of a variable is defined, it remains the same for all instances of that variable in a given expression.
- ➢ Point out that some expressions will have more than one unique variable. In these instances, each variable will have its own value.

Lesson 11

Evaluating Algebraic Expressions

To evaluate an algebraic expression, substitute a given numeric value for each variable in the expression. The same numeric value is used for every instance of the same variable. Follow the order of operations to simplify.

Evaluate $2x + 6$ for $x = -2$.

Substitute -2 for x in the expression. Remember that a coefficient next to a variable indicates multiplication.

$2(-2) + 6 = -4 + 6 = 2$

When there are two or more unique variables in an expression, each variable will have its own value. Make sure you substitute the correct value for each variable.

Evaluate $3x^2 + 2y - 4$ for $x = 2$ and $y = -3$.

Substitute 2 for x and -3 for y. Follow the order of operations to simplify.

$3(2)^2 + 2(-3) - 4 = 3(4) - 6 - 4 =$
$12 - 6 - 4 = 6 - 4 = 2$

① **Classwork**
Evaluate each algebraic expression.

$4x + 5$ for $x = 3$

$4(3) + 5 = 12 + 5 = 17$

$-5m + 3$ for $m = -1$

$-5(-1) + 3 = 5 + 3 = 8$

$7y - 2$ for $y = 2$

$7(2) - 2 = 14 - 2 = 12$

$2p^2 - 3p + 1$ for $p = -3$
$2(-3)^2 - 3(-3) + 1 = 2(9) + 9 + 1 =$
$18 + 9 + 1 = 27 + 1 = 28$

$3x - 2xy + 4y$ for $x = 4$ and $y = -2$
$3(4) - 2(4)(-2) + 4(-2) = 12 - 8(-2) - 8 =$
$12 + 16 - 8 = 28 - 8 = 20$

Activities
② Evaluate each algebraic expression.

$3x + 7$ for $x = 4$

$3(4) + 7 = 12 + 7 = 19$

$-9p + 8$ for $p = -2$

$-9(-2) + 8 = 18 + 8 = 26$

$3b - 5$ for $b = -2$

$3(-2) - 5 = -6 - 5 = -11$

$5r^2 - 2r + 3$ for $r = -2$
$5(-2)^2 - 2(-2) + 3 = 5(4) + 4 + 3 =$
$20 + 4 + 3 = 24 + 3 = 27$

$-9c + 4$ for $c = 3$

$-9(3) + 4 = -27 + 4 = -23$

$-6k + 5$ for $k = 3$

$-6(3) + 5 = -18 + 5 = -13$

$3t^2 - 7t + 4$ for $t = 3$
$3(3)^2 - 7(3) + 4 = 3(9) - 21 + 4 =$
$27 - 21 + 4 = 6 + 4 = 10$
$8g - 3gh + 5h$ for $g = -5$ and $h = 4$
$8(-5) - 3(-5)(4) + 5(4) =$
$-40 + 15(4) + 20 = -40 + 60 + 20 =$
$20 + 20 = 40$

Additional information about Euler's Formula

(See Activity 5)

There are several different formulas known as Euler's Formula. This exercise uses Euler's Polyhedral Formula, which states that the sum of the number of faces (flat surfaces) and the number of edges in a solid figure, specifically any convex polyhedron, is exactly two more than the number of edges in that figure.

For a soccer ball, there are a total of 32 faces – 12 pentagons and 20 hexagons.

You may wish to show the students a soccer ball so they can see the faces and count the faces, vertices, and edges for this exercise.

③ Simplify the expressions. You do not have to solve exponents greater than 3.

$33^0 = 1$

$41^1 = 41$

$16^3 \times 16^5 = 16^8$

$5^9 \div 5^7 = 5^2 = 25$

$(2 \times 5)^3 = 2^3 \times 5^3 = 8 \times 125 = 1000$

$15^{-2} = \left(\frac{1}{15}\right)^2 = \frac{1^2}{15^2} = \frac{1}{225}$

$\left(\frac{3}{4}\right)^3 = \frac{3^3}{4^3} = \frac{27}{64}$

$\left(\frac{6}{5}\right)^{-3} = \left(\frac{5}{6}\right)^3 = \frac{5^3}{6^3} = \frac{125}{216}$

④ Solve the absolute values.

$|23 + 31| = 54$

$|16 - 32| = |-16| = 16$

$-|27 - 15| = -12$

$-|43 - 59| = -|-16| = -16$

$|-51| + |24| = 51 + 24 = 75$

$|-26| - |-18| = 26 - 18 = 8$

$|36 - 47| - |25 - 18| = |-11| - |7| =$
$11 - 7 = 4$

$-|52 - 65| - |47 - 59| =$
$-|-13| - |-12| = -13 - 12 = -25$

⑤ Solve.

Euler's Polyhedral Formula gives the relationship between the number of faces, edges, and vertices of a solid figure. From the information in the chart below, write an algebraic equation showing the relationship of the number of faces, *F*, vertices, *V*, and edges, *E*, to yield a constant, 2. Hint: The same relationship applies to every solid figure.

Shape	Faces, *F*	Vertices, *V*	Edges, *E*
Tetrahedron	4	4	6
Square pyramid	5	5	8
Cube	6	8	12
Dodecahedron	12	20	30
Icosahedron	20	12	30
Soccer ball	32	60	90

$F + V - E = 2$

Teaching Tips, Cont.

- Draw the students' attention to Activity 5. Information regarding Euler's Polyhedral Formula is given at the bottom of the previous page. Specific information regarding soccer balls is included. If you brought a soccer ball, show the students the pattern of the pentagons and hexagons and have them count the number of faces, vertices, and edges. You may wish to complete Activity 5 as a class.
- Complete the Classwork exercises. Have some students work the problems on the board for the class and explain their answers. All students should work the problems in their books.

Assignment

- Complete Lesson 11, Activities 2-5.

Lesson 12

Concepts
- Adding polynomials
- Adding, subtracting, multiplying, and dividing signed numbers
- Math in the real world

Learning Objectives
The student will be able to:
- Add polynomials by combining like terms
- Write polynomials vertically with like terms aligned
- Use algebra tiles to check algebraic operations

Materials Needed
- Student Book, Lesson 12
- Algebra tiles
- Worksheet 6

Teaching Tips
- Have students complete Worksheet 6 in class. This may be for added practice of earlier topics, or graded as a quiz, if desired.
- Ask the students why it is important to line up the decimal points when adding a column of decimal numbers. (Lining up the decimal points keeps all digits of the same place value lined up.)
- Explain that it is just as important to keep terms of the same variable order lined up when adding polynomials vertically.
- Teach adding polynomials from the teaching box.

Adding Polynomials

Adding polynomials is simply the process of combining like terms. Look at this equation.

$(x^2+2x+3)+(2x^2-x+1)=$

Clear the parentheses to get

$x^2+2x+3+2x^2-x+1=$

and then combine like terms.

$x^2+2x+3+2x^2-x+1=3x^2+x+4$

Polynomials may also be added vertically. Recall that when adding integers and decimals vertically, digits in the same place value must be lined up. In the case of polynomials, terms with the same variable and degree (exponent) must be lined up in the same column. Add the columns to get the answer.

$$\begin{array}{r} (x^2+2x+3) \\ \underline{+(2x^2-x+1)} \\ 3x^2+x+4 \end{array}$$

You may use algebra tiles to check your answer.

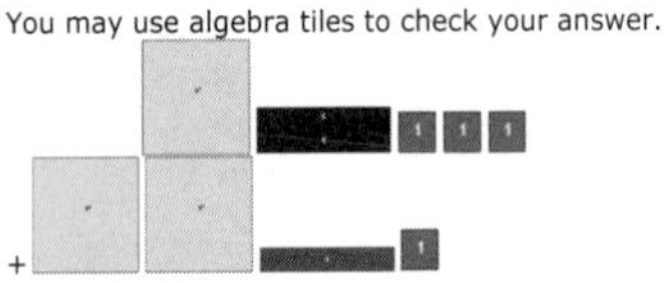

When adding with algebra tiles, a red piece paired with a different color of the same size will always result in both pieces being removed because the red is the negative of the other color and 1 − 1 = 0. Therefore, the sum looks like the diagram below.

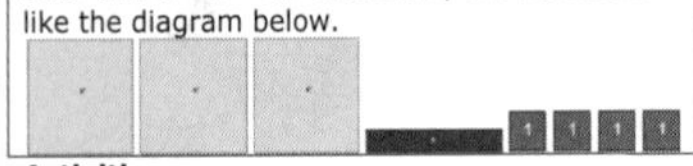

① **Classwork**

Write the problem vertically and add.

$(4x^2+3x+5)+(2x^2+x+3)=$

$$\begin{array}{r} 4x^2+3x+5 \\ \underline{+2x^2+x+3} \\ 6x^2+4x+8 \end{array}$$

$(2x^2+2x+7)+(5x^2-x+4)=$

$$\begin{array}{r} 2x^2+2x+7 \\ \underline{+5x^2-x+4} \\ 7x^2+x+11 \end{array}$$

$(3x^2+2x+4)+(x^2-3x-7)=$

$$\begin{array}{r} 3x^2+2x+4 \\ \underline{+x^2-3x-7} \\ 4x^2-x-3 \end{array}$$

Activities

② Add.

$$\begin{array}{r} 6x^2+2x+3 \\ \underline{+\ 4x^2+3x+5} \\ 10x^2+5x+8 \end{array} \qquad \begin{array}{r} 7x^2+3x+8 \\ \underline{+x^2-5x-4} \\ 8x^2-2x+4 \end{array} \qquad \begin{array}{r} 3x^2-6x+5 \\ \underline{+4x^2+4x-9} \\ 7x^2-2x-4 \end{array}$$

③ Write the problem vertically and add.

$(3x^2+4x+2)+(x^2+5x+3)=$

$$\begin{array}{r} 3x^2+4x+2 \\ \underline{+\ x^2+5x+3} \\ 4x^2+9x+5 \end{array}$$

$(3x^2+5x+4)+(7x^2+4x+2)=$

$$\begin{array}{r} 3x^2+5x+4 \\ \underline{+7x^2+4x+2} \\ 10x^2+9x+6 \end{array}$$

$(4x^2+5x+3)+(5x^2-3x+4)=$

$$\begin{array}{r} 4x^2+5x+3 \\ \underline{+5x^2-3x+4} \\ 9x^2+2x+7 \end{array}$$

$(5x^2+4x-2)+(3x^2-5x+3)=$

$$\begin{array}{r} 5x^2+4x-2 \\ \underline{+3x^2-5x+3} \\ 8x^2-x+1 \end{array}$$

$(3x^2-4x+3)+(-2x^2+3x-4)=$

$$\begin{array}{r} 3x^2-4x+3 \\ \underline{-2x^2+3x-4} \\ x^2-x-1 \end{array}$$

$(6x^2+3x+4)+(-3x^2-6x-7)=$

$$\begin{array}{r} 6x^2+3x+4 \\ \underline{-3x^2-6x-7} \\ 3x^2-3x-3 \end{array}$$

④ Solve, using the rules for signed numbers. Write the problem vertically, if necessary.

(-62) + (+23) =
$-(62-23)=-39$

(-46) - (-91) =
$(-46)+91=91-46=45$

(+57) + (+72) =
$57+72=129$

(+103) - (-25) =
$103+25=128$

(-58) + (+79) =
$79-58=21$

(-68) - (92) =
$-(68+92)=-160$

(14)(5) = 70

(-16)(-7) = 112

(11)(-5)(2) = $(-55)(2)=-110$

(-12)(-4)(-9) = $(48)(-9)=-432$

(-75) ÷ (15) = -5

(-108) ÷ (-4) = 27

⑤ Write an algebraic expression.

A soccer player should consume 1g of carbohydrates per kg of body weight each hour for the first four hours after a game or heavy exercise to replace lost carbohydrates. Write an algebraic equation showing how many carbohydrates, *c*, a player with weight, *w*, should consume in the first 4 hours.

$c=4w$

Translating Words into Mathematical Statements, Distributive Property Worksheet 6

① Translate the following words into a mathematical expression.

The total of a number and 42 $x + 42$

The product of 72 and a number $72x$

The ratio of a number to 15 $x \div 15$

A number increased by 100 $x + 100$

22 fewer than a number $x - 22$

A number times 18 $18x$

A number increased by a factor of 7 $7x$

95 more than a number $x + 95$

A number less than 89 $89 - x$

The sum of 69 and a number $69 + x$

The quotient of a number and 12 $x \div 12$

14 less than a number $x - 14$

② Use the distributive property to simplify each expression.

$9(90 + 4) = 810 + 36 = 846$

$6(20 + 8) = 120 + 48 = 168$

$12(30 + 3) = 360 + 36 = 396$

$7(20 + 4) = 140 + 28 = 168$

$11(20 + 7) = 220 + 77 = 297$

$8(40 + 3) = 320 + 24 = 344$

$4(50 + 7 + 15) = 200 + 28 + 60 = 288$

$8(25 + 9 + 5) = 200 + 72 + 40 = 312$

Teaching Tips, Cont.

- Note: While it is not necessary to write polynomials vertically to add them, some exercises have the students re-write polynomials vertically for added practice in lining up like terms. In the Classwork exercises and in Activity 3, you may wish to encourage students to find the sum without writing the problem vertically and then check their answer by working the same problem vertically.
- Complete the Classwork exercises. Have some students work the problems on the board for the class and explain their answers. All students should work the problems in their books.

Assignment

- Complete Lesson 12, Activities 2-5.

Lesson 13

Concepts

- Subtracting polynomials
- Distributive property
- Order of operations

Learning Objectives

The student will be able to:

- Subtract polynomials
- Write polynomials vertically with like terms aligned
- Use algebra tiles to check algebraic operations

Materials Needed

- Student Book, Lesson 13
- Algebra tiles
- Worksheet 7

Teaching Tips

- ➢ Review adding polynomials from Lesson 12.
- ➢ Review the rules for subtracting signed numbers. (See Lesson 1)
- ➢ Teach subtracting polynomials from the teaching box. Explain that the rules for subtracting signed numbers apply to subtracting polynomials.
- ➢ Remind students that like terms must be aligned when subtracting vertically.
- ➢ Explain that algebra tiles may be used to check answers when subtracting polynomials, but the problem should be re-written as an addition problem first, following the rules for subtracting signed numbers.

Subtracting Polynomials

Recall the rules for working with signed numbers. When you are subtracting a number, change the sign and add. This rule also applies to subtracting polynomials. Look at this problem.

$(2x^2+2x+3)-(x^2-x+1)=$

The negative applies to everything in the second set of parentheses. Change each sign in the second parentheses and add.

$(2x^2+2x+3)+(-x^2+x-1)=$

$2x^2+2x+3-x^2+x-1=$

x^2+3x+2

Polynomials may also be subtracted by writing the problem vertically. Like addition problems, like terms must appear in the same column.

$$\begin{array}{rcr} (2x^2+2x+3) & & (2x^2+2x+3) \\ \underline{-(x^2-x+1)} & \text{becomes} & \underline{+(-x^2+x-1)} \\ & & x^2+3x+2 \end{array}$$

You may use algebra tiles to check your answer.

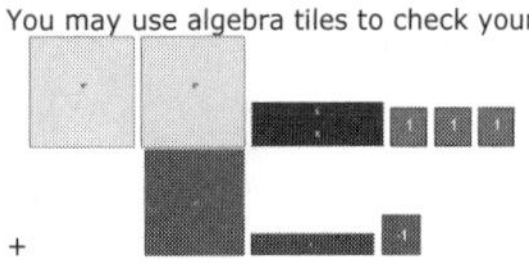

When adding with algebra tiles, a red piece paired with a different color of the same size will always result in both pieces being removed because the red is the negative of the other color and 1 - 1 = 0. Therefore, the sum looks like the diagram below.

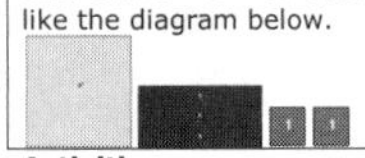

① **Classwork**

Write the problem vertically and subtract.

$(4x^2+3x+4)-(x^2+x+3)=$

$$\begin{array}{rcr} (4x^2+3x+4) & & 4x^2+3x+4 \\ \underline{-(x^2+x+3)} & \text{becomes} & \underline{-x^2-x-3} \\ & & 3x^2+2x+1 \end{array}$$

$(3x^2+3x+6)-(x^2-x+2)=$

$$\begin{array}{rcr} (3x^2+3x+6) & & 3x^2+3x+6 \\ \underline{-(x^2-x+2)} & \text{becomes} & \underline{-x^2+x-2} \\ & & 2x^2+4x+4 \end{array}$$

$(6x^2-x+2)-(4x^2-3x-2)=$

$$\begin{array}{rcr} (6x^2-x+2) & & 6x^2-x+2 \\ \underline{-(4x^2-3x-2)} & \text{becomes} & \underline{-4x^2+3x+2} \\ & & 2x^2+2x+4 \end{array}$$

Activities

② Subtract.

$$\begin{array}{r} (6x^2+6x+4) \\ \underline{-(4x^2+3x+2)} \\ 2x^2+3x+2 \end{array} \qquad \begin{array}{r} (6x^2-3x+4) \\ \underline{-(x^2-5x-2)} \\ 5x^2+2x+6 \end{array} \qquad \begin{array}{r} (8x^2-x-2) \\ \underline{-(6x^2+3x-4)} \\ 2x^2-4x+2 \end{array}$$

③ Write the problem vertically and subtract.

$(4x^2+6x+5)-(x^2+3x+4)=$

$$\begin{array}{rcr} (4x^2+6x+5) & & 4x^2+6x+5 \\ \underline{-(x^2+3x+4)} & \text{becomes} & \underline{-x^2-3x-4} \\ & & 3x^2+3x+1 \end{array}$$

$(9x^2+8x+5)-(5x^2+2x+2)=$

$$\begin{array}{rcr} (9x^2+8x+5) & & 9x^2+8x+5 \\ \underline{-(5x^2+2x+2)} & \text{becomes} & \underline{-5x^2-2x-2} \\ & & 4x^2+6x+3 \end{array}$$

$(8x^2+3x+6)-(3x^2-x+2)=$

$$\begin{array}{rcr} (8x^2+3x+6) & & 8x^2+3x+6 \\ \underline{-(3x^2-x+2)} & \text{becomes} & \underline{-3x^2+x-2} \\ & & 5x^2+4x+4 \end{array}$$

$(7x^2-2x+2)-(x^2-3x+1)=$

$$\begin{array}{rcr} (7x^2-2x+2) & & 7x^2-2x+2 \\ \underline{-(x^2-3x+1)} & \text{becomes} & \underline{-x^2+3x-1} \\ & & 6x^2+x+1 \end{array}$$

$(2x^2-2x-3)-(-3x^2+4x-5)=$

$$\begin{array}{rcr} (2x^2-2x-3) & & 2x^2-2x-3 \\ \underline{-(-3x^2+4x-5)} & \text{becomes} & \underline{+3x^2-4x+5} \\ & & 5x^2-6x+2 \end{array}$$

$(5x^2-5x-7)-(-3x^2-4x-7)=$

$$\begin{array}{rcr} (5x^2-5x-7) & & 5x^2-5x-7 \\ \underline{-(-3x^2-4x-7)} & \text{becomes} & \underline{+3x^2+4x+7} \\ & & 8x^2-x \end{array}$$

④ Solve. You may use the distributive property where appropriate.

$4(25+8)=100+32=132$

$7(20+9)=140+63=203$

$13(1+30)=13+390=403$

$11(20+8)=220+88=308$

$14(10+2)=140+28=168$

$8(25+9+12)=200+72+96=368$

$(11-5)^2-15\div3-2^4=$

$6^2-15\div3-16=36-15\div3-16=36-5-16=31-16=15$

$(5+3)^2-4^3+2(13-7)+18^0=$

$8^2-4^3+2(6)+18^0=64-64+2(6)+1=0+12+1=13$

$6+9\div3-21^1-2^3=$

$6+9\div3-21-8=6+3-21-8=9-21-8=-12-8=-20$

$\left((27\div3)^2\times(3)^{-2}+31^0\right)^2\div(13-8)=$

$\left(9^2\times\frac{1}{9}+31^0\right)^2\div5=\left(81\times\frac{1}{9}+1\right)^2\div5=(9+1)^2\div5=100\div5=20$

Evaluating Algebraic Expressions, Adding and Subtracting Polynomials Worksheet 7

① Evaluate each algebraic expression.

$12x - 7$ for $x = 6$
$12(6) - 7 = 72 - 7 = 65$

$8m + 21$ for $m = -7$
$8(-7) + 21 = -56 + 21 = -35$

$11y - 15$ for $y = -9$
$11(-9) - 15 = -99 - 15 = -114$

$2p^3 - 3p^2 + 4p$ for $p = -2$
$2(-2)^3 - 3(-2)^2 + 4(-2) = 2(-8) - 3(4) + 4(-2) =$
$-16 - 12 - 8 = -28 - 8 = -36$
$6x - 2xy + 3y$ for $x = -4$ and $y = 7$
$6(-4) - 2(-4)(7) + 3(7) = -24 + 8(7) + 21 =$
$-24 + 56 + 21 = 32 + 21 = 53$

② Solve.

$$\begin{array}{r} 13x^2 + 6x + 9 \\ \underline{+\ 12x^2 + 8x + 3} \\ 25x^2 + 14x + 12 \end{array} \qquad \begin{array}{r} 2x + 10 \\ \underline{+x^2 - 8x - 5} \\ x^2 - 6x + 5 \end{array} \qquad \begin{array}{r} x^2 \qquad + 17 \\ \underline{+3x^2 + 18x - 3} \\ 4x^2 + 18x + 14 \end{array}$$

$$\begin{array}{r} 4x^2 + 3x \\ \underline{+\ 7x^2 + 9x + 2} \\ 11x^2 + 12x + 2 \end{array} \qquad \begin{array}{r} 12x^2 + 3x + 2 \\ \underline{+7x^2 - 13x - 16} \\ 19x^2 - 10x - 14 \end{array} \qquad \begin{array}{r} 2x^2 - 9x + 2 \\ \underline{+\ x^2 + 4x + 3} \\ 3x^2 - 5x + 5 \end{array}$$

$$\begin{array}{r} (3x^2 \qquad + 8) \\ \underline{-(5x^2 + 8x + 2)} \\ -2x^2 - 8x + 6 \end{array} \qquad \begin{array}{r} (12x^2 - 7x) \\ \underline{-(12x^2 - 9x - 6)} \\ 2x + 6 \end{array} \qquad \begin{array}{r} (-5x - 12) \\ \underline{-(3x^2 + 6x - 9)} \\ -3x^2 - 11x - 3 \end{array}$$

$$\begin{array}{r} (x^2 + 3x + 8) \\ \underline{-(10x^2 \qquad + 12)} \\ -9x^2 + 3x - 4 \end{array} \qquad \begin{array}{r} (6x^2 - 7x + 8) \\ \underline{-(3x^2 - 5x)} \\ 3x^2 - 2x + 8 \end{array} \qquad \begin{array}{r} (x^2 - x - 2) \\ \underline{-(-9x - 4)} \\ x^2 + 8x + 2 \end{array}$$

Teaching Tips, Cont.

- Complete the Classwork exercises. Have some students work the problems on the board for the class and explain their answers. All students should work the problems in their books.

Assignments

- Complete Lesson 13, Activities 2-4.
- Worksheet 7 (Optional).

Lesson 14

Concepts

- Multiplying monomials
- Adding polynomials
- Subtracting polynomials
- Math in the real world

Learning Objectives

The student will be able to:

- Multiply coefficients of monomials
- Multiply variables in monomials
- Arrange coefficients and variables in the proper order in the product of monomials

Materials Needed

- Student Book, Lesson 14

Teaching Tips

- Review the rules for working with exponents. (See Lesson 2)
- Teach multiplying monomials from the teaching box. Explain that coefficients are always multiplied to form a single coefficient in the product. The rules of multiplying with exponents apply to multiplying the variables.
- Remind students that variables are only added when the bases are identical. When different bases appear in the factors, the same bases will appear in the product.
- Emphasize that answers should be written with coefficients first, followed by variables in alphabetical order.

Multiplying Monomials

When multiplying monomials, multiply the coefficients to get the new coefficient, and multiply the variables to get the new variable. The following rules apply to all instances of multiplying with variables.

- When multiplying like variables, add the exponents to get the new exponent.
- When multiplying different variables, write all variables as a single product.
- List like variables in order from highest degree to lowest degree.
- List unlike variables in alphabetical order.

$x^2(2x) = (1 \cdot 2)x^{2+1} = 2x^3$

Notice that the coefficients were multiplied and the exponents were added.

$(3x)(2y) = (3 \cdot 2)(xy) = 6xy$

Notice that the coefficients were multiplied. The variables are different, so they were written in alphabetical order as a product.

① Classwork

Multiply.

$x(4x^2)$

$(1 \cdot 4)x^{1+2} = 4x^3$

$3x(4y^2)$

$(3 \cdot 4)(xy^2) = 12xy^2$

$5x(3xy^2)$

$(5 \cdot 3)(x^{1+1})(y^2) = 15x^2y^2$

Activities

② Multiply.

$2x(5x^2)$

$(2 \cdot 5)x^{1+2} = 10x^3$

$7x^2(3x^2)$

$(7 \cdot 3)x^{2+2} = 21x^4$

$x^3(8x^2)$

$(1 \cdot 8)x^{3+2} = 8x^5$

$y(7y^2)$

$(1 \cdot 7)y^{1+2} = 7y^3$

$4y^2(6y^2)$

$(4 \cdot 6)y^{2+2} = 24y^4$

$9y^3(4y^2)$

$(9 \cdot 4)y^{3+2} = 36y^5$

$6y^3(5y^4)$

$(6 \cdot 5)y^{3+4} = 30y^7$

$2x(5y^2)$

$(2 \cdot 5)(xy^2) = 10xy^2$

$7x^2(3y^2)$

$(7 \cdot 3)(x^2y^2) = 21x^2y^2$

$x^3(8y^2)$

$(1 \cdot 8)(x^3y^2) = 8x^3y^2$

$x(7y^2)$

$(1 \cdot 7)(xy^2) = 7xy^2$

$4x^2(6y^2)$

$(4 \cdot 6)(x^2y^2) = 24x^2y^2$

$9x^3(4y^2)$

$(9 \cdot 4)(x^3y^2) = 36x^3y^2$

$6x^3(5y^4)$

$(6 \cdot 5)(x^3y^4) = 30x^3y^4$

$2x(5xy^2)$

$(2 \cdot 5)(x^{1+1})(y^2) = 10x^2y^2$

$7x^2(3xy^2)$

$(7 \cdot 3)(x^{2+1})(y^2) = 21x^3y^2$

$x^3(8xy^2)$

$(1 \cdot 8)(x^{3+1})(y^2) = 8x^4y^2$

$x(7x^2y^2)$

$(1 \cdot 7)(x^{2+1})(y^2) = 7x^3y^2$

$4x^2(6x^2y^2)$

$(4 \cdot 6)(x^{2+2})(y^2) = 24x^4y^2$

$9x^3(4x^2y^2)$

$(9 \cdot 4)(x^{3+2})(y^2) = 36x^5y^2$

$6x^3(5x^2y^4)$

$(6 \cdot 5)(x^{3+2})(y^4) = 30x^5y^4$

③ Add or subtract as indicated.

$\begin{array}{r} 8x^2+3x+2 \\ +\ 6x^2+4x+4 \\ \hline 14x^2+7x+6 \end{array}$	$\begin{array}{r} 9x^2+4x+7 \\ +2x^2-4x-5 \\ \hline 11x^2 \quad +2 \end{array}$	$\begin{array}{r} 5x^2-7x+4 \\ +6x^2+5x-8 \\ \hline 11x^2-2x-4 \end{array}$
$\begin{array}{r} 7x^2+4x+4 \\ +\ 5x^2+5x+6 \\ \hline 12x^2+9x+10 \end{array}$	$\begin{array}{r} 8x^2+5x+9 \\ +2x^2-3x-3 \\ \hline 10x^2+2x+6 \end{array}$	$\begin{array}{r} 4x^2-4x+6 \\ +5x^2+6x-8 \\ \hline 9x^2+2x-2 \end{array}$
$\begin{array}{r} 8x^2+\ x+4 \\ +\ 6x^2+2x+6 \\ \hline 14x^2+3x+10 \end{array}$	$\begin{array}{r} 9x^2+2x+10 \\ +\ 3x^2-6x-2 \\ \hline 12x^2-4x+8 \end{array}$	$\begin{array}{r} 5x^2-7x+6 \\ +6x^2+3x-8 \\ \hline 11x^2-4x-2 \end{array}$
$\begin{array}{r} (8x^2+7x+6) \\ -(6x^2+4x+4) \\ \hline 2x^2+3x+2 \end{array}$	$\begin{array}{r} (8x^2-1x+6) \\ -(3x^2-3x) \\ \hline 5x^2+2x+6 \end{array}$	$\begin{array}{r} (10x^2-2x-3) \\ -(7x^2+5x-6) \\ \hline 3x^2-7x+3 \end{array}$
$\begin{array}{r} (8x^2+8x+5) \\ -(5x^2+4x+4) \\ \hline 3x^2+4x+1 \end{array}$	$\begin{array}{r} (7x^2-5x+6) \\ -(2x^2-6x-3) \\ \hline 5x^2+\ x+9 \end{array}$	$\begin{array}{r} (7x^2-2x-3) \\ -(7x^2+4x-5) \\ \hline -6x+2 \end{array}$
$\begin{array}{r} (4x^2+5x+3) \\ -(5x^2+4x+1) \\ \hline -x^2+\ x+2 \end{array}$	$\begin{array}{r} (4x^2-5x+2) \\ -(2x^2-3x) \\ \hline 2x^2-2x+2 \end{array}$	$\begin{array}{r} (5x^2-3x-5) \\ -(3x^2+6x-1) \\ \hline 2x^2-9x-4 \end{array}$

④ Solve.

The area of a rectangle is given by the formula $A = Lw$, where A is the area, L is the length, and w is the width. What is the minimum area required for a soccer field if the minimum width is 150 feet and the minimum length is 300 feet?

$A = Lw$

$A = (300 \text{ feet})(150 \text{ feet})$

$A = 45{,}000$ sq. ft.

What is the maximum area required for a soccer field if the maximum width is 300 feet and the maximum length is 390 feet?

$A = Lw$

$A = (390 \text{ feet})(300 \text{ feet})$

$A = 117{,}000$ sq. ft.

Teaching Tips, Cont.

- Make sure students understand that each variable that appears in any factor should appear exactly one time in the answer.
- Complete the Classwork exercises. Have some students work the problems on the board for the class and explain their answers. All students should work the problems in their books.

Assignment

- Complete Lesson 14, Activities 2-4.

Lesson 15

Concepts

- Dividing monomials
- Adding polynomials
- Subtracting polynomials
- Multiplying monomials

Learning Objectives

The student will be able to:

- Divide coefficients of monomials
- Divide variables in monomials
- Arrange coefficients and variables in the proper order in the quotient of monomials

Materials Needed

- Student Book, Lesson 15
- Worksheet 8

Teaching Tips

- ➤ Have students complete Worksheet 8 in class. This may be for added practice of earlier topics, or graded as a quiz, if desired.
- ➤ Review the rules for working with exponents. (See Lesson 2)
- ➤ Teach dividing monomials from the teaching box. Explain that coefficients are always divided to form a single coefficient in the quotient. The rules of dividing with exponents apply to dividing the variables.
- ➤ Remind students that variables are only subtracted when the bases are identical. When different bases appear in the original problem, the same bases will appear in the quotient.

Dividing Monomials

When dividing monomials, divide the coefficients to get the new coefficient, and divide the variables to get the new variable. The following rules apply to all instances of dividing with variables.

- When dividing like variables, subtract the exponents to get the new exponent.
- When dividing different variables, write the divisor in the denominator.
- List like variables in order from highest degree to lowest degree.
- List unlike variables in alphabetical order.

$2x^2 \div x = (2 \div 1)x^{2-1} = x$

This may also be solved this way.

$2x^2 \div x = \frac{2x\not{x}}{\not{x}} = 2x$

Notice that the coefficients were divided and the exponents were subtracted.

$(3x) \div (2y) = (3 \div 2)(x \div y) = \frac{3}{2}\left(\frac{x}{y}\right) = \frac{3x}{2y}$

This may also be solved in one step by writing the divisor in the denominator.

$(3x) \div (2y) = \frac{3x}{2y}$

① Classwork

Divide.

$8x^3 \div 4x^2$

$(8 \div 4)x^{3-2} = 2x$

$8xy^2 \div 4y^2$

$(8 \div 4)(xy^{2-2}) = 2x$

$8x^2y^2 \div 4xy^2$

$(8 \div 4)(x^{2-1})(y^{2-2}) = 2x$

Activities

② Divide.

$9x^5 \div x^3$

$\frac{9x^5}{x^3} = 9x^{5-3} = 9x^2$

$12x^3 \div x$

$\frac{12x^3}{x} = 12x^{3-1} = 12x^2$

$24y^4 \div 8y^2$

$\frac{24y^4}{8y^2} = 3y^{4-2} = 3y^2$

$36y^5 \div 6y^2$

$\frac{36y^5}{6y^2} = 6y^{5-2} = 6y^3$

$21y^7 \div 3y^3$

$\frac{21y^7}{3y^3} = 7y^{7-3} = 7y^4$

$9x^3y^2 \div x^3$

$\frac{9x^3y^2}{x^3} = 9x^{3-3}y^2 = 9y^2$

$12xy^2 \div 2x$

$\frac{12xy^2}{2x} = 6x^{1-1}y^2 = 6y^2$

$24x^2y^3 \div 8y^2$

$\frac{24x^2y^3}{8y^2} = 3x^2y^{3-2} = 3x^2y$

$36x^3y^2 \div 6y$

$\frac{36x^3y^2}{6y} = 6x^3y^{2-1} = 6x^3y$

$21x^3y^4 \div 3xy$

$\frac{21x^3y^4}{3xy} = 7x^{3-1}y^{4-1} = 7x^2y^3$

$8x^4y^3 \div 2xy^2$

$\frac{8x^4y^3}{2xy^2} = 4x^{4-1}y^{3-2} = 4x^3y$

$12x^3y^3 \div 4x^2y^2$

$\frac{12x^3y^3}{4x^2y^2} = 3x^{3-2}y^{3-2} = 3xy$

$24x^4y^2 \div 8x^2y^2$

$\frac{24x^4y^2}{8x^2y^2} = 3x^{4-2}y^{2-2} = 3x^2$

$36x^5y^4 \div 6x^2y^2$

$\frac{36x^5y^4}{6x^2y^2} = 6x^{5-2}y^{4-2} = 6x^3y^2$

$21x^5y^4 \div 3x^2y^3$

$\frac{21x^5y^4}{3x^2y^3} = 7x^{5-2}y^{4-3} = 7x^3y$

③ Solve.

$$\begin{array}{r} 7a^2 + 2a + 1 \\ \underline{+\ 7a^2 + 5a + 5} \\ 14a^2 + 7a + 6 \end{array} \quad \begin{array}{r} 11b^2 + 6b + 9 \\ \underline{+b^2 - 5b - 6} \\ 12b^2 + b + 3 \end{array} \quad \begin{array}{r} 7c^2 - 5c + 6 \\ \underline{+5c^2 + 4c - 9} \\ 12c^2 - c - 3 \end{array}$$

$$\begin{array}{r} 9d^2 + 6d + 6 \\ \underline{+\ 4d^2 + 4d + 5} \\ 13d^2 + 10d + 11 \end{array} \quad \begin{array}{r} 10e^2 + 7e + 11 \\ \underline{+e^2 - 4e - 4} \\ 11e^2 + 3e + 7 \end{array} \quad \begin{array}{r} 6f^2 - 6f + 8 \\ \underline{+4f^2 + 5f - 9} \\ 10f^2 - f - 1 \end{array}$$

$$\begin{array}{r} 10g^2 + 2g + 6 \\ \underline{+\ 5g^2 + g + 5} \\ 15g^2 + 3g + 11 \end{array} \quad \begin{array}{r} 11h^2 + 4h + 12 \\ \underline{+\ 2h^2 - 7h - 3} \\ 13h^2 - 3h + 9 \end{array} \quad \begin{array}{r} 7i^2 - 5i + 4 \\ \underline{+5i^2 + 2i - 9} \\ 12i^2 - 3i - 5 \end{array}$$

$$\begin{array}{r} (10j^2 + 9j + 8) \\ \underline{-(5j^2 + 3j + 3)} \\ 5j^2 + 6j + 5 \end{array} \quad \begin{array}{r} (10k^2 + k + 4) \\ \underline{-(2k^2 - 4k + 1)} \\ 8k^2 + 5k + 3 \end{array} \quad \begin{array}{r} (8m^2 - 4m - 5) \\ \underline{-(9m^2 + 7m - 4)} \\ -m^2 - 11m - 1 \end{array}$$

$$\begin{array}{r} (6n^2 + 6n + 3) \\ \underline{-(7n^2 + 6n + 6)} \\ -n^2 \qquad - 3 \end{array} \quad \begin{array}{r} (5p^2 - 7p + 4) \\ \underline{-(4p^2 - 4p - 1)} \\ p^2 - 3p + 5 \end{array} \quad \begin{array}{r} (5r^2 - 4r - 5) \\ \underline{-(9r^2 + 6r - 3)} \\ -4r^2 - 10r - 2 \end{array}$$

$$\begin{array}{r} (x^2 + 2x) \\ \underline{-(6x^2 + 5x + 2)} \\ -5x^2 - 3x - 2 \end{array} \quad \begin{array}{r} (x^2 - 2x - 1) \\ \underline{-(3x^2 - 2x)} \\ -2x^2 \qquad - 1 \end{array} \quad \begin{array}{r} (2x^2 - 6x - 8) \\ \underline{-(4x^2 + 7x - 2)} \\ -2x^2 - 13x - 6 \end{array}$$

$9a^3(4b^2)(5a^2b^4)$

$(9 \cdot 4 \cdot 5)(a^{3+2})(b^{2+4}) = 180a^5b^6$

$7c^4(3d)(4c^3d^3)$

$(7 \cdot 3 \cdot 4)(c^{4+3})(d^{1+3}) = 84c^7d^4$

$6e^5(4f^4)(5ef^2)$

$(6 \cdot 4 \cdot 5)(e^{5+1})(f^{4+2}) = 120e^6f^6$

$9g^2(7h^3)(2g^3h^5)$

$(9 \cdot 7 \cdot 2)(g^{2+3})(h^{3+5}) = 126g^5h^8$

$2j^3(7k^2)(j^2k^4)$

$(2 \cdot 7 \cdot 1)(j^{3+2})(k^{2+4}) = 14j^5k^6$

$4m^5(2n^4)(3m^4n^6)$

$(4 \cdot 2 \cdot 3)(m^{5+4})(n^{4+6}) = 24m^9n^{10}$

$8r(5t^{-1})(7r^2t^3)$

$(8 \cdot 5 \cdot 7)(r^{1+2})(t^{-1+3}) = 280r^3t^2$

$5v^{-3}(3w^{-2})(4v^4w^5)$

$(5 \cdot 3 \cdot 4)(v^{-3+4})(w^{-2+5}) = 60vw^3$

$2x^4(-y^3)(3x^{-2}y)$

$(2 \cdot -1 \cdot 3)(x^{4-2})(y^{3+1}) = -6x^2y^4$

$8z^3(3z^2a^4)(7z^2a^4)$

$(8 \cdot 3 \cdot 7)(a^{4+4})(z^{3+2+2}) = 168a^8z^7$

$5b^4(4b^6c^3)(6b^5c^4)$

$(5 \cdot 4 \cdot 6)(b^{4+6+5})(c^{3+4}) = 120b^{15}c^7$

$9d^5(2d^3e^2)(8d^3e)$

$(9 \cdot 2 \cdot 8)(d^{5+3+3})(e^{2+1}) = 144d^{11}e^3$

$2f^7(f^{-2}g^3)(3f^4g^{-4})$

$(2 \cdot 1 \cdot 3)(f^{7-2+4})(g^{3-4}) = 6f^9g^{-1}$

$7h^3(4h^4j^2)(6h^{-2}j^{-5})$

$(7 \cdot 4 \cdot 6)(h^{3+4-2})(j^{2-5}) = 168h^5j^{-3}$

$13k^5(k^{-2}m^7)(k^{-3}m^{-6})$

$(13 \cdot 1 \cdot 1)(k^{5-2-3})(m^{7-6}) = 13m$

Evaluating Algebraic Expressions, Adding and Subtracting Polynomials Worksheet 8

① Evaluate each algebraic expression.

$7x + 3$ for $x = 8$
$7(8) + 3 = 56 + 3 = 59$

$-9m + 11$ for $m = -2$
$-9(-2) + 11 = 18 + 11 = 29$

$10y - 6$ for $y = 3$
$10(3) - 6 = 30 - 6 = 24$

$3p^2 - 2p + 5$ for $p = -3$
$3(-3)^2 - 2(-3) + 5 = 3(9) + 6 + 5 =$
$27 + 6 + 5 = 33 + 5 = 38$
$4x - 3xy + 5y$ for $x = -3$ and $y = 5$
$4(-3) - 3(-3)(5) + 5(5) = -12 + 9(5) + 25 =$
$-12 + 45 + 25 = 33 + 25 = 58$

② Solve.

$$\begin{array}{r} 8x^2+3x+5 \\ \underline{+\ 5x^2+2x+4} \\ 13x^2+5x+9 \end{array} \qquad \begin{array}{r} 4x^2+6x+7 \\ \underline{+x^2-9x-2} \\ 5x^2-3x+5 \end{array} \qquad \begin{array}{r} 8x^2-3x+7 \\ \underline{+x^2+7x-11} \\ 9x^2+4x-4 \end{array}$$

$$\begin{array}{r} 7x^2+5x+6 \\ \underline{+\ 2x^2+4x+4} \\ 9x^2+9x+10 \end{array} \qquad \begin{array}{r} 2x^2+3x+2 \\ \underline{+7x^2-3x-6} \\ 9x^2\qquad -4 \end{array} \qquad \begin{array}{r} 9x^2+\ x+2 \\ \underline{+\ 2x^2+4x+7} \\ 11x^2+5x+9 \end{array}$$

$$\begin{array}{r} (4x^2+8x+5) \\ \underline{-(2x^2+4x+3)} \\ 2x^2+4x+2 \end{array} \qquad \begin{array}{r} (8x^2-2x+7) \\ \underline{-(3x^2-4x-5)} \\ 5x^2+2x+12 \end{array} \qquad \begin{array}{r} (3x^2-\ x-2) \\ \underline{-(5x^2+7x-2)} \\ -2x^2-8x \end{array}$$

$$\begin{array}{r} (9x^2+5x+1) \\ \underline{-(7x^2+2x+3)} \\ 2x^2+3x-2 \end{array} \qquad \begin{array}{r} (2x^2-x+1) \\ \underline{-(x^2\qquad -5)} \\ x^2-\ x+6 \end{array} \qquad \begin{array}{r} (4x^2-8x-3) \\ \underline{-(9x^2-8x-7)} \\ -5x^2\qquad +4 \end{array}$$

Teaching Tips, Cont.

- Remind students that answers should be written with coefficients first, followed by variables in alphabetical order, and that each variable in the original problem must appear exactly one time in the quotient.
- Complete the Classwork exercises. Have some students work the problems on the board for the class. All students should work the problems in their books.

Assignment

- Complete Lesson 15, Activities 2-3.

Lesson 16

Concepts
- Properties of equality
- Solving algebraic equations
- Greatest common factor

Learning Objectives
The student will be able to:
- Define seven different properties of equality
- Apply the properties of equality to solve algebraic equations
- Identify the property of equality used in each step of the solution for an algebraic equation

Materials Needed
- Student Book, Lesson 16

Teaching Tips
- Introduce the properties of equality from the teaching box. It is essential that the students fully comprehend these properties because they are the foundation for upper-level algebra.
- Write $4(x + 3) = 32$ on the board. Ask the students what property they would use first to solve this equation. (Distributive property.)
- Write $4x + 12 = 32$ on the board, showing the effect of applying the distributive property. Ask the students what property they would apply next. (Subtraction property.)
- Write $4x = 20$ on the board, showing the effect of applying the subtraction property. Ask the students what property they would apply next. (Division property.)

Lesson 16

Properties of Equality

Although there are numerous algebraic properties of equality, this book will focus on the seven properties that are used most often for solving algebraic equations.

1. Addition property of equality: You may add the same value to both sides of an equation.
If $a = b$ then $a + c = b + c$.

2. Subtraction property of equality: You may subtract the same value from both sides of an equation.
If $a = b$ then $a - c = b - c$.

3. Multiplication property of equality: You may multiply both sides of an equation by the same value.
If $a = b$ then $ac = bc$.

4. Division property of equality: You may divide both sides of an equation by the same value.
If $a = b$ then $a \div c = b \div c$.

5. Distributive property: Multiplication and division may be distributed across values inside parentheses.
$a(b + c) = ab + ac$
The distributive property also works in reverse.
$ab + ac = a(b + c)$

6. Transitive property: If one value is equal to two other values, then the other two values are equal to each other.
If $a = b$ and $a = c$ then $b = c$.

7. Substitution property: If one value is equal to another value, then the two values may be interchanged in an equation.
If $a = b$ then a may be substituted for b and b may be substituted for a in an equation.

① **Classwork**

Solve each algebraic equation. For each step, identify the property of equality that was used.

$x + 8 = 13$
$x + 8 - 8 = 13 - 8 \Rightarrow x = 5$
Subtraction property

$2x + 12 = 26$
$2x + 12 - 12 = 26 - 12 \Rightarrow 2x = 14$
Subtraction property
$2x \div 2 = 14 \div 2 \Rightarrow x = 7$
Division property

$6x - 5 = 49$
$6x - 5 + 5 = 49 + 5 \Rightarrow 6x = 54$
Addition property
$6x \div 6 = 54 \div 6 \Rightarrow x = 9$
Division property

$2(x + 1) = 22$
$2x + 2 = 22$
Distributive property
$2x + 2 - 2 = 22 - 2 \Rightarrow 2x = 20$
Subtraction property
$2x \div 2 = 20 \div 2 \Rightarrow x = 10$
Division property

Activities

② Solve each algebraic equation. For each step, identify the property of equality that was used.

$3x + 5 = 17$
$3x + 5 - 5 = 17 - 5 \Rightarrow 3x = 12$
Subtraction property
$3x \div 3 = 12 \div 3 \Rightarrow x = 4$
Division property

$5x - 5 = 30$
$5x - 5 + 5 = 30 + 5 \Rightarrow 5x = 35$
Addition property
$5x \div 5 = 35 \div 5 \Rightarrow x = 7$
Division property

$3(x + 2) = 21$
$3x + 6 = 21$
Distributive property
$3x + 6 - 6 = 21 - 6 \Rightarrow 3x = 15$
Subtraction property
$3x \div 3 = 15 \div 3 \Rightarrow x = 5$
Division property

③ Solve each algebraic equation. For each step, identify the property of equality that was used.

$6x + 5 = 23$
$6x + 5 - 5 = 23 - 5 \Rightarrow 6x = 18$
Subtraction property
$6x \div 6 = 18 \div 6 \Rightarrow x = 3$
Division property

$5x - 7 = 28$
$5x - 7 + 7 = 28 + 7 \Rightarrow 5x = 35$
Addition property
$5x \div 5 = 35 \div 5 \Rightarrow x = 7$
Division property

$3(x + 2) = 27$
$3(x + 2) \div 3 = 27 \div 3 \Rightarrow x + 2 = 9$
Division property
$x + 2 - 2 = 9 - 2 \Rightarrow x = 7$
Subtraction property

$7(x + 3) = 49$
$7(x + 3) \div 7 = 49 \div 7 \Rightarrow x + 3 = 7$
Division property
$x + 3 - 3 = 7 - 3 \Rightarrow x = 4$
Subtraction property

$4(x - 1) = 20$
$4x - 4 = 20$
Distributive property
$4x - 4 + 4 = 20 + 4 \Rightarrow 4x = 24$
Addition property
$4x \div 4 = 24 \div 4 \Rightarrow x = 6$
Division property

$5(x - 2) = 45$
$5x - 10 = 45$
Distributive property
$5x - 10 + 10 = 45 + 10 \Rightarrow 5x = 55$
Addition property
$5x \div 5 = 55 \div 5 \Rightarrow x = 11$
Division property

$2(x + 1) - 5 = 31$
$2(x + 1) - 5 + 5 = 31 + 5 \Rightarrow 2(x + 1) = 36$
Addition property
$2(x + 1) = 36 \Rightarrow 2x + 2 = 36$
Distributive property
$2x + 2 - 2 = 36 - 2 \Rightarrow 2x = 34$
Subtraction property
$2x \div 2 = 34 \div 2 \Rightarrow x = 17$
Division property

$6(x - 5) + 7 = 55$
$6(x - 5) + 7 - 7 = 55 - 7 \Rightarrow 6(x - 5) = 48$
Subtraction property
$6(x - 5) \div 6 = 48 \div 6 \Rightarrow x - 5 = 8$
Division property
$x - 5 + 5 = 8 + 5 \Rightarrow x = 13$
Addition property

④ Find the greatest common factor of each set of numbers.

12, 15, and 18	6, 9, and 15	10, 18, and 30
12 = 2 × 2 × ③	6 = 2 × ③	10 = ② × 5
15 = ③ × 5	9 = ③ × 3	18 = ② × 3 × 3
18 = 2 × ③ × 3	15 = ③ × 5	30 = ② × 3 × 5
GCF is 3	GCF is 3	GCF is 2

9, 12, and 24	12, 15, and 21	16, 18, and 24
9 = ③ × 3	12 = 2 × 2 × ③	16 = ② × 2 × 2 × 2
12 = 2 × 2 × ③	15 = ③ × 5	18 = ② × 3 × 3
24 = 2 × 2 × 2 × ③	21 = ③ × 7	24 = ② × 2 × 2 × 3
GCF is 3	GCF is 3	GCF is 2

Teaching Tips, Cont.

- Write $x = 5$ on the board, showing the effect of applying the division property. Some students may suggest using the division property in the second step, rather than the subtraction property. This is also correct, but students should be encouraged to combine like terms from both sides of the equal sign before dividing.
- Complete the Classwork exercises. Have some students work the problems on the board for the class. All students should work the problems in their books.

Assignment

- Complete Lesson 16, Activities 2-4.

Lesson 17

Concepts

- Solving algebraic equations
- Properties of equality
- Adding and subtracting polynomials
- Multiplying and dividing monomials

Learning Objectives

The student will be able to:

- Solve algebraic equations with variables on both sides
- Apply the properties of equality to solve algebraic equations
- Identify the property of equality used in each step of the solution for an algebraic equation

Materials Needed

- Student Book, Lesson 17
- Algebra tiles, optional

Teaching Tips

- ➢ Review the properties of equality from Lesson 16.
- ➢ Teach how to solve algebraic equations with variables on both sides of the equation.
- ➢ Show the students that the process is identical to what they were doing in Lesson 16, except they are combining like terms with variables as well as constants.
- ➢ Tell the students that they must be able to apply one of the properties of equality for each step in the solution. If there is no property of equality that applies to what they have done, they most likely have an error.

Solving Algebraic Equations: Variables on Both Sides

When variables appear on both sides of the equal sign in an equations, use the Properties of Equality to isolate the variable on one side and the constants on the other side. Generally, the variable terms are moved to the left side and the constant terms are moved to the right side, although the specific sides are not mandatory.

Solve the algebraic equation.
$5x + 8 = 4x + 13$

Begin by moving the variable to the left side.
$5x + 8 - 4x = 4x + 13 - 4x \Rightarrow x + 8 = 13$
Subtraction property

Next move all constants to the right side.
$x + 8 - 8 = 13 - 8 \Rightarrow x = 5$
Subtraction property

① Classwork
Solve each algebraic equation. For each step, identify the property of equality that was used.

$7x + 12 = 5x + 26$
$7x + 12 - 5x = 5x + 26 - 5x \Rightarrow 2x + 12 = 26$
Subtraction property
$2x + 12 - 12 = 26 - 12 \Rightarrow 2x = 14$
Subtraction property
$2x \div 2 = 14 \div 2 \Rightarrow x = 7$
Division property

$4x - 5 = -2x + 49$
$4x - 5 + 2x = -2x + 49 + 2x \Rightarrow 6x - 5 = 49$
Addition property
$6x - 5 + 5 = 49 + 5 \Rightarrow 6x = 54$
Addition property
$6x \div 6 = 54 \div 6 \Rightarrow x = 9$
Division property

Activities
② Solve each algebraic equation. For each step, identity the property of equality that was used.

$4x + 7 = x + 19$
$4x + 7 - x = x + 19 - x \Rightarrow 3x + 7 = 19$
Subtraction property
$3x + 7 - 7 = 19 - 7 \Rightarrow 3x = 12$
Subtraction property
$3x \div 3 = 12 \div 3 \Rightarrow x = 4$
Division property

$7x - 5 = 4x + 7$
$7x - 5 - 4x = 4x + 7 - 4x \Rightarrow 3x - 5 = 7$
Subtraction property
$3x - 5 + 5 = 7 + 5 \Rightarrow 3x = 12$
Addition property
$3x \div 3 = 12 \div 3 \Rightarrow x = 4$
Division property

$4(x + 1) = x + 19$
$4x + 4 = x + 19$
Distributive property
$4x + 4 - x = x + 19 - x \Rightarrow 3x + 4 = 19$
Subtraction property
$3x + 4 - 4 = 19 - 4 \Rightarrow 3x = 15$
Subtraction property
$3x \div 3 = 15 \div 3 \Rightarrow x = 5$
Division property

$8x - 9 = 3x + 26$
$8x - 9 - 3x = 3x + 26 - 3x \Rightarrow 5x - 9 = 26$
Subtraction property
$5x - 9 + 9 = 26 + 9 \Rightarrow 5x = 35$
Addition property
$5x \div 5 = 35 \div 5 \Rightarrow x = 7$
Division property

$2x - 8 = -3x + 27$
$2x - 8 + 3x = -3x + 27 + 3x \Rightarrow 5x - 8 = 27$
Addition property
$5x - 8 + 8 = 27 + 8 \Rightarrow 5x = 35$
Addition property
$5x \div 5 = 35 \div 5 \Rightarrow x = 7$
Division property

$7(x + 2) = 2x + 29$
$7x + 14 = 2x + 29$
Distributive property
$7x + 14 - 2x = 2x + 29 - 2x \Rightarrow 5x + 14 = 29$
Subtraction property
$5x + 14 - 14 = 29 - 14 \Rightarrow 5x = 15$
Subtraction property
$5x \div 5 = 15 \div 5 \Rightarrow x = 3$
Division property

$3x + 5 = -x + 17$
$3x + 5 + x = -x + 17 + x \Rightarrow 4x + 5 = 17$
Addition property
$4x + 5 - 5 = 17 - 5 \Rightarrow 4x = 12$
Subtraction property
$4x \div 4 = 12 \div 4 \Rightarrow x = 3$
Division property

$9x - 2 = 2x + 33$
$9x - 2 - 2x = 2x + 33 - 2x \Rightarrow 7x - 2 = 33$
Subtraction property
$7x - 2 + 2 = 33 + 2 \Rightarrow 7x = 35$
Addition property
$7x \div 7 = 35 \div 7 \Rightarrow x = 5$
Division property

$3(x + 4) = -4x - 16$
$3x + 12 = -4x - 16$
Distributive property
$3x + 12 + 4x = -4x - 16 + 4x \Rightarrow 7x + 12 = -16$
Addition property
$7x + 12 - 12 = -16 - 12 \Rightarrow 7x = -28$
Subtraction property
$7x \div 7 = -28 \div 7 \Rightarrow x = -4$
Division property

③ Solve.

$6d^2+3d+7$ $\underline{+\ d^2+d+2}$ $7d^2+4d+9$	$7e^2+4e+8$ $\underline{-2e^2-e-1}$ $5e^2+3e+7$	$4f^2-4f+7$ $\underline{+2f^2+7f-10}$ $6f^2+3f-3$
$6g^2-2g+2$ $\underline{+\ g^2-3g+1}$ $7g^2-5g+3$	$6h^2-h+7$ $\underline{-3h^2-2h+2}$ $3h^2-3h+9$	$4i^2-2i+1$ $\underline{+2i^2+5i-12}$ $6i^2+3i-11$
$(3n^2+3n)$ $\underline{-(4n^2+2n+5)}$ $-n^2+n-5$	$(2p^2-4p+1)$ $\underline{-(5p^2-3p-2)}$ $-3p^2-p+3$	$(7r^2-2r-3)$ $\underline{-(10r^2+7r-2)}$ $-3r^2-9r-1$
$(3x^2+5x+2)$ $\underline{-(5x^2+4x)}$ $-2x^2+x+2$	$(3x^2\quad+2)$ $\underline{-(5x^2-3x)}$ $-2x^2+3x+2$	$(-x^2-3x-5)$ $\underline{-(2x^2+5x-3)}$ $-3x^2-8x-2$
$7y^5(4y^3z^4)(8y^5z^3)$ $(7\cdot4\cdot8)(y^{5+3+5})(z^{4+3})=$ $224y^{13}z^7$	$3b^7(8b^5c^4)(5b^2c^9)$ $(3\cdot8\cdot5)(b^{7+5+2})(c^{4+9})=$ $120b^{14}c^{13}$	$7d^6(3d^2e^5)(9de^3)$ $(7\cdot3\cdot9)(d^{6+2+1})(e^{5+3})=$ $189d^9e^8$
$3f^6(-4f^{-3}g^8)(7f^2g^{-5})$ $(3\cdot-4\cdot7)(f^{6-3+2})(g^{8-5})=$ $-84f^5g^3$	$-h^4(5hj^3)(9h^{-5}j^{-2})$ $(-1\cdot5\cdot9)(h^{4+1-5})(j^{3-2})=$ $-45j$	$-7k^6(6k^{-4}m^3)(-9k^{-5}m^{-4})$ $(-7\cdot6\cdot-9)(k^{6-4-5})(m^{3-4})=$ $378k^{-3}m^{-1}$
$39a^5\div13a^2$ $\frac{39a^5}{13a^2}=3a^{5-2}=3a^3$	$42b^9\div7b^4$ $\frac{42b^9}{7b^4}=6b^{9-4}=6b^5$	$77c^{15}\div11c^{-3}$ $\frac{77c^{15}}{11c^{-3}}=7c^{15-(-3)}=7c^{18}$
$32d^5e^8\div4e^6$ $\frac{32d^5e^8}{4e^6}=8d^5e^{8-6}=8d^5e^2$	$63f^4g\div9g^6$ $\frac{63f^4g}{9g^6}=7f^4g^{1-6}=7f^4g^{-5}$ or $\frac{7f^4}{g^5}$	$36hi^{-4}\div4i^{-5}$ $\frac{36hi^{-4}}{4i^{-5}}=9hi^{-4-(-5)}=9hi$
$48j^9k^6\div12j^7k^2$ $\frac{48j^9k^6}{12j^7k^2}=4j^{9-7}k^{6-2}=4j^2k^4$	$72m^3n^2\div9m^{-4}n$ $\frac{72m^3n^2}{9m^{-4}n}=8m^{3-(-4)}n^{2-1}=8m^7n$	$75p^{-6}r^2\div3p^{-4}r^5$ $\frac{75p^{-6}r^2}{3p^{-4}r^5}=25p^{-6-(-4)}r^{2-5}=$ $25p^{-2}r^{-3}$ or $\frac{25}{p^2r^3}$
$27t^2u\div9t^4u$ $\frac{27t^2u}{9t^4u}=3t^{2-4}u^{1-1}=3t^{-2}$ or $\frac{3}{t^2}$	$60v^3w^2\div12vw^5$ $\frac{60v^3w^2}{12vw^5}=5v^{3-1}w^{2-5}=$ $5v^2w^{-3}$ or $\frac{5v^2}{w^3}$	$32x^3y^4\div2x^5y^2$ $\frac{32x^3y^4}{2x^5y^2}=16x^{3-5}y^{4-2}=$ $16x^{-2}y^2$ or $\frac{16y^2}{x^2}$

Teaching Tips, Cont.

- Note: The 7 properties of equality covered in this book are not an exhaustive list, but they are the primary properties used in algebra. Additional properties of equality will be introduced in geometry.
- Students who are having difficulty solving algebraic equations on paper may find it easier to work with algebra tiles. Tell them the properties of equality apply to algebra tiles just like they apply to equations on paper.
- Complete the Classwork exercises. Have some students work the problems on the board for the class. All students should work the problems in their books.

Assignment

- Complete Lesson 17, Activities 2-3.

Lesson 18

Concepts

- Solving algebraic equations
- Fractions
- Properties of equality
- Least common multiple
- Roots
- Math in the real world

Learning Objectives

The student will be able to:

- Find the least common multiple of all terms in an algebraic equation
- Re-write the terms in an algebraic equation to have a common denominator
- Solve algebraic expressions involving fractions
- Apply the properties of equality to algebraic equations with fractions

Materials Needed

- Student Book, Lesson 18
- Worksheet 9

Teaching Tips

- Have students complete Worksheet 9 in class. This may be for added practice of earlier topics or graded as a quiz.
- Review least common multiple. (See Lesson 6)
- Review the properties of equality as needed. (See Lesson 16)
- Teach how to solve algebraic expressions containing fractions. Emphasize that the first step is ALWAYS to find the least common multiple of the denominators of the terms. Remind students that non-fraction terms have a denominator of 1.

Solving Algebraic Equations: Fractions

If an algebraic equation contains one or more fractions, it is essential to eliminate the fractions before solving the equation. If the equation has more than one term with a fraction, find the least common multiple of the denominators. Multiply every term on both sides of the equation by the least common multiple. Important: EVERY term must be multiplied, not just the fraction terms. Once all fractions have been eliminated, solve the equation using the Properties of Equality.

$\frac{x}{3}+\frac{x+2}{2}=12$

The least common multiple of 3 and 2 is 6. Multiply each term on BOTH sides of the equation by 6. (Multiplication property)

$\frac{x}{\not 3}\left(\not 6^{2}\right)+\frac{x+2}{\not 2}\left(\not 6^{3}\right)=12(6)\Rightarrow 2x+3(x+2)=72$

Now that all fractions have been eliminated, use the properties of equality to solve for x.

$2x+3x+6=72\Rightarrow 5x+6=72$
Distributive property

$5x+6-6=72-6\Rightarrow 5x=66$
Subtraction property

$5x\div 5=66\div 5\Rightarrow x=\frac{66}{5}$
Division property

① **Classwork**

Solve each algebraic equation. For each step, identify the property of equality that was used.

$\frac{x}{4}+\frac{3x+1}{2}=16$

$\frac{x}{\not 4}\left(\not 4\right)+\frac{3x+1}{\not 2}\left(\not 4^{2}\right)=16(4)\Rightarrow x+(3x+1)(2)=64$
Multiplication property
$x+6x+2=64\Rightarrow 7x+2=64$
Distributive property
$7x+2-2=64-2\Rightarrow 7x=62$
Subtraction property
$7x\div 7=62\div 7\Rightarrow x=\frac{62}{7}$
Division property

$\frac{6}{x}+\frac{5}{x^2}=\frac{1}{x}$

$\frac{6}{\not x}\left(x^{\not 2}\right)+\frac{5}{\not x^2}\left(\not x^2\right)=\frac{1}{\not x}\left(x^{\not 2}\right)\Rightarrow 6x+5=x$
Multiplication property
$6x+5-x=x-x\Rightarrow 5x+5=0$
Subtraction property
$5x+5-5=0-5\Rightarrow 5x=-5$
Subtraction property
$5x\div 5=-5\div 5\Rightarrow x=-1$
Division property

Activities

② Solve each algebraic equation. For each step, identity the property of equality that was used.

$\frac{2x}{3}+\frac{x+1}{5}=4$

$\frac{2x}{\not 3}\left(\not 15^{5}\right)+\frac{x+1}{\not 5}\left(\not 15^{3}\right)=4(15)\Rightarrow 10x+(x+1)(3)=60$
Multiplication property
$10x+3x+3=60\Rightarrow 13x+3=60$
Distributive property
$13x+3-3=60-3\Rightarrow 13x=57$
Subtraction property
$13x\div 13=57\div 13\Rightarrow x=\frac{57}{13}$
Division property

$\frac{4x}{5}-\frac{2x-3}{2}=3$

$\frac{4x}{\not 5}\left(\not 10^{2}\right)-\frac{2x-3}{\not 2}\left(\not 10^{5}\right)=3(10)\Rightarrow 8x-(2x-3)(5)=3$
Multiplication property
$8x-10x+15=30\Rightarrow -2x+15=30$
Distributive property
$-2x+15-15=30-15\Rightarrow -2x=15$
Subtraction property
$-2x\div(-2)=15\div(-2)\Rightarrow x=-\frac{15}{2}$
Division property

③ Solve each algebraic equation. For each step, identity the property of equality that was used.

$3+\frac{5}{x}=-2$

$3(x)+\frac{5}{\not x}\left(\not x\right)=-2(x)\Rightarrow 3x+5=-2x$
Multiplication property
$3x+5+2x=-2x+2x\Rightarrow 5x+5=0$
Addition property
$5x+5-5=0-5\Rightarrow 5x=-5$
Subtraction property
$5x\div 5=-5\div 5\Rightarrow x=-1$
Division property

$4-\frac{3}{x}=\frac{5}{x}$

$4(x)-\frac{3}{\not x}\left(\not x\right)=\frac{5}{\not x}\left(\not x\right)\Rightarrow 4x-3=5$
Multiplication property
$4x-3+3=5+3\Rightarrow 4x=8$
Addition property
$4x\div 4=8\div 4\Rightarrow x=4$
Division property

$\frac{8}{x}-\frac{3}{x^2}=-\frac{1}{x}$

$\frac{8}{\not x}\left(x^{\not 2}\right)-\frac{3}{\not x^2}\left(\not x^2\right)=-\frac{1}{\not x}\left(x^{\not 2}\right)\Rightarrow 8x-3=-x$
Multiplication property
$8x-3+x=-x+x\Rightarrow 9x-3=0$
Addition property
$9x-3+3=0+3\Rightarrow 9x=3$
Addition property
$9x\div 9=3\div 9\Rightarrow x=\frac{3}{9}=\frac{1}{3}$
Division property

$\frac{7}{x}+\frac{5}{x^2}=\frac{4}{x}+\frac{17}{x^2}$

$\frac{7}{\not x}\left(x^{\not 2}\right)+\frac{5}{\not x^2}\left(\not x^2\right)=\frac{4}{\not x}\left(x^{\not 2}\right)+\frac{17}{\not x^2}\left(\not x^2\right)\Rightarrow 7x+5=4x+17$
Multiplication property
$7x+5-4x=4x+17-4x\Rightarrow 3x+5=17$
Subtraction property
$3x+5-5=17-5\Rightarrow 3x=12$
Subtraction property
$3x\div 3=12\div 3\Rightarrow x=4$
Division property

④ Solve the following roots.

$\left(\sqrt{12}\right)\left(\sqrt{18}\right)=\left(2\sqrt{3}\right)\left(3\sqrt{2}\right)=6\sqrt{6}$

$3\left(5\sqrt{20}\right)=$

$15\sqrt{20}=15\sqrt{2\times 2\times 5}=(15\times 2)\sqrt{5}=30\sqrt{5}$

$20\sqrt{60}\div 4\sqrt{12}=(20\div 4)\sqrt{60\div 12}=5\sqrt{5}$

$\sqrt{75}\div 5=\sqrt{75}\div\sqrt{25}=\sqrt{75\div 25}=\sqrt{3}$

⑤ Solve.

The width of a soccer field is $\frac{1}{2}$ the length of the field. If the sum of the length and width is 150 yards, what are the dimensions of the soccer field? Hint: Use the substitution property of equality.

$W=\frac{1}{2}L$
$L+W=150$ yards
$L+\frac{1}{2}L=150$ yards
$L(2)+\frac{1}{2}L(2)=150(2)$ yards
$2L+L=300$ yards
$3L=300$ yards
$L=100$ yards
$W=\frac{1}{2}(100\text{ yards})=50$ yards

Multiplying and Dividing Monomials	Worksheet 9
① Multiply.	
$10j^2(5j^2k^2)$	$(10\cdot5)(j^{2+2})(k^2)=50j^4k^2$
$5c^2(9cd^2)$	$(5\cdot9)(c^{2+1})(d^2)=45c^3d^2$
$9g(g^2h^2)$	$(9\cdot1)(g^{1+2})(h^2)=9g^3h^2$
$9p^3(11p^2r^4)$	$(9\cdot11)(p^{3+2})(r^4)=99p^5r^4$
$12m^3(3m^2n^2)$	$(12\cdot3)(m^{3+2})(n^2)=36m^5n^2$
$3a(6ab^2)$	$(3\cdot6)(a^{1+1})(b^2)=18a^2b^2$
$2e^3(13ef^2)$	$(2\cdot13)(e^{3+1})(f^2)=26e^4f^2$
② Divide.	
$70m^5n^4\div7m^2n^2$	$\frac{70m^5n^4}{7m^2n^2}=10m^{5-2}n^{4-2}=10m^3n^2$
$42g^5h^4\div7g^2h^2$	$\frac{42g^5h^4}{7g^2h^2}=6g^{5-2}h^{4-2}=6g^3h^2$
$18c^3d^3\div6c^2d^2$	$\frac{18c^3d^3}{6c^2d^2}=3c^{3-2}d^{3-2}=3cd$
$84p^5r^4\div12p^2r^3$	$\frac{84p^5r^4}{12p^2r^3}=7p^{5-2}r^{4-3}=7p^3r$
$15a^4b^3\div3ab^2$	$\frac{15a^4b^3}{3ab^2}=5a^{4-1}b^{3-2}=5a^3b$
$36e^4f^2\div4e^2f^2$	$\frac{36e^4f^2}{4e^2f^2}=9e^{4-2}f^{2-2}=9e^2$
$63j^5k^4\div9j^2k^3$	$\frac{63j^5k^4}{9j^2k^3}=7j^{5-2}k^{4-3}=7j^3k$

Teaching Tips, Cont.

- Emphasize that ALL terms on both sides of the equal sign must be multiplied by the least common multiple of the denominators — not just the terms with fractions.
- Remind students that a property of equality must be used every time anything is done to the equation. If they cannot support their math with a property of equality, they cannot do that calculation.
- Complete the Classwork exercises. Have some students work the problems on the board for the class. All students should work the problems in their books.

Assignment

- Complete Lesson 18, Activities 2-5.

Lesson 19

Concepts

- Solving algebraic equations
- Decimals
- Fractions
- Math in the real world

Learning Objectives

The student will be able to:

- Solve algebraic expressions containing decimals
- Choose the proper power of 10 to eliminate decimals in an algebraic equation

Materials Needed

- Student Book, Lesson 19

Teaching Tips

➢ Teach how to solve algebraic equations that contain decimals. Explain that the easiest way to know what to multiply each term by is to count the number of digits to the right of the decimal point in each term. The greatest number of digits to the right of the decimal point in any term of the equation is the number each term should be multiplied by. Note: This is equivalent to multiplying each term by a power of 10, where the exponent is the highest number of digits to the right of the decimal point.

Solving Algebraic Equations: Decimals

Although it is possible to solve algebraic equations that contain decimals, it is much easier to solve the equation once all decimals have been eliminated. To eliminate decimals, first find the term with the greatest number of digits to the right of the decimal point. Then multiply each term on both sides of the equal sign by the power of 10 having that number as the exponent.

For example, the equation 3x + 2.4 = 2.94 has one term with no decimal, one term with one digit to the right of the decimal point, and one term with two digits to the right of the decimal point. Because the greatest number of digits to the right of the decimal point is 2, then multiply each term on both sides of the equal sign by 10^2 or 100.

100(3x) + 100(2.4) = 100(2.94)
300x + 240 = 294
300x = 294 - 240
300x = 54
x = 0.18

① Classwork

Solve.

$0.2x - 1 = 1.4$
$0.2x(10) - 1(10) = 1.4(10)$
$2x - 10 = 14$
$2x - 10 + 10 = 14 + 10$
$2x = 24$
$2x \div 2 = 24 \div 2$
$x = 12$

$5x + 0.3 = 2.05$
$5x(100) + 0.3(100) = 2.05(100)$
$500x + 30 = 205$
$500x + 30 - 30 = 205 - 30$
$500x = 175$
$500x \div 500 = 175 \div 500$
$x = \frac{175}{500} = \frac{7}{20} = 0.35$

Activities

② Solve.

$1.1x + 0.5 = 0.3x - 1.1$
$1.1x(10) + 0.5(10) = 0.3x(10) - 1.1(10)$
$11x + 5 = 3x - 11$
$8x + 5 = -11$
$8x = -16$
$x = -2$

$3(x - 0.2) + 0.1x = 5.6$
$3x - 0.6 + 0.1x = 5.6$
$3x(10) - 0.6(10) + 0.1x(10) = 5.6(10)$
$30x - 6 + x = 56$
$31x - 6 = 56$
$31x = 62$
$x = 2$

$0.7x - 2 = 1.5$
$0.7x(10) - 2(10) = 1.5(10)$
$7x - 20 = 15$
$7x = 35$
$x = 5$

$2.4x + 0.07 = 5(0.3x + 0.23)$
$2.4x + 0.07 = 1.5x + 1.15$
$2.4x(100) + 0.07(100) = 1.5x(100) + 1.15(100$
$240x + 7 = 150x + 115$
$90x + 7 = 115$
$90x = 108$
$x = \frac{108}{90} = \frac{6}{5} = 1.2$

③ Solve.

$2(0.09x - 1) = 5(0.03x + 0.23)$
$0.18x - 2 = 0.15x + 1.15$
$0.18x(100) - 2(100) = 0.15x(100) + 1.15(100)$
$18x - 200 = 15x + 115$
$3x - 200 = 115$
$3x = 315$
$x = 105$

$7(x + 0.6) = 2(x - 5.6) + 3.4$
$7x + 4.2 = 2x - 11.2 + 3.4$
$7x(10) + 4.2(10) = 2x(10) - 11.2(10) + 3.4(10)$
$70x + 42 = 20x - 112 + 34$
$50x + 42 = -78$
$50x = -120$
$x = -\frac{120}{50} = -\frac{12}{5} = -2.4$

$5 + \frac{14}{x} = -2$
$5(x) + \frac{14}{\cancel{x}}(\cancel{x}) = -2(x)$
$5x + 14 = -2x$
$7x + 14 = 0$
$7x = -14$
$x = -2$

$14 + \frac{37}{x} = \frac{9}{x}$
$14(x) + \frac{37}{\cancel{x}}(\cancel{x}) = \frac{9}{\cancel{x}}(\cancel{x})$
$14x + 37 = 9$
$14x = -28$
$x = -2$

$3(0.06x + 7) = 4(0.01x - 0.31) + 0.12$
$0.18x + 21 = 0.04x - 1.24 + 0.12$
$0.18x(100) + 21(100) = 0.04x(100) - 1.24(100) + 0.12(100)$
$18x + 2100 = 4x - 124 + 12$
$14x + 2100 = -112$
$14x = -2212$
$x = -158$

$3(0.3x + 0.5) = 2(0.2x - 0.9) + 0.3$
$0.9x + 1.5 = 0.4x - 1.8 + 0.3$
$0.9x(10) + 1.5(10) = 0.4x(10) - 1.8(10) + 0.3(10)$
$9x + 15 = 4x - 18 + 3$
$5x + 15 = -15$
$5x = -30$
$x = -6$

$\frac{23}{x} - \frac{9}{x^2} = -\frac{4}{x}$
$\frac{23}{\cancel{x}}(x^{\cancel{2}}) - \frac{9}{\cancel{x^2}}(\cancel{x^2}) = -\frac{4}{\cancel{x}}(x^{\cancel{2}})$
$23x - 9 = -4x$
$27x - 9 = 0$
$27x = 9$
$x = \frac{9}{27} = \frac{1}{3}$

$\frac{33}{x} - \frac{13}{x^2} = \frac{6}{x} + \frac{5}{x^2}$
$\frac{33}{\cancel{x}}(x^{\cancel{2}}) - \frac{13}{\cancel{x^2}}(\cancel{x^2}) = \frac{6}{\cancel{x}}(x^{\cancel{2}}) + \frac{5}{\cancel{x^2}}(\cancel{x^2})$
$33x - 13 = 6x + 5$
$27x - 13 = 5$
$27x = 18$
$x = \frac{18}{27} = \frac{2}{3}$

④ Solve.

The length of a soccer field is 1.3 times its width. If the sum of the length and width of the soccer field is 690 feet, what are the dimensions of the field? Hint: Use the substitution property of equality.

$L = 1.3w$ and $L + w = 690$ feet
Substitute $1.3w$ for the value of L in the second equation.
$1.3w + w = 690$ feet
Now solve for w.
$2.3w = 690$ feet
$2.3w(10) = 690$ feet (10)
$23w = 6900$ feet
$w = 300$ feet
From the original problem, $L = 1.3w$, so $L = 1.3(300$ feet$) = 390$ feet
Check: 300 feet + 390 feet = 690 feet

Teaching Tips, Cont.

- Remind students that according to the multiplication property of equality, every term on both sides of the equal sign must be multiplied by the same number.
- If you have students who have forgotten how to multiply by powers of 10, you may want to show them this shortcut: Move the decimal point to the right the number of places equal to the exponent in the power of ten. For example, if each term is multiplied by 10^3 then every term on both sides of the equal sign would have the decimal point moved to the right 3 places.
- Remind students that whole numbers have an understood decimal point to the right of the number. For example, the number 42 can be treated as 42.0 for the sake of decimal placement.
- Complete the Classwork exercises. Have some students work the problems on the board for the class. All students should work the problems in their books.

Assignment

- Complete Lesson 19, Activities 2-4.

Lesson 20

Concepts

- Solving algebraic equations
- Absolute value
- Multiplying monomials
- Dividing monomials
- Fractions
- Decimals

Learning Objectives

The student will be able to:

- Solve algebraic equations with absolute values
- Find all possible solutions when absolute values are involved
- Eliminate extraneous solutions from solutions of algebraic equations

Materials Needed

- Student Book, Lesson 20
- Worksheet 10

Teaching Tips

➤ Review absolute value. (See Lesson 5)

➤ Teach how to solve algebraic equations with absolute values. Explain that equations like this will occasionally produce extraneous roots — roots that are not true solutions of the equation. For this reason, it is imperative that all solutions are checked in the original equation to ensure they are real solutions.

➤ Write $|x+3|+10=2x+25$ on the board as an example of an equation with an extraneous solution. The complete solution is shown at the right.

Solving Algebraic Equations: Absolute Value

Algebraic equations that contain an absolute value cannot be solved like a normal algebraic equation. Because the value inside the absolute value sign may be positive or negative, you must work the problem out twice to allow for either answer. In most cases, there are two possible solutions to an algebraic equation with absolute values. It is important that you solve for both solutions.

For example, find all possible solutions of $|x+3|+5=13$.

First, isolate the term in the absolute value sign:
$|x+3|=13-5$
$|x+3|=8$

Because the value inside the absolute value sign may be positive or negative, you must solve for both cases.
$x+3=8$ or $x+3=-8$
$x=5$ or $x=-11$

Once you have solved for all possible value of the variable, substitute each value in the original problem to check. Occasionally you may get a solution that does not work when checked in the original.
$|5+3|=8$ and $|-11+3|=8$
$8=8$ $\quad |-8|=8$

① Classwork
Find all possible solutions.

$|2x+5|+7=18$
$|2x+5|=11$
$2x+5=11$ or $2x+5=-11$
$2x=6$ $\quad 2x=-16$
$x=3$ $\quad x=-8$

$|4x-3|+2=17$
$|4x-3|=15$
$4x-3=15$ or $4x-3=-15$
$4x=18$ $\quad 4x=-12$
$x=\frac{18}{4}=\frac{9}{2}$ $\quad x=-3$

$|3x+1|-4=x+5$
$|3x+1|=x+9$
$3x+1=x+9$ or $3x+1=-(x+9)$
$2x=8$ $\quad 3x+1=-x-9$
$x=4$ $\quad 4x=-10$
$x=-\frac{10}{4}=-\frac{5}{2}$

Activities

② Find all possible solutions.

$|3x+3|+6=21$
$|3x+3|=15$
$3x+3=15$ or $3x+3=-15$
$3x=12$ $\quad 3x=-18$
$x=4$ $\quad x=-6$

$|6x-5|+4=27$
$|6x-5|=23$
$6x-5=23$ or $6x-5=-23$
$6x=28$ $\quad 6x=-18$
$x=\frac{28}{6}=\frac{14}{3}$ $\quad x=-3$

$|5x-11|-17=32$
$|5x-11|=49$
$5x-11=49$ or $5x-11=-49$
$5x=60$ $\quad 5x=-38$
$x=12$ $\quad x=-\frac{38}{5}$

$|7x-40|-42=-19$
$|7x-40|=23$
$7x-40=23$ or $7x-40=-23$
$7x=63$ $\quad 7x=17$
$x=9$ $\quad x=\frac{17}{7}$

③ Find all possible solutions. Identify any extraneous solutions.

$|7x+9|-12=3x-23$
$|7x+9|=3x-11$
$7x+9=3x-11$ or $7x+9=-(3x-11)$
$4x=-20$ $\quad 7x+9=-3x+11$
$x=-5$ $\quad 10x=2 \Rightarrow x=\frac{2}{10}=\frac{1}{5}$
check:
$|7(-5)+9|-12=3(-5)-23$
$|-35+9|-12=-15-23$
$|-26|-12=-38$
$26-12\neq-38$ extraneous

$|7(\frac{1}{5})+9|-12=3(\frac{1}{5})-23$
$|\frac{36}{5}+\frac{45}{5}|-12=\frac{3}{5}-23$
$\frac{81}{5}-\frac{60}{5}=\frac{3}{5}-\frac{115}{5}$
$\frac{21}{5}\neq-\frac{112}{5}$ extraneous

$|3x-2|-3=-2x+25$
$|3x-2|=-2x+28$
$3x-2=-2x+28$ or $3x-2=-(-2x+28)$
$5x=30$ $\quad 3x-2=2x-28$
$x=6$ $\quad x=-26$
check:
$|3(6)-2|-3=-2(6)+25$
$|18-2|-3=-12+25$
$16-3=13$

$|3(-26)-2|-3=-2(-26)+25$
$|-78-2|-3=52+25$
$|-80|-3=77$
$80-3=77$

④ Solve.

$5a^5b^3(-3b^{-2}c^7)(6a^3c^{-4})$
$(5\cdot-3\cdot6)(a^{5+3})(b^{3-2})(c^{7-4})=$
$-90a^8bc^3$

$-5d^9e^5(2e^4f^6)(12d^{-2}f^{-1})$
$(-5\cdot2\cdot12)(d^{9-2})(e^{5+4})(f^{6-1})=$
$-120d^7e^9f^5$

$-11g^2h^5(4h^{-8}i^5)(-7g^4i^{-3})$
$(-11\cdot4\cdot-7)(g^{2+4})(h^{5-8})(i^{5-3})=$
$308g^6h^{-3}i^2$

$144j^5k^{13}m^8\div36j^2k^7m^5$
$\frac{144j^5k^{13}m^8}{36j^2k^7m^5}=4j^{5-2}k^{13-7}m^{8-5}=$
$4j^3k^6m^3$

$105n^5p^8\div15n^8p^5$
$\frac{105n^5p^8}{15n^8p^5}=7n^{5-8}p^{8-5}=$
$7n^{-3}p^3$ or $\frac{7p^3}{n^3}$

$18r^4t^7\div72r^{13}t^{19}$
$\frac{18r^4t^7}{72r^{13}t^{19}}=\frac{1}{4}r^{4-13}t^{7-19}=$
$\frac{1}{4}r^{-9}t^{-12}$ or $\frac{1}{4r^9t^{12}}$

$6(v+5)=2v+66$
$6v+30=2v+66$
$4v+30=66$
$4v=36$
$v=9$

$\frac{5x}{7}+\frac{2x-3}{4}=\frac{251}{28}$
$\frac{5x}{\not7}(\not{28}^{4})+\frac{2x-3}{\not4}(\not{28}^{7})=\frac{251}{\not{28}}(\not{28})$
$20x+(2x-3)(7)=251$
$20x+14x-21=251$
$34x-21=251$
$34x=272$
$x=8$

$12(w-3)=-3w-111$
$12w-36=-3w-111$
$15w-36=-111$
$15w=-75$
$w=-5$

$1.3x+0.16=0.9x-0.2$
$1.3x(100)+0.16(100)=0.9x(100)-0.2(100)$
$130x+16=90x-20$
$40x+16=-20$
$40x=-36$
$x=-\frac{36}{40}=-\frac{9}{10}=-0.9$

Algebraic Equations, Extraneous Solutions Worksheet 10

① Solve each algebraic equation. Identify extraneous solutions where necessary.

$5(0.05x - 0.1) = 3(0.05x + 0.3)$

$0.25x - 0.5 = 0.15x + 0.9$
$0.25x(100) - 0.5(100) = 0.15x(100) + 0.9(100)$
$25x - 50 = 15x + 90$
$10x - 50 = 90$
$10x = 140$
$x = 14$

$9 + \frac{23}{x} = -\frac{4}{x}$

$9(x) + \frac{23}{\cancel{x}}(\cancel{x}) = -\frac{4}{\cancel{x}}(\cancel{x})$
$9x + 23 = -4$
$9x = -27$
$x = -3$

$|5x + 3| - 8 = 7x - 9$

$|5x + 3| = 7x - 1$
$5x + 3 = 7x - 1$ or $5x + 3 = -(7x - 1)$
$-2x = -4$ $5x + 3 = -7x + 1$
$x = 2$ $12x = -2 \Rightarrow x = -\frac{2}{12} = -\frac{1}{6}$
check:
$|5(2) + 3| - 8 = 7(2) - 9$
$|10 + 3| - 8 = 14 - 9$
$13 - 8 = 5$
$5 = 5$

$|5(-\frac{1}{6}) + 3| - 8 = 7(-\frac{1}{6}) - 9$
$|-\frac{5}{6} + 3| - 8 = -\frac{7}{6} - 9$
$\frac{13}{6} - 8 = -\frac{7}{6} - 9$
$-\frac{35}{6} \neq -\frac{61}{6}$ extraneous

$|x + 3| + 10 = 2x + 25$
$|x + 3| = 2x + 15$
$x + 3 = 2x + 15$
$-x = 12$
$x = -12$
check:
$|-12 + 3| + 10 = 2(-12) + 25$
$|-9| + 10 = -24 + 25$
$9 + 10 = 1$
$19 = 1$
this solution does not work and is extraneous

$x + 3 = -(2x + 15)$
$x + 3 = -2x - 15$
$3x = -18$
$x = -6$
check:
$|-6 + 3| + 10 = 2(-6) + 25$
$|-3| + 10 = -12 + 25$
$3 + 10 = 13$
$13 = 13$
this solution works

Teaching Tips, Cont.

- Tell the students that most of the time the solutions will work. Finding an extraneous solution is uncommon, but the students should get in the habit of checking all solutions.
- Complete the Classwork exercises. Have some students work the problems on the board for the class. All students should work the problems in their books.
- Review for Test 2 using worksheets 6-10. These worksheets were assigned in previous lessons.

Assignments

- Complete Lesson 20, Activities 2-4.
- Worksheet 10.
- Study for Test 2 (Lessons 8-17).

Test 2

Testing Objectives

The student will:

- Translate phrases into algebraic expressions
- Use the distributive property to simplify expressions
- Evaluate algebraic expressions
- Add polynomials
- Subtract polynomials
- Multiply monomials
- Divide monomials
- Solve algebraic equations
- Identify the properties of equality used when solving algebraic equations

Materials Needed

- Test 2
- *It's College Test Prep Time!* from Student Book
- Exploring Math through … Volleyball from Student Book

Teaching Tips

- Administer Test 2, allowing the students 30-40 minutes to complete the test.
- When all students are finished taking the test, introduce the College Test Prep Time from the student book. This page may be completed in class or assigned as homework.
- Have students read the Exploring Math feature for Lessons 21-30.

① Translate the following words into a mathematical expression. **12 points**

The total of a number and 19 $x+19$

32 fewer than a number $x-32$

A number times 17 $17x$

The sum of 41 and a number $41+x$

The quotient of a number and 2 $x \div 2$

25 less than a number $x-25$

A number increased by a factor of 10 $10x$

54 more than a number $x+54$

A number less than 97 $97-x$

The product of 24 and a number $24x$

The ratio of a number to 4 $x \div 4$

A number increased by 70 $x+70$

② Use the distributive property to simplify each expression. **6 points**

$4(15+7)=60+28=88$

$3(20+9)=60+27=87$

$9(1+90)=9+810=819$

$7(40+7)=280+49=329$

$8(70+7)=560+56=616$

$6(25+7+15)=150+42+90=282$

③ Evaluate each algebraic expression. **8 points**

$4x + 9$ for $x = 3$
$4(3) + 9 = 12 + 9 = 21$

$-11p + 6$ for $p = -3$
$-11(-3) + 6 = 33 + 6 = 39$

$7b - 5$ for $b = -4$
$7(-4) - 5 = -28 - 5 = -33$

$2r^2 - 4r + 7$ for $r = -2$
$2(-2)^2 - 4(-2) + 7 = 2(4) + 8 + 7 =$
$8 + 8 + 7 = 16 + 7 = 23$

$-5c + 12$ for $c = 7$
$-5(7) + 12 = -35 + 12 = -23$

$-3k + 8$ for $k = 5$
$-3(5) + 8 = -15 + 8 = -7$

$3t^2 - 9t + 10$ for $t = 2$
$3(2)^2 - 9(2) + 10 = 3(4) - 18 + 10 =$
$12 - 18 + 10 = -6 + 10 = 4$

$9g - 4gh + 3h$ for $g = -6$ and $h = 3$
$9(-6) - 4(-6)(3) + 3(3) =$
$-54 + 24(3) + 9 = -54 + 72 + 9 =$
$18 + 9 = 27$

④ Solve. **6 points**

$$\begin{array}{r} 7x^2+4x+6 \\ +\ 3x^2+\ x+2 \\ \hline 10x^2+5x+8 \end{array} \qquad \begin{array}{r} 6x^2+2x+6 \\ +3x^2-3x-2 \\ \hline 9x^2-\ x+4 \end{array} \qquad \begin{array}{r} 3x^2 \qquad +5 \\ +2x^2+6x-7 \\ \hline 5x^2+6x-2 \end{array}$$

$$\begin{array}{r} (7x^2+5x+6) \\ -(3x^2+2x+4) \\ \hline 4x^2+3x+2 \end{array} \qquad \begin{array}{r} (4x^2-2x+5) \\ -(x^2-3x) \\ \hline 3x^2+\ x+5 \end{array} \qquad \begin{array}{r} (5x^2 \qquad -3) \\ -(7x^2-4x-3) \\ \hline -2x^2+4x \end{array}$$

⑤ Solve. **8 points**

$3a(4ab^2)$

$(3\cdot4)(a^{1+1})(b^2)=12a^2b^2$

$5c^3(9cd^2)$

$(5\cdot9)(c^{3+1})(d^2)=45c^4d^2$

$7e^3(6ef^2)$

$(7\cdot6)(e^{3+1})(f^2)=42e^4f^2$

$2g^2(11g^2h^2)$

$(2\cdot11)(g^{2+2})(h^2)=22g^4h^2$

$13j^3 \div j$

$\frac{13j^3}{j}=13j^{3-1}=13j^2$

$36k^4 \div 9k^2$

$\frac{36k^4}{9k^2}=4k^{4-2}=4k^2$

$15m^3n^2 \div m^3$

$\frac{15m^3n^2}{m^3}=15m^{3-3}n^2=15n^2$

$28p^5r^4 \div 7p^2r^3$

$\frac{28p^5r^4}{7p^2r^3}=4p^{5-2}r^{4-3}=4p^3r$

⑥ Solve each algebraic equation. Identify the property of equality used in each step. **24 points**

$7(x+5)=28$
$7(x+5)\div7=28\div7 \Rightarrow x+5=4$
Division property
$x+5-5=4-5 \Rightarrow x=-1$
Subtraction property

$6(x-9)=42$
$6x-54=42$
Distributive property
$6x-54+54=42+54 \Rightarrow 6x=96$
Addition property
$6x\div6=96\div6 \Rightarrow x=16$
Division property

$4(x-3)+7=59$
$4(x-3)+7-7=59-7 \Rightarrow 4(x-3)=52$
Subtraction property
$4(x-3)\div4=52\div4 \Rightarrow x-3=13$
Division property
$x-3+3=13+3 \Rightarrow x=16$
Addition property

$3x+8=x+12$
$3x+8-x=x+12-x \Rightarrow 2x+8=12$
Subtraction property
$2x+8-8=12-8 \Rightarrow 2x=4$
Subtraction property
$2x\div2=4\div2 \Rightarrow x=2$
Division property

$9x-5=5x+19$
$9x-5-5x=5x+19-5x \Rightarrow 4x-5=19$
Subtraction property
$4x-5+5=19+5 \Rightarrow 4x=24$
Addition property
$4x\div4=24\div4 \Rightarrow x=6$
Division property

$3(x+4)=x+18$
$3x+12=x+18$
Distributive property
$3x+12-x=x+18-x \Rightarrow 2x+12=18$
Subtraction property
$2x+12-12=18-12 \Rightarrow 2x=6$
Subtraction property
$2x\div2=6\div2 \Rightarrow x=3$
Division property

Note: These are sample methods of solution. Other uses of properties of equality are acceptable.

64 points total

It's College Test Prep Time!

1. Given $(3+m)(6-n)=0$ and m is a natural number, what is the value of n?
   - A. -6
   - B. -3
   - C. 0
   - D. 3
   - <u>E.</u> 6 A natural number is positive, making the first parentheses positive. The second parentheses MUST then equal zero.

2. Given $4(p+r)-3=5$, what is the value of $p+r$?
   - A. 1
   - <u>B.</u> 2 $4(p+r)=8;\ p+r=8\div4=2$
   - C. 4
   - D. 8
   - E. 16

3. If $12^6\times12^x=12^{15}$, what is the value of x?
   - A. 2.5
   - B. 4.5
   - <u>C.</u> 9 $12^{6+x}=12^{15};\ 6+x=15;\ x=9$
   - D. 21
   - E. 90

4. The soccer team scored 42 goals during the entire season. The starters scored 36 of the goals during regular game play. The second string players scored half of the remaining goals. The rest were made as sudden death goals in overtime play. How many goals were scored in sudden death overtime play during the season?
   - <u>A.</u> 3 $42-36=6;\ 6\div2=3$
   - B. 6
   - C. 18
   - D. 36
   - E. 39

5. Let c represent any even integer and d represent any odd integer. Then, $3c+5d$ MUST be
   - A. an even integer.
   - <u>B.</u> an odd integer.
   - C. a multiple of 3.
   - D. a multiple of 5.
   - E. a positive integer.

   Odd times even is always even. Odd times odd is always odd. The sum of an even and an odd is always odd. Therefore this is always an odd integer.

Exploring Math through... Volleyball

Math is heavily used in volleyball including the court design, match statistics, and the game play itself. Precise calculations must be done when striping the court and mounting the net. There are different requirements for the court depending on whether it is in a gym or outside. Additional math is required for outdoor courts when planning for drainage after rain, the slope of the playing surface, and the coarseness of the sand or other material used for the playing surface. To complicate the math involved in setting up a volleyball court even further, the rules for mounting the net change when switching between men's and women's volleyball. When using the English system, the net heights are measured to the nearest eighth of an inch. When using the metric system, the net heights are measured to the nearest millimeter.

Individual players' strengths and weaknesses become evident when applying the various hitting, serving, blocking, passing, and setting formulas. Some formulas are simple addition or division. Others, such as those used to calculate the various percentages or efficiency ratings, require the proper use of the order of operations to arrive at a correct statistic.

Individual players in a volleyball game use math in almost every aspect of the game without even thinking about it. The angle of a serve must be precise or the ball will either hit the net or go out of bounds. A player whose arms are off by even a few degrees when hitting the ball can send the ball ricocheting in an undesired direction. Trajectory is crucial in all aspects of game play. Even the timing and height of a jump can make or break a block attempt. Volleyball is a game of mathematical precision, and miscues can change the outcome of the game.

Assignments

- Complete *It's College Test Prep Time!*
- Read Exploring Math through ... Volleyball

Lesson 21

Concepts

- Solving algebraic equations
- Fractions
- Decimals
- Absolute value
- Math in the real world

Learning Objectives

The student will be able to:

- Solve algebraic equations involving multiple steps
- Eliminate fractions from algebraic equations
- Eliminate decimals from algebraic equations

Materials Needed

- Student Book, Lesson 21

Teaching Tips

- Review solving algebraic equations with fractions. (See Lesson 18)
- Review solving algebraic equations with decimals. (See Lesson 19)
- Teach how to solve algebraic equations with multiple steps from the teaching box. Explain that this type of equation is much easier to solve if the fractions are eliminated first. This is because the number of digits after the decimal point will sometimes change when the fraction is eliminated. If the decimals are eliminated first, there is a chance you will end up with much larger numbers than necessary when the fractions are eliminated. This will then require additional reducing to get the final answer.

Solving Algebraic Equations: Multiple Steps

When solving algebraic equations with multiple steps, following the order of operations does not always work because of the variables. Follow these steps to make the process simpler.
1. Eliminate fractions.
2. Eliminate decimals.
3. Simplify each side of the equal sign.
4. Isolate the variable using the Properties of Equality.
5. Solve for the variable using the Properties of Equality.

Solve the equation $3x + \frac{1}{4} = 2.95$ following the steps.
1. Multiply each term by 4 to eliminate the fraction. $12x + 1 = 11.8$
2. Multiply each term by 10 to eliminate the decimal. $120x + 10 = 118$
3. Each side is already simplified.
4. Use the Subtraction Property of Equality to isolate the variable. $120x = 108$
5. Use the Division Property of Equality to solve for the variable. $x = 0.9$

Answers may be expressed as proper or improper fractions or as decimals.

① Classwork

Solve.

$\frac{1}{3}x - 2 = 0.6$

$3(\frac{1}{3}x) - 3(2) = 3(0.6)$

$x - 6 = 1.8$

$x = 7.8$

$4x + \frac{1}{3} = 1.95$

$3(4x) + 3(\frac{1}{3}) = 3(1.95)$

$12x + 1 = 5.85$

$100(12x) + 100(1) = 100(5.85)$

$1200x + 100 = 585$

$1200x = 485$

$x = \frac{485}{1200} = \frac{97}{240} = 0.4041\overline{6}$

Activities

② Solve.

$\frac{1}{5}x - 3 = 1.2$

$5(\frac{1}{5}x) - 5(3) = 5(1.2)$

$x - 15 = 6$

$x = 21$

$\frac{3}{4}x - 5 = 0.2$

$4(\frac{3}{4}x) - 4(5) = 4(0.2)$

$3x - 20 = 0.8$

$10(3x) = 10(20.8)$

$30x = 208$

$x = \frac{208}{30} = \frac{104}{15} = 6.9\overline{3}$

$\frac{1}{7}x + 2 = 4.8$

$7(\frac{1}{7}x) + 7(2) = 7(4.8)$

$x + 14 = 33.6$

$x = 19.6$

$\frac{2}{3}x + \frac{3}{4} = 1.44$

$\cancel{12}^4(\frac{2}{\cancel{3}}x) + \cancel{12}^3(\frac{3}{\cancel{4}}) = 12(1.44)$

$8x + 9 = 17.28$

$100(8x) + 100(9) = 100(17.28)$

$800x + 900 = 1728$

$800x = 828$

$x = \frac{207}{200} = 1.035$

③ Find all possible solutions. Identify any extraneous solutions.

$|6x+11|-3=x-22$
$|6x+11|=x-19$
$6x+11=x-19$ or $6x+11=-(x-19)$
$5x=-30$ $\quad 6x+11=-x+19$
$x=-6$ $\quad 7x=8 \Rightarrow x=\frac{8}{7}$
check:
$|6(-6)+11|-3=-6-22$
$|-36+11|-3=-6-22$
$|-25|-3=-28$
$25-3\neq-28$ extraneous

$|6(\frac{8}{7})+11|-3=\frac{8}{7}-22$
$|\frac{50}{7}+\frac{77}{7}|-3=\frac{8}{7}-22$
$\frac{127}{7}-\frac{21}{7}=\frac{8}{7}-\frac{154}{7}$
$\frac{106}{7}\neq-\frac{146}{7}$ extraneous

$|7x-6|-2=-3x+32$
$|7x-6|=-3x+34$
$7x-6=-3x+34$ or $7x-6=-(-3x+34)$
$10x=40$ $\quad 7x-6=3x-34$
$x=4$ $\quad 4x=-28 \Rightarrow x=-7$
check:
$|7(4)-6|-2=-3(4)+32$
$|28-6|-2=-12+32$
$22-2=20$

$|7(-7)-6|-2=-3(-7)+32$
$|-49-6|-2=21+32$
$|-55|-2=53$
$55-2=53$

④ Solve.

$8(x+0.5)=3(x-4.2)+2.6$
$8x+4=3x-12.6+2.6$
$8x(10)+4(10)=3x(10)-12.6(10)+2.6(10)$
$80x+40=30x-126+26$
$50x+40=-100$
$50x=-140$
$x=-2.8$

$3(x+0.1)=4(x-1.01)+2.4$
$3x+0.3=4x-4.04+2.4$
$3x(100)+0.3(100)=4x(100)-4.04(100)+2.4(100)$
$300x+30=400x-404+240$
$-100x+30=-164$
$-100x=-194$
$x=1.94$

$26+\frac{17}{x}=-8$
$26(x)+\frac{17}{\not{x}}(\not{x})=-8(x)$
$26x+17=-8x$
$34x+17=0$
$34x=-17$
$x=-\frac{1}{2}$

$23-\frac{39}{x}=-16$
$23(x)-\frac{39}{\not{x}}(\not{x})=-16(x)$
$23x-39=-16x$
$39x-39=0$
$39x=39$
$x=1$

⑤ Solve.

A volleyball net is 39 inches high. If the top of the net is 7 ft. $11\frac{5}{8}$ in. off the surface of the court for men's volleyball, how high off the surface of the court is the bottom of the net? If the top of the net is 7 ft. $4\frac{1}{8}$ in. off the surface of the court for women's volleyball, how high off the surface of the court is the bottom of the net?

$\frac{12\text{ inches}}{1\text{ foot}}\cdot 7$ ft. $+11\frac{5}{8}$ in. -39 in. $=84$ in. $+11\frac{5}{8}$ in. -39 in. $=95\frac{5}{8}$ in. -39 in. $=56\frac{5}{8}$ in. for the men

$\frac{12\text{ inches}}{1\text{ foot}}\cdot 7$ ft. $+4\frac{1}{8}$ in. -39 in. $=84$ in. $+4\frac{1}{8}$ in. -39 in. $=88\frac{1}{8}$ in. -39 in. $=49\frac{1}{8}$ in. for the women

Alternate solution:

Solve the equation $3x+\frac{1}{4}=2.95$ following these steps.

1. Multiply each term by 100 to eliminate the decimal.
   $300x+25=295$

2. Subtract 25 from each side.
   $300x=270$

3. Divide each side by 300.
   $x=\frac{270}{300}=0.9$

Teaching Tips, Cont.

- Depending on the students' understanding, you may wish to show them that eliminating decimals first will save a step if all denominators are factors of the power of 10 necessary to eliminate the decimals. The example from the teaching box is re-worked below, eliminating the decimal first, for your convenience.

- Complete the Classwork exercises. Have students work the problems on the board for the class and explain their answers. All students should work the problems in their books.

Assignment

- Complete Lesson 21, Activities 2-5.

Lesson 22

Concepts

- Radical expressions
- Rationalizing the denominator
- Absolute value
- Real world math

Learning Objectives

The student will be able to:

- Rationalize expressions containing square roots
- Rationalize expressions containing higher-order roots
- Simplify expressions with radicals

Materials Needed

- Student Book, Lesson 22
- Worksheet 11

Teaching Tips

➢ Have students complete Worksheet 11 in class. This may be for added practice of earlier topics, or graded as a quiz, if desired.

➢ Review roots and radicals. (See Lesson 7)

➢ Tell the students that an important rule when working with radicals is that a radical can NEVER be left in the denominator of an expression in simplest form.

➢ Draw the students' attention to the three possible scenarios presented in the teaching box. (Square root in the denominator, higher-order root in the denominator, and the sum or difference of a radical in the denominator) Explain that this book will focus only on the first two scenarios. (Denominators with polynomials containing radicals will be introduced in Algebra 2.)

Rationalizing the Denominator

One rule of working with roots is that you can never leave a radical in the denominator of a fraction. Occasionally, you will have a problem that seems to simplify with a radical left in the denominator. When this happens, you must **rationalize the denominator** – a process that eliminates the radical from the denominator.

There are three possible scenarios for radicals in the denominator. First, there may be a simple square root in the denominator, such as $\frac{5}{\sqrt{2}}$.

The second option is a higher-order radical in the denominator, such as $\frac{5}{\sqrt[3]{2}}$.

The third option is the sum or difference of a radical in the denominator, such as $\frac{5}{1+\sqrt{2}}$.

This book will consider the first two options. To rationalize a denominator containing a square root, multiply both the numerator and the denominator of that fraction by the root in the denominator.

$\frac{5}{\sqrt{2}} = \frac{5\sqrt{2}}{\sqrt{2}\cdot\sqrt{2}} = \frac{5\sqrt{2}}{\sqrt{2\times 2}} = \frac{5\sqrt{2}}{2}$

This is an equivalent fraction with no radical in the denominator.

To rationalize a denominator containing a higher-order root, use the formula below.

$\frac{a}{\sqrt[r]{b^p}} = \frac{a}{\sqrt[r]{b^p}} \cdot \frac{\sqrt[r]{b^{r-p}}}{\sqrt[r]{b^{r-p}}} = \frac{a\sqrt[r]{b^{r-p}}}{b}$

Study this example.

$\frac{2}{\sqrt[3]{5}} = \frac{2}{\sqrt[3]{5}} \cdot \frac{\sqrt[3]{5^{3-1}}}{\sqrt[3]{5^{3-1}}} = \frac{2\sqrt[3]{5^{3-1}}}{5} = \frac{2\sqrt[3]{5^2}}{5} = \frac{2\sqrt[3]{25}}{5}$

① **Classwork**

Rationalize the denominator.

$\frac{4}{\sqrt{7}}$

$\frac{4}{\sqrt{7}} \cdot \frac{\sqrt{7}}{\sqrt{7}} = \frac{4\sqrt{7}}{7}$

$\frac{5\sqrt{2}}{\sqrt{6}}$

$\frac{5\sqrt{2}}{\sqrt{6}} \cdot \frac{\sqrt{6}}{\sqrt{6}} = \frac{5\sqrt{12}}{\sqrt{36}} = \frac{5\sqrt{12}}{6} =$

$\frac{5\sqrt{3\cdot 4}}{6} = \frac{2\cdot 5\sqrt{3}}{6} = \frac{\cancel{10}^{5}\sqrt{3}}{\cancel{6}^{3}} = \frac{5\sqrt{3}}{3}$

$\frac{3}{\sqrt[3]{12}}$

$\frac{3}{\sqrt[3]{12}} \cdot \frac{\sqrt[3]{12^{3-1}}}{\sqrt[3]{12^{3-1}}} = \frac{3}{\sqrt[3]{12}} \cdot \frac{\sqrt[3]{12^2}}{\sqrt[3]{12^2}} =$

$\frac{3\sqrt[3]{144}}{\sqrt[3]{12^3}} = \frac{3\sqrt[3]{3\cdot 3\cdot 2\cdot 2\cdot 2\cdot 2}}{12} = \frac{3\cdot 2\sqrt[3]{18}}{12} =$

$\frac{\cancel{6}\sqrt[3]{18}}{\cancel{12}_2} = \frac{\sqrt[3]{18}}{2}$

Activities

② Rationalize the denominator.

$\frac{3}{\sqrt{11}}$

$\frac{3}{\sqrt{11}} \cdot \frac{\sqrt{11}}{\sqrt{11}} = \frac{3\sqrt{11}}{11}$

$\frac{7\sqrt{3}}{6\sqrt{12}}$

$\frac{7\sqrt{3}}{6\sqrt{12}} \cdot \frac{\sqrt{12}}{\sqrt{12}} = \frac{7\sqrt{36}}{6\cdot 12} =$

$\frac{7\cdot\cancel{6}}{\cancel{6}\cdot 12} = \frac{7}{12}$

$\frac{8\sqrt{3}}{\sqrt{5}}$

$\frac{8\sqrt{3}}{\sqrt{5}} \cdot \frac{\sqrt{5}}{\sqrt{5}} = \frac{8\sqrt{15}}{5}$

$\frac{5\sqrt{7}}{4\sqrt{3}}$

$\frac{5\sqrt{7}}{4\sqrt{3}} \cdot \frac{\sqrt{3}}{\sqrt{3}} = \frac{5\sqrt{21}}{4\cdot 3} = \frac{5\sqrt{21}}{12}$

③ Rationalize the denominator.

$\frac{5}{\sqrt[3]{75}}$

$\frac{5}{\sqrt[3]{75}} \cdot \frac{\sqrt[3]{75^{3-1}}}{\sqrt[3]{75^{3-1}}} = \frac{5}{\sqrt[3]{75}} \cdot \frac{\sqrt[3]{75^2}}{\sqrt[3]{75^2}} =$

$\frac{5\sqrt[3]{3\cdot 3\cdot 5\cdot 5\cdot 5\cdot 5}}{\sqrt[3]{75^3}} = \frac{5\cdot\cancel{5}\sqrt[3]{3\cdot 3\cdot 5}}{\cancel{75}_{15}} = \frac{5\sqrt[3]{45}}{15} =$

$\frac{\cancel{5}\sqrt[3]{45}}{\cancel{15}_3} = \frac{\sqrt[3]{45}}{3}$

$\frac{12}{\sqrt[4]{8}}$

$\frac{12}{\sqrt[4]{2^3}} \cdot \frac{\sqrt[4]{2^{4-3}}}{\sqrt[4]{2^{4-3}}} = \frac{12}{\sqrt[4]{2^3}} \cdot \frac{\sqrt[4]{2}}{\sqrt[3]{2}} =$

$\frac{12\sqrt[4]{2}}{\sqrt[4]{2^4}} = \frac{{}^{6}\cancel{12}\sqrt[4]{2}}{\cancel{2}} = 6\sqrt[4]{2}$

$\frac{6\sqrt[3]{2}}{\sqrt[3]{32}}$

$\frac{6\sqrt[3]{2}}{\sqrt[3]{2^5}} = \frac{6\sqrt[3]{2}}{2\sqrt[3]{2^2}} \cdot \frac{\sqrt[3]{2^{3-2}}}{\sqrt[3]{2^{3-2}}} = \frac{6\sqrt[3]{2}}{2\sqrt[3]{2^2}} \cdot \frac{\sqrt[3]{2}}{\sqrt[3]{2}} =$

$\frac{6\sqrt[3]{4}}{2\sqrt[3]{8}} = \frac{6\sqrt[3]{4}}{2\sqrt[3]{2\cdot 2\cdot 2}} = \frac{{}^{3}\cancel{6}\sqrt[3]{4}}{\cancel{2}\cdot 2} = \frac{3\sqrt[3]{4}}{2}$

$\frac{10}{\sqrt[4]{50}}$

$\frac{10}{\sqrt[4]{2\cdot 5^2}} \cdot \frac{\sqrt[4]{2^{4-1}\cdot 5^{4-2}}}{\sqrt[4]{2^{4-1}\cdot 5^{4-2}}} = \frac{10}{\sqrt[4]{2\cdot 5^2}} \cdot \frac{\sqrt[4]{2^3\cdot 5^2}}{\sqrt[4]{2^3\cdot 5^2}} =$

$\frac{10\sqrt[4]{200}}{\sqrt[4]{2^4\cdot 5^4}} = \frac{\cancel{10}\sqrt[4]{200}}{\cancel{2\cdot 5}} = \sqrt[4]{200}$

Note: This is an alternate method of solution. You may use the same process as shown for the first problem in this section.

④ Find all possible solutions. Identify any extraneous solutions.

$|-4x+3|-7 = x+14$

$|-4x+3| = x+21$

$-4x+3 = x+21$ or $-4x+3 = -(x+21)$

$-5x = 18$ $-4x+3 = -x-21$

$x = -\frac{18}{5}$ $-3x = -24 \Rightarrow x = 8$

check:

$\left|-4\left(-\frac{18}{5}\right)+3\right|-7 = -\frac{18}{5}+14$

$\left|\frac{72}{5}+\frac{15}{5}\right|-7 = -\frac{18}{5}+\frac{70}{5}$

$\left|\frac{87}{5}\right|-\frac{35}{5} = \frac{52}{5}$

$\frac{87}{5}-\frac{35}{5} = \frac{52}{5}$

$|-4(8)+3|-7 = 8+14$

$|-32+3|-7 = 22$

$|-29|-7 = 22$

$29-7 = 22$

$|2x-3|+2 = -3x-14$

$|2x-3| = -3x-16$

$2x-3 = -3x-16$ or $2x-3 = -(-3x-16)$

$5x = -13$ $2x-3 = 3x+16$

$x = -\frac{13}{5}$ $-x = 19 \Rightarrow x = -19$

check:

$\left|2\left(-\frac{13}{5}\right)-3\right|+2 = -3\left(-\frac{13}{5}\right)-14$

$\left|-\frac{26}{5}-\frac{15}{5}\right|+\frac{10}{5} = \frac{39}{5}-\frac{70}{5}$

$\frac{41}{5}+\frac{10}{5} \neq -\frac{31}{5}$ extraneous

$|2(-19)-3|+2 = -3(-19)-14$

$|-38-3|+2 = 57-14$

$|-41|+2 = 43$

$41+2 = 43$

⑤ Solve.

The USA Volleyball rule book requires a minimum of 23 feet of space above the playing surface of a volleyball court. If the court is 59 feet long and 29 feet 6 inches wide, what is the minimum volume of space required for a volleyball court? $V = Lwh$, where L is the length, w is the width, and h is the height.

$V = Lwh$ $V = (59 \text{ feet})(29.5 \text{ feet})(23 \text{ feet})$ $V = 40{,}031.5$ cubic feet

Algebraic Equations, Properties of Equality Worksheet 11

① Solve each algebraic equation. For each step, identify the property of equality that was used.

$7 + \frac{36}{x} = -5$

$7(x) + \frac{36}{\cancel{x}}(\cancel{x}) = -5(x) \Rightarrow 7x + 36 = -5x$

Multiplication property

$7x + 36 + 5x = -5x + 5x \Rightarrow 12x + 36 = 0$

Addition property

$12x + 36 - 36 = 0 - 36 \Rightarrow 12x = -36$

Subtraction property

$12x \div 12 = -36 \div 12 \Rightarrow x = -3$

Division property

$4 - \frac{3}{x} = \frac{25}{x}$

$4(x) - \frac{3}{\cancel{x}}(\cancel{x}) = \frac{25}{\cancel{x}}(\cancel{x}) \Rightarrow 4x - 3 = 25$

Multiplication property

$4x - 3 + 3 = 25 + 3 \Rightarrow 4x = 28$

Addition property

$4x \div 4 = 28 \div 4 \Rightarrow x = 7$

Division property

$\frac{7}{x} - \frac{2}{x^2} = -\frac{1}{x}$

$\frac{7}{\cancel{x}}(x^{\cancel{2}}) - \frac{2}{\cancel{x^2}}(\cancel{x^2}) = -\frac{1}{\cancel{x}}(x^{\cancel{2}}) \Rightarrow 7x - 2 = -x$

Multiplication property

$7x - 2 + x = -x + x \Rightarrow 8x - 2 = 0$

Addition property

$8x - 2 + 2 = 0 + 2 \Rightarrow 8x = 2$

Addition property

$8x \div 8 = 2 \div 8 \Rightarrow x = \frac{2}{8} = \frac{1}{4}$

Division property

$\frac{7}{x} + \frac{2}{x^2} = \frac{4}{x} + \frac{17}{x^2}$

$\frac{7}{\cancel{x}}(x^{\cancel{2}}) + \frac{2}{\cancel{x^2}}(\cancel{x^2}) = \frac{4}{\cancel{x}}(x^{\cancel{2}}) + \frac{17}{\cancel{x^2}}(\cancel{x^2}) \Rightarrow 7x + 2 = 4x + 17$

Multiplication property

$7x + 2 - 4x = 4x + 17 - 4x \Rightarrow 3x + 2 = 17$

Subtraction property

$3x + 2 - 2 = 17 - 2 \Rightarrow 3x = 15$

Subtraction property

$3x \div 3 = 15 \div 3 \Rightarrow x = 5$

Division property

② Solve.

$0.7(x - 1) + 0.1x = 4.1$

$0.7x - 0.7 + 0.1x = 4.1$

$0.7x(10) - 0.7(10) + 0.1x(10) = 4.1(10)$

$7x - 7 + x = 41$

$8x - 7 = 41$

$8x = 48$

$x = 6$

$4(0.06x - 1) = 0.22x - 2.06$

$0.24x - 4 = 0.22x - 2.06$

$0.24x(100) - 4(100) = 0.22x(100) - 2.06(100)$

$24x - 400 = 22x - 206$

$2x - 400 = -206$

$2x = 194$

$x = 97$

$1.3x + 0.7 = 0.4x - 1.1$

$1.3x(10) + 0.7(10) = 0.4x(10) - 1.1(10)$

$13x + 7 = 4x - 11$

$9x + 7 = -11$

$9x = -18$

$x = -2$

$9(0.02x + 5) = 3(0.01x - 0.41) + 0.18$

$0.18x + 45 = 0.03x - 1.23 + 0.18$

$0.18x(100) + 45(100) = 0.03x(100) - 1.23(100) + 0.18(100)$

$18x + 4500 = 3x - 123 + 18$

$15x + 4500 = -105$

$15x = -4605$

$x = -307$

Teaching Tips, Cont.

- Explain that a fraction appearing as part of the radicand is the same thing as a radical appearing in the denominator. In other words, a denominator in a radical is just as wrong in an answer as a radical in a denominator. Both must be eliminated for an expression to be in simplest form.
- Ask the students if the value of an expression changes when the expression is multiplied by 1. (No.) Ask the students what the quotient is when something is divided by itself. (1)
- Teach how to rationalize the denominator from the teaching box. Students do not have to memorize the formula for rationalizing the denominator of higher-order radicals, but they must understand the concept well enough to do the work without the aid of the formula by the next test date.
- Complete the Classwork exercises. Have some students work the problems on the board for the class and explain their answers. All students should work the problems in their books.

Assignment

- Complete Lesson 22, Activities 2-5.

Lesson 23

Concepts

- Dividing radicals
- Rationalizing the denominator
- Decimals
- Fractions
- Absolute value

Learning Objectives

The student will be able to:

- Divide expressions containing radicals
- Rationalize the denominator of the quotient
- Simplify the quotient when necessary

Materials Needed

- Student Book, Lesson 23
- Worksheet 12

Teaching Tips

➢ Review rationalizing denominators. (See Lesson 22)

➢ Introduce dividing radicals as a situation that will often result in the need to rationalize the denominator.

➢ Teach dividing radicals from the teaching box. Emphasize that coefficients may be divided by coefficients and radicands may be divided by radicands, but one cannot cancel out the other. In other words, a coefficient in the numerator cannot be divided by or cancel out a radicand in the denominator. The same holds true for a radicand in the numerator and a coefficient in the denominator.

Dividing Radicals

When dividing radicals, follow these steps.

1. Divide the coefficients (the numbers outside the radicals) to get the coefficient of the quotient.
2. Divide the radicands (the portion under the radical) to get the radicand of the quotient.
3. Rationalize the denominator if necessary so there are no fractions in the radical, and no radicals in the denominator of the answer.
4. Reduce, if necessary.

Consider this example.

$12\sqrt{10} \div 4\sqrt{15}$ rewrite as $\frac{12\sqrt{10}}{4\sqrt{15}}$

Divide the coefficients first. $\frac{\cancel{12}^{3}\sqrt{10}}{\cancel{4}\sqrt{15}} = \frac{3\sqrt{10}}{\sqrt{15}}$

Divide the radicands next. $\frac{3\sqrt{\cancel{10}^{2}}}{\sqrt{\cancel{15}^{3}}} = \frac{3\sqrt{2}}{\sqrt{3}}$

Rationalize the denominator. $\frac{3\sqrt{2}}{\sqrt{3}} \cdot \frac{\sqrt{3}}{\sqrt{3}} = \frac{3\sqrt{6}}{3}$

Reduce. $\frac{\cancel{3}\sqrt{6}}{\cancel{3}} = \sqrt{6}$

① Classwork

Divide.

$18\sqrt{6} \div 3\sqrt{2}$

$\frac{\cancel{18}^{6}\sqrt{6}}{\cancel{3}\sqrt{2}} = \frac{6\sqrt{\cancel{6}^{3}}}{\sqrt{\cancel{2}}} = 6\sqrt{3}$

$20\sqrt{24} \div 5\sqrt{3}$

$\frac{\cancel{20}^{4}\sqrt{24}}{\cancel{5}\sqrt{3}} = \frac{4\sqrt{\cancel{24}^{8}}}{\sqrt{\cancel{3}}} = 4\sqrt{8} =$

$4\sqrt{4 \cdot 2} = 4 \cdot 2\sqrt{2} = 8\sqrt{2}$

$9\sqrt{3} \div 3\sqrt{12}$

$\frac{\cancel{9}^{3}\sqrt{3}}{\cancel{3}\sqrt{12}} = \frac{3\sqrt{\cancel{3}}}{\sqrt{\cancel{12}^{4}}} = \frac{3}{\sqrt{4}} = \frac{3}{2}$

$25\sqrt{3} \div 10\sqrt{18}$

$\frac{\cancel{25}^{5}\sqrt{3}}{\cancel{10}^{2}\sqrt{18}} = \frac{5\sqrt{\cancel{3}}}{2\sqrt{\cancel{18}^{6}}} = \frac{5}{2\sqrt{6}} \cdot \frac{\sqrt{6}}{\sqrt{6}} =$

$\frac{5\sqrt{6}}{2\sqrt{36}} = \frac{5\sqrt{6}}{2 \cdot 6} = \frac{5\sqrt{6}}{12}$

Activities

② Solve.

$35\sqrt{10} \div 7\sqrt{2}$

$\frac{\cancel{35}^{5}\sqrt{10}}{\cancel{7}\sqrt{2}} = \frac{5\sqrt{\cancel{10}^{5}}}{\sqrt{\cancel{2}}} = 5\sqrt{5}$

$8\sqrt{3} \div 4\sqrt{27}$

$\frac{\cancel{8}^{2}\sqrt{3}}{\cancel{4}\sqrt{27}} = \frac{2\sqrt{\cancel{3}}}{\sqrt{\cancel{27}^{9}}} = \frac{2}{\sqrt{9}} = \frac{2}{3}$

$42\sqrt{30} \div 12\sqrt{5}$

$\frac{\cancel{42}^{7}\sqrt{30}}{\cancel{12}^{2}\sqrt{5}} = \frac{7\sqrt{\cancel{30}^{6}}}{2\sqrt{\cancel{5}}} = \frac{7\sqrt{6}}{2}$

$28\sqrt{5} \div 21\sqrt{30}$

$\frac{\cancel{28}^{4}\sqrt{5}}{\cancel{21}^{3}\sqrt{30}} = \frac{4\sqrt{\cancel{5}}}{3\sqrt{\cancel{30}^{6}}} = \frac{4}{3\sqrt{6}} \cdot \frac{\sqrt{6}}{\sqrt{6}} =$

$\frac{4\sqrt{6}}{3\sqrt{36}} = \frac{\cancel{4}^{2}\sqrt{6}}{3 \cdot \cancel{6}^{3}} = \frac{2\sqrt{6}}{9}$

③ Solve.

$\frac{\sqrt{32}}{4\sqrt{2}}$

$\frac{\sqrt{\cancel{32}^{16}}}{4\sqrt{\cancel{2}}} = \frac{\sqrt{16}}{4} = \frac{4}{4} = 1$

$\frac{12\sqrt[4]{100}}{\sqrt[4]{162}}$

$\frac{12\sqrt[4]{\cancel{100}^{50}}}{\sqrt[4]{\cancel{162}^{81}}} = \frac{12\sqrt[4]{50}}{\sqrt[4]{3^4}} =$

$\frac{{}^{4}\cancel{12}\sqrt[4]{50}}{\cancel{3}} = 4\sqrt[4]{50}$

$\frac{5\sqrt{10}}{\sqrt{50}}$

$\frac{5\sqrt{\cancel{10}}}{\sqrt{\cancel{50}^{5}}} = \frac{5}{\sqrt{5}} \cdot \frac{\sqrt{5}}{\sqrt{5}} = \frac{\cancel{5}\sqrt{5}}{\cancel{5}} = \sqrt{5}$

$\frac{5\sqrt[3]{30}}{\sqrt[3]{45}}$

$\frac{5\sqrt[3]{\cancel{30}^{2}}}{\sqrt[3]{\cancel{45}^{3}}} = \frac{5\sqrt[3]{2}}{\sqrt[3]{3}} \cdot \frac{\sqrt[3]{3^{3-1}}}{\sqrt[3]{3^{3-1}}} = \frac{5\sqrt[3]{2}}{\sqrt[3]{3}} \cdot \frac{\sqrt[3]{3^2}}{\sqrt[3]{3^2}} =$

$\frac{5\sqrt[3]{2 \cdot 9}}{\sqrt[3]{3^3}} = \frac{5\sqrt[3]{18}}{3}$

④ Solve. Identify extraneous roots where appropriate.

$9(0.1x + 0.05) = 5(0.04x + 0.37)$

$0.9x + 0.45 = 0.2x + 1.85$

$0.9x(100) + 0.45(100) = 0.2x(100) + 1.85(100)$

$90x + 45 = 20x + 185$

$70x + 45 = 185$

$70x = 140$

$x = 2$

$9 + \frac{20}{x} = -5 + \frac{41}{x}$

$9(x) + \frac{20}{\cancel{x}}(\cancel{x}) = -5(x) + \frac{41}{\cancel{x}}(\cancel{x})$

$9x + 20 = -5x + 41$

$14x + 20 = 41$

$14x = 21$

$x = \frac{21}{14} = \frac{3}{2}$

$|4x - 3| + 9 = -x + 31$

$|4x - 3| = -x + 22$

$4x - 3 = -x + 22$ or $4x - 3 = -(-x + 22)$

$5x = 25$ $\quad$ $4x - 3 = x - 22$

$x = 5$ $\quad$ $3x = -19 \Rightarrow x = -\frac{19}{3}$

check:

$|4(5) - 3| + 9 = -5 + 31$

$|20 - 3| + 9 = 26$

$|17| + 9 = 26$

$17 + 9 = 26$

$|4(-\frac{19}{3}) - 3| + 9 = \frac{19}{3} + 31$

$|-\frac{76}{3} - \frac{9}{3}| + 9 = \frac{19}{3} + \frac{93}{3}$

$|-\frac{85}{3}| + \frac{27}{3} = \frac{112}{3}$

$\frac{85}{3} + \frac{27}{3} = \frac{112}{3}$

$13(0.4x + 0.3) = 11(0.2x + 0.7) + 11.2$

$5.2x + 3.9 = 2.2x + 7.7 + 11.2$

$5.2x(10) + 3.9(10) = 2.2x(10) + 7.7(10) + 11.2(10)$

$52x + 39 = 22x + 77 + 112$

$30x + 39 = 189$

$30x = 150$

$x = 5$

$7 + \frac{14}{x} = -11 + \frac{8}{x}$

$7(x) + \frac{14}{\cancel{x}}(\cancel{x}) = -11(x) + \frac{8}{\cancel{x}}(\cancel{x})$

$7x + 14 = -11x + 8$

$18x + 14 = 8$

$18x = -6$

$x = -\frac{6}{18} = -\frac{1}{3}$

$|3x - 26| - 7 = -4x + 9$

$|3x - 26| = -4x + 16$

$3x - 26 = -4x + 16$ or $3x - 26 = -(-4x + 16)$

$7x = 42$ $\quad$ $3x - 26 = 4x - 16$

$x = 6$ $\quad$ $-x = 10 \Rightarrow x = -10$

check:

$|3(6) - 26| - 7 = -4(6) + 9$

$|18 - 26| - 7 = -24 + 9$

$8 - 7 \neq -15$ extraneous

$|3(-10) - 26| - 7 = -4(-10) + 9$

$|-30 - 26| - 7 = 40 + 9$

$|-56| - 7 = 49$

$56 - 7 = 49$

Dividing Radicals Worksheet 12

① Solve.

$63\sqrt{15} \div 7\sqrt{5}$

$$\frac{\cancel{63}^{9}\sqrt{15}}{\cancel{7}\sqrt{5}} = \frac{9\sqrt{\cancel{15}^{3}}}{\sqrt{\cancel{5}}} = 9\sqrt{3}$$

$36\sqrt{60} \div 24\sqrt{12}$

$$\frac{\cancel{36}^{3}\sqrt{60}}{\cancel{24}^{2}\sqrt{12}} = \frac{3\sqrt{\cancel{60}^{5}}}{2\sqrt{\cancel{12}}} = \frac{3\sqrt{5}}{2}$$

$18\sqrt{5} \div 3\sqrt{45}$

$$\frac{\cancel{18}^{6}\sqrt{5}}{\cancel{3}\sqrt{45}} = \frac{6\sqrt{\cancel{5}}}{\sqrt{\cancel{45}^{9}}} = \frac{6}{\sqrt{9}} = \frac{6}{3} = 2$$

$35\sqrt{11} \div 21\sqrt{132}$

$$\frac{\cancel{35}^{5}\sqrt{11}}{\cancel{21}^{3}\sqrt{132}} = \frac{5\sqrt{\cancel{11}}}{3\sqrt{\cancel{132}^{12}}} = \frac{5}{3\sqrt{12}} \cdot \frac{\sqrt{12}}{\sqrt{12}} =$$

$$\frac{5\sqrt{12}}{3\sqrt{144}} = \frac{5\sqrt{2 \cdot 2 \cdot 3}}{3 \cdot 12} = \frac{5 \cdot \cancel{2}\sqrt{3}}{3 \cdot \cancel{12}^{6}} = \frac{5\sqrt{3}}{18}$$

$\dfrac{\sqrt{27}}{6\sqrt{3}}$

$$\frac{\sqrt{\cancel{27}^{9}}}{6\sqrt{\cancel{3}}} = \frac{\sqrt{9}}{6} = \frac{3}{6} = \frac{1}{2}$$

$\dfrac{12\sqrt[4]{51}}{\sqrt[4]{48}}$

$$\frac{12\sqrt[4]{\cancel{51}^{17}}}{\sqrt[4]{\cancel{48}^{16}}} = \frac{12\sqrt[4]{17}}{\sqrt[4]{2^4}} =$$

$$\frac{{}^{6}\cancel{12}\sqrt[4]{17}}{\cancel{2}} = 6\sqrt[4]{17}$$

$\dfrac{7\sqrt{20}}{\sqrt{140}}$

$$\frac{7\sqrt{\cancel{20}}}{\sqrt{\cancel{140}^{7}}} = \frac{7}{\sqrt{7}} \cdot \frac{\sqrt{7}}{\sqrt{7}} = \frac{\cancel{7}\sqrt{7}}{\cancel{7}} = \sqrt{7}$$

$\dfrac{3\sqrt[3]{14}}{\sqrt[3]{21}}$

$$\frac{3\sqrt[3]{\cancel{14}^{2}}}{\sqrt[3]{\cancel{21}^{3}}} = \frac{3\sqrt[3]{2}}{\sqrt[3]{3}} \cdot \frac{\sqrt[3]{3^{3-1}}}{\sqrt[3]{3^{3-1}}} = \frac{3\sqrt[3]{2}}{\sqrt[3]{3}} \cdot \frac{\sqrt[3]{3^2}}{\sqrt[3]{3^2}} =$$

$$\frac{3\sqrt[3]{2 \cdot 9}}{\sqrt[3]{3^3}} = \frac{\cancel{3}\sqrt[3]{18}}{\cancel{3}} = \sqrt[3]{18}$$

$\dfrac{\sqrt{75}}{5\sqrt{3}}$

$$\frac{\sqrt{\cancel{75}^{25}}}{5\sqrt{\cancel{3}}} = \frac{\sqrt{25}}{5} = \frac{5}{5} = 1$$

$\dfrac{10\sqrt[4]{160}}{\sqrt[4]{405}}$

$$\frac{10\sqrt[4]{\cancel{160}^{32}}}{\sqrt[4]{\cancel{405}^{81}}} = \frac{10\sqrt[4]{2^5}}{\sqrt[4]{3^4}} =$$

$$\frac{10 \cdot 2\sqrt[4]{2}}{3} = \frac{20\sqrt[4]{2}}{3}$$

$\dfrac{12\sqrt{26}}{\sqrt{91}}$

$$\frac{12\sqrt{\cancel{26}^{2}}}{\sqrt{\cancel{91}^{7}}} = \frac{12\sqrt{2}}{\sqrt{7}} \cdot \frac{\sqrt{7}}{\sqrt{7}} = \frac{12\sqrt{14}}{7}$$

$\dfrac{4\sqrt[3]{48}}{\sqrt[3]{135}}$

$$\frac{4\sqrt[3]{2^3 \cdot 6}}{\sqrt[3]{3^3 \cdot 5}} = \frac{4 \cdot 2\sqrt[3]{6}}{3\sqrt[3]{5}} \cdot \frac{\sqrt[3]{5^{3-1}}}{\sqrt[3]{5^{3-1}}} = \frac{8\sqrt[3]{6}}{3\sqrt[3]{5}} \cdot \frac{\sqrt[3]{5^2}}{\sqrt[3]{5^2}} =$$

$$\frac{8\sqrt[3]{6 \cdot 25}}{3\sqrt[3]{5^3}} = \frac{8\sqrt[3]{150}}{3 \cdot 5} = \frac{8\sqrt[3]{150}}{15}$$

Teaching Tips, Cont.

- Remind students that all fractions must be checked for radicals in the denominator. Any fractions containing a radical in the denominator must be rationalized for the answer to be correct. (Note: For this course, all answers containing radicals must be rationalized. This is accepted and expected in high school math courses. In calculus and higher-level college math, it is often acceptable — and even encouraged — to leave radicals in the denominator.)
- Tell the students to simplify all answers. Occasionally, a radicand in the numerator can be simplified further after rationalizing the denominator.
- Complete the Classwork exercises. Have some students work the problems on the board for the class and explain their answers. All students should work the problems in their books.

Assignments

- Complete Lesson 23, Activities 2-4.
- Worksheet 12 (Optional).

Lesson 24

Concepts

- Multiplying radical expressions
- Dividing radicals
- Rationalizing the denominator
- Fractions
- Decimals
- Multi-step algebraic equations
- Math in the real world

Learning Objectives

The student will be able to:

- Multiply a binomial radical expression by a monomial radical
- Apply the distributive property to radical expressions
- Write the products of radical expressions in simplest form

Materials Needed

- Student Book, Lesson 24

Teaching Tips

> Review the distributive property. (See Lesson 10)

> Review multiplying radicals. (See Lesson 7)

> Teach multiplying radical expressions from the teaching box. Explain that the distributive property is applied just like before, except this time the rules for multiplying radicals are also used.

> Emphasize that the radicand will change only if two radicals are being multiplied. Any time a coefficient is one of the factors, the coefficient will change and the radicand will always remain the same.

Radical Expressions: Multiplication

When multiplying radical expressions, use the distributive property. Multiply constants and coefficients to get the new coefficient. Multiply radicands to get the new radicand. As always, simplify your answer.

$\sqrt{2}\left(3+\sqrt{6}\right)$

Use the distributive property.

$\sqrt{2}\left(3+\sqrt{6}\right)=3\sqrt{2}+\sqrt{12}$

Simplify.

$3\sqrt{2}+\sqrt{12}=3\sqrt{2}+\sqrt{2\cdot2\cdot3}=3\sqrt{2}+2\sqrt{3}$

① **Classwork**

Multiply.

$\sqrt{5}\left(4+\sqrt{2}\right)$

$4\sqrt{5}+\sqrt{5\cdot2}=4\sqrt{5}+\sqrt{10}$

$\sqrt{6}\left(7+\sqrt{3}\right)$

$7\sqrt{6}+\sqrt{6\cdot3}=7\sqrt{6}+\sqrt{2\cdot3\cdot3}=$

$7\sqrt{6}+3\sqrt{2}$

Activities

② Multiply.

$\sqrt{3}\left(7+\sqrt{5}\right)$

$7\sqrt{3}+\sqrt{5\cdot3}=7\sqrt{3}+\sqrt{15}$

$\sqrt{7}\left(8+\sqrt{3}\right)$

$8\sqrt{7}+\sqrt{7\cdot3}=8\sqrt{7}+\sqrt{21}$

$\sqrt{5}\left(2+\sqrt{7}\right)$

$2\sqrt{5}+\sqrt{5\cdot7}=2\sqrt{5}+\sqrt{35}$

$\sqrt{11}\left(2+\sqrt{2}\right)$

$2\sqrt{11}+\sqrt{11\cdot2}=2\sqrt{11}+\sqrt{22}$

$\sqrt{2}\left(6+\sqrt{3}\right)$

$6\sqrt{2}+\sqrt{2\cdot3}=6\sqrt{2}+\sqrt{6}$

$\sqrt{13}\left(6+\sqrt{5}\right)$

$6\sqrt{13}+\sqrt{13\cdot5}=6\sqrt{13}+\sqrt{65}$

$\sqrt{3}\left(4+\sqrt{12}\right)$

$4\sqrt{3}+\sqrt{3\cdot12}=4\sqrt{3}+\sqrt{36}=$

$4\sqrt{3}+6$ or $6+4\sqrt{3}$

$\sqrt{7}\left(3+\sqrt{14}\right)$

$3\sqrt{7}+\sqrt{7\cdot14}=3\sqrt{7}+\sqrt{2\cdot7\cdot7}=$

$3\sqrt{7}+7\sqrt{2}$

$\sqrt{5}\left(6+\sqrt{10}\right)$

$6\sqrt{5}+\sqrt{5\cdot10}=6\sqrt{5}+\sqrt{2\cdot5\cdot5}$

$=6\sqrt{5}+5\sqrt{2}$

$\sqrt{6}\left(4+\sqrt{2}\right)$

$4\sqrt{6}+\sqrt{6\cdot2}=4\sqrt{6}+\sqrt{2\cdot2\cdot3}=$

$4\sqrt{6}+2\sqrt{3}$

$\sqrt{2}\left(9+\sqrt{6}\right)$

$9\sqrt{2}+\sqrt{2\cdot6}=9\sqrt{2}+\sqrt{2\cdot2\cdot3}=$

$9\sqrt{2}+2\sqrt{3}$

$\sqrt{12}\left(4+\sqrt{6}\right)$

$4\sqrt{12}+\sqrt{12\cdot6}=4\sqrt{2\cdot2\cdot3}+\sqrt{2\cdot6\cdot6}=$

$8\sqrt{3}+6\sqrt{2}$

③ Solve.

$$\frac{4\sqrt[3]{9}}{18\sqrt[3]{24}}$$

$$\frac{{}^{2}\cancel{4}\sqrt[3]{\cancel{9}^{3}}}{{}_{9}\cancel{18}\sqrt[3]{\cancel{24}_{8}}} = \frac{2\sqrt[3]{3}}{9\sqrt[3]{2^3}} = \frac{\cancel{2}\sqrt[3]{3}}{9 \cdot \cancel{2}} = \frac{\sqrt[3]{3}}{9}$$

$$\frac{10\sqrt[4]{12}}{\sqrt[4]{32}}$$

$$\frac{10\sqrt[4]{\cancel{12}^{3}}}{\sqrt[4]{\cancel{32}_{8}}} = \frac{10\sqrt[4]{3}}{\sqrt[4]{2^3}} \cdot \frac{\sqrt[4]{2^{4-3}}}{\sqrt[4]{2^{4-3}}} = \frac{{}^{5}\cancel{10}\sqrt[4]{3 \cdot 2}}{\cancel{2}} = 5\sqrt[4]{6}$$

$$\frac{\sqrt[3]{24}}{\sqrt[3]{9}}$$

$$\frac{\sqrt[3]{\cancel{24}^{8}}}{\sqrt[3]{\cancel{9}_{3}}} = \frac{\sqrt[3]{2^3}}{\sqrt[3]{3}} \cdot \frac{\sqrt[3]{3^{3-1}}}{\sqrt[3]{3^{3-1}}} =$$

$$\frac{2\sqrt[3]{3^2}}{\sqrt[3]{3^3}} = \frac{2\sqrt[3]{9}}{3}$$

$$\frac{\sqrt[4]{32}}{\sqrt[4]{12}}$$

$$\frac{\sqrt[4]{\cancel{32}^{8}}}{\sqrt[4]{\cancel{12}_{3}}} = \frac{\sqrt[4]{8}}{\sqrt[4]{3}} \cdot \frac{\sqrt[4]{3^{4-1}}}{\sqrt[4]{3^{4-1}}} =$$

$$\frac{\sqrt[4]{8 \cdot 3^3}}{\sqrt[4]{3^4}} = \frac{\sqrt[4]{8 \cdot 27}}{3} = \frac{\sqrt[4]{216}}{3}$$

④ Solve.

$\frac{1}{8}x - 2 = 0.625$

$8\left(\frac{1}{8}x\right) - 8(2) = 8(0.625)$

$x - 16 = 5$

$x = 21$

$\frac{1}{9}x + 2 = 5.5$

$9\left(\frac{1}{9}x\right) + 9(2) = 9(5.5)$

$x + 18 = 49.5$

$x = 31.5$

$\frac{2}{5}x - 0.86 = 0.54$

$5\left(\frac{2}{5}x\right) - 5(0.86) = 5(0.54)$

$2x - 4.3 = 2.7$

$2x = 7$

$x = \frac{7}{2} = 3.5$

$\frac{3}{4}x + \frac{1}{3} = 0.17$

$\cancel{12}^{3}\left(\frac{3}{\cancel{4}}x\right) + \cancel{12}^{4}\left(\frac{1}{\cancel{3}}\right) = 12(0.17)$

$9x + 4 = 2.04$

$100(9x) + 100(4) = 100(2.04)$

$900x + 400 = 204$

$900x = -196$

$x = -\frac{196}{900} = -\frac{49}{225} = -0.21\overline{7}$

⑤ Solve.

A volleyball player's hitting percentage is calculated using the formula $P = (k - e) \div a$ where P is the hitting percentage, k is the number of kills, e is the number of errors, and a is the total number of attacks. What is the hitting percentage of a player that had 25 kills, 10 errors, and 75 total attacks? Express your answer as a decimal to the thousandths place.

Note: In sports, statistical percentages are expressed as decimals. For example, a statistic expressed as 0.250 means 25%. Percents are generally given as decimals rounded to the nearest thousandth.

$P = (25 - 10) \div 75$

$P = \frac{15}{75} = \frac{1}{5} = 0.200$

How many errors did a player make with a -0.100 hitting percentage, 5 kills, and 30 total attacks?

$-0.100 = (5 - e) \div 30$

$30(-0.100) = 5 - e$

$-3 = 5 - e$

$e = 5 + 3 = 8$

Teaching Tips, Cont.

- Remind students that in algebra, any time there is no coefficient written, then it is an understood coefficient of 1. This concept should be applied whenever coefficients are multiplied.
- Explain that all expressions should be simplified after applying the distributive property. Always check each radicand to see if it can be simplified.
- Tell the students to look for common terms. This includes terms containing radicals. If two or more terms have identical radicals (same degree and same radicand) then those terms must be combined for the answer to be in simplest form.
- Complete the Classwork exercises. Have some students work the problems on the board for the class and explain their answers. All students should work the problems in their books.

Assignments

- Complete Lesson 24, Activities 2-5.
- Bring graph paper beginning in Lesson 29.

Lesson 25

Concepts

- Dividing radical expressions
- Absolute value
- Fractions
- Properties of equality

Learning Objectives

The student will be able to:

- Divide a binomial radical expression by a monomial radical
- Rationalize the denominator of the resulting quotient
- Simplify the resulting quotient

Materials Needed

- Student Book, Lesson 25
- Worksheet 13

Teaching Tips

- ➢ Have students complete Worksheet 13 in class. This may be for added practice of earlier topics, or graded as a quiz, if desired.
- ➢ Review rationalizing the denominator. (See Lesson 22)
- ➢ Review multiplying radical expressions. (See Lesson 24)
- ➢ Teach dividing radical expressions from the teaching box. Explain that just like the term outside the parentheses was applied to each term inside the parentheses in multiplication, the term outside the parentheses is also applied to each term inside the parentheses in division. Although the term in these division problems is to the right of the parentheses, the same rule applies.

Lesson 25

Radical Expressions: Division

When dividing radical expressions, divide each term in the dividend by the divisor. Rationalize the denominator if necessary, and simplify your answer.

$\left(3\sqrt{2}+2\sqrt{3}\right)\div\sqrt{2}$

Divide each term in the dividend by the divisor.

$\frac{3\cancel{\sqrt{2}}}{\cancel{\sqrt{2}}}+\frac{2\sqrt{3}}{\sqrt{2}}=3+\frac{2\sqrt{3}}{\sqrt{2}}$

Rationalize the denominator.

$3+\frac{2\sqrt{3}}{\sqrt{2}}\cdot\frac{\sqrt{2}}{\sqrt{2}}=3+\frac{2\sqrt{6}}{2}$

Simplify the answer.

$3+\frac{\cancel{2}\sqrt{6}}{\cancel{2}}=3+\sqrt{6}$

① Classwork

Divide.

$\left(3\sqrt{10}+2\sqrt{14}\right)\div\sqrt{2}$

$\frac{3\sqrt{10}}{\sqrt{2}}+\frac{2\sqrt{14}}{\sqrt{2}}=\frac{3\sqrt{\cancel{10}^{5}}}{\cancel{\sqrt{2}}}+\frac{2\sqrt{\cancel{14}^{7}}}{\cancel{\sqrt{2}}}=$

$3\sqrt{5}+2\sqrt{7}$

$\left(5\sqrt{6}+3\sqrt{2}\right)\div\sqrt{3}$

$\frac{5\sqrt{\cancel{6}_{2}}}{\cancel{\sqrt{3}}}+\frac{3\sqrt{2}}{\sqrt{3}}=5\sqrt{2}+\frac{3\sqrt{2}}{\sqrt{3}}\cdot\frac{\sqrt{3}}{\sqrt{3}}=$

$5\sqrt{2}+\frac{\cancel{3}\sqrt{6}}{\cancel{3}}=5\sqrt{2}+\sqrt{6}$

Activities

② Divide.

$\left(5\sqrt{12}+3\sqrt{6}\right)\div\sqrt{3}$

$\frac{5\sqrt{\cancel{12}^{4}}}{\cancel{\sqrt{3}}}+\frac{3\sqrt{\cancel{6}^{2}}}{\cancel{\sqrt{3}}}=5\sqrt{4}+3\sqrt{2}=$

$5\cdot2+3\sqrt{2}=10+3\sqrt{2}$

$\left(4\sqrt{7}+6\sqrt{5}\right)\div\sqrt{5}$

$\frac{4\sqrt{7}}{\sqrt{5}}+\frac{6\cancel{\sqrt{5}}}{\cancel{\sqrt{5}}}=\frac{4\sqrt{7}}{\sqrt{5}}\cdot\frac{\sqrt{5}}{\sqrt{5}}+6=$

$\frac{4\sqrt{7\cdot5}}{\sqrt{5\cdot5}}+6=\frac{4\sqrt{35}}{5}+6$ or $\frac{30+4\sqrt{35}}{5}$

$\left(3\sqrt{5}+8\sqrt{10}\right)\div\sqrt{6}$

$\frac{3\sqrt{5}}{\sqrt{6}}+\frac{8\sqrt{10}}{\sqrt{6}}=\frac{3\sqrt{5}}{\sqrt{6}}\cdot\frac{\sqrt{6}}{\sqrt{6}}+\frac{8\sqrt{\cancel{10}^{5}}}{\sqrt{\cancel{6}^{3}}}\cdot\frac{\sqrt{3}}{\sqrt{3}}=$

$\frac{3\sqrt{5\cdot6}}{\sqrt{6\cdot6}}+\frac{8\sqrt{5\cdot3}}{\sqrt{3\cdot3}}=\frac{\cancel{3}\sqrt{30}}{\cancel{6}_{2}}+\frac{8\sqrt{15}}{3}=$

$\frac{\sqrt{30}}{2}+\frac{8\sqrt{15}}{3}$ or $\frac{3\sqrt{30}+16\sqrt{15}}{6}$

$\left(6\sqrt{18}+4\sqrt{15}\right)\div\sqrt{3}$

$\frac{6\sqrt{\cancel{18}^{6}}}{\cancel{\sqrt{3}}}+\frac{4\sqrt{\cancel{15}^{5}}}{\cancel{\sqrt{3}}}=6\sqrt{6}+4\sqrt{5}$

$\left(2\sqrt{7}+9\sqrt{21}\right)\div\sqrt{14}$

$\frac{2\cancel{\sqrt{7}}}{\sqrt{\cancel{14}_{2}}}+\frac{9\sqrt{\cancel{21}^{3}}}{\sqrt{\cancel{14}_{2}}}=\frac{2}{\sqrt{2}}\cdot\frac{\sqrt{2}}{\sqrt{2}}+\frac{9\sqrt{3}}{\sqrt{2}}\cdot\frac{\sqrt{2}}{\sqrt{2}}=$

$\frac{2\sqrt{2}}{\sqrt{2\cdot2}}+\frac{9\sqrt{6}}{\sqrt{2\cdot2}}=\frac{2\sqrt{2}+9\sqrt{6}}{2}$ or $\sqrt{2}+\frac{9\sqrt{6}}{2}$

$\left(7\sqrt{3}+4\sqrt{5}\right)\div\sqrt{7}$

$\frac{7\sqrt{3}}{\sqrt{7}}+\frac{4\sqrt{5}}{\sqrt{7}}=\frac{7\sqrt{3}}{\sqrt{7}}\cdot\frac{\sqrt{7}}{\sqrt{7}}+\frac{4\sqrt{5}}{\sqrt{7}}\cdot\frac{\sqrt{7}}{\sqrt{7}}=$

$\frac{7\sqrt{3\cdot7}}{\sqrt{7\cdot7}}+\frac{4\sqrt{5\cdot7}}{\sqrt{7\cdot7}}=\frac{\cancel{7}\sqrt{3\cdot7}}{\cancel{7}}+\frac{4\sqrt{5\cdot7}}{7}=$

$\frac{7\sqrt{21}+4\sqrt{35}}{7}$ or $\sqrt{21}+\frac{4\sqrt{35}}{7}$

③ Find all possible solutions. Identify any extraneous solutions.

$|3x+14|+2=-2x-9$

$|3x+14|=-2x-11$

$3x+14=-2x-11$ or $3x+14=-(-2x-11)$

$5x=-25$ $3x+14=2x+11$

$x=-5$ $x=-3$

check:

$|3(-5)+14|+2=-2(-5)-9$

$|-15+14|+2=10-9$

$|-1|+2=1$

$1+2\neq1$ extraneous

$|3(-3)+14|+2=-2(-3)-9$

$|-9+14|+2=6-9$

$|5|+2=-3$

$5+2\neq-3$ extraneous

$|6x+4|-2=2(3x+1)$

$|6x+4|-2=6x+2$

$|6x+4|=6x+4$

$6x+4=6x+4$ or $6x+4=-(6x+4)$

$0=0$ $6x+4=-6x-4$

all real numbers $12x=-8\Rightarrow x=-\frac{8}{12}=-\frac{2}{3}$

check:

$\left|{}^{2}\cancel{6}\left(-\frac{2}{\cancel{3}}\right)+4\right|-2=2\left(\cancel{3}\left(-\frac{2}{\cancel{3}}\right)+1\right)$

$|-4+4|-2=2(-2+1)$

$|0|-2=-2$

$-2=-2$

④ Solve each algebraic equation. For each step, identify the property of equality that was used.

$7+\frac{3}{x}=-2$

$7(x)+\frac{3}{\cancel{x}}\left(\cancel{x}\right)=-2(x)\Rightarrow7x+3=-2x$

Multiplication property

$7x+3+2x=-2x+2x\Rightarrow9x+3=0$

Addition property

$9x+3-3=0-3\Rightarrow9x=-3$

Subtraction property

$9x\div9=-3\div9\Rightarrow x=-\frac{1}{3}$

Division property

$\frac{11}{x}-\frac{4}{x^2}=-\frac{1}{x}$

$\frac{11}{\cancel{x}}\left(x^{\cancel{2}}\right)-\frac{4}{\cancel{x^2}}\left(\cancel{x^2}\right)=-\frac{1}{\cancel{x}}\left(x^{\cancel{2}}\right)\Rightarrow11x-4=-x$

Multiplication property

$11x-4+x=-x+x\Rightarrow12x-4=0$

Addition property

$12x-4+4=0+4\Rightarrow12x=4$

Addition property

$12x\div12=4\div12\Rightarrow x=\frac{4}{12}=\frac{1}{3}$

Division property

$9-\frac{2}{x}=4+\frac{3}{x}$

$9(x)-\frac{2}{\cancel{x}}\left(\cancel{x}\right)=4(x)+\frac{3}{\cancel{x}}\left(\cancel{x}\right)\Rightarrow9x-2=4x+3$

Multiplication property

$9x-2-4x=4x+3-4x\Rightarrow5x-2=3$

Subtraction property

$5x-2+2=3+2\Rightarrow5x=5$

Addition property

$5x\div5=5\div5\Rightarrow x=1$

Division property

$\frac{6}{x}+\frac{5}{x^2}=\frac{2}{x}+\frac{21}{x^2}$

$\frac{6}{\cancel{x}}\left(x^{\cancel{2}}\right)+\frac{5}{\cancel{x^2}}\left(\cancel{x^2}\right)=\frac{2}{\cancel{x}}\left(x^{\cancel{2}}\right)+\frac{21}{\cancel{x^2}}\left(\cancel{x^2}\right)\Rightarrow6x+5=2x+21$

Multiplication property

$6x+5-2x=2x+21-2x\Rightarrow4x+5=21$

Subtraction property

$4x+5-5=21-5\Rightarrow4x=16$

Subtraction property

$4x\div4=16\div4\Rightarrow x=4$

Division property

Dividing Radicals Worksheet 13

① Solve.

$72\sqrt{24} \div 9\sqrt{8}$

$\frac{\cancel{72}^{8}\sqrt{24}}{\cancel{9}\sqrt{8}} = \frac{8\sqrt{\cancel{24}^{3}}}{\sqrt{\cancel{8}}} = 8\sqrt{3}$

$45\sqrt{42} \div 25\sqrt{7}$

$\frac{\cancel{45}^{9}\sqrt{42}}{\cancel{25}^{5}\sqrt{7}} = \frac{9\sqrt{\cancel{42}^{6}}}{5\sqrt{\cancel{7}}} = \frac{9\sqrt{6}}{5}$

$30\sqrt{11} \div 8\sqrt{77}$

$\frac{\cancel{30}^{15}\sqrt{11}}{\cancel{8}^{4}\sqrt{77}} = \frac{15\sqrt{\cancel{11}}}{4\sqrt{\cancel{77}^{7}}} = \frac{15}{4\sqrt{7}} \cdot \frac{\sqrt{7}}{\sqrt{7}} =$

$\frac{15\sqrt{7}}{4 \cdot 7} = \frac{15\sqrt{7}}{28}$

$56\sqrt{10} \div 24\sqrt{75}$

$\frac{\cancel{56}^{7}\sqrt{10}}{\cancel{24}^{3}\sqrt{75}} = \frac{7\sqrt{\cancel{10}^{2}}}{3\sqrt{\cancel{75}^{15}}} = \frac{7\sqrt{2}}{3\sqrt{15}} \cdot \frac{\sqrt{15}}{\sqrt{15}} =$

$\frac{7\sqrt{30}}{3\sqrt{15^2}} = \frac{7\sqrt{30}}{3 \cdot 15} = \frac{7\sqrt{30}}{45}$

$\frac{\sqrt{125}}{4\sqrt{5}}$

$\frac{\sqrt{\cancel{125}^{25}}}{4\sqrt{\cancel{5}}} = \frac{\sqrt{25}}{4} = \frac{5}{4}$

$\frac{11\sqrt[4]{26}}{\sqrt[4]{32}}$

$\frac{11\sqrt[4]{\cancel{26}^{13}}}{\sqrt[4]{\cancel{32}^{16}}} = \frac{11\sqrt[4]{13}}{\sqrt[4]{2^4}} = \frac{11\sqrt[4]{13}}{2}$

$\frac{4\sqrt{35}}{\sqrt{112}}$

$\frac{4\sqrt{\cancel{35}^{5}}}{\sqrt{\cancel{112}^{16}}} = \frac{4\sqrt{5}}{\sqrt{16}} = \frac{\cancel{4}\sqrt{5}}{\cancel{4}} = \sqrt{5}$

$\frac{6\sqrt[3]{15}}{\sqrt[3]{35}}$

$\frac{6\sqrt[3]{\cancel{15}^{3}}}{\sqrt[3]{\cancel{35}^{7}}} = \frac{6\sqrt[3]{3}}{\sqrt[3]{7}} \cdot \frac{\sqrt[3]{7^{3-1}}}{\sqrt[3]{7^{3-1}}} = \frac{6\sqrt[3]{3}}{\sqrt[3]{7}} \cdot \frac{\sqrt[3]{7^2}}{\sqrt[3]{7^2}} =$

$\frac{6\sqrt[3]{3 \cdot 49}}{\sqrt[3]{7^3}} = \frac{6\sqrt[3]{147}}{7}$

$\frac{\sqrt{72}}{6\sqrt{2}}$

$\frac{\sqrt{\cancel{72}^{36}}}{6\sqrt{\cancel{2}}} = \frac{\sqrt{36}}{6} = \frac{6}{6} = 1$

$\frac{12\sqrt[4]{486}}{\sqrt[4]{96}}$

$\frac{12\sqrt[4]{\cancel{486}^{81}}}{\sqrt[4]{\cancel{96}^{16}}} = \frac{12\sqrt[4]{3^4}}{\sqrt[4]{2^4}} =$

$\frac{\cancel{12}^{6} \cdot 3}{\cancel{2}} = 6 \cdot 3 = 18$

$\frac{16\sqrt{65}}{\sqrt{104}}$

$\frac{16\sqrt{\cancel{65}^{5}}}{\sqrt{\cancel{104}^{8}}} = \frac{16\sqrt{5}}{\sqrt{2^3}} = \frac{\cancel{16}^{8}\sqrt{5}}{\cancel{2}\sqrt{2}} \cdot \frac{\sqrt{2}}{\sqrt{2}} =$

$\frac{\cancel{8}^{4}\sqrt{10}}{\cancel{2}} = 4\sqrt{10}$

$\frac{14\sqrt[3]{54}}{\sqrt[3]{56}}$

$\frac{14\sqrt[3]{3^3 \cdot 2}}{\sqrt[3]{2^3 \cdot 7}} = \frac{14 \cdot 3\sqrt[3]{2}}{2\sqrt[3]{7}} \cdot \frac{\sqrt[3]{7^{3-1}}}{\sqrt[3]{7^{3-1}}} =$

$\frac{\cancel{42}^{21}\sqrt[3]{2}}{\cancel{2}\sqrt[3]{7}} \cdot \frac{\sqrt[3]{7^2}}{\sqrt[3]{7^2}} = \frac{21\sqrt[3]{2 \cdot 49}}{\sqrt[3]{7^3}} = \frac{\cancel{21}^{3}\sqrt[3]{98}}{\cancel{7}} = 3\sqrt[3]{98}$

Teaching Tips, Cont.

- Remind students to rationalize each denominator after dividing. Students should also simplify radicals and combine terms where appropriate to get the answer in simplest form.
- Complete the Classwork exercises. Have some students work the problems on the board for the class. All students should work the problems in their books.

Assignments

- Complete Lesson 25, Activities 2-4.
- Bring graph paper beginning in Lesson 29.

Lesson 26

Concepts

- Algebraic equations with radicals
- Properties of equality
- Multiplying with exponents
- Dividing with exponents

Learning Objectives

The student will be able to:

- Isolate the radical in an algebraic equation
- Solve for all possible solutions of an algebraic equation containing a radical
- Check each possible solution to determine if it is extraneous

Materials Needed

- Student Book, Lesson 26

Teaching Tips

➢ Review solving algebraic equations. (See Lesson 17)

➢ Tell the students that when the variable appears as part of the radicand, it cannot be pulled out separately just to isolate the variable. Refer to the first example in the teaching box to show the students what happens when the radical is split. Emphasize that it is NEVER acceptable to split a radicand.

➢ Write 2^2 on the board. Ask a student what the value is. (4)
Write $(\sqrt{2})(\sqrt{2})$ on the board. Ask a student what the value is. (2)

Lesson 26

Solving Algebraic Equations: Radicals

You have learned to isolate the variable when solving an algebraic expression. But what happens if that variable is under a radical? You cannot just pull out the variable. Look at what happens when you remove part of a radicand.

$\sqrt{8} = \sqrt{4+4}$ So far, this is a true statement.

But, you cannot split a radicand!

$\sqrt{4+4} \neq \sqrt{4} + \sqrt{4}$

$\sqrt{8} \neq 2 + 2$; $\sqrt{8} \neq 4$ because $4^2 = 16$

If you have a square root as part of an algebraic equation, follow these steps.

1. Isolate the entire radical rather than just the variable. This is true no matter where the variable appears in the equation.
2. Square both sides of the equation.
3. Solve for the variable, following the properties of equality.
4. Check for extraneous solutions.

$\sqrt{5x+4} - 2 = 5$

Isolate the radical.

$\sqrt{5x+4} = 7$

Square both sides.

$\left(\sqrt{5x+4}\right)^2 = 7^2 \Rightarrow 5x + 4 = 49$

Solve for the variable.

$5x = 45 \Rightarrow x = 9$

Check.

$\sqrt{5(9)+4} - 2 = 5$

$\sqrt{45+4} - 2 = 5$

$\sqrt{49} - 2 = 5$

$7 - 2 = 5$

$5 = 5$

① Classwork

Solve and check for extraneous solutions.

$\sqrt{6x+7} - 2 = 5$

$\sqrt{6x+7} = 7$

$\left(\sqrt{6x+7}\right)^2 = 7^2$

$6x + 7 = 49$

$6x = 42$

$x = 7$

check:

$\sqrt{6(7)+7} - 2 = 5$

$\sqrt{42+7} - 2 = 5$

$\sqrt{49} - 2 = 5$

$7 - 2 = 5$

$\sqrt{3x-2} + 8 = 3$

$\sqrt{3x-2} = -5$

$\left(\sqrt{3x-2}\right)^2 = (-5)^2$

$3x - 2 = 25$

$3x = 27$

$x = 9$

check:

$\sqrt{3(9)-2} + 8 = 3$

$\sqrt{27-2} + 8 = 3$

$\sqrt{25} + 8 = 3$

$5 + 8 \neq 3$ extraneous

Activities

② Solve and check for extraneous solutions.

$\sqrt{2x-13} - 3 = 6$

$\sqrt{2x-13} = 9$

$\left(\sqrt{2x-13}\right)^2 = 9^2$

$2x - 13 = 81$

$2x = 94$

$x = 47$

check:

$\sqrt{2(47)-13} - 3 = 6$

$\sqrt{94-13} - 3 = 6$

$\sqrt{81} - 3 = 6$

$9 - 3 = 6$

$\sqrt{7x+1} + 13 = 7$

$\sqrt{7x+1} = -6$

$\left(\sqrt{7x+1}\right)^2 = (-6)^2$

$7x + 1 = 36$

$7x = 35$

$x = 5$

check:

$\sqrt{7(5)+1} + 13 = 7$

$\sqrt{35+1} + 13 = 7$

$\sqrt{36} + 13 = 7$

$6 + 13 \neq 7$ extraneous

③ Solve and check for extraneous solutions.

$\sqrt{-3x+1}-1=4$
$\sqrt{-3x+1}=5$
$\left(\sqrt{-3x+1}\right)^2=5^2$
$-3x+1=25$
$-3x=24$
$x=-8$
check:
$\sqrt{-3(-8)+1}-1=4$
$\sqrt{24+1}-1=4$
$\sqrt{25}-1=4$
$5-1=4$

$\sqrt{-2x-3}+4=7$
$\sqrt{-2x-3}=3$
$\left(\sqrt{-2x-3}\right)^2=3^2$
$-2x-3=9$
$-2x=12$
$x=-6$
check:
$\sqrt{-2(-6)-3}+4=7$
$\sqrt{12-3}+4=7$
$\sqrt{9}+4=7$
$3+4=7$

$\sqrt{-9x+1}+3=11$
$\sqrt{-9x+1}=8$
$\left(\sqrt{-9x+1}\right)^2=8^2$
$-9x+1=64$
$-9x=63$
$x=-7$
check:
$\sqrt{-9(-7)+1}+3=11$
$\sqrt{63+1}+3=11$
$\sqrt{64}+3=11$
$8+3=11$

$\sqrt{8x+41}+2=-7$
$\sqrt{8x+41}=-9$
$\left(\sqrt{8x+41}\right)^2=(-9)^2$
$8x+41=81$
$8x=40$
$x=5$
check:
$\sqrt{8(5)+41}+2=-7$
$\sqrt{40+41}+2=-7$
$\sqrt{81}+2=-7$
$9+2\neq-7$ extraneous

④ Solve each algebraic equation. For each step, identify the property of equality that was used.

$12x-9=5x+19$
$12x-9-5x=5x+19-5x \Rightarrow 7x-9=19$
Subtraction property
$7x-9+9=19+9 \Rightarrow 7x=28$
Addition property
$7x\div7=28\div7 \Rightarrow x=4$
Division property

$8x-18=-7x+27$
$8x-18+7x=-7x+27+7x \Rightarrow 15x-18=27$
Addition property
$15x-18+18=27+18 \Rightarrow 15x=45$
Addition property
$15x\div15=45\div15 \Rightarrow x=3$
Division property

$5(x+3)=2x+39$
$5x+15=2x+39$
Distributive property
$5x+15-2x=2x+39-2x \Rightarrow 3x+15=39$
Subtraction property
$3x+15-15=39-15 \Rightarrow 3x=24$
Subtraction property
$3x\div3=24\div3 \Rightarrow x=8$
Division property

$11(x+1)=5x+53$
$11x+11=5x+53$
Distributive property
$11x+11-5x=5x+53-5x \Rightarrow 6x+11=53$
Subtraction property
$6x+11-11=53-11 \Rightarrow 6x=42$
Subtraction property
$6x\div6=42\div6 \Rightarrow x=7$
Division property

⑤ Solve.

$4a^5\left(-5a^{-4}b^7\right)\left(2a^3b^{-6}\right)$
$(4\cdot-5\cdot2)\left(a^{5-4+3}\right)\left(b^{7-6}\right)=$
$-40a^4b$

$-c^7\left(4cd^5\right)\left(8c^{-9}d^{-1}\right)$
$(-1\cdot4\cdot8)\left(c^{7+1-9}\right)\left(d^{5-1}\right)=$
$-32c^{-1}d^4$

$-6e^2\left(7e^{-5}f^6\right)\left(-9e^{-7}f^{-1}\right)$
$(-6\cdot7\cdot-9)\left(e^{2-5-7}\right)\left(f^{6-1}\right)=$
$378e^{-10}f^5$

$51g^8\div3g^3$
$\frac{51g^8}{3g^3}=17g^{8-3}=17g^5$

$39h^{11}\div13h^8$
$\frac{39h^{11}}{13h^8}=3h^{11-8}=3h^3$

$55j^{17}\div5j^{-8}$
$\frac{55j^{17}}{5j^{-8}}=11j^{17-(-8)}=11j^{25}$

Teaching Tips, Cont.

- Remind students that when a radical of degree 2 (a square root) is squared, the result is equal to the value of the radicand.
- Teach how to solve algebraic equations with radicals using the example from the teaching box. Emphasize that the radical must be isolated before squaring each side. Some students may be concerned about what to do if there is more than one radical in an equation. While these cases do appear, this book will only have problems with one radical. Equations with multiple radicals will appear in Algebra 2.
- Complete the Classwork exercises. Have some students work the problems on the board for the class. All students should work the problems in their books.

Assignments

- Complete Lesson 26, Activities 2-5.
- Bring graph paper beginning in Lesson 29.

Lesson 27

Concepts

- Scientific notation
- Powers of 10
- Adding polynomials
- Subtracting polynomials
- Absolute value
- Radicals

Learning Objectives

The student will be able to:

- Use scientific notation to express very large and very small numbers
- Convert scientific notation to standard form
- Multiply powers of 10
- Divide powers of 10

Materials Needed

- Student Book, Lesson 27

Teaching Tips

- Review multiplying and dividing exponents with the same base. (See Lesson 2)
- Review the rules for zero exponents and negative exponents. (See Lesson 2)
- Write the Powers of 10 chart from this page on the board. Ask a student to identify the pattern formed as the value of the exponent increases. (The decimal point moves to the right.) Ask a student to identify the pattern formed as the value of the exponent decreases. (The decimal point moves to the left.)
- Teach how to write the expanded notation of a number using 345.127 in the example at the right.

Lesson 27

Scientific Notation

Do you find it difficult to read the number 0.0000000000000059 without losing track of the number of zeros? It is also difficult to work with large numbers like 467,000,000,000,000 since most calculators will not accommodate that number of characters.

Scientists and mathematicians have a different way to handle these kinds of numbers to make them easier to work with. **Scientific notation** is a method of writing very large and very small numbers. Using this notation, numbers are written in the format $m \times 10^p$, where m is the **mantissa** (also called the **significand**) and p is the exponent, or power of 10. The mantissa, or significand, is ALWAYS a number greater than or equal to 1 and less than 10. In other words, $1 \le m < 10$.

The mantissa begins with the first non-zero digit of the standard form number, and ends with the last non-zero digit. In the first example above, the mantissa is 5.9 because 5 is the first non-zero digit. A decimal point is always placed after the first non-zero digit so the mantissa will be less than 10.

In the second example, the mantissa is 4.67 because 4 is the first non-zero digit.

To find the value of p, count the number of places the decimal point must move from its place in the mantissa to its place in the standard form number. In the first example, the decimal point in 5.9 must move 15 places to the left. This makes p equal to -15 and the scientific notation is 5.9×10^{-15}.

In the second example, the decimal point in 4.67 moves 14 places to the right. This makes p equal to 14 and the scientific notation is 4.67×10^{14}.

① **Classwork**

Write each number in scientific notation.

354,000 3.54×10^5

98,000 9.8×10^4

7,600,000 7.6×10^6

25,600,000 2.56×10^7

0.00079 7.9×10^{-4}

0.00000011 1.1×10^{-7}

0.00000438 4.38×10^{-6}

0.000000002 2×10^{-9}

Write each number in standard form.

6.1×10^5 610,000

9.55×10^7 95,500,000

6.814×10^6 6,814,000

3×10^8 300,000,000

7.1×10^{-6} 0.0000071

7.99×10^{-7} 0.000000799

6.572×10^{-9} 0.000000006572

8×10^{-5} 0.00008

Activities

② Write each number in scientific notation.

550,000,000 5.5×10^8

93,000,000 9.3×10^7

4,270,000,000 4.27×10^9

1,000,000 1×10^6

0.000000763 7.63×10^{-7}

0.00012 1.2×10^{-4}

0.0000003492 3.492×10^{-7}

0.000000004 4×10^{-9}

Powers of 10

Hundreds	Tens	Ones	Decimal	point	Tenths	Hundredths
10^2	10^1	10^0	.	10^{-1}	10^{-2}	10^{-3}
100	10	1	.	0.1	0.01	0.001

3	4	5	.	1	2	7

The number 345.127 can be represented using exponents by the expression $(3 \times 10^2) + (4 \times 10^1) + (5 \times 10^0) + (1 \times 10^{-1}) + (2 \times 10^{-2}) + (7 \times 10^{-3})$

To represent a number in a different base, change the number in the base from 10 to whichever base you are looking for. The number twelve can be expressed in base 2 as $(1 \times 2^3) + (1 \times 2^2) + (0 \times 2^0)$, or the number 110_2.

③ Write each number in standard form.

2.4×10^{6} 2,400,000	6.6×10^{-7} 0.00000066
7.895×10^{9} 7,895,000,000	6.78×10^{-6} 0.00000678
9.56×10^{7} 95,600,000	9.567×10^{-8} 0.00000009567
7×10^{5} 700,000	8×10^{-5} 0.00008

④ Solve.

$$\begin{array}{r}46a^2+87a+64\\ \underline{+12a^2-43a+29}\\ 58a^2+44a+93\end{array} \qquad \begin{array}{r}34b^2+46b+51\\ \underline{+28b^2-19b-39}\\ 62b^2+27b+12\end{array} \qquad \begin{array}{r}24c^2-11c+42\\ \underline{+73c^2+25c-17}\\ 97c^2+14c+25\end{array}$$

$$\begin{array}{r}(63d^2+27d+51)\\ \underline{-(48d^2+72d+39)}\\ 15d^2-45d+12\end{array} \qquad \begin{array}{r}(58e^2+18e+35)\\ \underline{-(26e^2-41e+13)}\\ 32e^2+59e+22\end{array} \qquad \begin{array}{r}(89f^2-48f-51)\\ \underline{-(91f^2+72f-44)}\\ -2f^2-120f-7\end{array}$$

⑤ Find all possible solutions. Identify any extraneous solutions.

$|7x-11|-19=2x-5$

$|7x-11|=2x+14$

$7x-11=2x+14$ or $7x-11=-(2x+14)$

$5x=25$ $7x-11=-2x-14$

$x=5$ $9x=-3\Rightarrow x=-\frac{3}{9}=-\frac{1}{3}$

check:

$|7(5)-11|-19=2(5)-5$

$|35-11|-19=10-5$

$|24|-19=5$

$24-19=5$

$|7(-\frac{1}{3})-11|-19=2(-\frac{1}{3})-5$

$|-\frac{7}{3}-\frac{33}{3}|-19=-\frac{2}{3}-\frac{15}{3}$

$|-\frac{40}{3}|-\frac{57}{3}=-\frac{17}{3}$

$\frac{40}{3}-\frac{57}{3}=-\frac{17}{3}$

$|5x+3|-8=3x-17$

$|5x+3|=3x-9$

$5x+3=3x-9$ or $5x+3=-(3x-9)$

$2x=-12$ $5x+3=-3x+9$

$x=-6$ $8x=6\Rightarrow x=\frac{6}{8}=\frac{3}{4}$

check:

$|5(-6)+3|-8=3(-6)-17$

$|-30+3|-8=-18-17$

$|-27|-8=-35$

$27-8\neq-35$ extraneous

$|5(\frac{3}{4})+3|-8=3(\frac{3}{4})-17$

$|\frac{15}{4}+\frac{12}{4}|-8=\frac{9}{4}-\frac{68}{4}$

$\frac{27}{4}-\frac{32}{4}=-\frac{59}{4}$

$-\frac{5}{4}\neq-\frac{59}{4}$ extraneous

$\sqrt{-4x-3}-2=7$

$\sqrt{-4x-3}=9$

$(\sqrt{-4x-3})^2=9^2$

$-4x-3=81$

$-4x=84$

$x=-21$

check:

$\sqrt{-4(-21)-3}-2=7$

$\sqrt{84-3}-2=7$

$\sqrt{81}-2=7$

$9-2=7$

$\sqrt{-2x+1}+10=3$

$\sqrt{-2x+1}=-7$

$(\sqrt{-2x+1})^2=(-7)^2$

$-2x+1=49$

$-2x=48$

$x=-24$

check:

$\sqrt{-2(-24)+1}+10=3$

$\sqrt{48+1}+10=3$

$\sqrt{49}+10=3$

$7+10\neq3$ extraneous

Powers of 10 Summary

Operation	Exponent	Decimal Direction
Multiply	Positive	Right
Multiply	Negative	Left
Divide	Positive	Left
Divide	Negative	Right

Teaching Tips, Cont.

- Note: The information regarding changing bases is for your information only. If you have advanced students in your class, you may present this material to them at your own discretion.
- Teach scientific notation from the teaching box. Emphasize that the entire mantissa must be written when writing a number in scientific notation.
- Tell the students that scientific notation is a vital skill to master. It is used extensively in high school, especially chemistry classes.
- Complete the Classwork exercises. Have some students work the problems on the board for the class. All students should work the problems in their books.

Assignments

- Complete Lesson 27, Activities 2-5.
- Bring graph paper beginning in Lesson 29.

Lesson 28

Concepts

- Rational exponents
- Decimals
- Fractions
- Dividing radicals
- Rationalizing the denominator
- Math in the real world

Learning Objectives

The student will be able to:

- Define *rational exponent*
- Convert rational exponent expressions to radical expressions
- Simplify expressions with rational exponents

Materials Needed

- Student Book, Lesson 28
- Worksheet 14

Teaching Tips

- Have students complete Worksheet 14 in class. This may be for added practice of earlier topics, or graded as a quiz, if desired.
- Review roots and radicals as necessary. (See Lesson 7)
- Write the number 8^2 on the board. Ask the students what this means. (8 squared, or 8 x 8) Ask the students what the base is. (8) Ask the students what the exponent is. (2) Ask the students what the denominator of the exponent is. (Some students may suggest that the exponent does not have a denominator. Remind them that a whole number can be written as an improper fraction with a 1 as the denominator.)

Rational Exponents

A **rational exponent** is an exponent that is a fraction. The numerator of the exponent gives the power of the base. The denominator of the exponent gives the root of the base.

$b^{\frac{p}{r}} = \sqrt[r]{b^p}$

Simplify the following expression.

$8^{\frac{2}{3}}$

8 is the base; 2 is the power; 3 is the root.

$8^{\frac{2}{3}} = \sqrt[3]{8^2} = \sqrt[3]{8 \cdot 8}$

You should recognize $\sqrt[3]{8} = 2$.

Therefore $\sqrt[3]{8 \cdot 8} = 2 \cdot 2 = 4$.

① **Classwork**

Solve.

$4^{\frac{1}{2}} = \sqrt{4} = 2$

$27^{\frac{2}{3}} = \sqrt[3]{27^2} = \sqrt[3]{27 \cdot 27} = \sqrt[3]{3^3 \cdot 3^3} = 3 \cdot 3 = 9$

$16^{\frac{2}{3}} =$

$\sqrt[3]{16^2} = \sqrt[3]{16 \cdot 16} = \sqrt[3]{2^4 \cdot 2^4} = 2 \cdot 2\sqrt[3]{2 \cdot 2} = 4\sqrt[3]{4}$

Activities

② Solve.

$9^{\frac{1}{2}} =$

$\sqrt{9} = 3$

$8^{\frac{1}{3}} =$

$\sqrt[3]{8} = 2$

$24^{\frac{1}{3}} =$

$\sqrt[3]{24} = \sqrt[3]{3 \cdot 8} = \sqrt[3]{3 \cdot 2^3} = 2\sqrt[3]{3}$

$27^{\frac{1}{2}} =$

$\sqrt{27} = \sqrt{3^3} = 3\sqrt{3}$

$32^{\frac{1}{4}} =$

$\sqrt[4]{32} = \sqrt[4]{2^5} = 2\sqrt[4]{2}$

$40^{\frac{1}{3}} =$

$\sqrt[3]{40} = \sqrt[3]{5 \cdot 8} = \sqrt[3]{5 \cdot 2^3} = 2\sqrt[3]{5}$

$8^{\frac{1}{2}} =$

$\sqrt{8} = \sqrt{2^3} = 2\sqrt{2}$

$16^{\frac{1}{3}} =$

$\sqrt[3]{16} = \sqrt[3]{2^4} = 2\sqrt[3]{2}$

$24^{\frac{2}{3}} =$

$\sqrt[3]{24^2} = \sqrt[3]{24 \cdot 24} = \sqrt[3]{2^3 \cdot 3 \cdot 2^3 \cdot 3} =$
$2 \cdot 2\sqrt[3]{3 \cdot 3} = 4\sqrt[3]{9}$

$36^{\frac{2}{3}} =$

$\sqrt[3]{36^2} = \sqrt[3]{36 \cdot 36} = \sqrt[3]{6^2 \cdot 6^2} = \sqrt[3]{6^4} = 6\sqrt[3]{6}$

$54^{\frac{2}{3}} =$

$\sqrt[3]{54^2} = \sqrt[3]{54 \cdot 54} = \sqrt[3]{2 \cdot 3^3 \cdot 2 \cdot 3^3} =$
$3 \cdot 3\sqrt[3]{2 \cdot 2} = 9\sqrt[3]{4}$

$64^{\frac{2}{3}} =$

$\sqrt[3]{64^2} = \sqrt[3]{64 \cdot 64} = \sqrt[3]{4^3 \cdot 4^3} =$
$\sqrt[3]{4^6} = 4^2 = 16$

③ Solve.

$4(0.24x - 0.3) = 7(0.03x + 0.16) + 1.43$
$0.96x - 1.2 = 0.21x + 1.12 + 1.43$
$0.96x(100) - 1.2(100) =$
$0.21x(100) + 1.12(100) + 1.43(100)$
$96x - 120 = 21x + 112 + 143$
$75x - 120 = 255$
$75x = 375$
$x = 5$

$57 + \frac{14}{x} = -27$
$57(x) + \frac{14}{\cancel{x}}(\cancel{x}) = -27(x)$
$57x + 14 = -27x$
$84x + 14 = 0$
$84x = -14$
$x = -\frac{1}{6}$

$9(0.01x + 1.6) = 3(0.01x + 0.43) - 0.09$
$0.09x + 14.4 = 0.03x + 1.29 - 0.09$
$0.09x(100) + 14.4(100) =$
$0.03x(100) + 1.29(100) - 0.09(100)$
$9x + 1440 = 3x + 129 - 9$
$6x + 1440 = 120$
$6x = -1320$
$x = -220$

$89 - \frac{25}{x} = 14$
$89(x) - \frac{25}{\cancel{x}}(\cancel{x}) = 14(x)$
$89x - 25 = 14x$
$75x - 25 = 0$
$75x = 25$
$x = \frac{1}{3}$

④ Rationalize the denominator.

$\frac{7}{\sqrt[3]{49}}$

$\frac{7}{\sqrt[3]{7^2}} \cdot \frac{\sqrt[3]{7^{3-2}}}{\sqrt[3]{7^{3-2}}} = \frac{7\sqrt[3]{7}}{\sqrt[3]{7^3}} = \frac{\cancel{7}\sqrt[3]{7}}{\cancel{7}} = \sqrt[3]{7}$

$\frac{12}{\sqrt[4]{72}}$

$\frac{12}{\sqrt[4]{2^3 \cdot 3^2}} \cdot \frac{\sqrt[4]{2^{4-3} \cdot 3^{4-2}}}{\sqrt[4]{2^{4-3} \cdot 3^{4-2}}} = \frac{12}{\sqrt[4]{2^3 \cdot 3^2}} \cdot \frac{\sqrt[4]{2 \cdot 3^2}}{\sqrt[4]{2 \cdot 3^2}} =$

$\frac{12\sqrt[4]{2 \cdot 9}}{\sqrt[4]{2^4 \cdot 3^4}} = \frac{\overset{\cancel{6}^{2}}{\cancel{12}}\sqrt[4]{18}}{\cancel{2} \cdot \cancel{3}} = 2\sqrt[4]{18}$

$\frac{10\sqrt[5]{16}}{\sqrt[5]{12}}$

$\frac{10\sqrt[5]{2^4}}{\sqrt[5]{2^2 \cdot 3}} \cdot \frac{\sqrt[5]{2^{5-2} \cdot 3^{5-1}}}{\sqrt[5]{2^{5-2} \cdot 3^{5-1}}} = \frac{10\sqrt[5]{2^{4+3} \cdot 3^4}}{\sqrt[5]{2^5 \cdot 3^5}} = \frac{{}^{5}\cancel{10}\sqrt[5]{2^7 \cdot 3^4}}{\cancel{2} \cdot 3} =$

$\frac{5 \cdot 2\sqrt[5]{2^2 \cdot 3^4}}{3} = \frac{10\sqrt[5]{4 \cdot 81}}{3} = \frac{10\sqrt[5]{324}}{3}$

$\frac{3\sqrt[3]{32}}{12\sqrt[3]{54}}$

$\frac{\cancel{3}\sqrt[3]{2^5}}{{}_{4}\cancel{12}\sqrt[3]{2 \cdot 3^3}} = \frac{\cancel{2}\sqrt[3]{2^2}}{{}_{2}\cancel{4} \cdot 3\sqrt[3]{2}} \cdot \frac{\sqrt[3]{2^{3-1}}}{\sqrt[3]{2^{3-1}}} = \frac{\sqrt[3]{2^{2+2}}}{6\sqrt[3]{2^{1+2}}} =$

$\frac{\sqrt[3]{2^4}}{6\sqrt[3]{2^3}} = \frac{\cancel{2}\sqrt[3]{2}}{6 \cdot \cancel{2}} = \frac{\sqrt[3]{2}}{6}$

⑤ Solve.

The support poles for an outdoor volleyball court are 16 feet long and are sunk in the ground to a depth of 3 feet. If the volleyball net is 39 inches high, how far from the top of the pole should the top of the net be if the top of the net must be 7 ft. $11\frac{5}{8}$ in. from the playing surface? Express your answer in inches. 16 feet − 3 feet = 13 feet of pole above the ground $\frac{13 \text{ ft.}}{1} \cdot \frac{12 \text{ in.}}{1 \text{ ft.}} = 156$ in. $\frac{7 \text{ ft.}}{1} \cdot \frac{12 \text{ in.}}{1 \text{ ft.}} = 84$ in.

156 in. − 84 in. − $11\frac{5}{8}$ in. = 72 in. − $11\frac{5}{8}$ in. = $60\frac{3}{8}$ in. from the top of the pole

Note: The height of the net is irrelevant in this problem.

Multiplying Radicals, Dividing Radicals Worksheet 14

① Multiply.

$\sqrt{7}(8+\sqrt{2})$

$8\sqrt{7}+\sqrt{7\cdot 2}=8\sqrt{7}+\sqrt{14}$

$\sqrt{6}(2+\sqrt{5})$

$2\sqrt{6}+\sqrt{6\cdot 5}=2\sqrt{6}+\sqrt{30}$

$\sqrt{10}(4+\sqrt{3})$

$4\sqrt{10}+\sqrt{10\cdot 3}=4\sqrt{10}+\sqrt{30}$

$\sqrt{2}(5+\sqrt{18})$

$5\sqrt{2}+\sqrt{2\cdot 18}=5\sqrt{2}+\sqrt{36}=$

$5\sqrt{2}+6$ or $6+5\sqrt{2}$

$\sqrt{11}(8+\sqrt{7})$

$8\sqrt{11}+\sqrt{11\cdot 7}=8\sqrt{11}+\sqrt{77}$

$\sqrt{3}(8+\sqrt{13})$

$8\sqrt{3}+\sqrt{3\cdot 13}=8\sqrt{3}+\sqrt{39}$

$\sqrt{5}(9+\sqrt{7})$

$9\sqrt{5}+\sqrt{5\cdot 7}=9\sqrt{5}+\sqrt{35}$

$\sqrt{3}(4+\sqrt{15})$

$4\sqrt{3}+\sqrt{3\cdot 15}=4\sqrt{3}+\sqrt{3\cdot 3\cdot 5}=$

$4\sqrt{3}+3\sqrt{5}$

$\sqrt{5}(4+\sqrt{15})$

$4\sqrt{5}+\sqrt{5\cdot 15}=4\sqrt{5}+\sqrt{5\cdot 3\cdot 5}=$

$4\sqrt{5}+5\sqrt{3}$

$\sqrt{7}(9+\sqrt{42})$

$9\sqrt{7}+\sqrt{7\cdot 42}=9\sqrt{7}+\sqrt{7\cdot 6\cdot 7}=$

$9\sqrt{7}+7\sqrt{6}$

② Divide.

$(4\sqrt{15}+7\sqrt{35})\div\sqrt{5}$

$\frac{4\sqrt{\cancel{15}^{3}}}{\cancel{\sqrt{5}}}+\frac{7\sqrt{\cancel{35}^{7}}}{\cancel{\sqrt{5}}}=4\sqrt{3}+7\sqrt{7}$

$(2\sqrt{18}+5\sqrt{12})\div\sqrt{2}$

$\frac{2\sqrt{\cancel{18}^{9}}}{\sqrt{\cancel{2}}}+\frac{5\sqrt{\cancel{12}^{6}}}{\sqrt{\cancel{2}}}=2\cdot 3+5\sqrt{6}=$

$6+5\sqrt{6}$

$(4\sqrt{10}+3\sqrt{15})\div\sqrt{6}$

$\frac{4\sqrt{10}}{\sqrt{6}}+\frac{3\sqrt{15}}{\sqrt{6}}=\frac{4\sqrt{\cancel{10}^{5}}}{\sqrt{\cancel{6}^{3}}}\cdot\frac{\sqrt{3}}{\sqrt{3}}+\frac{3\sqrt{\cancel{15}^{5}}}{\sqrt{\cancel{6}^{2}}}\cdot\frac{\sqrt{2}}{\sqrt{2}}=$

$\frac{4\sqrt{5\cdot 3}}{\sqrt{3\cdot 3}}+\frac{3\sqrt{5\cdot 2}}{\sqrt{2\cdot 2}}=$

$\frac{4\sqrt{15}}{3}+\frac{3\sqrt{10}}{2}=$ or $\frac{8\sqrt{15}+9\sqrt{10}}{6}$

$(7\sqrt{21}+9\sqrt{14})\div\sqrt{7}$

$\frac{7\sqrt{\cancel{21}^{3}}}{\cancel{\sqrt{7}}}+\frac{9\sqrt{\cancel{14}^{2}}}{\cancel{\sqrt{7}}}=7\sqrt{3}+9\sqrt{2}$

$(10\sqrt{3}+2\sqrt{12})\div\sqrt{15}$

$\frac{10\cancel{\sqrt{3}}}{\sqrt{\cancel{15}_{5}}}+\frac{2\sqrt{\cancel{12}^{4}}}{\sqrt{\cancel{15}_{5}}}=\frac{10}{\sqrt{5}}\cdot\frac{\sqrt{5}}{\sqrt{5}}+\frac{2\sqrt{4}}{\sqrt{5}}\cdot\frac{\sqrt{5}}{\sqrt{5}}=$

$\frac{10\sqrt{5}}{\sqrt{5\cdot 5}}+\frac{2\cdot 2\sqrt{5}}{\sqrt{5\cdot 5}}=\frac{10\sqrt{5}+4\sqrt{5}}{5}=\frac{14\sqrt{5}}{5}$

$(4\sqrt{7}+11\sqrt{3})\div\sqrt{5}$

$\frac{4\sqrt{7}}{\sqrt{5}}+\frac{11\sqrt{3}}{\sqrt{5}}=\frac{4\sqrt{7}}{\sqrt{5}}\cdot\frac{\sqrt{5}}{\sqrt{5}}+\frac{11\sqrt{3}}{\sqrt{5}}\cdot\frac{\sqrt{5}}{\sqrt{5}}=$

$\frac{4\sqrt{7\cdot 5}}{\sqrt{5\cdot 5}}+\frac{11\sqrt{3\cdot 5}}{\sqrt{5\cdot 5}}=$

$\frac{4\sqrt{35}}{5}+\frac{11\sqrt{15}}{5}=$ or $\frac{4\sqrt{35}+11\sqrt{15}}{5}$

Teaching Tips, Cont.

- Teach rational exponents from the teaching box. Emphasize that in a fractional exponent, the numerator is the power of the base. Consider a base with a whole-number exponent. This is the same thing as that whole number over 1. The whole number is the power of the base, and the number 1 is the root. The first root of a number is the number itself.
- Students do not have to memorize the formula for rational exponents, but they must understand the concept well enough to do the work without the aid of the formula. This material will appear on the test following Lesson 40 and NOT on the test following Lesson 30. This will provide ample time for students to master the concept.
- Complete the Classwork exercises. Have some students work the problems on the board for the class. All students should work the problems in their books.

Assignments

- Complete Lesson 28, Activities 2-5.
- Bring graph paper beginning with the next lesson.

Lesson 29

Concepts

- Coordinate plane
- Graphing points
- Rational exponents
- Radicals

Learning Objectives

The student will be able to:

- Describe the coordinate plane (Cartesian plane)
- Identify and name the four quadrants of the coordinate plane
- Graph ordered pairs on the coordinate plane

Materials Needed

- Student Book, Lesson 29
- Graph paper
- City road map showing grid street plan (A map of Rochester, MN, is especially helpful for this lesson.)

Teaching Tips

➢ Before this lesson, try to obtain a road map of the downtown Rochester, Minnesota area. This city labels its roads according to the coordinate plane. Center St. corresponds to the *x*-axis, and Broadway (Hwy 63) corresponds to the *y*-axis. Roads parallel to the *x*-axis (Center St.) are labeled streets, and roads parallel to the *y*-axis (Broadway) are labeled avenues. The roads in each quadrant are numbered, beginning at the origin (intersection of Center St. and Broadway) and going out toward the edge of town. Roads northeast of the origin are labeled NE and correspond to Quadrant I on the coordinate plane. Roads northwest of the origin are labeled NW and correspond to Quadrant II, etc.

Lesson 29

The Coordinate Plane

If two number lines are placed on a plane perpendicular to each other and intersect at point zero, they can be used to describe the location of any point on the plane. The grid that is formed is known as the **coordinate plane** or the **Cartesian plane**.

The horizontal number line is called the ***x*-axis**. Negative values are on the left, and positive values are on the right.

The vertical number line is called the ***y*-axis**. Negative values are below the *x*-axis, and positive values are above the *x*-axis.

The point where the two axes cross (the zeros) is called the **origin**.

Points on the plane are defined by a **coordinate** in the format (x, y), where x is the value on the x-axis, and y is the value on the y-axis.

The intersecting axes divide the plane into four quadrants. The diagram below shows the location of each quadrant, as well as the signs of x and y in each coordinate.

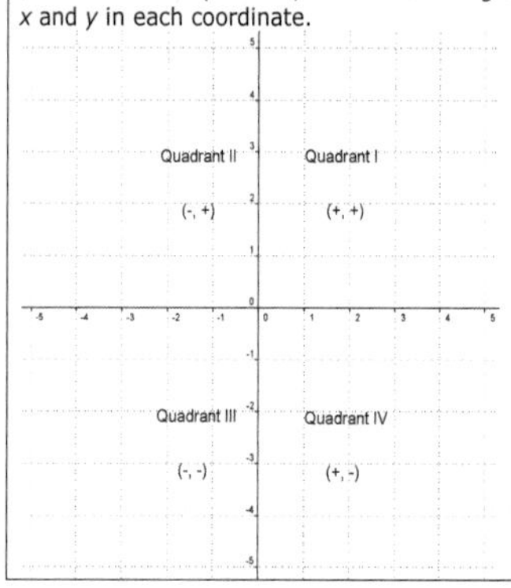

① **Classwork**

Give the coordinates for each point and identify the quadrant.

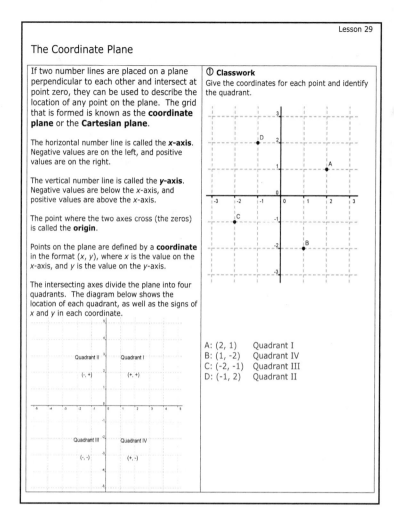

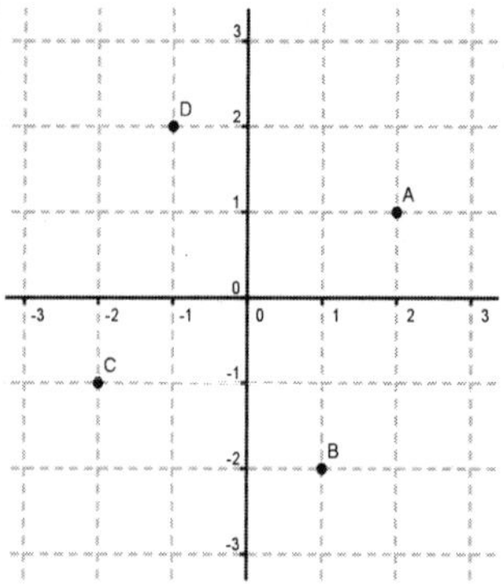

A: (2, 1) Quadrant I
B: (1, -2) Quadrant IV
C: (-2, -1) Quadrant III
D: (-1, 2) Quadrant II

Activities

② Graph each point and identify which quadrant it is in or if it is at the origin.

(1, 3) Quadrant I
(2, -1) Quadrant IV
(-3, 2) Quadrant II
(-1, -1) Quadrant III
(0, 0) Origin

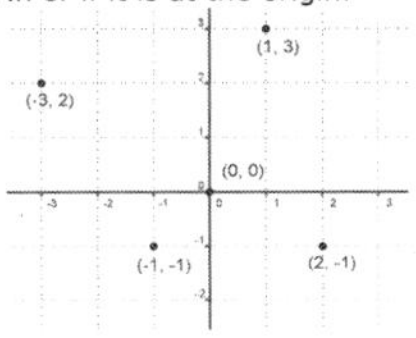

③ Graph the points on your own graph paper. Draw line segments between consecutive points. Draw a segment joining point *A* to point *J*.

A: (-4, -3)
B: (4, -3)
C: (4, 2)
D: (2, 4)
E: (-1, 4)
F: (-1, 5)
G: (-2, 5)
H: (-2, 4)
I: (-3, 4)
J: (-4, 2)

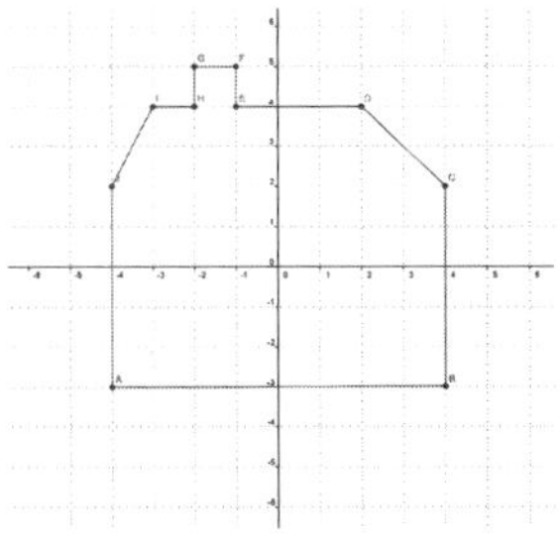

④ Solve.

$27^{\frac{1}{2}} =$

$\sqrt{27} = \sqrt{3^3} = 3\sqrt{3}$

$32^{\frac{1}{3}} =$

$\sqrt[3]{32} = \sqrt[3]{2^5} = 2\sqrt[3]{2^2} = 2\sqrt[3]{4}$

$16^{\frac{2}{3}} =$

$\sqrt[3]{16^2} = \sqrt[3]{16 \cdot 16} = \sqrt[3]{2^4 \cdot 2^4} =$
$2 \cdot 2\sqrt[3]{2 \cdot 2} = 4\sqrt[3]{4}$

$128^{\frac{2}{3}} =$

$\sqrt[3]{128^2} = \sqrt[3]{128 \cdot 128} = \sqrt[3]{2^7 \cdot 2^7} =$
$\sqrt[3]{2^{14}} = 2^4\sqrt[3]{2^2} = 16\sqrt[3]{4}$

$45^{\frac{2}{3}} =$

$\sqrt[3]{45^2} = \sqrt[3]{45 \cdot 45} = \sqrt[3]{3^2 \cdot 5 \cdot 3^2 \cdot 5} =$
$\sqrt[3]{3^4 \cdot 5^2} = 3\sqrt[3]{3 \cdot 25} = 3\sqrt[3]{75}$

$54^{\frac{2}{3}} =$

$\sqrt[3]{54^2} = \sqrt[3]{54 \cdot 54} = \sqrt[3]{2 \cdot 3^3 \cdot 2 \cdot 3^3} =$
$3 \cdot 3\sqrt[3]{2^2} = 9\sqrt[3]{4}$

Teaching Tips, Cont.

- Introduce the coordinate plane by showing students the map of Rochester, MN. Show them the origin (intersection of Center St. and Broadway) and the numbering pattern of the roads. Explain that the coordinate plane is set up in much the same way. Just like locations on a map can be identified by their addresses or intersections, points on a plane are also identified by their intersections.
- Teach the axes and origin of the coordinate plane from the teaching box. Tell the students that if arrows are drawn on the axes, they should only point in the positive direction. (To the right on the *x*-axis and up on the *y*-axis)
- Teach coordinate points from the teaching box. Explain that the first number in a coordinate point ALWAYS moves left or right from the origin, and the second number in a coordinate point ALWAYS moves up or down from the origin.
- Tell the students that the coordinate plane is also known as the Cartesian plane, after Rene Descartes, who created the coordinate plane.
- Complete the Classwork exercise. Have one student work the problem on the board for the class. All students should work the problem in their books.

Assignment

- Complete Lesson 29, Activities 2-4.

Lesson 30

Concepts

- Solving linear equations
- Graphing linear equations
- The coordinate plane
- Coordinate points

Learning Objectives

The student will be able to:

- Define *linear equation*
- Define *independent variable*
- Define *dependent variable*
- Solve linear equations for ordered pairs (x, y)
- Graph linear equations

Materials Needed

- Student Book, Lesson 30
- Worksheet 15
- Graph paper

Teaching Tips

- Review the coordinate plane. (See Lesson 29)
- Review solving algebraic equations. (See Lessons 16-17)
- Tell the students that so far, they have learned how to solve algebraic equations that have one variable. Now they are going to learn to solve algebraic equations that have two variables. Explain that two-variable equations are also called linear equations because they have multiple solutions that form a line when the points are connected on a coordinate plane.
- Teach the terms *independent variable* and *dependent variable* from the teaching box.

Linear Equations

So far, you have learned how to solve one-variable equations. These equations have exactly one solution. Some equations have an infinite number of solutions. These are **two-variable equations,** also called **linear equations**.

$2x - y = 3$ is a two-variable equation. To solve a two-variable equation, begin by rewriting the equation so that one variable is isolated on one side of the equal sign, and all other terms are on the other side of the equal sign.

$2x - y = 3$
$2x - 3 = y$

In this case, x is called the **independent variable,** because you can substitute any value for x. The **dependent variable** is y because its value depends on the value you substitute for x.

Once you have identified the independent and dependent variables, you can solve for values of those variable. Make a T-chart, with one variable on each side. Choose several values for the independent variable. Substitute each value into the equation and solve for the dependent variable. Solutions are written in coordinate format (x, y) for each solution combination.

x	y
0	$y = 2(0) - 3 = -3$
1	$y = 2(1) - 3 = -1$
2	$y = 2(2) - 3 = 1$
-1	$y = 2(-1) - 3 = -5$
-2	$y = 2(-2) - 3 = -7$

Possible solutions for this equation include (0, -3), (1, -1), (2, 1), (-1, -5), and (-2, -7)

① Classwork

Find 5 possible solutions for each equation.

$y = x$

x	y
0	$y = 0$
1	$y = 1$
2	$y = 2$
-1	$y = -1$
-2	$y = -2$

Possible solutions for this equation include (0, 0), (1, 1), (2, 2), (-1, -1), and (-2, -2)

$y = 2x - 1$

x	y
0	$y = 2(0) - 1 = -1$
1	$y = 2(1) - 1 = 1$
2	$y = 2(2) - 1 = 3$
-1	$y = 2(-1) - 1 = -3$
-2	$y = 2(-2) - 1 = -5$

Possible solutions for this equation include (0, -1), (1, 1), (2, 3), (-1, -3), and (-2, -5)

$y = 3(x + 1)$

x	y
0	$y = 3(0 + 1) = 3$
1	$y = 3(1 + 1) = 6$
2	$y = 3(2 + 1) = 9$
-1	$y = 3(-1 + 1) = 0$
-2	$y = 3(-2 + 1) = -3$

Possible solutions for this equation include (0, 3), (1, 6), (2, 9), (-1, 0), and (-2, -3)

Activities

② Solve each two-variable equation when $x = 5$.

$y = x - 2$
$y = 5 - 2$
$y = 3$

$y = 2x + 3$
$y = 2(5) + 3$
$y = 10 + 3$
$y = 13$

$y = 3(x + 1)$
$y = 3(5 + 1)$
$y = 3(6)$
$y = 18$

③ Find 5 possible solutions for each equation. Draw the graph of each equation.

$y = -2x$

x	y
0	$y = 0$
1	$y = -2$
2	$y = -4$
-1	$y = 2$
-2	$y = 4$

Possible solutions for this equation include (0, 0), (1, -2), (2, -4), (-1, 2), and (-2, 4)

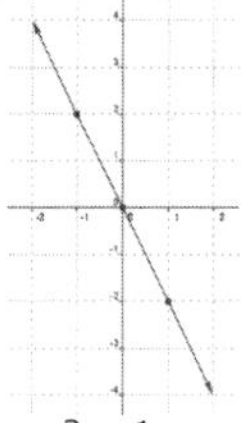

$y = 2x + 1$

x	y
0	$y = 2(0) + 1 = 1$
1	$y = 2(1) + 1 = 3$
2	$y = 2(2) + 1 = 5$
-1	$y = 2(-1) + 1 = -1$
-2	$y = 2(-2) + 1 = -3$

Possible solutions for this equation include (0, 1), (1, 3), (2, 5), (-1, -1), and (-2, -3)

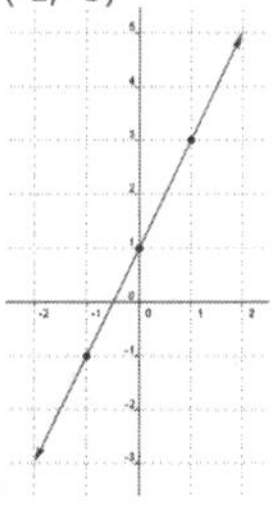

$y = x + 2$

x	y
0	$y = 0 + 2 = 2$
1	$y = 1 + 2 = 3$
2	$y = 2 + 2 = 4$
-1	$y = -1 + 2 = 1$
-2	$y = -2 + 2 = 0$

Possible solutions for this equation include (0, 2), (1, 3), (2, 4), (-1, 1), and (-2, 0)

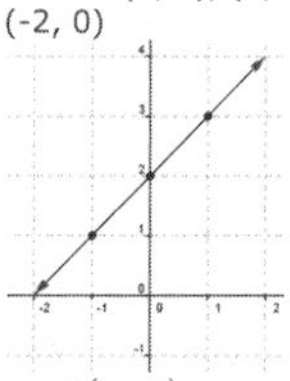

$y = 4(x - 1)$

x	y
0	$y = 4(0 - 1) = -4$
1	$y = 4(1 - 1) = 0$
2	$y = 4(2 - 1) = 4$
-1	$y = 4(-1 - 1) = -8$
-2	$y = 4(-2 - 1) = -12$

Possible solutions for this equation include (0, -4), (1, 0), (2, 4), (-1, -8), and (-2, -12)

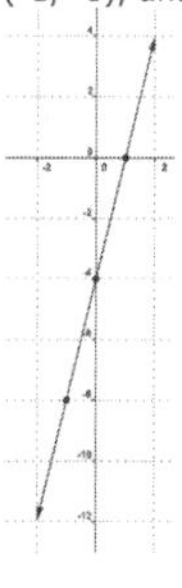

Graphing Linear Equations Worksheet 15

① Complete the chart to find 5 possible solutions for each equation. Draw the graph of each equation.

$y = -x + 1$

x	y
0	$y = 0 + 1 = 1$
1	$y = -1 + 1 = 0$
2	$y = -2 + 1 = -1$
-1	$y = 1 + 1 = 2$
-2	$y = 2 + 1 = 3$

Possible solutions for this equation include (0, 1), (1, 0), (2, -1), (-1, 2), and (-2, 3)

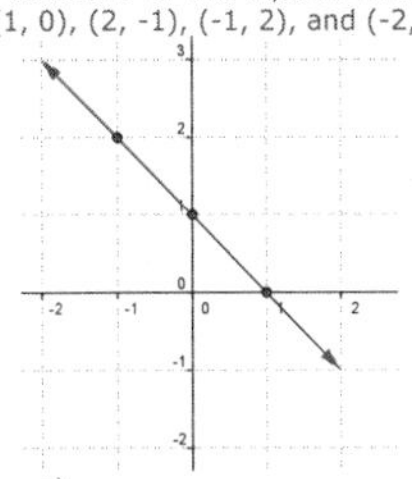

$y = 2x - 1$

x	y
0	$y = 0 - 1 = -1$
1	$y = 2 - 1 = 1$
2	$y = 4 - 1 = 3$
-1	$y = -2 - 1 = -3$
-2	$y = -4 - 1 = -5$

Possible solutions for this equation include (0, -1), (1, 1), (2, 3), (-1, -3), and (-2, -5)

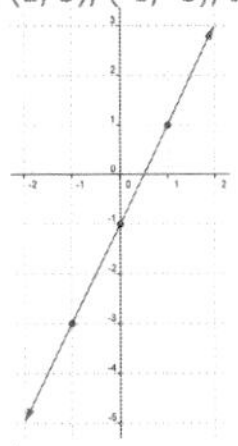

$y = 2(x + 1)$

x	y
0	$y = 2(0 + 1) = 2$
1	$y = 2(1 + 1) = 4$
2	$y = 2(2 + 1) = 6$
-1	$y = 2(-1 + 1) = 0$
-2	$y = 2(-2 + 1) = -2$

Possible solutions for this equation include (0, 2), (1, 4), (2, 6), (-1, 0), and (-2, -2)

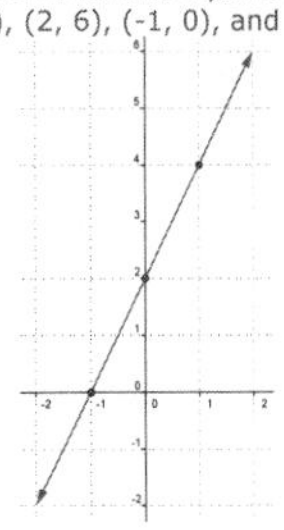

$y = 2(x - 1) + 1$

x	y
0	$y = 2(0 - 1) + 1 = -1$
1	$y = 2(1 - 1) + 1 = 1$
2	$y = 2(2 - 1) + 1 = 3$
-1	$y = 2(-1 - 1) + 1 = -3$
-2	$y = 2(-2 - 1) + 1 = -5$

Possible solutions for this equation include (0, -1), (1, 1), (2, 3), (-1, -3), and (-2, -5)

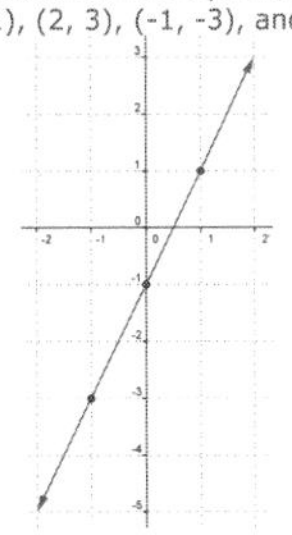

Teaching Tips, Cont.

- Teach how to solve linear equations from the teaching box. Tell the students that the easiest way to get points is to substitute numbers that are easy to work with for the independent variable. For example, 0, 1, and -1 are easy numbers to multiply by and will make solving the equation much faster.
- Show the students that a coordinate point can be obtained from each solution pair. Remind students that coordinate points are always written in the format (x, y) no matter which variable is the independent variable in the equation.
- Demonstrate how to graph the coordinate points on a graph and join them to form a line. Tell the students that if the points do not form a straight line, they have an error in their calculations.
- Complete the Classwork exercises. Have some students work the problems on the board for the class. All students should work the problems in their books.
- Review for Test 3 using worksheets 11-15. These worksheets were assigned in previous lessons.

Assignments

- Complete Lesson 30, Activities 2-3.
- Worksheet 15.
- Study for Test 3 (Lessons 18-27).

Test 3

Testing Objectives

The student will:

- Solve algebraic equations with fractions
- Solve algebraic equations with decimals
- Solve algebraic equations with fractions and decimals
- Solve algebraic equations with square roots
- Solve algebraic equations with absolute values
- Identify extraneous solutions
- Rationalize denominators
- Multiply radicals
- Divide radicals
- Convert numbers between scientific notation and standard form

Materials Needed

- Test 3
- *It's College Test Prep Time!* from Student Book
- Exploring Math through ... Multi-use Paths from Student Book

Teaching Tips

➢ Administer Test 3, allowing the students 30-40 minutes to complete the test.

➢ When all students are finished taking the test, introduce the College Test Prep Time from the student book. This page may be completed in class or assigned as homework.

➢ Have students read the Exploring Math feature for Lessons 31-40.

Test 3

① Solve each algebraic equation. **6 points**

$\frac{7}{x}+\frac{9}{x^2}=\frac{4}{x}+\frac{27}{x^2}$

$\frac{7}{\cancel{x}}\left(x^{\cancel{2}}\right)+\frac{9}{\cancel{x^2}}\left(\cancel{x^2}\right)=\frac{4}{\cancel{x}}\left(x^{\cancel{2}}\right)+\frac{27}{\cancel{x^2}}\left(\cancel{x^2}\right)$

$7x+9=4x+27$

$3x+9=27$

$3x=18$

$x=6$

$3(0.06x-1)=3(0.04x+0.7)$

$0.18x-3=0.12x+2.1$

$0.18x(100)-3(100)=0.12x(100)+2.1(100)$

$18x-300=12x+210$

$6x-300=210$

$6x=510$

$x=85$

Note: Students may begin by dividing both sides by 3 to simplify. The final answer remains the same.

$\frac{1}{5}x-3=1.8$

$5(\frac{1}{5}x)-5(3)=5(1.8)$

$x-15=9$

$x=24$

$3-\frac{4}{x}=\frac{5}{x}$

$3(x)-\frac{4}{\cancel{x}}(\cancel{x})=\frac{5}{\cancel{x}}(\cancel{x})$

$3x-4=5$

$3x=9$

$x=3$

$8(x+0.6)=3(x-4.7)+0.9$

$8x+4.8=3x-14.1+0.9$

$8x(10)+4.8(10)=3x(10)-14.1(10)+0.9(10)$

$80x+48=30x-141+9$

$50x+48=-132$

$50x=-180$

$x=-\frac{180}{50}=-\frac{18}{5}=-3.6$

$\frac{3}{4}x+\frac{2}{3}=1.2$

$\cancel{12}^3\left(\frac{3}{\cancel{4}}x\right)+\cancel{12}^4\left(\frac{2}{\cancel{3}}\right)=12(1.2)$

$9x+8=14.4$

$10(9x)+10(8)=10(14.4)$

$90x+80=144$

$90x=64$

$x=\frac{64}{90}=0.7\overline{1}$

Either answer is acceptable

② Solve and check. Identify any extraneous solutions. **8 points**

$\sqrt{7x-20}+3=9$

$\sqrt{7x-20}=6$

$\left(\sqrt{7x-20}\right)^2=(6)^2$

$7x-20=36$

$7x=56$

$x=8$

check:

$\sqrt{7(8)-20}+3=9$

$\sqrt{56-20}+3=9$

$\sqrt{36}+3=9$

$6+3=9$

$\sqrt{7x+43}+12=4$

$\sqrt{7x+43}=-8$

$\left(\sqrt{7x+43}\right)^2=(-8)^2$

$7x+43=64$

$7x=21$

$x=3$

check:

$\sqrt{7(3)+43}+12=4$

$\sqrt{21+43}+12=4$

$\sqrt{64}+12=4$

$8+12\neq 4$ extraneous

$|5x-3|-5=-4x+19$

$|5x-3|=-4x+24$

$5x-3=-4x+24$ or $5x-3=-(-4x+24)$

$9x=27$ $\quad$ $5x-3=4x-24$

$x=3$ $\quad$ $x=-21$

check:

$|5(3)-3|-5=-4(3)+19$

$|15-3|-5=-12+19$

$12-5=7$

$|5(-21)-3|-5=-4(-21)+19$

$|-105-3|-5=84+19$

$108-5=103$

Test 3

③ Rationalize the denominator. **4 points**

$\frac{5}{\sqrt{13}}$

$\frac{5}{\sqrt{13}}\cdot\frac{\sqrt{13}}{\sqrt{13}}=\frac{5\sqrt{13}}{13}$

$\frac{6}{\sqrt[4]{24}}$

$\frac{6}{\sqrt[4]{2^3\cdot 3}}\cdot\frac{\sqrt[4]{2^{4-3}\cdot 3^{4-1}}}{\sqrt[4]{2^{4-3}\cdot 3^{4-1}}}=\frac{6}{\sqrt[4]{2^3\cdot 3}}\cdot\frac{\sqrt[4]{2\cdot 3^3}}{\sqrt[4]{2\cdot 3^3}}=$

$\frac{6\sqrt[4]{54}}{\sqrt[4]{2^4\cdot 3^4}}=\frac{\cancel{6}\sqrt[4]{54}}{\cancel{2\cdot 3}}=\sqrt[4]{54}$

$\frac{3\sqrt{11}}{8\sqrt{5}}$

$\frac{3\sqrt{11}}{8\sqrt{5}}\cdot\frac{\sqrt{5}}{\sqrt{5}}=\frac{3\sqrt{55}}{8\cdot 5}=\frac{3\sqrt{55}}{40}$

$\frac{8}{\sqrt[3]{48}}$

$\frac{8}{\sqrt[3]{3\cdot 4^2}}\cdot\frac{\sqrt[3]{3^{3-1}\cdot 4^{3-2}}}{\sqrt[3]{3^{3-1}\cdot 4^{3-2}}}=\frac{8\sqrt[3]{3^2\cdot 4}}{\sqrt[3]{3^3\cdot 4^3}}=$

$\frac{{}_2\cancel{8}\sqrt[3]{36}}{3\cdot\cancel{4}}=\frac{2\sqrt[3]{36}}{3}$

④ Solve. **8 points**

$42\sqrt{10}\div 7\sqrt{5}$

$\frac{\cancel{42}^6\sqrt{10}}{\cancel{7}\sqrt{5}}=\frac{6\sqrt{\cancel{10}^2}}{\sqrt{\cancel{5}}}=6\sqrt{2}$

$60\sqrt{30}\div 15\sqrt{6}$

$\frac{\cancel{60}^4\sqrt{30}}{\cancel{15}\sqrt{6}}=\frac{4\sqrt{\cancel{30}^5}}{\sqrt{\cancel{6}}}=4\sqrt{5}$

$\sqrt{11}\left(3+\sqrt{7}\right)$

$3\sqrt{11}+\sqrt{11\cdot 7}=3\sqrt{11}+\sqrt{77}$

$\left(2\sqrt{5}+9\sqrt{10}\right)\div\sqrt{3}$

$\frac{2\sqrt{5}}{\sqrt{3}}+\frac{9\sqrt{10}}{\sqrt{3}}=\frac{2\sqrt{5}}{\sqrt{3}}\cdot\frac{\sqrt{3}}{\sqrt{3}}+\frac{9\sqrt{10}}{\sqrt{3}}\cdot\frac{\sqrt{3}}{\sqrt{3}}=$

$\frac{2\sqrt{5\cdot 3}}{\sqrt{3\cdot 3}}+\frac{9\sqrt{10\cdot 3}}{\sqrt{3\cdot 3}}=\frac{2\sqrt{15}}{3}+\frac{\cancel{9}^3\sqrt{30}}{\cancel{3}}=$

$\frac{2\sqrt{15}}{3}+3\sqrt{30}$ or $\frac{2\sqrt{15}+9\sqrt{30}}{3}$

$\sqrt{6}\left(4+\sqrt{3}\right)$

$4\sqrt{6}+\sqrt{6\cdot 3}=4\sqrt{6}+\sqrt{2\cdot 3\cdot 3}=$

$4\sqrt{6}+3\sqrt{2}$

$\sqrt{18}\left(3+\sqrt{2}\right)$

$3\sqrt{18}+\sqrt{18\cdot 2}=3\sqrt{2\cdot 3\cdot 3}+\sqrt{2\cdot 3\cdot 3\cdot 2}=$

$3\cdot 3\sqrt{2}+2\cdot 3=9\sqrt{2}+6$ or $6+9\sqrt{2}$

$\left(7\sqrt{24}+5\sqrt{42}\right)\div\sqrt{3}$

$\frac{7\sqrt{\cancel{24}^8}}{\cancel{\sqrt{3}}}+\frac{5\sqrt{\cancel{42}^{14}}}{\cancel{\sqrt{3}}}=7\sqrt{8}+5\sqrt{14}=$

$7\sqrt{2^3}+5\sqrt{14}=14\sqrt{2}+5\sqrt{14}$

$\sqrt{5}\left(9+\sqrt{10}\right)$

$9\sqrt{5}+\sqrt{5\cdot 10}=9\sqrt{5}+\sqrt{2\cdot 5\cdot 5}=$

$9\sqrt{5}+5\sqrt{2}$

⑤ Complete the chart to show scientific notation and standard form. **8 points**

Scientific notation	Standard form
1.209×10^6	1,209,000
5.00395×10^3	5003.95
9.31826×10^{-5}	0.0000931826
6.4972347×10^{-2}	0.064972347

Standard form	Scientific notation
83,080,000,000	8.308×10^{10}
2,000,430,000,000	2.00043×10^{12}
0.00005007	5.007×10^{-5}
0.0000000002	2.0×10^{-10}

34 points total

It's College Test Prep Time!

1. What number is a solution of both equations shown below?

   $|7x-21|-19=2x-15$

   $|4x-3|+5=-x+27$

   A. -19
   B. -6
   C. 5
   D. 17
   E. No common solution

   See Lesson 23 Activity 4 and Lesson 27 Activity 5 for a detailed solution. The problems are similar in format with some numbers changed. Both problems have 5 as the answer in these lessons as well.

2. What is the value of $|2x^2-75|$ when $x=6$?

   A. -69
   B. -39
   C. -3
   D. 3 $\quad |2(6)^2-75|=|2(36)-75|=|72-75|=|-3|=3$
   E. 39

3. If $a \& b=(a+2b)^2-(2a-b)^2$, what is the value of $\sqrt{3} \& \sqrt{3}$?

   A. 0
   B. 3
   C. 6
   D. 12 $\quad (\sqrt{3}+2\sqrt{3})^2-(2\sqrt{3}-\sqrt{3})^2=(3\sqrt{3})^2-(\sqrt{3})^2$
   E. 24 $\quad =(9)(3)-3=27-3=24$

4. If x>0, which of the following are equivalent to $x^{\frac{4}{3}}$?

   I. $\sqrt[3]{x^4}$ $\quad =\sqrt[3]{x\cdot x\cdot x\cdot x}=x\sqrt[3]{x}$
   II. $\sqrt[4]{x^3}$
   III. $x\sqrt[3]{x}$

   A. None
   B. I only
   C. II only
   D. III only
   E. I and III only

Exploring Math through... Multi-use Paths

Multi-use paths are designed in recreational areas for use by walkers, runners, cyclists, horseback riders, wheelchair users, roller skaters, etc. Most multi-use paths have posted regulations regarding which activities are or are not allowed on the path. These include which users must yield the right-of-way to others.

Math is especially important when considering a multi-use path for a particular activity. People on foot can navigate certain terrain easier than people on bicycles, roller skates, or in wheelchairs. The angle of ascent or descent can make the difference between an easy stroll or ride and one that becomes impossible. If the incline is too steep, all users may become fatigued and the path is no longer enjoyable by any group.

Potential speed is another issue that must be considered on a multi-use path. Runners may enjoy a long down-hill stretch, but if the path is too steep for too long, a person on skates or in a wheelchair may have a difficult time maintaining control. Even a slight downhill slope over a long distance can allow anyone on wheels to gain increasing momentum with little effort.

Angles and curves also play a role in multi-use paths. While some turns in the path may provide different scenery and a change from a monotonous straight line, a curve that is too sharp can be dangerous for a cyclist. Imagine a bicyclist trying to navigate a path with switchback curves!

Assignments

- Complete *It's College Test Prep Time!*
- Read Exploring Math through ... Multi-use Paths

Lesson 31

Concepts

- Slope
- Linear equations
- Coordinate points
- Graphing lines

Learning Objectives

The student will be able to:

- Define *slope*
- Calculate the slope when given two points
- Calculate the slope of a linear equation
- Identify the slope of horizontal and vertical lines

Materials Needed

- Student Book, Lesson 31
- Graph paper

Teaching Tips

- Define *slope* from the teaching box. Explain that *slope* is the same thing as *grade* when used to describe the incline of roads and paths.
- Ask the students where they have seen the word *slope* or *grade* used in this context. (Mountain road signs often warn truck drivers of a steep grade and tell them to use a lower gear; the grade of a ski slope affects its difficulty; bike paths and hiking trails are often described in terms of their grade.)
- Teach the formula for finding slope when two points are known. While the students are not required to memorize the formula, they must understand the concept well enough to do the work without the aid of a formula.

Lesson 31

Slope

The **slope** of a line is the ratio of its vertical change to its horizontal change. It is noted by the letter m and is described as $m = \frac{\text{rise}}{\text{run}}$.

The formula for slope is $m = \frac{y_2 - y_1}{x_2 - x_1}$, where (x_1, y_1) and (x_2, y_2) are two points on the line.

Find the slope of the line $-2x + y + 3 = 0$

Rewrite the equation to isolate y.

$y = 2x - 3$

Next, choose two values for x and solve for their corresponding values of y. Express the solution as coordinate points.

Let $x = 0$

$y = 2(0) - 3 = -3$

The first point (x_1, y_1) is (0, -3).

Let x = 1

y = 2(1) - 3 = 2 - 3 = -1

The second point (x_2, y_2) is (1, -1).

Finally, substitute the values from the coordinates into the formula for slope.

$m = \frac{y_2 - y_1}{x_2 - x_1} = \frac{-1-(-3)}{1-0} = \frac{2}{1} = 2$

This means the line rises two units for every one unit that it moves forward horizontally.

The slope of a horizontal line is 0.
A vertical line has no slope.

① Classwork

Find the slope of the line joining the points.

(7, 3) and (7, 8)

$m = \frac{8-3}{7-7} = \frac{5}{0} =$ no slope

(1, 2) and (4, 2)

$m = \frac{2-2}{4-1} = \frac{0}{3} = 0$

Find the slope of each line.

$4x + y + 1 = 0$

$y = -4x - 1$

(0, -1) and (1, -5)

$m = \frac{y_2 - y_1}{x_2 - x_1} = \frac{-5-(-1)}{1-0} = \frac{-4}{1} = -4$

$x + y - 2 = 0$

$y = -x + 2$

(0, 2) and (1, 1)

$m = \frac{y_2 - y_1}{x_2 - x_1} = \frac{1-2}{1-0} = \frac{-1}{1} = -1$

$x - 2y + 5 = 0$

$2y = x + 5$

$y = \frac{x+5}{2}$

(1, 3) and (3, 4)

$m = \frac{y_2 - y_1}{x_2 - x_1} = \frac{4-3}{3-1} = \frac{1}{2}$

$3x + 2y - 1 = 0$

$2y = -3x + 1$

$y = \frac{-3x+1}{2}$

(1, -1) and (3, -4)

$m = \frac{y_2 - y_1}{x_2 - x_1} = \frac{-4-(-1)}{3-1} = \frac{-3}{2}$

Activities

② Find the slope of the line joining the points.

(4, 1) and (6, 2)

$m = \frac{2-1}{6-4} = \frac{1}{2}$

(5, 3) and (3, 2)

$m = \frac{2-3}{3-5} = \frac{-1}{-2} = \frac{1}{2}$

(3, 2) and (3, 8)

$m = \frac{8-2}{3-3} = \frac{6}{0} =$ no slope

(1, -1) and (4, -2)

$m = \frac{-2-(-1)}{4-1} = \frac{-1}{3} = -\frac{1}{3}$

(7, -3) and (2, -8)

$m = \frac{-8-(-3)}{2-7} = \frac{-5}{-5} = 1$

(-1, 2) and (4, 2)

$m = \frac{2-2}{4-(-1)} = \frac{0}{5} = 0$

(-7, -3) and (1, 2)

$m = \frac{2-(-3)}{1-(-7)} = \frac{5}{8}$

(1, -2) and (-4, 2)

$m = \frac{2-(-2)}{-4-1} = \frac{4}{-5} = -\frac{4}{5}$

(7, 3) and (-3, 3)

$m = \frac{3-3}{-3-7} = \frac{0}{-10} = 0$

(-1, -2) and (-4, 2)

$m = \frac{2-(-2)}{-4-(-1)} = \frac{4}{-3} = -\frac{4}{3}$

Note regarding mountain roads:

Cars and trucks should adjust their speed and use a lower gear whenever the road grade is 6% or greater. Heavy trucks will often use a lower gear at lower grades when they are carrying heavy loads because gravity causes them to accelerate faster.

A 6% road grade means it has a slope of $\frac{6}{100} = \frac{3}{50}$ or greater.

Mountain roads in the western United States are generally no greater than a 6% grade. Mountain roads in the eastern United States tend to be much steeper. Grades up to 10% are common, while some locations have grades as high as 15%.

③ Find the slope of each line.

$x + y + 2 = 0$
$y = -x - 2$
(0, -2) and (1, -3)
$m = \frac{y_2 - y_1}{x_2 - x_1} = \frac{-3-(-2)}{1-0} = \frac{-1}{1} = -1$

$2x + y - 3 = 0$
$y = -2x + 3$
(0, 3) and (1, 1)
$m = \frac{y_2 - y_1}{x_2 - x_1} = \frac{1-3}{1-0} = \frac{-2}{1} = -2$

$-x + y - 1 = 0$
$y = x + 1$
(0, 1) and (1, 2)
$m = \frac{y_2 - y_1}{x_2 - x_1} = \frac{2-1}{1-0} = \frac{1}{1} = 1$

$-3x + y + 2 = 0$
$y = 3x - 2$
(0, -2) and (1, 1)
$m = \frac{y_2 - y_1}{x_2 - x_1} = \frac{1-(-2)}{1-0} = \frac{3}{1} = 3$

$-2x + y + 1 = 0$
$y = 2x - 1$
(0, -1) and (1, 1)
$m = \frac{y_2 - y_1}{x_2 - x_1} = \frac{1-(-1)}{1-0} = \frac{2}{1} = 2$

$3x + y - 5 = 0$
$y = -3x + 5$
(0, 5) and (1, 2)
$m = \frac{y_2 - y_1}{x_2 - x_1} = \frac{2-5}{1-0} = \frac{-3}{1} = -3$

$2x + 2y + 3 = 0$
$2y = -2x - 3$
$y = -x - \frac{3}{2}$
$\left(0, -\frac{3}{2}\right)$ and $\left(1, -\frac{5}{2}\right)$
$m = \frac{y_2 - y_1}{x_2 - x_1} = \frac{-\frac{5}{2}-\left(-\frac{3}{2}\right)}{1-0} = \frac{-1}{1} = -1$

$x + 2y + 2 = 0$
$2y = -x - 2$
$y = -\frac{1}{2}x - 1$
(0, -1) and (2, -2)
$m = \frac{y_2 - y_1}{x_2 - x_1} = \frac{-2-(-1)}{2-0} = \frac{-1}{2}$

$2x + 3y + 6 = 0$
$3y = -2x - 6$
$y = -\frac{2}{3}x - 2$
(0, -2) and (3, -4)
$m = \frac{y_2 - y_1}{x_2 - x_1} = \frac{-4-(-2)}{3-0} = \frac{-2}{3}$

④ Graph each of the equations from Activity ③ on your own graph paper.

$x + y + 2 = 0$

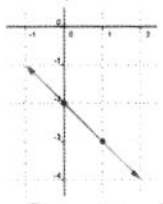

$2x + y - 3 = 0$

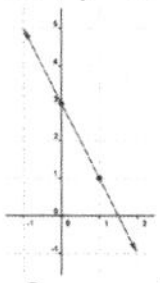

$-x + y - 1 = 0$

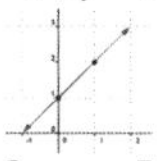

$-3x + y + 2 = 0$

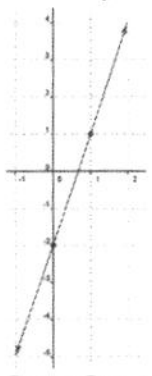

$-2x + y + 1 = 0$

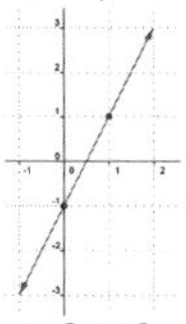

$3x + y - 5 = 0$

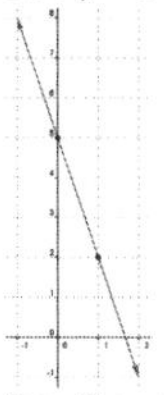

$2x + 2y + 3 = 0$

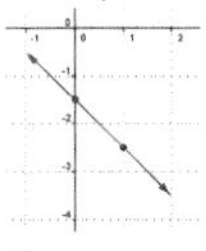

$x + 2y + 2 = 0$

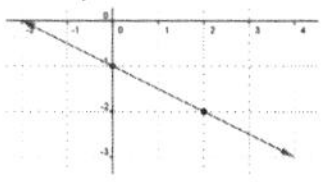

$2x + 3y + 6 = 0$

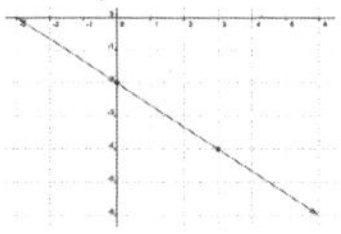

⑤ Simplify.

$\left(5^2 - \left(1^2 - 6^2\right)\right) \div (2 - 7) =$

$\left(25 - (1 - 36)\right) \div (-5) = \left(25 - (-35)\right) \div (-5) = (25 + 35) \div (-5) = 60 \div (-5) = -12$

Teaching Tips, Cont.

- Review linear equations. (See Lesson 30)
- Teach how to find the slope of a linear equation by solving for coordinate points and applying the slope formula.
- Tell the students that the slope of a horizontal line is zero. This means that the line has zero rise no matter how far horizontally the line moves. This is not the same thing as saying the line has no slope.
- Tell the students that a vertical line has no slope. The line has unlimited rise, but has zero movement horizontally. In the formula for slope, the denominator represents the horizontal movement. When there is no horizontal movement, the denominator is zero. Because you cannot divide by zero, there is no slope.
- Make sure all students understand the difference between zero slope (horizontal lines) and no slope (vertical lines).
- Complete the Classwork exercises. Have some students work the problems on the board for the class and explain their answers. All students should work the problems in their books.

Assignment

- Complete Lesson 31, Activities 2-5.

Lesson 32

Concepts

- y-intercepts
- Slope-intercept form
- Slope
- Graphing linear equations
- Radicals
- Extraneous solutions

Learning Objectives

The student will be able to:

- Define *y-intercept*
- Identify the slope and y-intercept of a linear equation
- Write linear equations in slope-intercept form

Materials Needed

- Student Book, Lesson 32
- Graph paper
- Worksheet 16

Teaching Tips

- Have students complete Worksheet 16 in class. This may be for added practice of earlier topics, or graded as a quiz, if desired.
- Review slope. (See Lesson 31)
- Review solving linear equations for coordinate points. (See Lesson 30)
- Tell the students that there is a much faster way of getting points to graph a linear equation.
- Define *y-intercept* from the teaching box. Ask the students what the value of x is at the point the graph crosses the y-axis. (0)

Graphing Linear Equations: Slope-Intercept Form

The ***y*-intercept** of a graph is the point at which the graph crosses the y-axis. The value of x is zero, making the coordinate appear in the format $(0, y)$. The y-intercept is represented by the letter b.

To find the y-intercept of a line, set $x = 0$ and solve for y.

Find the y-intercept of the line $-2x + y + 3 = 0$.
Begin by rewriting the equation to isolate y on one side of the equal sign.
$y = 2x - 3$

Next, substitute 0 for x and solve for the corresponding value of y.

Let $x = 0$
$y = 2(0) - 3 = -3$
The y-intercept is -3.

Look back at the example in Lesson 31. You found the slope of this equation to be $m = 2$. Now notice how the equation looked when you isolated y on one side of the equal sign.
$y = 2x - 3$
This equation is in the **slope-intercept form** $y = mx + b$, where m is the slope and b is the y-intercept. Any time you solve an equation for y, you know both the slope and the y-intercept.

① **Classwork**
Rewrite each equation in slope-intercept form. Give the slope and y-intercept of each equation.

$4x + y + 2 = 0$
$y = -4x - 2$
$m = -4$
$b = -2$

$3x + y - 5 = 0$
$y = -3x + 5$
$m = -3$
$b = 5$

$x - 2y + 6 = 0$
$2y = x + 6$
$y = \frac{x+6}{2}$
$y = \frac{1}{2}x + 3$
$m = \frac{1}{2}$
$b = 3$

$2x + 3y - 6 = 0$
$3y = -2x + 6$
$y = \frac{-2x+6}{3}$
$y = \frac{-2}{3}x + 2$
$m = \frac{-2}{3}$
$b = 2$

Activities

② Rewrite each equation in slope-intercept form. Give the slope and y-intercept of each equation.

$x + y - 4 = 0$ $y = -x + 4$ $m = -1$ $b = 4$	$2x + y - 6 = 0$ $y = -2x + 6$ $m = -2$ $b = 6$	$-4x + y - 3 = 0$ $y = 4x + 3$ $m = 4$ $b = 3$
$-5x + y - 3 = 0$ $y = 5x + 3$ $m = 5$ $b = 3$	$-3x + y + 1 = 0$ $y = 3x - 1$ $m = 3$ $b = -1$	$7x + y - 9 = 0$ $y = -7x + 9$ $m = -7$ $b = 9$
$4x + 2y + 1 = 0$ $2y = -4x - 1$ $y = -2x - \frac{1}{2}$ $m = -2$ $b = -\frac{1}{2}$	$x + 3y + 6 = 0$ $3y = -x - 6$ $y = -\frac{1}{3}x - 2$ $m = -\frac{1}{3}$ $b = -2$	$4x + 3y + 12 = 0$ $3y = -4x - 12$ $y = -\frac{4}{3}x - 4$ $m = -\frac{4}{3}$ $b = -4$

③ Write an equation having the given slope and y-intercept. Graph it on your own graph paper.

$m = 1$
$b = 3$
$y = x + 3$

$m = -1$
$b = 2$
$y = -x + 2$

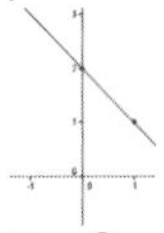

$m = 2$
$b = 2$
$y = 2x + 2$

$m = 3$
$b = -2$
$y = 3x - 2$

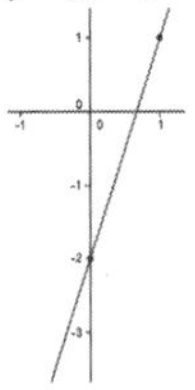

$m = -3$
$b = -1$
$y = -3x - 1$

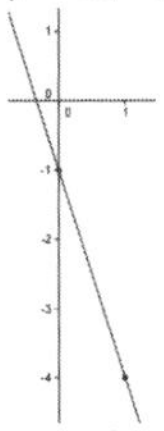

$m = -2$
$b = 3$
$y = -2x + 3$

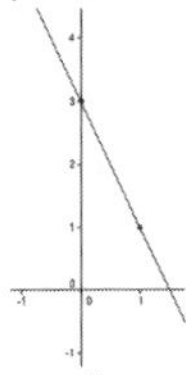

$m = -\frac{1}{2}$
$b = 2$
$y = -\frac{1}{2}x + 2$

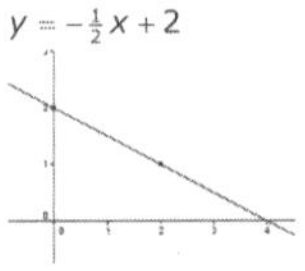

$m = -\frac{3}{2}$
$b = 1$
$y = -\frac{3}{2}x + 1$

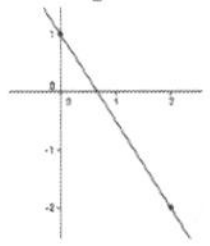

$m = \frac{3}{2}$
$b = -3$
$y = \frac{3}{2}x - 3$

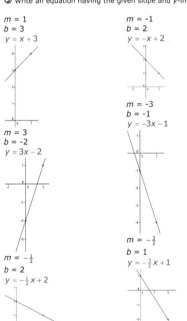

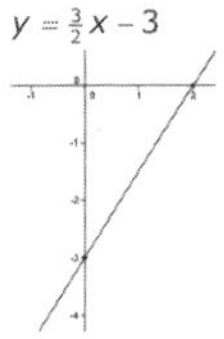

④ Find all possible solutions. Identify any extraneous solutions.

$\sqrt{-3x - 5} + 3 = 11$

$\sqrt{-3x - 5} = 8$
$\left(\sqrt{-3x - 5}\right)^2 = 8^2$
$-3x - 5 = 64$
$-3x = 69$
$x = -23$

check:
$\sqrt{-3(-23) - 5} + 3 = 11$
$\sqrt{69 - 5} + 3 = 11$
$\sqrt{64} + 3 = 11$
$8 + 3 = 11$

$\sqrt{-5x + 6} + 13 = 4$

$\sqrt{-5x + 6} = -9$
$\left(\sqrt{-5x + 6}\right)^2 = (-9)^2$
$-5x + 6 = 81$
$-5x = 75$
$x = -15$

check:
$\sqrt{-5(-15) + 6} + 13 = 4$
$\sqrt{75 + 6} + 13 = 4$
$\sqrt{81} + 13 = 4$
$9 + 13 \neq 4$ extraneous

Graphing Linear Equations Worksheet 16

① Complete the chart to find 5 possible solutions for each equation. Draw the graph of each equation.

$y = -2x + 3$

x	y
0	$y = 0 + 3 = 3$
1	$y = -2 + 3 = 1$
2	$y = -4 + 3 = -1$
-1	$y = 2 + 3 = 5$
-2	$y = 4 + 3 = 7$

Possible solutions for this equation include (0, 3), (1, 1), (2, -1), (-1, 5), and (-2, 7)

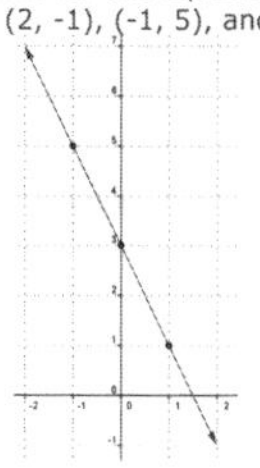

$y = 3x - 4$

x	y
0	$y = 0 - 4 = -4$
1	$y = 3 - 4 = -1$
2	$y = 6 - 4 = 2$
-1	$y = -3 - 4 = -7$
-2	$y = -6 - 4 = -10$

Possible solutions for this equation include (0, -4), (1, -1), (2, 2), (-1, -7), and (-2, -10)

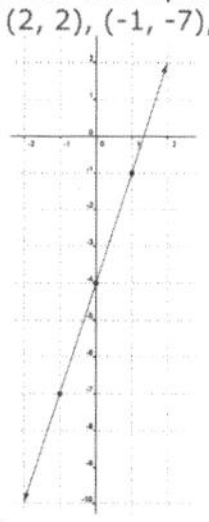

$y = 2(x - 2)$

x	y
0	$y = 2(0 - 2) = -4$
1	$y = 2(1 - 2) = -2$
2	$y = 2(2 - 2) = 0$
-1	$y = 2(-1 - 2) = -6$
-2	$y = 2(-2 - 2) = -8$

Possible solutions for this equation include (0, -4), (1, -2), (2, 0), (-1, -6), and (-2, -8)

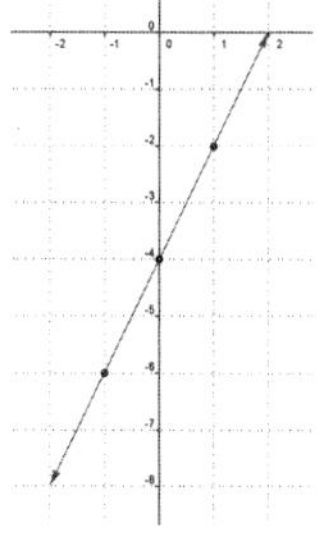

$y = 2(3 - x) - 3$

x	y
0	$y = 2(3 - 0) - 3 = 3$
1	$y = 2(3 - 1) - 3 = 1$
2	$y = 2(3 - 2) - 3 = -1$
-1	$y = 2(3 + 1) - 3 = 5$
-2	$y = 2(3 + 2) - 3 = 7$

Possible solutions for this equation include (0, 3), (1, 1), (2, -1), (-1, 5), and (-2, 7)

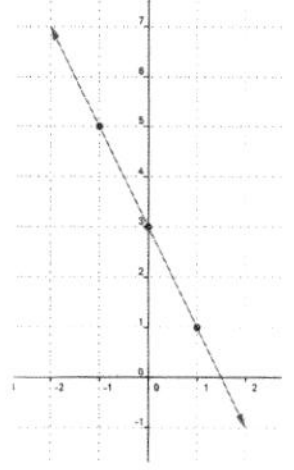

Teaching Tips, Cont.

- Explain that since the value of x is 0 where the graph crosses the y-axis, you can easily find the coordinate of the y-intercept by setting $x = 0$ and solving for y.
- Teach the slope-intercept form of a linear equation from the teaching box. Show the students that the y-intercept coordinate is a solution. Tell the students that they must memorize the forms of linear equations that are presented in this book.
- Point out the sample problem from the teaching box. It is the same sample problem from Lesson 31. Students should recognize the slope in the formula is the same as the slope they found in that problem in the previous lesson.
- Complete the Classwork exercises. Have some students work the problems on the board for the class and explain their answers. All students should work the problems in their books.

Assignment

- Complete Lesson 32, Activities 2-4.

Lesson 33

Concepts

- Point-slope form
- Slope-intercept form
- Graphing linear equations
- Real world math

Learning Objectives

The student will be able to:

- Write an equation of a line when given the slope and one point on the line
- Draw the graph of a line when given the slope and one point on the line
- Convert linear equations from point-slope form to slope-intercept form

Materials Needed

- Student Book, Lesson 33
- Graph paper
- Worksheet 17

Teaching Tips

- ➢ Review slope-intercept form. (See Lesson 32)
- ➢ Ask the students if there is a way to get an equation of a line if they know the slope and a point that is not on the *y*-axis. (There is, but not with what they have learned so far.)
- ➢ Teach the point-slope form of a linear equation from the teaching box. Emphasize that the coordinates from the points are substituted for the variables with subscripts.

Graphing Linear Equations: Point-Slope Form

So far you have learned to write the equation of a line when you know its slope and *y*-intercept. However, there will be times when you know the slope and one or more points on the graph, but not necessarily the *y*-intercept. In this situation, you can use a different formula for finding the equation of a line.

The point-slope form of a linear equation is used when at least one point and the slope of a line are known.

Use the formula $y - y_1 = m(x - x_1)$ where m is the slope of the line and (x_1, y_1) is a known point on the line. Any equation in point-slope form can be rewritten in slope-intercept form using the properties of equality to make graphing easier.

Find an equation of a line with slope 2 that passes through the point (1, 5).
The variable m represents the slope, so m = 2.
The point (x_1, y_1) is (1, 5), so the equation of the line is $y - 5 = 2(x - 1)$.

Rewrite the above equation in slope-intercept form.
$y - 5 = 2(x - 1)$
$y - 5 = 2x - 2$
$y = 2x + 3$

① Classwork
Write the point-slope form of the equation of a line. Rewrite each equation in slope-intercept form.

$m = 3$
(2, 1)

$y - 1 = 3(x - 2)$
$y - 1 = 3x - 6$
$y = 3x - 5$

$m = -2$
(3, 4)

$y - 4 = -2(x - 3)$
$y - 4 = -2x + 6$
$y = -2x + 10$

$m = 4$
(-1, -2)

$y - (-2) = 4(x - (-1))$
$y + 2 = 4(x + 1)$
$y + 2 = 4x + 4$
$y = 4x + 2$

Activities

② Write the point-slope form and slope-intercept form of the equation of a line.

$m = 1$ (4, 3) $y - 3 = 1(x - 4)$ $y - 3 = x - 4$ $y = x - 1$	$m = 2$ (1, -2) $y - (-2) = 2(x - 1)$ $y + 2 = 2x - 2$ $y = 2x - 4$	$m = -2$ (1, 3) $y - 3 = -2(x - 1)$ $y - 3 = -2x + 2$ $y = -2x + 5$
$m = -3$ (1, 4) $y - 4 = -3(x - 1)$ $y - 4 = -3x + 3$ $y = -3x + 7$	$m = 3$ (-2, 2) $y - 2 = 3(x - (-2))$ $y - 2 = 3(x + 2)$ $y - 2 = 3x + 6$ $y = 3x + 8$	$m = -3$ (-2, -2) $y - (-2) = -3(x - (-2))$ $y + 2 = -3(x + 2)$ $y + 2 = -3x - 6$ $y = -3x - 8$

③ Graph each equation from Activity ②.

$y = x - 1$

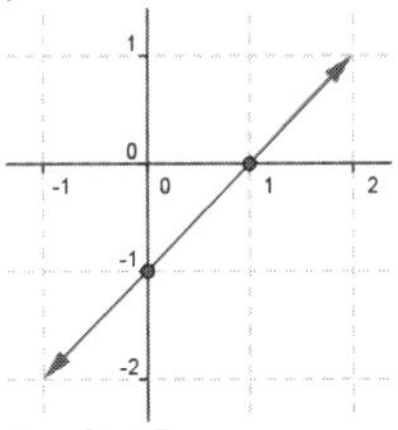

$y = 2x - 4$

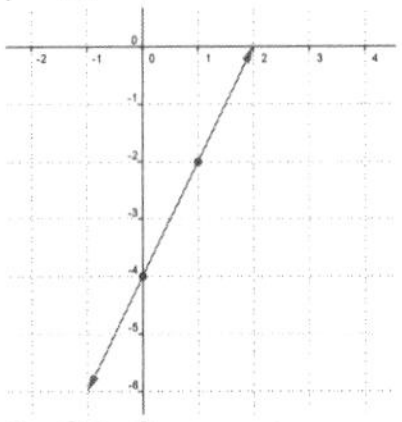

$y = -2x + 5$

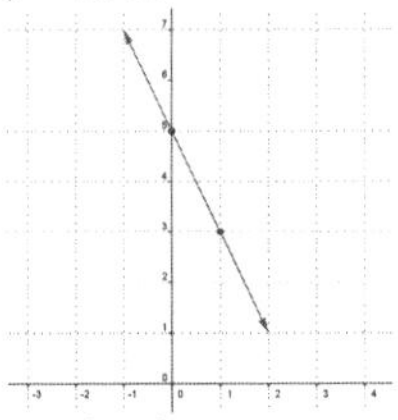

$y = -3x + 7$

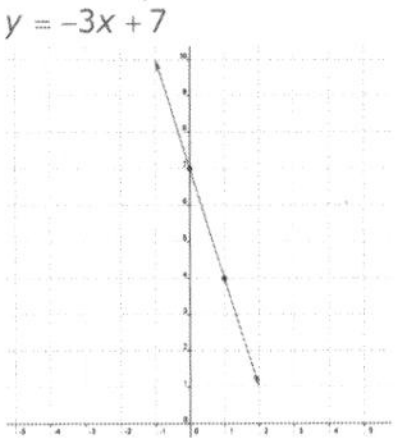

$y = 3x + 8$

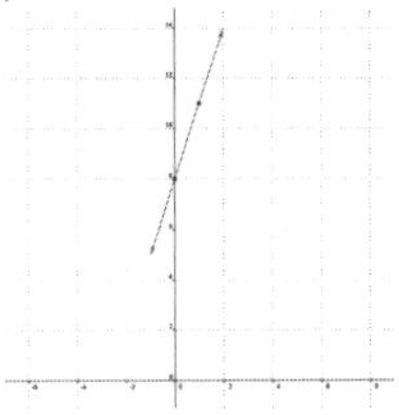

$y = -3x - 8$

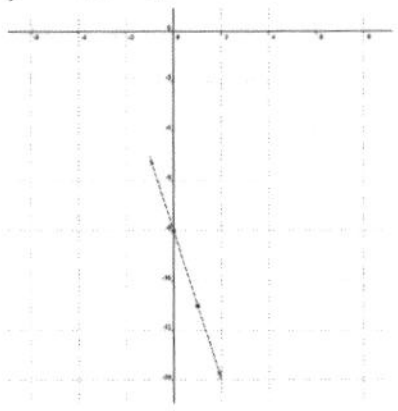

④ Solve.
Wheelchair accessibility guidelines state that the slope of a path may be 8.3% $\left(\frac{83}{1000}\right)$ for no more than 200 feet, 10 % $\left(\frac{1}{10}\right)$ for no more than 30 feet, and 12.5% $\left(\frac{1}{8}\right)$ for no more than 10 feet. What is the greatest change in elevation allowed in a 200-ft. section of a path? What is the greatest change in elevation allowed in a 30-ft. section of a path? What is the greatest change in elevation allowed in a 10-ft. section of a path? (Assume each path is a straight line.) Hint: Set up a proportion.

$\frac{83}{1000} = \frac{x}{200}$
$83(200) = 1000x$
$16600 = 1000x$
$x = 16.6$ feet

$\frac{1}{10} = \frac{x}{30}$
$30 = 10x$
$x = 3$ feet

$\frac{1}{8} = \frac{x}{10}$
$10 = 8x$
$x = 1.25$ feet

Point-slope Form, Slope-intercept Form Worksheet 17

① Write the point-slope form and slope-intercept form of the equation of a line.

$m = 4$
(2, 3)
$y - 3 = 4(x - 2)$
$y - 3 = 4x - 8$
$y = 4x - 5$

$m = \frac{1}{2}$
(4, -3)
$y - (-3) = \frac{1}{2}(x - 4)$
$y + 3 = \frac{1}{2}x - 2$
$y = \frac{1}{2}x - 5$

$m = -3$
(1, -2)
$y - (-2) = -3(x - 1)$
$y + 2 = -3x + 3$
$y = -3x + 1$

$m = -2$
(1, -1)
$y - (-1) = -2(x - 1)$
$y + 1 = -2x + 2$
$y = -2x + 1$

$m = 5$
(-3, 7)
$y - 7 = 5(x - (-3))$
$y - 7 = 5(x + 3)$
$y - 7 = 5x + 15$
$y = 5x + 22$

$m = -1$
(-3, -3)
$y - (-3) = -1(x - (-3))$
$y + 3 = -1(x + 3)$
$y + 3 = -x - 3$
$y = -x - 6$

② Graph each equation from Activity ①.

$y = 4x - 5$

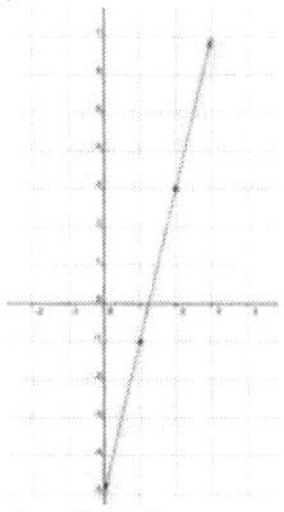

$y = \frac{1}{2}x - 5$

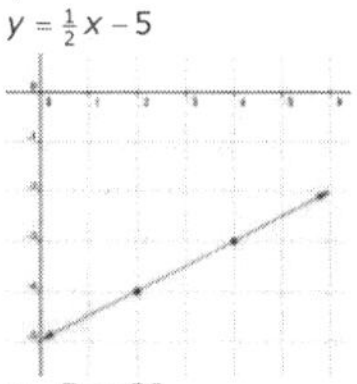

$y = -3x + 1$

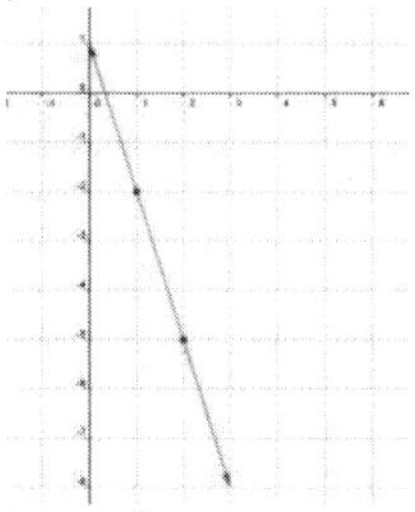

$y = 5x + 22$

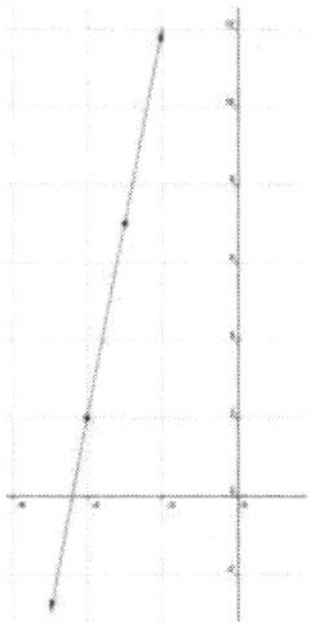

$y = -2x + 1$

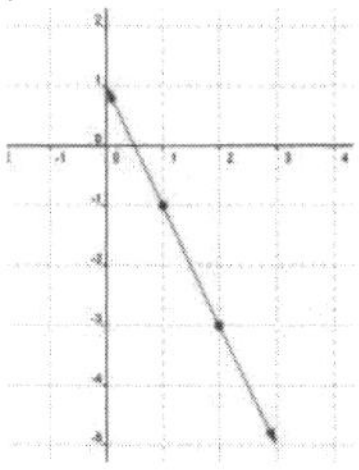

$y = -x - 6$

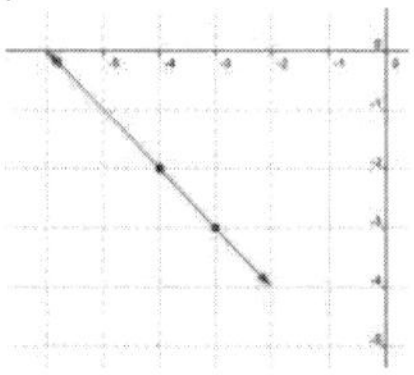

Teaching Tips, Cont.

- Review the rules of subtracting signed numbers, if necessary. (See Lesson 1) Tell the students to be careful when writing signs, especially when the coordinate point contains negative numbers.
- Remind the students that they must memorize all forms of linear equations presented in the book.
- Complete the Classwork exercises. Have some students work the problems on the board for the class and explain their answers. All students should work the problems in their books.

Assignments

- Complete Lesson 33, Activities 2-4.
- Worksheet 17.

Lesson 34

Concepts

- Horizontal and vertical lines
- Writing linear equations
- Graphing linear equations
- Math in the real world

Learning Objectives

The student will be able to:

- Define *horizontal line*
- Define *vertical line*
- Write linear equations of horizontal and vertical lines when given one point on the line
- Draw the graph of linear equations of horizontal and vertical lines

Materials Needed

- Student Book, Lesson 34
- Graph paper

Teaching Tips

➢ Review the difference between zero slope and no slope. (See Lesson 31)

➢ Define *horizontal line* from the teaching box. Ask the students what the slope of a horizontal line is. (0)

➢ Introduce the formula for the linear equation of a horizontal line, $y = c$. Ask the students why there is no x-variable in the equation. (The line does not cross the x-axis.)

➢ Ask a student to give the slope-intercept formula. ($y = mx + b$) Ask the students what the c in the equation of a horizontal line corresponds to in this formula. (b) Ask the students what b represents. (The y-intercept)

Graphing Linear Equations: Horizontal and Vertical Lines

A **horizontal line** is a line that is parallel to the x-axis. Because the line parallels the x-axis, the distance from the x-axis is constant. The formula for the equation of a horizontal line is $y = c$, where c is the constant distance from the x-axis. The slope of a horizontal line is always zero. A **vertical line** is a line that is parallel to the y-axis. Because the line parallels the y-axis, the distance from the y-axis is constant. The formula for the equation of a vertical line is $x = c$, where c is the constant distance from the y-axis. A vertical line has no slope. Write an equation of the line that passes through point (2, 4) and is parallel to the x-axis. Because the line is parallel to the x-axis, use the formula $y = c$. The y portion of the coordinate of the given point is 4, so the equation is $y = 4$.	① **Classwork** Write an equation for each line described below. A line that passes through the point (5, 2) and is parallel to the y-axis $x = 5$ A line that passes through the point (2, -3) and is parallel to the x-axis $y = -3$ A line that lies on the x-axis $y = 0$

Activities

② Write an equation for each line described below.

A line that passes through the point (4, 7) and is parallel to the y-axis
$x = 4$

A line that passes through the point (-2, -5) and is parallel to the x-axis
$y = -5$

A line that passes through the point (3, 1) and is parallel to the x-axis
$y = 1$

A line that passes through the point (-1, -4) and is parallel to the y-axis
$x = -1$

A line that passes through the point (-3, 3) and is parallel to the x-axis
$y = 3$

A line that lies on the y-axis
$x = 0$

③ Graph each equation from Activity ②.

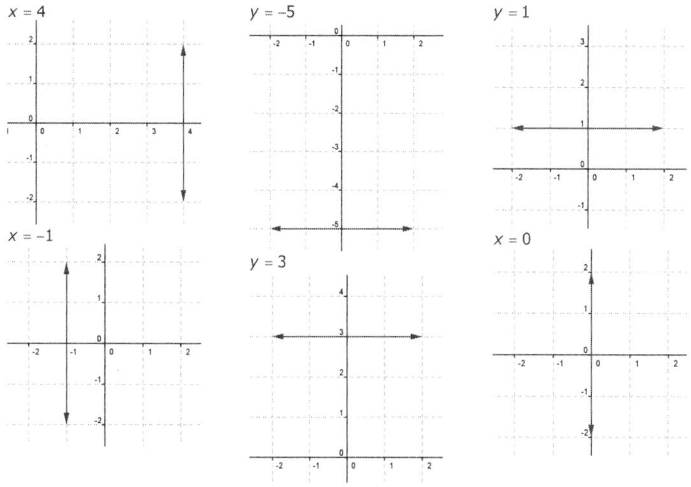

④ Solve.

Wheelchair accessibility guidelines state that the slope of a path may be 8.3% $\left(\frac{83}{1000}\right)$ for no more than 200 feet, 10 % $\left(\frac{1}{10}\right)$ for no more than 30 feet, and 12.5% $\left(\frac{1}{8}\right)$ for no more than 10 feet. Write an equation of a line to represent the maximum slope of a 200-ft. path, a 30-ft. path, and a 10-ft. path. Hint: Assume the *y*-intercept is the starting point of the path, or zero.

$y = \frac{83}{1000}x$ for the 200-ft. path

$y = \frac{1}{10}x$ for the 30-ft. path

$y = \frac{1}{8}x$ for the 10-ft. path

What is the slope of a level path?

The slope is zero.

Write an equation of the line formed by a level path at an elevation of 645 feet.

$y = 645$

Teaching Tips, Cont.

- Define *vertical line* from the teaching box. Ask the students what the slope of a vertical line is. (No slope)
- Introduce the formula for the linear equation of a vertical line, $x = c$. Ask the students why there is no *y*-variable in the equation. (The line does not cross the *y*-axis.)
- Ask students how this equation is similar to the equation of a horizontal line. (The only difference is the *y* changed to an *x*.) Point out that any time an equation contains a single variable, the line will be either horizontal or vertical, depending on which variable appears. Any time both variables appear in an equation, the line will be diagonal.
- Remind the students that they must memorize all forms of linear equations presented in the book.
- Complete the Classwork exercises. Have some students work the problems on the board for the class and explain their answers. All students should work the problems in their books.

Assignment

- Complete Lesson 34, Activities 2-4.

Lesson 35

Concepts

- Intercepts
- Linear equations
- Graphing linear equations
- Math in the real world

Learning Objectives

The student will be able to:

- Find the x-intercept of a linear equation
- Find the y-intercept of a linear equation
- Use the intercepts to draw a graph of a linear equation

Materials Needed

- Student Book, Lesson 35
- Worksheet 18
- Graph paper

Teaching Tips

➢ Have students complete Worksheet 18 in class. This may be for added practice of earlier topics, or graded as a quiz, if desired.

➢ Review the slope-intercept form of a linear equation. (See Lesson 32) Ask the students how they could write the y-intercept as a coordinate point. $(0, b)$

➢ Show the students that the x-coordinate of the y-intercept is always 0.

➢ Ask the students what should be true about the y-coordinate of the x-intercept. (It should always be 0.)

Graphing Linear Equations: Intercepts

Recall from Lesson 32 that the **y-intercept** of a graph is the point at which the graph crosses the y-axis. This is the point at which $x = 0$. Likewise, the **x-intercept** of a graph is the point at which the graph crosses the x-axis. This is the point at which $y = 0$.

To find the coordinate of the y-intercept of a graph, let $x = 0$ and solve for y.
To find the coordinate of the x-intercept of a graph, let $y = 0$ and solve for x.

Find the x- and y-intercepts of the equation $2x + 3y = 6$.

Let $y = 0$ to find the x-intercept.
$2x + 3(0) = 6$
$2x = 6$
$x = 3$
The x-intercept is the point (3, 0).

Let $x = 0$ to find the y-intercept.
$2(0) + 3y = 6$
$3y = 6$
$y = 2$
The y-intercept is the point (0, 2).

① **Classwork**
Find the x- and y-intercepts of each equation.

$2x + y = 4$
$2x + 0 = 4$
$2x = 4$
$x = 2$
$(2,0)$ is the x-intercept

$2(0) + y = 4$
$y = 4$
$(0,4)$ is the y-intercept

$x + 3y = 9$
$x + 3(0) = 9$
$x = 9$
$(9,0)$ is the x-intercept

$0 + 3y = 9$
$y = 3$
$(0,3)$ is the y-intercept

Activities

② Find the x- and y-intercepts of each equation.

$x + 4y = 12$
$x + 4(0) = 12$
$x = 12$
$(12,0)$ is the x-intercept

$0 + 4y = 12$
$y = 3$
$(0,3)$ is the y-intercept

$5x + 3y = 15$
$5x + 3(0) = 15$
$5x = 15$
$x = 3$
$(3,0)$ is the x-intercept

$5(0) + 3y = 15$
$3y = 15$
$y = 5$
$(0,5)$ is the y-intercept

$3x + 4y = 12$
$3x + 4(0) = 12$
$3x = 12$
$x = 4$
$(4,0)$ is the x-intercept

$3(0) + 4y = 12$
$4y = 12$
$y = 3$
$(0,3)$ is the y-intercept

③ Use the intercepts to graph each equation from Activity ②.

$x + 4y = 12$

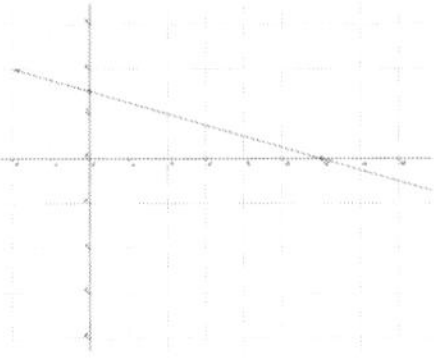

$5x + 3y = 15$

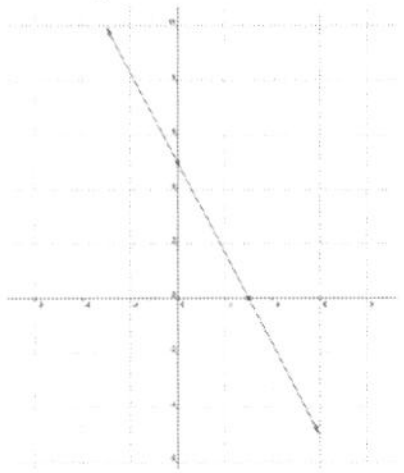

$3x + 4y = 12$

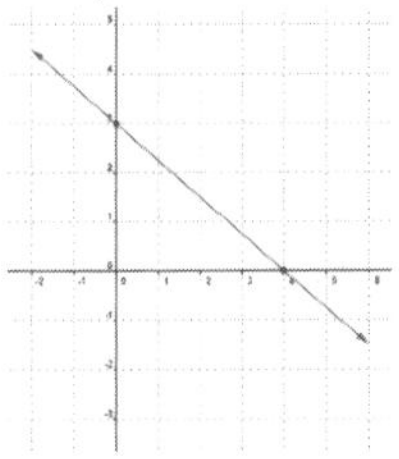

④ Solve.

The Silver Comet Trail is a 61-mile-long multi-use path that runs from Smyrna, Georgia, (near Atlanta) to the Georgia/Alabama line. The beginning section of the path has a 99-foot vertical change in elevation over a 2310-foot horizontal distance. If the designers wish to maintain a grade (slope) of less than 5% on the majority of the Silver Comet Trail, does this section of the trail fall within their specifications?

Slope $= \frac{99}{2310} = 0.043$ This is equivalent to a 4.3% grade, which falls within the specifications of the trail.

The elevation of the highest point on the Silver Comet Trail is 1065 feet. The elevation of the lowest point on the trail is 752 feet. The horizontal distance between these two points is 19.3 miles. What is the slope of a straight line joining these two points? (1 mile = 5280 feet)

First, convert miles to feet. (19.3)(5280) = 101,904 feet
The elevation change is 1065 − 752 = 313 feet
Slope $= \frac{313}{101{,}904} = 0.003$ This is equivalent to a less than 1% grade, which falls within the specifications of the trail. In fact, this is almost level!

If the trail's intended use was for walking, hiking, jogging, bike riding, roller blading, horseback riding, dog walking, and riding in wheelchairs, is the grade between the highest and lowest points considered safe for all of the above activities? (The grade must be less than 5% over that distance to be safe for all of the activities.)

Yes – the grade is almost level.

Slope, Slope-intercept Form Worksheet 18

① Find the slope of the line joining the points.

(3, 2) and (5, 3)

$m = \frac{3-2}{5-3} = \frac{1}{2}$

(-2, 8) and (5, 8)

$m = \frac{8-8}{5-(-2)} = \frac{0}{7} = 0$

(4, 3) and (6, 2)

$m = \frac{2-3}{6-4} = \frac{-1}{2} = -\frac{1}{2}$

(-2, -4) and (3, 4)

$m = \frac{4-(-4)}{3-(-2)} = \frac{8}{5}$

(1, 2) and (1, 8)

$m = \frac{8-2}{1-1} = \frac{6}{0} =$ no slope

(0, 0) and (-3, 4)

$m = \frac{4-0}{-3-0} = \frac{4}{-3} = -\frac{4}{3}$

(4, -1) and (7, -2)

$m = \frac{-2-(-1)}{7-4} = \frac{-1}{3} = -\frac{1}{3}$

(6, 2) and (-10, 2)

$m = \frac{2-2}{-10-6} = \frac{0}{-16} = 0$

(6, -2) and (3, -9)

$m = \frac{-9-(-2)}{3-6} = \frac{-7}{-3} = \frac{7}{3}$

(-4, -3) and (-4, 5)

$m = \frac{5-(-3)}{-4-(-4)} = \frac{8}{0} =$ no slope

② Rewrite each linear equation in slope-intercept form and state the slope of each line.

$x + y + 5 = 0$
$y = -x - 5$
$m = -1$

$2x + y - 1 = 0$
$y = -2x + 1$
$m = -2$

$-4x + y - 3 = 0$
$y = 4x + 3$
$m = 4$

$-5x + y + 1 = 0$
$y = 5x - 1$
$m = 5$

$-3x + y + 4 = 0$
$y = 3x - 4$
$m = 3$

$5x + y - 2 = 0$
$y = -5x + 2$
$m = -5$

$2x + 2y + 5 = 0$
$2y = -2x - 5$
$y = -x - \frac{5}{2}$
$m = -1$

$x + 2y + 4 = 0$
$2y = -x - 4$
$y = -\frac{1}{2}x - 2$
$m = -\frac{1}{2}$

$2x + 3y + 9 = 0$
$3y = -2x - 9$
$y = -\frac{2}{3}x - 3$
$m = -\frac{2}{3}$

Teaching Tips, Cont.

- Teach how to find the intercepts from the teaching box. Emphasize that one intercept is found by setting the opposite variable equal to zero and solving the equation. Make sure all students understand that the intercepts represent coordinate points on the graph.
- Remind the students that they must memorize all forms of linear equations presented in the book.
- Complete the Classwork exercises. Have some students work the problems on the board for the class. All students should work the problems in their books.

Assignment

- Complete Lesson 35, Activities 2-4.

Lesson 36

Concepts
- Perpendicular lines
- Slope
- Linear equations
- Graphing intersecting lines

Learning Objectives
The student will be able to:
- Find the reciprocal of a number
- Identify whether or not two linear equations represent perpendicular lines
- Draw the graph of intersecting lines

Materials Needed
- Student Book, Lesson 36
- Graph paper

Teaching Tips
- ➢ Review slope. (See Lesson 31)
- ➢ Review the slope-intercept form of a linear equation. (See Lesson 32 as well as the teaching box from this lesson.)
- ➢ Teach how to find the reciprocal of a number from the teaching box.
- ➢ Explain that lines that are perpendicular to each other have slopes that are negative reciprocals of each other. Ask the students what the word *negative* means in this context. (They have opposite signs.) Ask the students what the word *reciprocal* means in this context. (The numerator and the denominator switch places.)

Lesson 36

Graphing Linear Equations: Perpendicular Lines

Consider the graph of the line $y = 2x$ below.

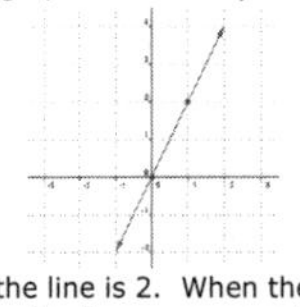

The slope of the line is 2. When the slope of a line is positive, the line goes up as it moves from left to right.

Consider the graph of the line $y = -\frac{1}{2}x$ below.

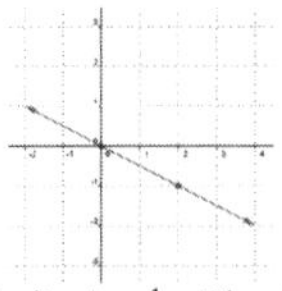

The slope of the line is $-\frac{1}{2}$. When the slope of a line is negative, the line goes down as it moves from left to right.

Notice what happens when both lines are graphed on the same plane.

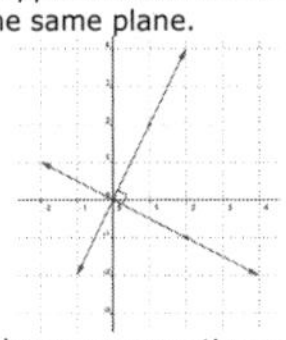

Lines whose slopes are negative reciprocals are perpendicular lines and form right angles at the point of intersection.

Negative reciprocals have opposite signs (one positive and one negative). To find the reciprocal, switch the numerator and the denominator. In the case of a whole number, the number becomes the denominator with a 1 in the numerator of the reciprocal.

In the examples above, 2 and $-\frac{1}{2}$ are negative reciprocals.

① **Classwork**

Find the negative reciprocal of each number.

-4 $\quad \frac{1}{4}$

$\frac{1}{7} \quad$ -7

$-\frac{6}{11} \quad \frac{11}{6}$

Identify whether or not the two lines are perpendicular. Tell why or why not.

$y = 4x + 7$
$y = -4x + 3$
The lines are not perpendicular because the slopes are 4 and -4. They have opposite signs, but they are not reciprocals.

$y = \frac{2}{3}x - 5$
$y = \frac{3}{2}x + 2$
The lines are not perpendicular because the slopes are $\frac{2}{3}$ and $\frac{3}{2}$. They are reciprocals, but they have the same sign.

$\frac{3}{5}x + y - 1 = 0$
$\frac{5}{3}x - y - 3 = 0$
The lines are perpendicular. Rewrite as
$y = -\frac{3}{5}x + 1$
$y = \frac{5}{3}x - 3$
and it is easy to see the slopes are $-\frac{3}{5}$ and $\frac{5}{3}$, which are negative reciprocals.

Activities

② Find the negative reciprocal of each number.

$\frac{12}{5}$ $-\frac{5}{12}$ $\frac{1}{3}$ -3 $-\frac{2}{5}$ $\frac{5}{2}$

③ Identify whether or not the two lines are perpendicular. Tell why or why not.

$y = \frac{7}{10}x - 8$
$y = -\frac{10}{7}x + 4$
The lines are perpendicular because the slopes are $\frac{7}{10}$ and $-\frac{10}{7}$, which are negative reciprocals.

$y = 2x - 5$
$y = -2x + \frac{1}{5}$
The lines are not perpendicular because the slopes are 2 and -2. They have opposite signs, but they are not reciprocals.

$\frac{5}{8}x + y - 3 = 0$
$-\frac{8}{5}x - y - 2 = 0$
The lines are not perpendicular because when they are rewritten as $y = -\frac{5}{8}x + 3$ and $y = -\frac{8}{5}x - 2$ it is easy to see the slopes are $-\frac{5}{8}$ and $-\frac{8}{5}$, which are reciprocals but have the same sign.

$y = 8x - 1$
$y = -8x + 6$
The lines are not perpendicular because the slopes are 8 and -8. They have opposite signs, but they are not reciprocals.

$\frac{2}{9}x + y - 7 = 0$
$\frac{9}{2}x - y - 4 = 0$
The lines are perpendicular. Rewrite as $y = -\frac{2}{9}x + 7$ and $y = \frac{9}{2}x - 4$ and it is easy to see the slopes are $-\frac{2}{9}$ and $\frac{9}{2}$, which are negative reciprocals.

$y = \frac{3}{7}x - 4$
$y = \frac{7}{3}x + 9$
The lines are not perpendicular because the slopes are $\frac{3}{7}$ and $\frac{7}{3}$. They are reciprocals, but they have the same sign.

④ Graph the equations from Activity ③. Graph each pair of equations on a single Cartesian plane.

$y = \frac{7}{10}x - 8$
$y = -\frac{10}{7}x + 4$

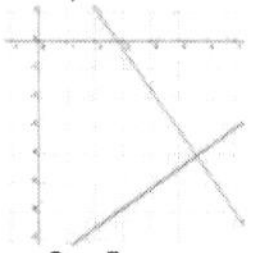

$\frac{5}{8}x + y - 3 = 0$
$-\frac{8}{5}x - y - 2 = 0$

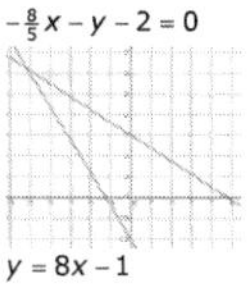

$\frac{2}{9}x + y - 7 = 0$
$\frac{9}{2}x - y - 4 = 0$

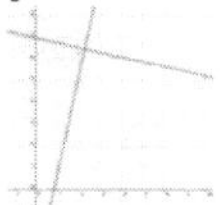

$y = 2x - 5$
$y = -2x + \frac{1}{5}$

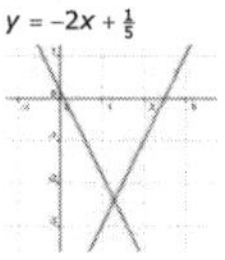

$y = 8x - 1$
$y = -8x + 6$

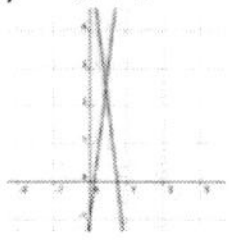

$y = \frac{3}{7}x - 4$
$y = \frac{7}{3}x + 9$

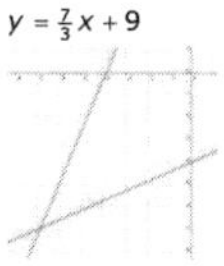

Teaching Tips, Cont.

- Point out the negative reciprocal slopes in the graphs of the lines in the teaching box. Show the students that the graph of the two lines forms perpendicular lines.
- Remind the students that they must memorize all forms of linear equations presented in the book.
- Complete the Classwork exercises. Have some students work the problems on the board for the class. All students should work the problems in their books.

Assignment

- Complete Lesson 36, Activities 2-4.

Lesson 37

Concepts

- Parallel lines
- Slope
- Slope-intercept form
- Perpendicular lines
- Graphing linear equations
- Writing linear equations

Learning Objectives

The student will be able to:

- Identify whether or not two linear equations represent parallel lines
- Write equations of parallel lines
- Write equations of perpendicular lines

Materials Needed

- Student Book, Lesson 37

Teaching Tips

➢ Review perpendicular lines. (See Lesson 36) Ask the students what is true about the slopes of perpendicular lines. (They are negative reciprocals of each other.)

➢ Draw the students' attention to the graphs in the teaching box of this lesson. Ask them what is true about the slopes of these lines. (The slopes are the same.)

➢ Tell the students that these graphs represent parallel lines. Ask the students if the slopes of parallel lines will always be the same. (Yes.)

Lesson 37

Graphing Linear Equations: Parallel Lines

Consider the graph of the line $y = 2x$ below.

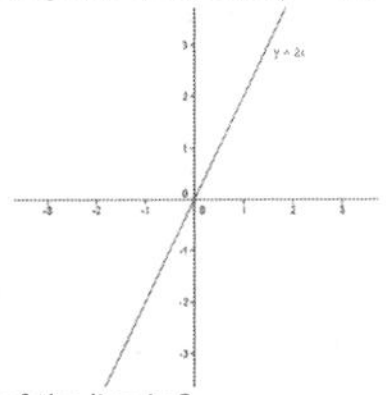

The slope of the line is 2.

Consider the graph of the line $y = 2x - 2$ below.

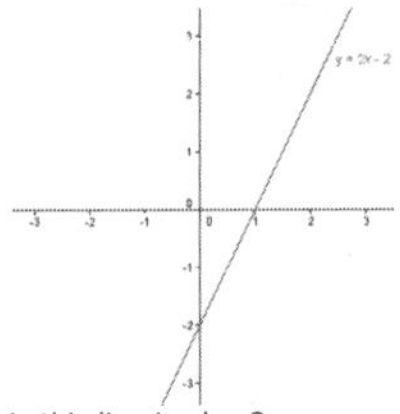

The slope is this line is also 2.

Notice what happens when both lines are graphed on the same plane.

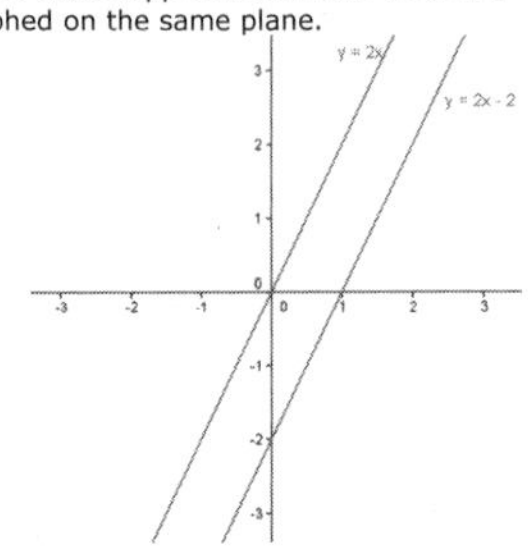

Lines with the same slope are always parallel.

① **Classwork**

Identify whether or not the two lines are parallel. Tell why or why not.

$y = 4x + 7$
$y = -4x + 3$
The lines are not parallel because the slopes are 4 and -4. They have opposite signs, so they are not equal.

$y = \frac{2}{3}x - 5$
$y = \frac{3}{2}x - 5$
The lines are not parallel because the slopes are $\frac{2}{3}$ and $\frac{3}{2}$. They are reciprocals, so they are not equal.

$-\frac{3}{5}x + y - 1 = 0$
$\frac{3}{5}x - y - 3 = 0$
The lines are parallel. Rewrite as $y = \frac{3}{5}x + 1$, $y = \frac{3}{5}x - 3$ and it is easy to see the slopes are the same.

Write an equation of a line parallel to the line $2x - y + 3 = 0$.
Rewrite the equation in slope-intercept form to easily find the slope.
$y = 2x + 3$ The slope is 2. Any line with a slope of 2 is a correct answer. To check, the x-coordinate should be twice the value of the y-coordinate when the x-term and y-term are on opposite sides of the equal sign.

Activities

② Identify whether or not the two lines are parallel. Tell why or why not.

$y = \frac{7}{10}x - 9$

$y = -\frac{7}{10}x + 3$

The lines are not parallel because the slopes are $\frac{7}{10}$ and $-\frac{7}{10}$, which have opposite signs.

$y = 2x - 6$

$y = 2x + \frac{1}{6}$

The lines are parallel because the slopes are equal.

$\frac{5}{8}x + y - 3 = 0$

$-\frac{5}{8}x - y - 2 = 0$

The lines are parallel because when they are rewritten as $y = -\frac{5}{8}x + 3$ and $y = -\frac{5}{8}x - 2$ it is easy to see the slopes are $-\frac{5}{8}$ and $-\frac{8}{5}$, which are equal.

$y = 8x - 1$

$y = \frac{1}{8}x + 6$

The lines are not parallel because the slopes are 8 and $\frac{1}{8}$. They are not equal.

$\frac{2}{9}x + y - 7 = 0$

$\frac{2}{9}x - y - 4 = 0$

The lines are not parallel. Rewrite as $y = -\frac{2}{9}x + 7$ and $y = \frac{2}{9}x - 4$ and it is easy to see the slopes are $-\frac{2}{9}$ and $\frac{2}{9}$, which have opposite signs.

$y = \frac{3}{7}x - 4$

$y = \frac{3}{7}x + 4$

The lines are parallel because the slopes are equal.

③ Rewrite each equation in slope-intercept form. Write an equation of a line parallel to the given line; then write an equation of a line perpendicular to the given line.

$x + 4y = 12$

Slope-intercept form: $4y = -x + 12 \Rightarrow y = -\frac{1}{4}x + 3$

Parallel line: Slope must equal $-\frac{1}{4}$. Sample equation: $y = -\frac{1}{4}x - 1$

Perpendicular line: Slope must equal 4. Sample equation: $y = 4x + 3$

$5x + 3y = 15$

Slope-intercept form: $3y = -5x + 15 \Rightarrow y = -\frac{5}{3}x + 5$

Parallel line: Slope must equal $-\frac{5}{3}$. Sample equation: $y = -\frac{5}{3}x - 1$

Perpendicular line: Slope must equal $\frac{3}{5}$. Sample equation: $y = \frac{3}{5}x + 3$

$3x + 4y = 12$

Slope-intercept form: $4y = -3x + 12 \Rightarrow y = -\frac{3}{4}x + 3$

Parallel line: Slope must equal $-\frac{3}{4}$. Sample equation: $y = -\frac{3}{4}x - 1$

Perpendicular line: Slope must equal $\frac{4}{3}$. Sample equation: $y = \frac{4}{3}x + 3$

Teaching Tips, Cont.

- Explain that parallel lines will always have equal slopes. This makes it possible to determine whether or not the graphs of two linear equations are parallel without having to draw the graphs.
- Complete the Classwork exercises. Have some students work the problems on the board for the class. All students should work the problems in their books.

Assignment

- Complete Lesson 37, Activities 2-3.

Lesson 38

Concepts
- Standard form
- Graphing linear equations
- Slope-intercept form
- Point-slope form
- Slope

Learning Objectives
The student will be able to:
- Convert a linear equation to standard form
- Graph an equation in standard form
- Write a standard form linear equation from a given set of data

Materials Needed
- Student Book, Lesson 38
- Graph paper
- Worksheet 19

Teaching Tips
- Have students complete Worksheet 19 in class. This may be for added practice of earlier topics, or graded as a quiz, if desired.
- Review the formula for slope. (See Lesson 31)
- Review the slope-intercept formula. (See Lesson 32)
- Review the point-slope formula. (See Lesson 33)
- Teach the standard form of an algebraic equation from the teaching box. Point out that the coefficient of *x* must be positive, and that the constant term must be isolated on the opposite side of the equal sign from the variables.

Graphing Linear Equations: Standard Form

The **standard form** of an algebraic equation is $Ax + By = C$, where *A*, *B*, and *C* are integers and $A > 0$. Because each coefficient is an integer, the standard form has no fractions or decimals.

The easiest way to graph an equation in standard form is to let $x = 0$ to solve for the corresponding *y*-coordinate and then let $y = 0$ to solve for the corresponding *x*-coordinate. Notice that this method give the two intercepts.

An alternate way to graph an equation in standard form is to rewrite the equation in slope-intercept form and plot points. Plotting two points will give a line. It is a good idea to plot a third point to make sure it lies on the same line as a way to check your work.

Write the equation $y = \frac{2}{3}x - 5$ in standard form.
First, multiply each term by 3 to eliminate the fraction.
$3y = 2x - 15$

Since there are no decimals to eliminate and all coefficients are integers, rearrange the terms in standard form, making sure the *x*-coefficient is positive.
$2x - 3y = 15$

① **Classwork**
Write each equation in standard form.

$\frac{3}{5}x + y - 1 = 0$
$5\left(\frac{3}{5}x\right) + 5y - 1(5) = 0(5)$
$3x + 5y - 5 = 0$
$3x + 5y = 5$

$y = \frac{3}{2}x + 2$
$2y = 2\left(\frac{3}{2}x\right) + 2(2)$
$2y = 3x + 4$
$3x - 2y = -4$

Graph the equation $2x - 3y = 15$.

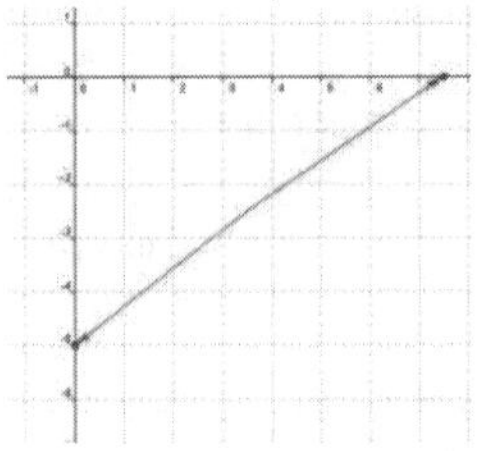

Activities

② Write each equation in standard form.

$y = -4x - 2$
$4x + y = -2$

$y = -2x - \frac{1}{2}$
$2y = 2(-2x) - 2\left(\frac{1}{2}\right)$
$2y = -4x - 1$
$4x + 2y = -1$

$y = \frac{1}{2}x + 3$
$2y = 2\left(\frac{1}{2}x\right) + 2(3)$
$2y = x + 6$
$x - 2y = -6$

$y = -\frac{1}{3}x - 2$
$3y = 3\left(-\frac{1}{3}x\right) - 3(2)$
$3y = -x - 6$
$x + 3y = -6$

$y = -\frac{4}{3}x - 4$
$3y = 3\left(-\frac{4}{3}x\right) - 3(4)$
$3y = -4x - 12$
$4x + 3y = -12$

$y = -\frac{2}{3}x + 2$
$3y = 3\left(-\frac{2}{3}x\right) + 3(2)$
$3y = -2x + 6$
$2x + 3y = 6$

③ Graph each equation from Activity ②.

$y = -4x - 2$

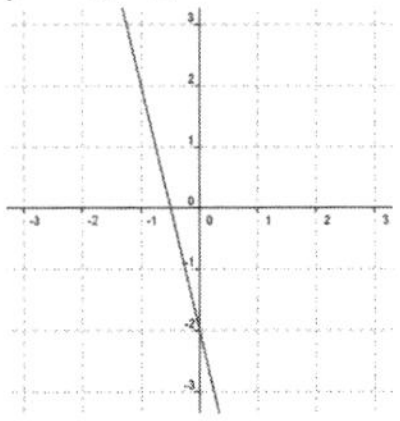

$y = -2x - \frac{1}{2}$

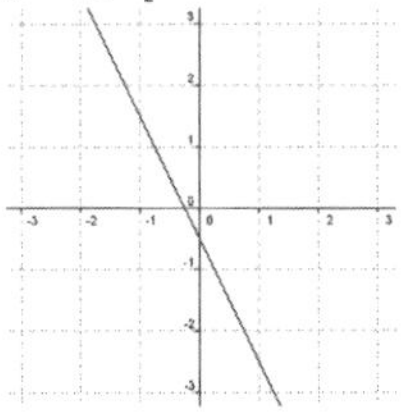

$y = \frac{1}{2}x + 3$

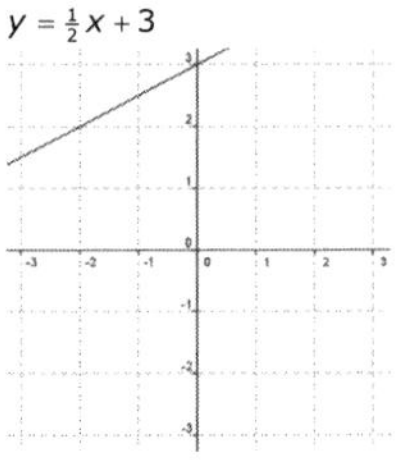

$y = -\frac{1}{3}x - 2$

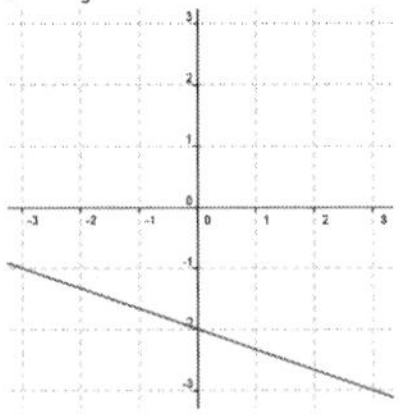

$y = -\frac{4}{3}x - 4$

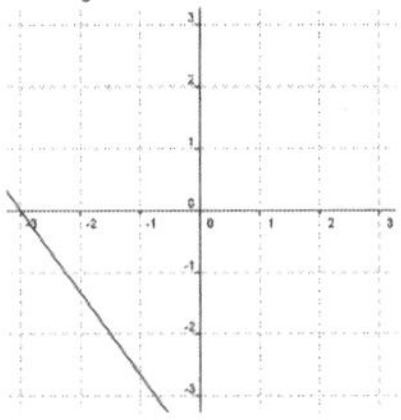

$y = -\frac{2}{3}x + 2$

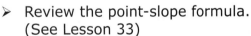

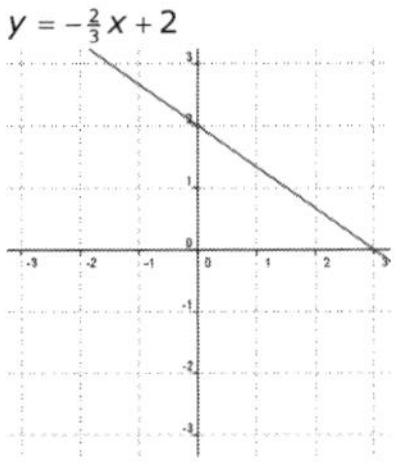

④ Write an equation for each line using the information provided. Convert each equation to standard form.

Slope = 3
y-intercept = -2
$y = 3x - 2$
$3x - y = 2$

Slope = $\frac{2}{3}$
Point: (4, 5)
$y - 5 = \frac{2}{3}(x - 4)$
$3(y) - 3(5) = 3\left(\frac{2}{3}x\right) - 3\left(\frac{8}{3}\right)$
$3y - 15 = 2x - 8$
$2x - 3y = -7$

Points (-2, 7) and (1, 3)
Slope = $\frac{3-7}{1-(-2)} = \frac{-4}{3}$
$y - 3 = -\frac{4}{3}(x - 1)$
$3(y) - 3(3) = 3\left(-\frac{4}{3}x\right) + 3\left(\frac{4}{3}\right)$
$3y - 9 = -4x + 4$
$4x + 3y = 13$

Slope = $\frac{1}{2}$
y-intercept = 3
$y = \frac{1}{2}x + 3$
$2(y) = 2\left(\frac{1}{2}x\right) + 2(3)$
$2y = x + 6$
$x - 2y = -6$

Slope = $-\frac{1}{4}$
Point: (-1, 1)
$y - 1 = -\frac{1}{4}(x + 1)$
$4(y) - 4(1) = 4\left(-\frac{1}{4}x\right) + 4\left(-\frac{1}{4}\right)$
$4y - 4 = -x - 1$
$x + 4y = 3$

Points (-3, 4) and (-1, -2)
Slope = $\frac{-2-4}{-1-(-3)} = \frac{-6}{2} = -3$
$y - (-2) = -3(x - (-1))$
$y + 2 = -3(x + 1)$
$y + 2 = -3x - 3$
$3x + y = -5$

Slope and *y*-intercept Worksheet 19

① Rewrite each equation in slope-intercept form. Give the slope and y-intercept of each equation.

$x + y - 9 = 0$ $y = -x + 9$ $m = -1$ $b = 9$	$2x + y - 3 = 0$ $y = -2x + 3$ $m = -2$ $b = 3$	$-5x + y - 2 = 0$ $y = 5x + 2$ $m = 5$ $b = 2$
$-4x + y - 7 = 0$ $y = 4x + 7$ $m = 4$ $b = 7$	$-2x + y + 9 = 0$ $y = 2x - 9$ $m = 2$ $b = -9$	$7x + y - 3 = 0$ $y = -7x + 3$ $m = -7$ $b = 3$
$4x + 2y + 6 = 0$ $2y = -4x - 6$ $y = -2x - 3$ $m = -2$ $b = -3$	$x + 3y + 8 = 0$ $3y = -x - 8$ $y = -\frac{1}{3}x - \frac{8}{3}$ $m = -\frac{1}{3}$ $b = -\frac{8}{3}$	$4x + 5y + 20 = 0$ $5y = -4x - 20$ $y = -\frac{4}{5}x - 4$ $m = -\frac{4}{5}$ $b = -4$

② Write an equation in slope-intercept form having the given slope and *y*-intercept.

$m = 1$ $b = 4$ $y = x + 4$	$m = -1$ $b = 3$ $y = -x + 3$	$m = 2$ $b = 7$ $y = 2x + 7$
$m = 4$ $b = -2$ $y = 4x - 2$	$m = -2$ $b = -1$ $y = -2x - 1$	$m = -3$ $b = 3$ $y = -3x + 3$
$m = -\frac{1}{2}$ $b = 5$ $y = -\frac{1}{2}x + 5$	$m = -\frac{3}{2}$ $b = 2$ $y = -\frac{3}{2}x + 2$	$m = \frac{3}{2}$ $b = -6$ $y = \frac{3}{2}x - 6$
$m = -\frac{1}{2}$ $b = 3$ $y = -\frac{1}{2}x + 3$	$m = -\frac{2}{3}$ $b = 2$ $y = -\frac{2}{3}x + 2$	$m = \frac{1}{4}$ $b = 5$ $y = \frac{1}{4}x + 5$

Teaching Tips, Cont.

- Explain that any standard form equation may be rewritten in slope-intercept form to make it easier to graph. This is easily done by isolating *y* on one side of the equal sign then dividing each term in the equation by the coefficient of *y*.
- Remind the students that they must memorize all forms of linear equations presented in the book.
- Complete the Classwork exercises. Have some students work the problems on the board for the class. All students should work the problems in their books.

Assignment

- Complete Lesson 38, Activities 2-4.

Lesson 39

Concepts

- Writing linear equations
- Slope-intercept form
- Slope
- Point-slope form

Learning Objectives

The student will be able to:

- Calculate the slope of a line on a graph
- Write a linear equation in slope-intercept form for a line on a graph

Materials Needed

- Student Book, Lesson 39

Teaching Tips

- Review slope-intercept form. (See Lesson 32)
- Review slope. (See Lesson 31)
- Teach how to find the slope of a line on a graph from the teaching box. Tell the students to use the *y*-intercept as one of the points even if there are multiple other identifiable points on the graph. This will make calculations easier.
- Ask the students how they can know the value of *b* in the slope-intercept form just by looking at the graph. (It is the *y*-coordinate of the point at which the graph crosses the *y*-axis.)

Lesson 39

Writing Linear Equations: Slope-Intercept Form

You already know how to get algebraic equations into slope-intercept form and how to draw the graph of the equation. In this lesson you will analyze graphs and write an equation of the graph in slope-intercept form. This is easily accomplished by following these steps.

1. Find the point at which the graph crosses the *y*-axis and note the coordinates of this point. The *y*-coordinate is *b* in the equation.
2. Find a second point on the graph and note the coordinates.
3. Apply the formula for slope using the coordinates of the points identified in steps 1 and 2. Reduce if necessary. This is the value of *m* in the equation.
4. Write the equation in slope-intercept form, substituting the values for *m* and *b* from the above steps.

Write an equation of the graph in slope-intercept form.

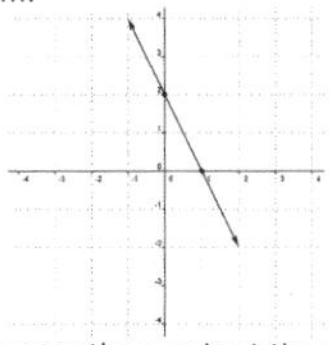

The graph crosses the *y*-axis at the point (0, 2) so $b = 2$.
Another point on the graph is (1, 0), so the slope is $\frac{0-2}{1-0} = \frac{-2}{1} = -2$. This is the value of *m*.
The equation of the graph in slope-intercept form is $y = -2x + 2$.

① **Classwork**
Write an equation of the graph in slope-intercept form.

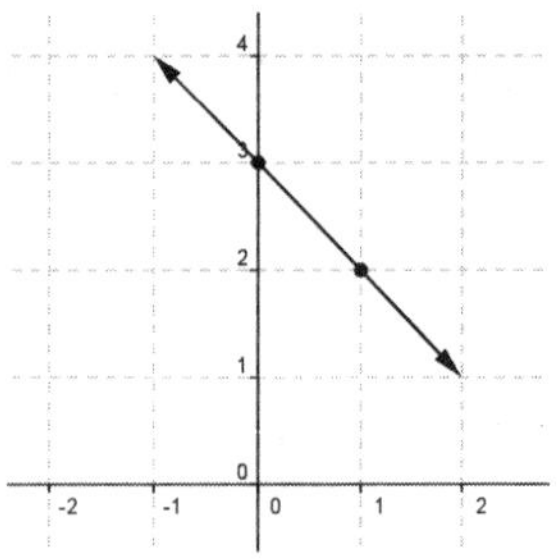

The graph crosses the *y*-axis at the point (0, 3) so $b = 3$.
Another point on the graph is (1, 2), so the slope is $\frac{2-3}{1-0} = \frac{-1}{1} = -1$. This is the value of *m*.
The equation of the graph in slope-intercept form is $y = -x + 3$.

Activities
② Write an equation of the graph in slope-intercept form.

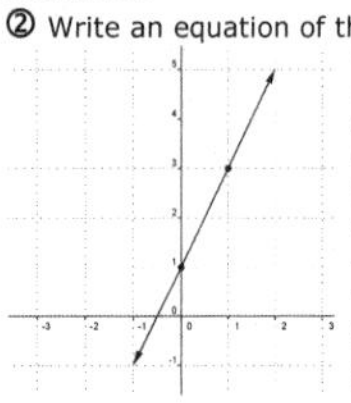

The graph crosses the *y*-axis at the point (0, 1) so $b = 1$.
Another point on the graph is (1, 3), so the slope is $\frac{3-1}{1-0} = \frac{2}{1} = 2$.
This is the value of *m*.
The equation of the graph in slope-intercept form is $y = 2x + 1$.

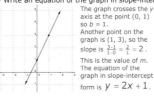

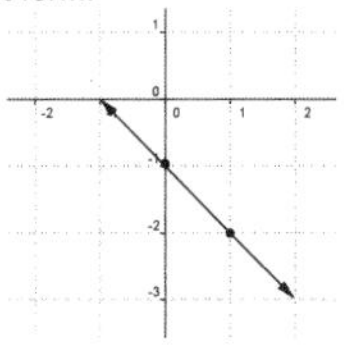

The graph crosses the *y*-axis at the point (0, -1) so $b = -1$. Another point on the graph is (1, -2), so the slope is $\frac{-2-(-1)}{1-0} = \frac{-1}{1} = -1$. This is the value of *m*.
The equation of the graph in slope-intercept form is $y = -x - 1$.

③ Write an equation of the graph in slope-intercept form.

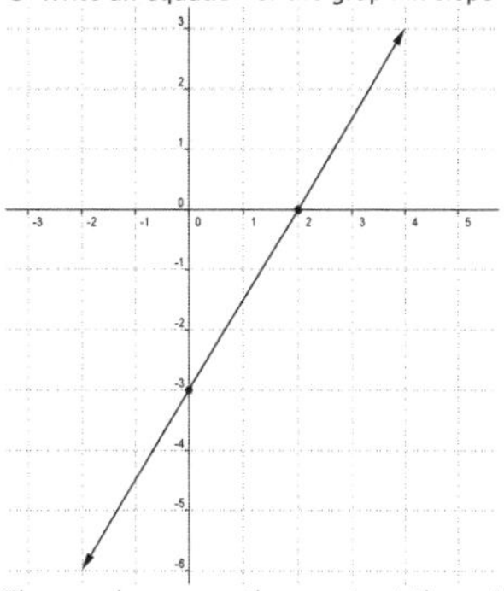

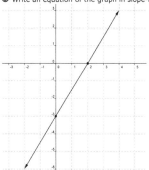

The graph crosses the y-axis at the point (0, -3) so b = -3. Another point on the graph is (2, 0), so the slope is $\frac{0-(-3)}{2-0} = \frac{3}{2}$. This is the value of m. The equation of the graph in slope-intercept form is $y = \frac{3}{2}x - 3$.

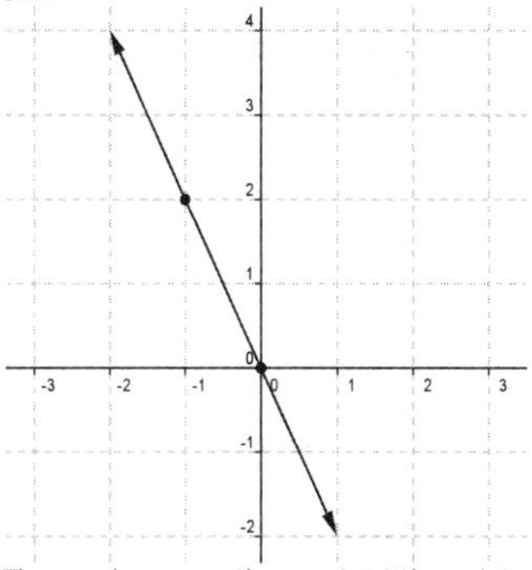

The graph crosses the y-axis at the point (0, 0) so b = 0. Another point on the graph is (-1, 2), so the slope is $\frac{2-0}{-1-0} = \frac{2}{-1} = -2$. This is the value of m. The equation of the graph in slope-intercept form is $y = -2x$.

④ Write an equation for each line using the information provided. Convert each equation to standard form.

Slope = -2
y-intercept = $\frac{2}{3}$

$y = -2x + \frac{2}{3}$
$3y = 3(-2x) + 3\left(\frac{2}{3}\right)$
$3y = -6x + 2$
$6x + 3y = 2$

Slope = $\frac{3}{5}$
y-intercept = $\frac{1}{4}$

$y = \frac{3}{5}x + \frac{1}{4}$
$20(y) = 20\left(\frac{3}{5}x\right) + 20\left(\frac{1}{4}\right)$
$20y = 12x + 5$
$12x - 20y = -5$

Slope = $\frac{1}{4}$
Point: (2, -5)

$y + 5 = \frac{1}{4}(x - 2)$
$4(y) + 4(5) = 4\left(\frac{1}{4}x\right) - 4\left(\frac{2}{4}\right)$
$4y + 20 = x - 2$
$x - 4y = 22$

Slope = $-\frac{2}{3}$
Point: (-3, -2)

$y + 2 = -\frac{2}{3}(x + 3)$
$3(y) + 3(2) = 3\left(-\frac{2}{3}x\right) + 3\left(-\frac{6}{3}\right)$
$3y + 6 = -2x - 6$
$2x + 3y = -12$

Points (-3, 1) and (2, -3)
Slope = $\frac{-3-1}{2-(-3)} = \frac{-4}{5}$

$y + 3 = -\frac{4}{5}(x - 2)$
$5(y) + 5(3) = 5\left(-\frac{4}{5}x\right) + 5\left(\frac{8}{5}\right)$
$5y + 15 = -4x + 8$
$4x + 5y = -7$

Points (-2, -5) and (3, 7)
Slope = $\frac{7-(-5)}{3-(-2)} = \frac{12}{5}$

$y - 7 = \frac{12}{5}(x - 3)$
$5y - 5(7) = 5\left(\frac{12}{5}x\right) - 5\left(\frac{36}{5}\right)$
$5y - 35 = 12x - 36$
$12x - 5y = 1$

Teaching Tips, Cont.

- Show the students that once they have calculated the slope and found the y-intercept, they have enough information to write an equation in slope-intercept form for the line in the graph.
- Complete the Classwork exercise. Have one student work the problem on the board for the class. All students should work the problem in their books.

Assignment

- Complete Lesson 39, Activities 2-4.

Lesson 40

Concepts

- Writing linear equations
- Point-slope form
- Standard form
- Absolute value
- Radicals
- Extraneous solutions

Learning Objectives

The student will be able to:

- Identify two unique points on the graph of a line
- Calculate the slope of a line on a graph
- Write an equation of a line on a graph in point-slope form
- Convert linear equations to standard form

Materials Needed

- Student Book, Lesson 40
- Worksheet 20

Teaching Tips

- Review writing linear equations in slope-intercept form. (See Lesson 39)
- Introduce writing linear equations in point-slope form. Explain that the process starts the same as writing linear equations in slope-intercept form, except that the points are not necessarily intercepts. The first step is still to find two points and calculate the slope.
- Tell the students that any point may be used when writing a linear equation in point-slope form.

Writing Linear Equations: Point-Slope Form

You already know how to get an algebraic equation when you are given the slope of a line and one point on the line, and you know how to draw the graph. In this lesson you will analyze graphs and write an equation of the graph in point-slope form. This is easily accomplished by following these steps.

1. Find two points on the graph and note their coordinates.
2. Apply the formula for slope using the coordinates of the points identified in step 1. Reduce if necessary. This is the value of m in the equation.
3. Choose the coordinates of one point from step 1. The x-coordinate is the value of x_1 in the equation and the y-coordinate is the value of y_1 in the equation.
4. Write the equation in point-slope form, substituting the values for m, x_1, and y_1 from the above steps and simplify inside the parentheses if necessary.

Write an equation of the graph in point-slope form.

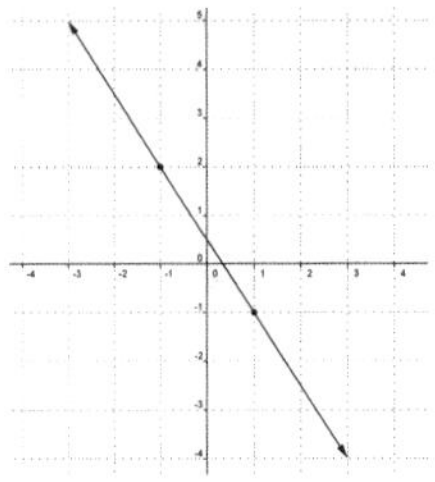

Two points on the line are (-1, 2) and (1, -1). The slope is $\frac{-1-2}{1-(-1)} = \frac{-3}{2} = -\frac{3}{2}$. Choose either point. For this exercise, we will use (-1, 2). Substitute all values into the equation.

$y - 2 = -\frac{3}{2}(x - (-1))$

$y - 2 = -\frac{3}{2}(x + 1)$

① Classwork

Write an equation of the graph in point-slope form.

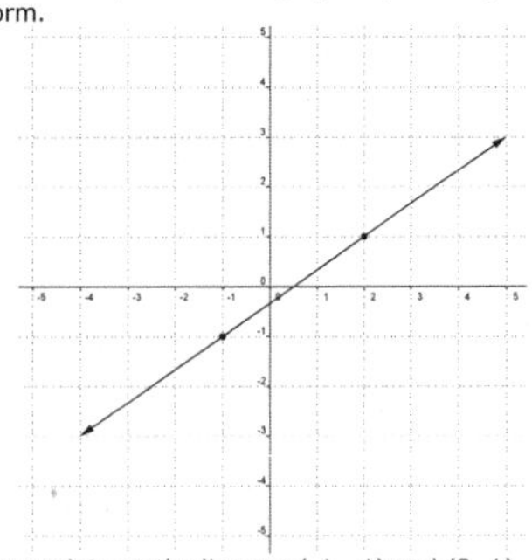

Two points on the line are (-1, -1) and (2, 1). The slope is $\frac{1-(-1)}{2-(-1)} = \frac{2}{3}$

$y + 1 = \frac{2}{3}(x + 1)$ or $y - 1 = \frac{2}{3}(x - 2)$

first point second point

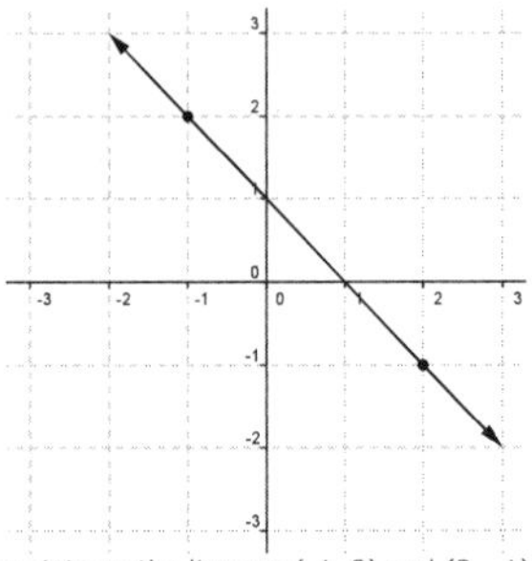

Two points on the line are (-1, 2) and (2, -1). The slope is $\frac{-1-2}{2-(-1)} = \frac{-3}{3} = -1$

$y - 2 = -(x + 1)$ or $y + 1 = -(x - 2)$

first point second point

Activities

② Write an equation of the graph in point-slope form. Convert each equation to standard form.

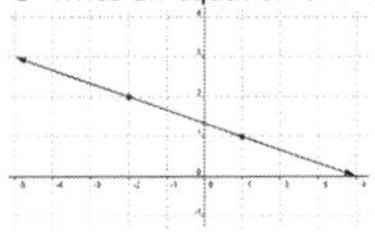

Two points on the line are (-2, 2) and (1, 1). The slope is $\frac{1-2}{1-(-2)} = \frac{-1}{3}$

$y - 2 = -\frac{1}{3}(x + 2)$ or $y - 1 = -\frac{1}{3}(x - 1)$

first point second point

$3y - 3(2) = -\frac{1}{3}(3)(x + 2)$

Standard form: $3y - 6 = -x - 2$

$x + 3y = 4$

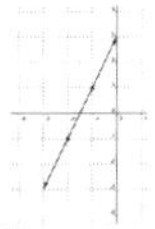

Two points are (-2, -1) and (-1, 1). The slope is $\frac{1-(-1)}{-1-(-2)} = \frac{2}{1} = 2$

$y + 1 = 2(x + 2)$ or $y - 1 = 2(x + 1)$

first point second point

Standard form: $y + 1 = 2x + 4$

$2x - y = -3$

③ Find all possible solutions. Identify any extraneous solutions.

$|4x - 18| - 11 = -3x - 8$

$|4x - 18| = -3x + 3$

$4x - 18 = -3x + 3$ or $4x - 18 = -(-3x + 3)$

$7x = 21$ $\quad$ $4x - 18 = 3x - 3$

$x = 3$ $\quad$ $x = 15$

check:

$|4(3) - 18| - 11 = -3(3) - 8$

$|12 - 18| - 11 = -9 - 8$

$|-6| - 11 = -17$

$6 - 11 \neq -17$ extraneous

$|4(15) - 18| - 11 = -3(15) - 8$

$|60 - 18| - 11 = -45 - 8$

$|42| - 11 = -53$

$42 - 11 \neq -53$ extraneous

$|-2x + 5| - 8 = 4x - 9$

$|-2x + 5| = 4x - 1$

$-2x + 5 = 4x - 1$ or $-2x + 5 = -(4x - 1)$

$-6x = -6$ $\quad$ $-2x + 5 = -4x + 1$

$x = 1$ $\quad$ $2x = -4 \Rightarrow x = -2$

check:

$|-2(1) + 5| - 8 = 4(1) - 9$

$|-2 + 5| - 8 = 4 - 9$

$|3| - 8 = -5$

$3 - 8 = -5$

$|-2(-2) + 5| - 8 = 4(-2) - 9$

$|4 + 5| - 8 = -8 - 9$

$|9| - 8 = -17$

$9 - 8 \neq -17$ extraneous

$\sqrt{-3x - 2} + 2 = 9$

$\sqrt{-3x - 2} = 7$

$\left(\sqrt{-3x - 2}\right)^2 = 7^2$

$-3x - 2 = 49$

$-3x = 51$

$x = -17$

check:

$\sqrt{-3(-17) - 2} + 2 = 9$

$\sqrt{51 - 2} + 2 = 9$

$\sqrt{49} + 2 = 9$

$7 + 2 = 9$

$\sqrt{-2x + 3} + 6 = 1$

$\sqrt{-2x + 3} = -5$

$\left(\sqrt{-2x + 3}\right)^2 = (-5)^2$

$-2x + 3 = 25$

$-2x = 22$

$x = -11$

check:

$\sqrt{-2(-11) + 3} + 6 = 1$

$\sqrt{22 + 3} + 6 = 1$

$\sqrt{25} + 6 = 1$

$5 + 6 \neq 1$ extraneous

Point-slope Form, Standard Form Worksheet 20

① Write an equation of the graph in point-slope form. Convert each equation to standard form.

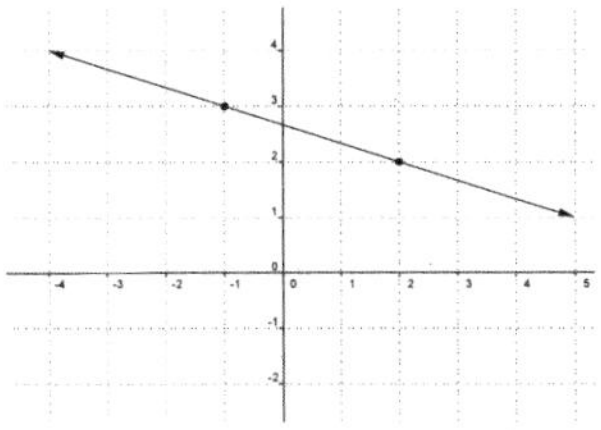

Two points on the line are (-1, 3) and (2, 2).

The slope is $\frac{2-3}{2-(-1)} = \frac{-1}{3} = -\frac{1}{3}$

$y - 3 = -\frac{1}{3}(x + 1)$ or $y - 2 = -\frac{1}{3}(x - 2)$

first point second point

Standard form:

$3y - 3(2) = -\frac{1}{3}(3)(x - 2)$

$3y - 6 = -x + 2$

$x + 3y = 8$

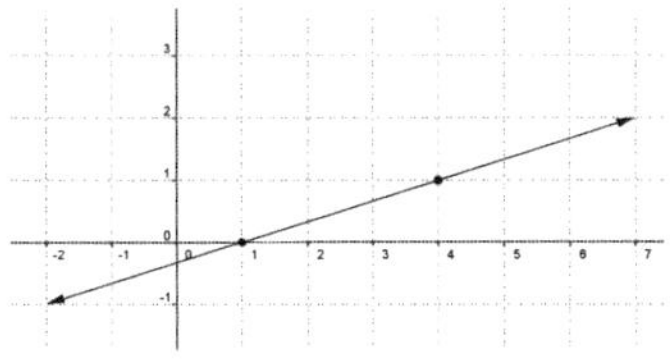

Two points on the line are (1, 0) and (4, 1).

The slope is $\frac{1-0}{4-1} = \frac{1}{3}$

$y - 0 = \frac{1}{3}(x - 1)$ or $y - 1 = \frac{1}{3}(x - 4)$

first point second point

Standard form:

$3y - 3(0) = \frac{1}{3}(3)(x - 1)$

$3y - 0 = x - 1$

$x - 3y = 1$

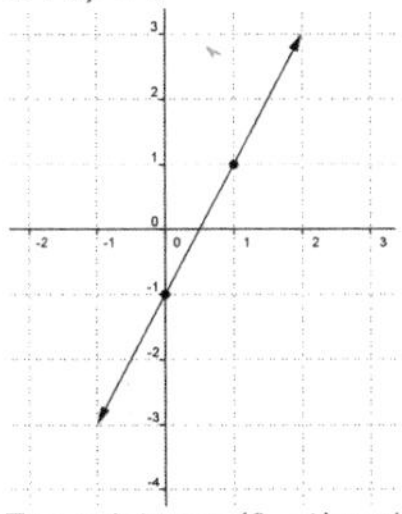

Two points are (0, -1) and (1, 1).

The slope is $\frac{1-(-1)}{1-0} = \frac{2}{1} = 2$

$y + 1 = 2(x - 0)$ or $y - 1 = 2(x - 1)$

first point second point

Standard form: $y + 1 = 2x - 0$

$2x - y = 1$

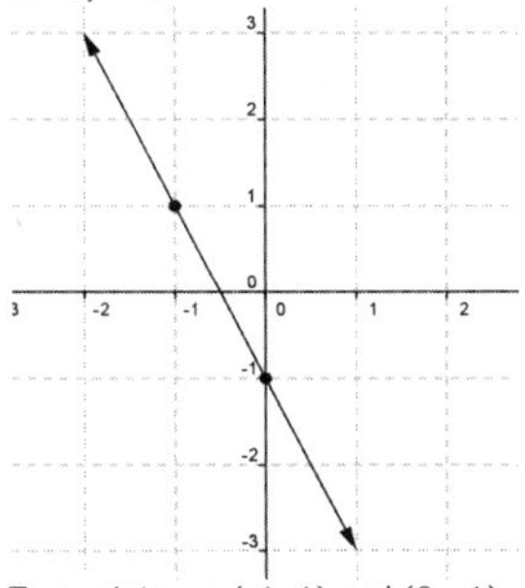

Two points are (-1, 1) and (0, -1).

The slope is $\frac{-1-1}{0-(-1)} = \frac{-2}{1} = -2$

$y - 1 = -2(x + 1)$ or $y + 1 = -2(x - 0)$

first point second point

Standard form: $y + 1 = -2x$

$2x + y = -1$

Teaching Tips, Cont.

- Make sure all students understand that there can be several correct answers for an equation of a line in point-slope form because there are an infinite number of points on a line. When the equations are written in standard form, there is only one correct answer.

- Complete the Classwork exercises. Have some students work the problems on the board for the class. All students should work the problems in their books.

- Review for Test 4 using worksheets 16-20. These worksheets were assigned in previous lessons.

- Review for Exam 1 using worksheets 1-20.

Assignments

- Complete Lesson 40, Activities 2-3.
- Worksheet 20.
- Study for Test 4 (Lessons 28-37).
- Study for Exam 1 (Lessons 1-37).

Test 4

Testing Objectives

The student will:

- Simplify expressions with rational exponents
- Plot points on a graph and identify the corresponding quadrant
- Solve two-variable equations when given the value of one variable
- Find the slope of a line formed by two given points
- Write equations in slope-intercept form and identify the slope and *y*-intercept of the line
- Write equations in point-slope form
- Graph linear equations
- Evaluate linear equations to identify pairs of lines as parallel, perpendicular, or neither
- Explain why two linear equations are parallel or perpendicular

Materials Needed

- Test 4
- *It's College Test Prep Time!* from Student Book
- Exploring Math through... Amusement Parks

Teaching Tips

- ➢ Administer Test 4, allowing the students 30-40 minutes to complete the test.
- ➢ When all students are finished taking the test, introduce the College Test Prep Time from the student book. This page may be completed in class or assigned as homework.
- ➢ Have students read the Exploring Math feature for Lessons 41-50.

① Solve. **12 points**

$49^{\frac{1}{2}} =$

$\sqrt{49} = 7$

$27^{\frac{1}{3}} =$

$\sqrt[3]{27} = 3$

$16^{\frac{1}{3}} =$

$\sqrt[3]{16} = \sqrt[3]{2 \cdot 8} = \sqrt[3]{2 \cdot 2^3} = 2\sqrt[3]{2}$

$8^{\frac{1}{2}} =$

$\sqrt{8} = \sqrt{2^3} = 2\sqrt{2}$

$243^{\frac{1}{4}} =$

$\sqrt[4]{243} = \sqrt[4]{3^5} = 3\sqrt[4]{3}$

$48^{\frac{1}{3}} =$

$\sqrt[3]{48} = \sqrt[3]{6 \cdot 8} = \sqrt[3]{6 \cdot 2^3} = 2\sqrt[3]{6}$

$12^{\frac{1}{2}} =$

$\sqrt{12} = \sqrt{3 \cdot 2^2} = 2\sqrt{3}$

$24^{\frac{1}{3}} =$

$\sqrt[3]{3 \cdot 8} = \sqrt[3]{3 \cdot 2^3} = 2\sqrt[3]{3}$

$40^{\frac{2}{3}} =$

$\sqrt[3]{40^2} = \sqrt[3]{40 \cdot 40} =$

$\sqrt[3]{2^3 \cdot 5 \cdot 2^3 \cdot 5} =$

$2 \cdot 2\sqrt[3]{5 \cdot 5} = 4\sqrt[3]{25}$

$12^{\frac{2}{3}} =$

$\sqrt[3]{12^2} = \sqrt[3]{12 \cdot 12} =$

$\sqrt[3]{3 \cdot 2^2 \cdot 3 \cdot 2^2} = \sqrt[3]{3^2 \cdot 2^4} =$

$2\sqrt[3]{3^2 \cdot 2} = 2\sqrt[3]{18}$

$36^{\frac{2}{3}} =$

$\sqrt[3]{36^2} = \sqrt[3]{36 \cdot 36} =$

$\sqrt[3]{6^2 \cdot 6^2} =$

$\sqrt[3]{6^4} = 6\sqrt[3]{6}$

$125^{\frac{2}{3}} =$

$\sqrt[3]{125^2} = \sqrt[3]{125 \cdot 125} = \sqrt[3]{5^3 \cdot 5^3} =$

$\sqrt[3]{5^6} = 5^2 = 25$

② Graph each point and identify which quadrant it is in or if it is at the origin. **10 points**

(3, 1) Quadrant I
(-2, -1) Quadrant III
(3, -2) Quadrant IV
(-1, 1) Quadrant II
(0, 0) Origin

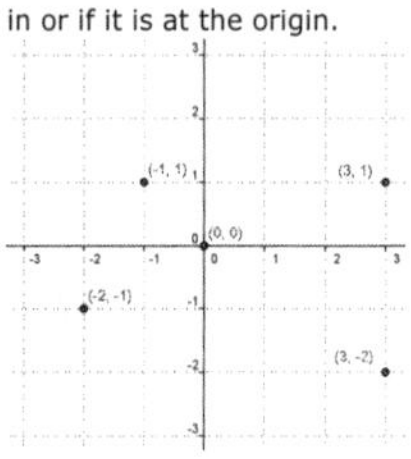

③ Solve each two-variable equation when $x = 7$. **6 points**

$y = x - 2$
$y = 7 - 2$
$y = 5$

$y = x + 9$
$y = 7 + 9$
$y = 16$

$y = 2x + 3$
$y = 2(7) + 3$
$y = 14 + 3$
$y = 17$

$y = 3x - 4$
$y = 3(7) - 4$
$y = 21 - 4$
$y = 17$

$y = 3(x + 1)$
$y = 3(7 + 1)$
$y = 3(8)$
$y = 24$

$y = 4(x - 5)$
$y = 4(7 - 5)$
$y = 4(2)$
$y = 8$

④ Find the slope of the line joining the points. **9 points**

(3, 2) and (5, 3)
$m = \frac{3-2}{5-3} = \frac{1}{2}$

(7, 5) and (4, 3)
$m = \frac{3-5}{4-7} = \frac{-2}{-3} = \frac{2}{3}$

(4, 1) and (4, 7)
$m = \frac{7-1}{4-4} = \frac{6}{0} =$ no slope

(2, -2) and (3, -1)
$m = \frac{-1-(-2)}{3-2} = \frac{1}{1} = 1$

(9, -5) and (4, -10)
$m = \frac{-10-(-5)}{4-9} = \frac{-5}{-5} = 1$

(-2, 1) and (3, 1)
$m = \frac{1-1}{3-(-2)} = \frac{0}{5} = 0$

(-8, -3) and (3, 2)
$m = \frac{2-(-3)}{3-(-8)} = \frac{5}{11}$

(4, 1) and (-1, 5)
$m = \frac{5-1}{-1-4} = \frac{4}{-5} = -\frac{4}{5}$

(7, 3) and (3, 7)
$m = \frac{7-3}{3-7} = \frac{4}{-4} = -1$

⑤ Rewrite each equation in slope-intercept form. Give the slope and *y*-intercept of each equation and draw its graph. **12 points**

$x + y - 3 = 0$
$y = -x + 3$
$m = -1$; $b = 3$

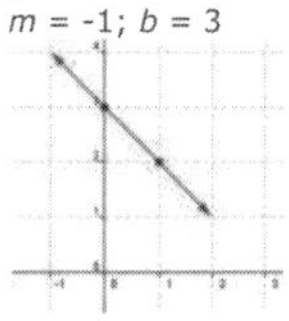

$3x + y - 6 = 0$
$y = -3x + 6$
$m = -3$; $b = 6$

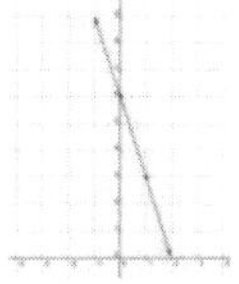

$-2x + y - 5 = 0$
$y = 2x + 5$
$m = 2$; $b = 5$

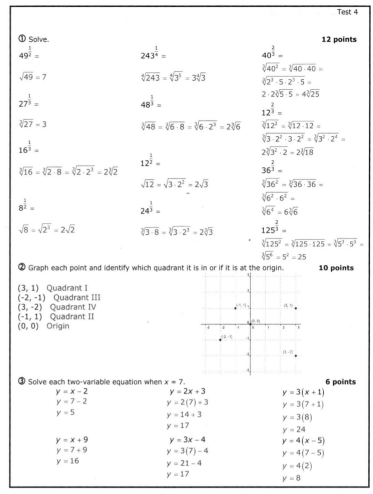

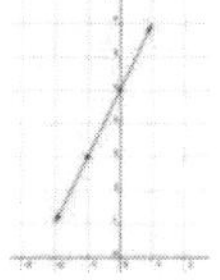

⑥ Write the point-slope form and the slope-intercept form of the equation of a line. **12 points**

$m = 2$
(4, 3)
$y - 3 = 2(x - 4)$
$y - 3 = 2x - 8$
$y = 2x - 5$

$m = -2$
(1, 4)
$y - 4 = -2(x - 1)$
$y - 4 = -2x + 2$
$y = -2x + 6$

$m = 3$
(1, -2)
$y - (-2) = 3(x - 1)$
$y + 2 = 3x - 3$
$y = 3x - 5$

$m = 1$
(-2, 2)
$y - 2 = 1(x - (-2))$
$y - 2 = 1(x + 2)$
$y - 2 = x + 2$
$y = x + 4$

$m = -4$
(1, 3)
$y - 3 = -4(x - 1)$
$y - 3 = -4x + 4$
$y = -4x + 7$

$m = -4$
(-2, -2)
$y - (-2) = -4(x - (-2))$
$y + 2 = -4(x + 2)$
$y + 2 = -4x - 8$
$y = -4x - 10$

⑦ Identify whether the two lines are parallel, perpendicular, or neither and tell why. **8 points**

$y = \frac{9}{13}x - 4$
$y = -\frac{9}{13}x + 7$
Neither. The slopes have opposite signs and are not reciprocals.

$y = \frac{9}{13}x - 4$
$y = \frac{9}{13}x + 7$
The lines are parallel because the slopes are equal.

$y = \frac{9}{13}x - 4$
$y = -\frac{13}{9}x + 7$
The lines are perpendicular because the slopes are negative reciprocals.

$y = \frac{9}{13}x - 4$
$y = \frac{13}{9}x + 7$
Neither. The slopes are reciprocals but have the same sign.

69 points total

It's College Test Prep Time!

1. In the coordinate plane, what is the slope of a line formed by the points (1, -5) and (-2, 3)?

   A. $-\frac{8}{3}$ $\frac{3-(-5)}{-2-1} = \frac{8}{-3} = -\frac{8}{3}$
   B. $-\frac{5}{6}$
   C. $-\frac{3}{8}$
   D. $\frac{1}{2}$
   E. 2

2. Given $x + 3 = 7$ and $y + 12 = 20$, what is the value of $2x + y$?
   A. 4
   B. 8 $x = 7 - 3$ $x = 4$
   C. 12 $y = 20 - 12$ $y = 8$
   D. 16 $2x + y = 2(4) + 8 = 8 + 8 = 16$
   E. 32

3. In a football game, a touchdown with an extra point is worth a total of 7 points. A field goal is worth 3 points. If a team has 37 points, how many field goals have they scored? (Assume all extra points were made and no safeties or 2-point conversions were scored.)
   A. 1
   B. 2 Use trial and error to solve.
   C. 3 5 touchdowns = 35 points. Only 2 points remain.
   D. 4 4 touchdowns = 28 points, leaving 9 points.
   E. 5 $9 \div 3 = 3$ field goals.

4. Given x is the square of an integer and a multiple of 12 and 18, find the value of x.
   A. 3 Since 18 is the larger number, look for multiples of
   B. 6 18 that are perfect squares. 18, 36, 54, . . .
   C. 9 You should recognize 36 as a perfect square. This
   D. 18 is also a multiple of 12. This is the value of x.
   E. 36 Notice that x is the square, not the integer.

Exploring Math through... Amusement Parks

When you visit an amusement park, you rarely think about the math involved outside of purchasing tickets and food. However, the very nature of an amusement park is a mathematics playground in itself. Park owners must consider the number of anticipated visitors when they set admission prices. If prices are too low, the park will not be able to handle the crowd. If prices are too high, not enough people will come to offset the day-to-day operating expenses. There are complex math formulas used to help maximize profit.

Every ride in an amusement park is a feat of mathematics. Rides designed for young children must have a low speed, height, and slope. Thrill rides have high speeds, heights, and slopes. If a ride has a speed or slope that is too high, it can be too scary or dangerous for people to ride.

Another mathematical consideration in thrill rides is the gravitational force at different points on the ride. If the gravitational force is too high, a rider's blood will be forced to his feet and could cause him to lose consciousness. On the other hand, low gravitational forces give the rider a sense of weightlessness and can increase a ride's thrill factor.

Assignments

- Complete *It's College Test Prep Time!*
- Read Exploring Math through ... Amusement Parks
- Study for Exam 1 (Lessons 1-37), if Exam 1 is being administered.

Exam 1

Testing Objectives

The student will:

- Apply the rules for signed numbers
- Simplify exponential expressions
- Apply the order of operations to mathematical expressions
- Apply the rules of absolute value
- Solve problems involving square roots and cube roots
- Translate words into mathematical expressions
- Evaluate algebraic expressions
- Add polynomials
- Subtract polynomials
- Multiply monomials
- Divide monomials
- Solve algebraic equations
- Identify properties of equality used in solving algebraic equations
- Solve algebraic equations with fractions and decimals
- Solve algebraic equations with roots and absolute values
- Identify extraneous solutions
- Simplify expressions with rational exponents
- Find the slope of a line formed by two given points
- Write equations in point-slope form
- Write equations in slope-intercept form
- Evaluate linear equations to identify pairs of lines as parallel, perpendicular, or neither
- Explain why two linear equations are parallel or perpendicular

① Solve, using the rules for signed numbers. **4 points**

(+175) + (-836) = -(836 − 175) = -661

(-12)(900) = -10,800

(-177) − (+516) = -(516 + 177) = -693

(891) ÷ (-99) = -9

② Simplify the expressions. You do not have to solve exponents greater than 3. **9 points**

$(24 \div 6)^2 = 4^2 = 16$

$7^{-3} = \left(\frac{1}{7}\right)^3 = \frac{1^3}{7^3} = \frac{1}{343}$

$19^5 \times 19^{12} = 19^{17}$

$10^{26} \div 10^{23} =$
$10^3 = 1{,}000$

$11^{-2} =$
$\left(\frac{1}{11}\right)^2 = \frac{1^2}{11^2} = \frac{1}{121}$

$\left(\frac{3}{5}\right)^3 = \frac{3^3}{5^3} = \frac{27}{125}$

$\left(\frac{3}{2}\right)^{-3} = \left(\frac{2}{3}\right)^3 = \frac{2^3}{3^3} = \frac{8}{27}$

$68^0 = 1$

$(3 \times 4)^3 =$
$3^3 \times 4^3 = 27 \times 64 = 1728$

③ Simplify each expression, following the proper order of operations. **2 points**

$2^3 \times 5 \div (17 - 12) - 9 = 2^3 \times 5 \div 5 - 9 = 8 \times 5 \div 5 - 9 = 40 \div 5 - 9 = 8 - 9 = -1$

$(6^2 - (29 - 16) + 5) \div 7 = (36 - 13 + 5) \div 7 = (23 + 5) \div 7 = 28 \div 7 = 4$

④ Solve, using the rules of absolute values. **6 points**

$|93| + |-107| =$ 93 + 107 = 200

$|28| - |-57| =$ 28 − 57 = -29

$-|45| + |-69| =$ -45 + 69 = 24

$-|-136| - |-149| =$
-136 − 149 = -285

$-|127 - 79| + |88 - 60| =$
-48 + 28 = -20

$-|240 + 128| - |416 - 152| =$
-368 − 264 = -632

⑤ Solve the following roots. **6 points**

$\sqrt{21} + \sqrt{21} = 2\sqrt{21}$

$39\sqrt[3]{25} - 17\sqrt[3]{25} = 22\sqrt[3]{25}$

$(4\sqrt{18})(5\sqrt{3}) = (4 \times 5)\sqrt{18 \times 3} = 20\sqrt{54} =$
$20\sqrt{2 \times 3 \times 3 \times 3} = 60\sqrt{6}$

$(\sqrt{27})(\sqrt{3}) = \sqrt{27 \times 3} = \sqrt{81} = \sqrt{9 \times 9} = 9$

$39\sqrt[3]{40} \div 3\sqrt[3]{5} =$
$(39 \div 3)\sqrt[3]{40 \div 5} = 13\sqrt[3]{8} = 13\sqrt[3]{2 \times 2 \times 2} = 13 \times 2 = 26$

$12 \div \sqrt{3} =$
$\sqrt{12 \times 12} \div \sqrt{3} = \sqrt{144 \div 3} = \sqrt{48} = \sqrt{3 \times 4 \times 4} = 4\sqrt{3}$

⑥ Translate the following words into a mathematical expression. **6 points**

The quotient of a number and 7 $x \div 7$

38 less than a number $x - 38$

A number less than 104 $104 - x$

The product of 33 and a number $33x$

The ratio of a number to 8 $x \div 8$

A number increased by 90 $x + 90$

⑦ Evaluate each algebraic expression. **2 points**

$8b - 3$ for $b = -2$
8(-2) − 3 = -16 − 3 = -19

$2r^2 - 4r + 5$ for $r = -3$
$2(-3)^2 - 4(-3) + 5 = 2(9) + 12 + 5 =$
18 + 12 + 5 = 30 + 5 = 35

⑧ Solve. **6 points**

$$\begin{array}{r} 8x^2 + 5x + 5 \\ +\ 2x^2 + 3x + 4 \\ \hline 10x^2 + 8x + 9 \end{array} \qquad \begin{array}{r} 7x^2 + 3x + 8 \\ +2x^2 - 2x - 6 \\ \hline 9x^2 + x + 2 \end{array} \qquad \begin{array}{r} 4x^2 \quad + 7 \\ +3x^2 + 5x - 8 \\ \hline 7x^2 + 5x - 1 \end{array}$$

$$\begin{array}{r} (8x^2 + 6x + 7) \\ -(2x^2 + 3x + 1) \\ \hline 6x^2 + 3x + 6 \end{array} \qquad \begin{array}{r} (5x^2 - 3x + 6) \\ -(x^2 - 7x) \\ \hline 4x^2 + 4x + 6 \end{array} \qquad \begin{array}{r} (6x^2 \quad - 4) \\ -(9x^2 - 7x - 4) \\ \hline -3x^2 + 7x \end{array}$$

⑨ Solve. **4 points**

$8a^3(6ab^2)$
$(8 \cdot 6)(a^{3+1})(b^2) = 48a^4b^2$

$3c^2(11c^2d^2)$
$(3 \cdot 11)(c^{2+2})(d^2) = 33c^4d^2$

$17e^3 \div e$
$\frac{17e^3}{e} = 17e^{3-1} = 17e^2$

$35f^5g^4 \div 7f^2g^3$
$\frac{35f^5g^4}{7f^2g^3} = 5f^{5-2}g^{4-3} = 5f^3g$

⑩ Solve each algebraic equation. Identify the property of equality used in each step. **9 points**

$9x - 9 = 5x + 19$
$9x - 9 - 5x = 5x + 19 - 5x \Rightarrow 4x - 9 = 19$
Subtraction property
$4x - 9 + 9 = 19 + 9 \Rightarrow 4x = 28$
Addition property
$4x \div 4 = 28 \div 4 \Rightarrow x = 7$
Division property

$5(x + 2) = 3x + 18$
$5x + 10 = 3x + 18$
Distributive property
$5x + 12 - 3x = 3x + 18 - 3x \Rightarrow 2x + 10 = 18$
Subtraction property
$2x + 10 - 10 = 18 - 10 \Rightarrow 2x = 8$
Subtraction property
$2x \div 2 = 8 \div 2 \Rightarrow x = 4$
Division property

Note: These are sample methods of solution. Other uses of properties of equality are acceptable.

⑪ Solve each algebraic equation. **2 points**

$\frac{8}{x} + \frac{9}{x^2} = \frac{5}{x} + \frac{24}{x^2}$
$\frac{8}{x}(x^2) + \frac{9}{x^2}(x^2) = \frac{5}{x}(x^2) + \frac{24}{x^2}(x^2)$
$8x + 9 = 5x + 24$
$3x + 9 = 24$
$3x = 15$
$x = 5$

$\frac{1}{6}x - 0.5 = 2$
$6(\frac{1}{6}x) - 6(0.5) = 6(2)$
$x - 3 = 12$
$x = 15$

⑫ Solve. **2 points**

$\sqrt{18}(2 + \sqrt{3})$
$2\sqrt{18} + \sqrt{18 \cdot 3} = 2\sqrt{2 \cdot 3 \cdot 3} + \sqrt{2 \cdot 3 \cdot 3 \cdot 3} =$
$2 \cdot 3\sqrt{2} + 3\sqrt{2 \cdot 3} =$
$6\sqrt{2} + 3\sqrt{6}$ or $3\sqrt{6} + 6\sqrt{2}$

$(5\sqrt{48} + 9\sqrt{42}) \div \sqrt{3}$
$\frac{5\sqrt{48}^{16}}{\sqrt{3}} + \frac{9\sqrt{42}^{14}}{\sqrt{3}} = 5\sqrt{16} + 9\sqrt{14} =$
$5\sqrt{4^2} + 9\sqrt{14} = 5 \cdot 4 + 9\sqrt{14} =$
$20 + 9\sqrt{14}$ or $9\sqrt{14} + 20$

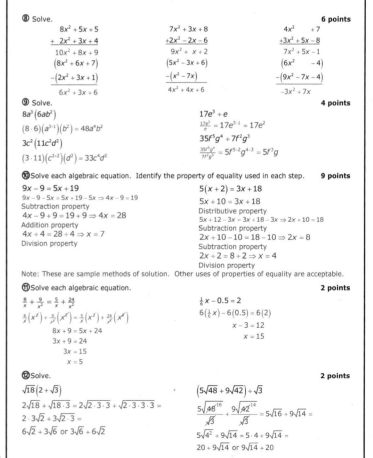

Exam 1

⑬ Solve and check. Identify any extraneous solutions. **6 points**

$\sqrt{7x+22}+15=7$
$\sqrt{7x+22}=-8$
$\left(\sqrt{7x+22}\right)^2=(-8)^2$
$7x+22=64$
$7x=42$
$x=6$

check:
$\sqrt{7(6)+22}+15=7$
$\sqrt{42+22}+15=7$
$\sqrt{64}+15=7$
$8+15\neq 7$ extraneous

$|5x-3|-3=-4x+21$
$|5x-3|=-4x+24$
$5x-3=-4x+24$ or $5x-3=-(-4x+24)$
$9x=27$ $\quad$ $5x-3=4x-24$
$x=3$ $\quad$ $x=-21$
check:
$|5(3)-3|-3=-4(3)+21$
$|15-3|-3=-12+21$
$12-3=9$

$|5(-21)-3|-3=-4(-21)+21$
$|-105-3|-3=84+21$
$108-3=105$

⑭ Solve. **4 points**

$54^{\frac{1}{3}}=$
$\sqrt[3]{54}=\sqrt[3]{2\cdot 27}=\sqrt[3]{2\cdot 3^3}=3\sqrt[3]{2}$

$18^{\frac{1}{2}}=$
$\sqrt{18}=\sqrt{2\cdot 3^2}=3\sqrt{2}$

$50^{\frac{1}{2}}=$
$\sqrt{50}=\sqrt{2\cdot 5^2}=5\sqrt{2}$

$32^{\frac{1}{3}}=$
$\sqrt[3]{4\cdot 8}=\sqrt[3]{4\cdot 2^3}=2\sqrt[3]{4}$

⑮ Find the slope of the line joining the points. **3 points**

(7, 2) and (7, 6)
$m=\frac{6-2}{7-7}=\frac{4}{0}=$ no slope

(-9, 3) and (4, 3)
$m=\frac{3-3}{4-(-9)}=\frac{0}{13}=0$

(8, 3) and (-5, 6)
$m=\frac{6-3}{-5-8}=\frac{3}{-13}=-\frac{3}{13}$

⑯ Write the point-slope form and the slope-intercept form of the equation of a line. **4 points**

m = 3; (5, 2)
$y-2=3(x-5)$
$y-2=3x-15$
$y=3x-13$

m = -4; (2, 7)
$y-7=-4(x-2)$
$y-7=-4x+8$
$y=-4x+15$

⑰ Identify whether the two lines are parallel, perpendicular, or neither and tell why. **8 points**

$y=\frac{3}{8}x-5$
$y=-\frac{3}{8}x+12$
Neither. The slopes have opposite signs and are not reciprocals.

$y=\frac{3}{8}x-5$
$y=-\frac{8}{3}x+12$
The lines are perpendicular because the slopes are negative reciprocals.

$y=\frac{3}{8}x-5$
$y=\frac{3}{8}x+12$
The lines are parallel because the slopes are equal.

$y=\frac{3}{8}x-5$
$y=\frac{8}{3}x+12$
Neither. The slopes are reciprocals but have the same sign.

83 points total

Materials Needed

- Exam 1

Teaching Tips

- Administer Exam 1, allowing the students 45-50 minutes to complete the test.

Assignment

- There is no assignment for this lesson.

Lesson 41

Concepts

- Writing linear equations in standard form
- Slope
- Writing linear equations in point-slope form
- Adding and subtracting polynomials
- Multiplying and dividing monomials
- Math in the real world

Learning Objectives

The student will be able to:

- Identify points on the graph of a line
- Calculate the slope of a line on a graph
- Write an equation in standard form of a line on a graph

Materials Needed

- Student Book, Lesson 41

Teaching Tips

➢ Review slope. (See Lesson 31)

➢ Review slope-intercept form. (See Lessons 32 and 39)

➢ Review point-slope form. (See Lessons 33 and 40)

➢ Review standard form. (See Lesson 38)

➢ Teach how to write equations in standard form from a graph. Explain that the easiest way to begin is to find the y-intercept. If the y-intercept is not obvious, use any two points and find the slope.

Lesson 41

Writing Linear Equations: Standard Form

An equation in standard form can be written for any graph of a line. Begin by finding two points on the graph and calculating the slope of the line. If one of the two points is the y-intercept, begin by writing an equation in slope-intercept form. If neither point is the y-intercept, choose one of the points and begin by writing an equation in point-slope form.

Once you have an initial equation written, apply the properties of equality to rearrange the terms into the standard form.

Write an equation of the graph in standard form.

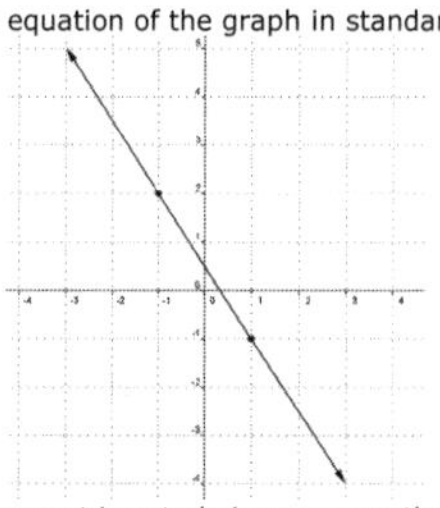

The y-intercept is not obvious, so use the two points that are marked to find the slope. Two points on the line are (-1, 2) and (1, -1). The slope is $\frac{-1-2}{1-(-1)} = \frac{-3}{2} = -\frac{3}{2}$.

Choose one point and write an equation in point-slope form. For this exercise, we will use (-1, 2). Substitute all values into the equation.

$y - 2 = -\frac{3}{2}(x - (-1))$

$y - 2 = -\frac{3}{2}(x + 1)$

Multiply both sides of the equation by 2 to eliminate the fraction.

$2(y - 2) = 2(-\frac{3}{2})(x + 1)$

$2y - 4 = -3(x + 1)$

$2y - 4 = -3x - 3$

Rearrange the terms to standard form.

$3x + 2y - 4 = -3$

$3x + 2y = 1$

① **Classwork**

Write an equation of the graph in standard form.

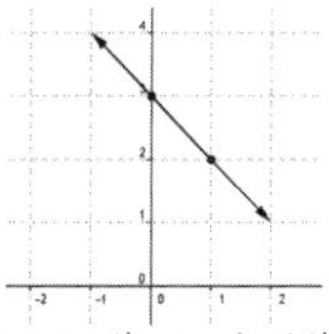

The graph crosses the y-axis at the point (0, 3) so $b = 3$.
Another point on the graph is (1, 2), so the slope is $\frac{2-3}{1-0} = \frac{-1}{1} = -1$. This is the value of m.
The equation of the graph in slope-intercept form is $y = -x + 3$.
There are no fractions to eliminate, so rearrange the terms to standard form.
$x + y = 3$

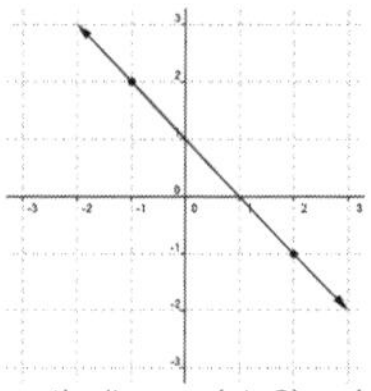

Two points on the line are (-1, 2) and (2, -1). The slope is $\frac{-1-2}{2-(-1)} = \frac{-3}{3} = -1$

$y - 2 = -(x + 1)$ or $y + 1 = -(x - 2)$
first point   second point

Standard form is
$y - 2 = -x - 1$ or $y + 1 = -x + 2$
$x + y = 1$ $x + y = 1$
first point   second point

Notice that the standard form is the same no matter which point was used.

Activities

② Write an equation of the graph in standard form.

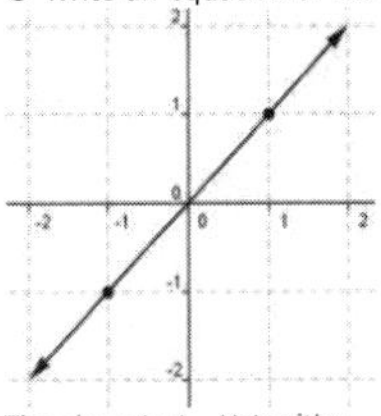

The slope is 1. Using the point (1, 1) gives the equation $y-1=1(x-1)$.

Convert to standard form.

$y-1=x-1$

$x-y=0$

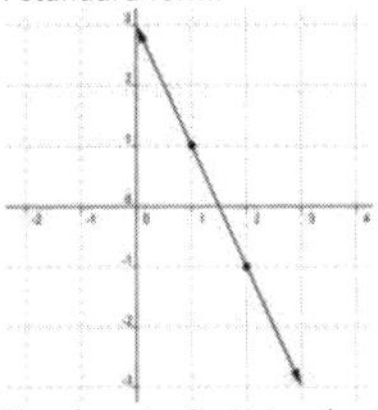

The slope is -2. Using the point (1, 1) gives the equation $y-1=-2(x-1)$.

Convert to standard form.

$y-1=-2x+2$

$2x+y=3$

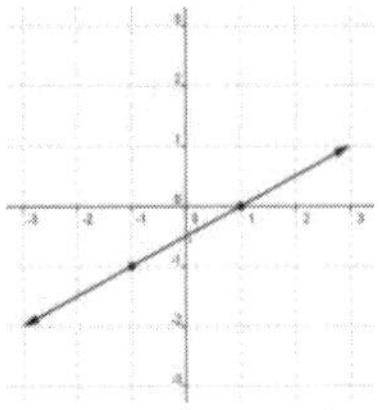

The slope is $\frac{1}{2}$. Using the point (1, 0) gives the equation $y-0=\frac{1}{2}(x-1)$.

Convert to standard form.

$2y=x-1$

$x-2y=1$

③ Solve.

$$\begin{array}{r} 64a^2+78a+37 \\ \underline{+21a^2-34a+49} \\ 85a^2+44a+86 \end{array} \qquad \begin{array}{r} 43b^2+64b+18 \\ \underline{+32b^2-79b-57} \\ 75b^2-15b-39 \end{array} \qquad \begin{array}{r} 42c^2-17c+29 \\ \underline{+37c^2+36c-12} \\ 79c^2+19c+17 \end{array}$$

$$\begin{array}{r} (35d^2+71d+18) \\ \underline{-(24d^2+22d+59)} \\ 11d^2+49d-41 \end{array} \qquad \begin{array}{r} (48e^2+28e+55) \\ \underline{-(27e^2-43e+14)} \\ 21e^2+71e+41 \end{array} \qquad \begin{array}{r} (68f^2-34f-27) \\ \underline{-(79f^2+42f-55)} \\ -11f^2-76f+28 \end{array}$$

$5g^4(-6g^{-5}h^8)(2g^4h^{-7})$

$(5\cdot -6\cdot 2)(g^{4-5+4})(h^{8-7})=$

$-60g^3h$

$-2j^5(6jk^3)(7j^{-6}k^{-3})$

$(-2\cdot 6\cdot 7)(j^{5+1-6})(k^{3-3})=$

-84

$-3m^4(4m^{-7}n^9)(-5m^{-3}n^{-4})$

$(-3\cdot 4\cdot -5)(m^{4-7-3})(n^{9-4})=$

$60m^{-6}n^5$

$54p^5 \div 6p^2$

$\frac{54p^5}{6p^2}=9p^{5-2}=9p^3$

$42r^2 \div 14r^5$

$\frac{42r^2}{14r^5}=3r^{2-5}=3r^{-3}$ or $\frac{3}{r^3}$

$77t^4 \div 11t^{-9}$

$\frac{77t^4}{11t^{-9}}=7t^{4-(-9)}=7t^{13}$

④ Solve.

The SheiKra roller coaster at Busch Gardens in Tampa, FL, takes riders up to a height of 200 feet before plunging them straight down toward the ground. What is the slope of the track of that drop?

Because the track is going straight down, it parallels the y-axis. Any line that is parallel to the y-axis has no slope. Note that this is not the same thing as a slope of zero, which would be the slope of a horizontal section of track.

Teaching Tips, Cont.

- Explain that it does not matter whether the student chooses to start with the y-intercept form or the slope-intercept form. The standard form will always be the same for a given line.
- Complete the Classwork exercises. Have some students work the problems on the board for the class and explain their answers. All students should work the problems in their books.
- Use the second exercise in the Classwork section to show that the chosen point in the point-slope form does not affect the standard form equation. You may wish to have the student who worked the problem on the board work it a second time using the second point to illustrate this concept.

Assignment

- Complete Lesson 41, Activities 2-4.

Lesson 42

Concepts

- Perpendicular lines
- Slope
- Writing algebraic equations in point-slope form
- Writing algebraic equations in standard form
- Graphing linear equations

Learning Objectives

The student will be able to:

- Calculate the slope of a line perpendicular to a line on a graph
- Write an equation of a line perpendicular to a line on a graph at a given point in point-slope form
- Write an equation of a line perpendicular to a line on a graph at a given point in standard form

Materials Needed

- Student Book, Lesson 42
- Worksheet 21

Teaching Tips

> Have students complete Worksheet 21 in class. This may be for added practice of earlier topics, or graded as a quiz, if desired.

> Review perpendicular lines. (See Lesson 36)

> Review point-slope form. (See Lessons 33 and 40)

> Review writing linear equations in standard form. (See Lesson 41)

> Explain that writing an equation of a perpendicular line follows the same rules the students learned in the previous lesson.

Writing Linear Equations: Perpendicular Lines

Recall from Lesson 36 that perpendicular lines have slopes that are negative reciprocals of each other. To write an equation of a line perpendicular to a given line on a graph, follow these steps.

- Find the slope of the given line.
- Find the negative reciprocal of the slope to get the slope of the perpendicular line.
- Choose a point on the given line and write an equation in point-slope form.
- Convert the equation to standard form.

Write an equation in standard form of a line perpendicular to the given line.

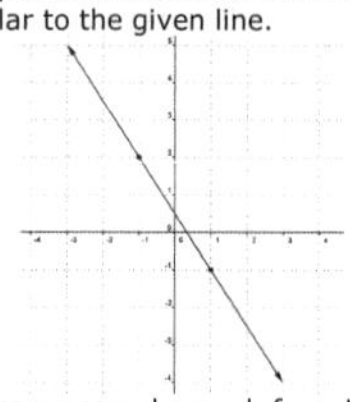

This is the same sample graph from Lesson 41, where we found the slope to be $-\frac{3}{2}$. The slope of a perpendicular line is the negative reciprocal of this number, or $\frac{2}{3}$.

Choose any point on the given line to write an equation. If you choose point (-1, 2), the point-slope form is $y-2=\frac{2}{3}(x+1)$. Now rewrite in standard form.

$3y-6=2(x+1)$

$3y-6=2x+2$

$2x-3y=-8$

If you choose point (1, -1), the point-slope form is $y+1=\frac{2}{3}(x-1)$. Now rewrite in standard form.

$3y+3=2(x-1)$

$3y+3=2x-2$

$2x-3y=5$

Because there are an infinite number of points on a line, there are also an infinite number of possible perpendicular lines and therefore an infinite number of possible equations. For all exercises in this book, choose a point shown on the graph unless otherwise instructed.

① Classwork

Write equations in standard form of the lines perpendicular to the given line at each of the points shown on the graph.

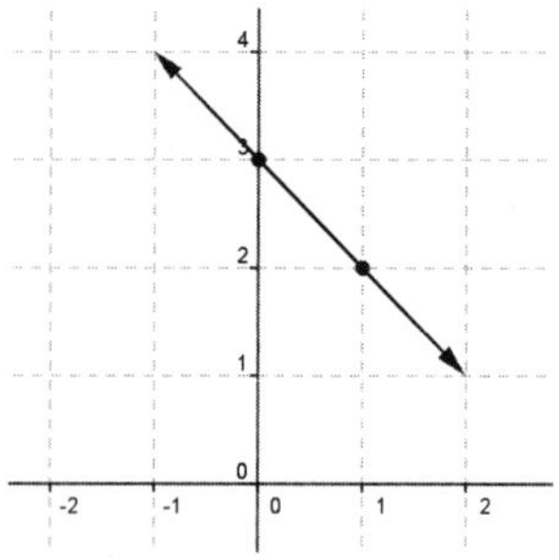

The slope is $\frac{2-3}{1-0}=\frac{-1}{1}=-1$. The negative reciprocal is 1. This is the slope of each perpendicular line.

The equation of the graph in point-slope form for the point (0, 3) is $y-3=1(x-0)$.

Rewrite in standard form.

$y-3=x$

$x-y=-3$

The equation of the graph in point-slope form for the point (1, 2) is $y-2=1(x-1)$.

Rewrite in standard form.

$y-2=x-1$

$x-y=-1$

Activities

② Write equations in standard form of the lines perpendicular to the given line at each of the points shown on the graph. Graph the original line and both perpendicular lines on your own graph paper.

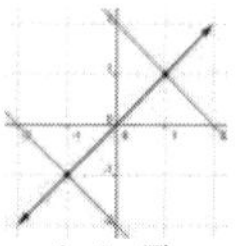

The slope is 1. The negative reciprocal is -1. This is the slope of each perpendicular line. The equation of the graph in point-slope form for the point (1, 1) is $y-1=-1(x-1)$. Rewrite in standard form.

$y-1=-x+1$

$x+y=2$

The equation of the graph in point-slope form for the point (-1, -1) is $y+1=-1(x+1)$. Rewrite in standard form.

$y+1=-x-1$

$x+y=-2$

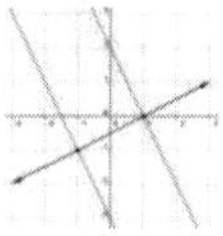

The slope is $\frac{1}{2}$. The negative reciprocal is -2. This is the slope of each perpendicular line. The equation of the graph in point-slope form for the point (1, 0) is $y-0=-2(x-1)$. Rewrite in standard form.

$y=-2x+2$

$2x+y=2$

The equation of the graph in point-slope form for the point (-1, -1) is $y+1=-2(x+1)$. Rewrite in standard form.

$y+1=-2x-2$

$2x+y=-3$

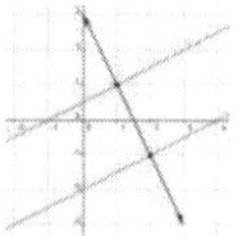

The slope is-2. The negative reciprocal is $\frac{1}{2}$. This is the slope of each perpendicular line. The equation of the graph in point-slope form for the point (1, 1) is $y-1=\frac{1}{2}(x-1)$. Rewrite in standard form.

$2y-2=x-1$

$x-2y=-1$

The equation of the graph in point-slope form for the point (2, -1) is $y+1=\frac{1}{2}(x-2)$. Rewrite in standard form.

$2y+2=x-2$

$x-2y=4$

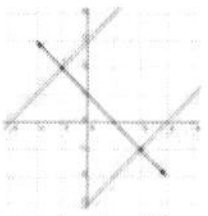

The slope is-1. The negative reciprocal is 1. This is the slope of each perpendicular line. The equation of the graph in point-slope form for the point (2, -1) is $y+1=1(x-2)$. Rewrite in standard form.

$y+1=x-2$

$x-y=3$

The equation of the graph in point-slope form for the point (-1, 2) is $y-2=1(x+1)$. Rewrite in standard form.

$y-2=x+1$

$x-y=-3$

Slope-intercept Form, Point-slope Form, Standard Form Worksheet 21

① Write an equation of the graph in slope-intercept form.

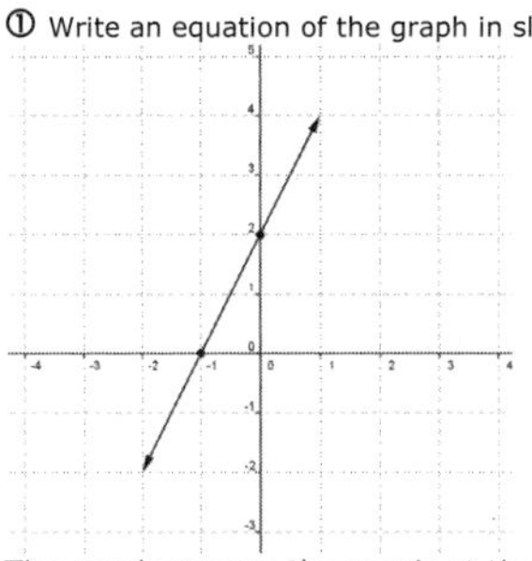

The graph crosses the y-axis at the point (0, 2) so b = 2. Another point on the graph is (-1, 0), so the slope is $\frac{0-2}{-1-0} = \frac{-2}{-1} = 2$. This is the value of m. The equation of the graph in slope-intercept form is $y = 2x + 2$.

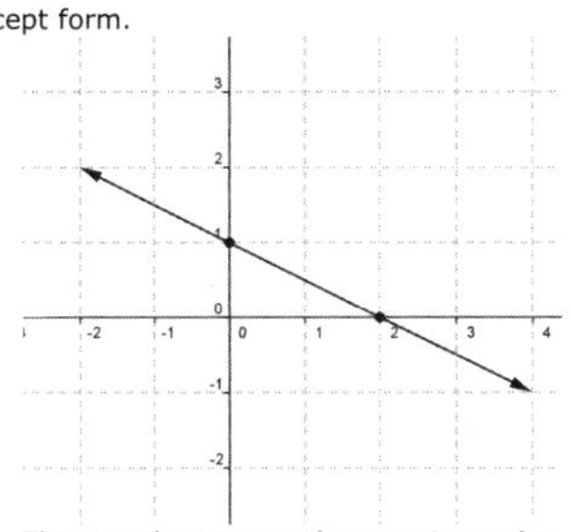

The graph crosses the y-axis at the point (0, 1) so b = 1. Another point on the graph is (2, 0), so the slope is $\frac{0-1}{2-0} = \frac{-1}{2} = -\frac{1}{2}$. This is the value of m. The equation of the graph in slope-intercept form is $y = -\frac{1}{2}x + 1$.

② Write an equation of the graph in point-slope form. Convert each equation to standard form.

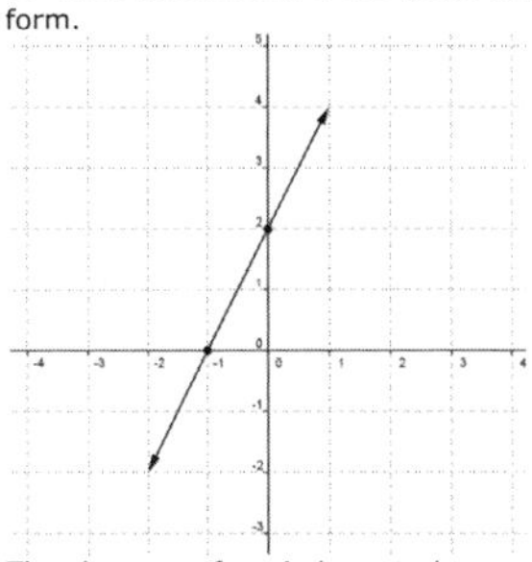

The slope was found above to be m = 2.

$y - 2 = 2(x - 0)$ or $y - 0 = 2(x + 1)$

first point second point

$y - 0 = 2x + 2$

Standard form: $y = 2x + 2$

$2x - y = -2$

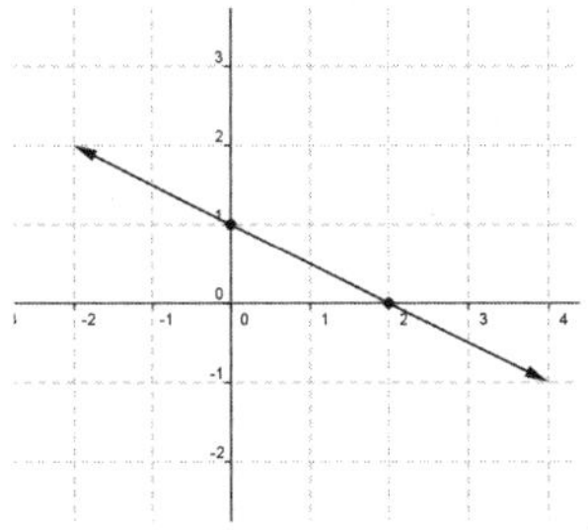

The slope was found above to be $m = -\frac{1}{2}$.

$y - 1 = -\frac{1}{2}(x - 0)$ or $y - 0 = -\frac{1}{2}(x - 2)$

first point second point

$2y - 2(0) = -\frac{1}{2}(2)(x - 2)$

Standard form: $2y = -x + 2$

$x + 2y = 2$

Teaching Tips, Cont.

- Ask the students if it is OK to use the slope of the line shown in the graph as the slope of a perpendicular line. (No) Why not? (Perpendicular lines have slopes that are negative reciprocals.)
- Ask the students what kind of line would have the same slope as the line on a graph. (Parallel line)
- Teach how to write an equation of a line perpendicular to a given line from the teaching box. Emphasize that the negative reciprocal of the slope MUST be used.
- Remind students to always convert equations to standard form when they are finished unless otherwise instructed.
- Complete the Classwork exercise. Have one student work the problem on the board for the class and explain the answers. All students should work the problem in their books.

Assignment

- Complete Lesson 42, Activity 2.

Lesson 43

Concepts
- Parallel lines
- Slope
- Equations in point-slope form
- Equations in standard form
- Graphing equations
- Math in the real world

Learning Objectives
The student will be able to:
- Define *ratio*
- Write a ratio in three different formats
- Reduce ratios to simplest form
- Calculate ratios from given sets of data
- Subtract mixed numbers without converting to improper fractions

Materials Needed
- Student Book, Lesson 43
- Worksheet 22

Teaching Tips
- Review parallel lines. (See Lesson 37)
- Review writing equations in point-slope form. (See Lesson 40)
- Ask the students what information they must know before they can write an equation of a line. (Any one of the following: two points, one point and the slope, or the *y*-intercept and the slope.)
- Ask the students how they can know the slope of a line parallel to a given line on a graph. (A parallel line has a slope equal to the slope of the line on the graph.)

Writing Linear Equations: Parallel Lines

Recall from Lesson 37 that parallel lines have equal slopes. To write an equation of a line parallel to a given line on a graph, follow these steps.
- Find the slope of the given line.
- Choose a point NOT on the given line and write an equation in point-slope form. The easiest point to use is the origin if it is available.
- Convert the equation to standard form.

Write an equation in standard form of a line parallel to the given line.

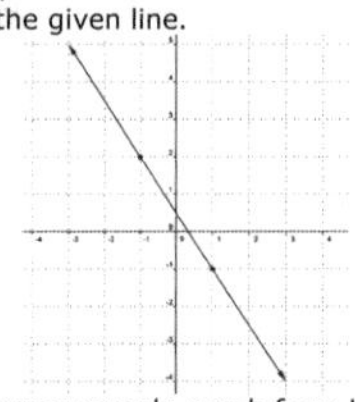

This is the same sample graph from Lesson 41, where we found the slope to be $-\frac{3}{2}$. The slope of a parallel line is also $-\frac{3}{2}$.

Choose any point not on the given line to write an equation. Using point (0, 0), the point-slope form is $y - 0 = -\frac{3}{2}(x - 0)$. Now rewrite in standard form.

$2y - 0 = -3(x - 0)$

$2y = -3x$

$3x + 2y = 0$

① **Classwork**

Write an equation in standard form of a line through the origin parallel to the given line.

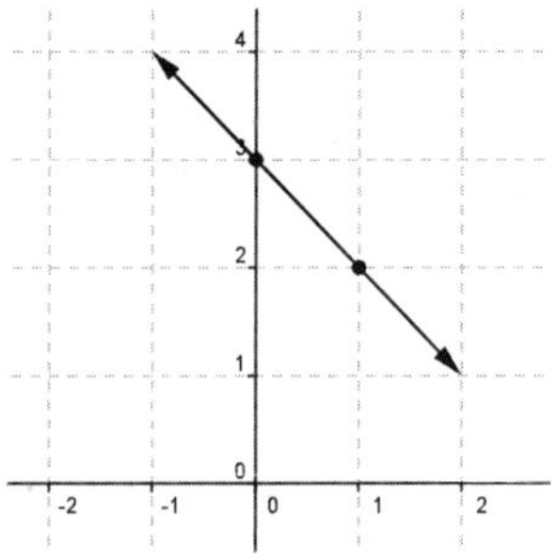

The slope is -1. This is the slope of each parallel line.

The equation of the graph in point-slope form for the point (0, 0) is $y - 0 = -1(x - 0)$.

Rewrite in standard form.

$y = -x$

$x + y = 0$

Activities

② Write an equation in standard form of a line through the origin parallel to the given line.

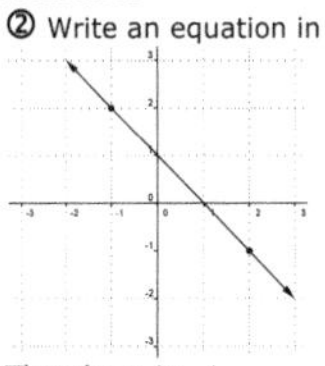

The slope is -1. This is the slope of each parallel line.

The equation of the graph in point-slope form for the point (0, 0) is $y - 0 = -1(x - 0)$.

Rewrite in standard form.

$y = -x$

$x + y = 0$

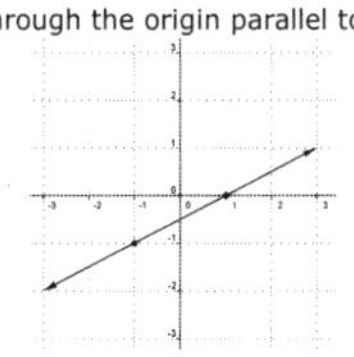

The slope is $\frac{1}{2}$. This is the slope of each parallel line.

The equation of the graph in point-slope form for the point (0, 0) is $y - 0 = \frac{1}{2}(x - 0)$.

Rewrite in standard form.

$2y = x$

$x - 2y = 0$

③ Write an equation in standard form of a line through the point (-1, 1) parallel to the given line. Graph the original line and the parallel line.

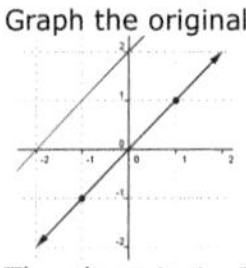

The slope is 1. This is the slope of each parallel line.

The equation of the graph in point-slope form for the point (-1, 1) is $y - 1 = 1(x + 1)$.

Rewrite in standard form.

$y - 1 = x + 1$

$x - y = -2$

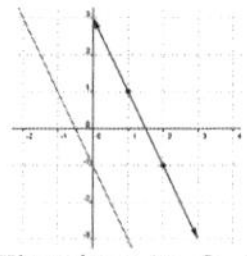

The slope is -2. This is the slope of each parallel line.

The equation of the graph in point-slope form for the point (-1, 1) is $y - 1 = -2(x + 1)$. Rewrite in standard form.

$y - 1 = -2x - 2$

$2x + y = -1$

④ Solve.

The Dominator roller coaster at King's Dominion in Doswell, VA, has a 148-ft. drop with a horizontal displacement of 96 feet. What is the slope of the drop? (Hint: Draw a picture if necessary and assign coordinate points to the top and bottom of the drop.)

Let the top of the drop be represented by the point (0, 148) and the bottom of the drop be represented by the point (96, 0). Use the slope formula with these two points.

$$\text{slope} = \frac{0 - 148}{96 - 0} = \frac{-148}{96} = -\frac{37}{24}$$

Note that it is also correct to assign the bottom of the drop the point (-96, 0) depending on how the coaster is pictured. Using this point would change the answer to

$$\text{slope} = \frac{0 - 148}{-96 - 0} = \frac{-148}{-96} = \frac{37}{24}$$

Either answer is correct for this problem.

The Great American Scream Machine at Six Flags over Georgia takes riders up to a height of 105 feet. If the initial hill has a slope of -1 and the base of the hill is 87 feet away horizontally from the peak, how far above the ground is the bottom of the first hill? (Hint: Draw a picture if necessary and assign coordinate points to the top and bottom of the hill.)

The slope is given as -1, so use this value in the formula for slope. Let the top of the hill be represented by the point (0, 105). The bottom of the hill must be represented by the point (87, *y*) since we do not know the height of the bottom of the hill.

$m = \frac{y_2 - y_1}{x_2 - x_1}$

$-1 = \frac{y - 105}{87 - 0}$

$-1 = \frac{y - 105}{87}$

$-87 = y - 105$

$y = 18$

The bottom of the hill is 18 feet above the ground.

Perpendicular and Parallel Lines Worksheet 22

① Write an equation in standard form of a line through the origin perpendicular to the given line.

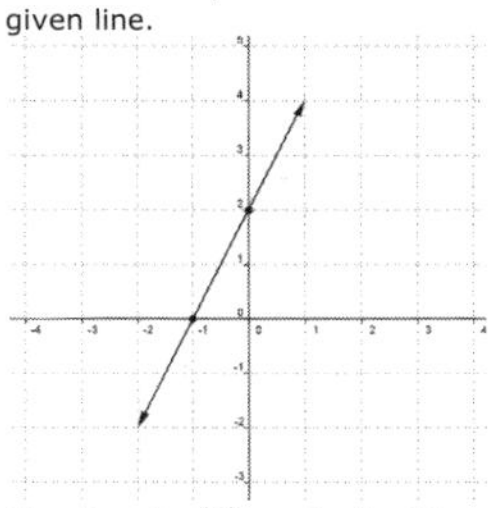

The slope is $\frac{0-2}{-1-0} = \frac{-2}{-1} = 2$. The negative reciprocal is $-\frac{1}{2}$. This is the slope of the perpendicular line.

The equation of the graph in point-slope form for the point (0, 0) is $y - 0 = -\frac{1}{2}(x - 0)$. Rewrite in standard form.

$2y - 0 = -x + 0$

$x + 2y = 0$

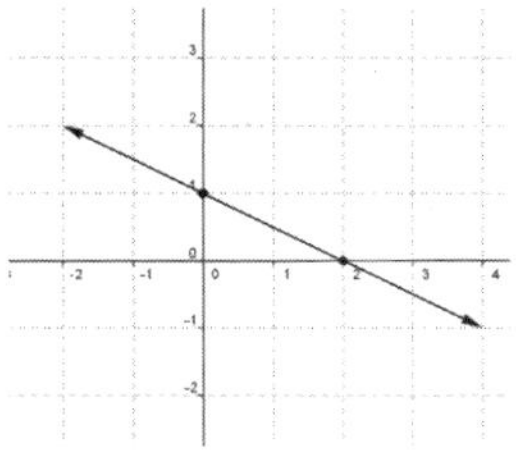

The slope is $\frac{0-1}{2-0} = \frac{-1}{2} = -\frac{1}{2}$. The negative reciprocal is 2. This is the slope of the perpendicular line.

The equation of the graph in point-slope form for the point (0, 0) is $y - 0 = 2(x - 0)$. Rewrite in standard form.

$y - 0 = 2x - 0$

$2x - y = 0$

② Write an equation in standard form of a line through the origin parallel to the given line.

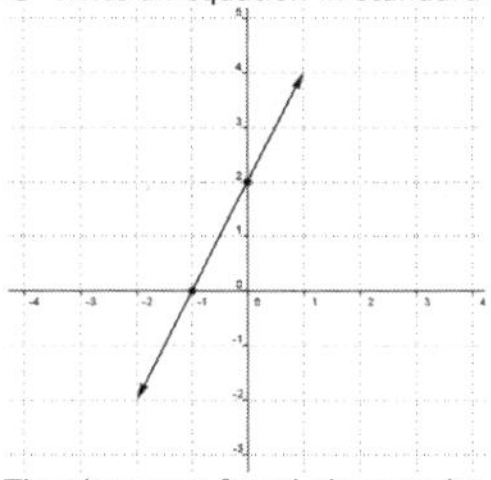

The slope was found above to be $m = 2$. This is the slope of the parallel line.

The equation of the graph in point-slope form for the point (0, 0) is $y - 0 = 2(x - 0)$. Rewrite in standard form.

$y - 0 = 2x - 0$

$2x - y = 0$

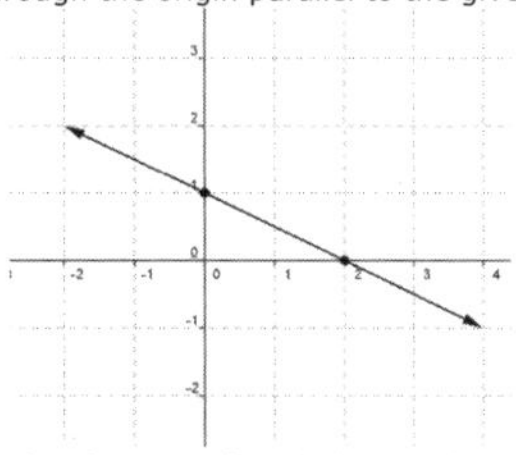

The slope was found above to be $m = -\frac{1}{2}$. This is the slope of the parallel line.

The equation of the graph in point-slope form for the point (0, 0) is $y - 0 = -\frac{1}{2}(x - 0)$. Rewrite in standard form.

$2y - 0 = -x + 0$

$x + 2y = 0$

Teaching Tips, Cont.

- Teach how to write a linear equation of a line parallel to a line on a graph. Emphasize that the slope of the parallel line MUST equal the slope of the line on the graph.
- Tell the students that once they know the slope of the parallel line, the only other piece of information they need is the coordinates of one point the parallel line passes through.
- Remind students to always convert equations to standard form when they are finished unless otherwise instructed.
- Complete the Classwork exercise. Have one student work the problem on the board for the class and explain the answers. All students should work the problem in their books.

Assignments

- Complete Lesson 43, Activities 2-4.
- Worksheet 22.

Lesson 44

Concepts

- Writing linear equations from graphs
- Horizontal lines
- Vertical lines
- Slope
- Parallel lines
- Perpendicular lines
- Math in the real world

Learning Objectives

The student will be able to:

- Write an equation in standard form of a line on a graph
- Write equations in standard form for lines that are parallel or perpendicular to a line on a graph
- Draw the graphs of standard form equations

Materials Needed

- Student Book, Lesson 44

Teaching Tips

➢ Review writing linear equations in slope-intercept form. (See Lesson 39)

➢ Review writing linear equations in point-slope form. (See Lesson 40)

➢ Review writing linear equations in standard form. (See Lesson 41)

➢ Review writing linear equations of perpendicular lines. (See Lesson 42)

➢ Review writing linear equations of parallel lines. (See Lesson 43)

Lesson 44

Writing Linear Equations from Graphs

So far you have learned about equations written in slope-intercept form, point-slope form, and standard form. You have also learned about horizontal and vertical lines, perpendicular lines, and parallel lines. In this lesson you will apply everything you have learned in the past 14 lessons.

When writing an equation from a graph, look for specific short-cuts.

- Is the line horizontal? If so, the equation is in the format $y = c$.
- Is the line vertical? If so, the equation is in the format $x = c$.
- Is the y-intercept shown? If so, use the equation $y = mx+b$.
- If none of the above are true, use the equation $y - y_1 = m(x - x_1)$.

Unless otherwise instructed, all equations, except those for horizontal and vertical lines, should be written in standard form.

Write an equation of the line in the graph. Then write an equation of a parallel line, a horizontal line through point *A*, a vertical line through point *B*, and a perpendicular line through point *C*.

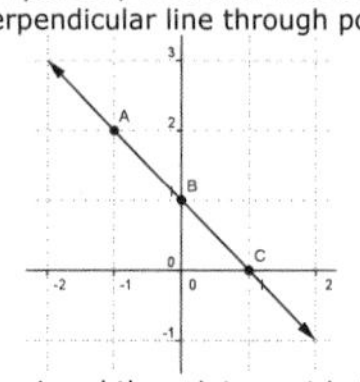

The slope is -1 and the *y*-intercept is (0, 1) so $b = 1$. The equation of the line is $y = -x + 1$ or $x + y = 1$ (standard form).
A parallel line has the same slope as the given line and any *y*-intercept except that of the given line. For example, $x + y = 2$
Point *A* is (-1, 2) so a horizontal line is $y = 2$.
Point *B* is (0, 1) so a vertical line is $x = 0$.
The negative reciprocal of the slope is 1, so a perpendicular line through point *C* is
$y - 0 = 1(x - 1) \Rightarrow y = x - 1 \Rightarrow$
$x - y = 1$

① **Classwork**

Write an equation of the line in the graph. Then write an equation of a parallel line, a horizontal line through point *A*, a vertical line through point *B*, and a perpendicular line through point *C*.

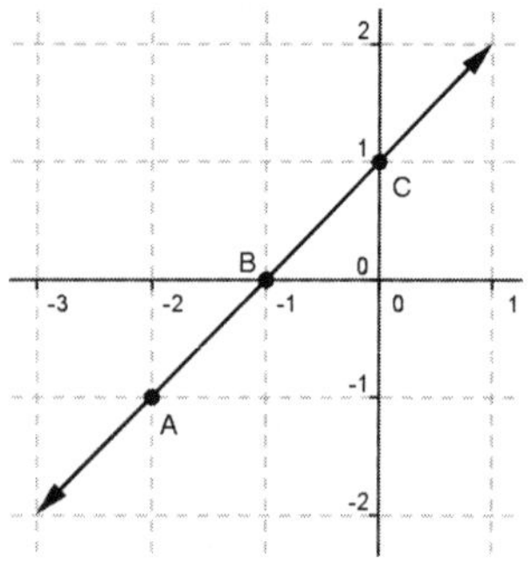

The slope is 1 and the *y*-intercept is (0, 1) so $b = 1$. The equation of the line is $y = x + 1$ or $x - y = -1$ (standard form).

A parallel line has the same slope as the given line and any *y*-intercept except that of the given line. For example, $x - y = 2$.

Point *A* is (-2, -1) so a horizontal line is $y = -1$.

Point *B* is (-1, 0) so a vertical line is $x = -1$.

The negative reciprocal of the slope is -1, so a perpendicular line through point *C* is

$y - 1 = -1(x - 0) \Rightarrow y - 1 = -x \Rightarrow$

$x + y = 1$

Activities

② Write an equation of the line in the graph. Then write an equation of a parallel line, a horizontal line through point *A*, a vertical line through point *B*, and a perpendicular line through point *C*.

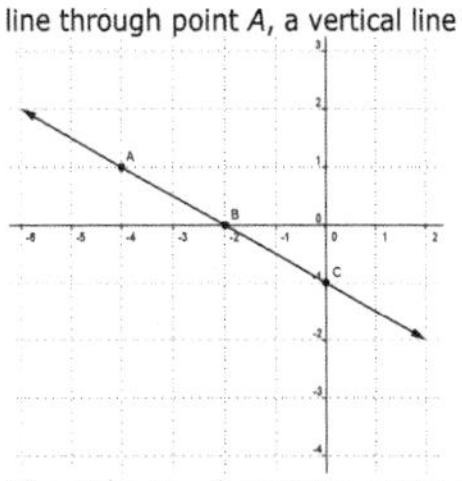

The slope is $-\frac{1}{2}$ and the y-intercept is (0, -1) so $b = -1$. The equation of the line is $y = -\frac{1}{2}x - 1$ or $x + 2y = -2$ (standard form).
A parallel line has the same slope as the given line and any y-intercept except that of the given line. For example, $x + 2y = 2$.
Point *A* is (-4, 1) so a horizontal line is $y = 1$.
Point *B* is (-2, 0) so a vertical line is $x = -2$.
The negative reciprocal of the slope is 2, so a perpendicular line through point *C* is
$y + 1 = 2(x - 0) \Rightarrow y + 1 = 2x \Rightarrow$
$2x - y = 1$

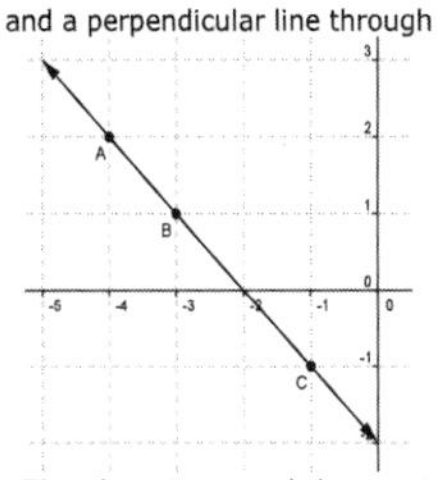

The slope is -1 and the y-intercept is (0, -2) so $b = -2$. The equation of the line is $y = -x - 2$ or $x + y = -2$ (standard form).
A parallel line has the same slope as the given line and any y-intercept except that of the given line. For example, $x + y = 2$.
Point *A* is (-4, 2) so a horizontal line is $y = 2$.
Point *B* is (-3, 1) so a vertical line is $x = -3$.
The negative reciprocal of the slope is 1, so a perpendicular line through point *C* is
$y + 1 = 1(x + 1) \Rightarrow y + 1 = x + 1 \Rightarrow$
$x - y = 0$

③ Solve.

A roller coaster train leaves the loading station, which is 16 feet above the ground, and moves horizontally to the base of the lift chain 20 feet away. The lift raises the train to a height of 97 feet off the ground. If the top of the lift is a horizontal distance of 18 feet from the bottom of the lift, what is the slope of the lift? Using the coordinate point (0, 16) for the bottom of the lift, write an equation of the line formed by the lift chain if the track heads in the positive direction.

The bottom of the lift is at the point (0, 16).
The top of the lift is at the point (18, 97). The slope of the lift is $\frac{97-16}{18-0} = \frac{81}{18} = \frac{9}{2}$.

$y - 16 = \frac{9}{2}(x - 0)$
$2y - 32 = 9x$
$9x - 2y = -32$

Teaching Tips, Cont.

- Tell the students that this lesson is a review of the material covered in the past 14 lessons. There is no new material to master. Rather, this is a summary application of everything they have learned about linear equations.
- Answer any questions the students have regarding linear equations. Refer to Lessons 30-43 as necessary.
- Complete the Classwork exercise. Have one student work the problem on the board for the class and explain the answer. All students should work the problem in their books.

Assignment

- Complete Lesson 44, Activities 2-3.

Lesson 45

Concepts

- Solving inequalities with positive divisors
- Absolute value
- Extraneous solutions
- Square roots
- Math in the real world

Learning Objectives

The student will be able to:

- Define *inequality*
- Solve inequalities with positive divisors

Materials Needed

- Student Book, Lesson 45
- Worksheet 23

Teaching Tips

- Have students complete Worksheet 23 in class. This may be for added practice of earlier topics, or graded as a quiz, if desired.
- Review the properties of equality. (See Lesson 16)
- Define *inequalities* from the teaching box.
- Tell the students that the properties of equality apply to inequalities as well, but with some restrictions.
- Teach the rules for working with inequalities from the teaching box.

Solving Inequalities: Positive Divisors

Inequalities show the relationship between two things that are not equal.

When working with inequalities in mathematical expressions, follow these rules:

- You may add or subtract the same amount from both sides of the inequality sign.
- You may multiply or divide both sides of the inequality sign by the same positive number.

For example, $3x < 12$.
Divide each side by 3 to get $x < 4$.

① Classwork
Solve the inequalities.

$5x < 30$
$5x \div 5 < 30 \div 5$
$x < 6$

$4x + 5 > 17$
$4x + 5 - 5 > 17 - 5$
$4x > 12$
$4x \div 4 > 12 \div 4$
$x > 3$

$x - 2 < -x + 8$
$x + x - 2 + 2 < -x + x + 8 + 2$
$2x < 10$
$x < 5$

Activities

② Solve the inequalities.

$4x < 12$
$4x \div 4 < 12 \div 4$
$x < 3$

$7x + 11 > 18$
$7x + 11 - 11 > 18 - 11$
$7x > 7$
$7x \div 7 > 7 \div 7$
$x > 1$

$3x - 9 < x + 13$
$3x - x - 9 < x - x + 13$
$2x - 9 + 9 < 13 + 9$
$2x < 22$
$x < 11$

$3x < 9$
$3x \div 3 < 9 \div 3$
$x < 3$

$4x + 7 > 3x - 2$
$4x - 3x + 7 > 3x - 3x - 2$
$x + 7 - 7 > -2 - 7$
$x > -9$

$9x + 7 < 5x + 3$
$9x - 5x + 7 < 5x - 5x + 3$
$4x + 7 - 7 < 3 - 7$
$4x < -4$
$x < -1$

$5x > -15$
$5x \div 5 > -15 \div 5$
$x > -3$

$6x + 7 > 13$
$6x + 7 - 7 > 13 - 7$
$6x \div 6 > 6 \div 6$
$x > 1$

$7x - 5 < -x + 11$
$7x + x - 5 < -x + x + 11$
$8x - 5 + 5 < 11 + 5$
$8x < 16$
$x < 2$

$2x + 3 < 9$
$2x + 3 - 3 < 9 - 3$
$2x < 6$
$x < 3$

$3x + 3 > -2x - 7$
$3x + 2x + 3 > -2x + 2x - 7$
$5x + 3 - 3 > -7 - 3$
$5x > -10$
$x > -2$

$6x + 17 < 2x + 13$
$6x - 2x + 17 < 2x - 2x + 13$
$4x + 17 - 17 < 13 - 17$
$4x < -4$
$x < -1$

$6x - 7 < 11$
$6x - 7 + 7 < 11 + 7$
$6x < 18$
$x < 3$

$5x > x + 12$
$5x - x > x - x + 12$
$4x > 12$
$x > 3$

$4x - 5 < -3x + 16$
$4x + 3x - 5 < -3x + 3x + 16$
$7x - 5 + 5 < 16 + 5$
$7x < 21$
$x < 3$

③ Find all possible solutions. Identify any extraneous solutions.

$|9x + 1| + 3 = 5x - 8$
$|9x + 1| = 5x - 11$
$9x + 1 = 5x - 11$ or $9x + 1 = -(5x - 11)$
$4x = -12$ $\quad$ $9x + 1 = -5x + 11$
$x = -3$ $\quad$ $14x = 10 \Rightarrow x = \frac{10}{14} = \frac{5}{7}$
check:
$|9(-3) + 1| + 3 = 5(-3) - 8$
$|-27 + 1| + 3 = -15 - 8$
$|-26| + 3 = -23$
$26 + 3 \neq -23$ extraneous

$|9(\frac{5}{7}) + 1| + 3 = 5(\frac{5}{7}) - 8$
$|\frac{45}{7} + \frac{7}{7}| + \frac{21}{7} = \frac{25}{7} - \frac{56}{7}$
$|\frac{52}{7}| + \frac{21}{7} = -\frac{31}{7}$
$\frac{52}{7} + \frac{21}{7} \neq -\frac{31}{7}$ extraneous

$|5x - 2| - 4 = -2x + 15$
$|5x - 2| = -2x + 19$
$5x - 2 = -2x + 19$ or $5x - 2 = -(-2x + 19)$
$7x = 21$ $\quad$ $5x - 2 = 2x - 19$
$x = 3$ $\quad$ $3x = -17 \Rightarrow x = -\frac{17}{3}$
check:
$|5(3) - 2| - 4 = -2(3) + 15$
$|15 - 2| - 4 = -6 + 15$
$13 - 4 = 9$

$|5(-\frac{17}{3}) - 2| - 4 = -2(-\frac{17}{3}) + 15$
$|-\frac{85}{3} - \frac{6}{3}| - \frac{12}{3} = \frac{34}{3} + \frac{45}{3}$
$|-\frac{91}{3}| - \frac{12}{3} = \frac{79}{3}$
$\frac{91}{3} - \frac{12}{3} = \frac{79}{3}$

$\sqrt{-11x - 10} - 1 = 9$
$\sqrt{-11x - 10} = 10$
$(\sqrt{-11x - 10})^2 = 10^2$
$-11x - 10 = 100$
$-11x = 110$
$x = -10$

check:
$\sqrt{-11(-10) - 10} - 1 = 9$
$\sqrt{110 - 10} - 1 = 9$
$\sqrt{100} - 1 = 9$
$10 - 1 = 9$

$\sqrt{6x + 7} + 2 = -5$
$\sqrt{6x + 7} = -7$
$(\sqrt{6x + 7})^2 = (-7)^2$
$6x + 7 = 49$
$6x = 42$
$x = 7$

check:
$\sqrt{6(7) + 7} + 2 = -5$
$\sqrt{42 + 7} + 2 = -5$
$\sqrt{49} + 2 = -5$
$7 + 2 \neq -5$ extraneous

④ Solve.

NASA (National Aeronautics and Space Administration) is using amusement park technology to design a roller coaster to use as an emergency escape for astronauts and other personnel at the launch pad of the new Orion spacecraft on the Ares I rocket. The train of the roller coaster will start at the level of the hatch on the spacecraft. It will then drop straight down 112 meters before curving to a horizontal track that takes the astronauts to a safety bunker. The time of descent is given by the formula $t = \sqrt{\frac{2d}{g}}$, where t is the time in seconds, d is the distance in meters, and g is the acceleration due to gravity, which is 9.8 m/s^2. Assuming there is no lost acceleration from friction, how long, to the nearest hundredth of a second, will it take the astronauts to make the 112-meter plunge once the brake is released? Use your calculator to solve this problem.

d = 112 meters $\quad$ g = 9.8 m/s^2

$t = \sqrt{\frac{2(112 \text{ meters})}{9.8 \text{ m/s}^2}}$

$t = \sqrt{\frac{224 \text{ meters}}{9.8 \text{ m/s}^2}} = \sqrt{\frac{112 \text{ meters}}{4.9 \text{ m/s}^2}} = 4.78$ seconds

Equations in Standard Form Worksheet 23

① Write an equation of the graph in standard form.

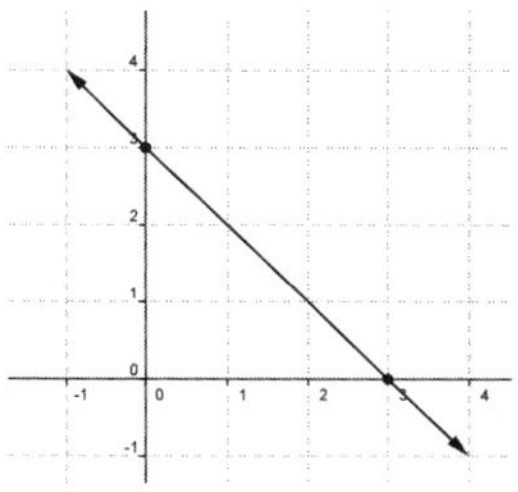

The slope is -1. Using the point (3, 0) gives the equation $y-0=-1(x-3)$.

Convert to standard form. $y=-x+3$
$x+y=3$

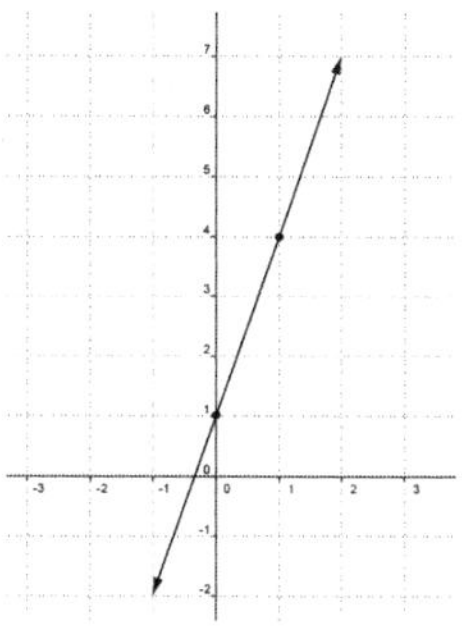

The slope is 3. Using the point (1, 4) gives the equation $y-4=3(x-1)$.

Convert to standard form. $y-4=3x-3$
$3x-y=-1$

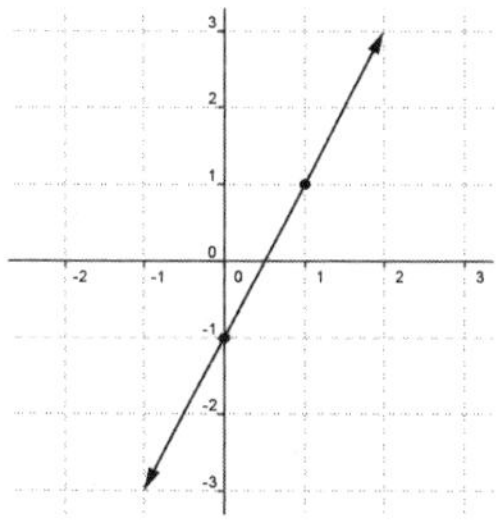

The slope is 2. Using the point (1, 1) gives the equation $y-1=2(x-1)$.

Convert to standard form. $y-1=2x-2$
$2x-y=1$

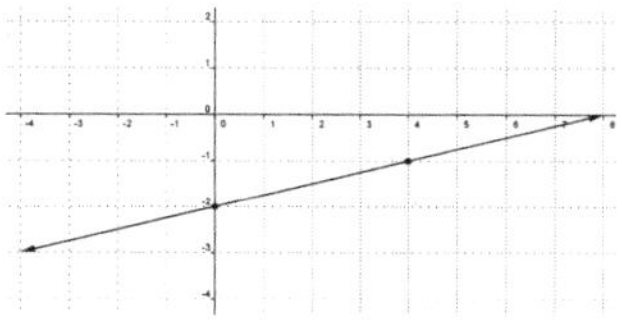

The slope is $\frac{1}{4}$. Using the point (4, -1) gives the equation $y-(-1)=\frac{1}{4}(x-4)$.

Convert to standard form. $4y+4=x-4$
$x-4y=8$

Note: Students may start with an equation in either slope-intercept form (since the y-intercept is shown for each graph) or an equation in point-slope form using either point shown. No matter which equation is used at the beginning, the standard form will be the same.

Teaching Tips, Cont.

- Emphasize that both sides may be multiplied or divided by the same POSITIVE number.
- Write the problem -3*x*<12 on the board. Notice that this is similar to the example in the teaching box, but with a negative sign.
- Ask the students what answer they would get if they divided by -3 instead of 3. (*x*<-4)
- Show the students that substituting a number less than -4, such as -5, produces a false result. [-3(-5)<12 gives 15<12, which is incorrect]
- Complete the Classwork exercises. Have some students work the problems on the board for the class. All students should work the problems in their books.

Assignment

Complete Lesson 45, Activities 2-4.

Lesson 46

Concepts
- Solving inequalities with negative divisors
- Solving algebraic equations with fractions
- Properties of equality

Learning Objectives
The student will be able to:
- Solve inequalities with negative divisors
- Determine whether or not to change the sign when solving inequalities
- Express the solution of inequalities using the proper sign

Materials Needed
- Student Book, Lesson 46

Teaching Tips
- Review solving inequalities with positive divisors. (See Lesson 45)
- Write the problem -3*x*<12 on the board. Notice that this is the same example problem you wrote on the board in Lesson 45. This is also the same example that appears in the teaching box of this lesson.
- Teach how to solve inequalities with negative divisors using the teaching box and the above problem.
- Emphasize that the direction of the sign MUST be changed when multiplying or dividing by a negative.

Solving Inequalities: Negative Divisors

Recall the following rules from Lesson 45 regarding inequalities.

- You may add or subtract the same amount from both sides of the inequality sign.
- You may multiply or divide both sides of the inequality sign by the same positive number.

When working with inequalities, a special rule applies when you multiply or divide by a negative number.
- If you multiply or divide both sides of the inequality sign by a negative number, you must reverse the inequality sign.

For example, $-3x < 12$.
If we add $3x$ to each side and subtract 12 from each side, we get:
$-3x + 3x < 12 + 3x$
$0 < 12 + 3x$
$-12 < 12 - 12 + 3x$
$-12 < 3x$

If we divide each side by 3, we know that $-4 < x$, which is the same as saying $x > -4$.

Looking back at the original problem $-3x < 12$, if we divide both sides by -3 to isolate the variable and do not reverse the sign, we have $x < -4$. Choose any number that is less than -4, such as -5, and test in the original problem: $-3(-5) < 12$ and $15 < 12$. This is clearly not correct! Reverse the inequality sign to get $-4 < x$ or $x > -4$.

① **Classwork**
Solve the inequalities.

$-4x < 20$
$-4x \div 4 < 20 \div 4$
$-x < 5$
$x > -5$

$-3x + 5 > 17$
$-3x + 5 - 5 > 17 - 5$
$-3x > 12$
$-3x \div (-3) > 12 \div (-3)$
$x < -4$

$-4x - 2 < x + 8$
$-4x - x - 2 + 2 < x - x + 8 + 2$
$-5x < 10$
$x > -2$

Activities
② Solve the inequalities.

$-3x < 27$
$-3x \div 3 < 27 \div 3$
$-x < 9$
$x > -9$

$3(x+3) < 4x + 11$
$3x + 9 < 4x + 11$
$3x - 4x + 5 - 5 < 4x - 4x + 7 - 5$
$-x < 2$
$x > -2$

$2(x-2) > 5(x+4)$
$2x - 4 > 5x + 20$
$-3x > 24$
$-x > 8$
$x < -8$

$5(x-3) < 6(x-3)$
$5x - 15 < 6x - 18$
$5x - 6x - 15 + 15 < 6x - 6x - 18 + 15$
$-x < -3$
$x > 3$

③ Solve the inequalities.

$-5(2x+7) > 2^2(-5-3x)+7x$
$-10x-35 > 4(-5-3x)+7x$
$-10x-35 > -20-12x+7x$
$-10x-35 > -20-5x$
$-5x > 15$
$-x > 3$
$x < -3$

$-10(x+3) < 2(-10-4x)+3x$
$-10x-30 < -20-8x+3x$
$-10x-30 < -20-5x$
$-5x < 10$
$-x < 2$
$x > -2$

$-11-5x < (3^2-3)(5x+4)$
$-11-5x < (9-3)(5x+4)$
$-11-5x < 6(5x+4)$
$-11-5x < 30x+24$
$-35x < 35$
$-x < 1$
$x > -1$

$-35-4x > (2^3-5)(7x+5)$
$-35-4x > (8-5)(7x+5)$
$-35-4x > 3(7x+5)$
$-35-4x > 21x+15$
$-25x > 50$
$-x > 2$
$x < -2$

$-4(3x+7) > 3(-2-3x)+8x$
$-12x-28 > -6-9x+8x$
$-12x-28 > -6-x$
$-11x > 22$
$-x > 2$
$x < -2$

$-7+7x > (4^2-3^2)(2x+3)$
$-7+7x > (16-9)(2x+3)$
$-7+7x > 7(2x+3)$
$-7+7x > 14x+21$
$-7x > 28$
$-x > 4$
$x < -4$

④ Solve each algebraic equation. For each step, identify the property of equality that was used.

$9+\frac{4}{x}=-7$
$9(x)+\frac{4}{x}(x)=-7(x) \Rightarrow 9x+4=-7x$
Multiplication property
$9x+4+7x=-7x+7x \Rightarrow 16x+4=0$
Addition property
$16x+4-4=0-4 \Rightarrow 16x=-4$
Subtraction property
$16x \div 16=-4 \div 16 \Rightarrow x=-\frac{4}{16}=-\frac{1}{4}$
Division property

$7-\frac{6}{x}=2+\frac{9}{x}$
$7(x)-\frac{6}{x}(x)=2(x)+\frac{9}{x}(x) \Rightarrow 7x-6=2x+9$
Multiplication property
$7x-6-2x=2x+9-2x \Rightarrow 5x-6=9$
Subtraction property
$5x-6+6=9+6 \Rightarrow 5x=15$
Addition property
$5x \div 5=15 \div 5 \Rightarrow x=3$
Division property

$\frac{13}{x}-\frac{2}{x^2}=-\frac{1}{x}$
$\frac{13}{x}(x^2)-\frac{2}{x^2}(x^2)=-\frac{1}{x}(x^2) \Rightarrow 13x-2=-x$
Multiplication property
$13x-2+x=-x+x \Rightarrow 14x-2=0$
Addition property
$14x-2+2=0+2 \Rightarrow 14x=2$
Addition property
$14x \div 14=2 \div 14 \Rightarrow x=\frac{2}{14}=\frac{1}{7}$
Division property

$\frac{14}{x}+\frac{3}{x^2}=\frac{6}{x}+\frac{27}{x^2}$
$\frac{14}{x}(x^2)+\frac{3}{x^2}(x^2)=\frac{6}{x}(x^2)+\frac{27}{x^2}(x^2) \Rightarrow 14x+3=6x+27$
Multiplication property
$14x+3-6x=6x+27-6x \Rightarrow 8x+3=27$
Subtraction property
$8x+3-3=27-3 \Rightarrow 8x=24$
Subtraction property
$8x \div 8=24 \div 8 \Rightarrow x=3$
Division property

Teaching Tips, Cont.

- Tell students to check their work by substituting a number that follows the rule in their answer. For example, if the answer is $x<4$, substitute 3 for x in the original problem to make sure it produces a true statement. If it produces a false statement, double check the direction of the sign. Did you remember to change the sign when multiplying or dividing by a negative number? Did you keep the sign the same when multiplying or dividing by a positive number? Did you keep the sign the same when adding or subtracting?
- Complete the Classwork exercises. Have some students work the problems on the board for the class. All students should work the problems in their books.

Assignment

- Complete Lesson 46, Activities 2-4.

Lesson 47

Concepts

- Solving inequalities
- Fractions
- Decimals
- Math in the real world

Learning Objectives

The student will be able to:

- Eliminate fractions from inequalities
- Eliminate decimals from inequalities
- Solve inequalities with multiple steps

Materials Needed

- Student Book, Lesson 47

Teaching Tips

➢ Review solving algebraic equations with multiple steps. (See Lesson 21)

➢ Review the rules for solving inequalities. (See Lessons 45 and 46)

➢ Tell students that the same rules you have just reviewed apply to solving inequalities with multiple steps.

➢ Remind the students to change the direction of the sign when they multiply or divide by a negative number.

Solving Inequalities: Multiple Steps

When solving algebraic inequalities with multiple steps, following the order of operations does not always work because of the variables. Follow these steps to make the process simpler.

1. Eliminate fractions.
2. Eliminate decimals.
3. Simplify each side of the inequality sign.
4. Isolate the variable.
5. Solve for the variable. Remember to change the direction of the sign if you multiply or divide by a negative number.

Solve the inequality $-3x + \frac{1}{4} < 2.95$ following the steps.

1. Multiply each term by 4 to eliminate the fraction. $-12x + 1 < 11.8$
2. Multiply each term by 10 to eliminate the decimal. $-120x + 10 < 118$
3. Each side is already simplified.
4. Use the Subtraction Property of Equality to isolate the variable. $-120x < 108$
5. Use the Division Property of Equality to solve for the variable. $x > -0.9$

Notice that the direction of the inequality sign was reversed because each term was divided by -120.

Answers may be expressed as proper or improper fractions or as decimals.

① Classwork

Solve the inequalities.

$\frac{1}{3}x - 2 > 0.6$
$3(\frac{1}{3}x) - 3(2) > 3(0.6)$
$x - 6 > 1.8$
$x > 7.8$

$-4x + \frac{1}{3} > 1.95$
$3(-4x) + 3(\frac{1}{3}) > 3(1.95)$
$-12x + 1 > 5.85$
$100(-12x) + 100(1) > 100(5.85)$
$-1200x + 100 > 585$
$-1200x > 485$
$x < -\frac{485}{1200}$
$x < -\frac{97}{240} \Rightarrow x < -0.4041\overline{6}$

Activities

② Solve the inequalities.

$\frac{1}{5}x - 3 < 1.2$
$5(\frac{1}{5}x) - 5(3) < 5(1.2)$
$x - 15 < 6$
$x < 21$

$-\frac{3}{4}x - 5 > 0.2$
$4(-\frac{3}{4}x) - 4(5) > 4(0.2)$
$-3x - 20 > 0.8$
$10(-3x) > 10(20.8)$
$-30x > 208$
$x < -\frac{208}{30}$
$x < -\frac{104}{15} \Rightarrow x < -6.9\overline{3}$

$\frac{1}{7}x + 2 > 4.8$
$7(\frac{1}{7}x) + 7(2) > 7(4.8)$
$x + 14 > 33.6$
$x > 19.6$

$-\frac{2}{3}x + \frac{3}{4} < 1.44$
$\cancel{12}^4(-\frac{2}{\cancel{3}}x) + \cancel{12}^3(\frac{3}{\cancel{4}}) < 12(1.44)$
$-8x + 9 < 17.28$
$100(-8x) + 100(9) < 100(17.28)$
$-800x + 900 < 1728$
$-800x < 828$
$x > -\frac{207}{200} \Rightarrow x > -1.035$

③ Solve.

$8(x+0.5) > 3(x-4.2)+2.6$
$8x+4 > 3x-12.6+2.6$
$8x(10)+4(10) > 3x(10)-12.6(10)+2.6(10)$
$80x+40 > 30x-126+26$
$50x+40 > -100$
$50x > -140$
$x > -2.8$

$3(x+0.1) < 4(x-1.01)+2.4$
$3x+0.3 < 4x-4.04+2.4$
$3x(100)+0.3(100) < 4x(100)-4.04(100)+2.4(100)$
$300x+30 < 400x-404+240$
$-100x+30 < -164$
$-100x < -194$
$x > 1.94$

$26+\frac{17}{x}=-8$
$26(x)+\frac{17}{\not x}(\not x)=-8(x)$
$26x+17=-8x$
$34x+17=0$
$34x=-17$
$x=-\frac{1}{2}$

$23-\frac{39}{x}=-16$
$23(x)-\frac{39}{\not x}(\not x)=-16(x)$
$23x-39=-16x$
$39x-39=0$
$39x=39$
$x=1$

④ Solve and graph.

The Intimidator 305 roller coaster at King's Dominion in Doswell, VA, has an initial drop of 300 feet that moves riders a mere 27 feet horizontally. What is the slope of the initial drop?

The slope is $\frac{300}{27}=\frac{100}{9}$ or $-\frac{300}{27}=-\frac{100}{9}$. The slope the students use will affect the graph in the second part.

Setting the y-intercept equal to the point (0, 300) to represent the height of the initial drop, write an equation of the line formed by the track on the initial drop. Sketch a graph of the drop.

$y=\frac{100}{9}x+300$ or $y=-\frac{100}{9}x+300$

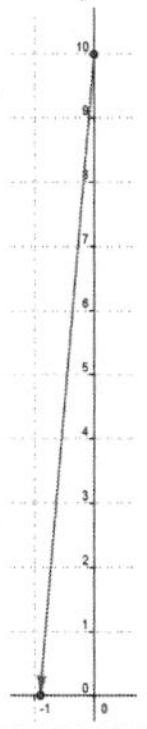

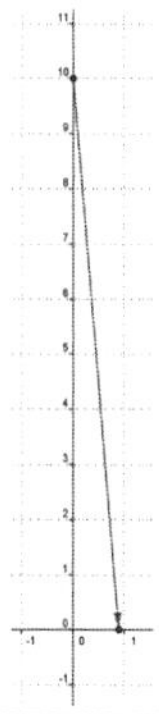

Teaching Tips, Cont.

- Teach solving inequalities with multiple steps from the teaching box.
- Tell students that they may express their answers as proper fractions, improper fractions, or decimals.
- Complete the Classwork exercises. Have some students work the problems on the board for the class. All students should work the problems in their books.

Assignment

- Complete Lesson 47, Activities 2-4.

Lesson 48

Concepts

- Inequalities
- Absolute value
- Multiplying monomials
- Dividing monomials

Learning Objectives

The student will be able to:

- Rewrite inequalities containing absolute value and a less than symbol
- Solve for all possible solutions of inequalities containing absolute value and a less than symbol
- Identify inequalities that have no solution

Materials Needed

- Student Book, Lesson 48
- Worksheet 24

Teaching Tips

- ➢ Have students complete Worksheet 24 in class. This may be for added practice of earlier topics, or graded as a quiz, if desired.
- ➢ Review solving algebraic equations with absolute value. (See Lesson 20)
- ➢ Explain that inequalities change the rules for working with absolute value.
- ➢ Review the rules for multiplying or dividing inequalities by a negative number. (See Lesson 46)

Solving Inequalities: Absolute Value with Less Than

Recall from Lesson 20: when you solve algebraic expressions with absolute values, you set the expression inside the absolute value sign equal to both the positive and negative values of the expression on the opposite side of the equal sign and solve two separate equations.

When the equal sign is replaced with the less than symbol (<), the rules change. Consider the expression $|x| < 3$. This means that $x < 3$ and $-x < 3$ (or $x > -3$, following the rules for multiplying or dividing by a negative). These expressions can be combined into a single expression $-3 < x < 3$. Notice that the expression inside the absolute value sign appears in the middle of this expression, and the expression on the opposite side of the less than sign appear as written on the right side, and has its negative value appearing on the left side.

The general pattern for solving absolute values with a less than symbol is shown below.
$|a| < b$ becomes $-b < a < b$

This pattern can then be split into two separate problems to solve.
$-b < a$ and $a < b$

Solve $|x+2| < 6$.
First, follow the pattern above to rewrite the problem.
$-6 < x+2 < 6$
Now split this expression into two separate problems.
$-6 < x+2$ and $x+2 < 6$
Solve each individual problem.
$-8 < x$ and $x < 4$
Join the two answers into a single expression.
$-8 < x < 4$

This shows that the value of x must be greater than -8 and less than 4.

Keep in mind that the absolute value of a number can NEVER be negative. If you ever see an expression such as $|x| < -2$, the answer is "no solution." Do not try to solve it!

① Classwork
Solve the inequalities.

$|5x| < x+12$
$-(x+12) < 5x < x+12$
$-x-12 < 5x < x+12$
$-x-12 < 5x$ and $5x < x+12$
$-12 < 6x$ $\quad 4x < 12$
$-2 < x$ $\quad x < 3$
$-2 < x < 3$

$|2x+5| + 7 < 18$
$|2x+5| < 11$
$-11 < 2x+5 < 11$
$-11 < 2x+5$ and $2x+5 < 11$
$-16 < 2x$ $\quad 2x < 6$
$-8 < x$ $\quad x < 3$
$-8 < x < 3$

$|3x+7| + 5 < 2$
$|3x+7| < -3$ NO SOLUTION
Stop working here. The absolute value of anything can never be negative, so the answer is no solution.

Activities
② Solve the inequalities.

$|4x| < x+15$
$-(x+15) < 4x < x+15$
$-x-15 < 4x < x+15$
$-x-15 < 4x$ and $4x < x+15$
$-15 < 5x$ $\quad 3x < 15$
$-3 < x$ $\quad x < 5$
$-3 < x < 5$

$|7x+2| + 6 < 5$
$|7x+2| < -1$ NO SOLUTION
Stop working here. The absolute value of anything can never be negative, so the answer is no solution.

$|4x-3| + 2 < 17$
$|4x-3| < 15$
$-15 < 4x-3 < 15$
$-15 < 4x-3$ and $4x-3 < 15$
$-12 < 4x$ $\quad 4x < 18$
$-3 < x$ $\quad x < \frac{18}{4} \Rightarrow x < \frac{9}{2}$
$-3 < x < \frac{9}{2}$

$|3x+1| - 4 < x+5$
$|3x+1| < x+9$
$-(x+9) < 3x+1 < x+9$
$-x-9 < 3x+1$ and $3x+1 < x+9$
$-10 < 4x$ $\quad 2x < 8$
$-\frac{10}{4} < x \Rightarrow -\frac{5}{2} < x$ $\quad x < 4$
$-\frac{5}{2} < x < 4$

$|5x+4| < x+16$
$-(x+16) < 5x+4 < x+16$
$-x-16 < 5x+4 < x+16$
$-x-16 < 5x+4$ and $5x+4 < x+16$
$-20 < 6x$ $\quad 4x < 12$
$-\frac{20}{6} < x \Rightarrow x < -\frac{10}{3}$ $\quad x < 3$
$-\frac{10}{3} < x < 3$

$|3x+3| + 6 < 21$
$|3x+3| < 15$
$-15 < 3x+3 < 15$
$-15 < 3x+3$ and $3x+3 < 15$
$-18 < 3x$ $\quad 3x < 12$
$-6 < x$ $\quad x < 4$
$-6 < x < 4$

$|6x-5| + 4 < 27$
$|6x-5| < 23$
$-23 < 6x-5 < 23$
$-23 < 6x-5$ and $6x-5 < 23$
$-18 < 6x$ $\quad 6x < 28$
$-3 < x$ $\quad x < \frac{28}{6} \Rightarrow x < \frac{14}{3}$
$-3 < x < \frac{14}{3}$

$|4x+3| + 6 < 4$
$|4x+3| < -2$ NO SOLUTION
Stop working here. The absolute value of anything can never be negative, so the answer is no solution.

③ Solve.

$6a^4(-2a^{-5}b^8)(5a^4b^{-7})$
$(6 \cdot -2 \cdot 5)(a^{4-5+4})(b^{8-7}) =$
$-60a^3b$

$-7c^5(2cd^3)(6c^{-6}d^{-3})$
$(-7 \cdot 2 \cdot 6)(c^{5+1-6})(d^{3-3}) =$
-84

$-5e^4(3e^{-7}f^9)(-4e^{-3}f^{-4})$
$(-5 \cdot 3 \cdot -4)(e^{4-7-3})(f^{9-4}) =$
$60e^{-6}f^5$

$63g^5 \div 7g^2$
$\frac{63g^5}{7g^2} = 9g^{5-2} = 9g^3$

$48h^2 \div 16h^5$
$\frac{48h^2}{16h^5} = 3h^{2-5} = 3h^{-3}$ or $\frac{3}{h^3}$

$91j^4 \div 13j^{-9}$
$\frac{91j^4}{13j^{-9}} = 7j^{4-(-9)} = 7j^{13}$

Inequalities Worksheet 24

① Solve the inequalities.

$7x < 35$ $7x \div 7 < 35 \div 7$ $x < 5$	$7x + 18 > 11$ $7x + 18 - 18 > 11 - 18$ $7x > -7$ $x > -1$	$4x - 9 < 7x + 12$ $4x - 7x - 9 < 7x - 7x + 12$ $-3x - 9 + 9 < 12 + 9$ $-3x < 21$ $x > -7$
$5x < -45$ $5x \div 5 < -45 \div 5$ $x < -9$	$8x + 13 > 6x - 5$ $8x - 6x + 13 > 6x - 6x - 5$ $2x + 13 - 13 > -5 - 13$ $2x > -18$ $x > -9$	$9x + 17 < -5x + 3$ $9x + 5x + 17 < -5x + 5x + 3$ $14x + 17 - 17 < 3 - 17$ $14x < -14$ $x < -1$
$-8x > 56$ $-8x \div (-8) < 56 \div (-8)$ $x < -7$	$-6x + 7 > 13$ $-6x + 7 - 7 > 13 - 7$ $-6x \div (-6) > 6 \div (-6)$ $x < -1$	$4x - 3 < -x + 22$ $4x + x - 3 < -x + x + 22$ $5x - 3 + 3 < 22 + 3$ $5x < 25$ $x < 5$
$3x + 4 < 13$ $3x + 4 - 4 < 13 - 4$ $3x < 9$ $x < 3$	$6x + 5 > -3x - 4$ $6x + 3x + 5 > -3x + 3x - 4$ $9x + 5 - 5 > -4 - 5$ $9x > -9$ $x > -1$	$-6x + 17 < -2x + 13$ $-6x + 2x + 17 < -2x + 2x + 13$ $-4x + 17 - 17 < 13 - 17$ $-4x < -4$ $x > 1$
$-6(2x + 5) > 7(-2 - x) - x$ $-12x - 30 > 7(-2 - x) - x$ $-12x - 30 > -14 - 7x - x$ $-12x - 30 > -14 - 8x$ $-4x > 16$ $-x > 4$ $x < -4$	$-11(x + 3) < 3(10 - 4x) + 4x$ $-11x - 33 < 30 - 12x + 4x$ $-11x - 33 < 30 - 8x$ $-3x < 63$ $-x < 21$ $x > -21$	$-3(3x + 7) > 4(-2 - 3x) + 16x$ $-9x - 21 > -8 - 12x + 16x$ $-9x - 21 > -8 + 4x$ $-13x > 13$ $-x > 1$ $x < -1$

Teaching Tips, Cont.

- Teach how to solve inequalities with absolute value and a less than symbol from the teaching box.
- Explain that two new inequalities are formed when the absolute value sign is removed. The answer is a combination of the answers from the two new inequalities.
- Ask the students what values can *never* be the answer to an absolute value expression. (Negative numbers)
- Tell the students that any time they have an absolute value expression equal to a negative number, the answer is "no solution." There is no need to work out the problem. Refer to the final paragraph in the teaching box or the last problem in the Classwork exercises for examples.
- Complete the Classwork exercises. Have some students work the problems on the board for the class. All students should work the problems in their books.

Assignment

- Complete Lesson 48, Activities 2-3.

Lesson 49

Concepts

- Inequalities
- Absolute value
- Math in the real world

Learning Objectives

The student will be able to:

- Rewrite inequalities containing absolute value and a greater than symbol
- Solve for all possible solutions of inequalities containing absolute value and a greater than symbol
- Identify inequalities that have all real numbers as the solution

Materials Needed

- Student Book, Lesson 49

Teaching Tips

- Review solving inequalities with absolute value and a less than symbol. (See Lesson 48)
- Explain that solving absolute value inequalities with a greater than symbol is similar to solving absolute value inequalities with a less than symbol. In both cases, two new inequalities are formed when the absolute value sign is removed. The answer is a combination of the answers from the two new inequalities.
- Teach how to solve inequalities with absolute value and a greater than symbol from the teaching box.

Solving Inequalities: Absolute Value with Greater Than

It is imperative that you check the direction of the inequality symbol when solving an inequality problem because the rules are different depending on which direction the symbol faces.

You learned in Lesson 48 how to solve expressions when a less than (<) symbol replaces the equal sign.

When the equal sign is replaced with the greater than symbol (>), the rules change again. Consider the expression $|x| > 3$. This means that $x > 3$ or $-x > 3$ (or $x < -3$, following the rules for multiplying or dividing by a negative).

Notice that these expressions cannot be combined into a single expression because x cannot be greater than 3 and less than -3 at the same time. Whenever you have a greater than symbol in an expression, rewrite the expression as two separate expressions joined by the word *or*.

The general pattern for solving absolute values with a greater than symbol is shown below.
$|a| > b$ becomes $a > b$ or $a < -b$

Solve $|x+2| > 6$.
First, follow the pattern above to rewrite the problem.
$x+2 > 6$ or $x+2 < -6$
Solve each individual problem.
$x > 4$ or $x < -8$

This shows that the value of x must be greater than 4 or less than -8. Leave the answer in this format.

Keep in mind that the absolute value of a number is ALWAYS positive. If you ever see an expression such as $|x| > -2$, the answer is "all real numbers" because the absolute value of all real numbers is positive, and therefore greater than any negative number. Do not try to solve it!

① Classwork
Solve the inequalities.

$|5x| > x+12$
$5x > x+12$ or $5x < -(x+12)$
$4x > 12$ $\quad$ $5x < -x-12$
$x > 3$ $\quad$ $6x < -12$
$x < -2$
$x > 3$ or $x < -2$

$|2x+5| + 7 > 18$
$|2x+5| > 11$
$2x+5 > 11$ or $2x+5 < -11$
$2x > 6$ $\quad$ $2x < -16$
$x > 3$ $\quad$ $x < -8$
$x > 3$ or $x < -8$

$|3x+7| + 5 > 2$
$|3x+7| > -3$ ALL REAL NUMBERS
Stop working here. The absolute value of anything can never be negative, so the answer is all real numbers.

Activities

② Solve the inequalities.

$|7x-40|-42>-19$

$|7x-40|>23$

$7x-40>23$ or $7x-40<-23$

$7x>63$ $\quad$ $7x<17$

$x>9$ $\quad$ $x<\frac{17}{7}$

$x>9$ or $x<\frac{17}{7}$

$|3x-2|-3>-2x+25$

$|3x-2|>-2x+28$

$3x-2>-2x+28$ or $3x-2<2x-28$

$5x>30$ $\quad$ $x<-26$

$x>6$ $\quad$ $x<-26$

$x>6$ or $x<-26$

$|4x-2|+9>5$

$|4x-2|>-4$ ALL REAL NUMBERS

Stop working here. The absolute value of anything can never be negative, so the answer is all real numbers.

$|5x-11|-17>32$

$|5x-11|>49$

$5x-11>49$ or $5x-11<-49$

$5x>60$ $\quad$ $5x<-38$

$x>12$ $\quad$ $x<-\frac{38}{5}$

$x>12$ or $x<-\frac{38}{5}$

$|7x+9|-13>3x+23$

$|7x+9|>3x+36$

$7x+9>3x+36$ or $7x+9<-3x-36$

$4x>27$ $\quad$ $10x<-45$

$x>\frac{27}{4}$ $\quad$ $x<-\frac{45}{10}\Rightarrow x<-\frac{9}{2}$

$x>\frac{27}{4}$ or $x<-\frac{9}{2}$

$|x+10|+6>3$

$|x+10|>-3$ ALL REAL NUMBERS

Stop working here. The absolute value of anything can never be negative, so the answer is all real numbers.

③ Solve.

$|7x-40|-42<-19$

$|7x-40|<23$

$-23<7x-40<23$

$-23<7x-40$ and $7x-40<23$

$17<7x$ $\quad$ $7x<63$

$\frac{17}{7}<x$ $\quad$ $x<9$

$\frac{17}{7}<x<9$

$|3x-2|-3<-2x+25$

$|3x-2|<-2x+28$

$2x-28<3x-2<-2x+28$

$2x-28<3x-2$ and $3x-2<-2x+28$

$-26<x$ $\quad$ $5x<30$

$x<6$

$-26<x<6$

$|7x+9|-13<3x+23$

$|7x+9|<3x+36$

$-3x-36<7x+9<3x+36$

$-3x-36<7x+9$ and $7x+9<3x+36$

$-45<10x$ $\quad$ $4x<27$

$-\frac{45}{10}<x\Rightarrow-\frac{9}{2}<x$ $\quad$ $x<\frac{27}{4}$

$-\frac{9}{2}<x<\frac{27}{4}$

$|5x-11|-17<32$

$|5x-11|<49$

$-49<5x-11<49$

$-49<5x-11$ and $5x-11<49$

$-38<5x$ $\quad$ $5x<60$

$-\frac{38}{5}<x$ $\quad$ $x<12$

$-\frac{38}{5}<x<12$

④ Solve.

The initial lift hill on a roller coaster lifts the train 129 feet. If the horizontal displacement of the lift hill is 60 feet, what is the slope of the lift hill?

Slope $=\frac{129}{60}=\frac{43}{20}$

Teaching Tips, Cont.

- Remind students to change the direction of the sign when they multiply or divide by a negative number.
- Explain that because the absolute value of anything is always positive, it does not matter what value is substituted for the variable inside an absolute value symbol when the absolute value is greater than a negative number. In this case, the answer is "all real numbers." Refer to the final paragraph in the teaching box or the last problem in the Classwork exercises for examples.
- Complete the Classwork exercises. Have some students work the problems on the board for the class. All students should work the problems in their books.

Assignment

- Complete Lesson 49, Activities 2-4.

Lesson 50

Concepts
- Graphing linear inequalities
- Graphing linear equations
- Parallel lines
- Perpendicular lines
- Slope
- Math in the real world

Learning Objectives
The student will be able to:
- Graph linear inequalities
- Determine whether the line should be solid or dotted on the graph of a linear inequality
- Shade the correct side of the line on the graph of a linear inequality

Materials Needed
- Student Book, Lesson 50
- Worksheet 25

Teaching Tips
- ➢ Review solving inequalities. (See Lessons 45-46)
- ➢ Review graphing linear equations. (See Lessons 32-38)
- ➢ Teach graphing inequalities from the teaching box.
- ➢ Explain that points are plotted to graph inequalities the same way they are plotted to graph linear equations.

Graphing Inequalities

Graphing linear inequalities follows the same procedure as graphing linear equations. Begin by making a T-chart and plotting some points. In this case, treat the inequality sign as an equal sign for the purpose of plotting points.

Recall from Lesson 30 that when graphing a linear equation, you joined the plotted points with a solid line. When graphing inequalities, you join the plotted points with a dotted line if the symbol is < or >. Use a solid line if the symbol is ≤ or ≥.

An additional aspect of graphing inequalities is that you must shade a portion of the graph to include all of the points less than or greater than the points on the line you drew.

Graph $y < x + 1$.

x	y
0	$y = 0 + 1 = 1$
1	$y = 1 + 1 = 2$
2	$y = 2 + 1 = 3$
-1	$y = -1 + 1 = 0$
-2	$y = -2 + 1 = -1$

Points on the line include (0, 1), (1, 2), (2, 3), (-1, 0), (-2, -1)

To determine which side of the line to shade, choose any point not on the line, and substitute the values in the original equation to see if it makes a true mathematical sentence. To make the process simpler, choose the origin if it is available. If not, choose a point on the y-axis or x-axis.

In this case, the origin is not on the line, so check the point (0, 0). 0 < 0 + 1 is a true mathematical sentence, so shade the side of the line containing the origin.

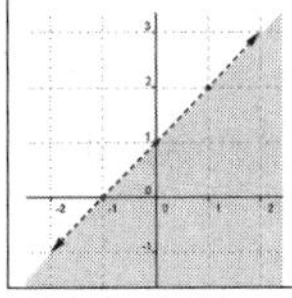

① Classwork
Graph the inequalities.

$y < -x$

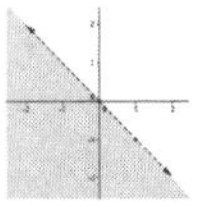

x	y
0	$y = 0$
1	$y = -1$
-1	$y = 1$

$y \le 2x - 3$

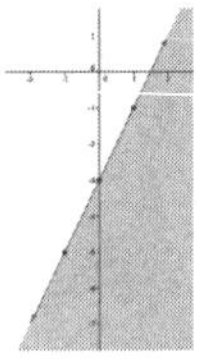

x	y
0	$y = 2(0) - 3 = -3$
1	$y = 2(1) - 3 = -1$
-1	$y = 2(-1) - 3 = -5$

$y \ge 2(x - 3)$

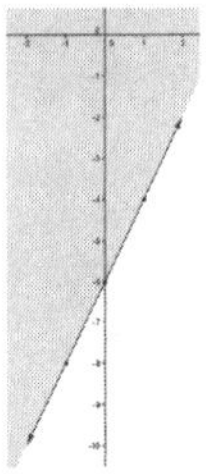

x	y
0	$y = 2(0 - 3) = -6$
1	$y = 2(1 - 3) = -4$
-1	$y = 2(-1 - 3) = -8$

Activities

② Graph the following inequalities on your own graph paper.

$y > x$

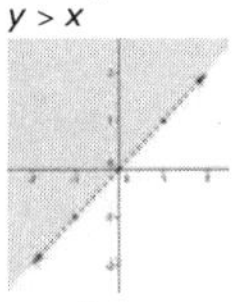

x	y
0	$y = 0$
1	$y = 1$
-1	$y = -1$

$y > x + 4$

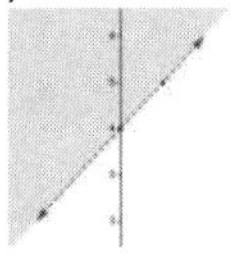

x	y
0	$y = 0 + 4 = 4$
1	$y = 1 + 4 = 5$
-1	$y = -1 + 4 = 3$

$y < 3x + 1$

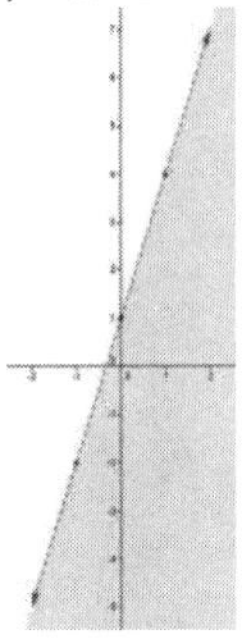

x	y
0	$y = 3(0) + 1 = 1$
1	$y = 3(1) + 1 = 4$
-1	$y = 3(-1) + 1 = -2$

$y \le 2(x + 1)$

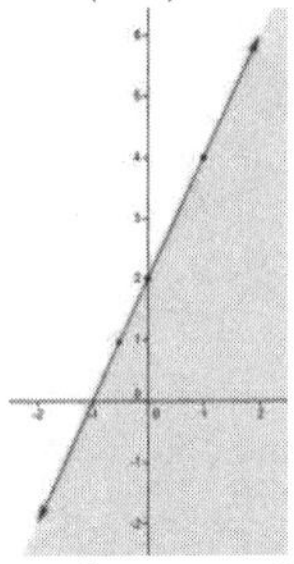

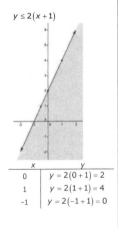

x	y
0	$y = 2(0 + 1) = 2$
1	$y = 2(1 + 1) = 4$
-1	$y = 2(-1 + 1) = 0$

③ For each equation, draw the graph of the equation, a line perpendicular to the equation through the origin, and a parallel line to the equation through the point (1, 1). (Think about the slope of parallel and perpendicular lines.)

$y = x + 4$

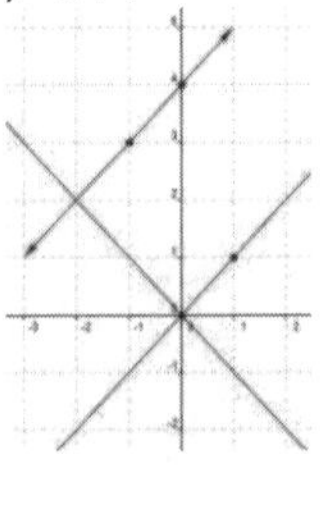

$y = 3x + 1$

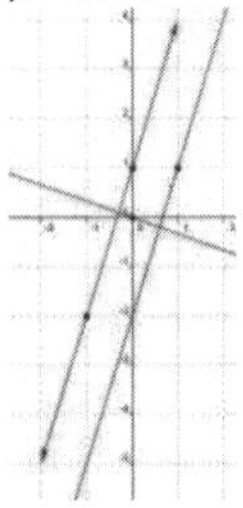

$y = 2(x + 1)$

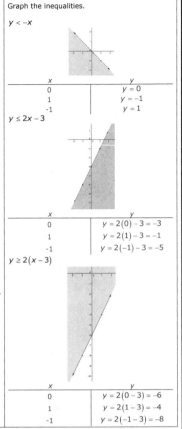

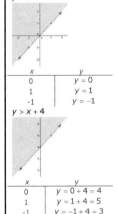

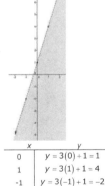

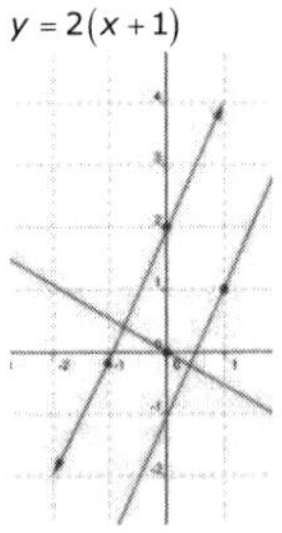

④ Solve.
The initial lift hill on a roller coaster lifts the train 90 feet. If the horizontal displacement of the lift hill is 9 feet, what is the slope of the lift hill?

Slope $= \frac{90}{9} = \frac{10}{1} = 10$

Graphing Inequalities Worksheet 25

① Graph the inequalities.

$y < -x$

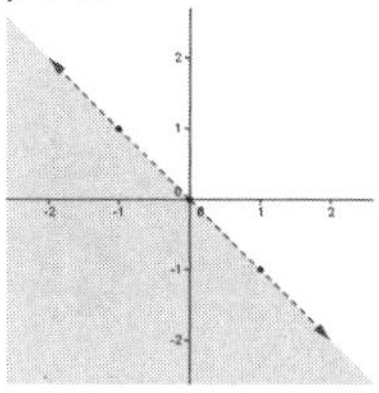

$y > 2x - 1$

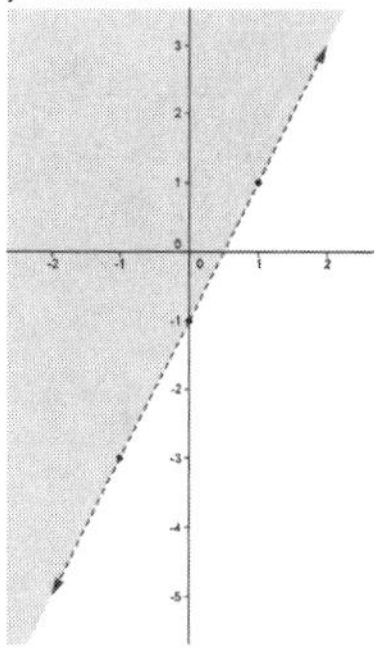

$y \le 2x - 3$

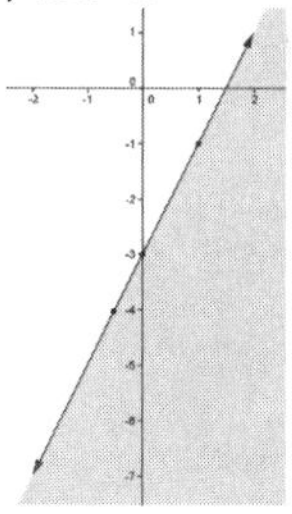

$y \le 3(x - 1)$

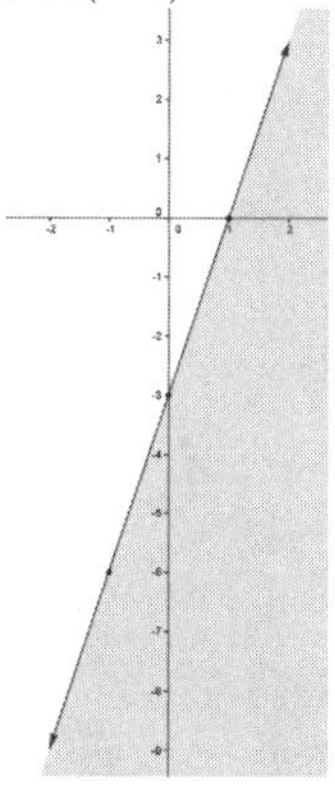

$y > x + 4$

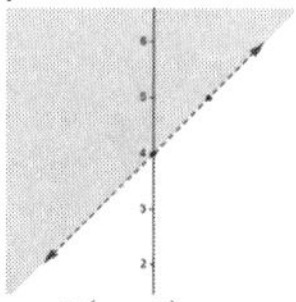

$y \ge 2(x - 3)$

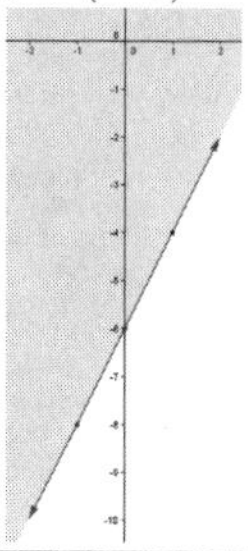

Teaching Tips, Cont.

- Write these symbols on the board.
  $<,\ \le,\ >,\ \ge$

  Ask the students what each symbol means. (Less than, less than or equal to, greater than, greater than or equal to)

- Tell the students that any time the symbol is less than or greater than, the graph will have a dotted line. If the symbol includes "equal to" then the graph will be a solid line just like the graphs of linear equations.

- Complete the Classwork exercises. Have some students work the problems on the board for the class. All students should work the problems in their books.

- Review for Test 5 using worksheets 21-25. These worksheets were assigned in previous lessons.

Assignments

- Complete Lesson 50, Activities 2-4.
- Worksheet 25.
- Study for Test 5 (Lessons 38-47).

Test 5

Testing Objectives

The student will:

- Write equations in standard form of the graph of a line
- Write an equation of a line parallel to a given line
- Write an equation of a horizontal line
- Write an equation of a vertical line
- Write an equation of a line perpendicular to a given line through a given point
- Convert equations to standard form
- Solve inequalities

Materials Needed

- Test 5
- *It's College Test Prep Time!* from Student Book
- Exploring Math through... Drama and Theater from Student Book

Teaching Tips

- ➢ Administer Test 5, allowing the students 30-40 minutes to complete the test.
- ➢ When all students are finished taking the test, introduce *It's College Test Prep Time* from the student book. This page may be completed in class or assigned as homework.

① Write an equation of the line in the graph. Then write an equation of a parallel line through the origin, a horizontal line through point *A*, a vertical line through point *B*, and a perpendicular line through point *C*. All two-variable equations should be written in standard form. **30 points**

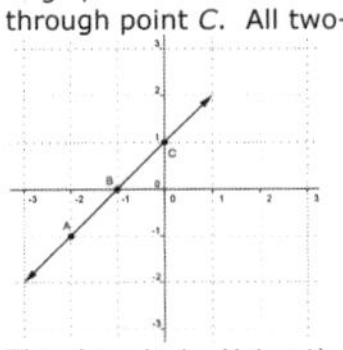

The slope is 1. Using the point (0, 1) gives the equation $y-1=1(x-0)$.
Convert to standard form.
$x-y=-1$
Parallel line: $x-y=0$
Horizontal line: $y=-1$
Vertical line: $x=-1$
Perpendicular line:
$y-1=-1(x-0)$
$y-1=-x$
$x+y=1$

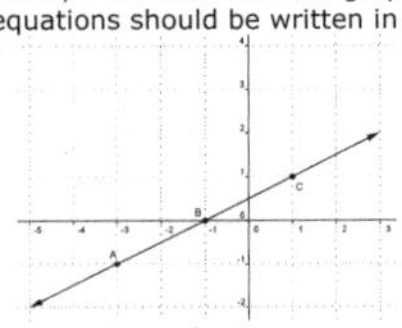

The slope is $\frac{1}{2}$. Using the point (1, 1) gives the equation $y-1=\frac{1}{2}(x-1)$.
Convert to standard form.
$2y-2=x-1$
$x-2y=-1$
Parallel line: $x-2y=0$
Horizontal line: $y=-1$
Vertical line: $x=-1$
Perpendicular line:
$y-1=-2(x-1)$
$y-1=-2x+2$
$2x+y=3$

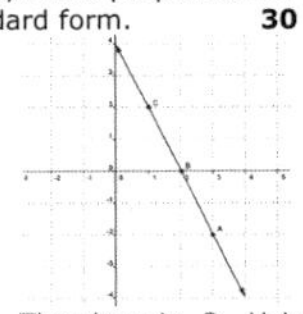

The slope is -2. Using the point (2, 0) gives the equation $y-0=-2(x-2)$.
Convert to standard form.
$y=-2x+4$
$2x+y=4$
Parallel line: $2x+y=0$
Horizontal line: $y=-2$
Vertical line: $x=2$
Perpendicular line:
$y-2=\frac{1}{2}(x-1)$
$2y-4=x-1$
$x-2y=-3$

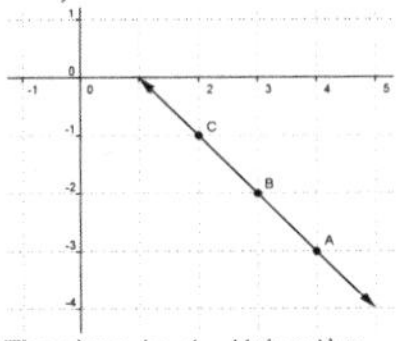

The slope is -1. Using the point (2, -1) gives the equation $y+1=-1(x-2)$.
Convert to standard form.
$y+1=-x+2$
$x+y=1$
Parallel line: $x+y=0$
Horizontal line: $y=-3$
Vertical line: $x=3$
Perpendicular line:
$y+1=1(x-2)$
$y+1=x-2$
$x-y=3$

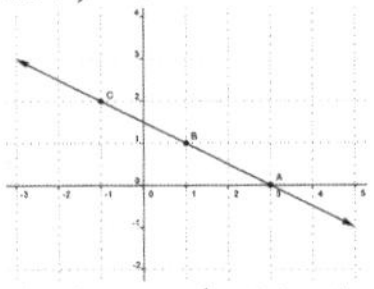

The slope is $-\frac{1}{2}$. Using the point (1, 1) gives the equation $y-1=-\frac{1}{2}(x-1)$.
Convert to standard form.
$2y-2=-x+1$
$x+2y=3$
Parallel line: $x+2y=0$
Horizontal line: $y=0$
Vertical line: $x=1$
Perpendicular line:
$y-2=2(x+1)$
$y-2=2x+2$
$2x-y=-4$

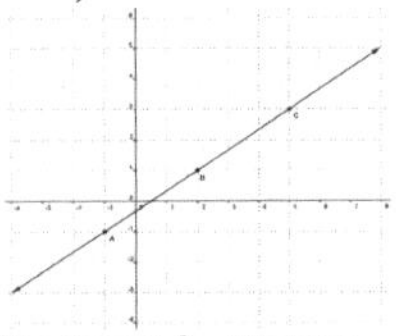

The slope is $\frac{2}{3}$. Using the point (2, 1) gives the equation $y-1=\frac{2}{3}(x-2)$.
Convert to standard form.
$3y-3=2x-4$
$2x-3y=1$
Parallel line: $2x-3y=0$
Horizontal line: $y=-1$
Vertical line: $x=2$
Perpendicular line:
$y-3=-\frac{3}{2}(x-5)$
$2y-6=-3x+15$
$3x+2y=21$

② Solve. **18 points**

$3x<27$
$3x\div3<27\div3$
$x<9$

$2x+17>35$
$2x+17-17>35-17$
$2x>18$
$x>9$

$5x-7<8x+11$
$5x-8x-7<8x-8x+11$
$-3x-7+7<11+7$
$-3x<18$
$x>-6$

$8x<-96$
$8x\div8<-96\div8$
$x<-12$

$11x+18>6x+3$
$11x-6x+18>6x-6x+3$
$5x+18-18>3-18$
$5x>-15$
$x>-3$

$8x-17<-5x+22$
$8x+5x-17<-5x+5x+22$
$13x-17+17<22+17$
$13x<39$
$x<3$

$-6x>48$
$-6x\div(-6)<48\div(-6)$
$x<-8$

$-4x+7>-13$
$-4x+7-7>-13-7$
$-4x>-20$
$x<5$

$-5x-6<2x+15$
$-5x-2x-6<2x-2x+15$
$-7x-6+6<15+6$
$-7x<21$
$x>-3$

$5x+4<19$
$5x+4-4<19-4$
$5x<15$
$x<3$

$3x+7>7x-5$
$3x-7x+7>7x-7x-5$
$-4x+7-7>-5-7$
$-4x>-12$
$x<3$

$-8x+25<-2x+13$
$-8x+2x+25<-2x+2x+13$
$-6x+25-25<13-25$
$-6x<-12$
$x>2$

$-5(3x+7)>9(-2-x)+1$
$-15x-35>-18-9x+1$
$-15x-35>-17-9x$
$-6x>18$
$x<-3$

$-12(2x+3)<7(10-7x)+19$
$-24x-36<70-49x+19$
$-24x-36<89-49x$
$25x<125$
$x<5$

$-4(3x+5)>5(-3-5x)-2x$
$-12x-20>-15-25x-2x$
$-12x-20>-15-27x$
$15x>5$
$x>\frac{5}{15}$
$x>\frac{1}{3}$

$\frac{1}{4}x-3<1.5$
$4(\frac{1}{4}x)-4(3)<4(1.5)$
$x-12<6$
$x<18$

$29+\frac{21}{x}=-13$
$29(x)+\frac{21}{\cancel{x}}(\cancel{x})=-13(x)$
$29x+21=-13x$
$42x+21=0$
$42x=-21$
$x=-\frac{1}{2}$

$38-\frac{57}{x}=-19$
$38(x)-\frac{57}{\cancel{x}}(\cancel{x})=-19(x)$
$23x-57=-16x$
$57x-57=0$
$57x=57$
$x=1$

48 points total

It's College Test Prep Time!

1. Which of the following equations satisfies the pairs of numbers listed in the table below?

x	y
-2	4
-1	-2
0	-4
1	-2
2	4

A. $y = x^2 + 4$
B. $y = 2x + 4$
C. $y = 2x^2 - 4$ This is easily solved by trial and error. Substitute
D. $y = -x^2 + 8$ each value of x and solve for y to test each pair.
E. $y = x^3 - 4$

2. In the figure below, line *a* crosses the *x*-axis at the point (-2, 0) and crosses the *y*-axis at the point (0, 3). What is the slope of a line that is perpendicular to line *a* and passes through the origin?

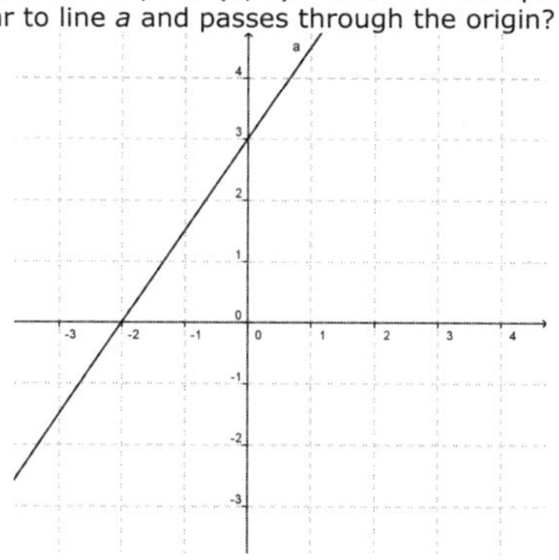

A. $-\frac{3}{2}$
B. $-\frac{2}{3}$ The slope of the given line is $\frac{3}{2}$. The slope of a
C. 0 perpendicular line is the negative reciprocal, or $-\frac{2}{3}$.
D. $\frac{2}{3}$
E. $\frac{3}{2}$

Exploring Math through... Drama and Theater

Stage productions are a mathematical feat for producers, directors, and stage hands. Even the smallest stage productions require a budget. This information, along with estimated ticket sales, helps determine ticket prices. If ticket prices are too low, even a sold-out show will not bring in enough money to cover expenses. If ticket prices are too high, it is possible that not enough tickets will be sold to cover expenses.

A director has the challenge of filling a stage without making the scene too crowded. This often involves the use of ratios and proportions. Directors also must calculate. The script may need to be adjusted so that the play fits the allotted time.

Stage hands may have the most mathematically challenging jobs in the theater industry, especially in theaters with manually-operated equipment. A system of weights and pulleys is used to operate scenery and lighting. Counterbalances must be properly calculated or the scene will not be set correctly. Precise measurements are necessary when building scenery and props. If the proportions are not equal, some items on the stage will look out of place – either too big or too small. If pieces are not cut exactly right, they will not fit together correctly. This could cause scenery to look strange. It could even have disastrous consequences, compromising the safety of the actors and actresses.

Teaching Tips, Cont.

- Have students read the Exploring Math feature for Lessons 51-60.

Assignments

- Complete *It's College Test Prep Time!*
- Read Exploring Math through... Drama and Theater

Lesson 51

Concepts

- Systems of equations
- Coordinate points
- Order of operations
- Math in the real world

Learning Objectives

The student will be able to:

- Solve systems of equations by setting equations equal
- Express the solution of a system of equations as a coordinate point

Materials Needed

- Student Book, Lesson 51

Teaching Tips

➢ Review solving linear equations. (See Lessons 16-17)

➢ Review slope-intercept form. (See Lesson 32)

➢ Explain that so far, all equations the students have solved have had just one variable. A system of equations allows for a single value for each variable. A system of equations has the same number of equations as there are unique variables. For example, if there are two unique variables, such as *x* and *y*, there will be two equations. If there are three unique variables, such as *x*, *y*, and *z*, there will be three equations.

➢ Tell the students that the systems of equations in this book will all have two equations and two unique variables. Systems of equations with three or more variables will appear in upper-level math courses.

Lesson 51

Solving Linear Systems: Set the Equations Equal

A **system of linear equations** is two or more equations that all use the same set of variables. The solution of a system of equations is the point or points that are common to all lines in the system. Lines that intersect will have exactly one point as the solution. Lines that are parallel will have no points as the solution. Lines that are on top of each other will have an infinite number of points as the solution.

Find the solution of the system of equations.

$-3x + y + 2 = 0$
$2x + y - 3 = 0$

Begin by writing both equations in slope-intercept form.

$y = 3x - 2$
$y = -2x + 3$

At this point, look at the slope in both equations. Parallel lines have equal slopes. If the slopes are equal, all points on the lines are the solution. Because the slopes are not equal, solve for the common point.

You are looking for a point whose *x*- and *y*-values are the same for both equations. Because the *y*-values are the same, set the right sides equal to each other.

$3x - 2 = -2x + 3$

Now combine terms to solve for *x*.

$3x - 2 = -2x + 3$
$5x = 5$
$x = 1$

Substitute 1 for *x* in either of the original equations and solve for *y*. Check your work by substituting in the other equation. If you are correct, you will get the same answer.

$-3(1) + y + 2 = 0$
$-3 + y + 2 = 0$
$y = 1$

Check:

$2(1) + y - 3 = 0$
$2 + y - 3 = 0$
$y = 1$

The solution is (1, 1)

① Classwork

Solve. Express the answer as a coordinate point.

$x + y = 0$
$2x + y - 3 = 0$
$y = -x$
$y = -2x + 3$
$-x = -2x + 3$
$x = 3$
$3 + y = 0$
$y = -3$
$(3, -3)$

$6x - y + 6 = 0$
$-2x + y - 2 = 0$
$y = 6x + 6$
$y = 2x + 2$
$6x + 6 = 2x + 2$
$4x = -4$
$x = -1$
$6(-1) - y + 6 = 0$
$y = -6 + 6$
$y = 0$
$(-1, 0)$

$-x + 2y + 1 = 0$
$3x - 2y - 7 = 0$
$2y = x - 1$
$2y = 3x - 7$ Divide each term by 2.
$y = \frac{1}{2}x - \frac{1}{2}$
$y = \frac{3}{2}x - \frac{7}{2}$
$\frac{1}{2}x - \frac{1}{2} = \frac{3}{2}x - \frac{7}{2}$
$-\frac{2}{2}x = -\frac{6}{2}$
$x = 3$

$-3 + 2y + 1 = 0$
$2y = 2$
$y = 1$
$(3, 1)$

Activities

② Solve. Express the answer as a coordinate point.

$-3x + y - 5 = 0$	$x - y + 2 = 0$	$-3x - y + 5 = 0$
$4x + y + 2 = 0$	$-2x + y - 5 = 0$	$2x - 2y - 6 = 0$
$y = 3x + 5$	$y = x + 2$	$y = -3x + 5$
$y = -4x - 2$	$y = 2x + 5$	$2y = 2x - 6$ Divide terms by 2.
$3x + 5 = -4x - 2$	$x + 2 = 2x + 5$	$y = x - 3$
$7x = -7$	$-x = 3$	$-3x + 5 = x - 3$
$x = -1$	$x = -3$	$-4x = -8$
$-3(-1) + y - 5 = 0$	$-3 - y + 2 = 0$	$x = 2$
$3 + y - 5 = 0$	$y = -1$	$-3(2) - y + 5 = 0$
$y = 2$	$(-3, -1)$	$-6 - y + 5 = 0$
$(-1, 2)$		$y = -1$
		$(2, -1)$

③ Solve. Remember to multiply each term by the denominator to eliminate fractions.

$3(x-2) + 7 = 5 + 12 \div 3 - x$	$5x + 14 \div 7 + 4 = 3(x-1) - x$	$4(2-x) - 3(1-x) = x - 3$
$3x - 6 + 7 = 5 + 4 - x$	$5x + 2 + 4 = 3x - 3 - x$	$8 - 4x - 3 + 3x = x - 3$
$3x + 1 = 9 - x$	$5x + 6 = 2x - 3$	$-x + 5 = x - 3$
$4x = 8$	$3x = -9$	$-2x = -8$
$x = 2$	$x = -3$	$x = 4$
$\frac{2x}{3} + 1 = -5$	$\frac{3x}{2} + 3 = 2x + 1$	$\frac{x+1}{2} - 5 = 2x - 3$
$\frac{2x}{3} = -6$	$\frac{3x}{2} = 2x - 2$	$\frac{x+1}{2} = 2x + 2$
$\cancel{3}\left(\frac{2x}{\cancel{3}}\right) = 3(-6)$	$\cancel{2}\left(\frac{3x}{\cancel{2}}\right) = 2(2x-2)$	$\cancel{2}\left(\frac{x+1}{\cancel{2}}\right) = 2(2x+2)$
$2x = -18$	$3x = 4x - 4$	$x + 1 = 4x + 4$
$x = -9$	$-x = -4$	$-3x = 3$
	$x = 4$	$x = -1$

④ Solve.

The director of the Mary Poppins musical had a total of 50 adults and children from which to cast 52 parts for the 2006 and 2007 seasons. (Some cast members were understudies, and some cast members filled multiple roles.) If the number of adults was 2 more than 3 times the number of children, how many adults and how many children participated in the Mary Poppins musical from 2006-2007?

Let a = the number of adults and let c = the number of children.

$a + c = 50$

$a = 3c + 2$

$3c + 2 + c = 50$	or	$a = 50 - c$
$4c = 48$		$50 - c = 3c + 2$
$c = 12$		$4c = 48;\ c = 12$

$a + 12 = 50$

$a = 38$

Teaching Tips, Cont.

- Teach how to solve a system of equations by setting two equations equal. If both equations have matching variables with equal coefficients, this is an easy way to solve.
- Explain that the value of one variable must be found at a time. Once the value of one variable is known, that value may be substituted into either original equation to solve for the value of the second variable.
- Tell the students that a good way to check their work is to substitute the values for the variables into both equations. If both equations give a true mathematical statement, the answer is correct. (This is assuming there were not math errors that canceled each other out.)
- Complete the Classwork exercises. Have some students work the problems on the board for the class and explain their answers. All students should work the problems in their books.

Assignment

- Complete Lesson 51, Activities 2-4.

Lesson 52

Concepts

- Adding polynomials
- Subtracting polynomials
- Systems of equations
- Inequalities
- Radicals
- Absolute value

Learning Objectives

The student will be able to:

- Add polynomials
- Subtract polynomials

Materials Needed

- Student Book, Lesson 52
- Worksheet 26

Teaching Tips

- Have students complete Worksheet 26 in class. This may be for added practice of earlier topics, or graded as a quiz, if desired.
- This lesson is a review of the material covered in Lessons 12 and 13. While there is no new material in this lesson, it is vital to reteach as necessary to ensure all students have mastered these concepts before proceeding with the lessons that follow.
- Review adding polynomials. (See Lesson 12)
- Review subtracting polynomials. (See Lesson 13)
- Make sure all students understand that subtraction applies to each term in the subtrahend (second polynomial).

Adding and Subtracting Polynomials

Recall from Lessons 12 and 13 that polynomials may be added or subtracted.

Terms with the same variable and degree (exponent) must be lined up in the same column. Add the columns to get the answer.

$$\begin{array}{r} (x^2+2x+3) \\ +(2x^2-x+1) \\ \hline 3x^2+x+4 \end{array}$$

When subtracting polynomials, remember to change the signs in the second polynomial and add.

$$\begin{array}{r} (2x^2+2x+3) \\ -(x^2-x+1) \\ \hline \end{array} \text{ becomes } \begin{array}{r} (2x^2+2x+3) \\ +(-x^2+x-1) \\ \hline x^2+3x+2 \end{array}$$

① **Classwork**

Write the problems vertically and add or subtract as indicated.

$(2x^2+x+1)+(x^2+x+2)=$

$$\begin{array}{r} 2x^2+x+1 \\ +\ x^2+x+2 \\ \hline 3x^2+2x+3 \end{array}$$

$(2x^2+2x+5)-(x^2-x+1)=$

$$\begin{array}{r} (2x^2+2x+5) \\ -(x^2-x+1) \\ \hline \end{array} \text{ becomes } \begin{array}{r} 2x^2+2x+5 \\ -x^2+x-1 \\ \hline x^2+3x+4 \end{array}$$

Activities

② Add or subtract as indicated.

$$\begin{array}{r} 3x^2+4x+1 \\ +\ 2x^2+5x+4 \\ \hline 5x^2+9x+5 \end{array} \qquad \begin{array}{r} 3x^2+3x+5 \\ +2x^2-2x-3 \\ \hline 5x^2+x+2 \end{array} \qquad \begin{array}{r} 4x^2-5x+3 \\ +3x^2+2x-5 \\ \hline 7x^2-3x-2 \end{array}$$

$$\begin{array}{r} (6x^2+4x+5) \\ -(2x^2+3x+2) \\ \hline 4x^2+x+3 \end{array} \qquad \begin{array}{r} (7x^2-3x+4) \\ -(2x^2-5x-3) \\ \hline 5x^2+2x+7 \end{array} \qquad \begin{array}{r} (3x^2-2x-4) \\ -(6x^2+5x-7) \\ \hline -3x^2-7x+3 \end{array}$$

$$\begin{array}{r} 2x^2+3x+2 \\ +\ 3x^2+2x+1 \\ \hline 5x^2+5x+3 \end{array} \qquad \begin{array}{r} 4x^2+2x+4 \\ +x^2-4x-1 \\ \hline 5x^2-2x+3 \end{array} \qquad \begin{array}{r} 2x^2-3x+2 \\ +5x^2+2x-3 \\ \hline 7x^2-x-1 \end{array}$$

$$\begin{array}{r} (5x^2+5x+3) \\ -(3x^2+2x+1) \\ \hline 2x^2+3x+2 \end{array} \qquad \begin{array}{r} (5x^2-2x+3) \\ -(x^2-4x-1) \\ \hline 4x^2+2x+4 \end{array} \qquad \begin{array}{r} (7x^2-x-1) \\ -(5x^2+2x-3) \\ \hline 2x^2-3x+2 \end{array}$$

③ Solve. Express the answer as a coordinate point.

$-2x+y-1=0$
$3x+y+24=0$
$y=2x+1$
$y=-3x-24$
$2x+1=-3x-24$
$5x=-25$
$x=-5$
$-2(-5)+y-1=0$
$10+y-1=0$
$9+y=0$
$y=-9$
$(-5,-9)$

$x-y+10=0$
$-3x-y-2=0$
$y=x+10$
$y=-3x-2$
$x+10=-3x-2$
$4x=-12$
$x=-3$
$-3-y+10=0$
$y=7$
$(-3,7)$

$-2x-y+12=0$
$2x+2y-6=0$
$y=-2x+12$
$2y=-2x+6$ Divide terms by 2.
$y=-x+3$
$-2x+12=-x+3$
$-x=-9$
$x=9$
$-2(9)-y+12=0$
$-18-y+12=0$
$y=-6$
$(9,-6)$

$-2x+y-9=0$
$x+y+6=0$
$y=2x+9$
$y=-x-6$
$2x+9=-x-6$
$3x=-15$
$x=-5$
$-5+y+6=0$
$1+y=0$
$y=-1$
$(-5,-1)$

$x-y-2=0$
$-2x+y+9=0$
$y=x-2$
$y=2x-9$
$x-2=2x-9$
$-x=-7$
$x=7$
$7-y-2=0$
$y=5$
$(7,5)$

$-2x-y+10=0$
$2x+2y-6=0$
$y=-2x+10$
$2y=-2x+6$ Divide terms by 2.
$y=-x+3$
$-2x+10=-x+3$
$-x=-7$
$x=7$
$-2(7)-y+10=0$
$-14-y+10=0$
$y=-4$
$(7,-4)$

④ Solve.

$9x+(6-9)^2>3(x+4)$
$9x+(-3)^2>3x+12$
$9x+9>3x+12$
$6x>3$
$x>\frac{1}{2}$

$8x+2(5-3x)<3x-(3^3\div3^2)$
$8x+10-6x<3x-3$
$2x+10<3x-3$
$-x<-13$
$x>13$

$4(2x-5)+\sqrt{3^2+2^2+3}<2(x+1)$
$8x-20+\sqrt{9+4+3}<2x+2$
$8x-20+\sqrt{16}<2x+2$
$8x-20+4<2x+2$
$8x-16<2x+2$
$6x<18$
$x<3$

⑤ Solve.

$|7x+5|+8<3$
$|7x+5|<-5$ NO SOLUTION
Stop working here. The absolute value of anything can never be negative, so the answer is no solution.

$|-3x-4|+5>2$
$|-3x-4|>-3$ ALL REAL NUMBERS
Stop working here. The absolute value of anything can never be negative, so the answer is all real numbers.

Inequalities with Absolute Value Worksheet 26

① Solve the inequalities.

$|3x| < x + 12$

$-(x+12) < 3x < x + 12$

$-x - 12 < 3x < x + 12$

$-x - 12 < 3x$ and $3x < x + 12$

$-12 < 4x \qquad 2x < 12$

$-3 < x \qquad x < 6$

$-3 < x < 6$

$|3x| > x + 12$

$3x > x + 12$ or $3x < -x - 12$

$2x > 12 \qquad 4x < -12$

$x > 6 \qquad x < -3$

$x > 6$ or $x < -3$

$|9x + 4| + 13 < 8$

$|9x + 4| < -5$ NO SOLUTION

Stop working here. The absolute value of anything can never be negative, so the answer is no solution.

$|6x - 5| + 11 > 7$

$|6x - 5| > -4$ ALL REAL NUMBERS

Stop working here. The absolute value of anything can never be negative, so the answer is all real numbers.

$|6x - 3| + 7 < 22$

$|6x - 3| < 15$

$-15 < 6x - 3 < 15$

$-15 < 6x - 3$ and $6x - 3 < 15$

$-12 < 6x \qquad 6x < 18$

$-2 < x \qquad x < 3$

$-2 < x < 3$

$|4x - 3| - 3 > -3x + 29$

$|4x - 3| > -3x + 32$

$4x - 3 > -3x + 32$ or $4x - 3 < 3x - 32$

$7x > 35 \qquad x < -29$

$x > 5$

$x > 5$ or $x < -29$

$|7x - 40| + 42 < 19$

$|7x - 40| < -23$ NO SOLUTION

Stop working here. The absolute value of anything can never be negative, so the answer is no solution.

$|5x - 11| - 7 > 2$

$|5x - 11| > 9$

$5x - 11 > 9$ or $5x - 11 < -9$

$5x > 20 \qquad 5x < 2$

$x > 4 \qquad x < \frac{2}{5}$

$x > 4$ or $x < \frac{2}{5}$

$|3x + 1| + 3 < x + 8$

$|3x + 1| < x + 5$

$-(x+5) < 3x + 1 < x + 5$

$-x - 5 < 3x + 1$ and $3x + 1 < x + 5$

$-6 < 4x \qquad 2x < 4$

$-\frac{6}{4} < x \Rightarrow -\frac{3}{2} < x \qquad x < 2$

$-\frac{3}{2} < x < 2$

$|2x + 5| + 8 > 2$

$|2x + 5| > -6$ ALL REAL NUMBERS

Stop working here. The absolute value of anything can never be negative, so the answer is all real numbers.

Teaching Tips, Cont.

- ➢ Remind students to change the sign of each term that is being subtracted.
- ➢ Complete the Classwork exercises. Have some students work the problems on the board for the class and explain their answers. All students should work the problems in their books.

Assignment

- Complete Lesson 52, Activities 2-5.

Lesson 53

Concepts

- Systems of equations
- Adding linear equations
- Standard form of linear equations
- Fractions
- Math in the real world

Learning Objectives

The student will be able to:

- Solve systems of equations by addition
- Write linear equations in standard form
- Express the solution of a system of equations as a coordinate point

Materials Needed

- Student Book, Lesson 53
- Worksheet 27

Teaching Tips

- Review solving systems of equations by setting two equations equal to each other. (See Lesson 51.)
- Tell the students that some systems of equations are not easily converted to slope-intercept form. This makes solving by setting two equations equal to each other difficult.
- Teach solving systems of equations by addition from the teaching box. The sample problem shown can be solved by converting to slope-intercept form and setting the two equations equal. You may wish to have the class solve the sample problem by this method as part of the review.

Solving Linear Systems: Addition

Adding equations is an alternate method of solving a system of equations. To add equations, write each equation in the form $Ax + By = C$, where A is the coefficient of x, B is the coefficient of y, and C is a constant. This is known as the **standard form** of an equation.

Solve the system of equations by adding.

$-3x + y + 4 = 0$
$3x + y - 2 = 0$

First, rewrite both equations in standard form.

$-3x + y = -4$
$3x + y = 2$

Add the terms vertically to get a new equation.

$-3x + y = -4$
$3x + y = 2$
$2y = -2$

Solve for the variable that remains.

$2y = -2$
$y = -1$

Substitute -1 for y in either of the original equations and solve for x. Check your work by substituting in the other equation. If you are correct, you will get the same answer.

$-3x + (-1) + 4 = 0$
$-3x + 3 = 0$
$-3x = -3$
$x = 1$

Check:

$3x + (-1) - 2 = 0$
$3x - 3 = 0$
$3x = 3$
$x = 1$

The solution is the point (1, -1).

① Classwork

Solve by adding.

$-4x + y - 6 = 0$
$3x - y + 5 = 0$
$-4x + y = 6$
$3x - y = -5$
$-x = 1$
$x = -1$
$-4(-1) + y - 6 = 0$
$4 + y - 6 = 0$
$y = 2$
$(-1, 2)$

$x - y + 2 = 0$
$-2x + y - 5 = 0$
$x - y = -2$
$-2x + y = 5$
$-x = 3$
$x = -3$
$-3 - y + 2 = 0$
$y = -1$
$(-3, -1)$

$-3x - y + 5 = 0$
$3x - 2y - 8 = 0$
$-3x - y = -5$
$3x - 2y = 8$
$-3y = 3$
$y = -1$
$-3x - (-1) + 5 = 0$
$-3x + 6 = 0$
$-3x = -6$
$x = 2$
$(2, -1)$

Activities

② Solve by adding.

$-4x + y + 8 = 0$
$4x - 2y - 4 = 0$
$-4x + y = -8$
$4x - 2y = 4$
$-y = -4$
$y = 4$
$-4x + 4 + 8 = 0$
$-4x = -12$
$x = 3$
$(3, 4)$

$3x - y + 6 = 0$
$-2x + y - 2 = 0$
$3x - y = -6$
$-2x + y = 2$
$x = -4$
$3(-4) - y + 6 = 0$
$-12 - y + 6 = 0$
$y = -6$
$(-4, -6)$

$-x + 2y + 1 = 0$
$3x - 2y - 7 = 0$
$-x + 2y = -1$
$3x - 2y = 7$
$2x = 6$
$x = 3$
$-3 + 2y + 1 = 0$
$2y = 2$
$y = 1$
$(3, 1)$

③ Solve by adding.

$-3x + y + 9 = 0$
$3x - 2y - 6 = 0$
$-3x + y = -9$
$3x - 2y = 6$
$-y = -3$
$y = 3$
$-3x + 3 + 9 = 0$
$-3x = -12$
$x = 4$
$(4, 3)$

$-x + 3y + 5 = 0$
$x - 2y - 2 = 0$
$-x + 3y = -5$
$x - 2y = 2$
$y = -3$
$-x + 3(-3) + 5 = 0$
$-x - 9 + 5 = 0$
$x = -4$
$(-4, -3)$

$-x + 2y + 7 = 0$
$3x - 2y - 1 = 0$
$-x + 2y = -7$
$3x - 2y = 1$
$2x = -6$
$x = -3$
$-(-3) + 2y + 7 = 0$
$3 + 2y + 7 = 0$
$2y = -10$
$y = -5$
$(-3, -5)$

④ Solve.

$\frac{3x+5}{2} - 3 = -11$
$\frac{3x+5}{2} = -8$
$\not{2}\left(\frac{3x+5}{\not{2}}\right) = 2(-8)$
$3x + 5 = -16$
$3x = -21$
$x = -7$

$\frac{3x+9}{5} + 4 = 2x + 3$
$\frac{3x+9}{5} = 2x - 1$
$\not{5}\left(\frac{3x+9}{\not{5}}\right) = 5(2x - 1)$
$3x + 9 = 10x - 5$
$-7x = -14$
$x = 2$

$\frac{4x-3}{9} - 4 = x - 6$
$\frac{4x-3}{9} = x - 2$
$\not{9}\left(\frac{4x-3}{\not{9}}\right) = 9(x - 2)$
$4x - 3 = 9x - 18$
$-5x = -15$
$x = 3$

⑤ Solve.

One scene in the Mary Poppins musical has birds and people. If there are 25 total people and birds and a total of 62 arms and legs (birds have 2 legs and no arms), how many people and how many birds are in the scene?

Let p = the number of people and let b = the number of birds

$p + b = 25$
$4p + 2b = 62$

$-4p - 4b = -100$
$4p + 2b = 62$
$-2b = -38$
$b = 19$

$p + 19 = 25$
$p = 6$

There are 6 people and 19 birds in the scene.

Solving Systems of Equations by Adding Worksheet 27

① Solve by adding.

$-3x + y + 8 = 0$
$3x - 2y - 4 = 0$
$-3x + y = -8$
$\underline{3x - 2y = 4}$
$-y = -4$
$y = 4$

$-3x + 4 + 8 = 0$
$-3x = -12$
$x = 4$
$(4, 4)$

$-2x - y + 13 = 0$
$2x + 3y + 5 = 0$
$-2x - y = -13$
$\underline{2x + 3y = -5}$
$2y = -18$
$y = -9$

$-2x + 9 + 13 = 0$
$-2x = -22$
$x = 11$
$(11, -9)$

$-4x - y + 5 = 0$
$4x + 2y + 6 = 0$
$-4x - y = -5$
$\underline{4x + 2y = -6}$
$y = -11$

$-4x + 11 + 5 = 0$
$-4x = -16$
$x = 4$
$(4, -11)$

$-x + 3y + 18 = 0$
$x - 2y - 11 = 0$
$-x + 3y = -18$
$\underline{x - 2y = 11}$
$y = -7$

$-x + 3(-7) + 18 = 0$
$-x - 21 + 18 = 0$
$x = -3$
$(-3, -7)$

$-x + 3y + 9 = 0$
$x - 4y - 15 = 0$
$-x + 3y = -9$
$\underline{x - 4y = 15}$
$-y = 6$
$y = -6$

$-x + 3(-6) + 9 = 0$
$-x - 18 + 9 = 0$
$x = -9$
$(-9, -6)$

$-2x - 3y + 17 = 0$
$2x + 2y - 10 = 0$
$-2x - 3y = -17$
$\underline{2x + 2y = 10}$
$-y = -7$
$y = 7$

$-2x + 3(-7) + 17 = 0$
$-2x - 21 + 17 = 0$
$-2x = 4$
$x = -2$
$(-2, 7)$

$-x - 2y - 14 = 0$
$3x + 2y + 10 = 0$
$-x - 2y = 14$
$\underline{3x + 2y = -10}$
$2x = 4$
$x = 2$

$-2 - 2y - 14 = 0$
$-2y = 16$
$y = -8$
$(2, -8)$

$-9x - y - 8 = 0$
$9x + 2y - 2 = 0$
$-9x - y = 8$
$\underline{9x + 2y = 2}$
$y = 10$

$-9x - 10 - 8 = 0$
$-9x = 18$
$x = -2$
$(-2, 10)$

$-2x + 3y + 2 = 0$
$3x - 3y + 6 = 0$
$-2x + 3y = -2$
$\underline{3x - 3y = -6}$
$x = -8$

$-2(-8) + 3y + 2 = 0$
$16 + 3y + 2 = 0$
$3y = -18$
$y = -6$
$(-8, -6)$

Teaching Tips, Cont.

- Show the students how to solve the sample problem by addition. Make sure all students realize that they will get the same answer no matter which method of solving the system of equations they choose to use.
- Tell the students that another good way to check their work is to solve the system of equations by an alternate method. However, it should be pointed out that not all systems of equations will solve easily by multiple methods.
- Complete the Classwork exercises. Have some students work the problems on the board for the class and explain their answers. All students should work the problems in their books.

Assignments

- Complete Lesson 53, Activities 2-5.
- Worksheet 27.

Lesson 54

Concepts

- Systems of equations
- Subtracting linear equations
- Standard form
- Slope-intercept form
- Perpendicular lines
- Parallel lines

Learning Objectives

The student will be able to:

- Solve systems of equations by subtraction
- Write linear equations in standard form
- Express the solution of a system of equations as a coordinate point

Materials Needed

- Student Book, Lesson 54

Teaching Tips

- Review solving systems of equations by setting two equations equal. (See Lesson 51)
- Review solving systems of equations by addition. (See Lesson 53)
- Tell the students there is a third method for solving systems of equations that is closely related to solving by addition.

Solving Linear Systems: Subtraction

Subtracting equations is a third method of solving a system of equations.

Solve the system of equations by subtracting.

$-3x + y + 4 = 0$
$3x + y - 2 = 0$

First, rewrite both equations in standard form.

$-3x + y = -4$
$3x + y = 2$

Subtract the terms vertically to get a new equation. This is the same as changing the sign of each term in the second equation and adding.

$-3x + y = -4$
$\underline{-3x - y = -2}$
$-6x = -6$

Solve for the variable that remains.

$-6x = -6$
$x = 1$

Substitute 1 for x in either of the original equations and solve for y. Check your work by substituting in the other equation. If you are correct, you will get the same answer.

$-3(1) + y + 4 = 0$
$-3 + y + 4 = 0$
$y = -1$

Check:

$3(1) + y - 2 = 0$
$3 + y - 2 = 0$
$y = -1$

The solution is the point (1, -1).

① Classwork

Solve by subtracting.

$-3x + y - 5 = 0$
$4x + y + 2 = 0$
$-3x + y = 5$
$\underline{4x + y = -2}$
$-7x = 7$
$x = -1$
$-3(-1) + y - 5 = 0$
$3 + y - 5 = 0$
$y = 2$
$(-1, 2)$

$x - y + 2 = 0$
$2x - y + 5 = 0$
$x - y = -2$
$\underline{2x - y = -5}$
$-x = 3$
$x = -3$
$-3 - y + 2 = 0$
$y = -1$
$(-3, -1)$

$3x + y - 5 = 0$
$3x - 2y - 8 = 0$
$3x + y = 5$
$\underline{3x - 2y = 8}$
$3y = -3$
$y = -1$
$3x - 1 - 5 = 0$
$3x - 6 = 0$
$3x = 6$
$x = 2$
$(2, -1)$

Activities

② Solve by subtracting.

$3x - y - 5 = 0$
$3x - 2y - 7 = 0$
$3x - y = 5$
$\underline{3x - 2y = 7}$
$y = -2$
$3x - (-2) - 5 = 0$
$3x + 2 - 5 = 0$
$3x = 3$
$x = 1$
$(1, -2)$

$4x - y + 2 = 0$
$2x - y + 4 = 0$
$4x - y = -2$
$\underline{2x - y = -4}$
$2x = 2$
$x = 1$
$4(1) - y + 2 = 0$
$4 - y + 2 = 0$
$y = 6$
$(1, 6)$

$x - 2y - 7 = 0$
$3x - 2y - 1 = 0$
$x - 2y = 7$
$\underline{3x - 2y = 1}$
$-2x = 6$
$x = -3$
$-3 - 2y - 7 = 0$
$-2y = 10$
$y = -5$
$(-3, -5)$

③ Solve by subtracting.

$$\begin{aligned} -3x + y - 2 &= 0 \\ 4x + y + 5 &= 0 \\ -3x + y &= 2 \\ 4x + y &= -5 \\ \hline -7x \quad &= 7 \\ x \quad &= -1 \end{aligned}$$

$$\begin{aligned} -3(-1) + y - 2 &= 0 \\ 3 + y - 2 &= 0 \\ y &= -1 \end{aligned}$$

$(-1, -1)$

$$\begin{aligned} x - y + 5 &= 0 \\ 2x - y + 2 &= 0 \\ x - y &= -5 \\ 2x - y &= -2 \\ \hline -x \quad &= -3 \\ x \quad &= 3 \end{aligned}$$

$$\begin{aligned} 3 - y + 5 &= 0 \\ y &= 8 \end{aligned}$$

$(3, 8)$

$$\begin{aligned} 7x + y - 8 &= 0 \\ 7x - 2y - 5 &= 0 \\ 7x + y &= 8 \\ 7x - 2y &= 5 \\ \hline 3y &= 3 \\ y &= 1 \\ 7x + 1 - 8 &= 0 \\ 7x - 7 &= 0 \\ 7x &= 7 \\ x &= 1 \end{aligned}$$

$(1, 1)$

④ Rewrite each equation below in slope-intercept form. Write the equation in standard form of a parallel line through the point (1, 2) and a perpendicular line through the point (-1, -2).

$-3x + y - 2 = 0$

$y = 3x + 2$ Slope = 3

$$\begin{aligned} y - 2 &= 3(x - 1) \\ y - 2 &= 3x - 3 \\ 3x - y - 1 &= 0 \end{aligned}$$

Parallel line: $3x - y = 1$

$$\begin{aligned} y - (-2) &= -\tfrac{1}{3}(x - (-1)) \\ y + 2 &= -\tfrac{1}{3}(x + 1) \\ y + 2 &= -\tfrac{1}{3}x - \tfrac{1}{3} \\ \tfrac{1}{3}x + y + \tfrac{7}{3} &= 0 \\ x + 3y + 7 &= 0 \end{aligned}$$

Perpendicular line: $x + 3y = -7$

$4x + y + 5 = 0$

$y = -4x - 5$ Slope = -4

$$\begin{aligned} y - 2 &= -4(x - 1) \\ y - 2 &= -4x + 4 \\ 4x + y + 6 &= 0 \end{aligned}$$

Parallel line: $4x + y = -6$

$$\begin{aligned} y - (-2) &= \tfrac{1}{4}(x - (-1)) \\ y + 2 &= \tfrac{1}{4}(x + 1) \\ y + 2 &= \tfrac{1}{4}x + \tfrac{1}{4} \\ \tfrac{1}{4}x - y - \tfrac{7}{4} &= 0 \\ x - 4y - 7 &= 0 \end{aligned}$$

Perpendicular line: $x - 4y = 7$

$x - y + 5 = 0$

$y = x + 5$ Slope = 1

$$\begin{aligned} y - 2 &= 1(x - 1) \\ y - 2 &= x - 1 \\ x - y + 1 &= 0 \end{aligned}$$

Parallel line: $x - y = -1$

$$\begin{aligned} y - (-2) &= -1(x - (-1)) \\ y + 2 &= -1(x + 1) \\ y + 2 &= -x - 1 \\ x + y + 3 &= 0 \end{aligned}$$

Perpendicular line: $x + y = -3$

$2x - y + 2 = 0$

$y = 2x + 2$ Slope = 2

$$\begin{aligned} y - 2 &= 2(x - 1) \\ y - 2 &= 2x - 2 \end{aligned}$$

Parallel line: $2x - y = 0$

$$\begin{aligned} y - (-2) &= -\tfrac{1}{2}(x - (-1)) \\ y + 2 &= -\tfrac{1}{2}(x + 1) \\ y + 2 &= -\tfrac{1}{2}x - \tfrac{1}{2} \\ \tfrac{1}{2}x + y + \tfrac{5}{2} &= 0 \\ x + 2y + 5 &= 0 \end{aligned}$$

Perpendicular line: $x + 2y = -5$

Teaching Tips, Cont.

- Teach solving systems of equations by subtraction from the teaching box. Tell the students that the only difference between solving by addition and solving by subtraction is that the variable that is eliminated by addition has like coefficients with opposite signs, and the variable that is eliminated by subtraction has like coefficients with the same sign.
- Remind the students to change the signs on each term when they are subtracting a polynomial or a linear equation. The subtraction applies to both sides of the equal sign.
- Complete the Classwork exercises. Have some students work the problems on the board for the class and explain their answers. All students should work the problems in their books.

Assignment

- Complete Lesson 54, Activities 2-4.

Lesson 55

Concepts

- Systems of equations
- Multiplying a polynomial by a constant
- Adding linear equations
- Subtracting linear equations
- Order of operations
- Inequalities

Learning Objectives

The student will be able to:

- Solve systems of equations by multiplication
- Apply combinations of methods learned to solve systems of equations
- Express the solution of a system of equations as a coordinate point

Materials Needed

- Student Book, Lesson 55
- Worksheet 28

Teaching Tips

- ➢ Have students complete Worksheet 28 in class. This may be for added practice of earlier topics, or graded as a quiz, if desired.
- ➢ Review solving systems of equations by addition and subtraction. (See Lessons 53-54)
- ➢ Tell the students there is a fourth method of solving systems of equations that can be used when no other method works easily.
- ➢ Introduce multiplication as another method of solving systems of equations. This method also uses either addition or subtraction to get the final answer.

Solving Linear Systems: Multiplication

Sometimes systems of linear equations cannot be easily solved by any of the methods you have learned so far. When this happens, one equation can be rewritten by multiplying each term of the equation by the same number to make one pair of variables match. In rare instances, both equations will need to be rewritten.

Solve the system of equations.

$3x + 2y - 4 = 0$
$x + 3y + 1 = 0$

Rewrite the equations in standard form.

$3x + 2y - 4 = 0 \Rightarrow 3x + 2y = 4$
$x + 3y + 1 = 0 \Rightarrow x + 3y = -1$

Notice that neither addition nor subtraction will eliminate a variable. In this case, multiplying each term in the second equation by 3 will make the *x*-terms match.

$3x + 2y = 4 \Rightarrow 3x + 2y = 4$
$3x + 3(3y) = 3(-1) \Rightarrow 3x + 9y = -3$

Subtract to solve the system of equations.

$3x + 2y = 4$
$\underline{-(3x + 9y = -3)}$
$-7y = 7$
$y = -1$

Substitute the value of *y* in either of the original equations to solve for *x*.

$x + 3(-1) + 1 = 0$
$x - 3 + 1 = 0$
$x = 2$

Express the answer as a coordinate point.
The solution is the point (2, -1).

As before, always remember to check your work by substituting the values in the other equation. If the values you found produce a true equation in both cases, your answer is correct.

① Classwork

Solve the systems of equations by multiplication.

$2x + y - 5 = 0$
$x + 3y - 5 = 0$

Write in standard form. $2x + y = 5$; $x + 3y = 5$

Multiply. $2x + y = 5$; $2x + 6y = 10$

Subtract. $-5y = -5$

Solve. $y = 1$

Substitute. $2x + 1 - 5 = 0$; $2x = 4$; $x = 2$

The solution is the point (2, 1).

$3x + 2y - 1 = 0$
$2x + 3y - 4 = 0$

Write in standard form. $3x + 2y = 1$; $2x + 3y = 4$

Multiply. $6x + 4y = 2$; $6x + 9y = 12$

Subtract. $-5y = -10$

Solve. $y = 2$

Substitute. $3x + 2(2) - 1 = 0$; $3x + 4 - 1 = 0$; $3x = -3$; $x = -1$

The solution is the point (-1, 2).

Activities

② Solve each system of equations by multiplication.

$3x + 2y - 7 = 0$ $x + 4y + 1 = 0$ $3x + 2y = 7$ $x + 4y = -1$ $6x + 4y = 14$ $\underline{x + 4y = -1}$ $5x = 15$ $x = 3$ $3(3) + 2y - 7 = 0$ $9 + 2y - 7 = 0$ $2y = -2$ $y = -1$ (3, -1)	$3x + 5y - 18 = 0$ $x + 2y - 9 = 0$ $3x + 5y = 18$ $x + 2y = 9$ $3x + 5y = 18$ $\underline{3x + 6y = 27}$ $-y = -9$ $y = 9$ $x + 2(9) - 9 = 0$ $x + 18 - 9 = 0$ $x = -9$ (-9, 9)	$4x - 3y + 1 = 0$ $3x + y - 9 = 0$ $4x - 3y = -1$ $3x + y = 9$ $4x - 3y = -1$ $\underline{9x + 3y = 27}$ $13x = 26$ $x = 2$ $3(2) + y - 9 = 0$ $6 + y - 9 = 0$ $y = 3$ (2, 3)	$2x + 3y - 8 = 0$ $5x - 6y + 7 = 0$ $2x + 3y = 8$ $5x - 6y = -7$ $4x + 6y = 16$ $\underline{5x - 6y = -7}$ $9x = 9$ $x = 1$ $2(1) + 3y - 8 = 0$ $2 + 3y - 8 = 0$ $3y = 6$ $y = 2$ (1, 2)
$5x + 3y + 3 = 0$ $2x + y + 2 = 0$ $5x + 3y = -3$ $2x + y = -2$ $5x + 3y = -3$ $\underline{6x + 3y = -6}$ $-x = 3$ $x = -3$ $2(-3) + y + 2 = 0$ $-6 + y + 2 = 0$ $y = 4$ (-3, 4)	$4x - 3y + 12 = 0$ $x - 2y - 7 = 0$ $4x - 3y = -12$ $x - 2y = 7$ $4x - 3y = -12$ $\underline{4x - 8y = 28}$ $5y = -40$ $y = -8$ $x - 2(-8) - 7 = 0$ $x + 16 - 7 = 0$ $x = -9$ (-9, -8)	$2x - y - 3 = 0$ $-x + 3y - 16 = 0$ $2x - y = 3$ $-x + 3y = 16$ $6x - 3y = 9$ $\underline{-x + 3y = 16}$ $5x = 25$ $x = 5$ $-5 + 3y - 16 = 0$ $3y = 21$ $y = 7$ (5, 7)	$2x + 5y - 6 = 0$ $3x + 4y + 5 = 0$ $2x + 5y = 6$ $3x + 4y = -5$ $6x + 15y = 18$ $\underline{6x + 8y = -10}$ $7y = 28$ $y = 4$ $2x + 5(4) - 6 = 0$ $2x + 20 - 6 = 0$ $2x = -14$ $x = -7$ (-7, 4)

③ Solve.

$5(x-2) + 7 < 5 + 24 \div 6 + 2x$ $5x - 10 + 7 < 5 + 4 + 2x$ $5x - 3 < 9 + 2x$ $3x < 12$ $x < 4$	$3x - 2 \times 3 + 2 > 4(x+2) - 5x$ $3x - 6 + 2 > 4x + 8 - 5x$ $3x - 4 > -x + 8$ $4x > 12$ $x > 3$	$6(1-2x) - 2(1-3x) < 5x - 7$ $6 - 12x - 2 + 6x < 5x - 7$ $-6x + 4 < 5x - 7$ $-11x < -11$ $x > 1$

Adding and Subtracting Polynomials, Systems of Equations Worksheet 28

① Add or subtract as indicated.

$$\begin{array}{r} 6x^2+7x+4 \\ +\ \underline{3x^2+6x+5} \\ 9x^2+13x+9 \end{array} \qquad \begin{array}{r} 6x^2+6x+8 \\ \underline{+4x^2-4x-5} \\ 10x^2+2x+3 \end{array} \qquad \begin{array}{r} 7x^2-8x+6 \\ \underline{+5x^2+4x-7} \\ 12x^2-4x-1 \end{array}$$

$$\begin{array}{r} (9x^2+7x+8) \\ \underline{-(4x^2+5x+4)} \\ 5x^2+2x+4 \end{array} \qquad \begin{array}{r} (10x^2-6x+7) \\ \underline{-(4x^2-7x-5)} \\ 6x^2+\ \ x+12 \end{array} \qquad \begin{array}{r} (6x^2-5x-7) \\ \underline{-(8x^2+7x-9)} \\ -2x^2-12x+2 \end{array}$$

$$\begin{array}{r} 5x^2+6x+5 \\ +\ \underline{5x^2+4x+3} \\ 10x^2+10x+8 \end{array} \qquad \begin{array}{r} 7x^2+5x+7 \\ \underline{+3x^2-6x-3} \\ 10x^2-\ \ x+4 \end{array} \qquad \begin{array}{r} 5x^2-6x+5 \\ \underline{+7x^2+4x-5} \\ 12x^2-2x \end{array}$$

$$\begin{array}{r} (8x^2+8x+6) \\ \underline{-(5x^2+4x+3)} \\ 3x^2+4x+3 \end{array} \qquad \begin{array}{r} (8x^2-5x+6) \\ \underline{-(3x^2-6x-3)} \\ 5x^2+\ \ x+9 \end{array} \qquad \begin{array}{r} (10x^2-4x-4) \\ \underline{-(7x^2+4x-5)} \\ 3x^2-8x+1 \end{array}$$

② Solve by setting the two equations equal. Express your answer as a coordinate point.

$-4x+y-6=0$
$5x+y+3=0$
$y=4x+6$
$y=-5x-3$
$4x+6=-5x-3$
$9x=-9$
$x=-1$
$-4(-1)+y-6=0$
$4+y-6=0$
$y=2$
$(-1,\ 2)$

$2x-y+5=0$
$-x+y-2=0$
$y=2x+5$
$y=x+2$
$2x+5=x+2$
$x=-3$
$2(-3)-y+5=0$
$-6-y+5=0$
$y=-1$
$(-3,\ -1)$

$-5x+y-7=0$
$3x+y+1=0$
$y=5x+7$
$y=-3x-1$
$5x+7=-3x-1$
$8x=-8$
$x=-1$
$-5(-1)+y-7=0$
$5+y-7=0$
$y=2$
$(-1,\ 2)$

$-5x-y+9=0$
$6x-2y-14=0$
$y=-5x+9$
$2y=6x-14$ Divide terms by 2.
$y=3x-7$
$-5x+9=3x-7$
$-8x=-16$
$x=2$
$-5(2)-y+9=0$
$-10-y+9=0$
$y=-1$
$(2,\ -1)$

$-5x-y+13=0$
$2x-2y-10=0$
$y=-5x+13$
$2y=2x-10$ Divide terms by 2.
$y=x-5$
$-5x+13=x-5$
$-6x=-18$
$x=3$
$-5(3)-y+13=0$
$-15-y+13=0$
$y=-2$
$(3,\ -2)$

$x-y+2=0$
$-2x+y-6=0$
$y=x+2$
$y=2x+6$
$x+2=2x+6$
$-x=4$
$x=-4$
$-4-y+2=0$
$y=-2$
$(-4,\ -2)$

Teaching Tips, Cont.

- Teach solving systems of equations by multiplication from the teaching box. Point out that multiplication alone will not give a solution to the system, but rather will transform one or both equations in the system so that either addition or subtraction can be used.
- Complete the Classwork exercises. Have some students work the problems on the board for the class and explain their answers. All students should work the problems in their books.
- The students can work these problems in many different ways but the final answers should be the same.

Assignment

- Complete Lesson 55, Activities 2-3.

Lesson 56

Concepts
- Systems of equations
- Dividing a polynomial by a constant
- Adding linear equations
- Subtracting linear equations
- Math in the real world

Learning Objectives
The student will be able to:
- Solve systems of equations by division
- Apply combinations of methods learned to solve systems of equations
- Express the solution of a system of equations as a coordinate point

Materials Needed
- Student Book, Lesson 56

Teaching Tips
- ➢ Review solving systems of equations by multiplication. (See Lesson 55)
- ➢ Tell the students that sometimes it is not desirable to multiply to make the coefficients match because that would cause you to work with very large numbers. It is much easier to work with equations that have small coefficients.
- ➢ Teach solving systems of equations by division from the teaching box. Explain that the same procedure for solving by multiplication applies to division.

Lesson 56

Solving Linear Systems: Division

Sometimes systems of linear equations cannot be easily solved by any of the methods you have learned so far. When this happens, one equation can be rewritten by dividing each term of the equation by the same number to make one pair of variables match. In rare instances, both equations will need to be rewritten.

Solve the system of equations.
$3x + 2y - 4 = 0$
$6x + 18y + 6 = 0$

Rewrite the equations in standard form.
$3x + 2y - 4 = 0 \quad 3x + 2y = 4$
$6x + 18y + 6 = 0 \Rightarrow 6x + 18y = -6$

Notice that neither addition nor subtraction will eliminate a variable. In this case, dividing each term in the second equation by 2 will make the *x*-terms match. (Note: You could multiply each term in the first equation by either 2 or 9, but that would give you large numbers to work with. Whenever possible, use smaller numbers.)
$3x + 2y = 4$
$3x + 9y = -3$

Subtract to solve the system of equations.
$$\begin{array}{r} 3x + 2y = 4 \\ -(3x + 9y = -3) \\ \hline -7y = 7 \\ y = -1 \end{array}$$

Substitute the value of *y* in either of the original equations to solve for *x*.
$x + 3(-1) + 1 = 0$
$x - 3 + 1 = 0$
$x = 2$

Express the answer as a coordinate point.
The solution is the point (2, -1).

As before, always remember to check your work by substituting the values in the other equation. If the values you found produce a true equation in both cases, your answer is correct.

① **Classwork**
Solve the systems of equations by division.

$2x + y - 5 = 0$
$4x + 12y - 20 = 0$

Write in standard form. $\begin{array}{l} 2x + y = 5 \\ 4x + 12y = 20 \end{array}$

Divide the second equation by 2.
$2x + y = 5$
$2x + 6y = 10$

Subtract. $-5y = -5$

Solve. $y = 1$

Substitute. $\begin{array}{l} 2x + 1 - 5 = 0 \\ 2x = 4 \\ x = 2 \end{array}$

The solution is the point (2, 1).

$18x + 12y - 6 = 0$
$6x + 9y - 12 = 0$

Write in standard form. $\begin{array}{l} 18x + 12y = 6 \\ 6x + 9y = 12 \end{array}$

Divide the first equation by 3. $\begin{array}{l} 6x + 4y = 2 \\ 6x + 9y = 12 \end{array}$

Subtract. $-5y = -10$

Solve. $y = 2$

Substitute. $\begin{array}{l} 6x + 9(2) - 12 = 0 \\ 6x + 18 - 12 = 0 \\ 6x = -6 \\ x = -1 \end{array}$

The solution is the point (-1, 2).

Activities

② Solve the systems of equations by division.

$6x+4y-14=0$ $2x+8y+2=0$ $6x+4y=14$ $2x+8y=-2$ $6x+4y=14$ $x+4y=-1$ $5x=15$ $x=3$ $2(3)+8y+2=0$ $6+8y+2=0$ $8y=-8$ $y=-1$ (3, -1)	$6x+10y-36=0$ $3x+6y-27=0$ $6x+10y=36$ $3x+6y=27$ $3x+5y=18$ $3x+6y=27$ $-y=-9$ $y=9$ $3x+6(9)-27=0$ $3x+54-27=0$ $3x=-27$ $x=-9$ (-9, 9)	$12x-9y+3=0$ $9x+3y-27=0$ $12x-9y=-3$ $9x+3y=27$ $4x-3y=-1$ $9x+3y=27$ $13x=26$ $x=2$ $9(2)+3y-27=0$ $18+3y-27=0$ $3y=9$ $y=3$ (2, 3)	$4x+6y-16=0$ $20x-24y+28=0$ $4x+6y=16$ $20x-24y=-28$ $4x+6y=16$ $5x-6y=-7$ $9x=9$ $x=1$ $4(1)+6y-16=0$ $4+6y-16=0$ $6y=12$ $y=2$ (1, 2)
$10x+6y+6=0$ $6x+3y+6=0$ $10x+6y=-6$ $6x+3y=-6$ $5x+3y=-3$ $6x+3y=-6$ $-x=3$ $x=-3$ $6(-3)+3y+6=0$ $-18+3y+6=0$ $3y=12$ $y=4$ (-3, 4)	$12x-9y+36=0$ $4x-8y-28=0$ $12x-9y=-36$ $4x-8y=28$ $4x-3y=-12$ $4x-8y=28$ $5y=-40$ $y=-8$ $4x-8(-8)-28=0$ $4x+64-28=0$ $4x=-36$ $x=-9$ (-9, -8)	$6x-3y-9=0$ $-5x+15y-80=0$ $6x-3y=9$ $-5x+15y=80$ $6x-3y=9$ $-x+3y=16$ $5x=25$ $x=5$ $-5(5)+15y-80=0$ $-25+15y-80=0$ $15y=105$ $y=7$ (5, 7)	$12x+30y-36=0$ $18x+24y+30=0$ (Divide both equations.) $12x+30y=36$ $18x+24y=-30$ $6x+15y=18$ $6x+8y=-10$ $7y=28$ $y=4$ $12x+30(4)-36=0$ $12x+120-36=0$ $12x=-84$ $x=-7$ (-7, 4)

③ Write a system of equations for the scenario below. You do not have to solve.
The New Amsterdam Theater in New York City has 740 seats in the orchestra section. Tickets for the center of the orchestra section cost \$162 and tickets for the edges of the orchestra section cost \$122. If the orchestra section is sold out for a performance, the theater brings in \$101,320 from ticket sales in that section.

Let c = the number of seats in the center of the orchestra section.

Let e = the number of seats on the edges of the orchestra section.

$c+e=740$

$162c+122e=101,320$

Teaching Tips, Cont.

- Tell the students that like multiplication, division will not provide an instant answer. They will have to either convert to slope-intercept form and set the equations equal to each other, add the equations, or subtract the equations to get a final answer.
- Complete the Classwork exercises. Have one student work the problem on the board for the class and explain the answer. All students should work the problem in their books.

Assignment

- Complete Lesson 56, Activities 2-3.

Lesson 57

Concepts

- Systems of equations
- Adding linear equations
- Multiplying a polynomial by a constant
- Math in the real world

Learning Objectives

The student will be able to:

- Solve systems of equations by linear combinations
- Express the solution of a system of equations as a coordinate point

Materials Needed

- Student Book, Lesson 57

Teaching Tips

- Review solving systems of equations by addition and multiplication. (See Lessons 53 and 55)
- Tell the students that there is a final method of solving systems of equations that is very similar to what they have already learned.
- Introduce linear combinations as a method of solving systems of equations that uses multiplication and addition.

Lesson 57

Solving Linear Systems: Linear Combinations

The linear combination method of solving linear systems uses two of the methods you have learned: multiplication and addition. Write all equations in standard form. Then multiply one or both of the given equations by a constant so that one of the variables has the same coefficient in each equation, but with opposite signs. This may require you to multiply by a negative number. Add the resulting equations and solve for the remaining variable.

If all variables are eliminated after adding, the answer is "all real numbers" if the resulting equation is true, such as 0 = 0, and "no solution" if the resulting equation if false, such as 0 = 4.

Solve using linear combinations.

$3x + 2y + 4 = 0$

$2x + 3y + 1 = 0$

Rewrite each equation in standard form.

$3x + 2y = -4$

$2x + 3y = -1$

Multiply the first equation by 2 and the second equation by -3 to eliminate the *x*-terms.

$2(3x) + 2(2y) = 2(-4) \Rightarrow 6x + 4y = -8$

$-3(2x) - 3(3y) = -3(-1) \Rightarrow -6x - 9y = 3$

Add the two new equations and solve for *y*.

$6x + 4y = -8$

$-6x - 9y = 3$

$-5y = -5$

$y = 1$

Substitute the value of *y* in one of the original equations to solve for *x*.

$3x + 2(1) + 4 = 0$

$3x + 2 + 4 = 0$

$3x = -6$

$x = -2$

The solution is the point (-2, 1).

Remember to check your work!

① Classwork

Solve the systems of equations using linear combinations.

$2x + y - 5 = 0$

$x + 3y - 5 = 0$

Write in standard form. $2x + y = 5$, $x + 3y = 5$

Multiply the second equation by -2.

$2x + y = 5$

$-2x - 6y = -10$

Add. $-5y = -5$

Solve. $y = 1$

Substitute. $2x + 1 - 5 = 0$, $2x = 4$, $x = 2$

The solution is the point (2, 1).

$3x + 2y - 1 = 0$

$2x + 3y - 4 = 0$

Write in standard form. $3x + 2y = 1$, $2x + 3y = 4$

Multiply the first equation by 2 and the second equation by -3. $6x + 4y = 2$, $-6x - 9y = -12$

Add. $-5y = -10$

Solve. $y = 2$

Substitute. $3x + 2(2) - 1 = 0$, $3x + 4 - 1 = 0$, $3x = -3$, $x = -1$

The solution is the point (-1, 2).

Activities

② Solve using linear combinations.

$$\begin{aligned} &3x+2y+11=0\\ &x+y+7=0\\ &3x+2y=-11\\ &x+y=-7\\ &3x+2y=-11\\ &\underline{-2x-2y=14}\\ &x=3\\ &3+y+7=0\\ &y=-10\\ &(3,\ -10) \end{aligned}$$

$$\begin{aligned} &5x+3y-9=0\\ &2x+y-2=0\\ &5x+3y=9\\ &2x+y=2\\ &5x+3y=9\\ &\underline{-6x-3y=-6}\\ &-x=3\\ &x=-3\\ &2(-3)+y-2=0\\ &-6+y-2=0\\ &y=8\\ &(-3,\ 8) \end{aligned}$$

$$\begin{aligned} &3x+5y+2=0\\ &x+2y-1=0\\ &3x+5y=-2\\ &x+2y=1\\ &3x+5y=-2\\ &\underline{-3x-6y=-3}\\ &-y=-5\\ &y=5\\ &x+2(5)-1=0\\ &x+10-1=0\\ &x=-9\\ &(-9,\ 5) \end{aligned}$$

$$\begin{aligned} &3x-y-2=0\\ &x-2y-14=0\\ &3x-y=2\\ &x-2y=14\\ &-6x+2y=-4\\ &\underline{x-2y=14}\\ &-5x=10\\ &x=-2\\ &-2-2y-14=0\\ &-2y=16\\ &y=-8\\ &(-2,\ -8) \end{aligned}$$

$$\begin{aligned} &x-3y-3=0\\ &2x-2y-18=0\\ &x-3y=3\\ &2x-2y=18\\ &-2x+6y=-6\\ &\underline{2x-2y=18}\\ &4y=12\\ &y=3\\ &x-3(3)-3=0\\ &x-9-3=0\\ &x=12\\ &(12,\ 3) \end{aligned}$$

$$\begin{aligned} &2x-y-1=0\\ &-x+2y-10=0\\ &2x-y=1\\ &-x+2y=10\\ &4x-2y=2\\ &\underline{-x+2y=10}\\ &3x=12\\ &x=4\\ &-4+2y-10=0\\ &2y=14\\ &y=7\\ &(4,\ 7) \end{aligned}$$

$$\begin{aligned} &2x-3y-16=0\\ &x-2y-7=0\\ &2x-3y=16\\ &x-2y=7\\ &2x-3y=16\\ &\underline{-2x+4y=-14}\\ &y=2\\ &x-2(2)-7=0\\ &x-4-7=0\\ &x=11\\ &(11,\ 2) \end{aligned}$$

$$\begin{aligned} &2x+5y+9=0\\ &x+4y+3=0\\ &2x+5y=-9\\ &x+4y=-3\\ &2x+5y=-9\\ &\underline{-2x-8y=6}\\ &-3y=-3\\ &y=1\\ &x+4(1)+3=0\\ &x+4+3=0\\ &x=-7\\ &(-7,\ 1) \end{aligned}$$

③ Solve.

The New Amsterdam Theater in New York City has 740 seats in the orchestra section. Tickets for the center of the orchestra section cost $162 and tickets for the edges of the orchestra section cost $122. If the orchestra section is sold out for a performance, the theater brings in $101,320 from ticket sales in that section. How many seats are in the center of the orchestra section? How many seats are on the edges of the orchestra section? (Use the system of equations you wrote in Lesson 55. You may use a calculator.)

Let c = the number of seats in the center of the orchestra section.

Let e = the number of seats on the edges of the orchestra section.

$$\begin{aligned} &c+e=740\\ &162c+122e=101{,}320 \end{aligned}$$

$$\begin{aligned} 162c+162e&=119{,}880\\ \underline{162c+122e}&\underline{=101{,}320}\\ 40e&=18{,}560\\ e&=464 \end{aligned}$$

$$\begin{aligned} &c+464=740\\ &c=276 \end{aligned}$$

There are 276 seats in the center and 464 seats on the edges.

Teaching Tips, Cont.

- Teach solving systems of equations by linear combinations from the teaching box. Point out that the only difference between this method and solving by multiplication is that this method *requires* multiplication followed by addition, whereas the general multiplication method allows the use of addition or subtraction.

- Complete the Classwork exercises. Have some students work the problems on the board for the class and explain their answers. All students should work the problems in their books.

Assignment

- Complete Lesson 57, Activities 2-3.

Lesson 58

Concepts
- Systems of equations
- Adding linear equations
- Subtracting linear equations
- Linear combinations
- Math in the real world

Learning Objectives
The student will be able to:
- Determine the best method to use to solve a system of equations
- Apply systems of equations to real world scenarios

Materials Needed
- Student Book, Lesson 58
- Worksheet 29

Teaching Tips
- Have students complete Worksheet 29 in class. This may be for added practice of earlier topics, or graded as a quiz, if desired.
- Review solving systems of equations by converting to slope-intercept form and setting the two equations equal. (See Lesson 51)
- Review solving systems of equations by addition. (See Lesson 53)
- Review solving systems of equations by subtraction. (See Lesson 54)
- Review solving systems of equations by multiplication. (See Lesson 55)

Solving Linear Systems: Review

Linear systems may be solved by setting the two equations equal, addition, subtraction, multiplication, division, a combination of these methods, or linear combinations. No matter which method you choose, there are three important things to remember.
- Write the equations in standard form.
- Express the answer as a coordinate point.
- Check your work to make sure your answer works in both original equations.

Solve the system of equations.

$3x + 2y - 7 = 0$
$6x + 4y - 15 = 0$

Rewrite each equation in standard form.

$3x + 2y = 7$
$6x + 4y = 15$

Multiply the first equation by 2.

$6x + 4y = 14$
$6x + 4y = 15$

Subtract the second equation from the first.

$6x + 4y = 14$
$-(6x + 4y = 15)$
$0 = -1$

Obviously this equation is false, so the answer is "no solution."

① **Classwork**
Solve the system of linear equations.

$5x - 2y - 5 = 0$
$-3x + 4y + 3 = 0$
$5x - 2y = 5$
$-3x + 4y = -3$

Multiply the first equation by 2.

$10x - 4y = 10$
$-3x + 4y = -3$

$7x = 7$
$x = 1$

$5(1) - 2y - 5 = 0$
$5 - 2y - 5 = 0$
$-2y = 0$
$y = 0$

(1, 0)

Activities
② Solve.

$x - y + 5 = 0$
$-2x + y - 7 = 0$
$x - y = -5$
$-2x + y = 7$

$2x - 2y = -10$
$-2x + y = 7$
$-y = -3$
$y = 3$

$x - 3 + 5 = 0$
$x = -2$

(-2, 3)

$10x - 3y + 2 = 0$
$7x + 2y - 15 = 0$
$10x - 3y = -2$
$7x + 2y = 15$

$20x - 6y = -4$
$21x + 6y = 45$
$41x = 41$
$x = 1$
$10(1) - 3y + 2 = 0$
$10 - 3y + 2 = 0$
$-3y = -12$
$y = 4$
(1, 4)

$11x + 22y - 11 = 0$
$-x - 4y - 1 = 0$
$11x + 22y = 11$
$-x - 4y = 1$

$x + 2y = 1$
$-x - 4y = 1$
$-2y = 2$
$y = -1$

$-x - 4(-1) - 1 = 0$
$-x + 4 - 1 = 0$
$-x = -3$
$x = 3$
(3, -1)

$5x - 3y - 6 = 0$
$10x - 6y - 12 = 0$
$5x - 3y = 6$
$10x - 6y = 12$

$5x - 3y = 6$
$5x - 3y = 6$
$0 = 0$

All real numbers

③ Solve.
The orchestra section of Broadway Theater in New York City has 560 seats in Section A. Some tickets for Section A cost \$310, and tickets for other seats in Section A cost \$237. If the theater brings in \$140,604 from a sold-out Section A, how many tickets at each price level are sold?

Let x = the number of tickets sold at the lower price.
Let y = the number of tickets sold at the higher price.

$x + y = 560$
$237x + 310y = 140,604$

$310x + 310y = 173,600$
$237x + 310y = 140,604$
$73x = 32,996$
$x = 452$

$452 + y = 560$
$y = 108$

There are 452 tickets sold for \$237 and 108 tickets sold for \$310.

A school play costs \$6715 to produce. If a school sells a total of 1000 tickets, how many of each type of ticket must be sold to break even if adult tickets cost \$10 and student tickets cost \$5? If 1000 tickets are sold, how many of each type of ticket must be sold to have a profit of \$500?

Let a = the number of adult tickets and t = the number of student tickets.

To break even:
$a + t = 1000$
$10a + 5t = 6715$

$10a + 10t = 10,000$
$10a + 5t = 6,715$
$5t = 3,285$
$t = 657$

$a + 657 = 1000$
$a = 343$

To profit \$500
$a + t = 1000$
$10a + 5t = 6715 + 500$

$10a + 10t = 10,000$
$10a + 5t = 7,215$
$5t = 2,785$
$t = 557$

$a + 557 = 1000$
$a = 443$

If the school in the problem above had only sold 650 tickets, would they be able to break even? Why or why not?
No. Even if all of the tickets were sold to adults, they would only bring in \$6500, which is less than the cost of production.

Systems of Equations Worksheet 29

① Solve each system of equations using the method of your choice. Express your answer as a coordinate point.

$3x + 2y - 10 = 0$
$x + 4y + 10 = 0$
$3x + 2y = 10$
$x + 4y = -10$

$6x + 4y = 20$
$\underline{x + 4y = -10}$
$5x = 30$
$x = 6$

$3(6) + 2y - 10 = 0$
$18 + 2y - 10 = 0$
$2y = -8$
$y = -4$

(6, -4)

$3x + 5y - 14 = 0$
$x + 2y - 7 = 0$
$3x + 5y = 14$
$x + 2y = 7$

$3x + 5y = 14$
$\underline{3x + 6y = 21}$
$-y = -7$
$y = 7$

$x + 2(7) - 7 = 0$
$x + 14 - 7 = 0$
$x = -7$

(-7, 7)

$4x - 3y - 2 = 0$
$3x + y - 21 = 0$
$4x - 3y = 2$
$3x + y = 21$

$4x - 3y = 2$
$\underline{9x + 3y = 63}$
$13x = 65$
$x = 5$

$3(5) + y - 21 = 0$
$15 + y - 21 = 0$
$y = 6$

(5, 6)

$5x + 3y + 6 = 0$
$2x + y + 4 = 0$
$5x + 3y = -6$
$2x + y = -4$

$5x + 3y = -6$
$\underline{6x + 3y = -12}$
$-x = 6$
$x = -6$

$2(-6) + y + 4 = 0$
$-12 + y + 4 = 0$
$y = 8$

(-6, 8)

$4x - 3y + 9 = 0$
$x - 2y - 4 = 0$
$4x - 3y = -9$
$x - 2y = 4$

$4x - 3y = -9$
$\underline{4x - 8y = 16}$
$5y = -25$
$y = -5$

$x - 2(-5) - 4 = 0$
$x + 10 - 4 = 0$
$x = -6$

(-6, -5)

$2x - y - 6 = 0$
$-x + 3y - 22 = 0$
$2x - y = 6$
$-x + 3y = 22$

$6x - 3y = 18$
$\underline{-x + 3y = 22}$
$5x = 40$
$x = 8$

$-8 + 3y - 22 = 0$
$3y = 30$
$y = 10$

(8, 10)

Solutions shown are samples. There are other acceptable methods that will result in the same answer.

Teaching Tips, Cont.

- Review solving systems of equations by division. (See Lesson 56)
- Review solving systems of equations by linear combinations. (See Lesson 57)
- Remind students to convert all equations to standard from unless they are converting to slope-intercept and setting the equations equal.
- There is no new material covered in this lesson. Reteach as necessary to ensure all students have mastered solving systems of equations before proceeding to the following lessons.
- Complete the Classwork exercise. Have one student work the problem on the board for the class and explain the answer. All students should work the problem in their books.

Assignment

- Complete Lesson 58, Activities 2-3.

Lesson 59

Concepts
- Systems of equations
- Graphing linear equations
- Math in the real world

Learning Objectives
The student will be able to:
- Graph multiple linear equations on the same Cartesian plane
- Use the graph of linear equations to find the solution to a system of equations

Materials Needed
- Student Book, Lesson 59

Teaching Tips
- Review graphing linear equations. (See Lesson 30)
- Tell the students that there is a way to solve systems of equations without having to do as much algebra.
- Introduce graphing as an alternate method of solving systems of equations.

Solving Linear Systems: Graphing

Graphing linear systems is simply graphing multiple lines on the same Cartesian plane. The point at which the lines intersect is the solution of the linear system.

Solve the system of equations by graphing.

$3x + 2y - 4 = 0$

$x + 3y + 1 = 0$

Graph both lines on the same Cartesian plane. On the graph below, the first equation is shown in blue and the second equation is shown in green. The point of intersection is the solution and is shown in red.

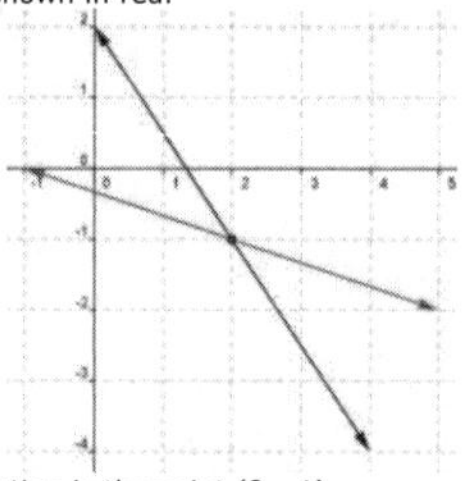

The solution is the point (2, -1).

① **Classwork**

Solve the systems of equations by graphing. Express the solution as a coordinate point.

$-4x + y - 6 = 0$

$3x - y + 5 = 0$

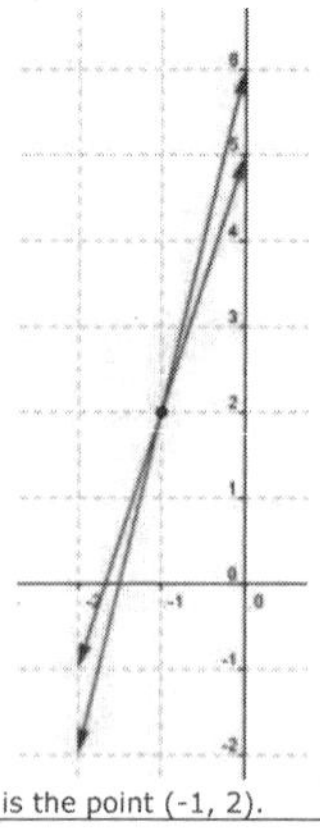

The solution is the point (-1, 2).

Activities

② Solve the systems of equations by graphing. Express the solution as a coordinate point.

$2x + y - 5 = 0$

$x + 3y - 5 = 0$

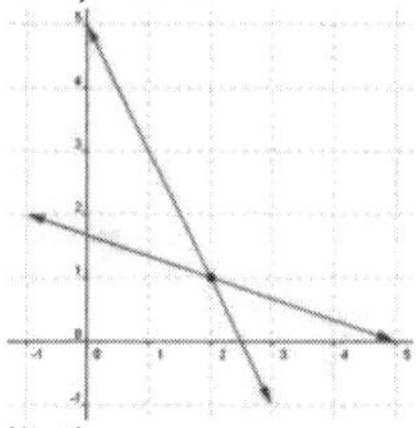

(2, 1)

$3x + 2y - 1 = 0$

$2x + 3y - 4 = 0$

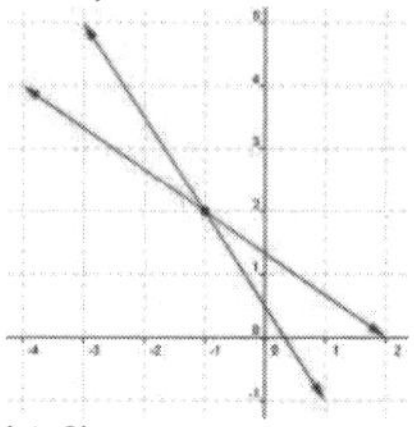

(-1, 2)

$-3x + y - 2 = 0$

$4x + y + 5 = 0$

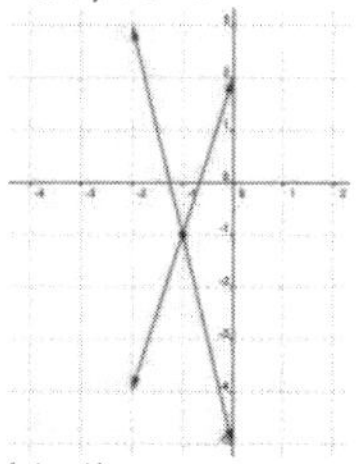

(-1, -1)

③ Solve the systems of equations by graphing. Express the solution as a coordinate point.

$-2x - y + 12 = 0$
$2x + 2y - 6 = 0$

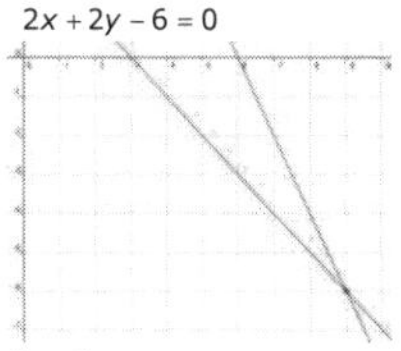

(9, -6)

$-2x + y - 9 = 0$
$x + y + 6 = 0$

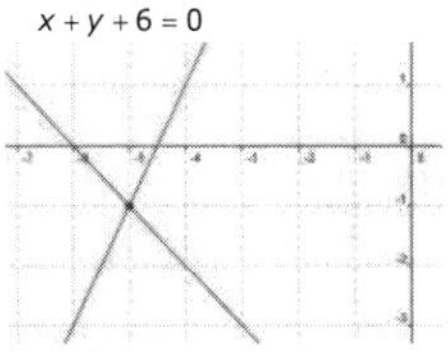

(-5, -1)

$x - y - 2 = 0$
$-2x + y + 9 = 0$

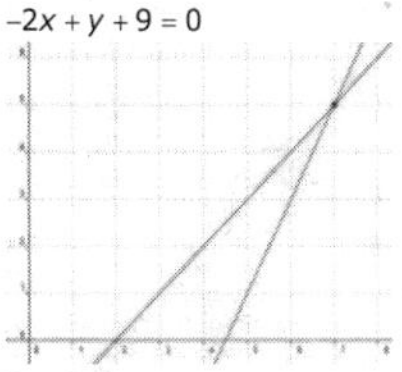

(7, 5)

$x - y + 10 = 0$
$-3x - y - 2 = 0$

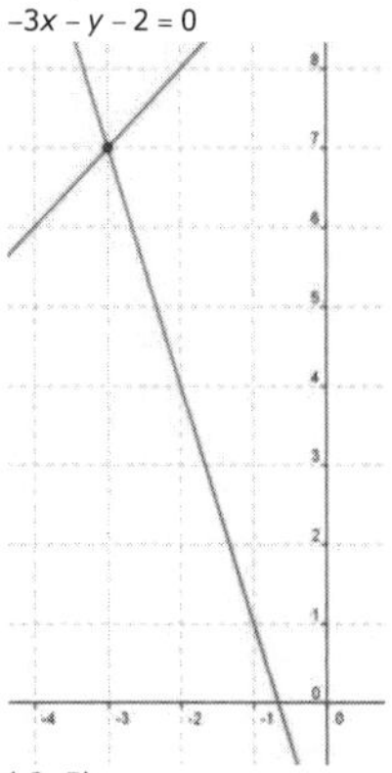

(-3, 7)

$-2x + y - 1 = 0$
$3x + y + 24 = 0$

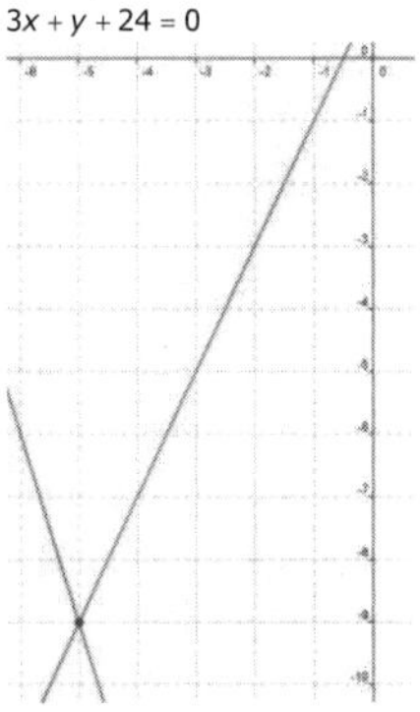

(-5, -9)

$-2x - y + 10 = 0$
$2x + 2y - 6 = 0$

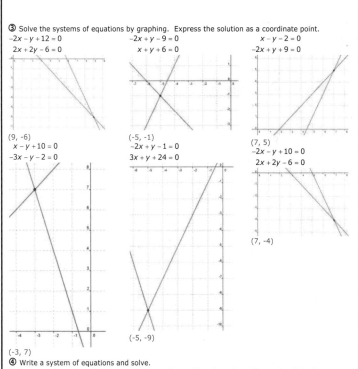

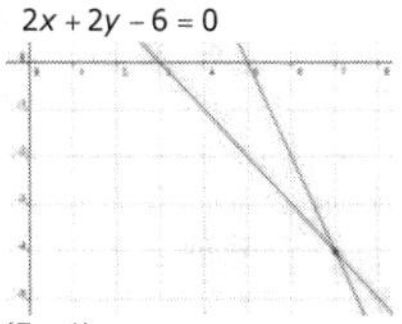

(7, -4)

④ Write a system of equations and solve.

Write a word problem that uses a system of equations to solve. There should be two variables in each equation. Make sure your word problem gives enough information to write two different equations. Write the system of equations for your word problem and solve to get the answer. It may be helpful to choose a scenario where you already know the answer and then write the equation. You may look at the word problems in Lessons 51-58 for ideas.

Answers may vary. Check to ensure that each student's answer makes sense for the stated problem. There must be two variables, and two relationships established so that two equations can be written.

Teaching Tips, Cont.

- Teach solving systems of equations by graphing from the teaching box. Tell the students that the two equations *must* be graphed on the same Cartesian plane for this method to work. If they use two separate graphs, they will not be able to see the point of intersection.
- If you feel the students need additional review on the traditional methods of solving systems of equations, you may have them work them out using one of the other methods and then check their work by graphing.
- Complete the Classwork exercise. Have one student work the problem on the board for the class and explain the answer. All students should work the problem in their books.

Assignment

- Complete Lesson 59, Activities 2-4.

Lesson 60

Concepts

- Multiplying a polynomial by a monomial
- Absolute value
- Radicals
- Extraneous solutions
- Fractions
- Properties of equality

Learning Objectives

The student will be able to:

- Multiply a polynomial by a monomial
- Use algebra tiles to represent algebraic multiplication

Materials Needed

- Student Book, Lesson 60
- Worksheet 30
- Algebra tiles

Teaching Tips

- ➢ Review multiplying monomials. (See Lesson 14)
- ➢ Teach multiplying a polynomial by a monomial from the teaching box.
- ➢ Show the students that multiplying a polynomial by a monomial is just an application of the distributive property.
- ➢ Illustrate multiplying a polynomial by a monomial using algebra tiles. Place tiles representing the polynomial and the monomial at right angles to each other. In the case of the sample problem, the polynomial is across the top (2*x*-1) and the monomial is down the left side (3*x*). Notice that the -1 is red to show it is negative.

Lesson 60

Multiplying by a Monomial

To multiply a polynomial by a monomial, use the distributive property and follow the rules of multiplying monomials for each term. (See Lesson 14.)

Distribute the monomial across the polynomial by multiplying each term of the polynomial by the monomial and adding.

$3x(2x-1) = 3x(2x) + 3x(-1)$

Solve each monomial product.

$3x(2x) + 3x(-1) = 6x^2 - 3x$

This can also be represented using algebra tiles. Place the monomial pieces vertically and the polynomial pieces horizontally to form the edges of a rectangle. Fill in the space in the middle of the rectangle to see the answer.

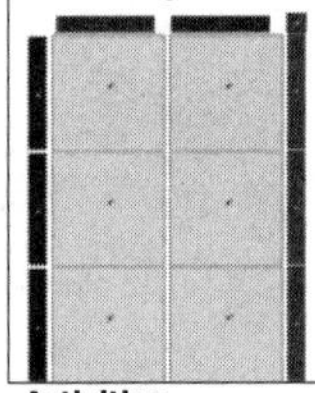

① Classwork

Multiply.

$5(3x-2)$

$5(3x) + 5(-2) = 15x - 10$

$2x(3x+4)$

$2x(3x) + 2x(4) = 6x^2 + 8x$

$2x(x^2 + 2x - 3)$

$2x(x^2) + 2x(2x) + 2x(-3) =$

$2x^3 + 4x^2 - 6x$

Activities

② Multiply.

$2(5x+2)$

$2(5x) + 2(2) = 10x + 4$

$3(4x-1)$

$3(4x) + 3(-1) = 12x - 3$

$5(3x-4)$

$5(3x) + 5(-4) = 15x - 20$

$2(2x+3)$

$2(2x) + 2(3) = 4x + 6$

$3(6x-1)$

$3(6x) + 3(-1) = 18x - 3$

$3x(3x+2)$

$3x(3x) + 3x(2) = 9x^2 + 6x$

$2x(4x-3)$

$2x(4x) + 2x(-3) = 8x^2 - 6x$

$3x(x-5)$

$3x(x) + 3x(-5) = 3x^2 - 15x$

$4x(2x-6)$

$4x(2x) + 4x(-6) = 8x^2 - 24x$

$3x(7x-3)$

$3x(7x) + 3x(-3) = 21x^2 - 9x$

$3x(3x^2 + x - 4)$

$3x(3x^2) + 3x(x) + 3x(-4) =$

$9x^3 + 3x^2 - 12x$

$3x(4x^2 + 2x - 3)$

$3x(4x^2) + 3x(2x) + 3x(-3) =$

$12x^3 + 6x^2 - 9x$

$2x(5x^2 - 2x + 7)$

$2x(5x^2) + 2x(-2x) + 2x(7) =$

$10x^3 - 4x^2 + 14x$

$3x(2x^2 - 3x + 5)$

$3x(2x^2) + 3x(-3x) + 3x(5) =$

$6x^3 - 9x^2 + 15x$

$3x(7x^2 + 2x - 6)$

$3x(7x^2) + 3x(2x) + 3x(-6) =$

$21x^3 + 6x^2 - 18x$

③ Find all possible solutions. Identify any extraneous solutions.

$|4x+3| + 3x = 2x - 2$

$|4x+3| = -x - 2$

$4x + 3 = -x - 2$ or $4x + 3 = -(-x-2)$

$5x = -5$ $\quad 4x + 3 = x + 2$

$x = -1$ $\quad 3x = -1 \Rightarrow x = -\frac{1}{3}$

check:

$|4(-1)+3| + 3(-1) = 2(-1) - 2$

$|-4+3| - 3 = -2 - 2$

$|-1| - 3 = -4$

$1 - 3 \neq -4$ extraneous

$|4(-\frac{1}{3})+3| + 3(-\frac{1}{3}) = 2(-\frac{1}{3}) - 2$

$|-\frac{4}{3}+3| - 1 = -\frac{2}{3} - 2$

$|\frac{5}{3}| - 1 = -\frac{8}{3}$

$\frac{5}{3} - 1 \neq -\frac{8}{3}$ extraneous

$|6x+5| - 4 = 2x + 9$

$|6x+5| = 2x + 13$

$6x + 5 = 2x + 13$ or $6x + 5 = -(2x+13)$

$4x = 8$ $\quad 6x + 5 = -2x - 13$

$x = 2$ $\quad 8x = -18 \Rightarrow x = -\frac{18}{8} = -\frac{9}{4}$

check:

$|6(2)+5| - 4 = 2(2) + 9$

$|12+5| - 4 = 4 + 9$

$17 - 4 = 13$

$|6(-\frac{9}{4})+5| - 4 = 2(-\frac{9}{4}) + 9$

$|-\frac{27}{2} + \frac{10}{2}| - 4 = -\frac{9}{2} + 9$

$|-\frac{17}{2}| - \frac{8}{2} = \frac{9}{2}$

$\frac{17}{2} - \frac{8}{2} = \frac{9}{2}$

$\sqrt{-6x-17} + 4 = 9$

$\sqrt{-6x-17} = 5$

$\left(\sqrt{-6x-17}\right)^2 = 5^2$

$-6x - 17 = 25$

$-6x = 42$

$x = -7$

check:

$\sqrt{-6(-7)-17} + 4 = 9$

$\sqrt{42-17} + 4 = 9$

$\sqrt{25} + 4 = 9$

$5 + 4 = 9$

$\sqrt{4x-3} + 7 = 4$

$\sqrt{4x-3} = -3$

$\left(\sqrt{4x-3}\right)^2 = (-3)^2$

$4x - 3 = 9$

$4x = 12$

$x = 3$

check:

$\sqrt{4(3)-3} + 7 = 4$

$\sqrt{12-3} + 7 = 4$

$\sqrt{9} + 7 = 4$

$3 + 7 \neq 4$ extraneous

④ Solve each algebraic equation. For each step, identify the property of equality that was used.

$\frac{2}{x} - \frac{5}{x^2} = -\frac{1}{x} + \frac{7}{x^2}$

$\frac{2}{\cancel{x}}(x^{\cancel{2}}) - \frac{5}{\cancel{x^2}}(\cancel{x^2}) = -\frac{1}{\cancel{x}}(x^{\cancel{2}}) + \frac{7}{\cancel{x^2}}(\cancel{x^2}) \Rightarrow$

$2x - 5 = -x + 7$

Multiplication property

$2x - 5 + x = -x + x + 7 \Rightarrow 3x - 5 = 7$

Addition property

$3x - 5 + 5 = 7 + 5 \Rightarrow 3x = 12$

Addition property

$3x \div 3 = 12 \div 3 \Rightarrow x = 4$

Division property

$7 - \frac{4}{x} = 1 - \frac{22}{x}$

$7(x) - \frac{4}{\cancel{x}}(\cancel{x}) = 1(x) - \frac{22}{\cancel{x}}(\cancel{x}) \Rightarrow 7x - 4 = x - 22$

Multiplication property

$7x - 4 - x = x - 22 - x \Rightarrow 6x - 4 = -22$

Subtraction property

$6x - 4 + 4 = -22 + 4 \Rightarrow 6x = -18$

Addition property

$6x \div 6 = -18 \div 6 \Rightarrow x = -3$

Division property

Multiplying Polynomials by Monomials Worksheet 30

① Multiply.

$3(5x+4) = 3(5x)+3(4) = 15x+12$

$4(3x-1) = 4(3x)+4(-1) = 12x-4$

$8(3x-5) = 8(3x)+8(-5) = 24x-40$

$7(2x+1) = 7(2x)+7(1) = 14x+7$

$5(6x-9) = 5(6x)+5(-9) = 30x-45$

$4x(3x+8) = 4x(3x)+4x(8) = 12x^2+32x$

$3x(5x-2) = 3x(5x)+3x(-2) = 15x^2-6x$

$2x(5x-11) = 2x(5x)+2x(-11) = 10x^2-22x$

$7x(2x-3) = 7x(2x)+7x(-3) = 14x^2-21x$

$12x(3x-1) = 12x(3x)+12x(-1) = 36x^2-12x$

$5x(3x^2+x-2) = 5x(3x^2)+5x(x)+5x(-2) = 15x^3+5x^2-10x$

$8x(4x^2+2x-7) = 8x(4x^2)+8x(2x)+8x(-7) = 32x^3+16x^2-56x$

$9x(5x^2-3x+7) = 9x(5x^2)+9x(-3x)+9x(7) = 45x^3-27x^2+63x$

$3x(4x^2-3x+6) = 3x(4x^2)+3x(-3x)+3x(6) = 12x^3-9x^2+18x$

$6x(7x^2+5x-6) = 6x(7x^2)+6x(5x)+6x(-6) = 42x^3+30x^2-36x$

Teaching Tips, Cont.

- Fill in the center of the rectangle with algebra tiles. Remember to follow the rules for signed numbers and use a red tile for any term that is negative.
- Complete the Classwork exercises. Have some students work the problems on the board for the class and explain their answers. All students should work the problems in their books.
- Review for Test 6 using worksheets 26-30. These worksheets were assigned in previous lessons.

Assignments

- Complete Lesson 60, Activities 2-4.
- Worksheet 30.
- Study for Test 6 (Lessons 48-57).

Test 6

Testing Objectives

The student will:

- Solve inequalities with absolute values
- Identify inequalities with no solution
- Graph inequalities
- Add polynomials
- Subtract polynomials
- Solve systems of equations
- Express the solution of a system of equations as a coordinate point

Materials Needed

- Test 6
- *It's College Test Prep Time!* from Student Book
- Exploring Math through... Swimming from Student Book

Teaching Tips

- ➢ Administer Test 6, allowing the students 30-40 minutes to complete the test.
- ➢ When all students are finished taking the test, introduce *It's College Test Prep Time* from the student book. This page may be completed in class or assigned as homework.
- ➢ Have students read the Exploring Math feature for Lessons 61-70.

① Solve the inequalities. **12 points**

$|7x| < x + 24$

$-(x+24) < 7x < x + 24$

$-x - 24 < 7x < x + 24$

$-x - 24 < 7x$ and $7x < x + 24$

$-24 < 8x \qquad 6x < 24$

$-3 < x \qquad x < 4$

$-3 < x < 4$

$|9x+5| + 7 < 3$

$|9x+5| < -4$ NO SOLUTION

Stop working here. The absolute value of anything can never be negative, so the answer is no solution.

$|3x+4| + 8 > 3$

$|3x+4| > -5$ ALL REAL NUMBERS

Stop working here. The absolute value of anything can never be negative, so the answer is all real numbers.

$|4x-2| - 3 > -3x + 23$

$|4x-2| > -3x + 26$

$4x - 2 > -3x + 26$ or $4x - 2 < 3x - 26$

$7x > 28 \qquad x < -24$

$x > 4$

$x > 4$ or $x < -24$

② Graph the inequalities. **9 points**

$y > x - 1$

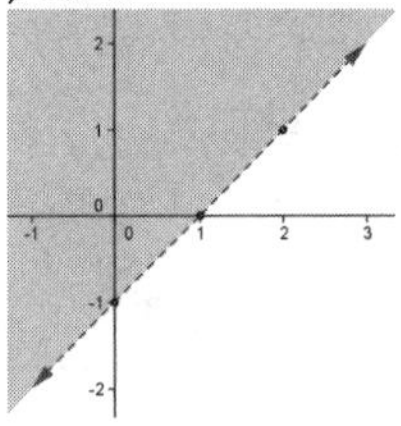

$y < 2x - 1$

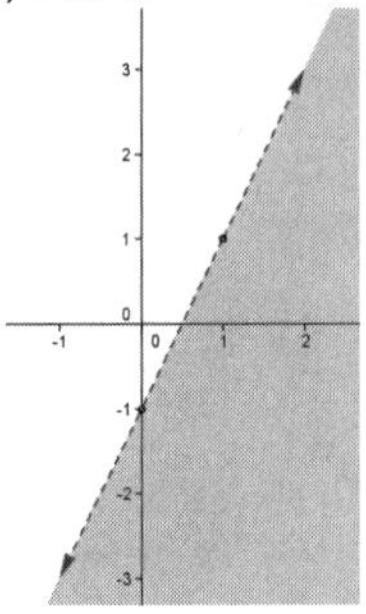

$y \le 2(x-2)$

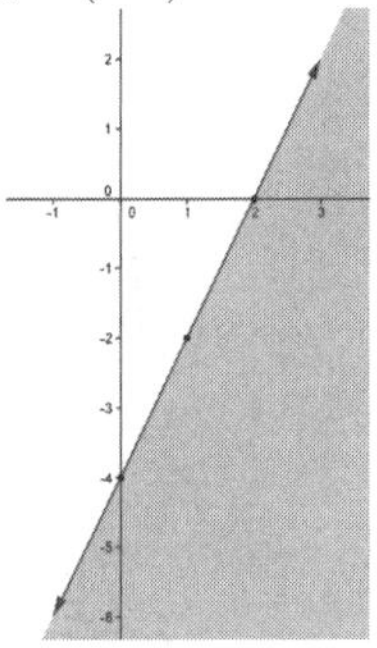

Note: Each problem has 1 point for the line in the correct place, 1 point for the line drawn properly (solid or dashed) and 1 point for the shading on the correct side of the line.

③ Add or subtract as indicated. **6 points**

$6x^2 + 7x + 4$
$+\ 4x^2 + 7x + 6$
$10x^2 + 14x + 10$

$6x^2 + 6x + 8$
$+4x^2 - 4x - 5$
$10x^2 + 2x + 3$

$7x^2 - 8x + 6$
$+5x^2 + 4x - 7$
$12x^2 - 4x - 1$

$(9x^2 + 7x + 8)$
$-(4x^2 + 5x + 4)$
$5x^2 + 2x + 4$

$(10x^2 - 6x + 7)$
$-(4x^2 - 7x - 5)$
$6x^2 + x + 12$

$(10x^2 - 4x - 4)$
$-(7x^2 + 3x - 5)$
$3x^2 - 7x + 1$

④ Solve. Express the answer as a coordinate point. **12 points**

$-3x - y - 24 = 0$
$3x + 2y + 12 = 0$
$-3x - y = 24$
$3x + 2y = -12$
$y = 12$
$-3x - 12 - 24 = 0$
$-3x = 36$
$x = -12$
$(-12, 12)$

$-x - 3y + 28 = 0$
$x - 2y + 32 = 0$
$-x - 3y = -28$
$x - 2y = -32$
$-5y = -60$
$y = 12$
$-x - 3(12) + 28 = 0$
$-x - 36 + 28 = 0$
$x = -8$
$(-8, 12)$

$10x + 6y + 46 = 0$
$6x + 3y + 30 = 0$
$10x + 6y = -46$
$6x + 3y = -30$
$5x + 3y = -23$
$6x + 3y = -30$
$-x = 7$
$x = -7$
$6(-7) + 3y + 30 = 0$
$-42 + 3y + 30 = 0$
$3y = 12$
$y = 4$
$(-7, 4)$

$-x + 2y + 21 = 0$
$3x - 2y - 19 = 0$
$-x + 2y = -21$
$3x - 2y = 19$
$2x = -2$
$x = -1$
$-(-1) + 2y + 21 = 0$
$1 + 2y + 21 = 0$
$2y = -22$
$y = -11$
$(-1, -11)$

$-3x + y + 15 = 0$
$4x + y - 41 = 0$
$-3x + y = -15$
$4x + y = 41$
$-7x = -56$
$x = 8$
$-3(8) + y + 15 = 0$
$-24 + y + 15 = 0$
$y = 9$
$(8, 9)$

$5x + 3y = 0$
$2x + y + 1 = 0$
$5x + 3y = 0$
$2x + y = -1$
$5x + 3y = 0$
$6x + 3y = -3$
$-x = 3$
$x = -3$
$2(-3) + y + 1 = 0$
$-6 + y + 1 = 0$
$y = 5$
$(-3, 5)$

$x - y + 14 = 0$
$-2x - y - 4 = 0$
$x - y = -14$
$-2x - y = 4$
$3x = -18$
$x = -6$
$-6 - y + 14 = 0$
$y = 8$
$(-6, 8)$

$7x + y + 52 = 0$
$7x - 2y + 85 = 0$
$7x + y = -52$
$7x - 2y = -85$
$3y = 33$
$y = 11$
$7x + 11 + 52 = 0$
$7x + 63 = 0$
$7x = -63$
$x = -9$
$(-9, 11)$

$3x + 2y - 16 = 0$
$x + 4y - 2 = 0$
$3x + 2y = 16$
$x + 4y = 2$
$6x + 4y = 32$
$x + 4y = 2$
$5x = 30$
$x = 6$
$3(6) + 2y - 16 = 0$
$18 + 2y - 16 = 0$
$2y = -2$
$y = -1$
$(6, -1)$

$6x - 4y - 46 = 0$
$2x + 8y - 34 = 0$
$6x - 4y = 46$
$2x + 8y = 34$
$6x - 4y = 46$
$x + 4y = 17$
$7x = 63$
$x = 9$
$2(9) + 8y - 34 = 0$
$18 + 8y - 34 = 0$
$8y = 16$
$y = 2$
$(9, 2)$

$3x + 2y + 7 = 0$
$x + y + 2 = 0$
$3x + 2y = -7$
$x + y = -2$
$3x + 2y = -7$
$2x + 2y = -4$
$x = -3$
$-3 + y + 2 = 0$
$y = 1$
$(-3, 1)$

$5x + 3y + 14 = 0$
$2x + y + 6 = 0$
$5x + 3y = -14$
$2x + y = -6$
$5x + 3y = -14$
$6x + 3y = -18$
$-x = 4$
$x = -4$
$2(-4) + y + 6 = 0$
$-8 + y + 6 = 0$
$y = 2$
$(-4, 2)$

39 points total

It's College Test Prep Time!

1. In the system of equations below, what is the value of $2(a+b)$?

   $a+b+4c=750$

   $a+b+2c=450$

   A. 75
   B. 150
   C. 300
   D. 450
   E. 600

   Subtract the bottom equation from the top equation to get $2c = 300$. Substitute this value for $2c$ in the second equation and get $a + b = 150$. Double this to get $2(a + b) = 300$.

2. Given that x is a positive integer less than 15, how many possible values are there for x in the solution of $3x+4 \le 52$?

   A. 13
   B. 14
   C. 15
   D. 16
   E. 17

   Solving for x gives you $x \le 16$. However, x must be less than 15, so there are 14 possible values of x.

3. Find the value of $\frac{x}{y}$ if x and y are positive real numbers and $27^x = 3^y$.

   A. 9
   B. 3
   C. $\sqrt{3}$
   D. $\frac{1}{3}$
   E. $\frac{1}{9}$

   $27^x = (3^3)^x = 3^{3x}$. Rewrite the equation as $3^{3x} = 3^y$. Because the bases are equal, set the exponents equal. $3x = y$. Substitute this value for y in the fraction and simplify. $\frac{x}{y} = \frac{x}{3x} = \frac{1}{3}$

4. Which of the following is NOT equivalent to $\frac{2x}{y}(yz-c)$?

   A. $2xz - \frac{2xc}{y}$
   B. $2x\left(z - \frac{c}{y}\right)$
   C. $\frac{2xyz - 2xc}{y}$
   D. $2x\left(-\frac{c}{y} + z\right)$
   E. $2x\left(\frac{z-c}{y}\right)$ The z should be yz for the equation to be equal.

Exploring Math through... Swimming

Math is an integral part of nearly every aspect of swimming. Competitive swimmers are concerned about their speed and do everything possible to reduce drag in the water. Most swimmers, both amateur and professional, care about the water temperature. Those responsible for pool maintenance have constant calculations to maintain safe, healthy conditions in the pool.

Professionals who do regular maintenance on pools must use algebra and geometry every day. Because chemical formulas depend on the volume of the pool, knowledge of geometry is essential. Slopes must be calculated to get an accurate volume of a pool that deepens.

Outdoor pools present their own mathematical challenges. During summer heat waves, the water in some pools gets too hot for people to enjoy. Employees wishing to cool the water to a comfortable temperature must calculate the number of pounds of ice necessary to cool the given volume of water the required number of degrees. Outdoor pools are also more susceptible to algae and climate changes. This requires a constant calculation of chemical amounts to keep the water clean and at a proper pH level.

All swimming pools must be chlorinated to help with germ control. The amount of chlorine that must be added to a pool depends on the volume of the pool, the current chlorine level, and the number of swimmers in the pool. Special formulas are used to ensure all chemical levels are kept in the proper balance.

Assignments

- Complete *It's College Test Prep Time!*
- Read Exploring Math through... Swimming

Lesson 61

Concepts
- Multiplying binomials
- Multiplying a polynomial by a monomial
- Systems of equations
- Adding linear equations
- Subtracting linear equations
- Multiplying linear equations
- Dividing linear equations

Learning Objectives
The student will be able to:
- Apply the rules of multiplying monomials to multiplying binomials
- Multiply two binomials
- Write the terms in the product of two binomials in order from highest degree to lowest degree

Materials Needed
- Student Book, Lesson 61
- Algebra tiles

Teaching Tips
- Review multiplying monomials. (See Lessons 14 and 60)
- Write the problem 45 x 72 on the board. Ask the students how they would solve that problem. (Write the problem vertically and follow the rules for multiplying.)
- Rewrite the problem vertically as shown in the second example to the right. Show the students that what they are really doing when multiplying is breaking each number down into place values and multiplying individual place values and adding.

Lesson 61

Multiplying Binomials

To multiply two binomials, multiply each term in the first binomial by each term in the second binomial and add the resulting products.
$(x+2)(2x+3) = x(2x) + x(3) + 2(2x) + 2(3)$

Follow the rules for multiplying monomials to simplify the answer.
$x(2x) + x(3) + 2(2x) + 2(3) = 2x^2 + 3x + 4x + 6$

Combine like terms. Remember to arrange the terms in order from the highest degree to the lowest degree, placing variables of equal degree in alphabetical order.
$2x^2 + 7x + 6$

This can also be represented using algebra tiles. Place one polynomial vertically and the other one horizontally. Fill in the center of the rectangle to get the answer.

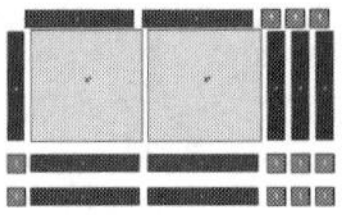

① Classwork
Multiply.

$(x-1)(x+2)$
$x(x) + x(2) - 1(x) - 1(2) =$
$x^2 + 2x - x - 2 = x^2 + x - 2$

$(x+1)(x-2)$
$x(x) + x(-2) + 1(x) + 1(-2) =$
$x^2 - 2x + x - 2 = x^2 - x - 2$

$(2x+1)(x+3)$
$2x(x) + 2x(3) + 1(x) + 1(3) =$
$2x^2 + 6x + x + 3 = 2x^2 + 7x + 3$

Activities
② Multiply.

$(x+3)(x+4)$
$x(x) + x(4) + 3(x) + 3(4) =$
$x^2 + 4x + 3x + 12 = x^2 + 7x + 12$

$(x-1)(x+2)$
$x(x) + x(2) - 1(x) - 1(2) =$
$x^2 + 2x - x - 2 = x^2 + x - 2$

$(x+1)(x-3)$
$x(x) + x(-3) + 1(x) + 1(-3) =$
$x^2 - 3x + x - 3 = x^2 - 2x - 3$

$(x+3)(x-3)$
$x(x) + x(-3) + 3(x) + 3(-3) =$
$x^2 - 3x + 3x - 9 = x^2 - 9$

$(2x-3)(x+2)$
$2x(x) + 2x(2) - 3(x) - 3(2) =$
$2x^2 + 4x - 3x - 6 = 2x^2 + x - 6$

$(2x+3)(x-5)$
$2x(x) + 2x(-5) + 3(x) + 3(-5) =$
$2x^2 - 10x + 3x - 15 = 2x^2 - 7x - 15$

$(3x-2)(x+1)$
$3x(x) + 3x(1) - 2(x) - 2(1) =$
$3x^2 + 3x - 2x - 2 = 3x^2 + x - 2$

$(2x+5)(3x-4)$
$2x(3x) + 2x(-4) + 5(3x) + 5(-4) =$
$6x^2 - 8x + 15x - 20 = 6x^2 + 7x - 20$

Multiplying numbers:

$$\begin{array}{r} 45 \\ \times 72 \\ \hline 90 \\ +3150 \\ \hline 3240 \end{array} \qquad \begin{array}{r} (40+5) \\ \times(70+2) \\ \hline 80+10 \\ +2800+350 \\ \hline 3240 \end{array}$$

$(40)(70) + (40)(2) + (5)(70) + (5)(2) =$
$2800 + 80 + 350 + 10 =$
3240

③ Multiply.

$3(4x+5)$
$3(4x)+3(5)=12x+15$

$4(2x-1)$
$4(2x)+4(-1)=8x-4$

$2(3x-7)$
$2(3x)+2(-7)=6x-14$

$5(3x+4)$
$5(3x)+5(4)=15x+20$

$7(2x-5)$
$7(2x)+7(-5)=14x-35$

$6x(2x+3)$
$6x(2x)+6x(3)=12x^2+18x$

$3x(5x-2)$
$3x(5x)+3x(-2)=15x^2-6x$

$4x(x-3)$
$4x(x)+4x(-3)=4x^2-12x$

$5x(4x-5)$
$5x(4x)+5x(-5)=20x^2-25x$

$2x(8x-7)$
$2x(8x)+2x(-7)=16x^2-14x$

$8x(2x^2+x-3)$
$8x(2x^2)+8x(x)+8x(-3)=$
$16x^3+8x^2-24x$

$4x(3x^2+2x-1)$
$4x(3x^2)+4x(2x)+4x(-1)=$
$12x^3+8x^2-4x$

$3x(5x^2-3x+7)$
$3x(5x^2)+3x(-3x)+3x(7)=$
$15x^3-9x^2+21x$

$2x(3x^2-4x+1)$
$2x(3x^2)+2x(-4x)+2x(1)=$
$6x^3-8x^2+2x$

$9x(4x^2+3x-8)$
$9x(4x^2)+9x(3x)+9x(-8)=$
$36x^3+27x^2-72x$

④ Solve each system of equations.

$x-y-5=0$
$-2x+y+7=0$
$x-y=5$
$\underline{-2x+y=-7}$
$-x=-2$
$x=2$
$2-y=5$
$y=-3$
(2, -3)

$10x-3y-37=0$
$7x+2y-30=0$
$10x-3y=37$
$7x+2y=30$
$20x-6y=74$
$\underline{21x+6y=90}$
$41x=164$
$x=4$
$10(4)-3y=37$
$40-3y=37$
$-3y=-3$
$y=1$
(4, 1)

$11x+22y+11=0$
$-x-4y+1=0$
$11x+22y=-11$
$-x-4y=-1$
$x+2y=-1$
$\underline{-x-4y=-1}$
$-2y=-2$
$y=1$
$-x-4(1)=-1$
$-x-4=-1$
$-x=3$
$x=-3$
(-3, 1)

$5x-10y-15=0$
$3x-6y-9=0$
$5x-10y=15$
$3x-6y=9$
$15x-30y=45$
$\underline{15x-30y=45}$
$0=0$
All real numbers

$3x+2y-11=0$
$x+y-7=0$
$3x+2y=11$
$x+y=7$
$3x+2y=11$
$\underline{2x+2y=14}$
$x=-3$
$-3+y=7$
$y=10$
(-3, 10)

$3x-y-14=0$
$x-2y-18=0$
$3x-y=14$
$x-2y=18$
$6x-2y=28$
$\underline{x-2y=18}$
$5x=10$
$x=2$
$2-2y=18$
$-2y=16$
$y=-8$
(2, -8)

$x-3y+21=0$
$2x-2y+30=0$
$x-3y=-21$
$2x-2y=-30$
$x-3y=-21$
$\underline{x-y=-15}$
$-2y=-6$
$y=3$
$x-3(3)=-21$
$x-9=-21$
$x=-12$
(-12, 3)

$2x-y+1=0$
$-x+2y+10=0$
$2x-y=-1$
$-x+2y=-10$
$4x-2y=-2$
$\underline{-x+2y=-10}$
$3x=-12$
$x=-4$
$4+2y=-10$
$2y=-14$
$y=-7$
(-4, -7)

Multiplying binomials:

$$
\begin{array}{r}
(x+2) \\
\times(2x+3) \\
\hline
3x+6 \\
+2x^2+4x \quad \\
\hline
2x^2+7x+6
\end{array}
$$

Teaching Tips, Cont.

- Write the last problem from the bottom of the previous page. Show the students that the same multiplication problem can be written horizontally and worked by following the same multiplication/addition pattern.

- Teach multiplying binomials from the teaching box. Show the students that this works the same way that multiplying two-digit numbers.

- An alternate method of multiplying binomials is shown at the lower left. Some students prefer to set up binomial multiplication the way they are used to setting up standard numerical multiplication.

- Students who are visual or hands-on learners may wish to use algebra tiles. Follow the same procedure as multiplying monomials. See Lesson 60 for details.

- Complete the Classwork exercises. Have some students work the problems on the board for the class and explain their answers. All students should work the problems in their books.

Assignment

- Complete Lesson 61, Activities 2-4.

Lesson 62

Concepts

- The FOIL method
- Multiplying binomials
- Absolute value
- Extraneous solutions
- Roots
- Math in the real world

Learning Objectives

The student will be able to:

- Use the FOIL method to multiply two binomials
- Write the terms in the product of two binomials in order from highest degree to lowest degree

Materials Needed

- Student Book, Lesson 62
- Worksheet 31

Teaching Tips

➢ Have students complete Worksheet 31 in class. This may be for added practice of earlier topics or graded as a quiz, if desired.

➢ Review multiplying two binomials. (See Lesson 61)

➢ If you are using algebra tiles, review the use of algebra tiles for multiplying binomials. Lesson 60 has information on the use of algebra tiles.

➢ Tell the students there is an easy way to remember how to multiply two binomials.

The FOIL Method

The **FOIL method** is a mnemonic device to help you remember how to multiply two binomials.

Look at this example from Lesson 61:

$(x+2)(2x+3) = x(2x) + x(3) + 2(2x) + 2(3)$

$= 2x^2 + 3x + 4x + 6$

$= 2x^2 + 7x + 6$

F: Multiply the **first** term of each binomial.
In this case, $x(2x)$

O: Multiply the two **outer** terms.
In this case, $x(3)$

I: Multiply the two **inner** terms.
In this case, $2(2x)$

L: Multiply the **last** term of each binomial.
In this case, $2(3)$

Add the result of each, and combine like terms to simplify.

$2x^2 + 3x + 4x + 6 = 2x^2 + 7x + 6$

This can also be represented using algebra tiles. See Lesson 61 for details.

① **Classwork**

Multiply, using the FOIL method.

$(x+1)(x+2)$

$x(x) + x(2) + 1(x) + 1(2) =$

$x^2 + 2x + x + 2 = x^2 + 3x + 2$

$(x-1)(x-1)$

$x(x) + x(-1) - 1(x) - 1(-1) =$

$x^2 - x - x + 1 = x^2 - 2x + 1$

$(2x+1)(x-2)$

$2x(x) + 2x(-2) + 1(x) + 1(-2) =$

$2x^2 - 4x + x - 2 = 2x^2 - 3x - 2$

Activities

② Multiply, using the FOIL method.

$(x+2)(x+3)$

$x(x) + x(3) + 2(x) + 2(3) =$

$x^2 + 3x + 2x + 6 = x^2 + 5x + 6$

$(x-3)(x-2)$

$x(x) + x(-2) - 3(x) - 3(-2) =$

$x^2 - 2x - 3x + 6 = x^2 - 5x + 6$

$(2x+1)(x-3)$

$2x(x) + 2x(-3) + 1(x) + 1(-3) =$

$2x^2 - 6x + x - 3 = 2x^2 - 5x - 3$

$(3x+2)(x-4)$

$3x(x) + 3x(-4) + 2(x) + 2(-4) =$

$3x^2 - 12x + 2x - 8 = 3x^2 - 10x - 8$

$(x+5)(x-3)$

$x(x) + x(-3) + 5(x) + 5(-3) =$

$x^2 - 3x + 5x - 15 = x^2 + 2x - 15$

$(2x+7)(x-3)$

$2x(x) + 2x(-3) + 7(x) + 7(-3) =$

$2x^2 - 6x + 7x - 21 = 2x^2 + x - 21$

$(2x+5)(3x-8)$

$2x(3x) + 2x(-8) + 5(3x) + 5(-8) =$

$6x^2 - 16x + 15x - 40 = 6x^2 - x - 40$

$(2x-7)(4x+3)$

$2x(4x) + 2x(3) - 7(4x) - 7(3) =$

$8x^2 + 6x - 28x - 21 = 8x^2 - 22x - 21$

③ Find all possible solutions. Identify any extraneous solutions.

$|-4x+3| + x - 2 = 2x + 16$

$|-4x+3| = x + 18$

$-4x + 3 = x + 18$ or $-4x + 3 = -(x+18)$

$-5x = 15$ $\quad$ $-4x + 3 = -x - 18$

$x = -3$ $\quad$ $-3x = -21 \Rightarrow x = 7$

check:

$|-4(-3)+3| - 3 - 2 = 2(-3) + 16$

$|12+3| - 3 - 2 = -6 + 16$

$|15| - 5 = 10$

$15 - 5 = 10$

$|-4(7)+3| + 7 - 2 = 2(7) + 16$

$|-28+3| + 7 - 2 = 14 + 16$

$|-25| + 5 = 30$

$25 + 5 = 30$

$|2x-3| - 2 = -3x - 25$

$|2x-3| = -3x - 23$

$2x - 3 = -3x - 23$ or $2x - 3 = -(-3x - 23)$

$5x = -20$ $\quad$ $2x - 3 = 3x + 23$

$x = -4$ $\quad$ $-x = 26 \Rightarrow x = -26$

check:

$|2(-4) - 3| - 2 = -3(-4) - 25$

$|-8-3| - 2 = 12 - 25$

$|-11| - 2 = 12 - 25$

$11 - 2 \neq -13$ extraneous

$|2(-26) - 3| - 2 = -3(-26) - 25$

$|-52-3| - 2 = 78 - 25$

$|-55| - 2 = 78 - 25$

$55 - 2 = 53$

④ Simplify the following roots.

$\sqrt[3]{56} + 5\sqrt[3]{189} = \sqrt[3]{2\times2\times2\times7} + 5\sqrt[3]{3\times3\times3\times7} = 2\sqrt[3]{7} + 5(3)\sqrt[3]{7} = 2\sqrt[3]{7} + 15\sqrt[3]{7} = 17\sqrt[3]{7}$

$6\sqrt{27} - \sqrt{75} = 6\sqrt{3\times3\times3} - \sqrt{3\times5\times5} = 6(3)\sqrt{3} - 5\sqrt{3} = 18\sqrt{3} - 5\sqrt{3} = 13\sqrt{3}$

$3\sqrt[4]{32}\left(3\sqrt[4]{128}\right) = 3\sqrt[4]{2\times2\times2\times2\times2}\left(3\sqrt[4]{2\times2\times2\times2\times2\times2\times2}\right) =$

$3(2)\sqrt[4]{2}\left(3(2)\sqrt[4]{8}\right) = 6\sqrt[4]{2}\left(6\sqrt[4]{8}\right) = 36\sqrt[4]{16} = 36\sqrt[4]{2\times2\times2\times2} = 36(2) = 72$

$4\sqrt[3]{270} \div 3\sqrt[3]{40} = 4\sqrt[3]{2\times3\times3\times3\times5} \div 3\sqrt[3]{2\times2\times2\times5} =$

$4(3)\sqrt[3]{2\times5} \div 3(2)\sqrt[3]{5} = 12\sqrt[3]{10} \div 6\sqrt[3]{5} = \frac{{}^{2}\cancel{12}\sqrt[3]{\cancel{10}^{2}}}{{}_{1}\cancel{6}\sqrt[3]{\cancel{5}_{1}}} = 2\sqrt[3]{2}$

⑤ Solve.

A rectangular diving pool's length, l, is 15 feet greater than its width, w. Express the length of the pool in terms of w.

length = $w + 15$

Express the perimeter (distance around) of the pool in terms of w.

perimeter = 2(length) + 2(width)

perimeter = $2(w + 15) + 2w = 2w + 30 + 2w = 4w + 30$

Express the area of the pool surface in terms of w. (Remember the area of a rectangle is length times width.)

Area = $(w+15)(w) = w^2 + 15w$

Solving Systems of Equations by Graphing Worksheet 31

① Solve the systems of equations by graphing. Express the solution as a coordinate point.

$3x + 2y - 7 = 0$
$x + 4y + 1 = 0$

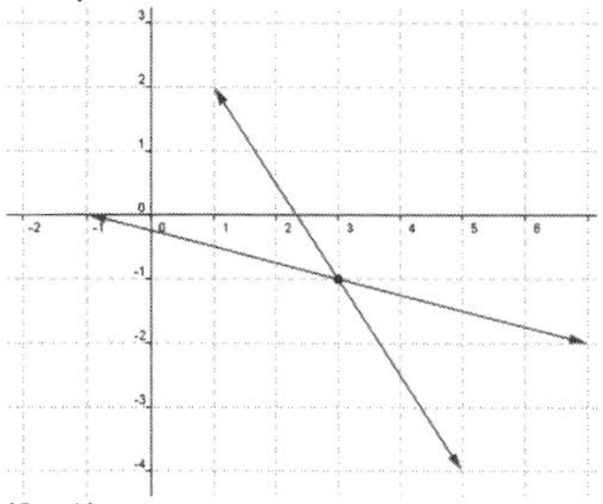

(3, -1)

$4x - 3y + 1 = 0$
$3x + y - 9 = 0$

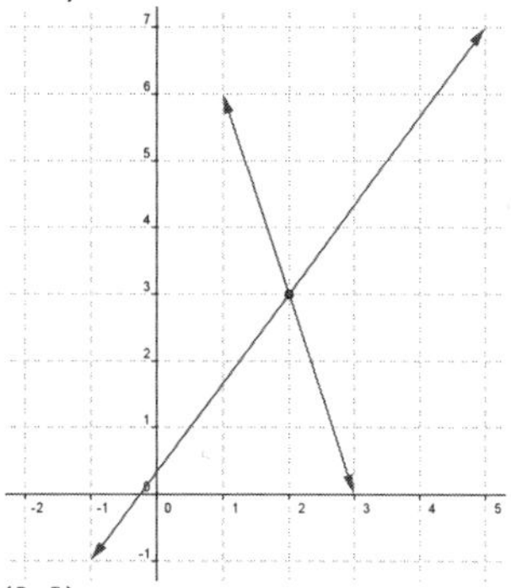

(2, 3)

$5x + 3y + 3 = 0$
$2x + y + 2 = 0$

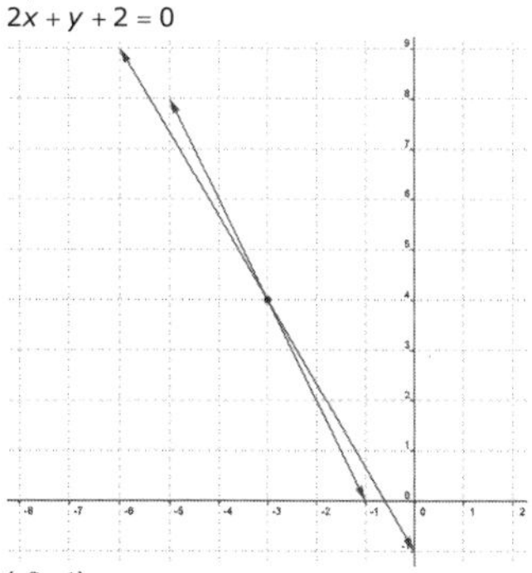

(-3, 4)

$2x + 3y - 8 = 0$
$5x - 6y + 7 = 0$

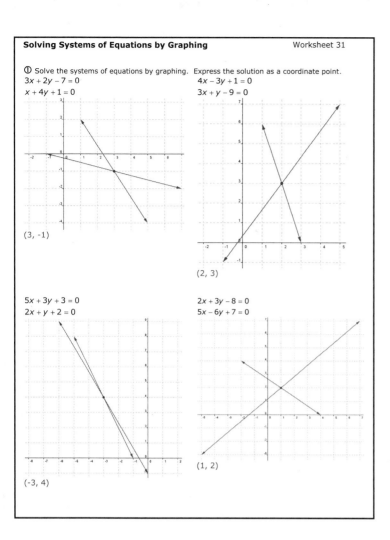

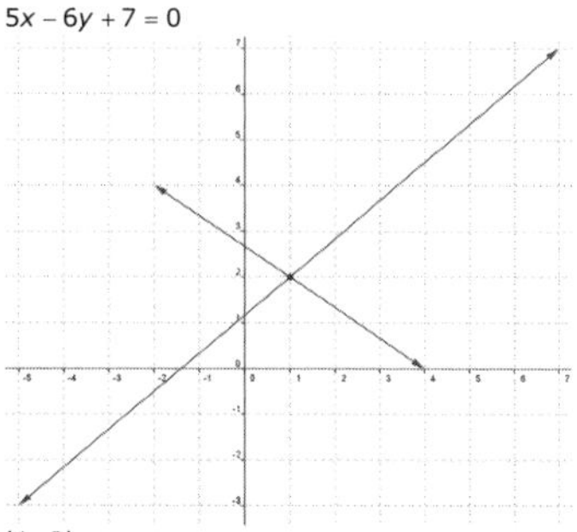

(1, 2)

Teaching Tips, Cont.

- Teach the FOIL method from the teaching box. This pattern calls for multiplying the **F**irst term of each binomial, the **O**uter terms (first term of the first binomial and last term of the second binomial), the **I**nner terms (the last term of the first binomial and the first term of the second binomial) and the **L**ast terms (the last term of each binomial).
- Tell the students that the FOIL method only works for multiplying two binomials, but the concept of multiplying each term of one polynomial by each term of the second polynomial applies to multiplying all polynomials.
- Complete the Classwork exercises. Have some students work the problems on the board for the class and explain their answers. All students should work the problems in their books.

Assignment

- Complete Lesson 62, Activities 2-5.

Lesson 63

Concepts

- Multiplying polynomials
- Multiplying monomials
- Solving linear equations
- Fractions
- Math in the real world

Learning Objectives

The student will be able to:

- Apply the rules of multiplying monomials to multiplying polynomials
- Multiply a binomial by a trinomial
- Multiply two trinomials

Materials Needed

- Student Book, Lesson 63
- Worksheet 32

Teaching Tips

- ➢ Review multiplying monomials. (See Lessons 14 and 60)
- ➢ Review multiplying binomials. (See Lesson 61)
- ➢ Tell the students that the most important thing to remember about multiplying binomials is that each term of one binomial must be multiplied by each term of the other binomial. Once the multiplication is completed, then like terms may be combined.

Multiplying Polynomials

To multiply two polynomials, multiply each term in the first polynomial by each term in the second polynomial and add the resulting products.

$(x+2)(x^2+2x+3)=$

$x(x^2)+x(2x)+x(3)+2(x^2)+2(2x)+2(3)$

Follow the rules for multiplying monomials to simplify the answer.

$x(x^2)+x(2x)+x(3)+2(x^2)+2(2x)+2(3)=$

$x^3+2x^2+3x+2x^2+4x+6$

Combine like terms. Remember to arrange the terms in order from the highest degree to the lowest degree, placing variables of equal degree in alphabetical order.

x^3+4x^2+7x+6

① **Classwork**

Multiply.

$(x+1)(x^2+x+2)$

$x(x^2)+x(x)+x(2)+1(x^2)+1(x)+1(2)=$

$x^3+x^2+2x+x^2+x+2=x^3+2x^2+3x+2$

$(x+1)(x^2-2x+3)$

$x(x^2)+x(-2x)+x(3)+1(x^2)+1(-2x)+1(3)=$

$x^3-2x^2+3x+x^2-2x+3=x^3-x^2+x+3$

$(2x-1)(x^2+3x-3)$

$2x(x^2)+2x(3x)+2x(-3)-1(x^2)-1(3x)-1(-3)=$

$2x^3+6x^2-6x-x^2-3x+3=2x^3+5x^2-9x+3$

Activities

② Multiply.

$(x+2)(x^2+x+1)$

$x(x^2)+x(x)+x(1)+2(x^2)+2(x)+2(1)=$

$x^3+x^2+x+2x^2+2x+2=$

x^3+3x^2+3x+2

$(x-3)(x^2-3x-2)$

$x(x^2)+x(-3x)+x(-2)-3(x^2)-3(-3x)-3(-2)=$

$x^3-3x^2-2x-3x^2+9x+6=$

x^3-6x^2+7x+6

$(x+5)(x^2-2x-3)$

$x(x^2)+x(-2x)+x(-3)+5(x^2)+5(-2x)+5(-3)=$

$x^3-2x^2-3x+5x^2-10x-15=$

$x^3+3x^2-13x-15$

$(x^2+2x+1)(x^2-x-3)$

$x^2(x^2)+x^2(-x)+x^2(-3)+2x(x^2)+2x(-x)+$

$2x(-3)+1(x^2)+1(-x)+1(-3)=$

$x^4-x^3-3x^2+2x^3-2x^2-6x+x^2-x-3=$

$x^4+x^3-4x^2-7x-3$

$(2x+1)(x^2+2x-5)$

$2x(x^2)+2x(2x)+2x(-5)+1(x^2)+1(2x)+1(-5)=$

$2x^3+4x^2-10x+x^2+2x-5=$

$2x^3+5x^2-8x-5$

$(2x+7)(x^2+4x-5)$

$2x(x^2)+2x(4x)+2x(-5)+7(x^2)+7(4x)+7(-5)=$

$2x^3+8x^2-10x+7x^2+28x-35=$

$2x^3+15x^2+18x-35$

$(2x-1)(x^2+3x-5)$

$2x(x^2)+2x(3x)+2x(-5)-1(x^2)-1(3x)-1(-5)=$

$2x^3+6x^2-10x-x^2-3x+5=$

$2x^3+5x^2-13x+5$

$(x^2-2x-5)(x^2+4x+1)$

$x^2(x^2)+x^2(4x)+x^2(1)-2x(x^2)-2x(4x)-$

$2x(1)-5(x^2)-5(4x)-5(1)=$

$x^4+4x^3+x^2-2x^3-8x^2-2x-5x^2-20x-5=$

$x^4+2x^3-12x^2-22x-5$

③ Solve.

$\frac{3x}{5}-1=-19$

$\frac{3x}{5}=-18$

$\cancel{5}\left(\frac{3x}{\cancel{5}}\right)=5(-18)$

$3x=-90$

$x=-30$

$\frac{3x}{4}+2=2x-3$

$\frac{3x}{4}=2x-5$

$\cancel{4}\left(\frac{3x}{\cancel{4}}\right)=4(2x-5)$

$3x=8x-20$

$-5x=-20$

$x=4$

$\frac{3x-1}{4}+7=x+5$

$\frac{3x-1}{4}=x-2$

$\cancel{4}\left(\frac{3x-1}{\cancel{4}}\right)=4(x-2)$

$3x-1=4x-8$

$-x=-7$

$x=7$

④ Solve.

A rectangular short course swimming pool has a width, w, that is 15 feet less than its length. Express the perimeter of the pool in terms of w.

length = $w + 15$

perimeter = 2(length) + 2(width)

perimeter = $2(w+15)+2w=2w+30+2w=4w+30$

Express the area of the pool in terms of w.

area = $(w+15)(w)=w^2+15w$

The pool has a concrete deck that extends 4 feet on each side of the pool. Express the width of the pool and deck in terms of w.

width of pool and deck = $w + 4 + 4 = w + 8$

Express the length of the pool and deck in terms of w.

length of pool and deck = $w + 15 + 4 + 4 = w + 23$

Express the perimeter of the pool and deck in terms of w.

perimeter of pool and deck = $2(w+23)+2(w+8)=2w+46+2w+16=4w+62$

Express the area of the pool and deck in terms of w.

area of pool and deck = $(w+23)(w+8)=w^2+8w+23w+184=w^2+31w+184$

Express the area of the concrete deck in terms of w.

area of concrete deck = area of pool and deck − area of pool

area of concrete deck = $(w^2+31w+184)-(w^2+15w)=w^2+31w+184-w^2-15w=$

$16w+184$

If the perimeter of the pool is 270 feet, what is the width of the pool?

270 feet $=4w+30$

240 feet $=4w$

60 feet $=w$

What is the length of the pool?

Length of pool = w + 15 = 60 + 15 = 75 feet

The FOIL Method, Multiplying Polynomials Worksheet 32

① Multiply, using the FOIL method.

$(x+3)(x+8)$
$x(x)+x(8)+3(x)+3(8)=$
$x^2+8x+3x+24=x^2+11x+24$

$(x+6)(x-7)$
$x(x)+x(-7)+6(x)+6(-7)=$
$x^2-7x+6x-42=x^2-x-42$

$(x-4)(x-1)$
$x(x)+x(-1)-4(x)-4(-1)=$
$x^2-x-4x+4=x^2-5x+4$

$(2x+5)(x-3)$
$2x(x)+2x(-3)+5(x)+5(-3)=$
$2x^2-6x+5x-15=2x^2-x-15$

$(2x+1)(x-2)$
$2x(x)+2x(-2)+1(x)+1(-2)=$
$2x^2-4x+x-2=2x^2-3x-2$

$(2x+7)(3x-4)$
$2x(3x)+2x(-4)+7(3x)+7(-4)=$
$6x^2-8x+21x-28=6x^2+13x-28$

$(3x+4)(x-5)$
$3x(x)+3x(-5)+4(x)+4(-5)=$
$3x^2-15x+4x-20=3x^2-11x-20$

$(2x-9)(3x+4)$
$2x(3x)+2x(4)-9(3x)-9(4)=$
$6x^2+8x-27x-36=6x^2-19x-36$

② Multiply.

$(x+3)(x^2+x+2)$
$x(x^2)+x(x)+x(2)+3(x^2)+3(x)+3(2)=$
$x^3+x^2+2x+3x^2+3x+6=$
x^3+4x^2+5x+6

$(2x+3)(x^2+4x-2)$
$2x(x^2)+2x(4x)+2x(-2)+3(x^2)+3(4x)+3(-2)=$
$2x^3+8x^2-4x+3x^2+12x-6=$
$2x^3+11x^2+8x-6$

$(x-4)(x^2-3x-5)$
$x(x^2)+x(-3x)+x(-5)-4(x^2)-4(-3x)-4(-5)=$
$x^3-3x^2-5x-4x^2+12x+20=$
$x^3-7x^2+7x+20$

$(3x+7)(x^2+2x-1)$
$3x(x^2)+3x(2x)+3x(-1)+7(x^2)+7(2x)+7(-1)=$
$3x^3+6x^2-3x+7x^2+14x-7=$
$3x^3+13x^2+11x-7$

$(x+2)(x^2-3x-4)$
$x(x^2)+x(-3x)+x(-4)+2(x^2)+2(-3x)+2(-4)=$
$x^3-3x^2-4x+2x^2-6x-8=$
$x^3-x^2-10x-8$

$(3x-2)(4x^2+3x-6)$
$3x(4x^2)+3x(3x)+3x(-6)-2(4x^2)-2(3x)-2(-6)=$
$12x^3+9x^2-18x-8x^2-6x+12=$
$12x^3+x^2-24x+12$

$(x^2+3x+4)(x^2-2x-1)$
$x^2(x^2)+x^2(-2x)+x^2(-1)+3x(x^2)+3x(-2x)+$
$3x(-1)+4(x^2)+4(-2x)+4(-1)=$
$x^4-2x^3-x^2+3x^3-6x^2-3x+4x^2-8x-4=$
$x^4+x^3-3x^2-11x-4$

$(x^2-3x-4)(2x^2+5x+3)$
$x^2(2x^2)+x^2(5x)+x^2(3)-3x(2x^2)-3x(5x)-$
$3x(3)-4(2x^2)-4(5x)-4(3)=$
$2x^4+5x^3+3x^2-6x^3-15x^2-9x-8x^2-20x-12=$
$2x^4-x^3-20x^2-29x-12$

Teaching Tips, Cont.

- Ask the students what would happen if one or both binomials had more than two terms. (Some students may say that they wouldn't be binomials any more — they would be trinomials or polynomials.) Elicit the idea that each term of one polynomial must be multiplied by each term of the other polynomial.
- Teach multiplying polynomials from the teaching box. Make sure the students understand that they are doing the same thing they did to multiply binomials, just with extra steps.
- If any students ask about using algebra tiles to multiply trinomials or polynomials, explain that the algebra tiles do not have pieces to allow for variables with an exponent greater than 2.
- Complete the Classwork exercises. Have some students work the problems on the board for the class and explain their answers. All students should work the problems in their books.

Assignments

- Complete Lesson 63, Activities 2-4.
- Worksheet 32.

Lesson 64

Concepts

- Special products of binomials
- FOIL method
- Multiplying polynomials
- Math in the real world

Learning Objectives

The student will be able to:

- Identify three patterns of special products for binomials
- Apply the patterns of special products to multiply binomials

Materials Needed

- Student Book, Lesson 64

Teaching Tips

- Review multiplying binomials and the FOIL method. (See Lessons 61 and 62)
- Review multiplying polynomials. (See Lesson 63)
- Tell the students that there are three patterns they can use to simplify multiplying binomials. If they memorize these patterns, they can shortcut the multiplication process.
- Write the following problems on the board and have the students work them out using the FOIL method.
  $(a + b)(a + b)$
  $(a - b)(a - b)$
  $(a + b)(a - b)$
  The patterns and their corresponding solutions are shown at the right.

Lesson 64

Special Products

There are three instances when multiplying two binomials forms a pattern that becomes a shortcut to arriving at the solution. If you memorize these special products now, it will save you much time later on. Consider these algebraic problems.

$(a+b)(a+b)$

Use the FOIL method to multiply.

$a^2 + ab + ba + b^2$

Remember that *ab* and *ba* are the same thing, according to the commutative property of multiplication. Now simplify the expression.

$a^2 + 2ab + b^2$

This is the formula for finding the square of a binomial.

$\mathbf{(a+b)(a+b) = (a+b)^2 = a^2 + 2ab + b^2}$

If the second term of the binomial is negative, the formula changes slightly.

$\mathbf{(a-b)(a-b) = (a-b)^2 = a^2 - 2ab + b^2}$

If the only difference between the two binomials is the sign of the second term, there is another formula.

$(a+b)(a-b) = a^2 - ab + ba - b^2 = a^2 - b^2$

Simplify to get the formula.

$\mathbf{(a+b)(a-b) = a^2 - b^2}$

This formula is also known as the difference of two squares due to the format of the answer.

① **Classwork**

Multiply, using the formulas for special products.

$(x+2)^2$
$x^2 + 2(2x) + 2^2 =$
$x^2 + 4x + 4$

$(2x+5)^2$
$(2x)^2 + 2(10x) + 5^2 =$
$4x^2 + 20x + 25$

$(x-3)^2$
$x^2 - 2(3x) + 3^2 =$
$x^2 - 6x + 9$

$(2x-1)^2$
$(2x)^2 - 2(2x) + 1^2 =$
$4x^2 - 4x + 1$

$(x+4)(x-4)$
$x^2 - 4^2 = x^2 - 16$

$(2x+3)(2x-3)$
$(2x)^2 - 3^2 = 4x^2 - 9$

Activities

② Multiply, using the formulas for special products.

$(x+1)^2$
$x^2 + 2x + 1$

$(2x+3)^2$
$4x^2 + 12x + 9$

$(x-7)^2$
$x^2 - 14x + 49$

$(2x-4)^2$
$4x^2 - 16x + 16$

$(x+5)(x-5)$
$x^2 - 5^2 = x^2 - 25$

$(2x+2)(2x-2)$
$(2x)^2 - 2^2 = 4x^2 - 4$

Shortcut patterns:

The square of a sum

$(a+b)(a+b)$

$a^2 + 2ab + b^2$

The square of a difference

$(a-b)(a-b)$

$a^2 - 2ab + b^2$

Difference of two squares

$(a+b)(a-b)$

$a^2 - b^2$

③ Multiply. Use the formulas for special products when possible.

$(x+9)^2$

$x^2+18x+81$

$(x+1)(x^2+x+3)$

$x(x^2)+x(x)+x(3)+1(x^2)+1(x)+1(3)=$

$x^3+x^2+3x+x^2+x+3=$

x^3+2x^2+4x+3

$(3x+2)(3x-2)$

$(3x)^2-2^2=9x^2-4$

$(x-3)(x^2-4x-3)$

$x(x^2)+x(-4x)+x(-3)-3(x^2)-3(-4x)-3(-3)=$

$x^3-4x^2-3x-3x^2+12x+9=$

x^3-7x^2+9x+9

$(x+5)(x^2-7x-4)$

$x(x^2)+x(-7x)+x(-4)+5(x^2)+5(-7x)+5(-4)=$

$x^3-7x^2-4x+5x^2-35x-20=$

$x^3-2x^2-39x-20$

$(x-1)^2$

x^2-2x+1

$(x^2+5x+6)(x^2-2x-3)$

$x^2(x^2)+x^2(-2x)+x^2(-3)+5x(x^2)+5x(-2x)+$

$5x(-3)+6(x^2)+6(-2x)+6(-3)=$

$x^4-2x^3-3x^2+5x^3-10x^2-15x+6x^2-12x-18=$

$x^4+3x^3-7x^2-27x-18$

$(2x+3)(x^2+7x-2)$

$2x(x^2)+2x(7x)+2x(-2)+3(x^2)+3(7x)+3(-2)=$

$2x^3+14x^2-4x+3x^2+21x-6=$

$2x^3+17x^2+17x-6$

$(4x-3)^2$

$16x^2-24x+9$

$(x+11)(x-11)$

$x^2-11^2=x^2-121$

$(2x+9)(3x^2+2x-6)$

$2x(3x^2)+2x(2x)+2x(-6)+9(3x^2)+9(2x)+9(-6)=$

$6x^3+4x^2-12x+27x^2+18x-54=$

$6x^3+31x^2+6x-54$

$(3x-1)(4x^2+2x-3)$

$3x(4x^2)+3x(2x)+3x(-3)-1(4x^2)-1(2x)-1(-3)=$

$12x^3+6x^2-9x-4x^2-2x+3=$

$12x^3+2x^2-11x+3$

$(4x+5)^2$

$16x^2+40x+25$

$(5x^2-2x-7)(3x^2+4x+8)$

$5x^2(3x^2)+5x^2(4x)+5x^2(8)-2x(3x^2)-2x(4x)-$

$2x(8)-7(3x^2)-7(4x)-7(8)=$

$15x^4+20x^3+40x^2-6x^3-8x^2-16x-21x^2-28x-56=$

$15x^4+14x^3+11x^2-44x-56$

④ Solve.

A swimming pool is 3 feet deep on the shallow end. The floor of the pool is level for a distance of 10 feet from the entrance steps, then slopes downward at an even rate until it is 8 feet deep at a distance of 15 feet from the entrance steps. What is the slope of the pool in the first 10 feet?

The pool floor is level, so the slope is 0.

What is the slope of the floor where the pool is getting deeper?

The change in depth is 8 feet − 3 feet = 5 feet. (Or 3 feet − 8 feet = -5 feet)

The distance covered is 15 feet − 10 feet = 5 feet.

The slope is $\frac{5}{5}=1$ or $\frac{-5}{5}=-1$

Teaching Tips, Cont.

- Teach the patterns of special products using the three problems the students just worked.
- Although you mentioned it earlier in the lesson, remind the students that memorizing these patterns will make multiplying some binomials easier. It is crucial that the students have these patterns memorized by Lesson 69 when factoring trinomials is introduced. These patterns are printed in bold print in the student book to make them easier to find.
- Complete the Classwork exercises. Have some students work the problems on the board for the class and explain their answers. All students should work the problems in their books.

Assignment

- Complete Lesson 64, Activities 2-4.

Lesson 65

Concepts

- Dividing a polynomial by a monomial
- Dividing a monomial by a monomial
- Exponents

Learning Objectives

The student will be able to:

- Use the distributive property to divide a polynomial by a monomial
- Apply the rules of dividing monomials to polynomials
- Use long division to divide polynomials

Materials Needed

- Student Book, Lesson 65
- Worksheet 33

Teaching Tips

➢ Have students complete Worksheet 33 in class. This may be for added practice of earlier topics or graded as a quiz, if desired.

➢ Review the distributive property. (See Lesson 10)

➢ Review dividing monomials. (See Lesson 15)

➢ Tell the students that the rules for dividing a monomial by a monomial also apply to dividing a polynomial by a monomial. In effect, the distributive property is used to apply the division by the monomial to each term of the polynomial.

Dividing by a Monomial

To divide a polynomial by a monomial, divide each term of the polynomial by the monomial. Follow the rules for dividing monomials. (See Lesson 15.)

$$(6x^2-3x)\div 3x=(6x^2)\div(3x)+(-3x)\div(3x)$$

Solve each monomial quotient.

$$(6x^2)\div(3x)+(-3x)\div(3x)=$$
$$(6\div 3)(x^{2-1})+(-3\div 3)(x^{1-1})=$$
$$2x+(-1)x^0$$

Remember that anything raised to the 0 power is equal to 1.

$$2x+(-1)x^0=2x-1$$

Alternately, polynomials may be written using long division. This method can make it easier to avoid mistakes, especially in long polynomials.

$$\begin{array}{r} 2x-1 \\ 3x\overline{)6x^2-3x} \\ \underline{6x^2} \\ -3x \\ \underline{-3x} \end{array}$$

This can also be represented using algebra tiles. Place the divisor vertically, and fill in the dividend next to the divisor so that all divided pieces are divided equally among the divisor pieces. The quotient will then go across the top, as in a long division problem.

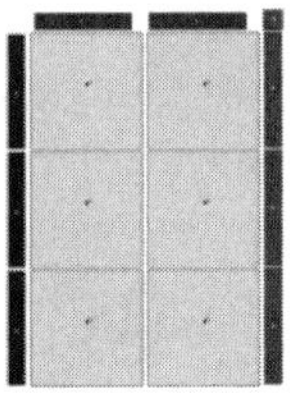

① Classwork

Divide.

$(20x-16)\div 4$

$$\begin{array}{r} 5x-4 \\ 4\overline{)20x-16} \\ \underline{20x} \\ -16 \\ \underline{-16} \end{array}$$

$(9x^2+12x)\div 3x$

$$\begin{array}{r} 3x+4 \\ 3x\overline{)9x^2+12x} \\ \underline{9x^2} \\ 12x \\ \underline{12x} \end{array}$$

$(2x^3+4x^2-6x)\div 2x$

$$\begin{array}{r} x^2+2x-3 \\ 2x\overline{)2x^3+4x^2-6x} \\ \underline{2x^3} \\ 4x^2 \\ \underline{4x^2} \\ -6x \\ \underline{-6x} \end{array}$$

Activities

② Divide.

$(20x+5)\div 5$

$$\begin{array}{r} 4x+1 \\ 5\overline{)20x+5} \\ \underline{20x} \\ 5 \\ \underline{5} \end{array}$$

$(15x^2+9x)\div 3x$

$$\begin{array}{r} 5x+3 \\ 3x\overline{)15x^2+9x} \\ \underline{15x^2} \\ 9x \\ \underline{9x} \end{array}$$

$(15x^3+9x^2-12x)\div 3x$

$$\begin{array}{r} 5x^2+3x-4 \\ 3x\overline{)15x^3+9x^2-12x} \\ \underline{15x^3} \\ 9x^2 \\ \underline{9x^2} \\ -12x \\ \underline{-12x} \end{array}$$

$(14x-14)\div 7$

$$\begin{array}{r} 2x-2 \\ 7\overline{)14x-14} \\ \underline{14x} \\ -14 \\ \underline{-14} \end{array}$$

$(8x^2-14x)\div 2x$

$$\begin{array}{r} 4x-7 \\ 2x\overline{)8x^2-14x} \\ \underline{8x^2} \\ -14x \\ \underline{-14x} \end{array}$$

$(12x^3+4x^2-20x)\div 4x$

$$\begin{array}{r} 3x^2+x-5 \\ 4x\overline{)12x^3+4x^2-20x} \\ \underline{12x^3} \\ 4x^2 \\ \underline{4x^2} \\ -20x \\ \underline{-20x} \end{array}$$

$(18x-12)\div 6$

$$\begin{array}{r} 3x-2 \\ 6\overline{)18x-12} \\ \underline{18x} \\ -12 \\ \underline{-12} \end{array}$$

$(12x^2-18x)\div 3x$

$$\begin{array}{r} 4x-6 \\ 3x\overline{)12x^2-18x} \\ \underline{12x^2} \\ -18x \\ \underline{-18x} \end{array}$$

$(18x^3-36x^2+42x)\div 6x$

$$\begin{array}{r} 3x^2-6x+7 \\ 6x\overline{)18x^3-36x^2+42x} \\ \underline{18x^3} \\ -36x^2 \\ \underline{-36x^2} \\ 42x \\ \underline{42x} \end{array}$$

$(6x+10)\div 2$

$$\begin{array}{r} 3x+5 \\ 2\overline{)6x+10} \\ \underline{6x} \\ 10 \\ \underline{10} \end{array}$$

$(20x^2-28x)\div 4x$

$$\begin{array}{r} 5x-7 \\ 4x\overline{)20x^2-28x} \\ \underline{20x^2} \\ -28x \\ \underline{-28x} \end{array}$$

$(20x^3-35x^2+45x)\div 5x$

$$\begin{array}{r} 4x^2-7x+9 \\ 5x\overline{)20x^3-35x^2+45x} \\ \underline{20x^3} \\ -35x^2 \\ \underline{-35x^2} \\ 45x \\ \underline{45x} \end{array}$$

$(12x-21)\div 3$

$$\begin{array}{r} 4x-7 \\ 3\overline{)12x-21} \\ \underline{12x} \\ -21 \\ \underline{-21} \end{array}$$

$(24x^2-33x)\div 3x$

$$\begin{array}{r} 8x-11 \\ 3x\overline{)24x^2-33x} \\ \underline{24x^2} \\ -33x \\ \underline{-33x} \end{array}$$

$(32x^3+56x^2-16x)\div 8x$

$$\begin{array}{r} 4x^2+7x-2 \\ 8x\overline{)32x^3+56x^2-16x} \\ \underline{32x^3} \\ 56x^2 \\ \underline{56x^2} \\ -16x \\ \underline{-16x} \end{array}$$

The FOIL Method, Multiplying Polynomials Worksheet 33

① Multiply, using the FOIL method.

$(x+4)(x+9)$
$x(x)+x(9)+4(x)+4(9)=$
$x^2+9x+4x+36=x^2+13x+36$

$(x+7)(x-9)$
$x(x)+x(-9)+7(x)+7(-9)=$
$x^2-9x+7x-63=x^2-2x-63$

$(x-3)(x-7)$
$x(x)+x(-7)-3(x)-3(-7)=$
$x^2-7x-3x+21=x^2-10x+21$

$(2x+7)(x-2)$
$2x(x)+2x(-2)+7(x)+7(-2)=$
$2x^2-4x+7x-14=2x^2+3x-14$

$(2x+5)(x-3)$
$2x(x)+2x(-3)+5(x)+5(-3)=$
$2x^2-6x+5x-15=2x^2-x-15$

$(2x+6)(3x-10)$
$2x(3x)+2x(-10)+6(3x)+6(-10)=$
$6x^2-20x+18x-60=6x^2-2x-60$

$(3x+5)(x-2)$
$3x(x)+3x(-2)+5(x)+5(-2)=$
$3x^2-6x+5x-10=3x^2-x-10$

$(2x-11)(3x+2)$
$2x(3x)+2x(2)-11(3x)-11(2)=$
$6x^2+4x-33x-22=6x^2-29x-22$

② Multiply.

$(x+4)(x^2+2x+5)$
$x(x^2)+x(2x)+x(5)+4(x^2)+4(2x)+4(5)=$
$x^3+2x^2+5x+4x^2+8x+20=$
$x^3+6x^2+13x+20$

$(2x+1)(x^2+8x-6)$
$2x(x^2)+2x(8x)+2x(-6)+1(x^2)+1(8x)+1(-6)=$
$2x^3+16x^2-12x+x^2+8x-6=$
$2x^3+17x^2-4x-6$

$(x-5)(x^2-4x-7)$
$x(x^2)+x(-4x)+x(-7)-5(x^2)-5(-4x)-5(-7)=$
$x^3-4x^2-7x-5x^2+20x+35=$
$x^3-9x^2+13x+35$

$(5x+8)(x^2+3x-2)$
$5x(x^2)+5x(3x)+5x(-2)+8(x^2)+8(3x)+8(-2)=$
$5x^3+15x^2-10x+8x^2+24x-16=$
$5x^3+23x^2+14x-16$

$(x+8)(x^2-5x-3)$
$x(x^2)+x(-5x)+x(-3)+8(x^2)+8(-5x)+8(-3)=$
$x^3-5x^2-3x+8x^2-40x-24=$
$x^3+3x^2-43x-24$

$(3x-4)(2x^2+5x-8)$
$3x(2x^2)+3x(5x)+3x(-8)-4(2x^2)-4(5x)-4(-8)=$
$6x^3+15x^2-24x-8x^2-20x+32=$
$6x^3+7x^2-44x+32$

$(x^2+2x+9)(x^2-3x-4)$
$x^2(x^2)+x^2(-3x)+x^2(-4)+2x(x^2)+2x(-3x)+$
$2x(-4)+9(x^2)+9(-3x)+9(-4)=$
$x^4-3x^3-4x^2+2x^3-6x^2-8x+9x^2-27x-36=$
$x^4-x^3-x^2-35x-36$

$(x^2-4x-7)(2x^2+9x+1)$
$x^2(2x^2)+x^2(9x)+x^2(1)-4x(2x^2)-4x(9x)-$
$4x(1)-7(2x^2)-7(9x)-7(1)=$
$2x^4+9x^3+x^2-8x^3-36x^2-4x-14x^2-63x-7=$
$2x^4+x^3-49x^2-67x-7$

Teaching Tips, Cont.

- If students question the use of the distributive property because the problem is division rather than multiplication, point out that dividing is the same thing as inverting and multiplying. Students should remember this concept from studying fractions in past years.
- Teach how to divide a polynomial by a monomial using long division. Explain that the problem is set up just like a regular long division problem with the dividend (the polynomial, in this case) inside and the divisor (the monomial, in this case) outside. The quotient goes on top as usual.
- Tell the students that just like they dealt with one digit at a time when dividing a large number by a single-digit number, they will deal with one term at a time when dividing a polynomial by a monomial.
- Encourage the students to use long division to complete the exercises in this lesson. If they get in the habit now, it will make future lessons easier and will reduce errors.
- Complete the Classwork exercises. Have some students work the problems on the board for the class and explain their answers. All students should work the problems in their books.

Assignment

- Complete Lesson 65, Activity 2.

Lesson 66

Concepts

- Dividing a polynomial by a binomial
- Order of operations
- Exponents
- Roots
- Inequalities

Learning Objectives

The student will be able to:

- Divide a polynomial by a binomial
- Use long division to divide polynomials

Materials Needed

- Student Book, Lesson 66

Teaching Tips

> Review dividing a polynomial by a monomial. (See Lesson 65)

> Have one student divide 276 by 12 and work it as a long division problem. The solution is shown at the right.

> Show the students how two digits of the dividend were used in the first step (27) and the last digit (6) was brought down for the second step. Tell them that dividing polynomials works the same way.

Dividing Polynomials

When dividing two polynomials, set up the problem as a long division problem.

$(2x^2+7x+6)\div(x+2)$ must be rewritten.

$x+2\overline{)2x^2+7x+6}$

Treat this just like long division, dividing the first term of the dividend by the first term of the divisor. In this case, think: $2x^2 \div x$. The answer to this is $2x$. Write this in the quotient area above the x-term of the dividend. Make sure you keep like terms lined up.

$$\begin{array}{r} 2x \\ x+2\overline{)2x^2+7x+6} \end{array}$$

Multiply the term in the quotient by the entire divisor. Write the product terms in their corresponding columns and subtract.

$$\begin{array}{r} 2x \\ x+2\overline{)2x^2+7x+6} \\ \underline{2x^2+4x} \\ 3x \end{array}$$

Bring down the next term in the dividend and repeat the above steps with the remaining polynomial.

$$\begin{array}{r} 2x+3 \\ x+2\overline{)2x^2+7x+6} \\ \underline{2x^2+4x} \\ 3x+6 \\ \underline{3x+6} \end{array}$$

The answer is $2x + 3$.

① **Classwork**

Divide.

$(x^2+5x+6)\div(x+2)$

$$\begin{array}{r} x+3 \\ x+2\overline{)x^2+5x+6} \\ \underline{x^2+2x} \\ 3x+6 \\ \underline{3x+6} \end{array}$$

$(x^2-2x+1)\div(x-1)$

$$\begin{array}{r} x-1 \\ x-1\overline{)x^2-2x+1} \\ \underline{x^2-x} \\ -x+1 \\ \underline{-x+1} \end{array}$$

Point out the pattern for the square of a binomial in the dividend. If students will learn to recognize these patterns for special products, they will have an easier time with division of polynomials.

$(2x^2-3x-2)\div(2x+1)$

$$\begin{array}{r} x-2 \\ 2x+1\overline{)2x^2-3x-2} \\ \underline{2x^2+x} \\ -4x-2 \\ \underline{-4x-2} \end{array}$$

Activities

② Divide.

$$\begin{array}{r} x+5 \\ x+2\overline{)x^2+7x+10} \\ \underline{x^2+2x} \\ 5x+10 \\ \underline{5x+10} \end{array} \qquad \begin{array}{r} x+4 \\ x-3\overline{)x^2+x-12} \\ \underline{x^2-3x} \\ 4x-12 \\ \underline{4x-12} \end{array} \qquad \begin{array}{r} 3x+2 \\ x-5\overline{)3x^2-13x-10} \\ \underline{3x^2-15x} \\ 2x-10 \\ \underline{2x-10} \end{array}$$

Long division:

$$\begin{array}{r} 23 \\ 12\overline{)276} \\ \underline{24} \\ 36 \\ \underline{36} \end{array}$$

③ Divide.

$(x^2 + 11x + 28) \div (x + 4)$

$$\begin{array}{r} x + 7 \\ x + 4\overline{)x^2 + 11x + 28} \\ \underline{x^2 + 4x} \\ 7x + 28 \\ \underline{7x + 28} \end{array}$$

$(2x^2 - 17x + 30) \div (x - 6)$

$$\begin{array}{r} 2x - 5 \\ x - 6\overline{)2x^2 - 17x + 30} \\ \underline{2x^2 - 12x} \\ -5x + 30 \\ \underline{-5x + 30} \end{array}$$

$(15x^2 - 11x - 56) \div (3x - 7)$

$$\begin{array}{r} 5x + 8 \\ 3x - 7\overline{)15x^2 - 11x - 56} \\ \underline{15x^2 - 35x} \\ 24x - 56 \\ \underline{24x - 56} \end{array}$$

$(x^2 + 5x - 36) \div (x + 9)$

$$\begin{array}{r} x - 4 \\ x + 9\overline{)x^2 + 5x - 36} \\ \underline{x^2 + 9x} \\ -4x - 36 \\ \underline{-4x - 36} \end{array}$$

$(2x^2 - 21x - 36) \div (x - 12)$

$$\begin{array}{r} 2x + 3 \\ x - 12\overline{)2x^2 - 21x - 36} \\ \underline{2x^2 - 24x} \\ 3x - 36 \\ \underline{3x - 36} \end{array}$$

$(54x^2 + 3x - 40) \div (6x - 5)$

$$\begin{array}{r} 9x + 8 \\ 6x - 5\overline{)54x^2 + 3x - 40} \\ \underline{54x^2 - 45x} \\ 48x - 40 \\ \underline{48x - 40} \end{array}$$

④ Solve.

$$\begin{aligned} 6x + (3 + 4)^2 &= 5(x + 7) \\ 6x + 7^2 &= 5x + 35 \\ 6x + 49 &= 5x + 35 \\ x &= -14 \end{aligned}$$

$$\begin{aligned} 8x + 3(5 - 2x) + 2 &= 5x - (3^3 - 2^3) \\ 8x + 15 - 6x + 2 &= 5x - (27 - 8) \\ 2x + 17 &= 5x - 19 \\ -3x &= -36 \\ x &= 12 \end{aligned}$$

$$\begin{aligned} 4(2x - 3) + \sqrt{2^3 \times 6 + 1} &= 3x + 2 \\ 8x - 12 + \sqrt{8 \times 6 + 1} &= 3x + 2 \\ 8x - 12 + \sqrt{49} &= 3x + 2 \\ 8x - 12 + 7 &= 3x + 2 \\ 8x - 5 &= 3x + 2 \\ 5x &= 7 \\ x &= \frac{7}{5} \end{aligned}$$

$$\begin{aligned} 6x + (5 - 9)^2 &> 4(x + 3) \\ 6x + (-4)^2 &> 4x + 12 \\ 6x + 16 &> 4x + 12 \\ 2x &> -4 \\ x &> -2 \end{aligned}$$

$$\begin{aligned} 7x + 3(4 - x) &< 3x - (2^3 \div 2^2) \\ 7x + 12 - 3x &< 3x - 2 \\ 4x + 12 &< 3x - 2 \\ x &< -14 \end{aligned}$$

$$\begin{aligned} 5(2x - 3) + \sqrt{3^2 + 2(2^3)} &< 3(x + 4) \\ 10x - 15 + \sqrt{9 + 2(8)} &< 3x + 12 \\ 10x - 15 + \sqrt{9 + 16} &< 3x + 12 \\ 10x - 15 + \sqrt{25} &< 3x + 12 \\ 10x - 15 + 5 &< 3x + 12 \\ 10x - 10 &< 3x + 12 \\ 7x &< 22 \\ x &< \frac{22}{7} \end{aligned}$$

Teaching Tips, Cont.

- Teach how to divide a polynomial by a polynomial. In this lesson, all of the dividends are trinomials and all of the divisors are binomials.

- Refer the students to the sample problem in the teaching box. Have them compare this problem with the long division problem they worked out earlier in this lesson. Point out that the 2-7-6 in the dividend of the problem they worked out corresponds to the coefficients in the trinomial dividend of the sample problem. The 1-2 in the divisor of the problem they worked out corresponds to the coefficients of the binomial divisor of the sample problem. The 2-3 in the quotient of the problem they worked out corresponds to the coefficients in the binomial quotient of the sample problem.

- It is important to note that the pattern in the above example is only true when the signs are the same in both binomials. If one has a plus sign and the other has a minus sign, the pattern will not work. Do not let the students assume they can ignore the variables and work these problems as normal numeric division.

- Complete the Classwork exercises. Have some students work the problems on the board for the class and explain their answers. All students should work the problems in their books.

Assignment

- Complete Lesson 66, Activities 2-4.

Lesson 67

Concepts

- Multiplying polynomials
- Dividing polynomials
- Special products of binomials

Learning Objectives

The student will be able to:

- Multiply polynomials
- Divide polynomials
- Recognize and apply patterns of special products of binomials

Materials Needed

- Student Book, Lesson 67

Teaching Tips

- Review multiplying polynomials. (See Lessons 61-63)
- Review special products of binomials. (See Lesson 64)
- Review dividing polynomials. (See Lesson 66)
- This lesson is the final review of multiplying and dividing polynomials before factoring is introduced. Make sure all students are confident in their ability to multiply and divide polynomials. Reteach concepts as necessary.

Review: Multiplying and Dividing Polynomials

When multiplying polynomials, remember to multiply the coefficients and add the exponents. Look for the patterns of special products to make multiplying certain binomials easier.

When dividing polynomials, remember to divide the coefficients and subtract the exponents. Look for the patterns of special products to make dividing certain polynomials easier.

When writing the answer to any polynomial problem, remember to write terms in order from greatest power to the lowest power, with constant terms at the end.

① Classwork

Multiply or divide as indicated.

$(3x+4)(3x-4)$

$(3x)^2-4^2=9x^2-16$

$(15x^2+34x-16)\div(5x-2)$

$$\begin{array}{r} 3x+8 \\ 5x-2\overline{)15x^2+34x-16} \\ \underline{15x^2-6x} \\ 40x-16 \\ \underline{40x-16} \end{array}$$

Activities

② Multiply. Remember to look for patterns of special products.

$(x+8)(x-4)$

$x(x)+x(-4)+8(x)+8(-4)=$

$x^2-4x+8x-32=x^2+4x-32$

$(x+12)^2$

$x^2+24x+144$

$(4x+1)(6x-5)$

$4x(6x)+4x(-5)+1(6x)+1(-5)=$

$24x^2-20x+6x-5=24x^2-14x-5$

$(x-11)^2$

$x^2-22x+121$

$(2x+6)(3x-3)$

$2x(3x)+2x(-3)+6(3x)+6(-3)=$

$6x^2-6x+18x-18=6x^2+12x-18$

$(3x-2)(7x+4)$

$3x(7x)+3x(4)-2(7x)-2(4)=$

$21x^2+12x-14x-8=21x^2-2x-8$

$(2x+4)(3x^2+2x-6)$

$2x(3x^2)+2x(2x)+2x(-6)+4(3x^2)+4(2x)+4(-6)=$

$6x^3+4x^2-12x+12x^2+8x-24=$

$6x^3+16x^2-4x-24$

$(5x-6)^2$

$25x^2-60x+36$

$(3x+1)(4x^2+2x-3)$

$3x(4x^2)+3x(2x)+3x(-3)+1(4x^2)+1(2x)+1(-3)=$

$12x^3+6x^2-9x+4x^2+2x-3=$

$12x^3+10x^2-7x-3$

$(3x+5)^2$

$9x^2+30x+25$

$(4x-6)(2x^2+7x-3)$

$4x(2x^2)+4x(7x)+4x(-3)-6(2x^2)-6(7x)-6(-3)=$

$8x^3+28x^2-12x-12x^2-42x+18=$

$8x^3+16x^2-54x+18$

$(3x+5)(3x-5)$

$9x^2-5^2=9x^2-25$

$(x^2-4x-2)(x^2+3x+7)$

$x^2(x^2)+x^2(3x)+x^2(7)-4x(x^2)-4x(3x)-$

$4x(7)-2(x^2)-2(3x)-2(7)=$

$x^4+3x^3+7x^2-4x^3-12x^2-28x-2x^2-6x-14=$

$x^4-x^3-7x^2-34x-14$

$(3x+8)(3x-8)$

$(3x)^2-8^2=9x^2-64$

③ Divide.

$(72x + 27) \div 9$

$$\begin{array}{r} 8x + 3 \\ 9\overline{)72x + 27} \\ \underline{72x} \quad\;\; \\ 27 \\ \underline{27} \end{array}$$

$(24x - 60) \div 12$

$$\begin{array}{r} 2x - 5 \\ 12\overline{)24x - 60} \\ \underline{24x} \quad\;\; \\ -60 \\ \underline{-60} \end{array}$$

$(45x - 90) \div 15$

$$\begin{array}{r} 3x - 6 \\ 15\overline{)45x - 90} \\ \underline{45x} \quad\;\; \\ -90 \\ \underline{-90} \end{array}$$

$(99x + 22) \div 11$

$$\begin{array}{r} 9x + 2 \\ 11\overline{)99x + 22} \\ \underline{99x} \quad\;\; \\ 22 \\ \underline{22} \end{array}$$

$(x^2 + 10x + 16) \div (x + 2)$

$$\begin{array}{r} x + 8 \\ x + 2\overline{)x^2 + 10x + 16} \\ \underline{x^2 + 2x} \quad\;\; \\ 8x + 16 \\ \underline{8x + 16} \end{array}$$

$(x^2 + 2x - 35) \div (x + 7)$

$$\begin{array}{r} x - 5 \\ x + 7\overline{)x^2 + 2x - 35} \\ \underline{x^2 + 7x} \quad\;\; \\ -5x - 35 \\ \underline{-5x - 35} \end{array}$$

$(3x^2 - 13x + 12) \div (3x - 4)$

$$\begin{array}{r} x - 3 \\ 3x - 4\overline{)3x^2 - 13x + 12} \\ \underline{3x^2 - 4x} \quad\;\; \\ -9x + 12 \\ \underline{-9x + 12} \end{array}$$

$(4x^2 + 4x - 24) \div (2x - 4)$

$$\begin{array}{r} 2x + 6 \\ 2x - 4\overline{)4x^2 + 4x - 24} \\ \underline{4x^2 - 8x} \quad\;\; \\ 12x - 24 \\ \underline{12x - 24} \end{array}$$

$(30x^2 - 34x - 36) \div (5x - 9)$

$$\begin{array}{r} 6x + 4 \\ 5x - 9\overline{)30x^2 - 34x - 36} \\ \underline{30x^2 - 54x} \quad\;\; \\ 20x - 36 \\ \underline{20x - 36} \end{array}$$

$(32x^2 + 4x - 6) \div (8x - 3)$

$$\begin{array}{r} 4x + 2 \\ 8x - 3\overline{)32x^2 + 4x - 6} \\ \underline{32x^2 - 12x} \quad\;\; \\ 16x - 6 \\ \underline{16x - 6} \end{array}$$

Teaching Tips, Cont.

- Tell the students they must have the patterns of special products of binomials memorized by the next lesson. Worksheet 34 is a quiz over the special products and appears in Lesson 68.
- Complete the Classwork exercises. Have some students work the problems on the board for the class and explain their answers. All students should work the problems in their books.

Assignment

- Complete Lesson 67, Activities 2-3.

Lesson 68

Concepts

- Factoring common monomials
- Prime factorization
- Dividing polynomials by monomials
- Math in the real world

Learning Objectives

The student will be able to:

- Write the prime factorization of each term of a polynomial
- Identify factors that are common to each term in a polynomial
- Express a polynomial as the product of a common monomial and a polynomial factor

Materials Needed

- Student Book, Lesson 68
- Worksheet 34

Teaching Tips

- Have students complete Worksheet 34 in class. This may be for added practice of earlier topics, or graded as a quiz, if desired.
- Review prime factorization. (See Lesson 4)
- Review dividing a polynomial by a monomial. (See Lesson 65)
- Review dividing with exponents. (See Lesson 2)
- Teach factoring polynomials from the teaching box. It is only necessary to prime factor the coefficients. The variables are already expressed in exponential form and cannot be factored further.

Factoring Common Monomials

Factoring a polynomial is similar to division, but you must determine the divisor and the quotient. You are supplied the dividend. To factor common monomials from a polynomial, follow these steps.

1. Write the prime factorization of each term.
2. Identify factors that are common to each term.
3. Multiply the common factors to get the common monomial.
4. Divide each term of the polynomial by the common monomial to get the new polynomial factor.
5. Write the answer as the product of the common monomial and the polynomial factor.

For example, factor $6x^3+2x^2+8x$.
Write the prime factorization of each term.
$2\cdot3\cdot x\cdot x\cdot x+2\cdot x\cdot x+2\cdot2\cdot2\cdot x$
Identify factors that are common to each term. These are written in red.
$2\cdot3\cdot x\cdot x\cdot x+2\cdot x\cdot x+2\cdot2\cdot2\cdot x$
The common monomial is $2\cdot x=2x$.
Divide each term of the polynomial by the common monomial to get the new polynomial factor.
$\frac{6x^3}{2x}+\frac{2x^2}{2x}+\frac{8x}{2x}=3x^2+x+4$
The factorization of $6x^3+2x^2+8x$ is $2x(3x^2+x+4)$. You can check your work by multiplying your answer to make sure it gives the original problem as the product.

① **Classwork**
Factor each polynomial.

$12x^3+6x^2+18x$
$\underline{2}\cdot2\cdot\underline{3}\cdot\underline{x}\cdot x\cdot x+\underline{2}\cdot\underline{3}\cdot\underline{x}\cdot x+\underline{2}\cdot\underline{3}\cdot3\cdot\underline{x}$
Common factors are underlined.
The common monomial is $6x$.
$\frac{12x^3}{6x}+\frac{6x^2}{6x}+\frac{18x}{6x}=2x^2+x+3$
Answer: $6x(2x^2+x+3)$

$15x^4+20x^3+10x^2$
$3\cdot\underline{5}\cdot\underline{x}\cdot\underline{x}\cdot x\cdot x+2\cdot2\cdot\underline{5}\cdot\underline{x}\cdot\underline{x}\cdot x+2\cdot\underline{5}\cdot\underline{x}\cdot\underline{x}$
Common factors are underlined.
The common monomial is $5x^2$.
$\frac{15x^4}{5x^2}+\frac{20x^3}{5x^2}+\frac{10x^2}{5x^2}=3x^2+4x+2$
Answer: $5x^2(3x^2+4x+2)$

Note: Students may not necessarily show all 5 steps on paper. Often, students will be able to do steps 1-4 in their heads and just write the problem and the answer on their papers. The individual steps will not be shown in this detail in the activity section.

Activities

② Factor each polynomial.

$12x+15$ $3(4x+5)$	$15x+20$ $5(3x+4)$	$15x^2-6x$ $3x(5x-2)$
$8x-4$ $4(2x-1)$	$14x-35$ $7(2x-5)$	$4x^2-12x$ $4x(x-3)$
$6x-14$ $2(3x-7)$	$12x^2+18x$ $6x(2x+3)$	$20x^2-25x$ $5x(4x-5)$

③ Factor each polynomial.

$16x^2-14x$ $2x(8x-7)$	$15x^3-9x^2+21x$ $3x(5x^2-3x+7)$
$16x^3+8x^2-24x$ $8x(2x^2+x-3)$	$6x^3-8x^2+2x$ $2x(3x^2-4x+1)$
$12x^3+8x^2-4x$ $4x(3x^2+2x-1)$	$36x^3+27x^2-72x$ $9x(4x^2+3x-8)$

④ Solve.

A swimming pool requires 1 ounce of swimming pool shock concentrate to raise the concentration of calcium hypochlorite in 5000 gallons of water 1 part per million. Write an algebraic expression that will serve as a formula for finding the number of ounces of shock concentrate, c, required to raise the concentration of calcium hypochlorite in g gallons of water 1 part per million.
$c=(1\text{ oz.})\left(\frac{g}{5000}\right)$

An Olympic-size swimming pool is 164 feet long, 82 feet wide, and $6\frac{1}{2}$ feet deep. What is the volume of the swimming pool in cubic feet? (Volume = length × width × depth)
$(164\text{ ft.})(82\text{ ft.})\left(6\frac{1}{2}\text{ ft.}\right)=87{,}412$ cubic feet

What is the volume of the pool in gallons if 1 cubic foot = 7.48 gallons? Round your answer to the nearest hundred.
$87{,}412(7.48)=653{,}841.76\approx653{,}800$ gallons

Will one gallon of shock concentrate be enough to raise the concentration of calcium hypochlorite in an Olympic-size pool 1 part per million? (One gallon is 128 ounces.)
$c=(1\text{ oz.})\left(\frac{g}{5000}\right)=(1\text{ oz.})\left(\frac{653{,}800}{5000}\right)=130.76\text{ oz.}$
No. One gallon is about 3 ounces short.

How many ounces of shock concentrate are needed to raise the concentration of calcium hypochlorite in an Olympic-size swimming pool 3 parts per million?
$(130.76\text{ oz.})(3)=392.28\text{ oz.}$

The maximum capacity of a swimming pool is 1 person per 24 square feet of surface area. What is the maximum capacity of an Olympic-size swimming pool?
Surface area = (164 feet)(82 feet) = 13,448 square feet
Maximum capacity = 13,448 ÷ 24 = 560 people

Special Products, Dividing Polynomials by Monomials Worksheet 34

① Multiply, using the formulas for special products.

$(x+6)^2$ $x^2+12x+36$	$(x+10)(x-10)$ $x^2-10^2=x^2-100$	$(x-2)^2$ x^2-4x+4
$(3x+2)^2$ $9x^2+12x+4$	$(2x+3)(2x-3)$ $(2x)^2-3^2=4x^2-9$	$(2x-7)^2$ $4x^2-28x+49$
$(x-8)^2$ $x^2-16x+64$	$(x+3)^2$ x^2+6x+9	$(x+11)(x-11)$ $x^2-11^2=x^2-121$
$(3x-5)^2$ $9x^2-30x+25$	$(4x+3)^2$ $16x^2+24x+9$	$(3x+4)(3x-4)$ $(3x)^2-4^2=9x^2-16$

② Divide.

$(32x^2-36x)\div 4x$ $8x-9$ $4x\overline{)32x^2-36x}$ $\underline{32x^2}$ $-36x$ $\underline{-36x}$	$(15x^3+3x^2-21x)\div 3x$ $5x^2+x-7$ $3x\overline{)15x^3+3x^2-21x}$ $\underline{15x^3}$ $3x^2$ $\underline{3x^2}$ $-21x$ $\underline{-21x}$	$(15x^3-20x^2+35x)\div 5x$ $3x^2-4x+7$ $5x\overline{)15x^3-20x^2+35x}$ $\underline{15x^3}$ $-20x^2$ $\underline{-20x^2}$ $35x$ $\underline{35x}$
$(18x^3+30x^2-12x)\div 6x$ $3x^2+5x-2$ $6x\overline{)18x^3+30x^2-12x}$ $\underline{18x^3}$ $30x^2$ $\underline{30x^2}$ $-12x$ $\underline{-12x}$	$(21x^3-35x^2+56x)\div 7x$ $3x^2-5x+8$ $7x\overline{)21x^3-35x^2+56x}$ $\underline{21x^3}$ $-35x^2$ $\underline{-35x^2}$ $56x$ $\underline{56x}$	$(40x^3+72x^2-48x)\div 8x$ $5x^2+9x-6$ $8x\overline{)40x^3+72x^2-48x}$ $\underline{40x^3}$ $72x^2$ $\underline{72x^2}$ $-48x$ $\underline{-48x}$

Teaching Tips, Cont.

- Explain that common factors include any common coefficient factors as well as any common variables. If all terms have the same variable, the common variable factor is the variable with the *lowest* exponent.
- Remind students to subtract exponents when they are dividing.
- Complete the Classwork exercises. Have some students work the problems on the board for the class and explain their answers. All students should work the problems in their books.

Assignment

- Complete Lesson 68, Activities 2-4.

Lesson 69

Concepts

- Factoring the difference of two squares
- Systems of equations
- Math in the real world

Learning Objectives

The student will be able to:

- Recognize polynomials that are the difference of two squares
- Apply the pattern of special products to factor the difference of two squares

Materials Needed

- Student Book, Lesson 69

Teaching Tips

- Review patterns of special products, with special attention to the difference of two squares. (See Lesson 64)
- Show the students how to rewrite the pattern from Lesson 64 to make it a formula for factoring the difference of two squares. (The formula is made by switching the left and right sides of the equal sign.)
- Teach how to factor the difference of two squares from the teaching box. Explain that the given formula works for any binomial in which the first term is positive and the second term is negative.

Factoring the Difference of Two Squares

Recall the formulas for special products from Lesson 64. If you have not yet memorized them, now would be a good time to do so.

This is the formula for the difference of two squares.

$(a+b)(a-b)=a^2-b^2$

This formula can be used to factor polynomials in the form a^2-b^2 and can be rewritten $a^2-b^2=(a+b)(a-b)$ for this purpose.

Factor the polynomial $9x^2-36$.

In this problem, $a^2=9x^2$ and $b^2=36$. Take the square root of each side to find a and b.

$a=3x$ and $b=6$.

Substitute these values in the formula to write the factorization.

$9x^2-36=(3x+6)(3x-6)$

If either term is not a perfect square, you will have a radical in the answer.

① Classwork

Factor each polynomial.

x^2-9

$a^2=x^2 \Rightarrow a=x$

$b^2=9 \Rightarrow b=3$

$(x+3)(x-3)$

$4x^2-25$

$a^2=4x^2 \Rightarrow a=2x$

$b^2=25 \Rightarrow b=5$

$(2x+5)(2x-5)$

x^2-7

$a^2=x^2 \Rightarrow a=x$

$b^2=7 \Rightarrow b=\sqrt{7}$

$(x+\sqrt{7})(x-\sqrt{7})$

Note: Often, students will be able to just write the problem and the answer. The individual steps will not be shown in this detail in the activity section.

Activities

② Factor each polynomial.

x^2-1
$(x+1)(x-1)$

x^2-49
$(x+7)(x-7)$

x^2-121
$(x+11)(x-11)$

x^2-16
$(x+4)(x-4)$

x^2-625
$(x+25)(x-25)$

x^2-196
$(x+14)(x-14)$

$9x^2-16$
$(3x+4)(3x-4)$

$4x^2-49$
$(2x+7)(2x-7)$

$4x^2-81$
$(2x+9)(2x-9)$

$9x^2-4$
$(3x+2)(3x-2)$

$25x^2-64$
$(5x+8)(5x-8)$

$49x^2-100$
$(7x+10)(7x-10)$

x^2-15
$(x+\sqrt{15})(x-\sqrt{15})$

x^2-39
$(x+\sqrt{39})(x-\sqrt{39})$

$4x^2-17$
$(2x+\sqrt{17})(2x-\sqrt{17})$

$25x^2-8$
$(5x+2\sqrt{2})(5x-2\sqrt{2})$

$36x^2-27$
$(6x+3\sqrt{3})(6x-3\sqrt{3})$

$49x^2-18$
$(7x+3\sqrt{2})(7x-3\sqrt{2})$

③ Solve.

An aquatics center charges $3.50 per adult and $2.50 per child. If the total charge for 10 people was $28, how many adults and how many children were in the group?

Let a = the number of adults.

Let c = the number of children.

$$\begin{aligned} a + c &= 10 \\ 3.5a + 2.5c &= 28 \end{aligned}$$

Multiply the top equation by 3.5.

$$\begin{aligned} 3.5a + 3.5c &= 35 \\ \underline{3.5a + 2.5c} &\underline{= 28} \\ c &= 7 \end{aligned}$$

$a + 7 = 10$

$a = 3$

There are 3 adults and 7 children in the group.

If the aquatics center charges $100 for a family pass, what is the minimum number of times a family with two adults and two children would have to visit the center for the cost of the pass to be a worthwhile investment?

2 adults + 2 children = 2($3.50) + 2($2.50) = $7 + $5 = $12 for one family admission.

Let v = the number of visits to make the pass a worthwhile investment.

$12v \geq 100$

$v \geq \frac{100}{12}$

$v \geq 8\frac{1}{3}$

The number of visits must be a whole number, so the family must visit at least 9 times.

If two adults and one child were visiting each time, how many visits would they need to make for the pass to be worthwhile?

2 adults + 1 child = 2($3.50) + 1($2.50) = $7 + $2.50 = $9.50 for one family admission.

Let v = the number of visits to make the pass a worthwhile investment.

$9.5v \geq 100$

$v \geq \frac{100}{9.5}$

$v \geq 10.5$

The number of visits must be a whole number, so the family must visit at least 11 times.

If one adult and two children were visiting each time, how many visits would they need to make for the pass to be worthwhile?

1 adult + 2 children = 1($3.50) + 2($2.50) = $3.50 + $5 = $8.50 for one family admission.

Let v = the number of visits to make the pass a worthwhile investment.

$8.5v \geq 100$

$v \geq \frac{100}{8.5}$

$v \geq 11.76$

The number of visits must be a whole number, so the family must visit at least 12 times.

Teaching Tips, Cont.

- Tell the students that every positive number has a square root. The square root may not be a whole number, however. In this case, a radical sign will appear in each binomial of the answer. The third problem in the Classwork section is an example of this situation.

- Complete the Classwork exercises. Have some students work the problems on the board for the class and explain their answers. All students should work the problems in their books.

Assignment

- Complete Lesson 69, Activities 2-3.

Lesson 70

Concepts

- Factoring perfect square trinomials
- Graphing linear equations
- Graphing linear inequalities
- Perpendicular lines
- Parallel lines

Learning Objectives

The student will be able to:

- Recognize perfect square trinomials
- Apply the patterns of special products to factor perfect square trinomials

Materials Needed

- Student Book, Lesson 70
- Worksheet 35

Teaching Tips

- Review patterns of special products, with special attention to squares of binomials. (See Lesson 64)
- Show the students how to rewrite the patterns from Lesson 64 to make them formulas for factoring perfect square trinomials. (The formulas are made by switching the left and right sides of the equal sign in the patterns for squaring a binomial, both positive and negative second terms.)
- Teach how to factor a perfect square trinomial when all terms are positive. Encourage the students to label the values of *a* and *b* for each problem, especially when they are learning the concept. This will make it easier to identify the value of $2ab$ and see the pattern.

Factoring Perfect Square Trinomials

Recall the formulas for special products from Lesson 64. If you have not yet memorized them, now would be a good time to do so.

These are the formulas for squaring a binomial.

$(a+b)^2 = a^2 + 2ab + b^2$

$(a-b)^2 = a^2 - 2ab + b^2$

These formulas can be used to factor polynomials in the form $a^2 \pm 2ab + b^2$ and can be rewritten $a^2 + 2ab + b^2 = (a+b)^2$ and $a^2 - 2ab + b^2 = (a-b)^2$ for this purpose. The formulas can be further simplified by combining the signs.

$a^2 \pm 2ab + b^2 = (a \pm b)^2$

Factor the polynomial $25x^2 - 60x + 36$.

In this problem, $a^2 = 25x^2$ and $b^2 = 36$. Take the square root of each side to find *a* and *b*.

$a = 5x$, $b = 6$, and $2ab = 2(5x)(6) = 60x$.

Substitute these values in the formula to write the factorization.

$25x^2 - 60x + 36 = (5x - 6)^2$

Because the middle term of the trinomial is negative, the sign in the answer is also negative. The sign of the answer will always match the sign of the middle term.

If the first and last terms are not perfect squares, you will have radicals in the answer.

① Classwork

Factor each polynomial.

$x^2 + 6x + 9$
$a^2 = x^2 \Rightarrow a = x$
$b^2 = 9 \Rightarrow b = 3$
$2ab = 6x$
$(x+3)^2$

$9x^2 - 30x + 25$
$a^2 = 9x^2 \Rightarrow a = 3x$
$b^2 = 25 \Rightarrow b = 5$
$2ab = 30x$
$(3x-5)^2$

$x^2 + 2\sqrt{10}x + 10$
$a^2 = x^2 \Rightarrow a = x$
$b^2 = 10 \Rightarrow b = \sqrt{10}$
$2ab = 2x\sqrt{10}$
$(x+\sqrt{10})^2$

Note: Often, students will be able to just write the problem and the answer. The individual steps will not be shown in this detail in the activity section.

Activities

② Factor each polynomial.

$x^2 + 2x + 1$
$(x+1)^2$

$x^2 - 16x + 64$
$(x-8)^2$

$x^2 + 22x + 121$
$(x+11)^2$

$x^2 - 10x + 25$
$(x-5)^2$

$9x^2 + 24x + 16$
$(3x+4)^2$

$4x^2 - 28x + 49$
$(2x-7)^2$

$4x^2 - 36x + 81$
$(2x-9)$

$9x^2 + 12x + 4$
$(3x+2)^2$

$x^2 - 2\sqrt{39}x + 39$
$(x-\sqrt{39})^2$

$4x^2 + 4\sqrt{17}x + 17$
$(2x+\sqrt{17})^2$

$25x^2 + 20\sqrt{2}x + 8$
$(5x+2\sqrt{2})^2$

$36x^2 - 36\sqrt{3}x + 27$
$(6x-3\sqrt{3})^2$

③ For each equation, draw the graph of the equation, a line perpendicular to the equation through the origin, and a parallel line to the equation through the point (1, 1).

$y = 2x + 1$

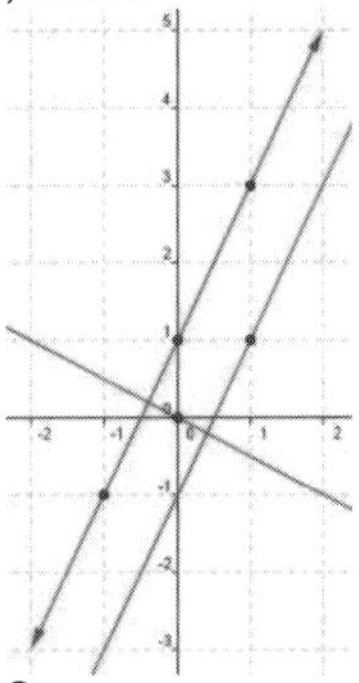

$y = -x + 4$

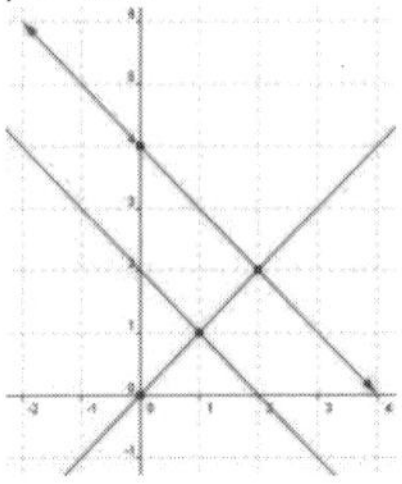

$y = 2(x-1)$

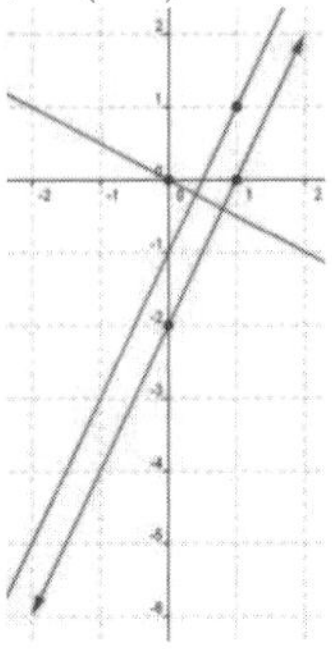

④ Graph the following inequalities on your own graph paper.

$y < 2x + 1$

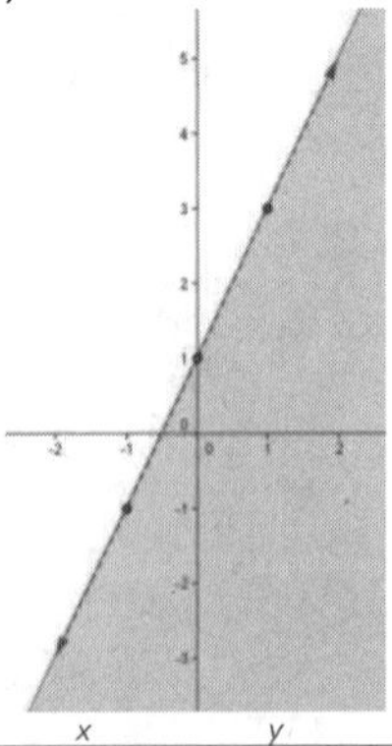

x	y
0	$y = 2(0) + 1 = 1$
1	$y = 2(1) + 1 = 3$
-1	$y = 2(-1) + 1 = -1$

$y \le 2(x-1)$

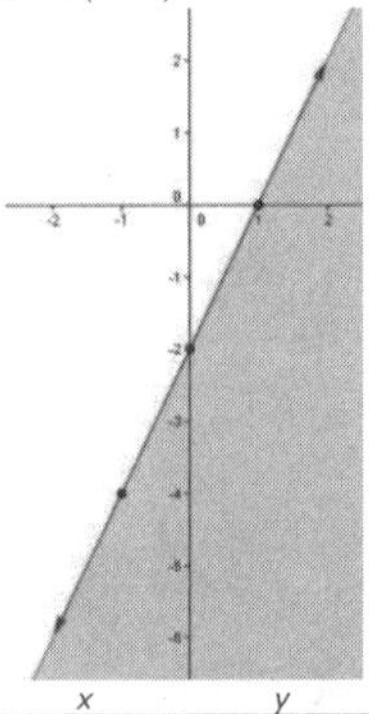

x	y
0	$y = 2(0-1) = -2$
1	$y = 2(1-1) = 0$
-1	$y = 2(-1-1) = -4$

$y < -x + 4$

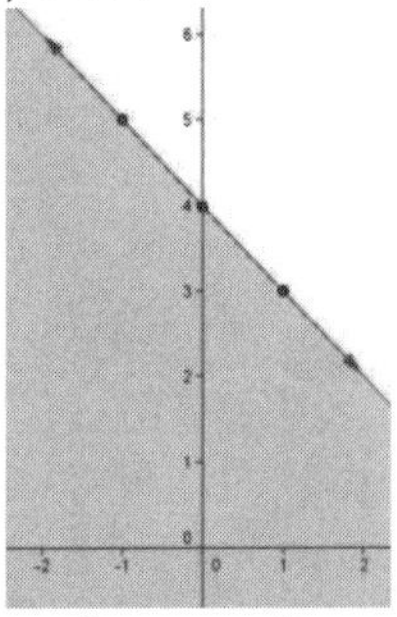

x	y
0	$y = -(0) + 4 = 4$
1	$y = -(1) + 4 = 3$
-1	$y = -(-1) + 4 = 5$

Factoring Polynomials with Special Products — Worksheet 35

① Factor each polynomial.

$12x+20$ $4(3x+5)$	$16x^2-25$ $(4x+5)(4x-5)$	$25x^2-48$ $(5x+4\sqrt{3})(5x-4\sqrt{3})$
$45x-10$ $5(9x-2)$	$144x^2-1$ $(12x+1)(12x-1)$	$36x^2-98$ $2(18x^2-49)$ $2(3x\sqrt{2}+7)(3x\sqrt{2}-7)$
$60x-72$ $12(5x-6)$	$4x^2-9$ $(2x+3)(2x-3)$	$81x^2+36x+4$ $(9x+2)^2$
$55x+20$ $5(11x+4)$	$144x^2-25$ $(12x+5)(12x-5)$	$9x^2-42x+49$ $(3x-7)^2$
$21x-56$ $7(3x-8)$	$25x^2-81$ $(5x+9)(5x-9)$	$16x^2-72x+81$ $(4x-9)^2$
$10x^2+15x$ $5x(2x+3)$	$64x^2-49$ $(8x+7)(8x-7)$	$16x^2+40x+25$ $(4x+5)^2$
$40x^2-72x$ $8x(5x-9)$	x^2-30 $(x+\sqrt{30})(x-\sqrt{30})$	$x^2-2\sqrt{23}x+23$ $(x-\sqrt{23})^2$
$3x^2-12x$ $3x(x-4)$	x^2-51 $(x+\sqrt{51})(x-\sqrt{51})$	$4x^2+4\sqrt{13}x+13$ $(2x+\sqrt{13})^2$
$30x^2-5x$ $5x(6x-1)$	$4x^2-83$ $(2x+\sqrt{83})(2x-\sqrt{83})$	$9x^2+12\sqrt{5}x+20$ $(3x+2\sqrt{5})^2$
$121x^2-220\sqrt{2}x+200$ $(11x-10\sqrt{2})^2$	$16x^2-18$ $(4x+3\sqrt{2})(4x-3\sqrt{2})$	$64x^2-48\sqrt{3}x+27$ $(8x-3\sqrt{3})^2$

Teaching Tips, Cont.

- Show the students how to substitute the values of *a* and *b* into the formula to get the proper factorization of the trinomial.
- Teach how to factor a perfect square trinomial when the second term is negative. As before, encourage the students to label the values of *a* and *b* for each problem, especially when they are learning the concept. This will make it easier to identify the value of *2ab* and see the pattern.
- Show the students how to substitute the values of *a* and *b* into the formula to get the proper factorization of the trinomial.
- Complete the Classwork exercises. Have some students work the problems on the board for the class and explain their answers. All students should work the problems in their books.
- Review for Test 7 using worksheets 31-35. These worksheets were assigned in previous lessons.

Assignments

- Complete Lesson 70, Activities 2-4.
- Worksheet 35.
- Study for Test 7 (Lessons 58-67).

Test 7

Testing Objectives

The student will:

- Solve systems of equations
- Express the solution of a system of equations as a coordinate point
- Use a graph to solve systems of equations
- Multiply a polynomial by a monomial
- Multiply binomials
- Use the formulas for special products to multiply binomials
- Multiply a trinomial by a binomial
- Divide a binomial by a monomial
- Divide a trinomial by a binomial

Materials Needed

- Test 7
- *It's College Test Prep Time!* from Student Book
- Exploring Math through... Vacation Planning from Student Book

Teaching Tips

➢ Administer Test 7, allowing the students 30-40 minutes to complete the test.

➢ When all students are finished taking the test, introduce *It's College Test Prep Time* from the student book. This page may be completed in class or assigned as homework.

① Solve. Express the solution as a coordinate point. **8 points**

$x - y + 11 = 0$
$-2x + y - 15 = 0$

$x - y = -11$
$-2x + y = 15$
$-x = 4$
$x = -4$

$-4 - y + 11 = 0$
$y = 7$

(-4, 7)

$10x - 3y - 24 = 0$
$7x + 2y - 25 = 0$
$10x - 3y = 24$
$7x + 2y = 25$

$20x - 6y = 48$
$21x + 6y = 75$
$41x = 123$
$x = 3$
$10(3) - 3y - 24 = 0$
$30 - 3y - 24 = 0$
$-3y = -6$
$y = 2$
(3, 2)

$11x + 22y + 44 = 0$
$-x - 4y - 14 = 0$
$11x + 22y = -44$
$-x - 4y = 14$

$x + 2y = -4$
$-x - 4y = 14$
$-2y = 10$
$y = -5$

$-x - 4(-5) - 14 = 0$
$-x + 20 - 14 = 0$
$-x = -6$
$x = 6$
(6, -5)

$5x - 2y - 7 = 0$
$10x - 4y - 14 = 0$
$5x - 2y = 7$
$10x - 4y = 14$

$5x - 2y = 7$
$5x - 2y = 7$
$0 = 0$

All real numbers

② Solve the systems of equations by graphing. Express the solution as a coordinate point. **6 points**

$2x + y - 4 = 0$
$x + 2y - 5 = 0$

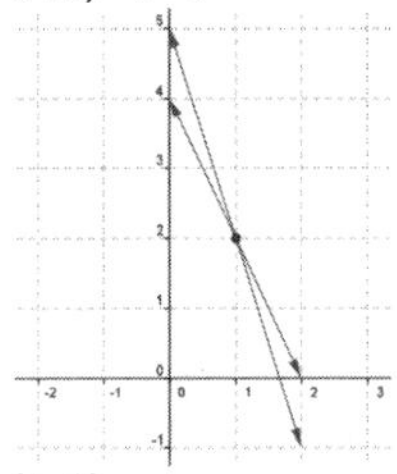

(1, 2)

$3x + 2y + 4 = 0$
$2x + 3y + 1 = 0$

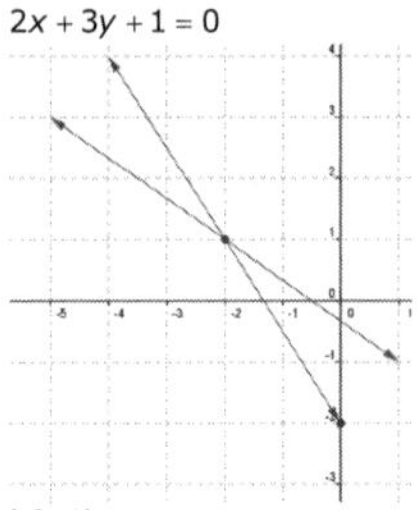

(-2, 1)

$-3x + y - 4 = 0$
$4x + y + 10 = 0$

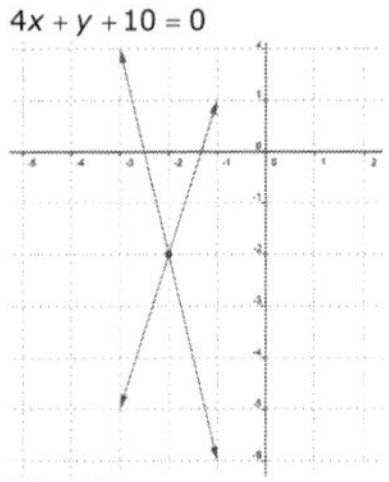

(-2, -2)

③ Multiply. **15 points**

$4x(x - 7)$

$4x(x) + 4x(-7) = 4x^2 - 28x$

$3x(2x - 9)$

$3x(2x) + 3x(-9) = 6x^2 - 27x$

$5x(3x^2 + 2x - 4)$

$5x(3x^2) + 5x(2x) + 5x(-4) =$
$15x^3 + 10x^2 - 20x$

$8x(7x - 4)$

$8x(7x) + 8x(-4) = 56x^2 - 32x$

$6x(5x^2 - 3x + 4)$

$6x(5x^2) + 6x(-3x) + 6x(4) =$
$30x^3 - 18x^2 + 24x$

$7x(2x^2 - 9x + 6)$

$7x(2x^2) + 7x(-9x) + 7x(6) =$
$14x^3 - 63x^2 + 42x$

④ Multiply. **45 points**

$(x + 8)(x - 8)$
$x^2 - 8^2 = x^2 - 64$

$(2x + 7)(2x - 7)$
$(2x)^2 - 7^2 = 4x^2 - 49$

$(x + 5)(x + 2)$
$x(x) + x(2) + 5(x) + 5(2) =$
$x^2 + 2x + 5x + 10 = x^2 + 7x + 10$

$(x + 8)(x - 6)$
$x(x) + x(-6) + 8(x) + 8(-6) =$
$x^2 - 6x + 8x - 48 = x^2 + 2x - 48$

$(2x - 5)(x + 5)$
$2x(x) + 2x(5) - 5(x) - 5(5) =$
$2x^2 + 10x - 5x - 25 = 2x^2 + 5x - 25$

$(3x - 4)(x + 2)$
$3x(x) + 3x(2) - 4(x) - 4(2) =$
$3x^2 + 6x - 4x - 8 = 3x^2 + 2x - 8$

$(x + 3)(x^2 + 2x + 4)$
$x(x^2) + x(2x) + x(4) + 3(x^2) + 3(2x) + 3(4) =$
$x^3 + 2x^2 + 4x + 3x^2 + 6x + 12 =$
$x^3 + 5x^2 + 10x + 12$

$(x + 6)^2$
$x^2 + 12x + 36$

$(2x + 5)^2$
$4x^2 + 20x + 25$

$(x - 10)^2$
$x^2 - 20x + 100$

$(3x - 7)^2$
$9x^2 - 42x + 49$

$(x + 4)(x^2 - 3x - 9)$
$x(x^2) + x(-3x) + x(-9) + 4(x^2) + 4(-3x) + 4(-9) =$
$x^3 - 3x^2 - 9x + 4x^2 - 12x - 36 =$
$x^3 + x^2 - 21x - 36$

$(x^2 + 3x + 2)(x^2 - 3x - 4)$
$x^2(x^2) + x^2(-3x) + x^2(-4) + 3x(x^2) + 3x(-3x) +$
$3x(-4) + 2(x^2) + 2(-3x) + 2(-4) =$
$x^4 - 3x^3 - 4x^2 + 3x^3 - 9x^2 - 12x + 2x^2 - 6x - 8 =$
$x^4 - 11x^2 - 18x - 8$

$(x - 3)(2x^2 - 5x - 4)$
$x(2x^2) + x(-5x) + x(-4) - 3(2x^2) - 3(-5x) - 3(-4) =$
$2x^3 - 5x^2 - 4x - 6x^2 + 15x + 12 =$
$2x^3 - 11x^2 + 11x + 12$

⑤ Divide. **12 points**

$(27x - 45) \div 9$

$3x - 5$
$9\overline{)27x - 45}$
$\underline{27x}$
-45
$\underline{-45}$

$(48x - 56) \div 8$

$6x - 7$
$8\overline{)48x - 56}$
$\underline{48x}$
-56
$\underline{-56}$

$(72x + 108) \div 12$

$6x + 9$
$12\overline{)72x + 108}$
$\underline{72x}$
108
$\underline{108}$

$(5x^2 - 26x + 24) \div (5x - 6)$

$x - 4$
$5x - 6\overline{)5x^2 - 26x + 24}$
$\underline{5x^2 - 6x}$
$-20x + 24$
$\underline{-20x + 24}$

$(3x^2 + 7x - 20) \div (x + 4)$

$3x - 5$
$x + 4\overline{)3x^2 + 7x - 20}$
$\underline{3x^2 + 12x}$
$-5x - 20$
$\underline{-5x - 20}$

$(6x^2 + 13x + 6) \div (3x + 2)$

$2x + 3$
$3x + 2\overline{)6x^2 + 13x + 6}$
$\underline{6x^2 + 4x}$
$9x + 6$
$\underline{9x + 6}$

86 points total

It's College Test Prep Time!

1. Given $x < 0$ and $8 < |x+2| < 9$, which of the following is a possible value of x?

A.	-11	Because x must be negative, use the equation
<u>B.</u>	-10.5	$8 < -(x+2)$, which gives $x < -10$. This eliminates
C.	-10	choices C, D, and E. Now use the equation
D.	-9.5	$-(x+2) < 9$, which gives $x > -11$. This eliminates
E.	-9	choice A. The answer is B.

2. Given $\frac{a}{b} = 48$ and $b = \frac{5}{4}$, find the value of $\frac{1}{3}a$.

A.	12.8	$a = 48b$
B.	16	$a = 48\left(\frac{5}{4}\right) = 60$
<u>C.</u>	20	$\frac{1}{3}a = \frac{1}{3}(60) = 20$
D.	51.2	
E.	60	

3. Given $(7r)t = 28$, what is the value of rt?

<u>A.</u>	4	Rewrite the equation as $7rt = 28$.
B.	14	Divide both sides by 7 and $rt = 4$.
C.	21	
D.	35	
E.	196	

4. Given the equation $y = 4x + 7$, what is the value of $3y - 5$?

A.	$7x + 2$	
B.	$7x + 5$	
C.	$12x + 2$	Begin by substituting the value of y in $3y - 5$.
D.	$12x + 6$	$3(4x+7) - 5$ Apply the distributive property.
<u>E.</u>	$12x + 16$	$12x + 21 - 5$ Combine like terms.

Exploring Math through... Vacation Planning

If your family has ever taken a vacation, your parents can tell you there is a great deal of math involved in the planning stage. Budget constraints must be considered when selecting accommodations, activities, transportation, food, and every other aspect of a vacation.

When choosing accommodations, you must consider the amenities included for the nightly cost. Some hotels will provide just a room for the nightly cost. Others include a continental breakfast, usually pastries and juice, or a full hot-cooked breakfast. Some rooms include a full-size kitchen so guests can cook their own meals. While many hotels now include a small refrigerator and microwave in each room, there are still some that have only a coffee maker.

When planning transportation costs, there is more to consider than just the cost of gas versus plane tickets. While it may seem cheaper initially to drive, you must also consider the added expenses of food and lodging en route if you are travelling a long distance. If flying will save several nights of hotel and food expenses, it may be a better deal to fly than to drive. If you are renting a car at your destination, those expenses must be considered as well.

Often, the activities are the most expensive part of a vacation. You must plan for the actual ticket expenses, as well as for food in the parks if the parks do not allow you to bring a picnic lunch. If you are planning to buy souvenirs, you must budget for that as well.

Another aspect of vacation planning that must be considered is the value of booking an all-inclusive vacation package versus planning and booking individual components yourself. Sometimes vacation packages offer a discount for booking as a package. Other times the vacation package costs more than the individual elements because you are paying for the convenience of booking everything at once.

No matter where you go on vacation or how long you stay, there is math involved at every level!

Teaching Tips, Cont.

- Have students read the Exploring Math feature for Lessons 71-80.

Assignments

- Complete *It's College Test Prep Time!*
- Read Exploring Math through... Vacation Planning

Lesson 71

Concepts

- Factoring trinomials of the form $x^2 + bx + c$
- Factoring common monomials
- Factoring the difference of two squares
- Factoring perfect square trinomials
- Dividing roots

Learning Objectives

The student will be able to:

- Factor trinomials of the form $x^2 + bx + c$

Materials Needed

- Student Book, Lesson 71

Teaching Tips

- Review the FOIL method. (See Lesson 62)
- Remind the students that using the FOIL method is multiplying two binomial factors.
- Ask the students how they can undo multiplication. (Division)
- Introduce factoring trinomials from the teaching box. Explain that factoring is the opposite of the FOIL method. In effect, the answer is given and they must find the original problem.

Factoring Trinomials of the Form $x^2 + bx + c$

Factoring trinomials is the opposite of using the FOIL method. Instead of multiplying two binomials to get a trinomial, you are now given the trinomial and must find the two binomials that were multiplied together. Some of the easiest trinomials to factor are those of the form $x^2 + bx + c$, where b and c are coefficients. To factor a trinomial in this form, follow these steps.

- Draw two sets of parentheses, leaving space for the binomials to be filled in.
- Find the square root of the first term in the trinomial. Write the result as the first term in each set of parentheses.
- Make a list of factor pairs that equal c, the third term. Pay attention to the sign. If c is positive, the factors will have the same sign as b. If c is negative, the factors will have opposite signs.
- Identify the factor pair whose sum is equal to b, the coefficient of the second term. Write each factor with its corresponding sign as the second term in one of the parentheses.

Factor $x^2 + 5x + 6$.
Draw two sets of parentheses.
(   )(   )
The square root of x^2 is x.
(x)(x)
Find factor pairs that equal +6 and have positive signs because the middle term is positive.
(+1)(+6) and (+2)(+3)
The value of b is 5, so the correct factor pair is (+2)(+3) because 2 + 3 = 5.
$(x + 2)(x + 3)$

① **Classwork**
Factor each polynomial.

$x^2 + 8x + 15$
$(x+3)(x+5)$

$x^2 - 12 + 11$
$(x-1)(x-11)$

$x^2 + 3x - 4$
$(x-1)(x+4)$

$x^2 - 2x - 8$
$(x+2)(x-4)$

Note: Factors may be written in any order as long as the terms within each set of parentheses are the same. For example, the last problem above may have $(x-4)(x+2)$ as the answer.

Activities

② Factor each polynomial.

$x^2 + 5x + 4$ $(x+1)(x+4)$	$x^2 + 4x - 12$ $(x-2)(x+6)$	$x^2 - 7x + 6$ $(x-1)(x-6)$
$x^2 - 8x + 15$ $(x-3)(x-5)$	$x^2 + 10x + 21$ $(x+3)(x+7)$	$x^2 + 7x - 18$ $(x-2)(x+9)$
$x^2 + 5x - 24$ $(x-3)(x+8)$	$x^2 - 4x - 5$ $(x+1)(x-5)$	$x^2 - 5x - 36$ $(x+4)(x-9)$
$x^2 - 3x - 18$ $(x+3)(x-6)$	$x^2 - 11x + 28$ $(x-4)(x-7)$	$x^2 + 7x + 10$ $(x+2)(x+5)$

③ Factor each polynomial.

$9x-12$	$16x+24$	$15x^2+40x$	$27x^2-36x$
$3(3x-4)$	$8(2x+3)$	$5x(3x+8)$	$9x(3x-4)$
$4x-20$	$18x-45$	$12x^2-18x$	$6x^2-30x$
$4(x-5)$	$9(2x-5)$	$6x(2x-3)$	$6x(x-5)$

④ Factor each difference of two squares.

$64x^2-25$	x^2-21	$9x^2-17$	$25x^2-27$
$(8x+5)(8x-5)$	$(x+\sqrt{21})(x-\sqrt{21})$	$(3x+\sqrt{17})(3x-\sqrt{17})$	$(5x+3\sqrt{3})(5x-3\sqrt{3})$
$81x^2-4$	x^2-47	$49x^2-12$	$100x^2-45$
$(9x+2)(9x-2)$	$(x+\sqrt{47})(x-\sqrt{47})$	$(7x+2\sqrt{3})(7x-2\sqrt{3})$	$(10x+3\sqrt{5})(10x-3\sqrt{5})$

⑤ Factor each perfect square trinomial.

$x^2+24x+144$	$4x^2+20x+25$	$16x^2-72x+81$	$x^2-2\sqrt{41}x+41$
$(x+12)^2$	$(2x+5)^2$	$(4x-9)$	$(x-\sqrt{41})^2$
$x^2-16x+64$	$9x^2-60x+100$	$25x^2+10x+1$	$4x^2+4\sqrt{19}x+19$
$(x-8)^2$	$(3x-10)^2$	$(5x+1)^2$	$(2x+\sqrt{19})^2$

⑥ Divide.

$$\frac{\sqrt{27}}{18}\div\frac{\sqrt{3}}{3}=\frac{3\sqrt{3}}{18}\div\frac{\sqrt{3}}{3}=\frac{3\sqrt{3}}{18}\times\frac{3}{\sqrt{3}}=\frac{1}{2}$$

$$\frac{\sqrt{75}}{20}\div 3\frac{3}{5}=\frac{5\sqrt{3}}{20}\div\frac{18}{5}=\frac{5\sqrt{3}}{20}\times\frac{5}{18}=\frac{5\sqrt{3}}{72}$$

$$\frac{\sqrt{32}}{8}\div\frac{\sqrt{8}}{2}=\frac{\sqrt{32}}{8}\times\frac{2}{\sqrt{8}}=\frac{\sqrt{4}}{4}\times\frac{1}{1}=\frac{2}{4}=\frac{1}{2}$$

Teaching Tips, Cont.

- Teach how to factor trinomials from the teaching box.
- Emphasize the importance of following each of the steps precisely. Future lessons build on the material in this lesson, so it is imperative that each student understands and follows the steps.
- Complete the Classwork exercises. Have some students work the problems on the board for the class and explain their answers. All students should work the problems in their books.
- If you plan to administer Exam 2 following Lesson 80 and Test 8, spend a few minutes reviewing for the Exam.

Assignment

- Complete Lesson 71, Activities 2-6.

Lesson 72

Concepts

- Factoring trinomials of the form $ax^2 + bx + c$
- Math in the real world

Learning Objectives

The student will be able to:

- Factor trinomials of the form $ax^2 + bx + c$

Materials Needed

- Student Book, Lesson 72
- Worksheet 36

Teaching Tips

- Have students complete Worksheet 36 in class. This may be for added practice of earlier topics, or graded as a quiz, if desired.
- Review factoring trinomials. (See Lesson 71)
- Have the students look at the lesson headings for Lessons 71 and 72 and tell what is different between the two. (Lesson 72 has an *a* at the beginning of the trinomial.)
- Tell the students that they have learned to factor trinomials whose first term has a coefficient of 1. In this lesson, they will factor trinomials with a coefficient other than 1.

Factoring Trinomials of the Form $ax^2 + bx + c$

In this lesson you will factor trinomials similar to those in the previous lesson, except the first term will have a coefficient other than 1. These trinomials are of the form $ax^2 + bx + c$. To factor these trinomials, follow these steps.

- See if *a* or a factor of *a* is also a factor of both *b* and *c*. If so, write this as the first factor in the answer and divide each term by this factor. Use the values of *a*, *b*, and *c* in the resulting trinomial in the rest of the steps.
- Find the value of *ac*. Make a list of factor pairs that equal *ac*. Pay attention to the sign. If *ac* is positive, the factors will have the same sign as *b*. If *ac* is negative, the factors will have opposite signs.
- Identify the factor pair whose sum is equal to *b*, the coefficient of the second term.
- Draw a box diagram and fill it in according to this pattern.

ax^2	(factor of *ac*)x
(factor of *ac*)x	c

- Find a common factor for each row and column, keeping the sign of the coefficient of the first term in each row or column.
- The common factors of the rows become one binomial in the answer, and common factors of the columns become the other binomial.

Factor $4x^2 - 2x - 12$.
The number 2 is a factor of all three terms.
$2(2x^2 - x - 6)$ Now $a = 2$; $b = -1$; $c = -6$

$ac = 2(-6) = -12$
Factors of -12 that add to -1 are -4 and 3.
Insert these values in the box and find the common factor of each row and column.

	x	-2
$2x$	$2x^2$	$-4x$
3	$3x$	-6

Factoring the rows gives $(2x + 3)$. Factoring the columns gives $(x - 2)$.
The factorization of $4x^2 - 2x - 12$ is $2(2x + 3)(x - 2)$. Don't forget to include the 2 that was factored out in the first step!

① Classwork
Factor each polynomial.

$2x^2 + 5x + 3$
$ac = 6$; factors that add to 5 are 2 and 3

	x	1
$2x$	$2x^2$	$2x$
3	$3x$	3

$(2x + 3)(x + 1)$

$2x^2 + 3x - 9$
$ac = -18$; factors that add to 3 are 6 and -3

	x	3
$2x$	$2x^2$	$6x$
-3	$-3x$	-9

$(2x - 3)(x + 3)$

$2x^2 + 4x - 16$
Factor out a 2. $2(x^2 + 2x - 8)$
$ac = -8$; factors that add to 2 are 4 and -2

	x	-2
x	x^2	$-2x$
4	$4x$	-8

$2(x + 4)(x - 2)$

$4x^3 + 16x^2 + 15x$
Factor out an x. $x(4x^2 + 16x + 15)$
$ac = 60$; factors that add to 16 are 10 and 6

	$2x$	5
$2x$	$4x^2$	$10x$
3	$6x$	15

$x(2x + 3)(2x + 5)$

$3x^3 - 9x^2 + 6x$
Factor out 3x. $3x(x^2 - 3x + 2)$
$ac = 2$; factors that add to -3 are -2 and -1

	x	-2
x	x^2	$-2x$
-1	$-x$	2

$3x(x - 2)(x - 1)$

Activities
② Factor each polynomial.

$2x^2 + 11x + 15$
$ac = 30$; factors that add to 11 are 5 and 6

	$2x$	5
x	$2x^2$	$5x$
3	$6x$	15

$(2x + 5)(x + 3)$

$3x^2 + 13x + 12$
$ac = 36$; factors that add to 13 are 9 and 4

	x	3
$3x$	$3x^2$	$9x$
4	$4x$	12

$(3x + 4)(x + 3)$

$x^2 - 4x - 12$
$ac = -12$; factors that add to -4 are 2 and -6

	x	-6
x	x^2	$-6x$
2	$2x$	-12

$(x + 2)(x - 6)$

$3x^2 + 10x - 8$
$ac = -24$; factors that add to 10 are 12 and -2

	x	4
$3x$	$3x^2$	$12x$
-2	$-2x$	-8

$(3x - 2)(x + 4)$

$4x^2 + x - 3$
$ac = -12$; factors that add to 1 are 4 and -3

	x	1
$4x$	$4x^2$	$4x$
-3	$-3x$	-3

$(4x - 3)(x + 1)$

$6x^2 + 17x + 12$
$ac = 72$; factors that add to 17 are 9 and 8

	$2x$	3
$3x$	$6x^2$	$9x$
4	$8x$	12

$(2x + 3)(3x + 4)$

$2x^2 + 2x - 12$
Factor out a 2.
$2(x^2 + x - 6)$
$ac = -6$; factors that add to 1 are 3 and -2

	x	-2
x	x^2	$-2x$
3	$3x$	-6

$2(x + 3)(x - 2)$

$2x^3 - 5x^2 + 2x$
Factor out x.
$x(2x^2 - 5x + 2)$
$ac = 4$; factors that add to -5 are -4 and -1

	x	-2
$2x$	$2x^2$	$-4x$
-1	$-x$	2

$x(2x - 1)(x - 2)$

$3x^3 + 6x^2 - 24x$
Factor out 3x.
$3x(x^2 + 2x - 8)$
$ac = -8$; factors that add to 2 are -2 and 4

	x	-2
x	x^2	$-2x$
4	$4x$	-8

$3x(x - 2)(x + 4)$

③ Solve.
An amusement park offers meal vouchers that allows park guests to have unlimited trips through the meal lines for an entire day. Vouchers for guests ages 10 and older cost $29.95 and vouchers for guests ages 3-9 cost $14.95. How many guests ages 10 and older bought meal vouchers in one day if the park sold a total of 255 vouchers for a total of $6107.25?
Let *a* = the number of adult vouchers
Let *c* = the number of child vouchers

$a + c = 255$
$29.95a + 14.95c = 6107.25$
Multiply the top equation by 29.95
$29.95a + 29.95c = 7637.25$
$\underline{29.95a + 14.95c = 6107.25}$
$15c = 1530$
$c = 102$

$a + 102 = 255$
$a = 153$

153 guests ages 10 and older bought vouchers.

Factoring Polynomials with Special Products Worksheet 36

① Factor each polynomial.

$24x - 56$
$8(3x - 7)$

$27x + 24$
$3(9x + 8)$

$30x^2 + 36x$
$6x(5x + 6)$

$20x^2 - 25x$
$5x(4x - 5)$

$50x^2 - 30x$
$10x(5x - 3)$

$8x^2 - 12x$
$4x(2x - 3)$

$x^2 - 81$
$(x + 9)(x - 9)$

$x^2 - 144$
$(x + 12)(x - 12)$

$81x^2 - 100$
$(9x + 10)(9x - 10)$

$25x^2 - 36$
$(5x + 6)(5x - 6)$

$16x^2 - 121$
$(4x + 11)(4x - 11)$

$9x^2 - 20$
$(3x + 2\sqrt{5})(3x - 2\sqrt{5})$

$49x^2 - 6$
$(7x + \sqrt{6})(7x - \sqrt{6})$

$x^2 - 8x + 16$
$(x - 4)^2$

$9x^2 - 64$
$(3x + 8)(3x - 8)$

$4x^2 + 20x + 25$
$(2x + 5)^2$

$16x^2 + 24x + 9$
$(4x + 3)^2$

$16x^2 - 56x + 49$
$(4x - 7)^2$

$9x^2 + 6\sqrt{19}x + 19$
$(3x + \sqrt{19})^2$

$16x^2 + 24\sqrt{2}x + 18$
$(4x + 3\sqrt{2})^2$

Teaching Tips, Cont.

- Teach factoring trinomials of the form $ax^2 + bx + c$ from the teaching box. As in the last lesson, emphasize the importance of following the steps exactly. Future lessons will build on the material in this lesson.

- Complete the Classwork exercises. Have some students work the problems on the board for the class and explain their answers. All students should work the problems in their books.

- If you plan to administer Exam 2 following Lesson 80 and Test 8, spend a few minutes reviewing for the Exam.

Assignment

- Complete Lesson 72, Activities 2-3.

Lesson 73

Concepts

- Factoring trinomials of the form $ax^2 + bxy + cy^2$
- Simplifying roots
- Math in the real world

Learning Objectives

The student will be able to:

- Factor trinomials of the form $ax^2 + bxy + cy^2$

Materials Needed

- Student Book, Lesson 73
- Worksheet 37

Teaching Tips

- Review factoring trinomials. (See Lessons 71 and 72)
- Have the students look at the lesson headings for Lessons 72 and 73 and tell what is different between the two. (Lesson 73 has a y added to the second term and a y^2 added to the third term.)
- Tell the students that they have learned to factor trinomials with one unique variable. In this lesson, they will factor trinomials with two variables.
- Teach factoring trinomials of the form $ax^2 + bxy + cy^2$ from the teaching box. Emphasize the importance of drawing the boxes, especially at the beginning.

Factoring Trinomials of the Form $ax^2 + bxy + cy^2$

So far, you have learned to factor trinomials with one variable. In this lesson, you will factor trinomials with two variables of the form $ax^2 + bxy + cy^2$. You will use the same box format as you used in Lesson 72, but with one slight modification. When the polynomial has two variables, follow the same steps you have been doing, but use the box shown below.

ax^2	(factor of ac)xy
(factor of ac)xy	cy^2

Notice that the upper right and lower left boxes have the factor of ac multiplied by xy instead of just x.

Factor $6x^2 - 3xy - 18y^2$.
The number 3 is a factor of all three terms.
$3(2x^2 - xy - 6y^2)$ Now a = 2; b = -1; c = -6
ac = 2(-6) = -12
Factors of -12 that add to -1 are -4 and 3.
Insert these values in the box and factor each row and column.

	x	$-2y$
$2x$	$2x^2$	$-4xy$
$3y$	$3xy$	$-6y^2$

Factoring the rows gives $(2x + 3y)$. Factoring the columns gives $(x - 2y)$.
The factorization of $6x^2 - 3xy - 18y^2$ is $3(2x + 3y)(x - 2y)$. Don't forget to include the 3 that was factored out in the first step!

① Classwork
Factor each polynomial.

$2x^2 + 3xy - 9y^2$
ac = -18; factors that add to 3 are 6 and -3

	x	$3y$
$2x$	$2x^2$	$6xy$
$-3y$	$-3xy$	$-9y^2$

$(2x - 3y)(x + 3y)$

$3x^2 + 6xy - 24y^2$
Factor out a 3. $3(x^2 + 2xy - 8y^2)$
ac = -8; factors that add to 2 are 4 and -2

	x	$-2y$
x	x^2	$-2xy$
$4y$	$4xy$	$-8y^2$

$3(x + 4y)(x - 2y)$

$8x^3 + 32x^2y + 30xy^2$
Factor out $2x$. $2x(4x^2 + 16xy + 15y^2)$
ac = 60; factors that add to 16 are 10 and 6

	$2x$	$5y$
$2x$	$4x^2$	$10xy$
$3y$	$6xy$	$15y^2$

$2x(2x + 3y)(2x + 5y)$

Activities

② Factor each polynomial.

$2x^2 - xy - 10y^2$
ac = -20; factors that add to -1 are 4 and -5

	x	$2y$
$2x$	$2x^2$	$4xy$
$-5y$	$-5xy$	$-10y^2$

$(2x - 5y)(x + 2y)$

$3x^2 + 6xy - 9y^2$
Factor out a 3.
$3(x^2 + 2xy - 3y^2)$
ac = -3; factors that add to 2 are 3 and -1

	x	$-y$
x	x^2	$-xy$
$3y$	$3xy$	$-3y^2$

$3(x + 3y)(x - y)$

$12x^3 + 26x^2y + 12xy^2$
Factor out $2x$.
$2x(6x^2 + 13xy + 6y^2)$
ac = 36; factors that add to 13 are 9 and 4

	$2x$	$3y$
$3x$	$6x^2$	$9xy$
$2y$	$4xy$	$6y^2$

$2x(3x + 2y)(2x + 3y)$

③ Factor each polynomial.

$8x^2 + 22xy - 21y^2$
ac = -168; factors that add to 22 are 28 and -6

	$2x$	$7y$
$4x$	$8x^2$	$28xy$
$-3y$	$-6xy$	$-21y^2$

$(4x - 3y)(2x + 7y)$

$6x^2 + 7xy - 3y^2$
ac = -18; factors that add to 7 are 9 and -2

	$2x$	$3y$
$3x$	$6x^2$	$9xy$
$-y$	$-2xy$	$-3y^2$

$(3x - y)(2x + 3y)$

$5x^2 + 18xy - 8y^2$
ac = -40; factors that add to 18 are 20 and -2

	x	$4y$
$5x$	$5x^2$	$20xy$
$-2y$	$-2xy$	$-8y^2$

$(5x - 2y)(x + 4y)$

$8x^2 + 20xy - 12y^2$
Factor out a 4.
$4(2x^2 + 5xy - 3y^2)$
ac = -6; factors that add to 5 are 6 and -1

	$2x$	$-y$
x	$2x^2$	$-xy$
$3y$	$6xy$	$-3y^2$

$4(x + 3y)(2x - y)$

$x^3 + x^2y - 2xy^2$
Factor out a x.
$x(x^2 + xy - 2y^2)$
ac = -2; factors that add to 1 are 2 and -1

	x	$-y$
x	x^2	$-xy$
$2y$	$2xy$	$-2y^2$

$x(x + 2y)(x - y)$

$6x^3 + 21x^2y + 9xy^2$
Factor out $3x$.
$3x(2x^2 + 7xy + 3y^2)$
ac = 6; factors that add to 7 are 1 and 6

	$2x$	y
x	$2x^2$	xy
$3y$	$6xy$	$3y^2$

$3x(x + 3y)(2x + y)$

④ Simplify the following roots.

$$\frac{4\sqrt{27}}{3} - \frac{\sqrt{48}}{3} = \frac{4\sqrt{3 \times 3 \times 3}}{3} - \frac{\sqrt{3 \times 4 \times 4}}{3} = \frac{4(3)\sqrt{3}}{3} - \frac{4\sqrt{3}}{3} = \frac{12\sqrt{3}}{3} - \frac{4\sqrt{3}}{3} = \frac{8\sqrt{3}}{3}$$

$$\frac{\sqrt[3]{32}}{2} + \frac{7\sqrt[3]{108}}{3} = \frac{\sqrt[3]{2 \times 2 \times 2 \times 2 \times 2}}{2} + \frac{7\sqrt[3]{2 \times 2 \times 3 \times 3 \times 3}}{3} = \frac{\cancel{2}\sqrt[3]{4}}{\cancel{2}} + \frac{7(\cancel{3})\sqrt[3]{4}}{\cancel{3}} = \sqrt[3]{4} + 7\sqrt[3]{4} = 8\sqrt[3]{4}$$

⑤ Solve.

Determine the most economical method of travel for a vacation for a family of 4. Airfare costs \$325 round trip per person, including all taxes and fees. Driving requires a one-night hotel stay in each direction, at a cost of \$107 including tax per night. Gas costs \$3.67 per gallon. Additional wear-and-tear on the car costs \$0.38 per mile. If the driving distance is 960 miles one way and the car gets 30 miles per gallon, should the family fly or drive? (Assume that transportation between the airport and hotel, as well as transportation between the hotel and attractions at the destination are provided by the hotel.) If a parent earns \$25 per hour and must lose an additional two days of work (16 hours additional time off), does this factor change the best method of travel?

Cost for 4 people to fly = 4(\$325) = \$1300
Total driving distance = 2(960) = 1920 miles
Gallons of gas needed = 1920 / 30 = 64 gallons
Cost of gas = 64(\$3.67) = \$234.88
Additional wear-and-tear = 1920(\$0.38) = \$729.60
Cost of two nights in a hotel = 2(\$107) = \$214
Total cost to drive = \$1178.48
Additional lost wages = 16(\$25) = \$400
Without the additional lost work, driving is the most economical. With the additional lost work, flying is the most economical.

Factoring Polynomials Worksheet 37

① Factor each polynomial.

$2x^2+13x+15$

ac = 30; factors that add to 13 are 10 and 3

	$2x$	3
x	$2x^2$	$3x$
5	$10x$	15

$(2x+3)(x+5)$

$3x^2+17x-6$

ac = -18; factors that add to 17 are 18 and -1

	x	6
$3x$	$3x^2$	$18x$
-1	$-x$	-6

$(3x-1)(x+6)$

$3x^2-6x-24$

Factor out a 3. $3(x^2-2x-8)$

ac = -8; factors that add to -2 are 2 and -4

	x	-4
x	x^2	$-4x$
2	$2x$	-8

$3(x+2)(x-4)$

$3x^2+13x+14$

ac = 42; factors that add to 13 are 6 and 7

	x	2
$3x$	$3x^2$	$6x$
7	$7x$	14

$(3x+7)(x+2)$

$5x^2-3x-8$

ac = -40; factors that add to -3 are 5 and -8

	x	1
$5x$	$5x^2$	$5x$
-8	$-8x$	-8

$(5x-8)(x+1)$

$4x^3-10x^2+4x$

Factor out $2x$. $2x(2x^2-5x+2)$

ac = 4; factors that add to -5 are -4 and -1

	x	-2
$2x$	$2x^2$	$-4x$
-1	$-x$	2

$2x(2x-1)(x-2)$

$49x^2-7xy-6y^2$

ac = -294; factors that add to -7 are 14 and -21

	$7x$	$2y$
$7x$	$49x^2$	$14xy$
$-3y$	$-21xy$	$-6y^2$

$(7x-3y)(7x+2y)$

$12x^2+30xy-18y^2$

Factor out a 6. $6(2x^2+5xy-3y^2)$

ac = -6; factors that add to 5 are 6 and -1

	$2x$	$-y$
x	$2x^2$	$-xy$
$3y$	$6xy$	$-3y^2$

$6(x+3y)(2x-y)$

$12x^2+17xy-5y^2$

ac = -60; factors that add to 17 are 3 and -20

	$3x$	$5y$
$4x$	$12x^2$	$20xy$
$-y$	$-3xy$	$-5y^2$

$(4x-y)(3x+5y)$

$3x^4+3x^3y-6x^2y^2$

Factor out $3x^2$. $3x^2(x^2+xy-2y^2)$

ac = -2; factors that add to 1 are 2 and -1

	x	$-y$
x	$2x^2$	$-xy$
$2y$	$2xy$	$-2y^2$

$3x^2(x+2y)(x-y)$

Teaching Tips, Cont.

- Note: As students become more proficient at factoring, they will be able to complete the process without drawing the boxes, and they may be able to complete some of the steps in their heads. It is important that they understand that they are still doing the steps even if they are not writing each step down. Students should be encouraged to show their work on all steps for the first couple of lessons. Students who have demonstrated understanding of the process may be allowed to complete the process without writing down every step.
- Complete the Classwork exercises. Have some students work the problems on the board for the class and explain their answers. All students should work the problems in their books.
- If you plan to administer Exam 2 following Lesson 80 and Test 8, spend a few minutes reviewing for the Exam.

Assignments

- Complete Lesson 73, Activities 2-5.
- Worksheet 37.

Lesson 74

Concepts

- Factoring the difference of two squares
- Factoring perfect square trinomials
- Identifying perfect square trinomials

Learning Objectives

The student will be able to:

- Identify whether or not a trinomial is a perfect square
- Calculate the value of a missing variable in a trinomial to make the trinomial a perfect square

Materials Needed

- Student Book, Lesson 74

Teaching Tips

➢ Review factoring the difference of two squares. (See Lesson 69)

➢ Review factoring perfect square trinomials. (See Lesson 70)

➢ Tell the students that if they have not already memorized the formulas for multiplying and factoring special products (the difference of two squares and perfect square trinomials), they must do so now!

➢ If necessary, review the formulas for the special products. These formulas are given in the teaching box of this lesson for your convenience.

Review: Factoring Special Products

If you have not already memorized the formulas for multiplying and factoring special products, you must do so now! Much of what you will be doing in the next several lessons depends on your ability to recognize and apply the formula patterns.

Factoring the difference of two squares
$a^2 - b^2 = (a+b)(a-b)$

Factoring perfect square trinomials
$a^2 \pm 2ab + b^2 = (a \pm b)^2$

Identify whether or not the polynomial is a perfect square trinomial.

$x^2 - 6x - 9$
No. Here, a = 1, b = 3, and $2ab$ = 6. However, the sign of the last term must be positive.

Determine what coefficient must go in place of the ? to make the polynomial a perfect square trinomial.

$x^2 + ?x + 25$
In this polynomial, a = 1 and b = 5. Therefore, 2ab must equal 10.

① **Classwork**
Identify whether or not each polynomial is a perfect square trinomial. Factor all perfect square trinomials.

$x^2 - 10x + 25$
Yes, this is a perfect square trinomial.
$(x-5)^2$

$x^2 + 7x + 49$
No. The coefficient of the middle term is equal to ab, not $2ab$.

Determine what coefficient must go in place of the ? to make the polynomial a perfect square trinomial.

$x^2 + ?x + 64$
a = 1 and b = 8, so $2ab$ = 16.

$x^2 + 22x + ?$
a = 1 and $2ab$ = 22, so b = 11. This is not what goes in place of the ? however. This is b^2, which is 121.

Activities

② Identify whether or not each polynomial is a perfect square trinomial. Factor all perfect square trinomials.

$x^2 - 16x + 64$
Yes, this is a perfect square trinomial.
$(x-8)^2$

$x^2 + 5x + 25$
No. The coefficient of the middle term is equal to ab, not $2ab$.

$x^2 + 9x + 9$
No. The coefficient of the middle term is equal to ab^2, not $2ab$.

$x^2 + 12x + 36$
Yes, this is a perfect square trinomial.
$(x+6)^2$

$9x^2 + 8x + 16$
No. The coefficient of the middle term is equal to $2b$, not $2ab$.

$4x^2 - 12x + 9$
Yes, this is a perfect square trinomial.
$(2x-3)^2$

$16x^2 - 8x + 1$
Yes, this is a perfect square trinomial.
$(4x-1)^2$

$49x^2 + 42x + 9$
Yes, this is a perfect square trinomial.
$(7x+3)^2$

③ Determine what coefficient must go in place of the ? to make the polynomial a perfect square trinomial.

$x^2 + ?x + 49$
$a = 1$ and $b = 7$, so $2ab = 14$.

$4x^2 + ?x + 9$
$a = 2$ and $b = 3$, so $2ab = 12$.

$x^2 + 10x + ?$
$a = 1$ and $2ab = 10$, so $b = 5$. This is not what goes in place of the ? however. This is b^2, which is 25.

$9x^2 + 66x + ?$
$a = 3$ and $2ab = 66$, so $b = 11$. This is not what goes in place of the ? however. This is b^2, which is 121.

$x^2 + ?x + 81$
$a = 1$ and $b = 9$, so $2ab = 18$.

$25x^2 + ?x + 4$
$a = 5$ and $b = 2$, so $2ab = 20$.

$? + 24x + 16$
$b^2 = 16$ and $2ab = 24$, so $b = 4$ and $a = 3$. This is not what goes in place of the ? however. This is a^2, which is $9x^2$.

$? + 28x + 49$
$b^2 = 49$ and $2ab = 28$, so $b = 7$ and $a = 2$. This is not what goes in place of the ? however. This is a^2, which is $4x^2$.

④ Factor.

$x^2 - 144$
$(x+12)(x-12)$

$x^2 - 81$
$(x+9)(x-9)$

$x^2 - 9$
$(x+3)(x-3)$

$x^2 - 25$
$(x+5)(x-5)$

$x^2 - 64$
$(x+8)(x-8)$

$121x^2 - 16$
$(11x+4)(11x-4)$

$25x^2 - 49$
$(5x+7)(5x-7)$

$4x^2 - 169$
$(2x+13)(2x-13)$

$49x^2 - 4$
$(7x+2)(7x-2)$

$64x^2 - 25$
$(8x+5)(8x-5)$

$100x^2 - 121$
$(10x+11)(10x-11)$

$x^2 - 43$
$(x+\sqrt{43})(x-\sqrt{43})$

$4x^2 - 77$
$(2x+\sqrt{77})(2x-\sqrt{77})$

$49x^2 - 8$
$(7x+2\sqrt{2})(7x-2\sqrt{2})$

$64x^2 - 27$
$(8x+3\sqrt{3})(8x-3\sqrt{3})$

$144x^2 - 18$
$(12x+3\sqrt{2})(12x-3\sqrt{2})$

$x^2 - 26x + 169$
$(x-13)^2$

$x^2 + 20x + 100$
$(x+10)^2$

$x^2 - 6x + 9$
$(x-3)^2$

$16x^2 + 40x + 25$
$(4x+5)^2$

$9x^2 - 48x + 64$
$(3x-8)^2$

$4x^2 - 28x + 49$
$(2x-7)^2$

$9x^2 + 30x + 25$
$(3x+5)^2$

$x^2 - 2\sqrt{65}x + 65$
$(x-\sqrt{65})^2$

$4x^2 + 4\sqrt{57}x + 57$
$(2x+\sqrt{57})^2$

$49x^2 + 28\sqrt{2}x + 8$
$(7x+2\sqrt{2})^2$

$25x^2 - 30\sqrt{3}x + 27$
$(5x-3\sqrt{3})^2$

Teaching Tips, Cont.

- Tell the students that the material appearing in the next several lessons relies on their ability to recognize and use the special product formulas.
- Complete the Classwork exercises. Have some students work the problems on the board for the class and explain their answers. All students should work the problems in their books.
- If you plan to administer Exam 2 following Lesson 80 and Test 8, spend a few minutes reviewing for the Exam.

Assignment

- Complete Lesson 74, Activities 2-4.

Lesson 75

Concepts

- Factoring completely
- Adding fractions with roots
- Subtracting fractions with roots
- Multiplying fractions with roots
- Dividing fractions with roots
- Math in the real world

Learning Objectives

The student will be able to:

- Identify polynomial factors that can be factored further
- Factor polynomials completely
- Apply the formulas for factoring special products to factor polynomials completely

Materials Needed

- Student Book, Lesson 75
- Worksheet 38

Teaching Tips

- ➢ Have students complete Worksheet 38 in class. This may be for added practice of earlier topics, or graded as a quiz, if desired.
- ➢ Review factoring special products. (See Lesson 74)
- ➢ Tell the students that occasionally a polynomial can be factored multiple times. When following the factoring rules they have learned so far, students may find a factor that can be factored again. This may be factoring out a constant, or may be factoring a polynomial that follows one of the previously learned patterns.

Factoring Completely

Occasionally, following the formula for factoring special products will yield a factor that can be factored further. For a polynomial to be factored completely, each factor must be reduced as far as possible.

Factor $x^4 - 1$.
You should recognize this as the difference of two squares.
$x^4 - 1 = (x^2 + 1)(x^2 - 1)$
There is no simplification for the sum of two squares, but the second factor is the difference of two squares and must be factored again.
$(x^2 + 1)(x^2 - 1) = (x^2 + 1)(x + 1)(x - 1)$
Remember that 1 raised to any power is still 1.

As long as the exponent of the variable is an even number, the term can be written as a square. Any number can be considered a square because you can always take the square root or the 4th root.

① **Classwork**
Factor each polynomial completely.

$x^4 - 16$
$(x^2 + 4)(x^2 - 4) =$
$(x^2 + 4)(x + 2)(x - 2)$

$4x^4 - 25$
$(2x^2 + 5)(2x^2 - 5) =$
$(2x^2 + 5)(x\sqrt{2} + \sqrt{5})(x\sqrt{2} - \sqrt{5})$

$x^4 - 10$
$(x^2 + \sqrt{10})(x^2 - \sqrt{10}) =$
$(x^2 + \sqrt{10})(x + \sqrt[4]{10})(x - \sqrt[4]{10})$

Activities

② Factor each polynomial completely.

$x^4 - 81$
$(x^2 + 9)(x^2 - 9) =$
$(x^2 + 9)(x + 3)(x - 3)$

$25x^4 - 256$
$(5x^2 + 16)(5x^2 - 16) =$
$(5x^2 + 16)(x\sqrt{5} + 4)(x\sqrt{5} - 4)$

$4x^4 - 64$
$4(x^4 - 16)$
$4(x^2 + 4)(x^2 - 4) =$
$4(x^2 + 4)(x + 2)(x - 2)$

$2x^4 - 50$
$2(x^4 - 25) =$
$2(x^2 + 5)(x^2 - 5) =$
$2(x^2 + 5)(x + \sqrt{5})(x - \sqrt{5})$

$x^4 - 10{,}000$
$(x^2 + 100)(x^2 - 100) =$
$(x^2 + 100)(x + 10)(x - 10)$

$x^3 - 25x$
$x(x^2 - 25) =$
$x(x + 5)(x - 5)$

$x^4 - 16x^2$
$x^2(x^2 - 16) =$
$x^2(x + 4)(x - 4)$

$2x^3 - 98x$
$2x(x^2 - 49) =$
$2x(x + 7)(x - 7)$

$x^5 - 10x^3$
$x^3(x^2 - 10) =$
$x^3(x + \sqrt{10})(x - \sqrt{10})$

$4x^4 - 16x^2$
$4x^2(x^2 - 4) =$
$4x^2(x + 2)(x - 2)$

$8x^4 - 200$
$8(x^4 - 25) =$
$8(x^2 + 5)(x^2 - 5) =$
$8(x^2 + 5)(x + \sqrt{5})(x - \sqrt{5})$

$3x^5 - 48x$
$3x(x^4 - 16) =$
$3x(x^2 + 4)(x^2 - 4) =$
$3x(x^2 + 4)(x + 2)(x - 2)$

③ Simplify the following roots.

$$\frac{\sqrt[3]{40}}{2} + \frac{4\sqrt[3]{135}}{3} = \frac{\sqrt[3]{2 \times 2 \times 2 \times 5}}{2} + \frac{4\sqrt[3]{3 \times 3 \times 3 \times 5}}{3} = \frac{\cancel{2}\sqrt[3]{5}}{\cancel{2}} + \frac{4(\cancel{3})\sqrt[3]{5}}{\cancel{3}} = \sqrt[3]{5} + 4\sqrt[3]{5} = 5\sqrt[3]{5}$$

$$\frac{3\sqrt{48}}{2} - \frac{\sqrt{75}}{5} = \frac{3\sqrt{3 \times 4 \times 4}}{2} - \frac{\sqrt{3 \times 5 \times 5}}{5} = \frac{3(\cancel{4}^2)\sqrt{3}}{\cancel{2}_1} - \frac{\cancel{5}\sqrt{3}}{\cancel{5}} = 6\sqrt{3} - \sqrt{3} = 5\sqrt{3}$$

$$\frac{3\sqrt[4]{48}}{2}\left(\frac{5\sqrt[4]{96}}{4}\right) = \frac{3\sqrt[4]{2 \times 2 \times 2 \times 2 \times 3}}{2}\left(\frac{5\sqrt[4]{2 \times 2 \times 2 \times 2 \times 2 \times 3}}{4}\right) = \frac{3(\cancel{2}^1)\sqrt[4]{3}}{\cancel{2}_1}\left(\frac{5(\cancel{2}^1)\sqrt[4]{6}}{\cancel{4}_2}\right) = 3\sqrt[4]{3}\left(\frac{5\sqrt[4]{6}}{2}\right) = \frac{15\sqrt[4]{18}}{2}$$

$$\frac{8\sqrt[3]{270}}{3} \div \frac{4\sqrt[3]{135}}{3} = \frac{8\sqrt[3]{2 \times 3 \times 3 \times 3 \times 5}}{3} \div \frac{4\sqrt[3]{3 \times 3 \times 3 \times 5}}{3} = \frac{8(\cancel{3})\sqrt[3]{2 \times 5}}{\cancel{3}} \div \frac{4(\cancel{3})\sqrt[3]{5}}{\cancel{3}} = 8\sqrt[3]{10} \div 4\sqrt[3]{5} = \frac{{}^2\cancel{8}\sqrt[3]{\cancel{10}^2}}{{}_1\cancel{4}\sqrt[3]{\cancel{5}_1}} = 2\sqrt[3]{2}$$

④ Solve.

You are planning a trip to visit as many national parks as possible. Some of the national parks are free, while others charge \$5 per person for ages 16 and older. An annual pass is available for \$80 that grants 4 people unlimited admission to all national parks for 1 year. What is the minimum number of national parks with an entrance fee that must be visited by a family with 2 people ages 16 and over to make the annual pass a good investment?
Let n = the number of visits.
Each visit would cost \$10 without the pass.
Set up an inequality and solve.
$10n \geq 80$
$n \geq 8$
It would take 8 visits to national parks with an entrance fee for the annual pass to be a good investment.

What is the minimum number of national parks with an entrance fee that must be visited by a family with 3 people ages 16 and over to make the annual pass a good investment?
Let n = the number of visits.
Each visit would cost \$15 without the pass.
Set up an inequality and solve.
$15n \geq 80$
$n \geq 5\frac{1}{3}$
You cannot have a partial visit. It would take 6 visits to national parks with an entrance fee for the annual pass to be a good investment.

What is the minimum number of national parks with an entrance fee that must be visited by a family with 4 people ages 16 and over to make the annual pass a good investment?
Let n = the number of visits.
Each visit would cost \$20 without the pass.
Set up an inequality and solve.
$20n \geq 80$
$n \geq 4$
It would take 4 visits to national parks with an entrance fee for the annual pass to be a good investment.

Factoring Polynomials Worksheet 38

① Factor each polynomial.

$4x^2+16x+15$

ac = 60; factors that add to 16 are 10 and 6

	$2x$	3
$2x$	$4x^2$	$6x$
5	$10x$	15

$(2x+3)(2x+5)$

$5x^2+14x-3$

ac = -15; factors that add to 14 are 15 and -1

	x	3
$5x$	$5x^2$	$15x$
-1	$-x$	-3

$(5x-1)(x+3)$

$15x^2-50x-40$

Factor out a 5. $5(3x^2-10x-8)$

ac = -24; factors that add to -10 are 2 and -12

	x	-4
$3x$	$3x^2$	$-12x$
2	$2x$	-8

$5(3x+2)(x-4)$

$15x^2+31x+10$

ac = 150; factors that add to 31 are 6 and 25

	$5x$	2
$3x$	$15x^2$	$6x$
5	$25x$	10

$(3x+5)(5x+2)$

$10x^2-9x-7$

ac = -70; factors that add to -9 are 5 and -14

	$2x$	1
$5x$	$10x^2$	$5x$
-7	$-14x$	-7

$(5x-7)(2x+1)$

$18x^3-63x^2+54x$

Factor out 9x. $9x(2x^2-7x+6)$

ac = 12; factors that add to -7 are -4 and -3

	x	-2
$2x$	$2x^2$	$-4x$
-3	$-3x$	6

$9x(2x-3)(x-2)$

$10x^2-11xy-6y^2$

ac = -60; factors that add to -11 are 4 and -15

	$5x$	$2y$
$2x$	$10x^2$	$4xy$
$-3y$	$-15xy$	$-6y^2$

$(2x-3y)(5x+2y)$

$28x^2+28xy-21y^2$

Factor out a 7. $7(4x^2+4xy-3y^2)$

ac = -12; factors that add to 4 are 6 and -2

	$2x$	$-y$
$2x$	$4x^2$	$-2xy$
$3y$	$6xy$	$-3y^2$

$7(2x+3y)(2x-y)$

$8x^2+2xy-45y^2$

ac = -360; factors that add to 2 are 20 and -18

	$2x$	$5y$
$4x$	$8x^2$	$20xy$
$-9y$	$-18xy$	$-45y^2$

$(4x-9y)(2x+5y)$

$4x^4-16x^2y^2$

Factor out $4x^2$. $4x^2(x^2-4y^2)$

You should recognize this as a special product pattern.

$4x^2(x+2y)(x-2y)$

Teaching Tips, Cont.

- Teach factoring polynomials completely from the teaching box.
- Tell the students they need to get in the habit of checking each factor to see if it can be factored further. From now on, students will be expected to factor completely unless otherwise instructed.
- Complete the Classwork exercises. Have some students work the problems on the board for the class and explain their answers. All students should work the problems in their books.
- If you plan to administer Exam 2 following Lesson 80 and Test 8, spend a few minutes reviewing for the Exam.

Assignment

- Complete Lesson 75, Activities 2-4.

Lesson 76

Concepts

- Factoring cubic polynomials
- Systems of equations
- Absolute value
- Extraneous solutions
- Math in the real world

Learning Objectives

The student will be able to:

- Factor the sum of two cubes
- Factor the difference of two cubes

Materials Needed

- Student Book, Lesson 76

Teaching Tips

- Review factoring trinomials. (See Lessons 71, 72, and 73)
- Review factoring special products. (See Lesson 74)
- Review factoring completely. (See Lesson 75)
- Tell the students that in this lesson, they are going to learn to factor binomials that do not have a corresponding multiplication rule.

Factoring Cubic Polynomials

You have already learned how to factor the difference of two squares. In this lesson you will factor the sum of two cubes and the difference of two cubes. There are two factoring formulas you should memorize.

Sum of two cubes
$a^3 + b^3 = (a+b)(a^2 - ab + b^2)$

Difference of two cubes
$a^3 - b^3 = (a-b)(a^2 + ab + b^2)$

These formulas can be combined into a singular formula as follows.
$a^3 \pm b^3 = (a \pm b)(a^2 \mp ab + b^2)$

Notice the change in signs before the *ab* in the second set of parentheses.

Factor $x^3 - 27$.
$a^3 = x^3$ so $a = x$. $b^3 = 27$ so $b = 3$.
Because the sign in the problem is negative, follow the bottom signs all the way across the formula.
$(x-3)(x^2 + 3x + 9)$

① Classwork
Factor each polynomial.

$x^3 + 27$
$a^3 = x^3$ so $a = x$. $b^3 = 27$ so $b = 3$.
$(x+3)(x^2 - 3x + 9)$

$x^3 - 8$
$a^3 = x^3$ so $a = x$. $b^3 = 8$ so $b = 2$.
$(x-2)(x^2 + 2x + 4)$

$8x^3 + 27$
$a^3 = 8x^3$ so $a = 2x$. $b^3 = 27$ so $b = 3$.
$(2x+3)(4x^2 - 6x + 9)$

Activities
② Factor each polynomial.

$x^3 + 64$
$a^3 = x^3$ so $a = x$. $b^3 = 64$ so $b = 4$.
$(x+4)(x^2 - 4x + 16)$

$x^3 - 125$
$a^3 = x^3$ so $a = x$. $b^3 = 125$ so $b = 5$.
$(x-5)(x^2 + 5x + 25)$

$27x^3 + 64$
$a^3 = 27x^3$ so $a = 3x$. $b^3 = 64$ so $b = 4$.
$(3x+4)(9x^2 - 12x + 16)$

$x^3 + 216$
$a^3 = x^3$ so $a = x$. $b^3 = 216$ so $b = 6$.
$(x+6)(x^2 - 6x + 36)$

$8x^3 - 27$
$a^3 = 8x^3$ so $a = 2x$. $b^3 = 27$ so $b = 3$.
$(2x-3)(4x^2 + 6x + 9)$

$8x^3 - 64$
$a^3 = 8x^3$ so $a = 2x$. $b^3 = 64$ so $b = 4$.
$(2x-4)(4x^2 + 8x + 16)$ or
$8(x-2)(x^2 + 2x + 4)$
Students may or may not notice the additional factoring possible.

③ Solve the systems of equations. Use the method of your choice.

$x - y - 5 = 0$
$-2x + y + 9 = 0$
$x - y = 5$
$\underline{-2x + y = -9}$
$-x = -4$
$x = 4$
$4 - y - 5 = 0$
$y = -1$
(4, -1)

$10x - 3y - 5 = 0$
$7x + 2y - 24 = 0$
$10x - 3y = 5$
$7x + 2y = 24$
$20x - 6y = 10$
$\underline{21x + 6y = 72}$
$41x = 82$
$x = 2$
$10(2) - 3y - 5 = 0$
$20 - 3y = 5$
$-3y = -15$
$y = 5$
(2, 5)

$11x + 22y - 44 = 0$
$-x - 4y + 10 = 0$
$11x + 22y = 44$
$-x - 4y = -10$
$x + 2y = 4$
$\underline{-x - 4y = -10}$
$-2y = -6$
$y = 3$
$-x - 4(3) + 10 = 0$
$-x - 12 = -10$
$-x = 2$
$x = -2$
(-2, 3)

$10x - 5y - 25 = 0$
$6x - 3y - 15 = 0$
$10x - 5y = 25$
$6x - 3y = 15$
Divide the top equation by 5 and the bottom equation by 3.
$2x - y = 5$
$\underline{2x - y = 5}$
$0 = 0$
All real numbers

④ Find all possible solutions. Identify any extraneous solutions.

$|-4x + 3| + x - 2 = 3x + 13$
$|-4x + 3| = 2x + 15$
$-4x + 3 = 2x + 15$ or $-4x + 3 = -(2x + 15)$
$-6x = 12$ $\quad -4x + 3 = -2x - 15$
$x = -2$ $\quad -2x = -18 \Rightarrow x = 9$
check:
$|-4(-2) + 3| - 2 - 2 = 3(-2) + 13$
$|8 + 3| - 2 - 2 = -6 + 13$
$|11| - 4 = 7$
$11 - 4 = 7$

$|-4(9) + 3| + 9 - 2 = 3(9) + 13$
$|-36 + 3| + 9 - 2 = 27 + 13$
$|33| + 7 = 40$
$33 + 7 = 40$

$|3x - 4| - 6 = -2x - 25$
$|3x - 4| = -2x - 19$
$3x - 4 = -2x - 19$ or $3x - 4 = -(-2x - 19)$
$5x = -15$ $\quad 3x - 4 = 2x + 19$
$x = -3$ $\quad x = 23$
check:
$|3(-3) - 4| - 6 = -2(-3) - 25$
$|-9 - 4| - 6 = 6 - 25$
$|-13| - 6 = 6 - 25$
$13 - 6 \neq -19$ extraneous

$|3(23) - 4| - 6 = -2(23) - 25$
$|69 - 4| - 6 = -46 - 25$
$|65| - 6 = -46 - 25$
$65 - 6 \neq -71$ extraneous

⑤ Solve.
A rectangular hotel room has an area of 572 square feet. Express the length in terms of the width if the width is 9 feet more than half the length. Write an equation in standard form in terms of the width to show the area of the room. Factor the equation completely.
Let w = the width and L = the length

$w = 9 + \frac{1}{2}L$
$2w = 18 + L$
$2w - 18 = L$

$(2w - 18)w = 572$
$2w^2 - 18w = 572$
$2w^2 - 18w - 572 = 0$

$2w^2 - 18w - 572 = 0$
$2(w^2 - 9w - 286) = 0$
$2(w + 13)(w - 22) = 0$

Note: Students may not necessarily have the equation set equal to zero when factoring.

Teaching Tips, Cont.

- Teach factoring cubic polynomials from the teaching box.
- Have the students pay special attention to the formulas for factoring cubic polynomials. Point out that the sign in the binomial factor matches the sign in the cubic polynomial. The first sign in the trinomial factor is the opposite sign from the cubic polynomial. The second sign in the trinomial factor is always positive.
- Complete the Classwork exercises. Have some students work the problems on the board for the class and explain their answers. All students should work the problems in their books.
- If you plan to administer Exam 2 following Lesson 80 and Test 8, spend a few minutes reviewing for the Exam.

Assignment

- Complete Lesson 76, Activities 2-5.

Lesson 77

Concepts

- Factoring by grouping
- Factoring completely
- Factoring the difference of two squares
- Factoring perfect square trinomials

Learning Objectives

The student will be able to:

- Group terms to factor polynomials with four terms
- Identify common binomial factors
- Factor out common binomial factors

Materials Needed

- Student Book, Lesson 77

Teaching Tips

- ➢ Review factoring trinomials. (See Lessons 71, 72, and 73)
- ➢ Review factoring special products. (See Lesson 74)
- ➢ Review factoring completely. (See Lesson 75)
- ➢ Review factoring cubic polynomials. (See Lesson 76)

Lesson 77

Factoring by Grouping

So far you have learned numerous ways to factor polynomials that fit certain patterns. But what happens when a polynomial has four or more terms and does not fit into any pattern? You can use a technique called **factoring by grouping**. Rather than tackling all four terms at once, break the polynomial up into groups of two terms and factor each group of two. Look for common factors and regroup.

Factor $4x + xy + 3y + 12$.

Split the polynomial up into two groups of two terms each. The xy term may be grouped with either the $4x$ term or the $3y$ term.

$(4x + xy) + (3y + 12)$

Factor each set of parentheses.

$x(4 + y) + 3(y + 4)$

Remember according to the commutative principle of addition that 4 + y is the same thing as y + 4.

Now factor out the y + 4 term from each group.

$(y + 4)(x + 3)$

This is the factorization of $4x + xy + 3y + 12$.

Note that this is the same as $(x + 3)(y + 4)$.

① **Classwork**

Factor each polynomial.

$5x + xy + 2y + 10$
$(5x + xy) + (2y + 10)$
$x(5 + y) + 2(y + 5)$
$(x + 2)(y + 5)$

$-2x + xy + y - 2$
$(-2x + xy) + (y - 2)$
$x(-2 + y) + 1(y - 2)$
$(x + 1)(y - 2)$

$-3x + xy - 2y + 6$
$(-3x + xy) + (-2y + 6)$
$x(-3 + y) - 2(y - 3)$
$(x - 2)(y - 3)$

Activities

② Factor each polynomial.

$2x + xy + 4y + 8$
$(2x + xy) + (4y + 8)$
$x(2 + y) + 4(y + 2)$
$(x + 4)(y + 2)$

$-6x + xy - 2y + 12$
$(-6x + xy) + (-2y + 12)$
$x(-6 + y) - 2(y - 6)$
$(x - 2)(y - 6)$

$4x + xy + 4y + 16$
$(4x + xy) + (4y + 16)$
$x(4 + y) + 4(y + 4)$
$(x + 4)(y + 4)$

$-2x + xy + 3y - 6$
$(-2x + xy) + (3y - 6)$
$x(-2 + y) + 3(y - 2)$
$(x + 3)(y - 2)$

$2x + xy + 7y + 14$
$(2x + xy) + (7y + 14)$
$x(2 + y) + 7(y + 2)$
$(x + 7)(y + 2)$

$-4x + xy - 3y + 12$
$(-4x + xy) + (-3y + 12)$
$x(-4 + y) - 3(y - 4)$
$(x - 3)(y - 4)$

$3x + xy - y - 3$
$(3x + xy) + (-y - 3)$
$x(3 + y) - 1(y + 3)$
$(x - 1)(y + 3)$

$-3x + 3xy - 2y + 2$
$(-3x + 3xy) + (-2y + 2)$
$3x(-1 + y) - 2(y - 1)$
$(3x - 2)(y - 1)$

$2x + 6xy + 15y + 5$
$(2x + 6xy) + (15y + 5)$
$2x(1 + 3y) + 5(3y + 1)$
$(2x + 5)(3y + 1)$

③ Factor each polynomial completely.

$6x^2 + 10xy - 4y^2$
Factor out a 2.
$2(3x^2 + 5xy - 2y^2)$
ac = -6; factors that add to 5 are 6 and -1

	$3x$	$-y$
x	$3x^2$	$-xy$
$2y$	$6xy$	$-2y^2$

$2(x + 2y)(3x - y)$

$6x^3 - 8x^2y - 8xy^2$
Factor out a $2x$.
$2x(3x^2 - 4xy - 4y^2)$
ac = -12; factors that add to -4 are 2 and -6

	x	$-2y$
$3x$	$3x^2$	$-6xy$
$2y$	$2xy$	$-4y^2$

$2x(3x + 2y)(x - 2y)$

$x^2 - 121$
$(x + 11)(x - 11)$

$64x^2 - 9$
$(8x + 3)(8x - 3)$

$100x^2 - 81$
$(10x + 9)(10x - 9)$

$x^2 - 71$
$(x + \sqrt{71})(x - \sqrt{71})$

$x^2 - 12x + 36$
$(x - 6)^2$

$4x^2 + 20x + 25$
$(2x + 5)^2$

$49x^2 + 28\sqrt{3}x + 12$
$(7x + 2\sqrt{3})^2$

$64x^2 - 48\sqrt{2}x + 18$
$(8x - 3\sqrt{2})^2$

$10x^2 + 25x - 60$
Factor out a 5.
$5(2x^2 + 5x - 12)$
ac = -24; factors that add to 5 are 8 and -3

	x	4
$2x$	$2x^2$	$8x$
-3	$-3x$	-12

$5(2x - 3)(x + 4)$

$6x^3 - 21x^2 + 9x$
Factor out $3x$.
$3x(2x^2 - 7x + 3)$
ac = 6; factors that add to -7 are -6 and -1

	x	-3
$2x$	$2x^2$	$-6x$
-1	$-x$	3

$3x(2x - 1)(x - 3)$

$x^2 - 169$
$(x + 13)(x - 13)$

$x^2 - 25$
$(x + 5)(x - 5)$

$x^2 - 144$
$(x + 12)(x - 12)$

$9x^2 - 60x + 100$
$(3x - 10)^2$

$16x^2 + 40x + 25$
$(4x + 5)^2$

$x^2 - 2\sqrt{83}x + 83$
$(x - \sqrt{83})^2$

$16x^2 - 72x + 81$
$(4x - 9)^2$

$4x^2 + 4\sqrt{17}x + 17$
$(2x + \sqrt{17})^2$

$4x^3 + 4x^2 - 8x$
Factor out 4x.
$4x(x^2 + x - 2)$
ac = -2; factors that add to 1 are -1 and 2

	x	-1
x	x^2	$-x$
2	$2x$	-2

$4x(x - 1)(x + 2)$

$42x^2 + 161x + 140$
Factor out a 7.
$7(6x^2 + 23x + 20)$
ac = 120; factors that add to 23 are 15 and 8

	$2x$	5
$3x$	$6x^2$	$15x$
4	$8x$	20

$7(2x + 5)(3x + 4)$

$x^2 - 49$
$(x + 7)(x - 7)$

$25x^2 - 121$
$(5x + 11)(5x - 11)$

$25x^2 - 169$
$(5x + 13)(5x - 13)$

$9x^2 - 64$
$(3x + 8)(3x - 8)$

$4x^2 - 25$
$(2x + 5)(2x - 5)$

$9x^2 - 101$
$(3x + \sqrt{101})(3x - \sqrt{101})$

$36x^2 - 75$
$(6x + 5\sqrt{3})(6x - 5\sqrt{3})$

$81x^2 - 32$
$(9x + 4\sqrt{2})(9x - 4\sqrt{2})$

Teaching Tips, Cont.

- Tell the students that sometimes they will have a polynomial with 4 terms that does not fit any of the factoring patterns they have learned. In this case, there is a short-cut they can use to easily factor the polynomial.

- Teach factoring by grouping from the teaching box. Ask the students if $y + 2$ is the same thing as $2 + y$. (Yes.) Make sure the students understand that binomials with identical terms can be factored out. The order of the terms does not matter as long as the signs and values of the coefficients are the same.

- Complete the Classwork exercises. Have some students work the problems on the board for the class and explain their answers. All students should work the problems in their books.

- If you plan to administer Exam 2 following Lesson 80 and Test 8, spend a few minutes reviewing for the Exam.

Assignment

- Complete Lesson 77, Activities 2-3.

Lesson 78

Concepts

- Rational expressions
- Exclusions
- Fractions
- Math in the real world

Learning Objectives

The student will be able to:

- Define *rational expression*
- Simplify rational expressions
- State exclusions that apply to simplified rational expressions

Materials Needed

- Student Book, Lesson 78
- Worksheet 39

Teaching Tips

➢ Have students complete Worksheet 39 in class. This may be for added practice of earlier topics, or graded as a quiz, if desired.

➢ Review factoring polynomials. (See Lessons 71, 72, and 73)

➢ Tell the students that sometimes polynomials appear in fractions. Define *rational expression* from the teaching box.

➢ Remind students that a polynomial must have positive integers as exponents and no variable may appear in the denominator.

Simplifying Rational Expressions

A **rational expression** is a fraction whose numerator and denominator are both polynomials. Remember from Lesson 8 that a polynomial is an algebraic expression in which variables must have positive integers as exponents, and no variable may appear in a denominator.

Because a rational expression is a fraction, a variable will likely appear in the denominator of the rational expression, but never in the denominator of an individual polynomial.

All of the rules that apply to simplifying fractions apply to simplifying rational expressions. Be careful when dividing by a variable. A variable represents an unknown value, and could cause you to divide by zero, which is not allowed. Whenever you divide by a factor containing a variable, you must determine what value will make the factor equal to zero and state as part of your answer that the zero-causing value is excluded.

Simplify the rational expression $\frac{2x+2}{x+1}$.

Begin by factoring the numerator and denominator completely.

$\frac{2x+2}{x+1} = \frac{2(x+1)}{x+1}$

Only entire identical factors can be cancelled. individual terms may not be cancelled. In this case, $x + 1$ appears as a factor in both the numerator and denominator.

$\frac{2(\cancel{x+1})}{\cancel{x+1}} = 2$

The rational expression simplifies to 2, but because we cannot divide by zero, we must state the values of x that are excluded. To do this, set each factor in the denominator of the original problem not equal to zero and solve for x. $x+1 \neq 0; x \neq -1$

The complete simplification of the rational expression is 2; $x \neq -1$.

① **Classwork**

Simplify. Remember to state any exclusions.

$\frac{2x}{6x^2}$

$\frac{\cancel{2}\cancel{x}}{{}_3\cancel{6}x\cancel{^2}} = \frac{1}{3x}; x \neq 0$

$\frac{6x^2+4x}{3x+2}$

$\frac{2x(\cancel{3x+2})}{\cancel{3x+2}} = 2x; x \neq -\frac{2}{3}$

$\frac{x^2+2x-3}{x^2+x-2}$

$\frac{(x+3)(\cancel{x-1})}{(x+2)(\cancel{x-1})} = \frac{x+3}{x+2}; x \neq -2, 1$

$\frac{x^2+6x+9}{x^2-9}$

$\frac{(\cancel{x+3})(x+3)}{(\cancel{x+3})(x-3)} = \frac{x+3}{x-3}; x \neq -3, 3$

Activities

② Simplify. Remember to state any exclusions.

$\frac{3x}{12x^2}$

$\frac{\cancel{3}\cancel{x}}{{}_4\cancel{12}x\cancel{^2}} = \frac{1}{4x}; x \neq 0$

$\frac{5x}{15x^2}$

$\frac{\cancel{5}\cancel{x}}{{}_3\cancel{15}x\cancel{^2}} = \frac{1}{3x}; x \neq 0$

$\frac{4x^2}{20x^3}$

$\frac{\cancel{4}\cancel{x^2}}{{}_5\cancel{20}x\cancel{^3}} = \frac{1}{5x}; x \neq 0$

③ Simplify. Remember to state any exclusions.

$\frac{3x^2+4x}{3x+4}$

$\frac{x(\cancel{3x+4})}{\cancel{3x+4}} = x; x \neq -\frac{4}{3}$

$\frac{6x+10}{3x+5}$

$\frac{2(\cancel{3x+5})}{\cancel{3x+5}} = 2; x \neq -\frac{5}{3}$

$\frac{12x^2+9x}{4x+3}$

$\frac{3x(\cancel{4x+3})}{\cancel{4x+3}} = 3x; x \neq -\frac{3}{4}$

$\frac{12x^2+22x}{6x+11}$

$\frac{2x(\cancel{6x+11})}{\cancel{6x+11}} = 2x; x \neq -\frac{11}{6}$

$\frac{14x^2-21x}{2x-3}$

$\frac{7x(\cancel{2x-3})}{\cancel{2x-3}} = 7x; x \neq \frac{3}{2}$

$\frac{20x^2-8x}{5x-2}$

$\frac{4x(\cancel{5x-2})}{\cancel{5x-2}} = 4x; x \neq \frac{2}{5}$

$\frac{x^2+3x-4}{x^2+2x-3}$

$\frac{(x+4)(\cancel{x-1})}{(x+3)(\cancel{x-1})} = \frac{x+4}{x+3}; x \neq -3, 1$

$\frac{x^2+4x-12}{x^2-4}$

$\frac{(x+6)(\cancel{x-2})}{(x+2)(\cancel{x-2})} = \frac{x+6}{x+2}; x \neq -2, 2$

$\frac{x^2-2x+1}{x^2-3x+2}$

$\frac{(x-1)(\cancel{x-1})}{(x-2)(\cancel{x-1})} = \frac{x-1}{x-2}; x \neq 1, 2$

$\frac{x^2-9x+20}{x^2+3x-28}$

$\frac{(\cancel{x-4})(x-5)}{(\cancel{x-4})(x+7)} = \frac{x-5}{x+7}; x \neq -7, 4$

$\frac{x^2+10x+16}{x^2+9x+8}$

$\frac{(\cancel{x+8})(x+2)}{(\cancel{x+8})(x+1)} = \frac{x+2}{x+1}; x \neq -8, -1$

$\frac{x^2-9}{x^2-6x+9}$

$\frac{(\cancel{x-3})(x+3)}{(\cancel{x-3})(x-3)} = \frac{x+3}{x-3}; x \neq 3$

④ Solve.

$\frac{3x}{4} - 1 = -7$

$\frac{3x}{4} = -6$

$\cancel{4}\left(\frac{3x}{\cancel{4}}\right) = 4(-6)$

$3x = -24$

$x = -8$

$\frac{3x}{2} - 2 = 4x + 3$

$\frac{3x}{2} = 4x + 5$

$\cancel{2}\left(\frac{3x}{\cancel{2}}\right) = 2(4x+5)$

$3x = 8x + 10$

$-5x = 10$

$x = -2$

$\frac{3x-1}{4} - 6 = 5x - 2$

$\frac{3x-1}{4} = 5x + 4$

$\cancel{4}\left(\frac{3x-1}{\cancel{4}}\right) = 4(5x+4)$

$3x - 1 = 20x + 16$

$-17x = 17$

$x = -1$

⑤ Solve.

The fuel efficiency, f, of a car is the average number of miles a car can run on 1 gallon of gasoline. Write an equation in terms of f, g, and m, that can be used to determine the number of gallons of gasoline, g, a car will need to travel a given number of miles, m. Using this equation, how many gallons of gas will a car with a fuel efficiency of 33 miles per gallon need to complete a 858-mile trip?

$g = \frac{m}{f}$ $\quad g = \frac{858 \text{ miles}}{33 \text{ miles per gallon}} = 26 \text{ gallons}$

Factoring Special Products Worksheet 39

① Factor.

$x^2 - 121$	$25x^2 - 27$
$(x+11)(x-11)$	$(5x+3\sqrt{3})(5x-3\sqrt{3})$
$x^2 - 64$	$4x^2 - 18$
$(x+8)(x-8)$	$(2x+3\sqrt{2})(2x-3\sqrt{2})$
$81x^2 - 25$	$169x^2 - 121$
$(9x+5)(9x-5)$	$(13x+11)(13x-11)$
$25x^2 - 64$	$x^2 - 53$
$(5x+8)(5x-8)$	$(x+\sqrt{53})(x-\sqrt{53})$
$9x^2 - 169$	$4x^2 - 17$
$(3x+13)(3x-13)$	$(2x+\sqrt{17})(2x-\sqrt{17})$
$49x^2 - 100$	$49x^2 - 112x + 64$
$(7x+10)(7x-10)$	$(7x-8)^2$
$36x^2 - 25$	$9x^2 + 12x + 4$
$(6x+5)(6x-5)$	$(3x+2)^2$

Teaching Tips, Cont.

- Ask the students what the difference is between a polynomial and a rational expression. (Rational expressions have variables in the denominator; polynomials do not.)
- Emphasize that rational expressions are fractions with two separate polynomials — one in the numerator and one in the denominator.
- Teach simplifying rational expressions from the teaching box.
- Ask the students if it is mathematically possible to divide by zero. (No.) Tell them that the same rule applies to rational expressions. Each factor in the denominator of the original problem must be set equal to zero to determine what values of the variable cannot be possible answers. These values must be stated as exclusions as part of the answer.
- Complete the Classwork exercises. Have some students work the problems on the board for the class and explain their answers. All students should work the problems in their books.
- If you plan to administer Exam 2 following Lesson 80 and Test 8, spend a few minutes reviewing for the Exam.

Assignment

- Complete Lesson 78, Activities 2-5.

Lesson 79

Concepts
- Adding rational expressions
- Subtracting rational expressions
- Exclusions
- Inequalities
- Fractions

Learning Objectives
The student will be able to:
- Find a common denominator for rational expressions
- Add rational expressions
- Subtract rational expressions
- State the exclusions for equations containing rational expressions

Materials Needed
- Student Book, Lesson 79

Teaching Tips
- Review rational expressions (See Lesson 78)
- Ask the students what must be true for any two fractions to be added or subtracted. (The denominators must be the same.)
- Teach adding and subtracting rational expressions from the teaching box.
- Remind the students that the numerators are added or subtracted, but the denominators stay the same.

Lesson 79

Adding and Subtracting Rational Expressions

When adding or subtracting rational expressions, follow the same rules for adding or subtracting fractions. You may only add or subtract rational expressions that have a common denominator. Simplify the answer if necessary. As in the previous lesson, you must state any exclusions.

$\frac{1}{x+2}+\frac{1}{x+2}=$
The common denominator is $x + 2$.

Because the denominators match, add the numerators and write the answer as a single fraction.
$\frac{1+1}{x+2}=\frac{2}{x+2}$
Because a variable appears in the denominator, you must state exclusions as part of the answer.
$\frac{2}{x+2}; x \neq -2$

Notice that the fraction cannot be reduced any further. The 2 in the numerator cannot cancel with the 2 in the denominator. Remember that only whole factors can cancel with other whole factors. Individual terms cannot cancel each other.

① **Classwork.**
Solve. Remember to state any exclusions.

$\frac{1}{x-1}+\frac{1}{x-1}=$
$\frac{1+1}{x-1}=\frac{2}{x-1}; x \neq 1$

$\frac{2x}{x+3}-\frac{x+5}{x+3}=$
$\frac{2x-(x+5)}{x+3}=\frac{x-5}{x+3}; x \neq -3$

Activities
② State whether or not each problem can be solved as written and explain why.

$\frac{5}{x+3}+\frac{2}{x-3}=$
No. The denominators have opposite signs.

$\frac{4}{x+4}-\frac{4}{x+2}=$
No. The numerators match, but the denominators are different.

$\frac{5}{x-4}+\frac{7}{x-4}=$
Yes. The denominators are the same.

$\frac{x}{x+2}-\frac{3x}{2+x}=$
Yes. The denominators have the same value.

$\frac{2x}{x^2+2x+1}+\frac{x}{(x+1)^2}=$
Yes. The denominators have the same value.

$\frac{6}{2x-1}-\frac{3}{2x-1}=$
Yes. The denominators are the same.

$\frac{1}{2x+1}+\frac{2}{2x+1}=$
Yes. The denominators have the same value.

$\frac{3x}{x-4}-\frac{7x}{x-5}=$
No. The denominators are different.

$\frac{2}{2x+2}+\frac{2}{3x+3}=$
No. The denominators factor to have 1 factor in common, but not all factors are common.

③ Solve. Remember to state any exclusions.

$\frac{5}{x+3}+\frac{2}{x+3}=$

$\frac{5+2}{x+3}=\frac{7}{x+3}; x \neq -3$

$\frac{4x}{x-5}-\frac{x}{x-5}=$

$\frac{4x-x}{x-5}=\frac{3x}{x-5}; x \neq 5$

$\frac{x+1}{2x+3}+\frac{3x-2}{2x+3}=$

$\frac{(x+1)+(3x-2)}{2x+3}=$

$\frac{4x-1}{2x+3}; x \neq -\frac{3}{2}$

$\frac{3}{x+4}-\frac{4}{x+4}=$

$\frac{3-4}{x+4}=-\frac{1}{x+4}; x \neq -4$

$\frac{2}{2x+3}+\frac{x}{2x+3}=$

$\frac{2+x}{2x+3}; x \neq -\frac{3}{2}$

$\frac{3x-7}{x-5}-\frac{x+3}{x-5}=$

$\frac{(3x-7)-(x+3)}{x-5}=\frac{2x-10}{x-5}=$

$\frac{2\cancel{(x-5)}}{\cancel{x-5}}=2; x \neq 5$

$\frac{5}{x-4}+\frac{7}{x-4}=$

$\frac{5+7}{x-4}=\frac{12}{x-4}; x \neq 4$

$\frac{5x+3}{2x-1}-\frac{2x-2}{2x-1}=$

$\frac{(5x+3)-(2x-2)}{2x-1}=$

$\frac{3x+5}{2x-1}; x \neq \frac{1}{2}$

$\frac{2x}{x^2+2x+1}+\frac{x}{(x+1)^2}=$

$\frac{2x+x}{x^2+2x+1}=$

$\frac{3x}{x^2+2x+1}; x \neq -1$

④ Solve.

$\frac{3x}{5}+1<-8$

$\frac{3x}{5}<-9$

$\cancel{5}\left(\frac{3x}{\cancel{5}}\right)<5(-9)$

$3x<-45$

$x<-15$

$\frac{4x}{3}-1<3x+4$

$\frac{4x}{3}<3x+5$

$\cancel{3}\left(\frac{4x}{\cancel{3}}\right)<3(3x+5)$

$4x<9x+15$

$-5x<15$

$-x<3$

$x>-3$

$\frac{5x-4}{2}-7>4x-3$

$\frac{5x-4}{2}>4x+4$

$\cancel{2}\left(\frac{5x-4}{\cancel{2}}\right)>2(4x+4)$

$5x-4>8x+8$

$-3x>12$

$-x>4$

$x<-4$

⑤ Solve.

A car rental company charges $89 per day (or portion of a day) on a rental of a mid-size SUV. The same SUV is available for a weekly rate of $329. After how many days does the per-day cost exceed the weekly rate?

Let d = the number of days in the rental period.

$89d>329$

$d>3.7$

On day 4, the per-day cost exceeds the weekly rental rate.

Teaching Tips, Cont.

- Tell the students to pay special attention to the signs when subtracting a polynomial.
- Remind the students to factor their answers completely.
- Tell the students to list all exclusions as part of their answer anytime a variable appears in the denominator. The factors appearing in the denominator of the original problem should be used to determine any exclusions.
- Complete the Classwork exercises. Have some students work the problems on the board for the class and explain their answers. All students should work the problems in their books.
- If you plan to administer Exam 2 following Lesson 80 and Test 8, spend a few minutes reviewing for the Exam.

Assignment

- Complete Lesson 79, Activities 2-5.

Lesson 80

Concepts
- Multiplying rational expressions
- Exclusions
- Factoring trinomials
- Factoring completely
- Factoring the difference of two squares
- Factoring perfect square trinomials
- Factoring by grouping

Learning Objectives
The student will be able to:
- Multiply rational expressions
- Factor polynomials in rational expressions to cancel terms before multiplying
- State the exclusions in the product of rational expressions

Materials Needed
- Student Book, Lesson 80
- Worksheet 40

Teaching Tips
➢ Review simplifying rational expressions. (See Lesson 78)

➢ Review adding and subtracting rational expressions. (See Lesson 79)

➢ Teach multiplying rational expressions from the teaching box. Tell the students that the process is much easier if they factor each polynomial first and cancel terms.

➢ Remind the students that only entire factors can be cancelled. Individual terms cannot be cancelled.

Multiplying Rational Expressions

When multiplying rational expressions, follow the same rules for multiplying fractions. You will find it easier to factor each numerator and denominator and cancel like factors before you multiply. Remember to state any exclusions found in the original denominators.

$\frac{5x+10}{2x^2+6x}\cdot\frac{2x^2-2x}{x^2+x-2}=$

Factor each polynomial and cancel like factors.

$\frac{5\cancel{(x+2)}}{\cancel{2x}(x+3)}\cdot\frac{\cancel{2x}\cancel{(x-1)}}{\cancel{(x+2)}\cancel{(x-1)}}=\frac{5}{x+3}$

Identify values of x that must be excluded.

$\frac{5}{x+3}; x\neq -3,-2,0,1$

Remember to factor all denominators in the original problem to identify all exclusions.

① **Classwork**

Solve. Remember to state any exclusions.

$\frac{4x-8}{3x^2+6x}\cdot\frac{3x^2+9x}{x^2+x-6}=$

$\frac{4\cancel{(x-2)}}{\cancel{3x}(x+2)}\cdot\frac{\cancel{3x}\cancel{(x+3)}}{\cancel{(x+3)}\cancel{(x-2)}}=$

$\frac{4}{x+2}; x\neq -3,-2,0,2$

$\frac{2x^2+2x}{10x^2+15x}\cdot\frac{6x^2+9x}{3x^2-3x-6}=$

$\frac{2\cancel{x}\cancel{(x+1)}}{5\cancel{x}\cancel{(2x+3)}}\cdot\frac{\cancel{3}x\cancel{(2x+3)}}{\cancel{3}\cancel{(x+1)}(x-2)}=\frac{2x}{5(x-2)}=$

$\frac{2x}{5x-10}; x\neq -\frac{3}{2},-1,0,2$

Activities

② Solve. Remember to state any exclusions.

$\frac{3x+12}{x^2+5x}\cdot\frac{x^2-3x}{x^2+x-12}=$

$\frac{3\cancel{(x+4)}}{\cancel{x}(x+5)}\cdot\frac{\cancel{x}\cancel{(x-3)}}{\cancel{(x+4)}\cancel{(x-3)}}=$

$\frac{3}{x+5}; x\neq -5,-4,0,3$

$\frac{6x+42}{8x^2+16x}\cdot\frac{4x^2+8x}{x^2+3x-28}=$

$\frac{{}_3\cancel{6}\cancel{(x+7)}}{{}_2\cancel{8x}\cancel{(x+2)}}\cdot\frac{\cancel{4x}\cancel{(x+2)}}{\cancel{(x+7)}(x-4)}=$

$\frac{3}{x-4}; x\neq -7,-2,0,4$

$\frac{x^2-3x-10}{2x^2+7x+3}\cdot\frac{2x^2-x-1}{x^2+x-2}=$

$\frac{(x-5)\cancel{(x+2)}}{\cancel{(2x+1)}(x+3)}\cdot\frac{\cancel{(2x+1)}\cancel{(x-1)}}{\cancel{(x+2)}\cancel{(x-1)}}=$

$\frac{x-5}{x+3}; x\neq -3,-2,-\frac{1}{2},1$

$\frac{8x^2+40x}{6x^3-12x^2}\cdot\frac{3x^2-6x}{2x^2+10x}=$

$\frac{{}_2\cancel{8x}\cancel{(x+5)}}{{}_x\cancel{6x^2}\cancel{(x-2)}}\cdot\frac{\cancel{3x}\cancel{(x-2)}}{\cancel{2x}\cancel{(x+5)}}=$

$\frac{2}{x}; x\neq -5,0,2$

$\frac{3x+21}{3x^2+5x-12}\cdot\frac{6x^2-8x}{x^2+5x-14}=$

$\frac{3\cancel{(x+7)}}{\cancel{(3x-4)}(x+3)}\cdot\frac{2x\cancel{(3x-4)}}{\cancel{(x+7)}(x-2)}=\frac{3}{x+3}\cdot\frac{2x}{x-2}=$

$\frac{6x}{x^2+x-6}; x\neq -7,-3,\frac{4}{3},2$

$\frac{3x^2-5x-2}{2x^2+3x-9}\cdot\frac{x^2+2x-3}{x^2-3x+2}=$

$\frac{(3x+1)\cancel{(x-2)}}{(2x-3)\cancel{(x+3)}}\cdot\frac{\cancel{(x+3)}\cancel{(x-1)}}{\cancel{(x-2)}\cancel{(x-1)}}=$

$\frac{3x+1}{2x-3}; x\neq -3,1,\frac{3}{2},2$

③ Factor each polynomial completely.

$x^2-9x+20$
$(x-5)(x-4)$

$2x^2+2x-24$
$2(x^2+x-12)=$
$2(x+4)(x-3)$

x^2-x-72
$(x+8)(x-9)$

$x^2-4x-21$
$(x-7)(x+3)$

$15x^2+34xy-16y^2$
$(5x-2y)(3x+8y)$

$2x^3+5x^2y-3xy^2$
$x(2x^2+5xy-3y^2)=$
$x(x+3y)(2x-y)$

x^2+9x+8
$(x+8)(x+1)$

$25x^2+90xy-40y^2$
$5(5x^2+18xy-8y^2)=$
$5(x+4y)(5x-2y)$

x^3+27
$(x+3)(x^2-3x+9)$

$6x^2+19x+15$
$(3x+5)(2x+3)$

$6x^2+11xy-10y^2$
$(3x-2y)(2x+5y)$

x^3-216
$(x-6)(x^2+6x+36)$

$15x^2+14x-8$
$(5x-2)(3x+4)$

$x^2-14x+49$
$(x-7)^2$

$64x^3+27$
$(4x+3)(16x^2-12x+9)$

$2x^3-18x$
$2x(x^2-9)=$
$2x(x+3)(x-3)$

$x^2+22x+121$
$(x+11)^2$

$6x^4-150x^2$
$6x^2(x^2-25)=$
$6x^2(x+5)(x-5)$

$5x+xy+3y+15$
$(5x+xy)+(3y+15)$
$x(5+y)+3(y+5)$
$(x+3)(y+5)$

$9x^2-12x+4$
$(3x-2)^2$

x^4-36x^2
$x^2(x^2-36)=$
$x^2(x+6)(x-6)$

x^5-15x^3
$x^3(x^2-15)=$
$x^3(x+\sqrt{15})(x-\sqrt{15})$

$-x+xy+4y-4$
$(-x+xy)+(4y-4)$
$x(-1+y)+4(y-1)$
$(x+4)(y-1)$

$3x+xy-7y-21$
$(3x+xy)+(-7y-21)$
$x(3+y)-7(y+3)$
$(x-7)(y+3)$

$8x+xy+6y+48$
$(8x+xy)+(6y+48)$
$x(8+y)+6(y+8)$
$(x+6)(y+8)$

$9x+xy-5y-45$
$(9x+xy)+(-5y-45)$
$x(9+y)-5(y+9)$
$(x-5)(y+9)$

$-8x+xy+2y-16$
$(-8x+xy)+(2y-16)$
$x(-8+y)+2(y-8)$
$(x+2)(y-8)$

Rational Expressions Worksheet 40

① Solve. Remember to state any exclusions.

$$\frac{5}{x+5}+\frac{3}{x+5}=$$
$$\frac{5+3}{x+5}=\frac{8}{x+5};x\neq -5$$

$$\frac{7x}{x-2}-\frac{3x}{x-2}=$$
$$\frac{7x-3x}{x-2}=\frac{4x}{x-2};x\neq 2$$

$$\frac{x+1}{2x+7}+\frac{3x-2}{2x+7}=$$
$$\frac{(x+1)+(3x-2)}{2x+7}=$$
$$\frac{4x-1}{2x+7};x\neq -\tfrac{7}{2}$$

$$\frac{3x+12}{5x^2+11x-12}\cdot\frac{10x^2-8x}{x^2+2x-8}=$$
$$\frac{3\cancel{(x+4)}}{\cancel{(5x-4)}(x+3)}\cdot\frac{2x\cancel{(5x-4)}}{\cancel{(x+4)}(x-2)}=\frac{3}{x+3}\cdot\frac{2x}{x-2}=$$
$$\frac{6x}{x^2+x-6};x\neq -4,-3,\tfrac{4}{5},2$$

$$\frac{3x^2-17x-6}{2x^2-x-3}\cdot\frac{x^2-1}{x^2-7x+6}=$$
$$\frac{(3x+1)\cancel{(x-6)}}{(2x-3)\cancel{(x+1)}}\cdot\frac{\cancel{(x+1)}\cancel{(x-1)}}{\cancel{(x-6)}\cancel{(x-1)}}=$$
$$\frac{3x+1}{2x-3};x\neq -1,1,\tfrac{3}{2},6$$

$$\frac{12x+42}{8x^2+24x}\cdot\frac{4x^2+12x}{2x^2-x-28}=$$
$$\frac{{}_3\cancel{6}\cancel{(2x+7)}}{{}_{\cancel{2}}\cancel{8x}\cancel{(x+3)}}\cdot\frac{\cancel{4x}\cancel{(x+3)}}{\cancel{(2x+7)}(x-4)}=$$
$$\frac{3}{x-4};x\neq -\tfrac{7}{2},-3,0,4$$

$$\frac{3x}{x+4}-\frac{4}{x+4}=$$
$$\frac{3x-4}{x+4};x\neq -4$$

$$\frac{2}{2x+3}+\frac{4x}{2x+3}=$$
$$\frac{2+4x}{2x+3};x\neq -\tfrac{3}{2}$$

$$\frac{3x-7}{x-11}-\frac{2x+3}{x-11}=$$
$$\frac{(3x-7)-(2x+3)}{x-11}=$$
$$\frac{x-10}{x-11};x\neq 11$$

$$\frac{9x+12}{x^2+5x}\cdot\frac{2x^2-3x}{6x^2-x-12}=$$
$$\frac{3\cancel{(3x+4)}}{\cancel{x}(x+5)}\cdot\frac{\cancel{x}\cancel{(2x-3)}}{\cancel{(3x+4)}\cancel{(2x-3)}}=$$
$$\frac{3}{x+5};x\neq -5,-\tfrac{4}{3},0,\tfrac{3}{2}$$

$$\frac{5x^2-23x-10}{2x^2+7x+3}\cdot\frac{8x^2+2x-1}{20x^2+3x-2}=$$
$$\frac{(x-5)\cancel{(5x+2)}}{\cancel{(2x+1)}(x+3)}\cdot\frac{\cancel{(2x+1)}\cancel{(4x-1)}}{\cancel{(5x+2)}\cancel{(4x-1)}}=$$
$$\frac{x-5}{x+3};x\neq -3,-\tfrac{1}{2},-\tfrac{2}{5},\tfrac{1}{4}$$

$$\frac{16x^2+40x}{18x^3-12x^2}\cdot\frac{9x^2-6x}{4x^2+10x}=$$
$$\frac{{}_{2}\cancel{4}\cancel{8x}\cancel{(2x+5)}}{{}_{\cancel{2}x}\cancel{6x^2}\cancel{(3x-2)}}\cdot\frac{\cancel{3x}\cancel{(3x-2)}}{\cancel{2x}\cancel{(2x+5)}}=$$
$$\frac{2}{x};x\neq -\tfrac{5}{2},0,\tfrac{2}{3}$$

Teaching Tips, Cont.

- Remind students to find any exclusions based on the factors in the denominator of the original problem. If they use the denominator of the answer, they will likely miss some of the exclusions.
- Complete the Classwork exercises. Have some students work the problems on the board for the class and explain their answers. All students should work the problems in their books.
- If you plan to administer Exam 2, spend a few minutes reviewing.
- Review for Test 8 using worksheets 36-40. These worksheets were assigned in previous lessons.
- Review for Exam 2 using worksheets 1-40.

Assignments

- Complete Lesson 80, Activities 2-3.
- Worksheet 40.
- Study for Test 8 (Lessons 68-77).

Test 8

Testing Objectives
The student will:

- Factor out monomials
- Factor the difference of two squares
- Factor perfect square trinomials
- Factor trinomials
- Factor the difference of two cubes
- Factor by grouping
- Factor completely

Materials Needed
- Test 8
- *It's College Test Prep Time!* from the Student Book
- Exploring Math through... Basketball from Student Book

Teaching Tips
- ➢ Administer Test 8, allowing the students 30-40 minutes to complete the test.
- ➢ When all students are finished taking the test, introduce *It's College Test Prep Time* from the student book. This page may be completed in class or assigned as homework.

① Factor each polynomial completely. **21 points**

$7x - 21$ → $7(x-3)$

$x^2 - 64$ → $(x+8)(x-8)$

$x^2 + x - 12$ → $(x-3)(x+4)$

$6x + 8$ → $2(3x+4)$

$49x^2 - 16$ → $(7x+4)(7x-4)$

$x^2 + 11x + 28$ → $(x+4)(x+7)$

$15x - 24$ → $3(5x-8)$

$9x^2 - 25$ → $(3x+5)(3x-5)$

$x^2 - 3x - 10$ → $(x+2)(x-5)$

$12x^2 - 9x + 15$ → $3(4x^2 - 3x + 5)$

$16x^2 - 13$ → $(4x+\sqrt{13})(4x-\sqrt{13})$

$25x^2 - 30x + 9$ → $(5x-3)^2$

$15x^2 + 20x + 5$ → $5(3x^2+4x+1) =$ $5(3x+1)(x+1)$

$9x^2 - 50$ → $(3x+5\sqrt{2})(3x-5\sqrt{2})$

$4x^2 + 28x + 49$ → $(2x+7)^2$

$22x^3 + 33x^2 - 77x$ → $11x(2x^2+3x-7)$

$9x^2 + 48x + 64$ → $(3x+8)^2$

$x^2 - 24x + 144$ → $(x-12)^2$

$x^2 - 100$ → $(x+10)(x-10)$

$25x^2 - 90x + 81$ → $(5x-9)^2$

$x^2 + 14x + 49$ → $(x+7)^2$

② Factor each polynomial completely. **15 points**

$5x^2 + 23x + 12$
ac = 60; factors that add to 23 are 20 and 3

	x	4
$5x$	$5x^2$	$20x$
3	$3x$	12

$(5x+3)(x+4)$

$5x^2 + 7xy - 6y^2$
ac = -30; factors that add to 7 are 10 and -3

	x	$2y$
$5x$	$5x^2$	$10xy$
$-3y$	$-3xy$	$-6y^2$

$(5x-3y)(x+2y)$

$6x^2 + 7xy - 10y^2$
ac = -60; factors that add to 7 are 12 and -5

	x	$2y$
$6x$	$6x^2$	$12xy$
$-5y$	$-5xy$	$-10y^2$

$(6x-5y)(x+2y)$

$6x^3 + 15x^2y + 6xy^2$
Factor out 3*x*.
$3x(2x^2+5xy+2y^2)$
ac = 4; factors that add to 5 are 1 and 4

	$2x$	y
x	$2x^2$	xy
$2y$	$4xy$	$2y^2$

$3x(x+2y)(2x+y)$

$8x^3 + 52x^2y + 60xy^2$
Factor out 4*x*.
$4x(2x^2+13xy+15y^2)$
ac = 30; factors that add to 13 are 10 and 3

	$2x$	$3y$
x	$2x^2$	$3xy$
$5y$	$10xy$	$15y^2$

$4x(x+5y)(2x+3y)$

$21x^3 + 49x^2y + 14xy^2$
Factor out 7*x*.
$7x(3x^2+7xy+2y^2)$
ac = 6; factors that add to 7 are 1 and 6

	$3x$	y
x	$3x^2$	xy
$2y$	$6xy$	$2y^2$

$7x(x+2y)(3x+y)$

$x^4 - 9x^2$
$x^2(x^2-9) =$
$x^2(x+3)(x-3)$

$2x^3 - 128x$
$2x(x^2-64) =$
$2x(x+8)(x-8)$

$6x + xy + 6y + 36$
$(6x+xy)+(6y+36) =$
$x(6+y)+6(y+6) =$
$(x+6)(y+6)$

$x^3 + 125$
$a^3 = x^3$ so $a = x$.
$b^3 = 125$ so $b = 5$.
$(x+5)(x^2-5x+25)$

$x^3 - 8$
$a^3 = x^3$ so $a = x$. $b^3 = 8$
so $b = 2$.
$(x-2)(x^2+2x+4)$

$-3x + xy - 4y + 12$
$(-3x+xy)+(-4y+12)$
$x(-3+y)-4(y-3)$
$(x-4)(y-3)$

$x^3 + 64$
$a^3 = x^3$ so $a = x$. $b^3 = 64$
so $b = 4$.
$(x+4)(x^2-4x+16)$

$x^3 - 1$
$a^3 = x^3$ so $a = x$. $b^3 = 1$
so $b =$.
$(x-1)(x^2+x+1)$

$2x + 10xy + 15y + 3$
$(2x+10xy)+(15y+3)$
$2x(1+5y)+3(5y+1)$
$(2x+3)(5y+1)$

36 points total

It's College Test Prep Time!

1. Given $-1 < x < 0$, which of the following statements is FALSE?
   Choose a value and substitute.

A.	$x < x^2$	$-\frac{1}{2} < \left(-\frac{1}{2}\right)^2 \Rightarrow -\frac{1}{2} < \frac{1}{4}$ true
B.	$2x < x$	$2\left(-\frac{1}{2}\right) < -\frac{1}{2} \Rightarrow -1 < -\frac{1}{2}$ true
C.	$\frac{1}{x} < x$	$\frac{1}{-\frac{1}{2}} < -\frac{1}{2} \Rightarrow -2 < -\frac{1}{2}$ true
D.	$\frac{x}{2} < x$	$\frac{-\frac{1}{2}}{2} < -\frac{1}{2} \Rightarrow -\frac{1}{4} < -\frac{1}{2}$ false
E.	$3x < x$	$3\left(-\frac{1}{2}\right) < -\frac{1}{2} \Rightarrow -\frac{3}{2} < -\frac{1}{2}$ true

2. For all real numbers *a*, *b*, *c*, and *d*, let (*a*, *b*) ⌘ (*c*, *d*) be defined as (*a*, *b*) ⌘ (*c*, *d*) = *ad* + *bc*. If (2, 3) ⌘ (*x*, 4) = 29, find the value of *x*.

A.	5	
B.	$5\frac{3}{4}$	$a = 2;\ b = 3;\ c = x;\ d = 4$ so $2(4) + 3x = 29$
C.	7	$8 + 3x = 29;\ 3x = 21;\ x = 7$
D.	$7\frac{2}{5}$	
E.	$8\frac{1}{2}$	

3. For all real numbers *x*, let 🗁*x* be defined as 🗁*x* = 2 − x. What is the value of 🗁(🗁*x*)?

A.	x	🗁(2 − x) = 2 − (2 − x) = 2 − 2 + *x* = *x*
B.	$2 - x$	
C.	$4 - x$	
D.	$x + 2$	
E.	$x + 4$	

Exploring Math through... Basketball

Most sports involve math in ways the players do not even consider. Basketball is no exception. While the obvious use of math includes scoring and marking the lines on the court, there are numerous other uses of math that have become vital to franchise success on the professional level.

One of the biggest areas that basketball uses math is in statistics. This behind-the-scene use of math is used to rank teams and players on all levels, but it is crucial on the professional level.

In basketball, simple statistics are used to calculate the number of possessions, points, rebounds, and assists per game. Math is also used to do more in-depth calculations in areas such as offensive and defensive ratings, floor percentage, play percentage, and field goal percentage. Sports statisticians use math to calculate expected win percentages for teams. This allows sportscasters to tell which team is favored to win and by how many points.

One area that professional basketball depends on math is calculating the trade value of a player. Teams must know what each player involved in a trade is worth so they can negotiate the best trade deal possible for the team.

Teaching Tips, Cont.

- Have students read the Exploring Math feature for Lessons 81-90.
- If you plan to administer Exam 2, review as time permits when all students have finished Test 8.
- Review for Exam 2 using worksheets 1-40.

Assignments

- Complete *It's College Test Prep Time!*
- Read Exploring Math through... Basketball
- Study for Exam 2 (Lessons 1-77)

Exam 2

Testing Objectives

The student will:

- Add, subtract, multiply, and divide signed numbers
- Simplify exponential expressions
- Follow proper order of operations
- Solve absolute values
- Add, subtract, multiply, and divide roots
- Translate words into mathematical expressions
- Evaluate algebraic expressions
- Add and subtract polynomials
- Multiply and divide monomials
- Solve algebraic equations
- Identify properties of equality
- Solve algebraic equations with roots
- Solve algebraic equations with absolute values
- Calculate the slope between two points
- Write equations of a line
- Identify lines as parallel or perpendicular
- Solve inequalities with absolute values
- Solve systems of equations
- Multiply and divide polynomials
- Factor polynomials completely

Materials Needed

- Exam 2

Teaching Tips

➢ Administer Exam 2, allowing the students 75-90 minutes to complete the test.

① Solve, using the rules for signed numbers. **4 points**

$(+275) + (-736) = -(736 - 275) = -461$ $(-11)(800) = -8{,}800$

$(-167) - (+526) = -(526 + 167) = -693$ $(264) \div (-33) = -8$

② Simplify the expressions. You do not have to solve exponents greater than 3. **9 points**

$(42 \div 6)^2 = 7^2 = 49$ $10^{32} \div 10^{29} = 10^3 = 1{,}000$ $\left(\frac{5}{4}\right)^{-3} =$

$6^{-3} =$ $12^{-2} = \left(\frac{1}{12}\right)^2 = \frac{1^2}{12^2} = \frac{1}{144}$ $\left(\frac{4}{5}\right)^3 = \frac{4^3}{5^3} = \frac{64}{125}$

$\left(\frac{1}{6}\right)^3 = \frac{1^3}{6^3} = \frac{1}{216}$

$23^5 \times 23^{12} = 23^{17}$ $\left(\frac{2}{5}\right)^3 = \frac{2^3}{5^3} = \frac{8}{125}$ $54^0 = 1$

$(12 \div 4)^3 = 3^3 = 27$

③ Simplify each expression, following the proper order of operations. **2 points**

$2^3 \times 5 \div (22 - 17) - 9 = 2^3 \times 5 \div 5 - 9 = 8 \times 5 \div 5 - 9 = 40 \div 5 - 9 = 8 - 9 = -1$

$(6^2 - (36 - 22) + 6) \div 7 = (36 - 14 + 6) \div 7 = (22 + 6) \div 7 = 28 \div 7 = 4$

④ Solve, using the rules of absolute values. **6 points**

$|47| + |-119| = 47 + 119 = 166$ $-|33| + |-82| = -33 + 82 = 49$ $-|141 - 72| + |98 - 57| = -69 + 41 = -28$

$|51| - |-78| = 51 - 78 = -27$ $-|-178| - |-199| = -178 - 199 = -377$ $-|265 + 133| - |444 - 217| = -398 - 227 = -625$

⑤ Solve the following roots. **6 points**

$\sqrt{33} + \sqrt{33} = 2\sqrt{33}$ $(\sqrt{8})(\sqrt{2}) = \sqrt{8 \times 2} = \sqrt{16} = \sqrt{4 \times 4} = 4$

$22\sqrt[3]{49} - 15\sqrt[3]{49} = 7\sqrt[3]{49}$ $51\sqrt[3]{54} \div 3\sqrt[3]{2} = (51 \div 3)\sqrt[3]{54 \div 2} = 17\sqrt[3]{27} = 17\sqrt[3]{3 \times 3 \times 3} = 17 \times 3 = 51$

$(5\sqrt{12})(6\sqrt{2}) = (5 \times 6)\sqrt{12 \times 2} = 30\sqrt{24} = 30\sqrt{2 \times 2 \times 2 \times 3} = 60\sqrt{6}$

$20 \div \sqrt{5} = \sqrt{20 \times 20} \div \sqrt{5} = \sqrt{400 \div 5} = \sqrt{80} = \sqrt{4 \times 4 \times 5} = 4\sqrt{5}$

⑥ Translate the following words into a mathematical expression. **6 points**

The quotient of a number and 6 $x \div 6$ The product of 14 and a number $14x$

45 less than a number $x - 45$ The ratio of a number to 7 $x \div 7$

A number less than 125 $125 - x$ A number increased by 87 $x + 87$

⑦ Evaluate each algebraic expression. **2 points**

$7b - 5$ for $b = -3$ $2r^2 - 3r + 6$ for $r = -2$

$7(-3) - 5 = -21 - 5 = -26$ $2(-2)^2 - 3(-2) + 6 = 2(4) + 6 + 6 = 8 + 6 + 6 = 14 + 6 = 20$

⑧ Solve. **6 points**

$$\begin{array}{r} 9x^2 + 4x + 7 \\ +\ 3x^2 + 5x + 2 \\ \hline 12x^2 + 9x + 9 \end{array} \qquad \begin{array}{r} 6x^2 + 5x + 4 \\ +3x^2 - 3x - 7 \\ \hline 9x^2 + 2x - 3 \end{array} \qquad \begin{array}{r} 2x^2 \qquad + 6 \\ +6x^2 + 3x - 4 \\ \hline 8x^2 + 3x - 2 \end{array}$$

$$\begin{array}{r} (7x^2 + 4x + 5) \\ -(3x^2 + 2x + 2) \\ \hline 4x^2 + 2x + 3 \end{array} \qquad \begin{array}{r} (6x^2 - 2x + 7) \\ -(x^2 - 5x) \\ \hline 5x^2 + 3x + 7 \end{array} \qquad \begin{array}{r} (4x^2 \qquad - 5) \\ -(6x^2 - 8x - 5) \\ \hline -2x^2 + 8x \end{array}$$

⑨ Solve. **8 points**

$5a^3(7ab^2) = (5 \cdot 7)(a^{3+1})(b^2) = 35a^4b^2$ $23e^3 \div e = \frac{23e^3}{e} = 23e^{3-1} = 23e^2$

$4c^2(9c^2d^2) = (4 \cdot 9)(c^{2+2})(d^2) = 36c^4d^2$ $54f^5g^4 \div 9f^2g^3 = \frac{54f^5g^4}{9f^2g^3} = 6f^{5-2}g^{4-3} = 6f^3g$

$54^{\frac{1}{3}} = \sqrt[3]{54} = \sqrt[3]{2 \cdot 27} = \sqrt[3]{2 \cdot 3^3} = 3\sqrt[3]{2}$ $75^{\frac{1}{2}} = \sqrt{75} = \sqrt{3 \cdot 5^2} = 5\sqrt{3}$

$72^{\frac{1}{2}} = \sqrt{72} = \sqrt{2 \cdot 6^2} = 6\sqrt{2}$ $24^{\frac{1}{3}} = \sqrt[3]{3 \cdot 8} = \sqrt[3]{3 \cdot 2^3} = 2\sqrt[3]{3}$

⑩ Solve each algebraic equation. Identify the property of equality used in each step. **9 points**

$11x - 5 = 7x + 19$

$11x - 5 - 7x = 7x + 19 - 7x \Rightarrow 4x - 5 = 19$

Subtraction property

$4x - 5 + 5 = 19 + 5 \Rightarrow 4x = 24$

Addition property

$4x \div 4 = 24 \div 4 \Rightarrow x = 6$

Division property

$8(x + 2) = 5x + 43$

$8x + 16 = 5x + 43$

Distributive property

$8x + 16 - 5x = 5x + 43 - 5x \Rightarrow 3x + 16 = 43$

Subtraction property

$3x + 16 - 16 = 43 - 16 \Rightarrow 3x = 27$

Subtraction property

$3x \div 3 = 27 \div 3 \Rightarrow x = 9$

Division property

Note: These are sample methods of solution. Other uses of properties of equality are acceptable.

⑪ Solve each algebraic equation. **2 points**

$\frac{8}{x} + \frac{7}{x^2} = \frac{5}{x} + \frac{25}{x^2}$

$\frac{8}{x}(x^2) + \frac{7}{x^2}(x^2) = \frac{5}{x}(x^2) + \frac{25}{x^2}(x^2)$

$8x + 7 = 5x + 25$

$3x + 7 = 25$

$3x = 18$

$x = 6$

$\frac{1}{8}x - 0.5 = 2$

$8(\frac{1}{8}x) - 8(0.5) = 8(2)$

$x - 4 = 16$

$x = 20$

⑫ Solve. **2 points**

$\sqrt{21}(5 + \sqrt{3}) =$

$5\sqrt{21} + \sqrt{21 \cdot 3} = 5\sqrt{21} + \sqrt{7 \cdot 3 \cdot 3} =$

$5\sqrt{21} + 3\sqrt{7}$

$(4\sqrt{24} + 3\sqrt{32}) \div \sqrt{2} =$

$\frac{4\sqrt{24}^{12}}{\sqrt{2}} + \frac{3\sqrt{32}^{16}}{\sqrt{2}} = 4\sqrt{12} + 3\sqrt{16} =$

$4\sqrt{2 \cdot 2 \cdot 3} + 3\sqrt{4 \cdot 4} = 4 \cdot 2\sqrt{3} + 3 \cdot 4 =$

$8\sqrt{3} + 12$ or $12 + 8\sqrt{3}$

Teaching Tips, Cont.

Assignment

- There is no assignment for this lesson.

⑬ Solve and check. Identify any extraneous solutions. **6 points**

$\sqrt{6x+25}+43=36$

$\sqrt{6x+25}=-7$

$\left(\sqrt{6x+25}\right)^2=(-7)^2$

$6x+25=49$

$6x=24$

$x=4$

check:

$\sqrt{6(4)+25}+43=36$

$\sqrt{24+25+43}=36$

$\sqrt{49}+43=36$

$7+\sqrt{43}\neq 36$ extraneous

$|3x-7|-5=-4x+9$

$|3x-7|=-4x+14$

$3x-7=-4x+14$ or $3x-7=-(-4x+14)$

$7x=21$ $\quad$ $3x-7=4x-14$

$x=3$ $\quad$ $-x=-7$

$x=7$

check:

$|3(3)-7|-5=-4(3)+9$

$|9-7|-5=-12+9$

$2-5=-3$

$|3(7)-7|-5=-4(7)+9$

$|21-7|-5=-28+9$

$14-5\neq-19$ extraneous

⑭ Find the slope of the line joining the points. **3 points**

(8, 4) and (8, -6)

$m=\frac{-6-4}{8-8}=\frac{-10}{0}=$ no slope

(5, -3) and (-7, -3)

$m=\frac{-3-(-3)}{-7-5}=\frac{0}{-12}=0$

(7, -3) and (-5, 6)

$m=\frac{6-(-3)}{-5-7}=\frac{9}{-12}=-\frac{3}{4}$

⑮ Write the point-slope form and the slope-intercept form of the equation of a line. **4 points**

m = 2; (5, 4)

$y-4=2(x-5)$

$y-4=2x-10$

$y=2x-6$

m = -3; (2, -7)

$y-(-7)=-3(x-2)$

$y+7=-3x+6$

$y=-3x-1$

⑯ Identify whether the two lines are parallel, perpendicular, or neither and tell why. **6 points**

$y=\frac{3}{5}x-4$

$y=-\frac{3}{5}x+2$

Neither. The slopes have opposite signs but are not reciprocals.

$y=\frac{3}{5}x-4$

$y=\frac{3}{5}x+2$

The lines are parallel because the slopes are equal.

$y=\frac{3}{5}x-4$

$y=-\frac{5}{3}x+2$

The lines are perpendicular because the slopes are negative reciprocals.

⑰ Solve. **3 points**

$|7x|<x+24$

$-(x+24)<7x<x+24$

$-x-24<7x<x+24$

$-x-24<7x$ and $7x<x+24$

$-24<8x$ $\quad$ $6x<24$

$-3<x$ $\quad$ $x<4$

$-3<x<4$

$|3x+8|+6<1$

$|3x+8|<-5$ NO SOLUTION

Stop working here. The absolute value of anything can never be negative, so the answer is no solution.

$|7x+1|+6>2$

$|7x+1|>-4$ ALL REAL NUMBERS

Stop working here. The absolute value of anything can never be negative, so the answer is all real numbers.

⑱ Solve. Express the answer as a coordinate point. **3 points**

$-3x-y-14=0$

$3x+2y+10=0$

$-3x-y=14$

$\underline{3x+2y=-10}$

$y=4$

$-3x-4-14=0$

$-3x=18$

$x=-6$

$(-6,4)$

$-x-3y+18=0$

$x-2y+17=0$

$-x-3y=-18$

$\underline{x-2y=-17}$

$-5y=-35$

$y=7$

$-x-3(7)+18=0$

$-x-21+18=0$

$x=-3$

$(-3,7)$

$-3x+y+14=0$

$4x+y-14=0$

$-3x+y=-14$

$\underline{4x+y=14}$

$-7x=-28$

$x=4$

$-3(4)+y+14=0$

$-12+y+14=0$

$y=-2$

$(4,-2)$

⑲ Solve. **4 points**

$(3x-5)^2$

$9x^2-30x+25$

$(3x^2-26x+48)\div(3x-8)$

$$\begin{array}{r}
x-6 \\
3x-8\,\overline{)\,3x^2-26x+48} \\
\underline{3x^2-8x} \\
-18x+48 \\
\underline{-18x+48}
\end{array}$$

$(3x+2)(x^2-4x-1)$

$3x(x^2)+3x(-4x)+3x(-1)+2(x^2)+2(-4x)+2(-1)=$

$3x^3-12x^2-3x+2x^2-8x-2=$

$3x^3-10x^2-11x-2$

$(27x-45)\div 9$

$$\begin{array}{r}
3x-5 \\
9\,\overline{)\,27x-45} \\
\underline{27x} \\
-45 \\
\underline{-45}
\end{array}$$

⑳ Factor completely. **6 points**

$6x^2-12x+15$

$3(2x^2-4x+5)$

$16x^2-72x+81$

$(4x-9)^2$

$2x^3-18x$

$2x(x^2-9)=$

$2x(x+3)(x-3)$

$4x+10xy+25y+10$

$(4x+10xy)+(25y+10)$

$2x(2+5y)+5(5y+2)$

$(2x+5)(5y+2)$

x^3+64

$a^3=x^3$ so $a=x$. $b^3=64$

so $b=4$.

$(x+4)(x^2-4x+16)$

$25x^2-2$

$(5x+\sqrt{2})(5x-\sqrt{2})$

97 points total

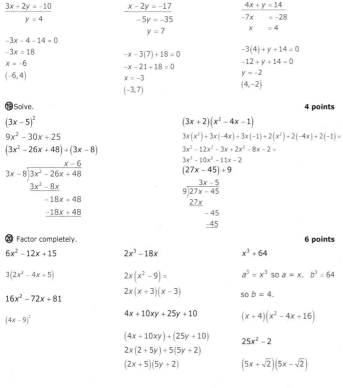

Lesson 81

Concepts

- Dividing rational expressions
- Exclusions
- Systems of equations

Learning Objectives

The student will be able to:

- Divide rational expressions
- Find the reciprocal of a rational expression
- Factor rational expressions and cancel like factors

Materials Needed

- Student Book, Lesson 81

Teaching Tips

- ➢ Review the rules for dividing fractions. Remind the students that they must take the reciprocal of the second fraction (the divisor).
- ➢ Review multiplying rational expressions. (See Lesson 80) Ask the students what parts of the rational expressions may be cancelled. (Like factors) Emphasize that only entire factors may be cancelled, not individual terms.

Lesson 81

Dividing Rational Expressions

When dividing rational expressions, follow the same rules for dividing fractions. After you have taken the reciprocal of the divisor, you will find it easier to factor each numerator and denominator and cancel like factors before you multiply. When dividing rational expressions, you must consider the denominators of the original problem as well as the denominator after you have taken the reciprocal of the divisor when stating the exclusions.

$\frac{5x+10}{2x^2+6x} \div \frac{x^2+x-2}{2x^2-2x} =$

Take the reciprocal of the divisor.

$\frac{5x+10}{2x^2+6x} \cdot \frac{2x^2-2x}{x^2+x-2} =$

Factor each polynomial and cancel like factors.

$\frac{5\cancel{(x+2)}}{\cancel{2x}(x+3)} \cdot \frac{\cancel{2x}\cancel{(x-1)}}{\cancel{(x+2)}\cancel{(x-1)}} = \frac{5}{x+3}$

Identify values of x that must be excluded.

$\frac{5}{x+3}; x \neq -3, -2, 0, 1$

① Classwork

Solve. Remember to state any exclusions.

$\frac{4x-8}{3x^2+6x} \div \frac{x^2+x-6}{3x^2+9x} =$

$\frac{4x-8}{3x^2+6x} \cdot \frac{3x^2+9x}{x^2+x-6} =$

$\frac{4\cancel{(x-2)}}{\cancel{3x}(x+2)} \cdot \frac{\cancel{3x}\cancel{(x+3)}}{\cancel{(x+3)}\cancel{(x-2)}} =$

$\frac{4}{x+2}; x \neq -3, -2, 0, 2$

$\frac{2x^2+2x}{10x^2+15x} \div \frac{3x^2-3x-6}{6x^2+9x} =$

$\frac{2x^2+2x}{10x^2+15x} \cdot \frac{6x^2+9x}{3x^2-3x-6} =$

$\frac{2\cancel{x}\cancel{(x+1)}}{5\cancel{x}\cancel{(2x+3)}} \cdot \frac{\cancel{3}x\cancel{(2x+3)}}{\cancel{3}\cancel{(x+1)}(x-2)} = \frac{2x}{5(x-2)} =$

$\frac{2x}{5x-10}; x \neq -\frac{3}{2}, -1, 0, 2$

Activities

② Solve. Remember to state any exclusions.

$\frac{3x+12}{x^2+5x} \div \frac{x^2+x-12}{x^2-3x} =$

$\frac{3x+12}{x^2+5x} \cdot \frac{x^2-3x}{x^2+x-12} =$

$\frac{3\cancel{(x+4)}}{\cancel{x}(x+5)} \cdot \frac{\cancel{x}\cancel{(x-3)}}{\cancel{(x+4)}\cancel{(x-3)}} =$

$\frac{3}{x+5}; x \neq -5, -4, 0, 3$

$\frac{6x+42}{8x^2+16x} \div \frac{x^2+3x-28}{4x^2+8x} =$

$\frac{6x+42}{8x^2+16x} \cdot \frac{4x^2+8x}{x^2+3x-28} =$

$\frac{{}_3\cancel{6}\cancel{(x+7)}}{{}_2\cancel{8x}\cancel{(x+2)}} \cdot \frac{\cancel{4x}\cancel{(x+2)}}{\cancel{(x+7)}(x-4)} =$

$\frac{3}{x-4}; x \neq -7, -2, 0, 4$

Note: The exercises in Activities 2 and 3 are the same as the exercises found in Lesson 80, but written as division problems. These problems also serve as a review of multiplying rational expressions since Lesson 80, Test 4, and Exam 2 conclude the first semester and many schools have a break at this point in the school year.

③ Solve. Remember to state any exclusions.

$\frac{x^2-3x-10}{2x^2+7x+3} \div \frac{x^2+x-2}{2x^2-x-1} =$

$\frac{x^2-3x-10}{2x^2+7x+3} \cdot \frac{2x^2-x-1}{x^2+x-2} =$

$\frac{(x-5)\cancel{(x+2)}}{\cancel{(2x+1)}(x+3)} \cdot \frac{\cancel{(2x+1)}\cancel{(x-1)}}{\cancel{(x+2)}\cancel{(x-1)}} =$

$\frac{x-5}{x+3}; x \neq -3, -2, -\frac{1}{2}, 1$

$\frac{8x^2+40x}{6x^3-12x^2} \div \frac{2x^2+10x}{3x^2-6x} =$

$\frac{8x^2+40x}{6x^3-12x^2} \cdot \frac{3x^2-6x}{2x^2+10x} =$

$\frac{{}_{2}{}_{\cancel{4}}\cancel{8x}\cancel{(x+5)}}{{}_{\cancel{2}x}\cancel{6x^2}\cancel{(x-2)}} \cdot \frac{\cancel{3x}\cancel{(x-2)}}{\cancel{2x}\cancel{(x+5)}} =$

$\frac{2}{x}; x \neq -5, 0, 2$

$\frac{3x+21}{3x^2+5x-12} \div \frac{x^2+5x-14}{6x^2-8x} =$

$\frac{3x+21}{3x^2+5x-12} \cdot \frac{6x^2-8x}{x^2+5x-14} =$

$\frac{3\cancel{(x+7)}}{\cancel{(3x-4)}(x+3)} \cdot \frac{2x\cancel{(3x-4)}}{\cancel{(x+7)}(x-2)} = \frac{3}{x+3} \cdot \frac{2x}{x-2} =$

$\frac{6x}{x^2+x-6}; x \neq -7, -3, 0, \frac{4}{3}, 2$

$\frac{3x^2-5x-2}{2x^2+3x-9} \div \frac{x^2-3x+2}{x^2+2x-3} =$

$\frac{3x^2-5x-2}{2x^2+3x-9} \cdot \frac{x^2+2x-3}{x^2-3x+2} =$

$\frac{(3x+1)\cancel{(x-2)}}{(2x-3)\cancel{(x+3)}} \cdot \frac{\cancel{(x+3)}\cancel{(x-1)}}{\cancel{(x-2)}\cancel{(x-1)}} =$

$\frac{3x+1}{2x-3}; x \neq -3, 1, \frac{3}{2}, 2$

④ Solve each system of equations. State the solution as a coordinate point.

$x-y-9=0$
$-2x+y+13=0$
$x-y=9$
$\underline{-2x+y=-13}$
$-x=-4$
$x=4$
$4-y=9$
$y=-5$
(4, -5)

$8x-3y-39=0$
$7x+2y-48=0$
$8x-3y=39$
$7x+2y=48$
$16x-6y=78$
$\underline{21x+6y=144}$
$37x=222$
$x=6$
$8(6)-3y-39=0$
$48-3y=39$
$-3y=-9$
$y=3$
(6, 3)

$7x+14y-7=0$
$-x-4y+5=0$
$7x+14y=7$
$-x-4y=-5$
$x+2y=1$
$\underline{-x-4y=-5}$
$-2y=-4$
$y=2$
$-x-4(2)+5=0$
$-x-8=-5$
$-x=3$
$x=-3$
(-3, 2)

$4x-8y-12=0$
$7x-14y-21=0$
$4x-8y=12$
$7x-14y=21$
$x-2y=3$
$\underline{x-2y=3}$
$0=0$
All real numbers

$3x+2y-3=0$
$x+y-4=0$
$3x+2y=3$
$x+y=4$
$3x+2y=3$
$\underline{2x+2y=8}$
$x=-5$
$-5+y-4=0$
$y=9$
(-5, 9)

$3x-y-19=0$
$x-2y-18=0$
$3x-y=19$
$x-2y=18$
$6x-2y=38$
$\underline{x-2y=18}$
$5x=20$
$x=4$
$4-2y-18=0$
$-2y=14$
$y=-7$
(4, -7)

$x-3y+21=0$
$2x-2y+26=0$
$x-3y=-21$
$2x-2y=-26$
$x-3y=-21$
$\underline{x-y=-13}$
$-2y=-8$
$y=4$
$x-3(4)+21=0$
$x-12=-21$
$x=-9$
(-9, 4)

$2x-y+13=0$
$-x+2y-2=0$
$2x-y=-13$
$-x+2y=2$
$4x-2y=-26$
$\underline{-x+2y=2}$
$3x=-24$
$x=-8$
$8+2y-2=$
$2y=-6$
$y=-3$
(-8, -3)

Teaching Tips, Cont.

- Teach dividing rational expressions from the teaching box. Explain that dividing rational expressions follows the same rules as dividing fractions.
- Remind the students that only entire factors can be cancelled, not just like terms.
- Explain that the quotients will have exclusions, just like any other problem involving rational expressions. The difference here is that the denominators of the original problem, as well as the denominator after the reciprocal has been taken, must be considered when determining exclusions.
- Complete the Classwork exercises. Have some students work the problems on the board for the class and explain their answers. All students should work the problems in their books.

Assignment

- Complete Lesson 81, Activities 2-4.

Lesson 82

Concepts

- Adding rational expressions
- Subtracting rational expressions
- Inequalities
- Absolute value
- Math in the real world

Learning Objectives

The student will be able to:

- Add rational expressions with a whole number denominator
- Add a whole number to a rational expression
- Subtract rational expressions with whole number denominators

Materials Needed

- Student Book, Lesson 82
- Worksheet 41

Teaching Tips

- Have students complete Worksheet 41 in class. This may be for added practice of earlier topics or graded as a quiz, if desired.
- Review adding and subtracting rational expressions. (See Lesson 79)
- Review least common multiple. (See Lesson 6)
- Tell the students that when the denominators of rational expressions are different, they must find the lowest common denominator. This is the same as the least common multiple of the denominators.

Rational Expressions and Numeric Denominators

Recall from Lesson 78 that a rational expression is a fraction whose numerator and denominator are both polynomials. So far you have learned to add and subtract rational expressions that have the same polynomial denominator. But what happens when one denominator is a single constant term?

$\frac{2x}{x+1}+\frac{3x}{2}=$

You must first find a common denominator. The simplest way to do this is to reduce each fraction, if possible, and then multiply the two denominators to get the new denominator. Remember to multiply both the numerator and denominator of a fraction by the same thing to get an equivalent fraction.

The common denominator in the example above is $(x+1)(2)=2x+2$.

Rewrite each fraction with the common denominator.

$\frac{(2x)(2)}{(x+1)(2)}+\frac{(3x)(x+1)}{(2)(x+1)}=$

$\frac{4x}{2x+2}+\frac{3x^2+3x}{2x+2}$

Add the numerators to get the new numerator and keep the common denominator.

$\frac{4x}{2x+2}+\frac{3x^2+3x}{2x+2}=\frac{3x^2+7x}{2x+2}$

As before, you must state all exclusions based on the denominators in the original problem.

$\frac{3x^2+7x}{2x+2}; x\neq -1$

① **Classwork**

Solve. Remember to state any exclusions.

$\frac{1}{x+2}+\frac{2}{3}=$

$\frac{(1)(3)}{(x+2)(3)}+\frac{(2)(x+2)}{(3)(x+2)}=$

$\frac{3+2x+4}{3x+6}=\frac{2x+7}{3x+6}; x\neq -2$

$\frac{1}{2x+1}-\frac{x}{2}=$

$\frac{(1)(2)}{(2x+1)(2)}-\frac{(x)(2x+1)}{(2)(2x+1)}=$

$\frac{2-2x^2-x}{4x+2}=\frac{-2x^2-x+2}{4x+2}; x\neq -\frac{1}{2}$

$\frac{x^2}{3x+2}+2=$

$\frac{(x^2)(1)}{(3x+2)(1)}+\frac{(2)(3x+2)}{(1)(3x+2)}=$

$\frac{x^2+6x+4}{3x+2}; x\neq -\frac{2}{3}$

Activities

② Solve. Remember to state any exclusions.

$\frac{1}{x+3}+\frac{4}{5}=$

$\frac{(1)(5)}{(x+3)(5)}+\frac{(4)(x+3)}{(5)(x+3)}=$

$\frac{5+4x+12}{5x+15}=\frac{4x+17}{5x+15}; x\neq -3$

$\frac{x}{3x+2}-\frac{x}{4}=$

$\frac{(x)(4)}{(3x+2)(4)}-\frac{(x)(3x+2)}{(4)(3x+2)}=$

$\frac{4x-3x^2-2x}{12x+8}=\frac{-3x^2+2x}{12x+8}; x\neq -\frac{2}{3}$

③ Solve. Remember to state any exclusions.

$\frac{2x}{x+4}+\frac{1}{3}=$

$\frac{(2x)(3)}{(x+4)(3)}+\frac{(1)(x+4)}{(3)(x+4)}=$

$\frac{6x+x+4}{3x+12}=\frac{7x+4}{3x+12}; x\neq -4$

$\frac{3x^2}{2x+5}+7=$

$\frac{(3x^2)(1)}{(2x+5)(1)}+\frac{(7)(2x+5)}{(1)(2x+5)}=$

$\frac{3x^2+14x+35}{2x+5}; x\neq -\frac{5}{2}$

$\frac{3x^2}{2x+1}+9=$

$\frac{(3x^2)(1)}{(2x+1)(1)}+\frac{(9)(2x+1)}{(1)(2x+1)}=$

$\frac{3x^2+18x+9}{2x+1}; x\neq -\frac{1}{2}$

$\frac{6x}{5x+1}-\frac{2x}{3}=$

$\frac{(6x)(3)}{(5x+1)(3)}-\frac{(2x)(5x+1)}{(3)(5x+1)}=$

$\frac{18x-10x^2-2x}{15x+3}=$

$\frac{-10x^2+16x}{15x+3}; x\neq -\frac{1}{5}$

$\frac{4}{3x+5}+\frac{3x}{2}=$

$\frac{(4)(2)}{(3x+5)(2)}+\frac{(3x)(3x+5)}{(2)(3x+5)}=$

$\frac{8+9x^2+15x}{6x+10}=$

$\frac{9x^2+15x+8}{6x+10}; x\neq -\frac{5}{3}$

$\frac{4}{5x+4}-\frac{3x}{7}=$

$\frac{(4)(7)}{(5x+4)(7)}-\frac{(3x)(5x+4)}{(7)(5x+4)}=$

$\frac{28-15x^2-12x}{35x+28}=$

$\frac{-15x^2-12x+28}{35x+28}; x\neq -\frac{4}{5}$

④ Solve.

$3(2x-3)>5|7-10|$
$6x-9>5|-3|$
$6x-9>5(3)$
$6x-9>15$
$6x>24$
$x>4$

$3(2x-3)<(-5)|7-10|$
$6x-9<(-5)|-3|$
$6x-9<(-5)(3)$
$6x-9<-15$
$6x<-6$
$x<-1$

$(-3)(2x-3)<5|7-10|$
$-6x+9<5|-3|$
$-6x+9<5(3)$
$-6x+9<15$
$-6x<6$
$x>-1$

⑤ Solve.

The Lions and the Hawks had a total of 25 players in the championship basketball game. The Lions averaged 7 points per player, and the Hawks averaged 8 points per player. A total of 186 points was scored in the game. How many players were on each team, which team won the game, and what was the final score? Hint: Set up a system of equations.

Let L = the number of players on the Lions
Let h = the number of players on the Hawks

$L+h=25$
$7L+8h=186$

$8L+8h=200$
$7L+8h=186$
$L\quad=14$

$14+h=25$
$h=11$

The Lions had 14 players and the Hawks had 11 players.
The Lions scored 7(14) = 98 points and the Hawks scored 8(11) = 88 points.
The Lions won the game with a final score of 98-88.

Rational Expressions Worksheet 41

① Simplify. Remember to state any exclusions.

$\frac{5x}{20x^2}$

$\frac{\cancel{5}\cancel{x}}{{}_4\cancel{20}x\cancel{^2}} = \frac{1}{4x}; x \neq 0$

$\frac{4x^3}{36x^2}$

$\frac{\cancel{4}x^{\cancel{3}}}{{}_9\cancel{36}\cancel{x^2}} = \frac{x}{9}; x \neq 0$

$\frac{15x^2 + 6x}{5x + 2}$

$\frac{3x\left(\cancel{5x+2}\right)}{\cancel{5x+2}} = 3x; x \neq -\frac{2}{5}$

$\frac{8x^3 + 6x^2}{4x + 3}$

$\frac{2x^2\left(\cancel{4x+3}\right)}{\cancel{4x+3}} = 2x^2; x \neq -\frac{3}{4}$

$\frac{10x^2 + x - 3}{6x^2 + x - 2}$

$\frac{(5x+3)\left(\cancel{2x-1}\right)}{(3x+2)\left(\cancel{2x-1}\right)} = \frac{5x+3}{3x+2}; x \neq -\frac{2}{3}, \frac{1}{2}$

$\frac{x^2 - 4x + 3}{x^2 - 1}$

$\frac{(x-3)\left(\cancel{x-1}\right)}{(x+1)\left(\cancel{x-1}\right)} = \frac{x-3}{x+1}; x \neq -1, 1$

$\frac{x^2 - 16}{x^2 + 8x + 16}$

$\frac{\left(\cancel{x+4}\right)(x-4)}{\left(\cancel{x+4}\right)(x+4)} = \frac{x-4}{x+4}; x \neq -4$

$\frac{4x^2 + 12x + 9}{4x^2 - 9}$

$\frac{\left(\cancel{2x+3}\right)(2x+3)}{\left(\cancel{2x+3}\right)(2x-3)} = \frac{2x+3}{2x-3}; x \neq -\frac{3}{2}, \frac{3}{2}$

② Solve. Remember to state any exclusions.

$\frac{5}{x-6} + \frac{8}{x-6} =$

$\frac{5+8}{x-6} = \frac{13}{x-6}; x \neq 6$

$\frac{3}{2x-1} + \frac{6}{2x-1} =$

$\frac{3+6}{2x-1} = \frac{9}{2x-1}; x \neq \frac{1}{2}$

$\frac{7x}{4x-3} - \frac{3x+5}{4x-3} =$

$\frac{7x-(3x+5)}{4x-3} = \frac{4x-5}{4x-3}; x \neq \frac{3}{4}$

$\frac{6x}{5x+2} - \frac{3x-8}{5x+2} =$

$\frac{6x-(3x-8)}{5x+2} = \frac{3x+8}{5x+2}; x \neq -\frac{2}{5}$

Teaching Tips, Cont.

- Teach adding and subtracting rational expressions with whole number denominators from the teaching box.
- Tell the students that the easiest way to find the lowest common denominator when one denominator is a polynomial and the other denominator is a whole number is to multiply the two denominators.
- Remind the students to factor both the numerator and denominator and cancel like *factors*.
- Complete the Classwork exercises. Have some students work the problems on the board for the class and explain their answers. All students should work the problems in their books.

Assignment

- Complete Lesson 82, Activities 2-5.

Lesson 83

Concepts

- Adding rational expressions with different denominators
- Common denominators of rational expressions
- Exclusions
- Factoring polynomials

Learning Objectives

The student will be able to:

- Find the lowest common denominator of rational expressions with different polynomial denominators
- Add rational expressions with different denominators
- State all exclusions of the sum of rational expressions with different denominators

Materials Needed

- Student Book, Lesson 83
- Worksheet 42

Teaching Tips

➢ Review adding rational expressions. (See Lesson 79)

➢ Review finding the lowest common denominator of rational expressions. (See Lesson 82)

➢ Write the sample problem from the teaching box on the board. Ask the students if these rational expressions can be added as they are written. (No.) Why or why not? (The signs are not equal in the denominators.) Ask the students what they have to do to be able to add these rational expressions. (Find a common denominator.)

Adding Rational Expressions with Different Denominators

When adding rational expressions, follow the same rules for adding fractions. You must find a common denominator, and then simplify the answer if necessary. As in the previous lesson, you must state any exclusions.

$\frac{1}{x+2}+\frac{1}{x-2}=$

The common denominator is $(x+2)(x-2)$ or x^2-4.

$\frac{x-2}{(x+2)(x-2)}+\frac{x+2}{(x+2)(x-2)}=$

Now that the denominators match, add the numerators and write the answer as a single fraction.

$\frac{x-2+x+2}{(x+2)(x-2)}=\frac{2x}{(x+2)(x-2)}$

Simplify.

$\frac{2x}{x^2-4}; x \neq -2, 2$

Notice that the fraction cannot be reduced any further. The x cannot cancel with the x^2, and the 2 cannot cancel with the 4. Remember that only whole factors can cancel with other whole factors. Individual terms cannot cancel each other.

① Classwork

Solve. Remember to state any exclusions.

$\frac{1}{x+1}+\frac{1}{x-1}=$

The common denominator is $(x+1)(x-1)$ or x^2-1.

$\frac{1(x-1)}{(x+1)(x-1)}+\frac{1(x+1)}{(x+1)(x-1)}=$

$\frac{(x-1)+(x+1)}{(x+1)(x-1)}=\frac{2x}{x^2-1}; x \neq -1, 1$

$\frac{2}{x+3}+\frac{3}{x-2}=$

The common denominator is $(x+3)(x-2)$ or x^2+x-6.

$\frac{2(x-2)}{(x+3)(x-2)}+\frac{3(x+3)}{(x+3)(x-2)}=$

$\frac{(2x-4)+(3x+9)}{(x+3)(x-2)}=\frac{5x+5}{x^2+x-6}; x \neq -3, 2$

Point out that although the numerator can be factored, neither factor is a factor of the denominator, so it is impossible to reduce.

Activities

② State the common denominator in each problem.

$\frac{5}{x+3}+\frac{2}{x-1}=$

The common denominator is $(x+3)(x-1)$ or x^2+2x-3.

$\frac{2}{x+3}+\frac{x}{x+1}=$

The common denominator is $(x+3)(x+1)$or x^2+4x+3.

$\frac{1}{2x+1}+\frac{2}{x-1}=$

The common denominator is $(2x+1)(x-1)$ or $2x^2-x-1$.

$\frac{5}{x-4}+\frac{7}{x+3}=$

The common denominator is $(x-4)(x+3)$ or x^2-x-12.

③ Solve each problem from Activity ②. Remember to state any exclusions.

$\frac{5}{x+3}+\frac{2}{x-1}=$

$\frac{5(x-1)}{(x+3)(x-1)}+\frac{2(x+3)}{(x+3)(x-1)}=$

$\frac{5x-5}{x^2+2x-3}+\frac{2x+6}{x^2+2x-3}=$

$\frac{7x+1}{x^2+2x-3}; x \neq -3, 1$

$\frac{1}{2x+1}+\frac{2}{x-1}=$

$\frac{1(x-1)}{(2x+1)(x-1)}+\frac{2(2x+1)}{(2x+1)(x-1)}=$

$\frac{x-1}{2x^2-x-1}+\frac{4x+2}{2x^2-x-1}=$

$\frac{5x+1}{2x^2-x-1}; x \neq -\frac{1}{2}, 1$

$\frac{2}{x+3}+\frac{x}{x+1}=$

$\frac{2(x+1)}{(x+3)(x+1)}+\frac{x(x+3)}{(x+3)(x+1)}=$

$\frac{2x+2}{x^2+4x+3}+\frac{x^2+3x}{x^2+4x+3}=$

$\frac{x^2+5x+2}{x^2+4x+3}; x \neq -3, -1$

$\frac{5}{x-4}+\frac{7}{x+3}=$

$\frac{5(x+3)}{(x-4)(x+3)}+\frac{7(x-4)}{(x-4)(x+3)}=$

$\frac{5x+15}{x^2-x-12}+\frac{7x-28}{x^2-x-12}=$

$\frac{12x-13}{x^2-x-12}; x \neq -3, 4$

④ Factor each polynomial completely.

$6x^3-3x^2y-45xy^2$
$3x(2x+5y)(x-3y)$

$9x^2-64$
$(3x+8)(3x-8)$

$16x^2-9$
$(4x+3)(4x-3)$

$4x^2-169$
$(2x+13)(2x-13)$

$100x^2+220x+121$
$(10x+11)^2$

$9x^2+12\sqrt{7}+28$
$(3x+2\sqrt{7})^2$

$2x^2-5x-12$
$(2x+3)(x-4)$

$15x^3-85x^2+100x$
$5x(3x^2-17x+20)=$
$5x(3x-5)(x-4)$

x^2-225
$(x+15)(x-15)$

x^2-4
$(x+2)(x-2)$

x^2-169
$(x+13)(x-13)$

$81x^2-198x+121$
$(9x-11)^2$

$16x^2+88x+121$
$(4x+11)^2$

$x^2-2\sqrt{29}+29$
$(x-\sqrt{29})^2$

$49x^2-140x+100$
$(7x-10)^2$

$32x^2+16\sqrt{7}+14$
$2(16x^2+8x\sqrt{7}+7)=$
$2(4x+\sqrt{7})^2$

x^2+4x-5
$(x-1)(x+5)$

$6x^2+23x+20$
$(2x+5)(3x+4)$

x^2-144
$(x+12)(x-12)$

$16x^2-81$
$(4x+9)(4x-9)$

$64x^2-25$
$(8x+5)(8x-5)$

$9x^2-50$
$(3x+5\sqrt{2})(3x-5\sqrt{2})$

$49x^2-80$
$(7x+4\sqrt{5})(7x-4\sqrt{5})$

$12x^2-27$
$3(4x^2-9)=$
$3(2x+3)(2x-3)$

Adding Rational Expressions with Different Denominators Worksheet 42

① Solve. Remember to state any exclusions.

$\frac{5x}{4x+3}+\frac{3}{2x-1}=$

$\frac{5x(2x-1)}{(4x+3)(2x-1)}+\frac{3(4x+3)}{(4x+3)(2x-1)}=$

$\frac{10x^2-5x}{8x^2+2x-3}+\frac{12x+9}{8x^2+2x-3}=$

$\frac{10x^2+7x+9}{8x^2+2x-3}; x \neq -\frac{3}{4}, \frac{1}{2}$

$\frac{4x}{x+2}+\frac{x}{3x-1}=$

$\frac{4x(3x-1)}{(x+2)(3x-1)}+\frac{x(x+2)}{(x+2)(3x-1)}=$

$\frac{12x^2-4x}{3x^2+5x-2}+\frac{x^2+2x}{3x^2+5x-2}=$

$\frac{13x^2-2x}{3x^2+5x-2}; x \neq -2, \frac{1}{3}$

$\frac{x+1}{2x+1}+\frac{x-2}{x-1}=$

$\frac{(x+1)(x-1)}{(2x+1)(x-1)}+\frac{(x-2)(2x+1)}{(2x+1)(x-1)}=$

$\frac{x^2-1}{2x^2-x-1}+\frac{2x^2-3x-2}{2x^2-x-1}=$

$\frac{3x^2-3x-3}{2x^2-x-1}; x \neq -\frac{1}{2}, 1$

$\frac{2x-1}{3x-1}+\frac{2x+3}{x+1}=$

$\frac{(2x-1)(x+1)}{(3x-1)(x+1)}+\frac{(2x+3)(3x-1)}{(3x-1)(x+1)}=$

$\frac{2x^2+x-1}{3x^2+2x-1}+\frac{6x^2+7x-3}{3x^2+2x-1}=$

$\frac{8x^2+8x-4}{3x^2+2x-1}; x \neq -1, \frac{1}{3}$

$\frac{7x}{3x-2}+\frac{3x}{4x+5}=$

$\frac{7x(4x+5)}{(3x-2)(4x+5)}+\frac{3x(3x-2)}{(3x-2)(4x+5)}=$

$\frac{28x^2+35x}{12x^2+7x-10}+\frac{9x^2-6x}{12x^2+7x-10}=$

$\frac{37x^2+29x}{12x^2+7x-10}; x \neq -\frac{5}{4}, \frac{2}{3}$

$\frac{3x-7}{3x-4}+\frac{4x-1}{2x-5}=$

$\frac{(3x-7)(2x-5)}{(3x-4)(2x-5)}+\frac{(4x-1)(3x-4)}{(3x-4)(2x-5)}=$

$\frac{6x^2-29x+35}{6x^2-23x+20}+\frac{12x^2-19x+4}{6x^2-23x+20}=$

$\frac{18x^2-48x+39}{6x^2-23x+20}; x \neq \frac{4}{3}, \frac{5}{2}$

$\frac{5x^2}{x-4}+\frac{7x}{x+3}=$

$\frac{5x^2(x+3)}{(x-4)(x+3)}+\frac{7x(x-4)}{(x-4)(x+3)}=$

$\frac{5x^3+15x^2}{x^2-x-12}+\frac{7x^2-28x}{x^2-x-12}=$

$\frac{5x^3+22x^2-28x}{x^2-x-12}; x \neq -3, 4$

$\frac{x^2-1}{x^2-5x+4}+\frac{x+1}{x-4}=$

$\frac{(x+1)\cancel{(x-1)}}{(x-4)\cancel{(x-1)}}+\frac{x+1}{x-4}=$

$\frac{x+1}{x-4}+\frac{x+1}{x-4}=$

$\frac{2x+2}{x-4}; x \neq 1, 4$

Teaching Tips, Cont.

- Teach adding rational expression with different denominators from the teaching box.
- Remind the students to find all exclusions from the denominators of the original problem.
- Complete the Classwork exercises. Have some students work the problems on the board for the class and explain their answers. All students should work the problems in their books.

Assignments

- Complete Lesson 83, Activities 2-4.
- Worksheet 42.

Lesson 84

Concepts

- Subtracting rational expressions with different denominators
- Lowest common denominator
- Exclusions
- Math in the real world

Learning Objectives

The student will be able to:

- Find the lowest common denominator of rational expressions with different polynomial denominators
- Subtract rational expressions with different denominators
- State all exclusions of the difference of rational expressions with different denominators

Materials Needed

- Student Book, Lesson 84

Teaching Tips

➢ Review subtracting rational expressions. (See Lesson 79)

➢ Review finding the lowest common denominator of rational expressions. (See Lesson 82)

➢ Write the sample problem from the teaching box on the board. Ask the students if these rational expressions can be subtracted as they are written. (No.) Why or why not? (The signs are not equal in the denominators.) Ask the students what they have to do to be able to subtract these rational expressions. (Find a common denominator.)

Subtracting Rational Expressions with Different Denominators

When subtracting rational expressions, follow the same rules for subtracting fractions. You must find a common denominator, and then simplify the answer if necessary. As in the previous lesson, you must state any exclusions.

$\frac{1}{x+2}-\frac{1}{x-2}=$

The common denominator is $(x+2)(x-2)$ or x^2-4.

$\frac{x-2}{(x+2)(x-2)}-\frac{x+2}{(x+2)(x-2)}=$

Now that the denominators match, subtract the numerators and write the answer as a single fraction.

$\frac{(x-2)-(x+2)}{(x+2)(x-2)}=\frac{-4}{(x+2)(x-2)}$

Simplify.

$\frac{-4}{x^2-4}; x\neq -2,2$

Notice that the fraction cannot be reduced any further. The -4 in the numerator cannot cancel with the -4 in the denominator. Remember that only whole factors can cancel with other whole factors. Individual terms cannot cancel each other.

① **Classwork**

Solve. Remember to state any exclusions.

$\frac{1}{x+1}-\frac{1}{x-1}=$

The common denominator is $(x+1)(x-1)$ or x^2-1.

$\frac{1(x-1)}{(x+1)(x-1)}-\frac{1(x+1)}{(x+1)(x-1)}=$

$\frac{(x-1)-(x+1)}{(x+1)(x-1)}=\frac{-2}{x^2-1}; x\neq -1,1$

$\frac{2}{x+3}-\frac{3}{x-2}=$

The common denominator is $(x+3)(x-2)$ or x^2+x-6.

$\frac{2(x-2)}{(x+3)(x-2)}-\frac{3(x+3)}{(x+3)(x-2)}=$

$\frac{(2x-4)-(3x+9)}{(x+3)(x-2)}=\frac{-x-13}{x^2+x-6}; x\neq -3,2$

Activities

② State the common denominator in each problem.

$\frac{x}{x+2}-\frac{x}{x-5}=$

The common denominator is $(x+2)(x-5)$ or $x^2-3x-10$.

$\frac{3x}{x-4}-\frac{7x}{x-5}=$

The common denominator is $(x-4)(x-5)$ or $x^2-9x+20$.

$\frac{3}{x+4}-\frac{4}{x+2}=$

The common denominator is $(x+4)(x+2)$ or x^2+6x+8.

$\frac{6}{2x-1}-\frac{3}{x-2}=$

The common denominator is $(2x-1)(x-2)$ or $2x^2-5x+2$.

③ Solve each problem from exercise ②. Remember to state any exclusions.

$$\frac{x}{x+2}-\frac{x}{x-5}=$$
$$\frac{x(x-5)}{(x+2)(x-5)}-\frac{x(x+2)}{(x+2)(x-5)}=$$
$$\frac{x^2-5x}{x^2-3x-10}-\frac{x^2+2x}{x^2-3x-10}=$$
$$\frac{-7x}{x^2-3x-10};x\neq -2,5$$

$$\frac{3x}{x-4}-\frac{7x}{x-5}=$$
$$\frac{3x(x-5)}{(x-4)(x-5)}-\frac{7x(x-4)}{(x-4)(x-5)}=$$
$$\frac{3x^2-15x}{x^2-9x+20}-\frac{7x^2-28x}{x^2-9x+20}=$$
$$\frac{-4x^2+13x}{x^2-9x+20};x\neq 4,5$$

$$\frac{3}{x+4}-\frac{4}{x+2}=$$
$$\frac{3(x+2)}{(x+4)(x+2)}-\frac{4(x+4)}{(x+4)(x+2)}=$$
$$\frac{3x+6}{(x+4)(x+2)}-\frac{4x+16}{(x+4)(x+2)}=$$
$$\frac{-x-10}{x^2+6x+8};x\neq -4,-2$$

$$\frac{6}{2x-1}-\frac{3}{x-2}=$$
$$\frac{6(x-2)}{(2x-1)(x-2)}-\frac{3(2x-1)}{(2x-1)(x-2)}=$$
$$\frac{6x-12}{(2x-1)(x-2)}-\frac{6x-3}{(2x-1)(x-2)}=$$
$$\frac{-9}{2x^2-5x+2};x\neq \tfrac{1}{2},2$$

④ Solve.

A basketball player's estimated number of years left to play, y, is found using the formula $y = 27 - \frac{3a}{4}$, where a is the player's current age. How many additional years can a 28-year-old basketball player expect to play?

$y = 27 - \frac{3(28)}{4} = 27 - 21 = 6$ additional years of play

The trade value, v, of a player is found using the formula $v = \frac{(e-y)^2(y+1)e}{190} + \frac{ey^2}{13}$. Rewrite this formula as a single fraction.

$$v=\frac{13\left[(e-y)^2(y+1)e\right]}{13(190)}+\frac{190\left(ey^2\right)}{190(13)}=\frac{13\left[\left(e^2-2ey+y^2\right)(y+1)e\right]}{2470}+\frac{190ey^2}{2470}=$$
$$\frac{13\left[\left(e^2y-2ey^2+y^3+e^2-2ey+y^2\right)e\right]}{2470}+\frac{190ey^2}{2470}=$$
$$\frac{13\left(e^3y-2e^2y^2+ey^3+e^3-2e^2y+ey^2\right)}{2470}+\frac{190ey^2}{2470}=$$
$$\frac{13e^3y-26e^2y^2+13ey^3+13e^3-26e^2y+13ey^2}{2470}+\frac{190ey^2}{2470}$$
$$=\frac{13e^3y-26e^2y^2+13ey^3+13e^3-26e^2y+203ey^2}{2470}$$

Teaching Tips, Cont.

- Teach subtracting rational expression with different denominators from the teaching box.
- Remind the students to find all exclusions from the denominators of the original problem.
- Complete the Classwork exercises. Have some students work the problems on the board for the class and explain their answers. All students should work the problems in their books.

Assignment

- Complete Lesson 84, Activities 2-4.

Lesson 85

Concepts
- Multiplying rational expressions
- Exclusions
- Adding rational expressions
- Subtracting rational expressions
- Lowest common denominator

Learning Objectives
The student will be able to:
- Factor polynomials in rational expressions
- Simplify rational expressions
- Multiply rational expressions

Materials Needed
- Student Book, Lesson 85
- Worksheet 43

Teaching Tips
- ➢ Have students complete Worksheet 43 in class. This may be for added practice of earlier topics, or graded as a quiz, if desired.
- ➢ Review multiplying rational expressions. (See Lesson 80)
- ➢ Review factoring polynomials as needed. (See Lessons 68-77)
- ➢ Review simplifying rational expressions as needed. (See Lesson 78)

Review: Multiplying Rational Expressions

Recall from Lesson 80 that multiplying rational expressions follows the same rules as multiplying fractions. Factor each numerator and denominator and cancel like factors before you multiply. Remember that entire factors must be cancelled. You cannot cancel individual terms. When writing the answer, remember to state any exclusions found in the denominators of the original problem.

① Classwork

Solve. Remember to state any exclusions.

$$\frac{3x-12}{4x^2+8x}\cdot\frac{4x^2+8x}{x^2-2x-8}=$$
$$\frac{3(\cancel{x-4})}{\cancel{4x}(x+2)}\cdot\frac{\cancel{4x}(\cancel{x+2})}{(\cancel{x+2})(\cancel{x-4})}=$$
$$\frac{3}{x+2};x\neq-2,0,4$$

Activities

② Solve. Remember to state any exclusions.

$$\frac{18x+6}{2x^2+8x}\cdot\frac{4x^2-6x}{6x^2-7x-3}=$$
$$\frac{6(\cancel{3x+1})}{\cancel{2x}(x+4)}\cdot\frac{\cancel{2x}(\cancel{2x-3})}{(\cancel{3x+1})(\cancel{2x-3})}=$$
$$\frac{6}{x+4};x\neq-4,-\tfrac{1}{3},0,\tfrac{3}{2}$$

$$\frac{16x+40}{6x^3+6x^2}\cdot\frac{3x^3+3x^2}{6x^2-3x-45}=$$
$$\frac{{}_4\cancel{8}(\cancel{2x+5})}{{}_2\cancel{6x^2}(\cancel{x+1})}\cdot\frac{\cancel{3x^2}(\cancel{x+1})}{3(\cancel{2x+5})(x-3)}=$$
$$\frac{4}{3(x-3)}=\frac{4}{3x-9};x\neq-\tfrac{5}{2},-1,0,3$$

$$\frac{x^2-4x+3}{4x^2+22x+28}\cdot\frac{2x^2+5x-7}{3x^2-6x+3}=$$
$$\frac{(x-3)(\cancel{x-1})}{2(\cancel{2x+7})(x+2)}\cdot\frac{(\cancel{2x+7})(\cancel{x-1})}{3(\cancel{x-1})(\cancel{x-1})}=$$
$$\frac{x-3}{6x+12};x\neq-\tfrac{7}{2},-2,1$$

$$\frac{2x^2-x-1}{4x^3-x}\cdot\frac{4x^3-4x^2+x}{2x^2+3x-2}=$$
$$\frac{(x-1)(\cancel{2x+1})}{\cancel{x}(\cancel{2x+1})(\cancel{2x-1})}\cdot\frac{\cancel{x}(\cancel{2x-1})(\cancel{2x-1})}{(x+2)(\cancel{2x-1})}=$$
$$\frac{x-1}{x+2};x\neq-2,-\tfrac{1}{2},0,\tfrac{1}{2}$$

$$\frac{28x^2+20x}{18x^3-12x^2}\cdot\frac{3x^2-2x}{14x^2+10x}=$$
$$\frac{{}_2\cancel{4x}(\cancel{7x+5})}{{}_{3x}\cancel{6x^2}(\cancel{3x-2})}\cdot\frac{\cancel{x}(\cancel{3x-2})}{\cancel{2}\cancel{x}(\cancel{7x+5})}=$$
$$\frac{1}{3x};x\neq-\tfrac{5}{7},0,\tfrac{2}{3}$$

$$\frac{15x+10}{28x^2+66x-10}\cdot\frac{42x^2-6x}{6x^3+x^2-2x}=$$
$$\frac{5(\cancel{3x+2})}{\cancel{2}(\cancel{7x-1})(2x+5)}\cdot\frac{{}_3\cancel{6}\cancel{x}(\cancel{7x-1})}{\cancel{x}(\cancel{3x+2})(2x-1)}=$$
$$\frac{5}{2x+5}\cdot\frac{3}{2x-1}=\frac{15}{4x^2+8x-5};x\neq-\tfrac{5}{2},-\tfrac{2}{3},0,\tfrac{1}{7},\tfrac{1}{2}$$

$$\frac{45x^2+42x-24}{108x^2+120x-32}\cdot\frac{2x^2-6x+4}{5x^3-12x^2+4x}=$$
$$\frac{3(\cancel{3x+4})(\cancel{5x-2})}{{}_2\cancel{4}(9x-2)(\cancel{3x+4})}\cdot\frac{\cancel{2}(\cancel{x-2})(x-1)}{x(\cancel{5x-2})(\cancel{x-2})}=$$
$$\frac{3}{2(9x-2)}\cdot\frac{x-1}{x}=\frac{3x-3}{18x^2-4x};x\neq-\tfrac{4}{3},0,\tfrac{2}{9},\tfrac{2}{5},2$$

$$\frac{x^2-2x+1}{x^2+5x+6}\cdot\frac{x^2+4x+4}{x^2-2x+1}=$$
$$\frac{(\cancel{x-1})(\cancel{x-1})}{(\cancel{x+2})(x+3)}\cdot\frac{(x+2)(\cancel{x+2})}{(\cancel{x-1})(\cancel{x-1})}=$$
$$\frac{x+2}{x+3};x\neq-3,-2,1$$

③ Solve. Remember to state any exclusions.

$$\frac{4}{x+3}+\frac{1}{x-2}=$$
$$\frac{4(x-2)}{(x+3)(x-2)}+\frac{1(x+3)}{(x+3)(x-2)}=$$
$$\frac{4x-8}{x^2+x-6}+\frac{x+3}{x^2+x-6}=$$
$$\frac{5x-5}{x^2+x-6};x\neq-3,2$$

$$\frac{3}{2x+5}+\frac{6}{x-5}=$$
$$\frac{3(x-5)}{(2x+5)(x-5)}+\frac{6(2x+5)}{(2x+5)(x-5)}=$$
$$\frac{3x-15}{2x^2-5x-25}+\frac{12x+30}{2x^2-5x-25}=$$
$$\frac{15x+15}{2x^2-5x-25};x\neq-\tfrac{5}{2},5$$

$$\frac{4}{3x+5}+\frac{3x}{6x-1}=$$
$$\frac{4(6x-1)}{(3x+5)(6x-1)}+\frac{3x(3x+5)}{(3x+5)(6x-1)}=$$
$$\frac{24x-4}{18x^2+27x-5}+\frac{9x^2+15x}{18x^2+27x-5}=$$
$$\frac{9x^2+39x-4}{18x^2+27x-5};x\neq-\tfrac{5}{3},\tfrac{1}{6}$$

$$\frac{5x}{4x-3}+\frac{7}{5x+3}=$$
$$\frac{5x(5x+3)}{(4x-3)(5x+3)}+\frac{7(4x-3)}{(4x-3)(5x+3)}=$$
$$\frac{25x^2+15x}{20x^2-3x-9}+\frac{28x-21}{20x^2-3x-9}=$$
$$\frac{25x^2+43x-21}{20x^2-3x-9};x\neq-\tfrac{3}{5},\tfrac{3}{4}$$

$$\frac{6}{3x-4}+\frac{7x}{2x+3}=$$
$$\frac{6(2x+3)}{(3x-4)(2x+3)}+\frac{7x(3x-4)}{(3x-4)(2x+3)}=$$
$$\frac{12x+18}{6x^2+x-12}+\frac{21x^2-28x}{6x^2+x-12}=$$
$$\frac{21x^2-16x+18}{6x^2+x-12};x\neq-\tfrac{3}{2},\tfrac{4}{3}$$

$$\frac{2x}{x+3}-\frac{3x}{x-7}=$$
$$\frac{2x(x-7)}{(x+3)(x-7)}-\frac{3x(x+3)}{(x+3)(x-7)}=$$
$$\frac{2x^2-14x}{x^2-4x-21}-\frac{3x^2+9x}{x^2-4x-21}=$$
$$\frac{-x^2-23x}{x^2-4x-21};x\neq-3,7$$

$$\frac{2}{x-5}-\frac{8}{x-3}=$$
$$\frac{2(x-3)}{(x-5)(x-3)}-\frac{8(x-5)}{(x-5)(x-3)}=$$
$$\frac{2x-6}{x^2-8x+15}-\frac{8x-40}{x^2-8x+15}=$$
$$\frac{-6x+34}{x^2-8x+15};x\neq3,5$$

$$\frac{4x}{2x-5}-\frac{6x}{4x-3}=$$
$$\frac{4x(4x-3)}{(2x-5)(4x-3)}-\frac{6x(2x-5)}{(2x-5)(4x-3)}=$$
$$\frac{16x^2-12x}{8x^2-26x+15}-\frac{12x^2-30x}{8x^2-26x+15}=$$
$$\frac{4x^2+18x}{8x^2-26x+15};x\neq\tfrac{3}{4},\tfrac{5}{2}$$

$$\frac{2}{2x-1}-\frac{3}{x-3}=$$
$$\frac{2(x-3)}{(2x-1)(x-3)}-\frac{3(2x-1)}{(2x-1)(x-3)}=$$
$$\frac{2x-6}{2x^2-7x+3}-\frac{6x-3}{2x^2-7x+3}=$$
$$\frac{-4x-3}{2x^2-7x+3};x\neq\tfrac{1}{2},3$$

$$\frac{7x}{2x-5}-\frac{8x}{4x-9}=$$
$$\frac{7x(4x-9)}{(2x-5)(4x-9)}-\frac{8x(2x-5)}{(2x-5)(4x-9)}=$$
$$\frac{28x^2-63x}{8x^2-38x+45}-\frac{16x^2-40x}{8x^2-38x+45}=$$
$$\frac{12x^2-23x}{8x^2-38x+45};x\neq\tfrac{9}{4},\tfrac{5}{2}$$

Multiplying and Dividing Rational Expressions Worksheet 43

① Multiply. Remember to state any exclusions.

$$\frac{24x+32}{x^2+9x}\cdot\frac{2x^2-3x}{6x^2-x-12}=$$
$$\frac{8\cancel{(3x+4)}}{\cancel{x}(x+9)}\cdot\frac{\cancel{x}\cancel{(2x-3)}}{\cancel{(3x+4)}\cancel{(2x-3)}}=$$
$$\frac{8}{x+9};x\neq-9,-\tfrac{4}{3},0,\tfrac{3}{2}$$

$$\frac{18x^2-29x+3}{4x^2+27x+18}\cdot\frac{9x^2+47x-42}{18x^2-41x+21}=$$
$$\frac{(9x+1)\cancel{(2x-3)}}{\cancel{(x+6)}(4x+3)}\cdot\frac{\cancel{(x+6)}\cancel{(9x-7)}}{\cancel{(2x-3)}\cancel{(9x-7)}}=$$
$$\frac{9x+1}{4x+3};x\neq-6,-\tfrac{3}{4},\tfrac{3}{2},\tfrac{7}{9}$$

$$\frac{12x+48}{40x^2+16x}\cdot\frac{10x^2+4x}{x^2-3x-28}=$$
$$\frac{{}_{3}\cancel{12}\cancel{(x+4)}}{{}_{\cancel{4}}\cancel{8x}\cancel{(5x+2)}}\cdot\frac{\cancel{2x}\cancel{(5x+2)}}{\cancel{(x+4)}(x-7)}=$$
$$\frac{3}{x-7};x\neq-4,-\tfrac{2}{5},0,7$$

$$\frac{45x^2+54x}{42x^3-12x^2}\cdot\frac{14x^2-4x}{15x^2+18x}=$$
$$\frac{{}_{\cancel{3}}\cancel{9x}\cancel{(5x+6)}}{{}_{\cancel{3}x}\cancel{6x^2}\cancel{(7x-2)}}\cdot\frac{\cancel{2x}\cancel{(7x-2)}}{\cancel{3x}\cancel{(5x+6)}}=$$
$$\frac{1}{x};x\neq-\tfrac{6}{5},0,\tfrac{2}{7}$$

② Divide. Remember to state any exclusions.

$$\frac{7x^2-19x-6}{2x^2+11x+12}\div\frac{7x^2-12x-4}{2x^2-x-6}=$$
$$\frac{7x^2-19x-6}{2x^2+11x+12}\cdot\frac{2x^2-x-6}{7x^2-12x-4}=$$
$$\frac{(x-3)\cancel{(7x+2)}}{\cancel{(2x+3)}(x+4)}\cdot\frac{\cancel{(2x+3)}\cancel{(x-2)}}{\cancel{(7x+2)}\cancel{(x-2)}}=$$
$$\frac{x-3}{x+4};x\neq-\tfrac{3}{2},-4,-\tfrac{2}{7},2$$

$$\frac{24x+56}{15x^2-31x-24}\div\frac{3x^2-2x-21}{15x^2-40x}=$$
$$\frac{24x+56}{15x^2-31x-24}\cdot\frac{15x^2-40x}{3x^2-2x-21}=$$
$$\frac{8\cancel{(3x+7)}}{\cancel{(3x-8)}(5x+3)}\cdot\frac{5x\cancel{(3x-8)}}{\cancel{(3x+7)}(x-3)}=\frac{8}{5x+3}\cdot\frac{5x}{x-3}=$$
$$\frac{40x}{5x^2-12x-9};x\neq-\tfrac{7}{3},-\tfrac{3}{5},\tfrac{8}{3},3$$

$$\frac{16x^2+20x}{42x^3-28x^2}\div\frac{8x^2+10x}{21x^2-14x}=$$
$$\frac{16x^2+20x}{42x^3-28x^2}\cdot\frac{21x^2-14x}{8x^2+10x}=$$
$$\frac{{}_{\cancel{2}}\cancel{4x}\cancel{(4x+5)}}{{}_{\cancel{2}x}\cancel{14x^2}\cancel{(3x-2)}}\cdot\frac{\cancel{7x}\cancel{(3x-2)}}{\cancel{2x}\cancel{(4x+5)}}=$$
$$\frac{1}{x};x\neq-\tfrac{5}{4},0,\tfrac{2}{3}$$

$$\frac{3x^2-7x-6}{4x^2+15x-4}\div\frac{x^2-5x+6}{x^2+2x-8}=$$
$$\frac{3x^2-7x-6}{4x^2+15x-4}\cdot\frac{x^2+2x-8}{x^2-5x+6}=$$
$$\frac{(3x+2)\cancel{(x-3)}}{(4x-1)\cancel{(x+4)}}\cdot\frac{\cancel{(x+4)}\cancel{(x-2)}}{\cancel{(x-3)}\cancel{(x-2)}}=$$
$$\frac{3x+2}{4x-1};x\neq-4,\tfrac{1}{4},2,3$$

Teaching Tips, Cont.

- Remind students to state all exclusions when giving the answer to any rational expression problem.
- Complete the Classwork exercise. Have one student work the problem on the board for the class and explain the answer. All students should work the problem in their books.

Assignment

- Complete Lesson 85, Activities 2-3.

Lesson 86

Concepts
- Dividing rational expressions
- Exclusions
- Math in the real world

Learning Objectives
The student will be able to:
- Factor polynomials in rational expressions
- Simplify rational expressions
- Divide rational expressions

Materials Needed
- Student Book, Lesson 86

Teaching Tips
- Review dividing rational expressions. (See Lesson 81)
- Review factoring polynomials as needed. (See Lessons 68-77)
- Review simplifying rational expressions as needed. (See Lesson 78)
- Remind students to state all exclusions any time they are working a problem with rational expressions.
- Ask the students what special rule applies to exclusions for division with rational expressions. (The denominators in the original problem as well as the denominator of the reciprocal must be considered when stating the exclusions.)

Review: Dividing Rational Expressions

Recall from Lesson 81 that dividing rational expressions follows the same rules as dividing fractions. Factor each numerator and denominator and cancel like factors before you divide. Remember that entire factors must be cancelled. You cannot cancel individual terms. When writing the answer, remember to state any exclusions found in the original problem as well as the denominator after you have taken the reciprocal of the divisor when stating the exclusions.

① **Classwork**

Solve. Remember to state any exclusions.

$$\frac{3x-15}{4x^2+12x} \div \frac{x^2-x-20}{4x^2+16x} =$$
$$\frac{3x-15}{4x^2+12x} \cdot \frac{4x^2+16x}{x^2-x-20} =$$
$$\frac{3\cancel{(x-5)}}{\cancel{4x}(x+3)} \cdot \frac{\cancel{4x}\cancel{(x+4)}}{\cancel{(x+4)}\cancel{(x-5)}} =$$
$$\frac{3}{x+3}; x \neq -4, -3, 0, 5$$

Activities

② Solve. Remember to state any exclusions.

$$\frac{x^2-4}{2x^2+11x+12} \div \frac{2x^2+x-6}{4x^2-9} =$$
$$\frac{x^2-4}{2x^2+11x+12} \cdot \frac{4x^2-9}{2x^2+x-6} =$$
$$\frac{(x-2)\cancel{(x+2)}}{\cancel{(2x+3)}(x+4)} \cdot \frac{\cancel{(2x+3)}\cancel{(2x-3)}}{\cancel{(x+2)}\cancel{(2x-3)}} =$$
$$\frac{x-2}{x+4}; x \neq -4, -2, -\tfrac{3}{2}, \tfrac{3}{2}$$

$$\frac{3x^2+11x-20}{5x^2-7x-6} \div \frac{4x^2+21x+5}{4x^2-7x-2} =$$
$$\frac{3x^2+11x-20}{5x^2-7x-6} \cdot \frac{4x^2-7x-2}{4x^2+21x+5} =$$
$$\frac{(3x-4)\cancel{(x+5)}}{(5x+3)\cancel{(x-2)}} \cdot \frac{\cancel{(4x+1)}\cancel{(x-2)}}{\cancel{(4x+1)}\cancel{(x+5)}} =$$
$$\frac{3x-4}{5x+3}; x \neq -5, -\tfrac{3}{5}, -\tfrac{1}{4}, 2$$

$$\frac{12x^3+44x^2-16x}{6x^4+6x^3-36x^2} \div \frac{6x^3+22x^2-8x}{9x^3-36x} =$$
$$\frac{12x^3+44x^2-16x}{6x^4+6x^3-36x^2} \cdot \frac{9x^3-36x}{6x^3+22x^2-8x} =$$
$$\frac{{}_{2}\cancel{4x}\cancel{(3x-1)}\cancel{(x+4)}}{{}_{3x}\cancel{6x^2}(x+3)\cancel{(x-2)}} \cdot \frac{{}_{3}\cancel{9x}(x+2)\cancel{(x-2)}}{\cancel{2x}\cancel{(3x-1)}\cancel{(x+4)}} =$$
$$\frac{3(x+2)}{x(x+3)} = \frac{3x+6}{x^2+3x}; x \neq -4, -3, -2, 0, \tfrac{1}{3}, 2$$

$$\frac{2x^2+11x+12}{4x^2+3x-1} \div \frac{4x^2+12x+9}{8x^2+18x-5} =$$
$$\frac{2x^2+11x+12}{4x^2+3x-1} \cdot \frac{8x^2+18x-5}{4x^2+12x+9} =$$
$$\frac{(x+4)\cancel{(2x+3)}}{\cancel{(4x-1)}(x+1)} \cdot \frac{(2x+5)\cancel{(4x-1)}}{\cancel{(2x+3)}(2x+3)} =$$
$$\frac{(x+4)}{(x+1)} \cdot \frac{(2x+5)}{(2x+3)} =$$
$$\frac{2x^2+13x+20}{2x^2+5x+3}; x \neq -\tfrac{3}{2}, -1, \tfrac{1}{4}, -\tfrac{5}{2}$$

$$\frac{12x^2+x-6}{12x^2-19x-21} \div \frac{9x^2-12x+4}{9x^2-4} =$$
$$\frac{12x^2+x-6}{12x^2-19x-21} \cdot \frac{9x^2-4}{9x^2-12x+4} =$$
$$\frac{\cancel{(3x-2)}\cancel{(4x+3)}}{(3x-7)\cancel{(4x+3)}} \cdot \frac{(3x+2)\cancel{(3x-2)}}{\cancel{(3x-2)}\cancel{(3x-2)}} =$$
$$\frac{3x+2}{3x-7}; x \neq -\tfrac{3}{4}, \tfrac{2}{3}, \tfrac{7}{3}, -\tfrac{2}{3}$$

$$\frac{8x^2-5x-3}{10x^2-33x-54} \div \frac{x^2-3x+2}{5x^2-4x-12} =$$
$$\frac{8x^2-5x-3}{10x^2-33x-54} \cdot \frac{5x^2-4x-12}{x^2-3x+2} =$$
$$\frac{(8x+3)\cancel{(x-1)}}{(2x-9)\cancel{(5x+6)}} \cdot \frac{\cancel{(5x+6)}\cancel{(x-2)}}{\cancel{(x-2)}\cancel{(x-1)}} =$$
$$\frac{8x+3}{2x-9}; x \neq 1, -\tfrac{6}{5}, 2, \tfrac{9}{2}$$

③ Solve. Round answers to the nearest hundredth. You will want to use your scientific calculator.

The trade value, *v*, of a player is found using the formula $v = \frac{(e-y)^2(y+1)e}{190} + \frac{ey^2}{13}$, where *e* is the player's estimated value and *y* is the player's estimated number of years left to play. The value of *y* is found using the formula $y = 27 - \frac{3a}{4}$, where *a* is the player's current age. The value of *e* is found using the formula

$$e = \frac{(p + 0.85r + 0.35d + 0.79a + 1.2s + 0.85b - 1.2t - 0.85g - 1.45m - 0.41f)^{\frac{3}{4}}}{21}$$

where the variables represent the following information for the season:

p is the number of points scored
r is the number of offensive rebounds
d is the number of defensive rebounds
a is the number of assists
s is the number of steals
b is the number blocks
t is the number of turnovers
g is the number of field goals missed
m is the number of missed free throws
f is the number of personal fouls

How many additional years can a team expect a 32-year-old player to play?

$y = 27 - \frac{3(32)}{4} = 27 - 24 = 3$ additional years

What is the estimated value, *e*, of a player with the following season stats?

2075 points scored
82 offensive rebounds
336 defensive rebounds
385 assists
98 steals
16 blocks
246 turnovers
1066 field goals missed
82 missed free throws
172 personal fouls

$$e = \frac{(2075 + 0.85(82) + 0.35(336) + 0.79(385) + 1.2(98) + 0.85(16) - 1.2(246) - 0.85(1066) - 1.45(82) - 0.41(172))^{\frac{3}{4}}}{21}$$

$$e = \frac{(2075 + 69.7 + 117.6 + 304.15 + 117.6 + 13.6 - 295.2 - 906.1 - 118.9 - 70.52)^{\frac{3}{4}}}{21} = \frac{(1306.93)^{\frac{3}{4}}}{21} = 10.35$$

What is the trade value of a 32-year-old with the above stats?

$$v = \frac{(10.35-3)^2(3+1)(10.35)}{190} + \frac{(10.35)(3^2)}{13} = \frac{(7.35)^2(4)(10.35)}{190} + \frac{(10.35)(9)}{13} = \frac{(54.0225)(4)(10.35)}{190} + \frac{93.15}{13} =$$

$$\frac{13(2236.5315)}{13(190)} + \frac{190(93.15)}{190(13)} = \frac{29074.9095}{2470} + \frac{17698.5}{2470} = \frac{46773.4095}{2470} = 18.94$$

The trade value is used to compare players being considered in a trade to determine if the trade is fair and which team is getting the better deal. It is not a measure of salary.

Teaching Tips, Cont.

- Complete the Classwork exercise. Have one student work the problem on the board for the class and explain the answers. All students should work the problem in their books.

Assignment

- Complete Lesson 86, Activities 2-3.

Lesson 87

Concepts

- Complex fractions
- Systems of equations
- Graphing

Learning Objectives

The student will be able to:

- Define *complex fraction*
- Simplify complex fractions

Materials Needed

- Student Book, Lesson 87

Teaching Tips

- Review lowest common multiple as needed. (See Lesson 6)
- Define *complex fraction* from the teaching box.
- Teach simplifying complex fractions from the teaching box.
- Ask the students what mathematical operator is indicated by a fraction bar. (Division)
- An alternate method of simplifying complex fractions is shown at the right. You may teach the alternate method at your own discretion. Students who have a difficult time simplifying complex fractions with the LCD may find it easier using the alternate method. However, students should be encouraged to use the LCD method as much as possible because it will make complex fractions with rational expressions easier to simplify later.

Lesson 87

Complex Fractions

A **complex fraction** is a fraction that has a fraction in the numerator, the denominator, or both. The following are all complex fractions.

$\frac{\frac{1}{2}}{3}$ Fraction in the numerator

$\frac{2}{\frac{3}{4}}$ Fraction in the denominator

$\frac{\frac{2}{3}}{\frac{3}{4}}$ Fractions in the numerator and denominator

To simplify a complex fraction, find the lowest common denominator (LCD) of all fractions in both the numerator and the denominator. Do not use whole numbers that appear in the numerator or denominator of the complex fraction. Multiply the numerator and denominator of the complex fraction by the LCD.

Simplify $\frac{\frac{2}{3}}{\frac{3}{4}}$. The LCD is $3(4) = 12$.

Multiply the numerator and denominator by 12.

$$\frac{{}_4\cancel{12}\left(\frac{2}{\cancel{3}}\right)}{{}_3\cancel{12}\left(\frac{3}{\cancel{4}}\right)} = \frac{4(2)}{3(3)} = \frac{8}{9}$$

① **Classwork**

Simplify the complex fractions.

$\frac{\frac{1}{2}}{3}$

The LCD is 2. (The 3 in the denominator is not a fraction and is not used in finding the LCD.)

$$\frac{\cancel{2}\left(\frac{1}{\cancel{2}}\right)}{2(3)} = \frac{1}{6}$$

$\frac{2}{\frac{3}{4}}$

The LCD is 4. (The 2 in the numerator is not a fraction and is not used in finding the LCD.)

$$\frac{4(2)}{\cancel{4}\left(\frac{3}{\cancel{4}}\right)} = \frac{8}{3}$$

$\frac{\frac{1}{4}}{\frac{3}{5}+\frac{1}{2}}$

The LCD is $5(2^2) = 20$.

$$\frac{{}_5\cancel{20}\left(\frac{1}{\cancel{4}}\right)}{20\left(\frac{3}{5}+\frac{1}{2}\right)} = \frac{5}{{}_4\cancel{20}\left(\frac{3}{\cancel{5}}\right) + {}_{10}\cancel{20}\left(\frac{1}{\cancel{2}}\right)} =$$

$$\frac{5}{12+10} = \frac{5}{22}$$

Activities

② Simplify the complex fractions.

$\frac{\frac{1}{3}}{5}$ LCD = 3.

$$\frac{\cancel{3}\left(\frac{1}{\cancel{3}}\right)}{3(5)} = \frac{1}{15}$$

$\frac{\frac{3}{8}}{2}$ LCD = 8.

$$\frac{\cancel{8}\left(\frac{3}{\cancel{8}}\right)}{8(2)} = \frac{3}{16}$$

$\frac{\frac{5}{9}}{7}$ LCD = 9.

$$\frac{\cancel{9}\left(\frac{5}{\cancel{9}}\right)}{9(7)} = \frac{5}{63}$$

$\frac{7}{\frac{5}{6}}$ LCD = 6.

$$\frac{6(7)}{\cancel{6}\left(\frac{5}{\cancel{6}}\right)} = \frac{42}{5}$$

$\frac{6}{\frac{2}{7}}$ LCD = 7.

$$\frac{7(6)}{\cancel{7}\left(\frac{2}{\cancel{7}}\right)} = \frac{{}_{21}\cancel{42}}{\cancel{2}} = 21$$

$\frac{4}{\frac{6}{11}}$ LCD = 11.

$$\frac{11(4)}{\cancel{11}\left(\frac{6}{\cancel{11}}\right)} = \frac{44}{6} = \frac{22}{3}$$

$\frac{\frac{1}{4}}{\frac{3}{5}}$ LCD $= 5(4) = 20$.

$$\frac{{}_5\cancel{20}\left(\frac{1}{\cancel{4}}\right)}{{}_4\cancel{20}\left(\frac{3}{\cancel{5}}\right)} = \frac{5}{12}$$

$\frac{\frac{3}{4}}{\frac{5}{8}}$ LCD = 8.

$$\frac{{}_2\cancel{8}\left(\frac{3}{\cancel{4}}\right)}{\cancel{8}\left(\frac{5}{\cancel{8}}\right)} = \frac{6}{5}$$

$\frac{\frac{2}{5}}{\frac{3}{8}}$ LCD $= 5(8) = 40$.

$$\frac{{}_8\cancel{40}\left(\frac{2}{\cancel{5}}\right)}{{}_5\cancel{40}\left(\frac{3}{\cancel{8}}\right)} = \frac{16}{15}$$

Alternate Method for Complex Fractions

Rewrite as a division problem.

$$\frac{\frac{2}{3}}{\frac{3}{4}} = \frac{2}{3} \div \frac{3}{4}$$

Take the reciprocal of the divisor and multiply.

$$\frac{2}{3} \times \frac{4}{3} = \frac{8}{9}$$

③ Solve the systems of equations by graphing. Express the solution as a coordinate point.

$x + y - 3 = 0$
$2x - y - 3 = 0$

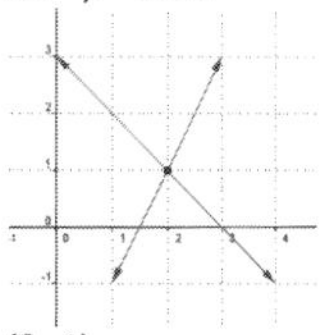

(2, 1)

$2x + y - 1 = 0$
$x - 2y - 3 = 0$

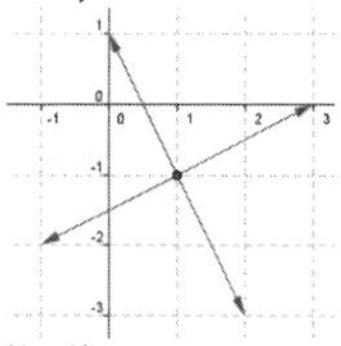

(1, -1)

$x + y - 1 = 0$
$x - 3y + 7 = 0$

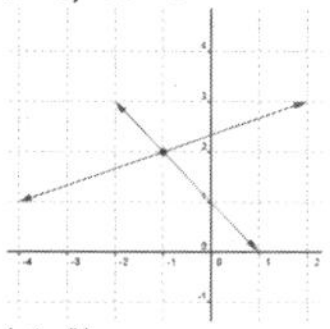

(-1, 2)

④ Solve the systems of equations using the method of your choice. Express the solution as a coordinate point.

$3x + y - 5 = 0$
$-2x - y + 6 = 0$
$3x + y = 5$
$-2x - y = -6$
$x = -1$

$3(-1) + y - 5 = 0$
$-3 + y = 5$
$y = 8$

(-1, 8)

$x + 2y + 11 = 0$
$-x - 3y - 20 = 0$
$x + 2y = -11$
$-x - 3y = 20$
$-y = 9$
$y = -9$

$x + 2(-9) + 11 = 0$
$x - 18 = -11$
$x = 7$

(7, -9)

$x + y - 7 = 0$
$2x + y - 5 = 0$
$x + y = 7$
$2x + y = 5$
$-x = 2$
$x = -2$

$-2 + y - 7 = 0$
$y = 9$

(-2, 9)

$3x + 4y + 9 = 0$
$-x - y - 1 = 0$
$3x + 4y = -9$
$-x - y = 1$

$3x + 4y = -9$
$-3x - 3y = 3$
$y = -6$

$-x - (-6) - 1 = 0$
$-x + 6 = 1$
$-x = -5$
$x = 5$

(5, -6)

$10x - 3y - 10 = 0$
$7x - 2y - 8 = 0$
$10x - 3y = 10$
$7x - 2y = 8$

$20x - 6y = 20$
$21x - 6y = 24$
$-x = -4$
$x = 4$

$10(4) - 3y - 10 = 0$
$40 - 3y = 10$
$-3y = -30$
$y = 10$

(4, 10)

$3x - 6y - 15 = 0$
$4x - 8y - 20 = 0$
$3x - 6y = 15$
$4x - 8y = 20$

$x - 2y = 5$
$x - 2y = 5$
$0 = 0$

All real numbers

$10x - 3y - 12 = 0$
$7x - 2y - 9 = 0$
$10x - 3y = 12$
$7x - 2y = 9$

$20x - 6y = 24$
$21x - 6y = 27$
$-x = -3$
$x = 3$

$10(3) - 3y - 12 = 0$
$30 - 3y = 12$
$-3y = -18$
$y = 6$

(3, 6)

$4x - 12y - 8 = 0$
$6x - 18y - 12 = 0$
$4x - 12y = 8$
$6x - 18y = 12$

$x - 3y = 2$
$x - 3y = 2$
$0 = 0$

All real numbers

Note: Solutions show one method of solving. Students may use a different method, but will still get the same answer.

Teaching Tips, Cont.

- If you have taught both methods of simplifying complex fractions, tell the students that they may use either method for this lesson.
- Encourage the students to use the method presented in the teaching box of this lesson. The complex fractions become more involved in the next two lessons and students should be used to the method presented in this lesson.
- Complete the Classwork exercises. Have some students work the problems on the board for the class and explain their answers. All students should work the problems in their books.

Assignment

- Complete Lesson 87, Activities 2-4.

Lesson 88

Concepts

- Complex rational expressions
- Equations with radicals
- Equations with absolute value
- Math in the real world

Learning Objectives

The student will be able to:

- Define *complex rational expression*
- Simplify complex rational expressions

Materials Needed

- Student Book, Lesson 88
- Worksheet 44

Teaching Tips

- Have students complete Worksheet 44 in class. This may be for added practice of earlier topics, or graded as a quiz, if desired.
- Review complex fractions. (See Lesson 87)
- Review rational expressions. (See Lessons 78-86)
- Have the students compare the complex fractions in the teaching boxes of Lessons 87 and 88. Ask the students what is different about the complex fractions in Lesson 88. (There are variables in the complex fractions in Lesson 88.)
- Teach complex rational expressions from the teaching box. Explain that the method used to solve complex fractions with rational expressions is the same as the method used to solve complex fractions in Lesson 87.

Lesson 88

Complex Rational Expressions

A **complex rational expression** is a fraction that has a rational expression in the numerator, the denominator, or both. The following are all complex rational expressions.

$\frac{\frac{1}{x+2}}{3}$ Rational expression in the numerator

$\frac{2}{\frac{3}{3x+4}}$ Rational expression in the denominator

$\frac{\frac{2}{x-3}}{\frac{3}{4x+1}}$ Rational expression in both

To simplify a complex rational expression, find the lowest common denominator (LCD) of all fractions in both the numerator and the denominator. Do not use whole numbers that appear in the numerator or denominator of the complex fraction. Leave the LCD as factors. Multiply the numerator and denominator of the complex fraction by the LCD.

Simplify $\frac{\frac{2}{x-3}}{\frac{3}{4x+1}}$. The LCD is $(x-3)(4x+1)$.

Multiply the numerator and denominator by $(x-3)(4x+1)$.

$$\frac{\cancel{(x-3)}(4x+1)\left(\frac{2}{\cancel{x-3}}\right)}{(x-3)\cancel{(4x+1)}\left(\frac{3}{\cancel{4x+1}}\right)}=\frac{2(4x+1)}{3(x-3)}=\frac{8x+2}{3x-9}$$

① Classwork

Simplify the complex rational expressions.

$\frac{\frac{1}{x+2}}{3}$

The LCD is $x+2$. (The 3 in the denominator is not a fraction and is not used in finding the LCD.)

$$\frac{\cancel{x+2}\left(\frac{1}{\cancel{x+2}}\right)}{(x+2)(3)}=\frac{1}{3x+6}$$

$\frac{2}{\frac{3}{3x+4}}$

The LCD is $3x+4$. (The 2 in the numerator is not a fraction and is not used in finding the LCD.)

$$\frac{(3x+4)(2)}{\cancel{(3x+4)}\left(\frac{3}{\cancel{3x+4}}\right)}=\frac{6x+8}{3}$$

$\frac{\frac{1}{x+4}}{\frac{3}{2x+5}}$

The LCD is $(x+4)(2x+5)$.

$$\frac{\cancel{(x+4)}(2x+5)\left(\frac{1}{\cancel{x+4}}\right)}{(x+4)\cancel{(2x+5)}\left(\frac{3}{\cancel{2x+5}}\right)}=$$

$$\frac{2x+5}{3x+12}$$

Activities

② Simplify the complex rational expressions.

$\frac{\frac{1}{x-3}}{5}$ LCD = $x-3$.

$$\frac{\cancel{(x-3)}\left(\frac{1}{\cancel{x-3}}\right)}{(x-3)(5)}=\frac{1}{5x-15}$$

$\frac{7}{\frac{5}{6x+1}}$ LCD = $6x+1$.

$$\frac{(6x+1)(7)}{\cancel{(6x+1)}\left(\frac{5}{\cancel{6x+1}}\right)}=\frac{42x+7}{5}$$

$\frac{\frac{1}{x-4}}{\frac{3}{x+5}}$ LCD = $(x-4)(x+5)$.

$$\frac{\cancel{(x-4)}(x+5)\left(\frac{1}{\cancel{x-4}}\right)}{(x-4)\cancel{(x+5)}\left(\frac{3}{\cancel{x+5}}\right)}=\frac{x+5}{3x-12}$$

$\frac{\frac{3}{3x-8}}{2}$ LCD = $3x-8$.

$$\frac{\cancel{(3x-8)}\left(\frac{3}{\cancel{3x-8}}\right)}{(3x-8)(2)}=\frac{3}{6x-16}$$

$\frac{6}{\frac{2}{2x+7}}$ LCD = $2x+7$.

$$\frac{(2x+7)(\cancel{6}_3)}{\cancel{(2x+7)}\left(\frac{\cancel{2}}{\cancel{2x+7}}\right)}=6x+21$$

$\frac{\frac{3}{5x-4}}{\frac{5}{8x+3}}$ LCD = $(5x-4)(8x+3)$.

$$\frac{\cancel{(5x-4)}(8x+3)\left(\frac{3}{\cancel{5x-4}}\right)}{(5x-4)\cancel{(8x+3)}\left(\frac{5}{\cancel{8x+3}}\right)}=\frac{24x+9}{25x-20}$$

③ Solve. Identify any extraneous solutions.

$\sqrt{-6x+10}+3=11$

$\sqrt{-6x+10}=8$

$\left(\sqrt{-6x+10}\right)^2=8^2$

$-6x+10=64$

$-6x=54$

$x=-9$

check:

$\sqrt{-6(-9)+10}+3=11$

$\sqrt{54+10}+3=11$

$\sqrt{64}+3=11$

$8+3=11$

$|-4x-9|+7>3$

$|-4x-9|>-4$ ALL REAL NUMBERS

The absolute value of anything can never be negative, so the answer is all real numbers.

$|4x-3|-2=x+10$

$|4x-3|=x+12$

$4x-3=x+12$ or $4x-3=-(x+12)$

$3x=15$ | $4x-3=-x-12$

$x=5$ | $5x=-9\Rightarrow x=-\frac{9}{5}$

check:

$|4(5)-3|-2=1(5)+10$

$|20-3|-2=5+10$

$17-2=15$

$\left|4\left(-\frac{9}{5}\right)-3\right|-2=1\left(-\frac{9}{5}\right)+10$

$\left|-\frac{36}{5}-\frac{15}{5}\right|-\frac{10}{5}=-\frac{9}{5}+\frac{50}{5}$

$\frac{51}{5}-\frac{10}{5}=\frac{41}{5}$

$|3x+6|+13<7$

$|3x+6|<-6$ NO SOLUTION

The absolute value of anything can never be negative, so the answer is no solution.

$|2x+7|+6x=3x-11$

$|2x+7|=-3x-11$

$2x+7=-3x-11$ or $2x+7=-(-3x-11)$

$5x=-18$ | $2x+7=3x+11$

$x=-\frac{18}{5}$ | $-x=4\Rightarrow x=-4$

check:

$\left|2\left(-\frac{18}{5}\right)+7\right|+6\left(-\frac{18}{5}\right)=3\left(-\frac{18}{5}\right)-11$

$\left|-\frac{36}{5}+\frac{35}{5}\right|-\frac{108}{5}=-\frac{54}{5}-\frac{55}{5}$

$\left|-\frac{1}{5}\right|-\frac{108}{5}=-\frac{109}{5}$

$\frac{1}{5}-\frac{108}{5}\neq-\frac{109}{5}$ extraneous

$|2(-4)+7|+6(-4)=3(-4)-11$

$|-8+7|-24=-12-11$

$|-1|-24=-23$

$1-24=-23$

$\sqrt{4x-7}+1=-4$

$\sqrt{4x-7}=-5$

$\left(\sqrt{4x-7}\right)^2=(-5)^2$

$4x-7=25$

$4x=32$

$x=8$

check:

$\sqrt{4(8)-7}+1=-4$

$\sqrt{32-7}+1=-4$

$\sqrt{25}+1=-4$

$5+1\neq-4$ extraneous

④ Solve.

According to the formula $y=27-\frac{3a}{4}$, where a is a basketball player's current age and y is the number of years left to play professional ball, what is the age of a basketball player when he is likely to end his career? State your answer as an inequality.

$0\le 27-\frac{3a}{4}$ | $3a\le 108$

$0\le 108-3a$ | $a\le 36$ A basketball player's age is less than or equal to 36 years.

Adding Rational Expressions with Different Denominators Worksheet 44

① Solve. Remember to state any exclusions.

$\frac{2x}{3x+4}+\frac{1}{3}=$
$\frac{(2x)(3)}{(3x+4)(3)}+\frac{(1)(3x+4)}{(3)(3x+4)}=$
$\frac{6x+3x+4}{9x+12}=\frac{9x+4}{9x+12}; x \neq -\frac{4}{3}$

$\frac{5x^2}{2x+5}+2=$
$\frac{(5x^2)(1)}{(2x+5)(1)}+\frac{(2)(2x+5)}{(1)(2x+5)}=$
$\frac{5x^2+4x+10}{2x+5}; x \neq -\frac{5}{2}$

$\frac{3x}{5x+2}-\frac{2x}{5}=$
$\frac{(3x)(5)}{(5x+2)(5)}-\frac{(2x)(5x+2)}{(5)(5x+2)}=$
$\frac{15x-10x^2-4x}{25x+10}=$
$\frac{-10x^2+11x}{25x+10}; x \neq -\frac{2}{5}$

$\frac{5}{4x+5}+\frac{3x}{7}=$
$\frac{(5)(7)}{(4x+5)(7)}+\frac{(3x)(4x+5)}{(7)(4x+5)}=$
$\frac{35+12x^2+15x}{28x+35}=$
$\frac{12x^2+15x+35}{28x+35}; x \neq -\frac{5}{4}$

$\frac{4}{2x+3}+\frac{1}{3x-1}=$
$\frac{4(3x-1)}{(2x+3)(3x-1)}+\frac{1(2x+3)}{(2x+3)(3x-1)}=$
$\frac{12x-4}{6x^2+7x-3}+\frac{2x+3}{6x^2+7x-3}=$
$\frac{14x-1}{6x^2+7x-3}; x \neq -\frac{3}{2}, \frac{1}{3}$

$\frac{3}{x+4}+\frac{2x}{4x+1}=$
$\frac{3(4x+1)}{(x+4)(4x+1)}+\frac{2x(x+4)}{(x+4)(4x+1)}=$
$\frac{12x+3}{4x^2+17x+4}+\frac{2x^2+8x}{4x^2+17x+4}=$
$\frac{2x^2+20x+3}{4x^2+17x+4}; x \neq -4, -\frac{1}{4}$

$\frac{5}{2x+1}+\frac{4}{2x-1}=$
$\frac{5(2x-1)}{(2x+1)(2x-1)}+\frac{4(2x+1)}{(2x+1)(2x-1)}=$
$\frac{10x-5}{4x^2-1}+\frac{8x+4}{4x^2-1}=$
$\frac{18x-1}{4x^2-1}; x \neq -\frac{1}{2}, \frac{1}{2}$

$\frac{8x}{x-2}+\frac{2x^2}{4x+3}=$
$\frac{8x(4x+3)}{(x-2)(4x+3)}+\frac{2x^2(x-2)}{(x-2)(4x+3)}=$
$\frac{32x^2+24x}{4x^2-5x-6}+\frac{2x^3-4x^2}{4x^2-5x-6}=$
$\frac{2x^3+28x^2+24x}{4x^2-5x-6}; x \neq -\frac{3}{4}, 2$

Teaching Tips, Cont.

- Make sure all students understand that the LCD is found using the denominators of the individual fractions. The numerators of the individual fractions are not used to determine the LCD.
- Note: When simplifying expressions with variables in the denominator, it is customary to list values of the variable that must be excluded as part of the solution. (The variable cannot equal anything that would cause a denominator to equal zero since you cannot divide by zero.) For now, it is important that the students understand the basic concept of simplifying complex rational expressions. Exclusions will be included when the complex expressions are solved.
- Complete the Classwork exercises. Have some students work the problems on the board for the class and explain their answers. All students should work the problems in their books.

Assignment

- Complete Lesson 88, Activities 2-4.

Lesson 89

Concepts

- Complex rational expressions
- Lowest common denominator

Learning Objectives

The student will be able to:

- Identify the lowest common denominator (LCD) of a complex rational expression
- Simplify complex rational expressions

Materials Needed

- Student Book, Lesson 89
- Worksheet 45

Teaching Tips

- Review complex fractions. (See Lesson 87)
- Review rational expressions. (See Lessons 78-86)
- Review complex rational expressions. (See Lesson 88)
- Remind students to use only the denominators when finding the LCD. If there are multiple fractions in the numerator or denominator of the main fraction, all denominators must be used to find the LCD.

Review of Complex Expressions

Recall that complex expressions are fractions that have a fraction, rational expression, or both in the numerator, denominator, or both. No matter what the configuration, find the LCD of all fractions in the complex expression and multiply each term in the numerator and denominator by the LCD.

Simplify the complex expression.

$$\frac{\frac{3}{x}+\frac{4}{x+1}}{\frac{x-1}{x^2-1}}$$

Factor each denominator and cancel like terms before finding the LCD.

$$\frac{\frac{3}{x}+\frac{4}{x+1}}{\frac{\cancel{x-1}}{(x+1)(\cancel{x-1})}}$$

The LCD is $x(x+1)$.

Multiply each term in the numerator and denominator by the LCD. Cancel where appropriate and combine like terms.

$$\frac{\cancel{x}(x+1)\left(\frac{3}{\cancel{x}}\right)+x\left(\cancel{x+1}\right)\left(\frac{4}{\cancel{x+1}}\right)}{x\left(\cancel{x+1}\right)\left(\frac{1}{\cancel{x+1}}\right)}=$$

$$\frac{3(x+1)+4x}{x}=\frac{3x+3+4x}{x}=\frac{7x+3}{x}$$

① **Classwork.**

Simplify the complex expression.

$$\frac{\frac{4}{x}+\frac{3}{x+2}}{\frac{x+1}{x^2-1}}$$

$$\frac{\frac{4}{x}+\frac{3}{x+2}}{\frac{\cancel{x+1}}{(\cancel{x+1})(x-1)}}$$

The LCD is $x(x+2)(x-1)$.

$$\frac{\cancel{x}(x+2)(x-1)\left(\frac{4}{\cancel{x}}\right)+x\left(\cancel{x+2}\right)(x-1)\left(\frac{3}{\cancel{x+2}}\right)}{x(x+2)\left(\cancel{x-1}\right)\left(\frac{1}{\cancel{x-1}}\right)}=$$

$$\frac{(x+2)(x-1)(4)+x(x-1)(3)}{x(x+2)(1)}=$$

$$\frac{\left(x^2+x-2\right)(4)+\left(x^2-x\right)(3)}{\left(x^2+2x\right)(1)}=$$

$$\frac{4x^2+4x-8+3x^2-3x}{x^2+2x}=$$

$$\frac{7x^2+x-8}{x^2+2x}$$

Activities

② Simplify the complex expressions.

$$\frac{\frac{2}{x}+\frac{3}{x+2}}{\frac{x-2}{x^2-4}}$$

$$\frac{\frac{2}{x}+\frac{3}{x+2}}{\frac{\cancel{x-2}}{(x+2)(\cancel{x-2})}}$$

The LCD is $x(x+2)$.

$$\frac{\cancel{x}(x+2)\left(\frac{2}{\cancel{x}}\right)+x\left(\cancel{x+2}\right)\left(\frac{3}{\cancel{x+2}}\right)}{x\left(\cancel{x+2}\right)\left(\frac{1}{\cancel{x+2}}\right)}=$$

$$\frac{(x+2)(2)+x(3)}{x(1)}=\frac{2x+4+3x}{x}=$$

$$\frac{5x+4}{x}$$

$$\frac{\frac{5}{x}+\frac{1}{2x-3}}{\frac{2x+3}{4x^2-9}}$$

$$\frac{\frac{5}{x}+\frac{1}{2x-3}}{\frac{\cancel{2x+3}}{(\cancel{2x+3})(2x-3)}}$$

The LCD is $x(2x-3)$.

$$\frac{\cancel{x}(2x-3)\left(\frac{5}{\cancel{x}}\right)+x\left(\cancel{2x-3}\right)\left(\frac{1}{\cancel{2x-3}}\right)}{x\left(\cancel{2x-3}\right)\left(\frac{1}{\cancel{2x-3}}\right)}=$$

$$\frac{(2x-3)(5)+x(1)}{x(1)}=\frac{10x-15+x}{x}=$$

$$\frac{11x-15}{x}$$

③ Simplify the complex expressions.

$$\frac{\frac{7}{3x}+\frac{5}{x+4}}{\frac{x-4}{x^2-16}}$$

$$\frac{\frac{7}{3x}+\frac{5}{x+4}}{\frac{\cancel{x-4}}{(x+4)(\cancel{x-4})}}$$

The LCD is $3x(x+4)$.

$$\frac{\cancel{3x}(x+4)\left(\frac{7}{\cancel{3x}}\right)+3x\left(\cancel{x+4}\right)\left(\frac{5}{\cancel{x+4}}\right)}{3x\left(\cancel{x+4}\right)\left(\frac{1}{\cancel{x+4}}\right)}=$$

$$\frac{(x+4)(7)+3x(5)}{3x(1)}=$$

$$\frac{7x+28+15x}{3x}=$$

$$\frac{22x+28}{3x}$$

$$\frac{\frac{2x+5}{2x}+\frac{3x+1}{x^2+2x+1}}{\frac{x+1}{6x^2+2x}}$$

$$\frac{\frac{2x+5}{2x}+\frac{3x+1}{(x+1)^2}}{\frac{x+1}{2x(3x+1)}}$$

The LCD is $2x(x+1)^2(3x+1)$.

$$\frac{\cancel{2x}(x+1)^2(3x+1)\left(\frac{2x+5}{\cancel{2x}}\right)+2x\cancel{(x+1)^2}(3x+1)\left(\frac{3x+1}{\cancel{(x+1)^2}}\right)}{\cancel{2x}(x+1)^2\left(\cancel{3x+1}\right)\left(\frac{x+1}{\cancel{2x}(\cancel{3x+1})}\right)}=$$

$$\frac{(x+1)^2(3x+1)(2x+5)+2x(3x+1)(3x+1)}{(x+1)^2(x+1)}=$$

$$\frac{\left(x^2+2x+1\right)\left(6x^2+17x+5\right)+\left(6x^2+2x\right)(3x+1)}{\left(x^2+2x+1\right)(x+1)}=$$

$$\frac{\left(6x^4+29x^3+45x^2+27x+5\right)+\left(18x^3+12x^2+2x\right)}{x^3+x^2+2x^2+2x+x+1}=$$

$$\frac{6x^4+47x^3+57x^2+29x+5}{x^3+3x^2+3x+1}$$

$$\frac{\frac{2}{2x+1}+\frac{3}{x-2}}{\frac{x+1}{x^2-x-2}-\frac{2x+4}{x^2-4}}$$

$$\frac{\frac{2}{2x+1}+\frac{3}{x-2}}{\frac{\cancel{x+1}}{(\cancel{x+1})(x-2)}-\frac{2(\cancel{x+2})}{(\cancel{x+2})(x-2)}}$$

The LCD is $(2x+1)(x-2)$.

$$\frac{\left(\cancel{2x+1}\right)(x-2)\left(\frac{2}{\cancel{2x+1}}\right)+(2x+1)\left(\cancel{x-2}\right)\left(\frac{3}{\cancel{x-2}}\right)}{(2x+1)\left(\cancel{x-2}\right)\left(\frac{1}{\cancel{x-2}}\right)-(2x+1)\left(\cancel{x-2}\right)\left(\frac{2}{\cancel{x-2}}\right)}=$$

$$\frac{(x-2)(2)+(2x+1)(3)}{(2x+1)(1)-(2x+1)(2)}=$$

$$\frac{(2x-4)+(6x+3)}{2x+1-4x-2}=$$

$$\frac{8x-1}{-2x-1}$$

$$\frac{\frac{x^2+7x+6}{x+1}-\frac{x^2+4x+3}{x+3}}{\frac{x+1}{x^2+7x+6}}$$

$$\frac{\frac{(x+6)(\cancel{x+1})}{\cancel{x+1}}-\frac{(x+1)(\cancel{x+3})}{\cancel{x+3}}}{\frac{\cancel{x+1}}{(x+6)(\cancel{x+1})}}$$

The LCD is $(x+6)$.

$$\frac{(x+6)(x+6)-(x+6)(x+1)}{\left(\cancel{x+6}\right)\left(\frac{1}{\cancel{x+6}}\right)}=$$

$$\frac{\left(x^2+12x+36\right)-\left(x^2+7x+6\right)}{1}=$$

$$5x+30$$

Complex Rational Expressions Worksheet 45

① Simplify the complex expressions.

$$\frac{\frac{9}{4x}+\frac{3}{x+2}}{\frac{2x-4}{x^2-4}}$$

$$\frac{\frac{9}{4x}+\frac{3}{x+2}}{\frac{2\cancel{(x-2)}}{(x+2)\cancel{(x-2)}}}$$

The LCD is $4x(x+2)$.

$$\frac{\cancel{4x}(x+2)\left(\frac{9}{\cancel{4x}}\right)+4x\cancel{(x+2)}\left(\frac{3}{\cancel{x+2}}\right)}{4x\cancel{(x+2)}\left(\frac{2}{\cancel{x+2}}\right)}=$$

$$\frac{(x+2)(9)+4x(3)}{4x(2)}=$$

$$\frac{9x+18+12x}{8x}=$$

$$\frac{21x+18}{8x}$$

$$\frac{\frac{2x+1}{5x}+\frac{2x+5}{x^2-2x+1}}{\frac{3x+1}{15x^2+10x}}$$

$$\frac{\frac{2x+1}{5x}+\frac{2x+5}{(x-1)^2}}{\frac{3x+1}{5x(3x+2)}}$$

The LCD is $5x(x-1)^2(3x+2)$.

$$\frac{\cancel{5x}(x-1)^2(3x+2)\left(\frac{2x+1}{\cancel{5x}}\right)+5x\cancel{(x-1)^2}(3x+2)\left(\frac{2x+5}{\cancel{(x-1)^2}}\right)}{\cancel{5x}(x-1)^2\cancel{(3x+2)}\left(\frac{3x+1}{\cancel{5x}\cancel{(3x+2)}}\right)}=$$

$$\frac{(x-1)^2(3x+2)(2x+1)+5x(3x+2)(2x+5)}{(x-1)^2(3x+1)}=$$

$$\frac{(x^2-2x+1)(6x^2+7x+2)+(15x^2+10x)(2x+5)}{(x^2-2x+1)(3x+1)}=$$

$$\frac{(6x^4-5x^3-6x^2+3x+2)+(30x^3+95x^2+50x)}{3x^3+x^2-6x^2-2x+3x+1}=$$

$$\frac{6x^4+25x^3+89x^2+53x+2}{3x^3-5x^2+x+1}$$

$$\frac{\frac{3}{x+6}+\frac{4}{7x-2}}{\frac{2x+2}{7x^2+5x-2}-\frac{5x+10}{7x^2+12x-4}}$$

$$\frac{\frac{3}{x+6}+\frac{4}{7x-2}}{\frac{2\cancel{(x+1)}}{\cancel{(x+1)}(7x-2)}-\frac{5\cancel{(x+2)}}{\cancel{(x+2)}(7x-2)}}$$

The LCD is $(x+6)(7x-2)$.

$$\frac{\cancel{(x+6)}(7x-2)\left(\frac{3}{\cancel{x+6}}\right)+(x+6)\cancel{(7x-2)}\left(\frac{4}{\cancel{7x-2}}\right)}{(x+6)\cancel{(7x-2)}\left(\frac{2}{\cancel{7x-2}}\right)-(x+6)\cancel{(7x-2)}\left(\frac{5}{\cancel{7x-2}}\right)}=$$

$$\frac{(7x-2)(3)+(x+6)(4)}{(x+6)(2)-(x+6)(5)}=$$

$$\frac{(21x-6)+(4x+24)}{2x+12-5x-30}=$$

$$\frac{25x+18}{-3x-18}$$

$$\frac{\frac{x^2+7x+6}{x+1}-\frac{x^2+4x+3}{x+3}}{\frac{5x+5}{x^2+7x+6}}$$

$$\frac{\frac{(x+6)\cancel{(x+1)}}{\cancel{x+1}}-\frac{(x+1)\cancel{(x+3)}}{\cancel{x+3}}}{\frac{5\cancel{(x+1)}}{(x+6)\cancel{(x+1)}}}$$

The LCD is $(x+6)$.

$$\frac{(x+6)(x+6)-(x+6)(x+1)}{\cancel{(x+6)}\left(\frac{5}{\cancel{x+6}}\right)}=$$

$$\frac{(x^2+12x+36)-(x^2+7x+6)}{5}=$$

$$\frac{5x+30}{5}=$$

$$\frac{\cancel{5}(x+6)}{\cancel{5}}=$$

$$x+6$$

Teaching Tips, Cont.

- Encourage the students to simplify the fractions by cancelling like terms as much as possible before multiplying.
- Complete the Classwork exercise. Have one student work the problem on the board for the class and explain the answer. All students should work the problem in their books.
- Note: The solution for the second problem in the first row of Worksheet 45 can be simplified by combining the terms in the denominator after the first step.

Assignment

- Complete Lesson 89, Activities 2-3.
- Worksheet 45.

Lesson 90

Concepts

- Quadratic equations
- Dividing rational expressions
- Multiplying rational expressions
- Adding rational expressions
- Subtracting rational expressions

Learning Objectives

The student will be able to:

- Define *quadratic equation*
- Identify whether or not an equation is a quadratic equation
- Explain why a given equation is not a quadratic equation

Materials Needed

- Student Book, Lesson 90

Teaching Tips

- Review multiplying by a binomial. (See Lesson 60)
- Review the FOIL method. (See Lesson 62)
- Define *quadratic equation* from the teaching box.
- Teach the conditions for an equation to be a quadratic equation:
  - The equation must be in the format $ax^2 + bx + c$.
  - The variable a cannot equal 0.
  - No variable may have an exponent greater than 2.

Lesson 90

Quadratic Equations

You are familiar with a variety of polynomials, such as monomials, binomials, trinomials, as well as polynomials with more than three terms. This lesson deals with a specific type of polynomial known as a quadratic equation. A **quadratic equation** is a polynomial of the second degree in the form $ax^2 + bx + c = 0$.

The standard form trinomials you have worked with already this year are quadratic equations. While the easiest quadratic equations to recognize are those that follow the rule exactly, the most important thing to remember is that $a \neq 0$ and no variable may have an exponent greater than 2.

Identify whether or not the equation simplifies to a quadratic equation. If not, explain why.

$8(x-1)=0$

Multiply to get $8x-8=0$. This is not a quadratic equation because it is missing the ax^2 term.

① **Classwork**

Identify whether or not the equation simplifies to a quadratic equation. If not, explain why.

$x(x+3)=0$

$x^2+3x=0$

This is a quadratic equation.

$(x^2)(x+5)=0$

$x^3+5x^2=0$

This is not a quadratic equation. The variable has an exponent greater than 2.

Activities

② Identify whether or not the equation simplifies to a quadratic equation. If not, explain why.

$x(x-4)=0$

$x^2-4x=0$

This is a quadratic equation.

$(x-2)(x+6)=0$

$x^2+4x-12=0$

This is a quadratic equation.

$2(x^2+5x)=0$

$2x^2+10x=0$

This is a quadratic equation.

$(3x-1)(x^2+4)=0$

$3x^3-x^2+12x-4=0$

This is not a quadratic equation. The variable has an exponent greater than 2.

$(x^2)(x-2)=x^3$

$x^3-2x^2=x^3$

$-2x^2=0$

This is a quadratic equation.

$(x^2-3)(2x+5)=0$

$2x^3+5x^2-6x-15=0$

This is not a quadratic equation. The variable has an exponent greater than 2.

$(x-3)(x+3)=0$

$x^2-9=0$

This is a quadratic equation.

$(3x+4)(2x+1)=0$

$6x^2+11x+4=0$

This is a quadratic equation.

$(7x-2)(x^2-4)=0$

$7x^3-2x^2-28x+8=0$

This is not a quadratic equation. The variable has an exponent greater than 2.

$(2x+5)(2x-5)=0$

$4x^2-25=0$

This is a quadratic equation.

$(x^2-4)(-x^2+4)=0$

$-x^4+8x^2-16=0$

This is not a quadratic equation. The variable has an exponent greater than 2.

$4(x^2+3x+2)=0$

$4x^2+12x+8=0$

This is a quadratic equation.

③ Solve. Remember to state any exclusions.

$$\frac{2x^2+x-6}{2x^2-x-6} \div \frac{2x^2+3x-2}{4x^2+4x-3} =$$
$$\frac{2x^2+x-6}{2x^2-x-6} \cdot \frac{4x^2+4x-3}{2x^2+3x-2} =$$
$$\frac{(2x-3)\cancel{(x+2)}}{\cancel{(2x+3)}(x-2)} \cdot \frac{\cancel{(2x+3)}\cancel{(2x-1)}}{\cancel{(x+2)}\cancel{(2x-1)}} =$$
$$\frac{2x-3}{x-2}; x \neq -2, -\tfrac{3}{2}, \tfrac{1}{2}, 2$$

$$\frac{8x+20}{8x^2+6x-9} \div \frac{2x^2-3x-20}{12x^2-9x} =$$
$$\frac{8x+20}{8x^2+6x-9} \cdot \frac{12x^2-9x}{2x^2-3x-20} =$$
$$\frac{4\cancel{(2x+5)}}{\cancel{(4x-3)}(2x+3)} \cdot \frac{3x\cancel{(4x-3)}}{\cancel{(2x+5)}(x-4)} = \frac{4}{2x+3} \cdot \frac{3x}{x-4} =$$
$$\frac{12x}{2x^2-5x-12}; x \neq -\tfrac{5}{2}, -\tfrac{3}{2}, \tfrac{3}{4}, 4, 0$$

$$\frac{10x^2+35x}{18x^3-12x^2} \div \frac{4x^2+14x}{6x^2-4x} =$$
$$\frac{10x^2+35x}{18x^3-12x^2} \cdot \frac{6x^2-4x}{4x^2+14x} =$$
$$\frac{5\cancel{x}\cancel{(2x+7)}}{6x^{\cancel{2}}\cancel{(3x-2)}} \cdot \frac{\cancel{2x}\cancel{(3x-2)}}{\cancel{2x}\cancel{(2x+7)}} =$$
$$\frac{5}{6x}; x \neq -\tfrac{7}{2}, 0, \tfrac{2}{3}$$

$$\frac{3x^2-14x-24}{4x^2-81} \div \frac{4x^2-25x+6}{8x^2+34x-9} =$$
$$\frac{3x^2-14x-24}{4x^2-81} \cdot \frac{8x^2+34x-9}{4x^2-25x+6} =$$
$$\frac{(3x+4)\cancel{(x-6)}}{(2x-9)\cancel{(2x+9)}} \cdot \frac{\cancel{(2x+9)}\cancel{(4x-1)}}{\cancel{(x-6)}\cancel{(4x-1)}} =$$
$$\frac{3x+4}{2x-9}; x \neq -\tfrac{9}{2}, \tfrac{1}{4}, \tfrac{9}{2}, 6$$

④ Solve. Remember to state any exclusions.

$$\frac{3x}{4x-5} + \frac{4}{5x+2} =$$
$$\frac{3x(5x+2)}{(4x-5)(5x+2)} + \frac{4(4x-5)}{(4x-5)(5x+2)} =$$
$$\frac{15x^2+6x}{20x^2-17x-10} + \frac{16x-20}{20x^2-17x-10} =$$
$$\frac{15x^2+22x-20}{20x^2-17x-10}; x \neq -\tfrac{2}{5}, \tfrac{5}{4}$$

$$\frac{4x}{3x+1} - \frac{4x}{2x-7} =$$
$$\frac{4x(2x-7)}{(3x+1)(2x-7)} - \frac{4x(3x+1)}{(3x+1)(2x-7)} =$$
$$\frac{8x^2-28x}{6x^2-19x-7} - \frac{12x^2+4x}{6x^2-19x-7} =$$
$$\frac{-4x^2-32x}{6x^2-19x-7}; x \neq -\tfrac{1}{3}, \tfrac{7}{2}$$

$$\frac{8}{5x-2} + \frac{3x}{2x-1} =$$
$$\frac{8(2x-1)}{(5x-2)(2x-1)} + \frac{3x(5x-2)}{(5x-2)(2x-1)} =$$
$$\frac{16x-8}{10x^2-9x+2} + \frac{15x^2-6x}{10x^2-9x+2} =$$
$$\frac{15x^2+10x-8}{10x^2-9x+2}; x \neq \tfrac{2}{5}, \tfrac{1}{2}$$

$$\frac{3x^2}{2x-3} - \frac{2x}{x+5} =$$
$$\frac{3x^2(x+5)}{(2x-3)(x+5)} - \frac{2x(2x-3)}{(2x-3)(x+5)} =$$
$$\frac{3x^3+15x^2}{2x^2+7x-15} - \frac{4x^2-6x}{2x^2+7x-15} =$$
$$\frac{3x^3+11x^2+6x}{2x^2+7x-15}; x \neq -5, \tfrac{3}{2}$$

Teaching Tips, Cont.

- Tell the students that it is important that the learn to identify quadratic equations quickly and accurately because they will have to use this information in upcoming Lessons.
- Complete the Classwork exercises. Have some students work the problems on the board for the class and explain their answers. All students should work the problems in their books.
- Review for Test 9 using worksheets 41-45. These worksheets were assigned in previous lessons.

Assignments

- Complete Lesson 90, Activities 2-4.
- Study for Test 9 (Lessons 78-87).

Test 9

Testing Objectives

The student will:

- Simplify rational expressions
- Add rational expressions
- Subtract rational expressions
- Multiply rational expressions
- Divide rational expressions
- Simplify complex numbers

Materials Needed

- Test 9
- *It's College Test Prep Time!* from the Student Book
- Exploring Math through... Ice Hockey from Student Book

Teaching Tips

➢ Administer Test 9, allowing the students 30-40 minutes to complete the test.

Test 9

① Simplify. Remember to state any exclusions. **7 points**

$\frac{20x^2-12x}{5x-3}$

$\frac{4x\cancel{(5x-3)}}{\cancel{5x-3}} = 4x; x \neq \frac{3}{5}$

$\frac{3x^2+16x-12}{9x^2-4}$

$\frac{(x+6)\cancel{(3x-2)}}{(3x+2)\cancel{(3x-2)}} = \frac{x+6}{3x+2}; x \neq -\frac{2}{3}, \frac{2}{3}$

$\frac{9x^2+26x+16}{9x^2+17x+8}$

$\frac{\cancel{(9x+8)}(x+2)}{\cancel{(9x+8)}(x+1)} = \frac{x+2}{x+1}; x \neq -\frac{8}{9}, -1$

② Solve. Remember to state any exclusions. **32 points**

$\frac{4}{x+2}+\frac{6}{x+2}=$

$\frac{4+6}{x+2}=\frac{10}{x+2}; x \neq -2$

$\frac{3x+1}{4x+3}+\frac{3x-2}{4x+3}=$

$\frac{(3x+1)+(3x-2)}{4x+3}=$

$\frac{6x-1}{4x+3}; x \neq -\frac{3}{4}$

$\frac{24x+42}{56x^2+16x}\cdot\frac{28x^2+8x}{4x^2-9x-28}=$

$\frac{{}_3\cancel{6}\cancel{(4x+7)}}{{}_1\cancel{8x}\cancel{(7x+2)}}\cdot\frac{\cancel{4x}\cancel{(7x+2)}}{\cancel{(4x+7)}(x-4)}=$

$\frac{3}{x-4}; x \neq -\frac{7}{4}, -\frac{2}{7}, 0, 4$

$\frac{3x+9}{x^2+5x}\div\frac{x^2-4x-21}{x^2-7x}=$

$\frac{3x+9}{x^2+5x}\cdot\frac{x^2-7x}{x^2-4x-21}=$

$\frac{3\cancel{(x+3)}}{\cancel{x}(x+5)}\cdot\frac{\cancel{x}\cancel{(x-7)}}{\cancel{(x+3)}\cancel{(x-7)}}=$

$\frac{3}{x+5}; x \neq -5, -3, 0, 7$

$\frac{1}{x+3}+\frac{4}{5}=$

$\frac{(1)(5)}{(x+3)(5)}+\frac{(4)(x+3)}{(5)(x+3)}=$

$\frac{5+4x+12}{5x+15}=\frac{4x+17}{5x+15}; x \neq -3$

$\frac{8x}{4x-5}-\frac{3x}{4x-5}=$

$\frac{8x-3x}{4x-5}=\frac{5x}{4x-5}; x \neq \frac{5}{4}$

$\frac{23x-7}{9x-5}-\frac{5x+3}{9x-5}=$

$\frac{(23x-7)-(5x+3)}{9x-5}=\frac{18x-10}{9x-5}=$

$\frac{2\cancel{(9x-5)}}{\cancel{9x-5}}=2; x \neq \frac{5}{9}$

$\frac{5x^2-23x-10}{2x^2+9x+9}\cdot\frac{8x^2+10x-3}{20x^2+3x-2}=$

$\frac{(x-5)\cancel{(5x+2)}}{\cancel{(2x+3)}(x+3)}\cdot\frac{\cancel{(2x+3)}\cancel{(4x-1)}}{\cancel{(5x+2)}\cancel{(4x-1)}}=$

$\frac{x-5}{x+3}; x \neq -3, -\frac{3}{2}, -\frac{2}{5}, \frac{1}{4}$

$\frac{6x+36}{8x^2+32x}\div\frac{x^2+2x-24}{4x^2+16x}=$

$\frac{6x+36}{8x^2+32x}\cdot\frac{4x^2+16x}{x^2+2x-24}=$

$\frac{{}_3\cancel{6}\cancel{(x+6)}}{{}_2\cancel{8x}\cancel{(x+4)}}\cdot\frac{\cancel{4x}\cancel{(x+4)}}{\cancel{(x+6)}(x-4)}=$

$\frac{3}{x-4}; x \neq -6, -4, 0, 4$

$\frac{x}{3x+2}-\frac{x}{4}=$

$\frac{(x)(4)}{(3x+2)(4)}-\frac{(x)(3x+2)}{(4)(3x+2)}=$

$\frac{4x-3x^2-2x}{12x+8}=\frac{-3x^2+2x}{12x+8}; x \neq -\frac{2}{3}$

Test 9

③ Solve. Remember to state any exclusions. **12 points**

$\frac{5}{x+3}+\frac{2}{x-1}=$

$\frac{5(x-1)}{(x+3)(x-1)}+\frac{2(x+3)}{(x+3)(x-1)}=$

$\frac{5x-5}{x^2+2x-3}+\frac{2x+6}{x^2+2x-3}=$

$\frac{7x+1}{x^2+2x-3}; x \neq -3, 1$

$\frac{1}{2x+1}+\frac{2}{x-1}=$

$\frac{1(x-1)}{(2x+1)(x-1)}+\frac{2(2x+1)}{(2x+1)(x-1)}=$

$\frac{x-1}{2x^2-x-1}+\frac{4x+2}{2x^2-x-1}=$

$\frac{5x+1}{2x^2-x-1}; x \neq -\frac{1}{2}, 1$

$\frac{x}{x+2}-\frac{x}{x-5}=$

$\frac{x(x-5)}{(x+2)(x-5)}-\frac{x(x+2)}{(x+2)(x-5)}=$

$\frac{x^2-5x}{x^2-3x-10}-\frac{x^2+2x}{x^2-3x-10}=$

$\frac{-7x}{x^2-3x-10}; x \neq -2, 5$

$\frac{3}{x+4}-\frac{4}{x+2}=$

$\frac{3(x+2)}{(x+4)(x+2)}-\frac{4(x+4)}{(x+4)(x+2)}=$

$\frac{3x+6}{(x+4)(x+2)}-\frac{4x+16}{(x+4)(x+2)}=$

$\frac{-x-10}{x^2+6x+8}; x \neq -4, -2$

④ Simplify the complex fractions. **9 points**

$\frac{\frac{1}{3}}{8}$ LCD = 3.

$\frac{\cancel{3}\left(\frac{1}{\cancel{3}}\right)}{3(8)}=\frac{1}{24}$

$\frac{\frac{5}{8}}{7}$ LCD = 8.

$\frac{\cancel{8}\left(\frac{5}{\cancel{8}}\right)}{8(7)}=\frac{5}{56}$

$\frac{\frac{4}{9}}{10}$ LCD = 9.

$\frac{\cancel{9}\left(\frac{4}{\cancel{9}}\right)}{9(10)}=\frac{4}{90}=\frac{2}{45}$

$\frac{5}{\frac{1}{6}}$ LCD = 6.

$\frac{6(5)}{\cancel{6}\left(\frac{1}{\cancel{6}}\right)}=\frac{30}{1}=30$

$\frac{8}{\frac{3}{7}}$ LCD = 7.

$\frac{7(8)}{\cancel{7}\left(\frac{3}{\cancel{7}}\right)}=\frac{56}{3}$

$\frac{6}{\frac{5}{11}}$ LCD = 11.

$\frac{11(6)}{\cancel{11}\left(\frac{5}{\cancel{11}}\right)}=\frac{66}{5}$

$\frac{\frac{3}{4}}{\frac{2}{5}}$ LCD = 5(4) = 20.

$\frac{{}_5\cancel{20}\left(\frac{3}{\cancel{4}}\right)}{{}_4\cancel{20}\left(\frac{2}{\cancel{5}}\right)}=\frac{15}{8}$

$\frac{\frac{1}{4}}{\frac{7}{8}}$ LCD = 8.

$\frac{{}_2\cancel{8}\left(\frac{1}{\cancel{4}}\right)}{\cancel{8}\left(\frac{7}{\cancel{8}}\right)}=\frac{2}{7}$

$\frac{\frac{2}{5}}{\frac{3}{8}}$ LCD = 5(8) = 40.

$\frac{{}_8\cancel{40}\left(\frac{2}{\cancel{5}}\right)}{{}_5\cancel{40}\left(\frac{3}{\cancel{8}}\right)}=\frac{16}{15}$

60 points total

It's College Test Prep Time!

1. Given (x, y) ♎ z is defined as $\frac{xy^z - x^z y}{xyz}$ for all nonzero numbers x, y, and z, what is the value of $(4, 5)$ ♎ 3?

   A. $\frac{41}{3}$ Substitute the given values in the formula. $\frac{4(5)^3 - 4^3(5)}{4(5)(3)}$

   <u>B.</u> 3 $\frac{4(125) - 64(5)}{20(3)} = \frac{500 - 320}{60} = \frac{180}{60} = 3$

   C. $\frac{1}{3}$

   D. 0

   E. $-\frac{13}{3}$

2. If a and b are both positive real numbers and $\frac{2a}{b} = c$, what is the value of $\frac{2a+3}{c+1}$?

   <u>A.</u> $\frac{2ab+3b}{2a+b}$ Substitute for c and simplify.

   B. $\frac{2a+3}{2a+1}$ $\frac{2a+3}{\frac{2a}{b}+1} = \frac{b(2a+3)}{b\left(\frac{2a}{b}+1\right)} = \frac{2ab+3b}{2a+b}$

   C. $\frac{3}{b+1}$

   D. $\frac{2ab+3b}{2a+1}$

   E. $\frac{a+3}{b+1}$

Exploring Math through... Ice Hockey

Ice hockey is a game that involves just about every facet of math imaginable. Without even thinking about it, players must do math calculations in their heads. Oftentimes, these calculations are done in a fraction of a second. Other calculations must be so precise that they cannot be rushed, and they may be computed more than once to ensure accuracy.

When a hockey rink is lined, a few thin layers of ice are put down first. The markings are then painted on the ice and topped with several more layers of ice, making the entire iced area about one inch thick. If even one measurement is done incorrectly, the entire rink will have to be redone because you cannot melt just a portion of the rink, and you cannot remove paint from ice without removing the ice.

During game play, players are tasked with the laws of physics and principles of geometry and trigonometry. It is said that the wall, also known as the boards, serves as extra men on a hockey team. This is especially true when the players have a working knowledge of the properties of angles. A key mathematical concept that applies to every game of ice hockey is that the angle of incidence equals the angle of reflection. As it applies to hockey, the angle the path of a puck forms with the wall at the moment the puck hits the wall is equal to the angle the path of the puck forms with the wall as it is leaving the wall.

Players must also consider speed and distance when determining how much force to use to hit the puck. Too much force can cause the puck to overshoot the target, and too little force could leave the puck in an undesired area. In either case, the player has just given the opponent an advantage.

There are numerous other ways in which math affects ice hockey including the angle the player's skates make with the ice to the degree to which a player bends his knees when controlling the puck. No matter what positions players have in the game, math will affect the way they play the game

Teaching Tips, Cont.

- When all students are finished taking the test, introduce *It's College Test Prep Time* from the student book. This page may be completed in class or assigned as homework.
- Have students read the Exploring Math feature for Lessons 91-100.

Assignments

- Complete *It's College Test Prep Time!*
- Read Exploring Math through... Ice Hockey

Lesson 91

Concepts

- Quadratic equations
- Solving quadratic equations by factoring
- Simplifying complex rational expressions

Learning Objectives

The student will be able to:

- Identify the solution of a quadratic equation as its *roots* or *zeros*
- Factor a quadratic equation
- Apply the zero-product property of quadratic equations to find the roots
- List all possible roots of a quadratic equation

Materials Needed

- Student Book, Lesson 91

Teaching Tips

- Review factoring polynomials. (See Lessons 68-74)
- Ask the students what they must multiply a number by to get zero. (Zero) Explain that this concept will be used to solve quadratic equations and is called the *zero-product property*.
- Teach how to solve quadratic equations by factoring from the teaching box.
- Emphasize the four steps shown in the teaching box. It is essential for the students to master these four steps.

Solving Quadratic Equations: Factoring

Each quadratic equation has two solutions. The solutions of a quadratic equation are also called **roots** or **zeros**. The terms *solution*, *root*, and *zero* may be used interchangeably when discussing equations. The number of solutions is equal to the value of the highest exponent. For quadratic equations, there are 2 roots because the highest exponent is 2.

There are three different methods of finding the roots of a quadratic equation: factoring, completing the square, and using the quadratic formula. This lesson will show you how to solve quadratic equations by factoring.

Factoring a quadratic equation to find the roots applies the **zero-product property**. This property states that if the product of two or more factors is zero, then at least one of those factors must be a zero.

To solve a quadratic equation by factoring, follow these steps.

- Set the equation equal to zero.
- Factor the polynomial
- Set each factor equal to zero
- Solve each factor equation

Solve the equation $x^2 + 5x + 6 = 0$.

The equation is set equal to zero, so factor the polynomial.
$(x + 2)(x + 3) = 0$

Set each factor equal to zero and solve.
$x + 2 = 0; x = -2$
$x + 3 = 0; x = -3$

The solution is x = -2 and -3.

① Classwork

Solve each quadratic equation by factoring.

$x^2 + 6x + 8 = 0$
$(x + 4)(x + 2) = 0$
$x + 4 = 0; x = -4$
$x + 2 = 0; x = -2$
The solution is x = -4 and -2.

$x^2 + 2x - 3 = 0$
$(x + 3)(x - 1) = 0$
$x + 3 = 0; x = -3$
$x - 1 = 0; x = 1$
The solution is x = -3 and 1.

$x^2 - 7x + 10 = 0$
$(x - 2)(x - 5) = 0$
$x - 2 = 0; x = 2$
$x - 5 = 0; x = 5$
The solution is x = 2 and 5.

$x^2 + 6x = -5$
$x^2 + 6x + 5 = 0$
$(x + 5)(x + 1) = 0$
$x + 5 = 0; x = -5$
$x + 1 = 0; x = -1$
The solution is x = -5 and -1.

Activities

② Solve each quadratic equation by factoring.

$x^2 + 9x + 18 = 0$
$(x + 6)(x + 3) = 0$
$x + 6 = 0; x = -6$
$x + 3 = 0; x = -3$
The solution is x = -6 and -3.

$x^2 + 5x - 14 = 0$
$(x + 7)(x - 2) = 0$
$x + 7 = 0; x = -7$
$x - 2 = 0; x = 2$
The solution is x = -7 and 2.

$x^2 - 13x + 36 = 0$
$(x - 4)(x - 9) = 0$
$x - 4 = 0; x = 4$
$x - 9 = 0; x = 9$
The solution is x = 4 and 9.

$x^2 - 9x = -20$
$x^2 - 9x + 20 = 0$
$(x - 5)(x - 4) = 0$
$x - 5 = 0; x = 5$
$x - 4 = 0; x = 4$
The solution is x = 5 and 4.

③ Solve each quadratic equation by factoring.

$x^2 - x - 12 = 0$
$(x-4)(x+3) = 0$
$x - 4 = 0; x = 4$
$x + 3 = 0; x = -3$
The solution is
$x = 4$ and -3.

$x^2 + 9x + 8 = 0$
$(x+8)(x+1) = 0$
$x + 8 = 0; x = -8$
$x + 1 = 0; x = -1$
The solution is
$x = -8$ and -1.

$x^2 - x = 2$
$x^2 - x - 2 = 0$
$(x-2)(x+1) = 0$
$x - 2 = 0; x = 2$
$x + 1 = 0; x = -1$
The solution is
$x = 2$ and -1.

$2x^2 + 11x + 12 = 0$
$(x+4)(2x+3) = 0$
$x + 4 = 0; x = -4$
$2x + 3 = 0; x = -\frac{3}{2}$
The solution is
$x = -4$ and $-\frac{3}{2}$.

$x^2 - 9 = 0$
$(x-3)(x+3) = 0$
$x - 3 = 0; x = 3$
$x + 3 = 0; x = -3$
The solution is
$x = 3$ and -3.

$6x^2 + 7x = -2$
$6x^2 + 7x + 2 = 0$
$(3x+2)(2x+1) = 0$
$3x + 2 = 0; x = -\frac{2}{3}$
$2x + 1 = 0; x = -\frac{1}{2}$
The solution is
$x = -\frac{2}{3}$ and $-\frac{1}{2}$.

$2x^2 + 10x + 8 = 0$
$2(x+1)(x+4) = 0$
$x + 1 = 0; x = -1$
$x + 4 = 0; x = -4$
The solution is
$x = -1$ and -4.

$2x^2 - 5x - 3 = 0$
$(2x+1)(x-3) = 0$
$2x + 1 = 0; x = -\frac{1}{2}$
$x - 3 = 0; x = 3$
The solution is
$x = -\frac{1}{2}$ and 3.

$10x^2 - 27x = -18$
$10x^2 - 27x + 18 = 0$
$(5x-6)(2x-3) = 0$
$5x - 6 = 0; x = \frac{6}{5}$
$2x - 3 = 0; x = \frac{3}{2}$
The solution is
$x = \frac{6}{5}$ and $\frac{3}{2}$.

$x^2 + 8x + 16 = 0$
$(x+4)(x+4) = 0$
$x + 4 = 0; x = -4$
$x + 4 = 0; x = -4$
The solution is
$x = -4$.

$x^2 - 12x + 35 = 0$
$(x-7)(x-5) = 0$
$x - 7 = 0; x = 7$
$x - 5 = 0; x = 5$
The solution is
$x = 7$ and 5.

$x^2 = 25$
$x^2 - 25 = 0$
$(x+5)(x-5) = 0$
$x + 5 = 0; x = -5$
$x - 5 = 0; x = 5$
The solution is
$x = 5$ and -5.

④ Simplify the complex expressions.

$$\frac{\frac{2x+3}{2x} + \frac{3x-1}{x^2+4x+4}}{\frac{x+2}{6x^2-2x}}$$

$$\frac{\frac{2x+3}{2x} + \frac{3x-1}{(x+2)^2}}{\frac{x+2}{2x(3x-1)}}$$

The LCD is $2x(x+2)^2(3x-1)$.

$$\frac{\cancel{2x}(x+2)^2(3x-1)\left(\frac{2x+3}{\cancel{2x}}\right) + 2x\cancel{(x+2)^2}(3x-1)\left(\frac{3x-1}{\cancel{(x+2)^2}}\right)}{\cancel{2x}(x+2)^2\cancel{(3x-1)}\left(\frac{x+2}{\cancel{2x}\cancel{(3x-1)}}\right)} =$$

$$\frac{(x+2)^2(3x-1)(2x+3) + 2x(3x-1)(3x-1)}{(x+2)^2(x+2)} =$$

$$\frac{(x^2+4x+4)(6x^2+7x-3) + (6x^2-2x)(3x-1)}{(x^2+4x+4)(x+2)} =$$

$$\frac{(6x^4+31x^3+49x^2+16x-12) + (18x^3-12x^2+2x)}{x^3+6x^2+12x+8} =$$

$$\frac{6x^4+49x^3+37x^2+18x-12}{x^3+6x^2+12x+8}$$

$$\frac{\frac{2x-1}{3x} - \frac{2x+1}{2x^2+x-1}}{\frac{x-1}{3x^2+3x}}$$

$$\frac{\frac{2x-1}{3x} - \frac{2x+1}{(x+1)(2x-1)}}{\frac{x-1}{3x(x+1)}}$$

The LCD is $3x(x+1)(2x-1)$.

$$\frac{\cancel{3x}(x+1)(2x-1)\left(\frac{2x-1}{\cancel{3x}}\right) - 3x\cancel{(x+1)}\cancel{(2x-1)}\left(\frac{2x+1}{\cancel{(x+1)}\cancel{(2x-1)}}\right)}{\cancel{3x}\cancel{(x+1)}(2x-1)\left(\frac{x-1}{\cancel{3x}\cancel{(x+1)}}\right)} =$$

$$\frac{(x+1)(2x-1)(2x-1) - 3x(2x+1)}{(2x-1)(x-1)} =$$

$$\frac{(2x^2+x-1)(2x-1) - (6x^2+3x)}{2x^2-3x+1} =$$

$$\frac{(4x^3-3x+1) - (6x^2+3x)}{2x^2-3x+1} =$$

$$\frac{4x^3-6x^2-6x+1}{2x^2-3x+1}$$

Teaching Tips, Cont.

- Tell the students to make sure they solve each individual factor equation when finding possible solutions.
- Explain that it is possible for the same answer to appear more than one time in the solution of a given quadratic equation. If this happens, it is only necessary to list the number once in the solution.
- Complete the Classwork exercises. Have some students work the problems on the board for the class and explain their answers. All students should work the problems in their books.

Assignment

- Complete Lesson 91, Activities 2-4.

Lesson 92

Concepts

- Quadratic equations
- Solving quadratic equations by taking roots
- Solving quadratic equations by factoring
- Math in the real world

Learning Objectives

The student will be able to:

- Identify quadratic equations of the form $x^2 + c = 0$
- Solve quadratic equations by taking roots
- List the possible values of x as both the positive and the negative values of the root

Materials Needed

- Student Book, Lesson 92
- Worksheet 46

Teaching Tips

- Have students complete Worksheet 46 in class. This may be for added practice of earlier topics, or graded as a quiz, if desired.
- Review Solving quadratic equations by factoring. (See Lesson 91)
- Introduce the special form of a quadratic equation, $x^2 + c = 0$. Explain that this quadratic equation is formed when $a = 1$ and $b = 0$.
- Tell the students there is a shortcut for solving quadratic equations if they are in the form $x^2 + c = 0$ and $c < 0$.

Solving Quadratic Equations: Taking Roots

So far you have learned to solve quadratic equations by factoring. In this lesson you will learn a short-cut that works for certain quadratic equations.

Anytime $a = 1$, $b = 0$, and $c < 0$ in a quadratic equation, leaving you with the format $x^2 + c = 0$, you can take the roots to find the solution.

Solve the equation $x^2 - 4 = 0$.

First, isolate the x^2 term.
$x^2 = 4$

Now take the square root of both sides.
$\sqrt{x^2} = \sqrt{4}$

Because squaring a negative number gives a positive number (negative times negative equals positive), the square root of a number may be positive or negative. This is how you get two roots of the quadratic equation.
$\sqrt{x^2} = \sqrt{4}$
$x = \pm 2$

You may leave the answer in this format, or you may list the roots separately as $x = 2$ and -2.

① Classwork
Solve each quadratic equation by taking the roots.

$x^2 - 25 = 0$
$x^2 = 25$
$\sqrt{x^2} = \sqrt{25}$
$x = \pm 5$

$x^2 - 13 = 0$
$x^2 = 13$
$\sqrt{x^2} = \sqrt{13}$
$x = \pm\sqrt{13}$

$x^2 - 18 = 0$
$x^2 = 18$
$\sqrt{x^2} = \sqrt{18}$
$\sqrt{x^2} = \sqrt{2 \cdot 3 \cdot 3}$
$x = \pm 3\sqrt{2}$

Activities
② Solve each quadratic equation by taking the roots.

$x^2 - 100 = 0$
$x^2 = 100$
$\sqrt{x^2} = \sqrt{100}$
$x = \pm 10$

$x^2 - 9 = 0$
$x^2 = 9$
$\sqrt{x^2} = \sqrt{9}$
$x = \pm 3$

$x^2 - 1 = 0$
$x^2 = 1$
$\sqrt{x^2} = \sqrt{1}$
$x = \pm 1$

$x^2 - 49 = 0$
$x^2 = 49$
$\sqrt{x^2} = \sqrt{49}$
$x = \pm 7$

$x^2 - 26 = 0$
$x^2 = 26$
$\sqrt{x^2} = \sqrt{26}$
$x = \pm\sqrt{26}$

$x^2 - 33 = 0$
$x^2 = 33$
$\sqrt{x^2} = \sqrt{33}$
$x = \pm\sqrt{33}$

$x^2 - 41 = 0$
$x^2 = 41$
$\sqrt{x^2} = \sqrt{41}$
$x = \pm\sqrt{41}$

$x^2 - 57 = 0$
$x^2 = 57$
$\sqrt{x^2} = \sqrt{57}$
$x = \pm\sqrt{57}$

$x^2 - 12 = 0$
$x^2 = 12$
$\sqrt{x^2} = \sqrt{12}$
$\sqrt{x^2} = \sqrt{2 \cdot 2 \cdot 3}$
$x = \pm 2\sqrt{3}$

$x^2 - 27 = 0$
$x^2 = 27$
$\sqrt{x^2} = \sqrt{27}$
$\sqrt{x^2} = \sqrt{3 \cdot 3 \cdot 3}$
$x = \pm 3\sqrt{3}$

$x^2 - 32 = 0$
$x^2 = 32$
$\sqrt{x^2} = \sqrt{32}$
$\sqrt{x^2} = \sqrt{2 \cdot 4 \cdot 4}$
$x = \pm 4\sqrt{2}$

$x^2 - 50 = 0$
$x^2 = 50$
$\sqrt{x^2} = \sqrt{50}$
$\sqrt{x^2} = \sqrt{2 \cdot 5 \cdot 5}$
$x = \pm 5\sqrt{2}$

③ Solve each quadratic equation by factoring.

$6x^2 + 13x - 5 = 0$
$(3x - 1)(2x + 5) = 0$
$3x - 1 = 0; x = \frac{1}{3}$
$2x + 5 = 0; x = -\frac{5}{2}$
The solution is $x = \frac{1}{3}$ and $-\frac{5}{2}$.

$4x^2 - 13x - 12 = 0$
$(4x + 3)(x - 4) = 0$
$4x + 3 = 0; x = -\frac{3}{4}$
$x - 4 = 0; x = 4$
The solution is $x = -\frac{3}{4}$ and 4.

$6x^2 - 7x = -2$
$6x^2 - 7x + 2 = 0$
$(3x - 2)(2x - 1) = 0$
$3x - 2 = 0; x = \frac{2}{3}$
$2x - 1 = 0; x = \frac{1}{2}$
The solution is $x = \frac{2}{3}$ and $\frac{1}{2}$.

④ Solve.
An official ice rink for the National Hockey League has a length that is 30 feet more than twice the width. If the area of the rink is 17,000 square feet, what are the dimensions of the rink?
Let w = the width of the rink. Then $2w + 30$ = the length of the rink. Set up a quadratic equation and solve by factoring.
$w(2w + 30) = 17{,}000$
$2w^2 + 30w - 17{,}000 = 0$
$(2w + 200)(w - 85) = 0$
$2w + 200 = 0 \quad w - 85 = 0$
$2w = -200 \quad w = 85$
$w = -100$
Because the width of the rink cannot be negative, the width must equal 85 feet.
Substitute this for w in the formula for the length of the rink.
$2(85) + 30 = 170 + 30 = 200$
The length of the rink is 200 feet.

Dimensions: 200 feet long by 85 feet wide
An official ice rink for the Olympics has a length that is 1 meter more than twice the width. If the area of the rink is 1830 square meters, what are the dimensions of the rink?
Let w = the width of the rink. Then $2w + 1$ = the length of the rink. Set up a quadratic equation and solve by factoring.
$w(2w + 1) = 1830$
$2w^2 + w - 1830 = 0$
$(2w + 61)(w - 30) = 0$
$2w + 61 = 0 \quad w - 30 = 0$
$2w = -61 \quad w = 30$
$w = -\frac{61}{2}$
Because the width of the rink cannot be negative, the width must equal 30 meters.
Substitute this for w in the formula for the length of the rink.
$2(30) + 1 = 60 + 1 = 61$
The length of the rink is 61 meters.

Dimensions: 61 meters long by 30 meters wide

Complex Rational Expressions, Quadratic Equations Worksheet 46

① Simplify the complex expressions.

$$\frac{\frac{6x}{x+3}+\frac{3}{x-1}}{\frac{3x^2+3x}{x^2-1}-\frac{9x+18}{x^2+x-2}}$$

$$\frac{\frac{6x}{x+3}+\frac{3}{x-1}}{\frac{3x(\cancel{x+1})}{(\cancel{x+1})(x-1)}-\frac{9(\cancel{x+2})}{(\cancel{x+2})(x-1)}}$$

The LCD is $(x+3)(x-1)$.

$$\frac{(\cancel{x+3})(x-1)\left(\frac{6x}{\cancel{x+3}}\right)+(x+3)(\cancel{x-1})\left(\frac{3}{\cancel{x-1}}\right)}{(x+3)(\cancel{x-1})\left(\frac{3x}{\cancel{x-1}}\right)-(x+3)(\cancel{x-1})\left(\frac{9}{\cancel{x-1}}\right)}=$$

$$\frac{(x-1)(6x)+(x+3)(3)}{(x+3)(3x)-(x+3)(9)}=$$

$$\frac{(6x^2-6x)+(3x+9)}{3x^2+9x-9x-27}=$$

$$\frac{6x^2-3x+9}{3x^2-27}=\frac{3(2x^2-x+3)}{3(x^2-9)}=$$

$$\frac{2x^2-x+3}{x^2-9}$$

$$\frac{\frac{x^2+6x+5}{x+1}-\frac{x^2+8x+15}{x+3}}{\frac{x+1}{x^2+6x+5}}$$

$$\frac{\frac{(x+5)(\cancel{x+1})}{\cancel{x+1}}-\frac{(x+5)(\cancel{x+3})}{\cancel{x+3}}}{\frac{\cancel{x+1}}{(x+5)(\cancel{x+1})}}$$

$$\frac{(x+5)-(x+5)}{\left(\frac{1}{x+5}\right)}=$$

$$\frac{0}{\left(\frac{1}{x+5}\right)}=0$$

② Identify whether or not the equation simplifies to a quadratic equation. If not, explain why.

$x(x-7)=0$

$x^2-7x=0$

This is a quadratic equation.

$(x-4)(x+1)=0$

$x^2-3x-4=0$

This is a quadratic equation.

$8(x^2+3x)=0$

$8x^2+24x=0$

This is a quadratic equation.

$(2x-1)(x^2+1)=0$

$2x^3-x^2+2x-1=0$

This is not a quadratic equation. The variable has an exponent greater than 2.

$(x^2)(x-3)=x^3$

$x^3-3x^2=x^3$

$-3x^2=0$

This is a quadratic equation.

$(x^2-1)(4x+3)=0$

$4x^3+3x^2-4x-3=0$

This is not a quadratic equation. The variable has an exponent greater than 2.

$(x-9)(x+9)=0$

$x^2-81=0$

This is a quadratic equation.

$(3x+1)(4x+1)=0$

$12x^2+7x+1=0$

This is a quadratic equation.

Teaching Tips, Cont.

- Teach how to solve quadratic equations by taking roots.
- Ask the students why it is important that $c < 0$ in this case. (If c were greater than zero then they would be taking the square root of a negative number, which does not exist.)
- Ask the students what would happen if $c = 0$ in this case. (If c were equal to zero then they would have exactly one root: 0.)
- Complete the Classwork exercises. Have some students work the problems on the board for the class and explain their answers. All students should work the problems in their books.
- Note: The solution for the first problem in the first row of Worksheet 46 can be simplified by combining the terms in the denominator after the first step.

Assignment

- Complete Lesson 92, Activities 2-4.

Lesson 93

Concepts

- Quadratic equations
- Solving quadratic equations by completing the square
- Simplifying complex rational expressions

Learning Objectives

The student will be able to:

- Complete the square of a quadratic equation
- Take the roots to find the zeros of the equation formed by completing the square
- List the possible values of *x* as both the positive and the negative values of the root

Materials Needed

- Student Book, Lesson 93
- Worksheet 47

Teaching Tips

- ➢ Review solving quadratic equations by taking roots. (See Lesson 92)
- ➢ Review factoring perfect square trinomials. (See Lesson 70)
- ➢ Ask the students if every quadratic equation will factor with whole number coefficients. (No.) Ask them to give an example of a quadratic equation that does not factor with whole number coefficients. (There are an infinite number of quadratic equations that will not factor with whole number coefficients. If students are having difficulty thinking of one, direct their attention to the sample problem in the teaching box.)

Solving Quadratic Equations: Completing the Square

A second way to solve quadratic equations is completing the square. This method uses the same principles you used to take the roots in Lesson 92, but with quadratic equations in the format $x^2 + bx + c = 0$ rather than $x^2 + c = 0$.

To complete the square, follow these steps.

- Isolate *c* on one side of the equal sign, leaving the *x*-terms on the other side.
- Add the value of $\left(\frac{b}{2}\right)^2$ to both sides.
  This creates a perfect square trinomial of the form $x^2 \pm 2xy + y^2$, where $c = y^2$ on one side of the equal sign.
- Factor the perfect square trinomial as $\left(x \pm \frac{b}{2}\right)^2$.
- Take the square root of each side. Remember that a square root has both a positive and a negative.
- Solve for x using both the positive and negative values of the square root.

Solve the equation $x^2 + 5x + 3 = 0$.
Isolate *c*.
$x^2 + 5x = -3$

Add $\left(\frac{5}{2}\right)^2 = \frac{25}{4}$ to both sides.
$x^2 + 5x + \frac{25}{4} = -3 + \frac{25}{4}$

Factor the perfect square trinomial.
$\left(x + \frac{5}{2}\right)^2 = -\frac{12}{4} + \frac{25}{4} \Rightarrow \left(x + \frac{5}{2}\right)^2 = \frac{13}{4}$

Take the square root of each side.
$\sqrt{\left(x + \frac{5}{2}\right)^2} = \sqrt{\frac{13}{4}} \Rightarrow \left(x + \frac{5}{2}\right) = \pm\frac{\sqrt{13}}{2}$

Solve for *x*.
$x + \frac{5}{2} = \frac{\sqrt{13}}{2}$ and $x + \frac{5}{2} = -\frac{\sqrt{13}}{2}$
$x = -\frac{5}{2} + \frac{\sqrt{13}}{2}$ and $x = -\frac{5}{2} - \frac{\sqrt{13}}{2}$
$x = \frac{-5 \pm \sqrt{13}}{2}$

① Classwork
Solve each quadratic equation by completing the square.

$x^2 + 4x + 2 = 0$
$x^2 + 4x = -2$
$x^2 + 4x + \left(\frac{4}{2}\right)^2 = -2 + \left(\frac{4}{2}\right)^2$
$x^2 + 4x + 4 = -2 + 4$
$x^2 + 4x + 4 = 2$
$(x + 2)^2 = 2$
$\sqrt{(x + 2)^2} = \sqrt{2}$
$x + 2 = \pm\sqrt{2}$
$x = -2 \pm \sqrt{2}$

$x^2 - 6x - 5 = 0$
$x^2 - 6x = 5$
$x^2 - 6x + \left(-\frac{6}{2}\right)^2 = 5 + \left(-\frac{6}{2}\right)^2$
$x^2 - 6x + 9 = 5 + 9$
$x^2 - 6x + 9 = 14$
$(x - 3)^2 = 14$
$\sqrt{(x - 3)^2} = \sqrt{14}$
$x - 3 = \pm\sqrt{14}$
$x = 3 \pm \sqrt{14}$

Activities

② Solve each quadratic equation by completing the square.

$x^2 + 8x + 5 = 0$
$x^2 + 8x = -5$
$x^2 + 8x + \left(\frac{8}{2}\right)^2 = -5 + \left(\frac{8}{2}\right)^2$
$x^2 + 8x + 16 = -5 + 16$
$x^2 + 8x + 16 = 11$
$(x + 4)^2 = 11$
$\sqrt{(x + 4)^2} = \sqrt{11}$
$x + 4 = \pm\sqrt{11}$
$x = -4 \pm \sqrt{11}$

$x^2 - 7x + 4 = 0$
$x^2 - 7x = -4$
$x^2 - 7x + \left(-\frac{7}{2}\right)^2 = -4 + \left(-\frac{7}{2}\right)^2$
$x^2 - 7x + \frac{49}{4} = -\frac{16}{4} + \frac{49}{4}$
$x^2 - 7x + \frac{49}{4} = \frac{33}{4}$
$\left(x - \frac{7}{2}\right)^2 = \frac{33}{4}$
$\sqrt{\left(x - \frac{7}{2}\right)^2} = \sqrt{\frac{33}{4}}$
$x - \frac{7}{2} = \pm\frac{\sqrt{33}}{2}$
$x = \frac{7 \pm \sqrt{33}}{2}$

$x^2 + 10x - 3 = 0$
$x^2 + 10x = 3$
$x^2 + 10x + \left(\frac{10}{2}\right)^2 = 3 + \left(\frac{10}{2}\right)^2$
$x^2 + 10x + 25 = 3 + 25$
$x^2 + 10x + 25 = 28$
$(x + 5)^2 = 28$
$\sqrt{(x + 5)^2} = \sqrt{28}$
$x + 5 = \pm\sqrt{2 \cdot 2 \cdot 7}$
$x = -5 \pm 2\sqrt{7}$

$x^2 - 9x - 2 = 0$
$x^2 - 9x = 2$
$x^2 - 9x + \left(-\frac{9}{2}\right)^2 = 2 + \left(-\frac{9}{2}\right)^2$
$x^2 - 9x + \frac{81}{4} = \frac{8}{4} + \frac{81}{4}$
$x^2 - 9x + \frac{81}{4} = \frac{89}{4}$
$\left(x - \frac{9}{2}\right)^2 = \frac{89}{4}$
$\sqrt{\left(x - \frac{9}{2}\right)^2} = \sqrt{\frac{89}{4}}$
$x - \frac{9}{2} = \pm\frac{\sqrt{89}}{2}$
$x = \frac{9 \pm \sqrt{89}}{2}$

$x^2 - 2x - 4 = 0$
$x^2 - 2x = 4$
$x^2 - 2x + \left(-\frac{2}{2}\right)^2 = 4 + \left(-\frac{2}{2}\right)^2$
$x^2 - 2x + 1 = 4 + 1$
$x^2 - 2x + 1 = 5$
$(x - 1)^2 = 5$
$\sqrt{(x - 1)^2} = \sqrt{5}$
$x - 1 = \pm\sqrt{5}$
$x = 1 \pm \sqrt{5}$

$x^2 + 3x - 8 = 0$
$x^2 + 3x = 8$
$x^2 + 3x + \left(\frac{3}{2}\right)^2 = 8 + \left(\frac{3}{2}\right)^2$
$x^2 + 3x + \frac{9}{4} = \frac{32}{4} + \frac{9}{4}$
$x^2 + 3x + \frac{9}{4} = \frac{41}{4}$
$\left(x + \frac{3}{2}\right)^2 = \frac{41}{4}$
$\sqrt{\left(x + \frac{3}{2}\right)^2} = \sqrt{\frac{41}{4}}$
$x + \frac{3}{2} = \pm\frac{\sqrt{41}}{2}$
$x = \frac{-3 \pm \sqrt{41}}{2}$

③ Simplify the complex expressions.

$$\frac{\frac{2}{3x} + \frac{3}{2x+3}}{\frac{2x-3}{4x^2-9}}$$

$$\frac{\frac{2}{3x} + \frac{3}{2x+3}}{\frac{\cancel{2x-3}}{(2x+3)\cancel{(2x-3)}}}$$

The LCD is $3x(2x + 3)$.

$$\frac{\cancel{3x}(2x+3)\left(\frac{2}{\cancel{3x}}\right) + 3x\cancel{(2x+3)}\left(\frac{3}{\cancel{2x+3}}\right)}{3x\cancel{(2x+3)}\left(\frac{1}{\cancel{2x+3}}\right)} =$$

$$\frac{(2x+3)(2) + 3x(3)}{3x(1)} = \frac{4x + 6 + 9x}{3x} =$$

$$\frac{13x + 6}{3x}$$

$$\frac{\frac{6}{x} + \frac{x}{x-4}}{\frac{x+2}{x^2-2x-8}}$$

$$\frac{\frac{6}{x} + \frac{x}{x-4}}{\frac{\cancel{x+2}}{\cancel{(x+2)}(x-4)}}$$

The LCD is $x(x - 4)$.

$$\frac{\cancel{x}(x-4)\left(\frac{6}{\cancel{x}}\right) + x\cancel{(x-4)}\left(\frac{x}{\cancel{x-4}}\right)}{x\cancel{(x-4)}\left(\frac{1}{\cancel{x-4}}\right)} =$$

$$\frac{(x-4)(6) + x(x)}{x(1)} = \frac{6x - 24 + x^2}{x} =$$

$$\frac{x^2 + 6x - 24}{x}$$

Solving Quadratic Equations Worksheet 47

① Solve each quadratic equation by factoring.

$x^2 - x - 6 = 0$
$(x-3)(x+2) = 0$
$x - 3 = 0; x = 3$
$x + 2 = 0; x = -2$
The solution is $x = 3$ and -2.

$x^2 + 8x + 12 = 0$
$(x+6)(x+2) = 0$
$x + 6 = 0; x = -6$
$x + 2 = 0; x = -2$
The solution is $x = -6$ and -2.

$x^2 + 2x = 35$
$x^2 + 2x - 35 = 0$
$(x-5)(x+7) = 0$
$x - 5 = 0; x = 5$
$x + 7 = 0; x = -7$
The solution is $x = 5$ and -7.

② Solve each quadratic equation by taking the roots.

$x^2 - 81 = 0$
$x^2 = 81$
$\sqrt{x^2} = \sqrt{81}$
$x = \pm 9$

$x^2 - 33 = 0$
$x^2 = 33$
$\sqrt{x^2} = \sqrt{33}$
$x = \pm\sqrt{33}$

$x^2 - 54 = 0$
$x^2 = 54$
$\sqrt{x^2} = \sqrt{54}$
$\sqrt{x^2} = \sqrt{3 \cdot 3 \cdot 6}$
$x = \pm 3\sqrt{6}$

③ Solve each quadratic equation by completing the square.

$x^2 + 12x + 5 = 0$
$x^2 + 12x = -5$
$x^2 + 12x + \left(\frac{12}{2}\right)^2 = -5 + \left(\frac{12}{2}\right)^2$
$x^2 + 12x + 36 = -5 + 36$
$x^2 + 12x + 36 = 31$
$(x+6)^2 = 31$
$\sqrt{(x+6)^2} = \sqrt{31}$
$x + 6 = \pm\sqrt{31}$
$x = -6 \pm \sqrt{31}$

$x^2 - 9x + 4 = 0$
$x^2 - 9x = -4$
$x^2 - 9x + \left(-\frac{9}{2}\right)^2 = -4 + \left(-\frac{9}{2}\right)^2$
$x^2 - 9x + \frac{81}{4} = -\frac{16}{4} + \frac{81}{4}$
$x^2 - 9x + \frac{81}{4} = \frac{65}{4}$
$\left(x - \frac{9}{2}\right)^2 = \frac{65}{4}$
$\sqrt{\left(x - \frac{9}{2}\right)^2} = \sqrt{\frac{65}{4}}$
$x - \frac{9}{2} = \pm\frac{\sqrt{65}}{2}$
$x = \frac{9 \pm \sqrt{65}}{2}$

$x^2 + 18x - 3 = 0$
$x^2 + 18x = 3$
$x^2 + 18x + \left(\frac{18}{2}\right)^2 = 3 + \left(\frac{18}{2}\right)^2$
$x^2 + 18x + 81 = 3 + 81$
$x^2 + 18x + 81 = 84$
$(x+9)^2 = 84$
$\sqrt{(x+9)^2} = \sqrt{84}$
$x + 9 = \pm\sqrt{2 \cdot 2 \cdot 21}$
$x = -9 \pm 2\sqrt{21}$

$x^2 + 8x + 1 = 0$
$x^2 + 8x = -1$
$x^2 + 8x + \left(\frac{8}{2}\right)^2 = -1 + \left(\frac{8}{2}\right)^2$
$x^2 + 8x + 16 = -1 + 16$
$x^2 + 8x + 16 = 15$
$(x+4)^2 = 15$
$\sqrt{(x+4)^2} = \sqrt{15}$
$x + 4 = \pm\sqrt{15}$
$x = -4 \pm \sqrt{15}$

$x^2 - 7x + 2 = 0$
$x^2 - 7x = -2$
$x^2 - 7x + \left(-\frac{7}{2}\right)^2 = -2 + \left(-\frac{7}{2}\right)^2$
$x^2 - 7x + \frac{49}{4} = -\frac{8}{4} + \frac{49}{4}$
$x^2 - 7x + \frac{49}{4} = \frac{41}{4}$
$\left(x - \frac{7}{2}\right)^2 = \frac{41}{4}$
$\sqrt{\left(x - \frac{7}{2}\right)^2} = \sqrt{\frac{41}{4}}$
$x - \frac{7}{2} = \pm\frac{\sqrt{41}}{2}$
$x = \frac{7 \pm \sqrt{41}}{2}$

$x^2 + 8x - 3 = 0$
$x^2 + 8x = 3$
$x^2 + 8x + \left(\frac{8}{2}\right)^2 = 3 + \left(\frac{8}{2}\right)^2$
$x^2 + 8x + 16 = 3 + 16$
$x^2 + 8x + 16 = 19$
$(x+4)^2 = 19$
$\sqrt{(x+4)^2} = \sqrt{19}$
$x + 4 = \pm\sqrt{19}$
$x = -4 \pm \sqrt{19}$

Teaching Tips, Cont.

- Use the steps listed in the teaching box to teach how to complete the square of a quadratic equation.
- Show the students that a perfect square trinomial is formed after completing the square. Make sure they all understand the importance of factoring the perfect square trinomial to solve the quadratic equation.
- Teach how to use completing the square to solve a quadratic equation. Make sure students remember to list the square root of a constant as both the positive and the negative values.
- Tell the students that if the constant term that is isolated on one side of the equal sign is not a perfect square, then leave the answer as a radical. Make sure all radicals are simplified.
- Complete the Classwork exercises. Have some students work the problems on the board for the class and explain their answers. All students should work the problems in their books.

Assignments

- Complete Lesson 93, Activities 2-3.
- Worksheet 47.

Lesson 94

Concepts

- Quadratic equations
- Quadratic formula
- Solving quadratic equations using the quadratic formula
- Solving quadratic equations by factoring
- Solving quadratic equations by taking roots

Learning Objectives

The student will be able to:

- Memorize the quadratic formula
- Use the quadratic formula to solve quadratic equations
- Simplify the radical in the solution of a quadratic equation

Materials Needed

- Student Book, Lesson 94

Teaching Tips

- Review solving quadratic equations by completing the square. (See Lesson 93)
- Tell the students there is another method of solving quadratic equations that do not factor easily.
- Introduce the quadratic formula from the teaching box. Tell the students they must memorize this formula.
- Teach how to find the roots of a quadratic equation using the quadratic formula.

Solving Quadratic Equations: Quadratic Formula

You have learned how to solve quadratic equations by factoring and completing the square. However, not every quadratic equation will factor nicely, and completing the square can be cumbersome at times. In these situations, the quadratic formula will provide the roots.

The **quadratic formula** is $x = \frac{-b \pm \sqrt{b^2 - 4ac}}{2a}$, where a, b, and c correspond to the coefficients in a quadratic equation, $ax^2 + bx + c = 0$.

Notice the operator in the numerator of the formula. The symbol $\pm$ means "plus or minus." This will produce two distinct roots in the solution. One by adding the square root, and one by subtracting the square root.

Solve the equation $x^2 + 5x + 3 = 0$.
This equation does not factor, so you need to use the quadratic formula.

First, identify the values of a, b, and c.
$a = 1$; $b = 5$, and $c = 3$

Substitute these values in the formula.

$$x = \frac{-5 \pm \sqrt{5^2 - 4(1)(3)}}{2(1)} = \frac{-5 \pm \sqrt{25 - 12}}{2} = \frac{-5 \pm \sqrt{13}}{2}$$

The answer can be left in this form. However, it is important that you understand that this is really two distinct roots:

$\frac{-5 + \sqrt{13}}{2}$ and $\frac{-5 - \sqrt{13}}{2}$

Notice this was the same example problem that was used in Lesson 93, but solved with the quadratic formula rather than completing the square. The answer is the same no matter which method you use.

① **Classwork**

Use the quadratic formula to solve each equation.

$x^2 + 4x + 2 = 0$

$x = \frac{-4 \pm \sqrt{4^2 - 4(1)(2)}}{2(1)}$

$x = \frac{-4 \pm \sqrt{16 - 8}}{2}$

$x = \frac{-4 \pm \sqrt{8}}{2}$

$x = \frac{-4 \pm 2\sqrt{2}}{2}$

$x = \frac{-4}{2} \pm \frac{2\sqrt{2}}{2}$

$x = -2 \pm \sqrt{2}$

$x^2 - 6x - 5 = 0$

$x = \frac{6 \pm \sqrt{(-6)^2 - 4(1)(-5)}}{2(1)}$

$x = \frac{6 \pm \sqrt{36 + 20}}{2}$

$x = \frac{6 \pm \sqrt{56}}{2}$

$x = \frac{6 \pm 2\sqrt{14}}{2}$

$x = \frac{6}{2} \pm \frac{2\sqrt{14}}{2}$

$x = 3 \pm \sqrt{14}$

Note: These are the same Classwork problems from Lesson 93.

Activities

② Use the quadratic formula to solve each equation.

$3x^2 + 5x - 4 = 0$

$x = \frac{-5 \pm \sqrt{5^2 - 4(3)(-4)}}{2(3)}$

$x = \frac{-5 \pm \sqrt{25 + 48}}{6}$

$x = \frac{-5 \pm \sqrt{73}}{6}$

$2x^2 + 4x - 3 = 0$

$x = \frac{-4 \pm \sqrt{4^2 - 4(2)(-3)}}{2(2)}$

$x = \frac{-4 \pm \sqrt{16 + 24}}{4}$

$x = \frac{-4 \pm \sqrt{40}}{4}$

$x = \frac{-4 \pm 2\sqrt{10}}{4}$

$x = \frac{-4}{4} \pm \frac{2\sqrt{10}}{4}$

$x = -1 \pm \frac{\sqrt{10}}{2}$

$x^2 - 3x - 6 = 0$

$x = \frac{-(-3) \pm \sqrt{(-3)^2 - 4(1)(-6)}}{2(1)}$

$x = \frac{3 \pm \sqrt{9 + 24}}{2}$

$x = \frac{3 \pm \sqrt{33}}{2}$

$2x^2 - 6x - 1 = 0$

$x = \frac{-(-6) \pm \sqrt{(-6)^2 - 4(2)(-1)}}{2(2)}$

$x = \frac{6 \pm \sqrt{36 + 8}}{4}$

$x = \frac{6 \pm \sqrt{44}}{4}$

$x = \frac{6 \pm 2\sqrt{11}}{4}$

$x = \frac{3 \pm \sqrt{11}}{2}$

$3x^2 + 9x + 5 = 0$

$x = \frac{-9 \pm \sqrt{9^2 - 4(3)(5)}}{2(3)}$

$x = \frac{-9 \pm \sqrt{81 - 60}}{6}$

$x = \frac{-9 \pm \sqrt{21}}{6}$

$5x^2 - 7x + 2 = 0$

$x = \frac{-(-7) \pm \sqrt{(-7)^2 - 4(5)(2)}}{2(5)}$

$x = \frac{7 \pm \sqrt{49 - 40}}{10}$

$x = \frac{7 \pm \sqrt{9}}{10}$

$x = \frac{7 \pm 3}{10}$

$x = \frac{10}{10}$ and $\frac{4}{10}$

$x = 1$ and $\frac{2}{5}$

③ Solve.

$12x^2 + 13x - 4 = 0$

$(4x - 1)(3x + 4) = 0$

$4x - 1 = 0; x = \frac{1}{4}$

$3x + 4 = 0; x = -\frac{4}{3}$

$x = \frac{1}{4}$ and $-\frac{4}{3}$.

$5x^2 - 21x = -4$

$5x^2 - 21x + 4 = 0$

$(5x - 1)(x - 4) = 0$

$5x - 1 = 0; x = \frac{1}{5}$

$x - 4 = 0; x = 4$

$x = \frac{1}{5}$ and 4.

$12x^2 + 4x - 5 = 0$

$(6x + 5)(2x - 1) = 0$

$6x + 5 = 0; x = -\frac{5}{6}$

$2x - 1 = 0; x = \frac{1}{2}$

$x = -\frac{5}{6}$ and $\frac{1}{2}$.

$6x^2 + 5x - 25 = 0$

$(2x + 5)(3x - 5) = 0$

$2x + 5 = 0; x = -\frac{5}{2}$

$3x - 5 = 0; x = \frac{5}{3}$

$x = -\frac{5}{2}$ and $\frac{5}{3}$.

$2x^2 - 11x - 21 = 0$

$(x - 7)(2x + 3) = 0$

$x - 7 = 0; x = 7$

$2x + 3 = 0; x = -\frac{3}{2}$

$x = 7$ and $-\frac{3}{2}$.

$x^2 - 36 = 0$

$x^2 = 36$

$x = \pm 6$

Teaching Tips, Cont.

- Note: The sample problem in the teaching box and the Classwork exercises of this lesson are the same as the sample problem and Classwork exercises in Lesson 93. When you are finished teaching this lesson, have the students look at the sample problem and Classwork exercises from Lesson 93 and compare the answers.
- Remind students to express the positive and negative values when using radicals.
- Complete the Classwork exercises. Have some students work the problems on the board for the class and explain their answers. All students should work the problems in their books.

Assignment

- Complete Lesson 94, Activities 2-3.

Lesson 95

Concepts
- Discriminant
- Double roots
- Math in the real world

Learning Objectives
The student will be able to:
- Define *discriminant*
- Calculate the value of the discriminant
- Use the value of the discriminant to determine the number of roots in a quadratic equation
- Identify quadratic equations with double roots

Materials Needed
- Student Book, Lesson 95
- Worksheet 48

Teaching Tips
- Have students complete Worksheet 48 in class. This may be for added practice of earlier topics, or graded as a quiz, if desired.
- Review solving quadratic equations by taking roots. (See Lesson 92)
- Review the quadratic formula. (See Lesson 94)
- Remind students that they must memorize the quadratic formula if they have not already done so. If they do not memorize this formula, they will have difficulty with this lesson as well as other future lessons.
- Teach the definition of *discriminant* from the teaching box.

Lesson 95

The Discriminant

So far, the quadratic equations you have solved have all had 2 real roots. However, that is not always the case. Some quadratic equations have one real root, known as a **double root**, in the case of perfect square trinomials set equal to zero. Other quadratic equations have no real roots. Fortunately, there is a simple way to discriminate between all the possible solutions.

The **discriminant** is the argument (portion under the radical) in the quadratic formula. If the discriminant is greater than zero, there are two real roots. If the discriminant is equal to zero, there is 1 real root - a double root. If the discriminant is less than zero, there are no real roots because you cannot take the square root of a negative number.

Consider the equation $x^2+6x+9=0$.
When this equation is factored, it gives
$(x+3)^2=0$.
Taking the square root of both sides gives
$\sqrt{(x+3)^2}=\sqrt{0}$
$x+3=0$
$x=-3$

There is no such thing as positive or negative zero, so it appears that a root is missing. In reality, -3 appears twice as a root - once for each identical factor $(x+3)$ - and is a double root. Double roots are listed once in the answer.

Notice the discriminant for this problem.
$b^2-4ac=6^2-4(1)(9)=36-36=0$
The discriminant equals zero, so there is one real root.

① **Classwork**
Find the discriminant and tell the number of real roots in each quadratic equation.

$x^2+8x+3=0$
$8^2-4(1)(3)=$
$64-12=$
52
The discriminant is greater than zero, so there are 2 real roots.

$5x^2-6x+2=0$
$(-6)^2-4(5)(2)=$
$36-40=$
-4
The discriminant is less than zero, so there are no real roots.

$4x^2-4x+1=0$
$(-4)^2-4(4)(1)=$
$16-16=$
0
The discriminant is equal to zero, so there is one real root.

Activities
② Find the discriminant and tell the number of real roots in each quadratic equation.

$3x^2+2x+4=0$
$2^2-4(3)(4)=$
$4-48=$
-44
The discriminant is less than zero, so there are no real roots.

$2x^2-8x+3=0$
$(-8)^2-4(2)(3)=$
$64-24=$
40
The discriminant is greater than zero, so there are 2 real roots.

$9x^2-6x+1=0$
$(-6)^2-4(9)(1)=$
$36-36=$
0
The discriminant is equal to zero, so there is one real root.

③ Find the discriminant and tell the number of real roots in each quadratic equation.

$2x^2+7x+3=0$
$7^2-4(2)(3)=$
$49-24=$
25
The discriminant is greater than zero, so there are 2 real roots.

$x^2-2x+1=0$
$(-2)^2-4(1)(1)=$
$4-4=$
0
The discriminant is equal to zero, so there is one real root.

$x^2-5x+7=0$
$(-5)^2-4(1)(7)=$
$25-28=$
-3
The discriminant is less than zero, so there are no real roots.

$2x^2-3x+2=0$
$(-3)^2-4(2)(2)=$
$9-16=$
-7
The discriminant is less than zero, so there are no real roots.

$3x^2+6x+2=0$
$6^2-4(3)(2)=$
$36-24=$
12
The discriminant is greater than zero, so there are 2 real roots.

$4x^2+12x+9=0$
$(12)^2-4(4)(9)=$
$144-144=$
0
The discriminant is equal to zero, so there is one real root.

④ Solve.
The distance a hockey player can reach with his stick is given by the formula $d=\sqrt{s^2-h^2}$, where s is the distance from the player's shoulder to the bottom of the stick when he is gripping the stick, and h is the shoulder height of the player with his skates on. If a player's shoulder height with his skates on is 63 inches and the distance from his shoulder to the bottom of the gripped stick is 87 inches, how far can the player reach with his stick?

s = 87 inches and h = 63 inches
$d=\sqrt{87^2-63^2}$
$d=\sqrt{7569-3969}$
$d=\sqrt{3600}$
$d=60$
The player can reach 60 inches with his stick.

If the player squats so that his shoulder height is reduced to 60 inches, how far can he reach with his stick?
s = 87 inches and h = 60 inches
$d=\sqrt{87^2-60^2}$
$d=\sqrt{7569-3600}$
$d=\sqrt{3969}$
$d=63$
The player can reach 63 inches with his stick.

Solving Quadratic Equations Worksheet 48

① Solve each quadratic equation by factoring.

$x^2+3x-4=0$
$(x-1)(x+4)=0$
$x-1=0; x=1$
$x+4=0; x=-4$
The solution is
$x = 1$ and -4.

$x^2+5x+6=0$
$(x+2)(x+3)=0$
$x+2=0; x=-2$
$x+3=0; x=-3$
The solution is
$x = -2$ and -3.

$x^2+x=20$
$x^2+x-20=0$
$(x-4)(x+5)=0$
$x-4=0; x=4$
$x+5=0; x=-5$
The solution is
$x = 4$ and -5.

② Solve each quadratic equation by taking the roots.

$x^2-144=0$
$x^2=144$
$\sqrt{x^2}=\sqrt{144}$
$x=\pm 12$

$x^2-41=0$
$x^2=41$
$\sqrt{x^2}=\sqrt{41}$
$x=\pm\sqrt{41}$

$x^2-48=0$
$x^2=48$
$\sqrt{x^2}=\sqrt{48}$
$\sqrt{x^2}=\sqrt{4\cdot 4\cdot 3}$
$x=\pm 4\sqrt{3}$

③ Solve each quadratic equation by completing the square.

$x^2+8x+3=0$
$x^2+8x=-3$
$x^2+8x+\left(\frac{8}{2}\right)^2=-3+\left(\frac{8}{2}\right)^2$
$x^2+8x+16=-3+16$
$x^2+8x+16=13$
$(x+4)^2=13$
$\sqrt{(x+4)^2}=\sqrt{13}$
$x+4=\pm\sqrt{13}$
$x=-4\pm\sqrt{13}$

$x^2-11x+2=0$
$x^2-11x=-2$
$x^2-11x+\left(-\frac{11}{2}\right)^2=-2+\left(-\frac{11}{2}\right)^2$
$x^2-11x+\frac{121}{4}=-\frac{8}{4}+\frac{121}{4}$
$x^2-11x+\frac{121}{4}=\frac{113}{4}$
$\left(x-\frac{11}{2}\right)^2=\frac{113}{4}$
$\sqrt{\left(x-\frac{11}{2}\right)^2}=\sqrt{\frac{113}{4}}$
$x-\frac{11}{2}=\pm\frac{\sqrt{113}}{2}$
$x=\frac{11\pm\sqrt{113}}{2}$

$x^2+10x-7=0$
$x^2+10x=7$
$x^2+10x+\left(\frac{10}{2}\right)^2=7+\left(\frac{10}{2}\right)^2$
$x^2+10x+25=7+25$
$x^2+10x+25=32$
$(x+5)^2=32$
$\sqrt{(x+5)^2}=\sqrt{32}$
$x+5=\pm\sqrt{4\cdot 4\cdot 2}$
$x=-5\pm 4\sqrt{2}$

$x^2+10x+5=0$
$x^2+10x=-5$
$x^2+10x+\left(\frac{10}{2}\right)^2=-5+\left(\frac{10}{2}\right)^2$
$x^2+10x+25=-5+25$
$x^2+10x+25=20$
$(x+5)^2=20$
$\sqrt{(x+5)^2}=\sqrt{20}$
$x+5=\pm\sqrt{2\cdot 2\cdot 5}$
$x=-5\pm 2\sqrt{5}$

$x^2-9x+4=0$
$x^2-9x=-4$
$x^2-9x+\left(-\frac{9}{2}\right)^2=-4+\left(-\frac{9}{2}\right)^2$
$x^2-9x+\frac{81}{4}=-\frac{16}{4}+\frac{81}{4}$
$x^2-9x+\frac{81}{4}=\frac{65}{4}$
$\left(x-\frac{9}{2}\right)^2=\frac{65}{4}$
$\sqrt{\left(x-\frac{9}{2}\right)^2}=\sqrt{\frac{65}{4}}$
$x-\frac{9}{2}=\pm\frac{\sqrt{65}}{2}$
$x=\frac{9\pm\sqrt{65}}{2}$

$x^2+10x-1=0$
$x^2+10x=1$
$x^2+10x+\left(\frac{10}{2}\right)^2=1+\left(\frac{10}{2}\right)^2$
$x^2+10x+25=1+25$
$x^2+10x+25=26$
$(x+5)^2=26$
$\sqrt{(x+5)^2}=\sqrt{26}$
$x+5=\pm\sqrt{26}$
$x=-5\pm\sqrt{26}$

Teaching Tips, Cont.

- Teach how to find the value of the discriminant.
- Explain that when the value of the discriminant is known, it is easy to determine the number of roots a quadratic equation has. This is helpful because if the discriminant indicates there are no real roots, then you do not have to waste your time trying to solve the equation. Simply list the solution as "no real roots."
- Complete the Classwork exercises. Have some students work the problems on the board for the class and explain their answers. All students should work the problems in their books.

Assignment

- Complete Lesson 95, Activities 2-4.

Lesson 96

Concepts

- Quadratic equations
- Discriminant
- Solving quadratic equations
- Solving systems of equations
- Solving equations with absolute value
- Dividing polynomials

Learning Objectives

The student will be able to:

- Calculate the discriminant of a quadratic equation
- Use the discriminant to determine the best way to solve a quadratic equation
- Solve quadratic equations with real solutions

Materials Needed

- Student Book, Lesson 96

Teaching Tips

➢ Review finding the discriminant. (See Lesson 95)

➢ Review solving quadratic equations by factoring. (See Lesson 91)

➢ Review solving quadratic equations by taking roots. (See Lesson 92)

➢ Review solving quadratic equations by completing the square. (See Lesson 93)

➢ Review solving quadratic equations by using the quadratic formula. (See Lesson 94)

Review of Quadratic Equations

Before attempting to solve a quadratic equation, you should find the discriminant. This will give you a clue about which method of solving will work best.

If the discriminant is a perfect square, solving by factoring may be your best option.

If the discriminant is a positive integer, the quadratic formula will most likely be your best choice. In either case, completing the square will work if you get stuck or just want to check your work.

If the discriminant is a negative number, do not attempt to solve the problem at this time. Simply state that there are no real roots.

① **Classwork**

Find the discriminant and solve the quadratic equations with real roots.

$2x^2 + 6x + 1 = 0$

$6^2 - 4(2)(1) = 36 - 8 = 28$

$x = \frac{-6 \pm \sqrt{28}}{2(2)} = \frac{-6 \pm 2\sqrt{7}}{4} = \frac{-3 \pm \sqrt{7}}{2}$

$2x^2 - 2x + 3 = 0$

$(-2)^2 - 4(2)(3) = 4 - 24 = -20$

There are no real roots.

Activities

② Find the discriminant and solve the quadratic equations with real roots.

$x^2 + 4x + 3 = 0$

$4^2 - 4(1)(3) = 16 - 12 = 4$

$(x + 3)(x + 1) = 0$

$x + 3 = 0 \quad x + 1 = 0$

$x = -3, -1$

$5x^2 - 5x + 2 = 0$

$(-5)^2 - 4(5)(2) = 25 - 40 = -15$

There are no real roots.

$4x^2 + 28x + 49 = 0$

$(28)^2 - 4(4)(49) = 784 - 784 = 0$

$(2x + 7)(2x + 7) = 0$

$2x + 7 = 0$

$x = -\frac{7}{2}$

$3x^2 + x - 5 = 0$

$1^2 - 4(3)(-5) = 1 + 60 = 61$

$x = \frac{-1 \pm \sqrt{61}}{2(3)} = \frac{-1 \pm \sqrt{61}}{6}$

$2x^2 + 7x + 7 = 0$

$(7)^2 - 4(2)(7) = 49 - 56 = -7$

There are no real roots.

$x^2 - 12x + 36 = 0$

$(-12)^2 - 4(1)(36) = 144 - 144 = 0$

$(x - 6)(x - 6) = 0$

$x - 6 = 0$

$x = 6$

$4x^2 + 7x + 2 = 0$

$7^2 - 4(4)(2) = 49 - 32 = 17$

$x = \frac{-7 \pm \sqrt{17}}{2(4)} = \frac{-7 \pm \sqrt{17}}{8}$

$4x^2 - 3x + 7 = 0$

$(-3)^2 - 4(4)(7) = 9 - 112 = -103$

There are no real roots.

$x^2 - 4x + 4 = 0$

$(-4)^2 - 4(1)(4) = 16 - 16 = 0$

$(x - 2)(x - 2) = 0$

$x - 2 = 0$

$x = 2$

$5x^2 + 9x + 3 = 0$

$9^2 - 4(5)(3) = 81 - 60 = 21$

$x = \frac{-9 \pm \sqrt{21}}{2(5)} = \frac{-9 \pm \sqrt{21}}{10}$

$3x^2 - 8x + 6 = 0$

$(-8)^2 - 4(3)(6) = 64 - 72 = -8$

There are no real roots.

$9x^2 + 6x + 1 = 0$

$(6)^2 - 4(9)(1) = 36 - 36 = 0$

$(3x + 1)(3x + 1) = 0$

$3x + 1 = 0$

$x = -\frac{1}{3}$

③ Solve the systems of equations.

$x - y - 7 = 0$
$-2x + y + 12 = 0$
$x - y = 7$
$\underline{-2x + y = -12}$
$-x = -5$
$x = 5$
$5 - y - 7 = 0$
$y = -2$
(5, -2)

$10x - 7y - 2 = 0$
$5x + 2y - 23 = 0$
$10x - 7y = 2$
$5x + 2y = 23$
$10x - 7y = 2$
$\underline{10x + 4y = 46}$
$-11y = -44$
$y = 4$
$10x - 7(4) - 2 = 0$
$10x - 28 = 2$
$10x = 30$
$x = 3$
(3, 4)

$11x + 22y - 11 = 0$
$-x - 4y + 5 = 0$
$11x + 22y = 11$
$-x - 4y = -5$
$x + 2y = 1$
$\underline{-x - 4y = -5}$
$-2y = -4$
$y = 2$
$-x - 4(2) + 5 = 0$
$-x - 8 = -5$
$-x = 3$
$x = -3$
(-3, 2)

$15x - 10y - 20 = 0$
$9x - 6y - 12 = 0$
$15x - 10y = 20$
$9x - 6y = 12$
Divide the top equation by 5 and the bottom equation by 3.
$3x - 2y = 4$
$\underline{3x - 2y = 4}$
$0 = 0$
All real numbers

④ Find all possible solutions. Identify any extraneous solutions.

$|-4x + 1| + 3x - 5 = 5x + 12$
$|-4x + 1| = 2x + 17$
$-4x + 1 = 2x + 17$ or $-4x + 1 = -(2x + 17)$
$-6x = 16$ $\quad$ $-4x + 1 = -2x - 17$
$x = -\frac{16}{6} = -\frac{8}{3}$ $\quad$ $-2x = -18 \Rightarrow x = 9$
check:
$|-4(-\frac{8}{3}) + 1| + 3(-\frac{8}{3}) - 5 = 5(-\frac{8}{3}) + 12$
$|\frac{32}{3} + 1| - \frac{24}{3} - \frac{15}{3} = -\frac{40}{3} + 12$
$|\frac{35}{3}| - \frac{39}{3} = -\frac{40}{3} + \frac{36}{3}$
$\frac{35}{3} - \frac{39}{3} = -\frac{4}{3}$

$|-4(9) + 1| + 3(9) - 5 = 5(9) + 12$
$|-36 + 1| + 27 - 5 = 45 + 12$
$|-35| + 22 = 57$
$35 + 22 = 57$

$|3x - 2| - 4 = -2x - 21$
$|3x - 2| = -2x - 17$
$3x - 2 = -2x - 17$ or $3x - 2 = -(-2x - 17)$
$5x = -15$ $\quad$ $3x - 2 = 2x + 17$
$x = -3$ $\quad$ $x = 19$
check:
$|3(-3) - 2| - 4 = -2(-3) - 21$
$|-9 - 2| - 4 = 6 - 21$
$|-11| - 4 = 6 - 21$
$11 - 4 \neq -15$ extraneous

$|3(19) - 2| - 4 = -2(19) - 21$
$|57 - 2| - 4 = -38 - 21$
$|55| - 4 = -38 - 21$
$55 - 4 \neq -59$ extraneous

⑤ Divide.

$(2x^2 + 11x + 12) \div (2x + 3)$

$$\begin{array}{r} x + 4 \\ 2x + 3\overline{)2x^2 + 11x + 12} \\ \underline{2x^2 + 3x} \\ 8x + 12 \\ \underline{8x + 12} \end{array}$$

$(12x^2 + 19x - 18) \div (4x + 9)$

$$\begin{array}{r} 3x - 2 \\ 4x + 9\overline{)12x^2 + 19x - 18} \\ \underline{12x^2 + 27x} \\ -8x - 18 \\ \underline{-8x - 18} \end{array}$$

$(9x^2 - 25) \div (3x - 5)$

$$\begin{array}{r} 3x + 5 \\ 3x - 5\overline{)9x^2 \qquad - 25} \\ \underline{9x^2 - 15x} \\ +15x - 25 \\ \underline{+15x - 25} \end{array}$$

Teaching Tips, Cont.

- Remind students to always find the discriminant before attempting to solve a quadratic equation. The value of the discriminant will give a clue about the easiest way to solve the equation.
- Tell the students that they should try to factor the quadratic equation if the discriminant is a perfect square. Completing the square or using the quadratic equation is a good choice if the discriminant is a positive, non perfect-square number. If the value of *a* is not equal to 1, they will have to use the quadratic formula. Completing the square when *a* is not equal to 1 will be taught in Lesson 100.
- Ask the students what method of solving they should use when the discriminant is negative. (None.) Why not? (There are no real roots.)
- Complete the Classwork exercises. Have some students work the problems on the board for the class and explain their answers. All students should work the problems in their books.

Assignment

- Complete Lesson 96, Activities 2-5.

Lesson 97

Concepts

- Functions
- Domain
- Range
- Graphing functions

Learning Objectives

The student will be able to:

- Define *function*
- Define *domain*
- Define *range*
- Apply the vertical line test to determine if a graph is a function
- Graph functions

Materials Needed

- Student Book, Lesson 97

Teaching Tips

- Teach the definitions of *function*, *domain*, and *range* from the teaching box.
- Explain that for an equation to be a function, each value of x must have no more than 1 corresponding value of y. However, a single value of y may have multiple corresponding values of x. Refer the students to the diagrams in the teaching box for clarity.
- Tell the students that a function is an equation written in the format $f(x) =$ rather than $y =$. In functions, $f(x)$ is treated as y when plotting points to graph.
- Show the students how to use the vertical line test to determine whether or not a graph is a function.

Functions

A **function** is an equation in which each value of the independent variable has exactly one corresponding value of the dependent variable.

The values assigned to the independent variable are called the **domain**.

The corresponding values of the dependent variable are called the **range**.

A function is written in the format $f(x)$ and is read, "the function f of x," or, "the f of x."

When graphing a function, the $f(x)$ side of the equation corresponds to the y portion of an equation. Plot points as usual and graph.

To look at a graph and instantly determine whether or not the graph is a function, use the **vertical line test**. If you can draw a vertical line on the graph and cross the graph in two or more points, the graph is not a function. Otherwise, the graph is a function.

Tell whether or not each graph is a function.

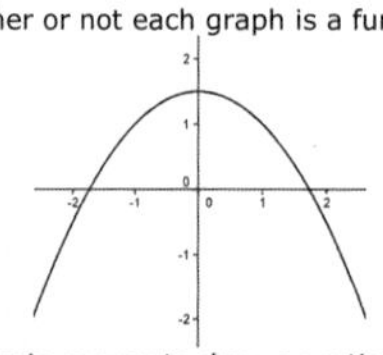

Yes. There is no way to draw a vertical line that intersects the graph in more than one point.

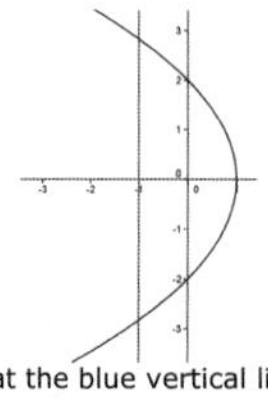

No. Notice that the blue vertical line intersects the graph in two places.

① Classwork

Tell whether or not each graph is a function.

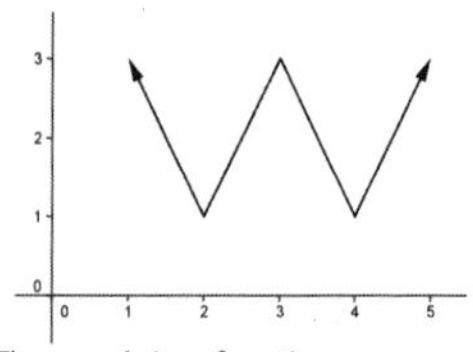

Yes. The graph is a function.

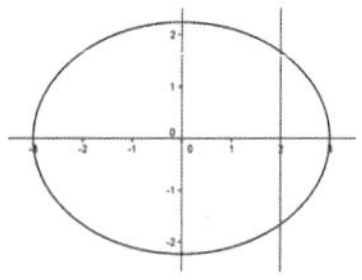

No. A vertical line intersects the graph in two places.

Graph the function $f(x) = 2(x - 1)$.

x	y
0	$y = 2(0-1) = 2(-1) = -2$
1	$y = 2(1-1) = 2(0) = 0$
-1	$y = 2(-1-1) = 2(-2) = -4$

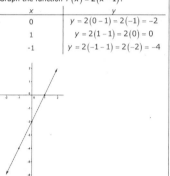

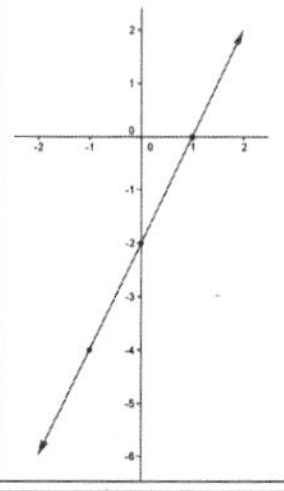

Activities

② Tell whether or not each graph is a function.

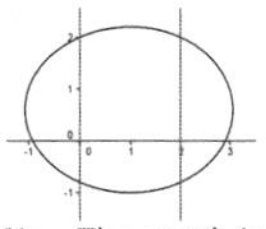

No. The graph is not a function.

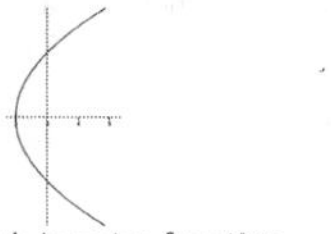

No. The graph is not a function.

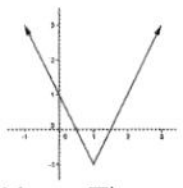

Yes. The graph is a function.

Yes. The graph is a function.

③ Graph the following functions on your own graph paper.

$f(x) = x + 1$

x	y
0	$y = 0 + 1 = 1$
1	$y = 1 + 1 = 2$
2	$y = 2 + 1 = 3$
-1	$y = -1 + 1 = 0$
-2	$y = -2 + 1 = -1$

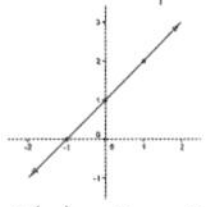

$f(x) = 2x - 1$

x	y
0	$y = 2(0) - 1 = 0 - 1 = -1$
1	$y = 2(1) - 1 = 2 - 1 = 1$
2	$y = 2(2) - 1 = 4 - 1 = 3$
-1	$y = 2(-1) - 1 = -2 - 1 = -3$
-2	$y = 2(-2) - 1 = -4 - 1 = -5$

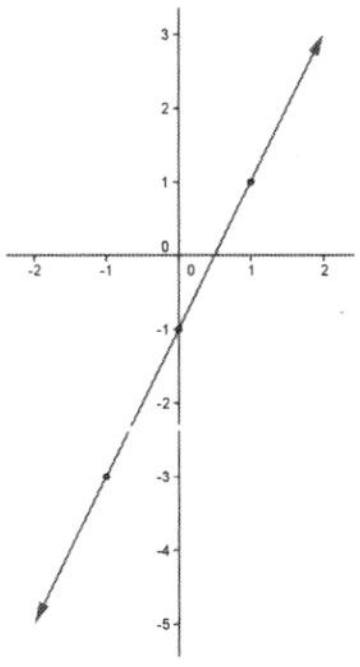

$f(x) = 3(x - 2)$

x	y
0	$y = 3(0 - 2) = 3(-2) = -6$
1	$y = 3(1 - 2) = 3(-1) = -3$
2	$y = 3(2 - 2) = 3(0) = 0$
-1	$y = 3(-1 - 2) = 3(-3) = -9$
-2	$y = 3(-2 - 2) = 3(-4) = -12$

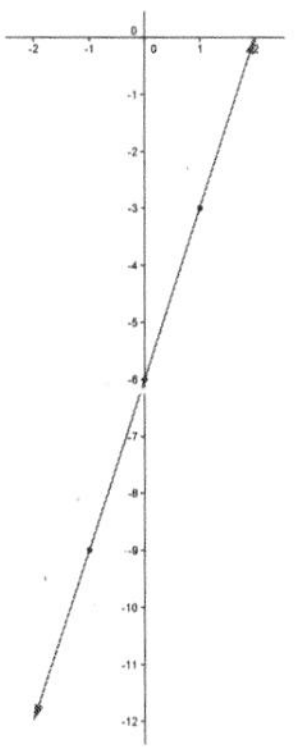

$f(x) = 2x - 3$

x	y
0	$y = 2(0) - 3 = 0 - 3 = -3$
1	$y = 2(1) - 3 = 2 - 3 = -1$
2	$y = 2(2) - 3 = 4 - 3 = 1$
-1	$y = 2(-1) - 3 = -2 - 3 = -5$
-2	$y = 2(-2) - 3 = -4 - 3 = -7$

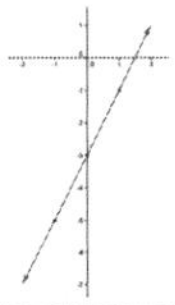

Teaching Tips, Cont.

- Have some students draw examples of graphs that are functions. Have other students draw examples of graphs that are not functions. In both cases, have the student tell whether or not the graph is a function and explain why or why not.
- Complete the Classwork exercises. Have some students work the problems on the board for the class and explain their answers. All students should work the problems in their books.

Assignment

- Complete Lesson 97, Activities 2-3.

Lesson 98

Concepts
- Quadratic functions
- Parabola
- Conic sections
- Math in the real world

Learning Objectives
The student will be able to:
- Define *conic section*
- Describe a parabola
- Sketch the graph of a parabola in the form $f(x) = ax^2$

Materials Needed
- Student Book, Lesson 98
- Worksheet 49
- 1 solid styrofoam cone (These are sold in most craft supply stores.)
- 1 sharp knife (long enough blade to cut through the styrofoam cone)

Teaching Tips
- Have students complete Worksheet 49 in class. This may be for added practice of earlier topics, or graded as a quiz, if desired.
- Introduce conic sections from the teaching box.
- Show the students the styrofoam cone. Use the knife to cut a section of the cone away, as shown in the picture in the teaching box. Start the cut on the edge of the circular base and slice at an angle. Show the students the parabola that is formed. (Because this can be messy depending on the type of styrofoam you get, you may wish to do the cutting over a trash can. You may also choose to cut the cone ahead of time and bring both pieces so you can just remove the cut portion to show the students the parabola that is formed.)

Quadratic Functions of the Form $f(x) = ax^2$

Quadratic functions will always graph to form a parabola. A **parabola** is one of several shapes known as conic sections. A **conic section** is a shape formed by slicing a cone. A parabola is formed by slicing a cone so that the slice is parallel to a line through the vertex of the cone.

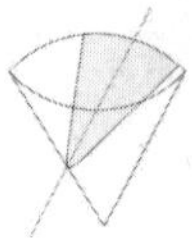

Quadratic functions of the form $f(x) = ax^2$ will have the **vertex** (the point at which the parabola turns around) at the origin. If a is positive, the parabola opens up. If a is negative, the parabola opens down.

To graph a parabola, plot at least 5 points, including the vertex. Be sure to choose both positive and negative values of x. Connect the points with a smooth curve.

Sketch the graph of $f(x) = 2x^2$.

x	y
0	0
1	2
2	8
-1	2
-2	8

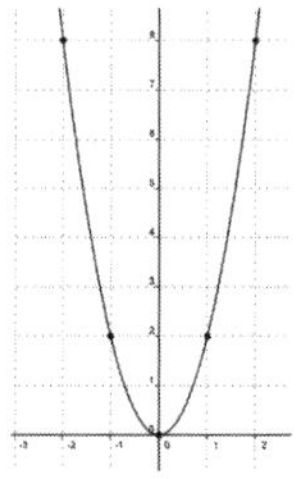

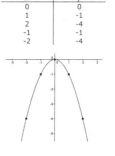

① Classwork
Sketch the graph of each parabola.

$f(x) = x^2$

x	y
0	0
1	1
2	4
-1	1
-2	4

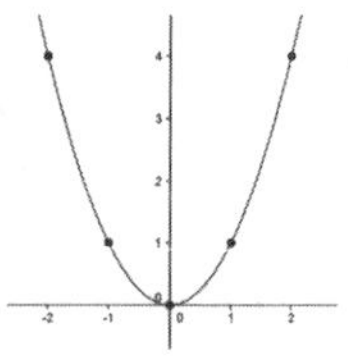

$f(x) = 3x^2$

x	y
0	0
1	3
2	12
-1	3
-2	12

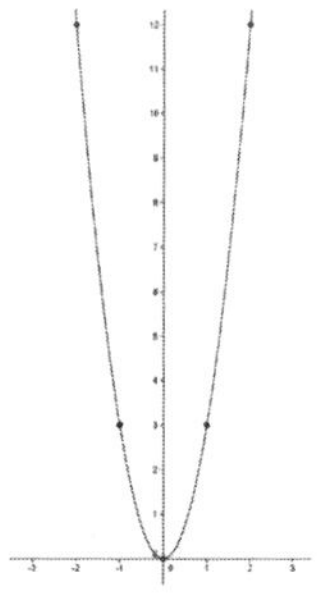

Activities
② Sketch the graph of each parabola.

$f(x) = -x^2$

x	y
0	0
1	-1
2	-4
-1	-1
-2	-4

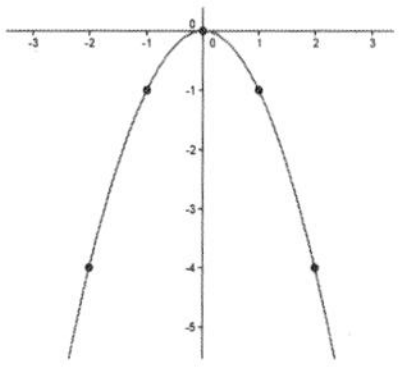

$f(x) = \frac{1}{2}x^2$

x	y
0	0
1	0.5
2	2
-1	0.5
-2	2

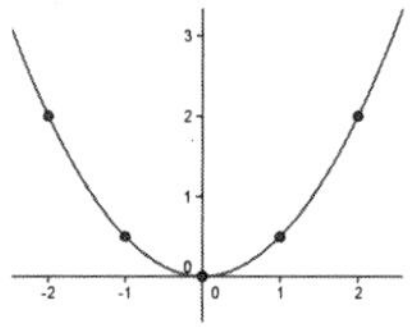

$f(x) = -2x^2$

x	y
0	0
1	-2
2	-8
-1	-2
-2	-8

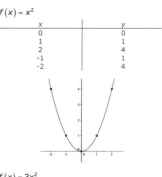

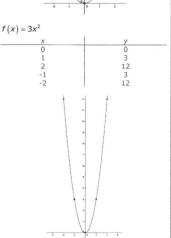

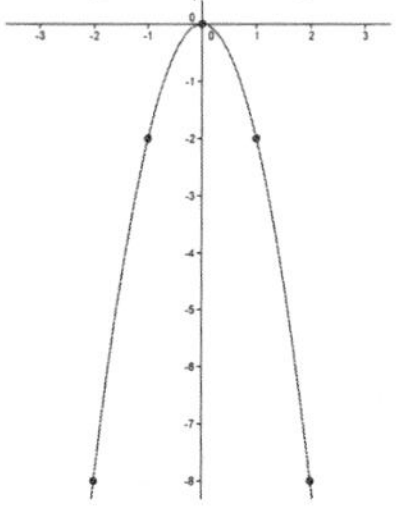

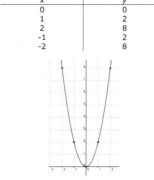

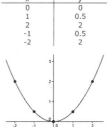

③ Solve.
The number of defensemen on an ice hockey team is 4 times the number of goalies and 4 less than the number of forwards. If there are a total of 14 forwards and goalies, how many players are at each position, and how many players total are on the team?

Let d = the number of defensemen.
Let g = the number of goalies.
Let f = the number of forwards.

Write equations based on the information in the problem.
$d = 4g$
$d = f - 4$
$f + g = 14$

Set the first two equations equal. $4g = f - 4$
Set up a system of equations and solve.
$4g = f - 4 \quad -f + 4g = -4$
$f + g = 14 \quad f + g = 14$
$5g = 10$
$g = 2$

There are 2 goalies, 4(2) = 8 defensemen, and 14 − 2 = 12 forwards for a total of 2 + 8 + 12 = 22 players on an ice hockey team.

The Quadratic Formula Worksheet 49

① Use the quadratic formula to solve each equation.

$x^2 + 8x + 3 = 0$

$x = \frac{-8 \pm \sqrt{8^2 - 4(1)(3)}}{2(1)}$

$x = \frac{-8 \pm \sqrt{64 - 12}}{2}$

$x = \frac{-8 \pm \sqrt{52}}{2}$

$x = \frac{-8}{2} \pm \frac{2\sqrt{13}}{2}$

$x = -4 \pm \sqrt{13}$

$x^2 - 11x + 2 = 0$

$x = \frac{-(-11) \pm \sqrt{(-11)^2 - 4(1)(2)}}{2(1)}$

$x = \frac{11 \pm \sqrt{121 - 8}}{2}$

$x = \frac{11 \pm \sqrt{113}}{2}$

$x^2 + 10x - 7 = 0$

$x = \frac{-10 \pm \sqrt{10^2 - 4(1)(-7)}}{2(1)}$

$x = \frac{-10 \pm \sqrt{100 + 28}}{2}$

$x = \frac{-10 \pm \sqrt{128}}{2}$

$x = \frac{-10 \pm 8\sqrt{2}}{2}$

$x = -5 \pm 4\sqrt{2}$

$3x^2 + 10x + 5 = 0$

$x = \frac{-(10) \pm \sqrt{(10)^2 - 4(3)(5)}}{2(3)}$

$x = \frac{-10 \pm \sqrt{100 - 60}}{6}$

$x = \frac{-10 \pm \sqrt{40}}{6}$

$x = \frac{-10 \pm 2\sqrt{10}}{6}$

$x = -\frac{10}{6} \pm \frac{2\sqrt{10}}{6}$

$x = -\frac{5}{3} \pm \frac{\sqrt{10}}{3}$ or $\frac{-5 \pm \sqrt{10}}{3}$

$3x^2 - 9x + 4 = 0$

$x = \frac{9 \pm \sqrt{(-9)^2 - 4(3)(4)}}{2(3)}$

$x = \frac{9 \pm \sqrt{81 - 48}}{6}$

$x = \frac{9 \pm \sqrt{33}}{6}$

$2x^2 + 10x - 1 = 0$

$x = \frac{-10 \pm \sqrt{10^2 - 4(2)(-1)}}{2(2)}$

$x = \frac{-10 \pm \sqrt{100 + 8}}{4}$

$x = \frac{-10 \pm \sqrt{108}}{4}$

$x = \frac{-10 \pm 6\sqrt{3}}{4}$

$x = \frac{-5 \pm 3\sqrt{3}}{2}$

$5x^2 + 8x - 1 = 0$

$x = \frac{-8 \pm \sqrt{8^2 - 4(5)(-1)}}{2(5)}$

$x = \frac{-8 \pm \sqrt{64 + 20}}{10}$

$x = \frac{-8 \pm \sqrt{84}}{10}$

$x = \frac{-8 \pm 2\sqrt{21}}{10}$

$x = \frac{-4 \pm \sqrt{21}}{5}$

$2x^2 - 7x - 2 = 0$

$x = \frac{-(-7) \pm \sqrt{(-7)^2 - 4(2)(-2)}}{2(2)}$

$x = \frac{7 \pm \sqrt{49 + 16}}{4}$

$x = \frac{7 \pm \sqrt{65}}{4}$

$3x^2 + 8x + 3 = 0$

$x = \frac{-8 \pm \sqrt{8^2 - 4(3)(3)}}{2(3)}$

$x = \frac{-8 \pm \sqrt{64 - 36}}{6}$

$x = \frac{-8 \pm \sqrt{28}}{6}$

$x = \frac{-8 \pm \sqrt{4 \cdot 7}}{6}$

$x = \frac{-8 \pm 2\sqrt{7}}{6}$

$x = \frac{-4 \pm \sqrt{7}}{3}$

Teaching Tips, Cont.

- Teach how to sketch the graph of a parabola from the teaching box. Explain that there is more to graphing a parabola than just plotting some points. This lesson just focuses on sketching a rough graph.
- Tell the students they need to plot at least 5 points when sketching the graph of a parabola. They need to include 0, 2 positive integers, and 2 negative integers as the value of *x* for this lesson.
- Complete the Classwork exercises. Have some students work the problems on the board for the class and explain their answers. All students should work the problems in their books.

Assignment

- Complete Lesson 98, Activities 2-3.

Lesson 99

Concepts

- Parabolas
- Vertex
- Sketching parabolas

Learning Objectives

The student will be able to:

- Find the vertex of a parabola from its quadratic function
- Sketch the graph of a parabola in the form $f(x) = ax^2 + k$
- Identify trends in the graphs of parabolas

Materials Needed

- Student Book, Lesson 99

Teaching Tips

- ➢ Review parabolas. (See Lesson 98)
- ➢ Have the students look back at their graphs from Lesson 98. Ask them where the vertex lies on each of those graphs. (At the origin)
- ➢ Tell the students that the vertex is not always at the origin when a parabola is graphed.
- ➢ Tell the students that when a constant is added to the end of the function $f(x) = ax^2$ to make it $f(x) = ax^2 + k$, the vertex moves higher on the y-axis if k is positive and lower on the y-axis if k is negative.

Quadratic Functions of the Form $f(x) = ax^2 + k$

In Lesson 98 you learned how to sketch the graph of a parabola with the vertex at the origin. In this lesson, you will graph parabolas with vertices on the y-axis, but not on the origin.

Quadratic functions of the form $f(x) = ax^2 + k$ have the vertex at the point (0, k).

As before, the parabola opens up if a is positive, and the parabola opens down if a is negative.

As the value of a increases, the parabola gets skinnier. As the value of a approaches 0, the parabola gets wider.

To graph a parabola, plot at least 5 points, including the vertex. Make sure you include both positive and negative values of x.

Sketch the graph of $f(x) = 2x^2 - 1$.

x	y
0	-1
1	1
2	7
-1	1
-2	7

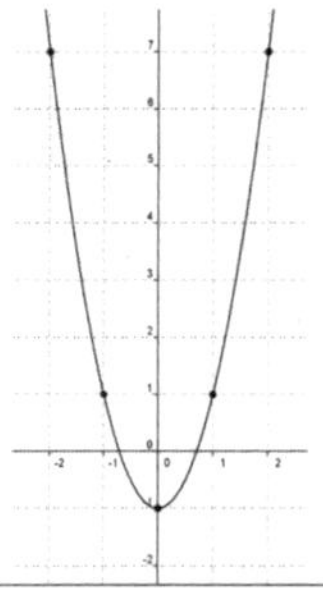

① **Classwork.**
Sketch the graph of each parabola.

$f(x) = x^2 - 1$

x	y
0	-1
1	0
2	3
-1	0
-2	3

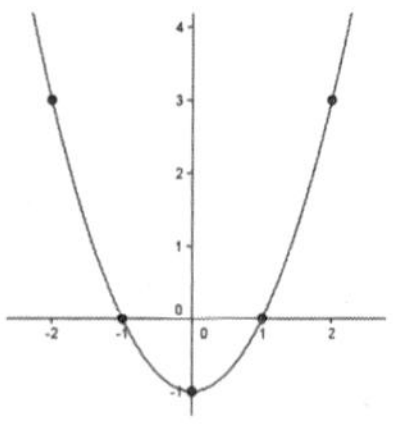

$f(x) = x^2 + 2$

x	y
0	2
1	3
2	6
-1	3
-2	6

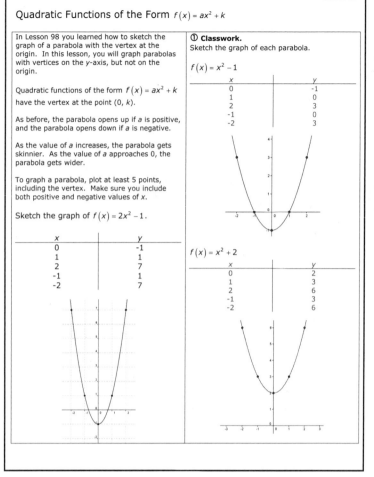

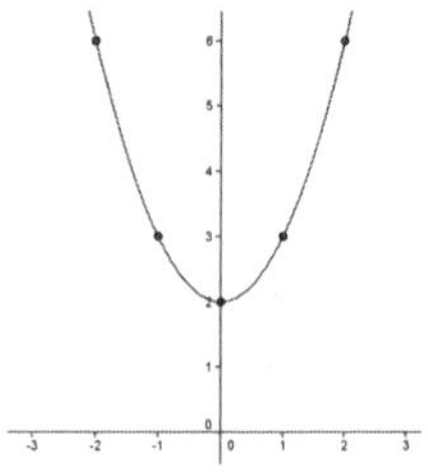

Activities

② Sketch the graph of each parabola.

$f(x) = x^2 - 2$

x	y
0	-2
1	-1
2	2
-1	-1
-2	2

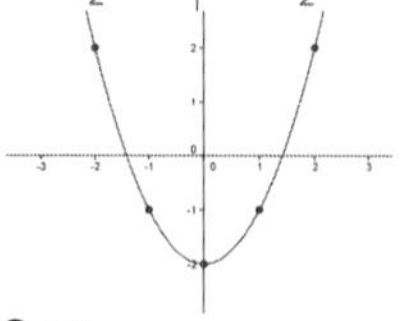

$f(x) = 2x^2 - 1$

x	y
0	-1
1	1
2	7
-1	1
-2	7

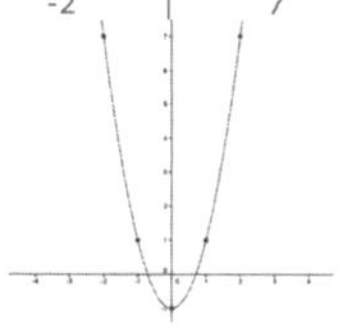

$f(x) = -x^2 - 1$

x	y
0	-1
1	-2
2	-5
-1	-2
-2	-5

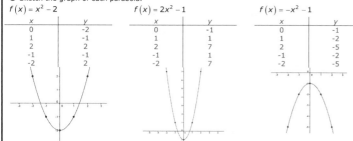

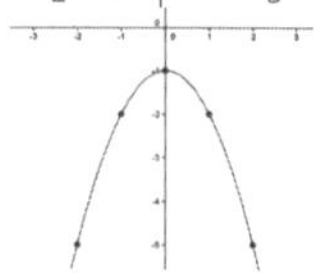

③ Solve.

Look back over the graphs you have done in Lessons 98 and 99. What happens to the parabola when the value of a is negative?
The graph opens downward.

What happens to the parabola as the absolute value of a gets larger?
The graph gets narrower.

What happens to the parabola as the absolute value of a gets smaller?
The graph gets wider.

What happens to the parabola when $k > 0$?
The vertex is higher on the y-axis.

What happens to the parabola when $k < 0$?
The vertex is lower on the y-axis.

How many times does the parabola touch the x-axis when $k = 0$?
1 (The vertex is on the x-axis.)

How many times does the parabola touch the x-axis when $a > 0$ and $k > 0$?
0 (The graph opens up and starts above the x-axis.)

How many times does the parabola touch the x-axis when $a > 0$ and $k < 0$?
2 (The graph opens up and starts below the x-axis.)

How many times does the parabola touch the x-axis when $a < 0$ and $k > 0$?
2 (The graph opens down and starts above the x-axis.)

How many times does the parabola touch the x-axis when $a < 0$ and $k < 0$?
0 (The graph opens down and starts below the x-axis.)

Teaching Tips, Cont.

- Teach the formula for finding the vertex of a parabola of the form $f(x) = ax^2 + k$.
- Remind the students they need to plot at least 5 points when sketching the graph of a parabola. They need to include 0, 2 positive integers, and 2 negative integers as the value of x for this lesson.
- Complete the Classwork exercises. Have some students work the problems on the board for the class and explain their answers. All students should work the problems in their books.

Assignment

- Complete Lesson 99, Activities 2-3.

Lesson 100

Concepts

- Completing the square
- Solving quadratic equations

Learning Objectives

The student will be able to:

- Complete the square with leading coefficients
- Use the positive and negative values of the radical to obtain all possible roots

Materials Needed

- Student Book, Lesson 100
- Worksheet 50

Teaching Tips

➢ Review completing the square. (See Lesson 93)

➢ Have the students look back at the problems they worked in Lesson 93 and notice that every equation had $a = 1$. Tell the students that in this lesson they will learn how to complete the square when a is not equal to 1.

➢ Teach completing the square from the teaching box. Explain that this is the identical process that was used in Lesson 93, but with one additional step. When a is not equal to 1, each term must be divided by a so that $a = 1$ to complete the square.

Completing the Square with Leading Coefficients

This lesson uses the same principles you used to complete the square in Lesson 93, but with quadratic equations in the format $ax^2 + bx + c = 0$ rather than $x^2 + bx + c = 0$.

To complete the square, follow these steps.

- Isolate c on one side of the equal sign, leaving the x-terms on the other side.
- If $a \neq 1$, divide all terms on both sides by a.
- Add the value of $\left(\frac{b}{2}\right)^2$ to both sides.
- Factor the perfect square trinomial as $\left(x \pm \frac{b}{2}\right)^2$.
- Take the square root of each side. Remember that a square root has both a positive and a negative.
- Solve for x using both the positive and negative values of the square root.

Solve the equation $2x^2 + 5x + 3 = 0$.
Isolate c.
$2x^2 + 5x = -3$

Divide each term by 2. This gives new values for a, b, and c.
$x^2 + \frac{5}{2}x = -\frac{3}{2}$

Add $\left(\frac{5}{4}\right)^2 = \frac{25}{16}$ to both sides.
$x^2 + \frac{5}{2}x + \frac{25}{16} = -\frac{3}{2} + \frac{25}{16}$

Factor the perfect square trinomial.
$\left(x + \frac{5}{4}\right)^2 = -\frac{24}{16} + \frac{25}{16} \Rightarrow \left(x + \frac{5}{4}\right)^2 = \frac{1}{16}$

Take the square root of each side.
$\sqrt{\left(x + \frac{5}{4}\right)^2} = \sqrt{\frac{1}{16}} \Rightarrow \left(x + \frac{5}{4}\right) = \pm\frac{1}{4}$

Solve for x.
$x + \frac{5}{4} = \frac{1}{4}$ and $x + \frac{5}{4} = -\frac{1}{4}$
$x = -\frac{5}{4} + \frac{1}{4}$ and $x = -\frac{5}{4} - \frac{1}{4}$
$x = -\frac{4}{4}, x = -\frac{6}{4} \Rightarrow x = -1, -\frac{3}{2}$

① Classwork
Complete the square to solve each equation.

$3x^2 + 8x + 5 = 0$
$3x^2 + 8x = -5$
$x^2 + \frac{8}{3}x = -\frac{5}{3}$
$x^2 + \frac{8}{3}x + \left(\frac{4}{3}\right)^2 = -\frac{5}{3} + \left(\frac{4}{3}\right)^2$
$\left(x + \frac{4}{3}\right)^2 = -\frac{5}{3} + \frac{16}{9}$
$\left(x + \frac{4}{3}\right)^2 = \frac{1}{9}$
$\sqrt{\left(x + \frac{4}{3}\right)^2} = \sqrt{\frac{1}{9}}$
$x + \frac{4}{3} = \pm\frac{1}{3}$
$x = -\frac{4}{3} \pm \frac{1}{3}$
$x = -1, -\frac{5}{3}$

$2x^2 + 3x - 4 = 0$
$2x^2 + 3x = 4$
$x^2 + \frac{3}{2}x = 2$
$x^2 + \frac{3}{2}x + \left(\frac{3}{4}\right)^2 = 2 + \left(\frac{3}{4}\right)^2$
$\left(x + \frac{3}{4}\right)^2 = 2 + \frac{9}{16}$
$\left(x + \frac{3}{4}\right)^2 = \frac{41}{16}$
$\sqrt{\left(x + \frac{3}{4}\right)^2} = \sqrt{\frac{41}{16}}$
$x + \frac{3}{4} = \pm\frac{\sqrt{41}}{4}$
$x = -\frac{3}{4} \pm \frac{\sqrt{41}}{4} = \frac{-3 \pm \sqrt{41}}{4}$

Activities
② Complete the square to solve each equation.

$4x^2 + 5x - 3 = 0$
$4x^2 + 5x = 3$
$x^2 + \frac{5}{4}x = \frac{3}{4}$
$x^2 + \frac{5}{4}x + \left(\frac{5}{8}\right)^2 = \frac{3}{4} + \left(\frac{5}{8}\right)^2$
$\left(x + \frac{5}{8}\right)^2 = \frac{3}{4} + \frac{25}{64}$
$\left(x + \frac{5}{8}\right)^2 = \frac{73}{64}$
$\sqrt{\left(x + \frac{5}{8}\right)^2} = \sqrt{\frac{73}{64}}$
$x + \frac{5}{8} = \pm\frac{\sqrt{73}}{8}$
$x = -\frac{5}{8} \pm \frac{\sqrt{73}}{8} = \frac{-5 \pm \sqrt{73}}{8}$

$4x^2 - 8x - 5 = 0$
$4x^2 - 8x = 5$
$x^2 - 2x = \frac{5}{4}$
$x^2 - 2x + (1)^2 = \frac{5}{4} + (1)^2$
$(x - 1)^2 = \frac{5}{4} + 1$
$(x - 1)^2 = \frac{9}{4}$
$\sqrt{(x - 1)^2} = \sqrt{\frac{9}{4}}$
$x - 1 = \pm\frac{3}{2}$
$x = 1 \pm \frac{3}{2}$
$x = \frac{5}{2}, -\frac{1}{2}$

$2x^2 + 7x + 4 = 0$
$2x^2 + 7x = -4$
$x^2 + \frac{7}{2}x = -2$
$x^2 + \frac{7}{2}x + \left(\frac{7}{4}\right)^2 = -2 + \left(\frac{7}{4}\right)^2$
$\left(x + \frac{7}{4}\right)^2 = -2 + \frac{49}{16}$
$\left(x + \frac{7}{4}\right)^2 = \frac{17}{16}$
$\sqrt{\left(x + \frac{7}{4}\right)^2} = \sqrt{\frac{17}{16}}$
$x + \frac{7}{4} = \pm\frac{\sqrt{17}}{4}$
$x = -\frac{7}{4} \pm \frac{\sqrt{17}}{4} = \frac{-7 \pm \sqrt{17}}{4}$

$3x^2 - 9x + 5 = 0$
$3x^2 - 9x = -5$
$x^2 - 3x = -\frac{5}{3}$
$x^2 - 3x + \left(\frac{3}{2}\right)^2 = -\frac{5}{3} + \left(\frac{3}{2}\right)^2$
$\left(x - \frac{3}{2}\right)^2 = -\frac{5}{3} + \frac{9}{4}$
$\left(x - \frac{3}{2}\right)^2 = \frac{7}{12}$
$\sqrt{\left(x - \frac{3}{2}\right)^2} = \sqrt{\frac{7}{12}}$
$x - \frac{3}{2} = \pm\frac{\sqrt{7}}{2\sqrt{3}} \cdot \frac{\sqrt{3}}{\sqrt{3}}$
$x = \frac{3}{2} \pm \frac{\sqrt{21}}{6} = \frac{9 \pm \sqrt{21}}{6}$

$2x^2 + 6x - 9 = 0$
$2x^2 + 6x = 9$
$x^2 + 3x = \frac{9}{2}$
$x^2 + 3x + \left(\frac{3}{2}\right)^2 = \frac{9}{2} + \left(\frac{3}{2}\right)^2$
$\left(x + \frac{3}{2}\right)^2 = \frac{9}{2} + \frac{9}{4}$
$\left(x + \frac{3}{2}\right)^2 = \frac{27}{4}$
$\sqrt{\left(x + \frac{3}{2}\right)^2} = \sqrt{\frac{27}{4}}$
$x + \frac{3}{2} = \pm\frac{\sqrt{27}}{2}$
$x = -\frac{3}{2} \pm \frac{3\sqrt{3}}{2} = \frac{-3 \pm 3\sqrt{3}}{2}$

$2x^2 - x - 3 = 0$
$2x^2 - x = 3$
$x^2 - \frac{1}{2}x = \frac{3}{2}$
$x^2 - \frac{1}{2}x + \left(\frac{1}{4}\right)^2 = \frac{3}{2} + \left(\frac{1}{4}\right)^2$
$\left(x - \frac{1}{4}\right)^2 = \frac{3}{2} + \frac{1}{16}$
$\left(x - \frac{1}{4}\right)^2 = \frac{25}{16}$
$\sqrt{\left(x - \frac{1}{4}\right)^2} = \sqrt{\frac{25}{16}}$
$x - \frac{1}{4} = \pm\frac{5}{4}$
$x = \frac{1}{4} \pm \frac{5}{4}$
$x = \frac{3}{2}, -1$

$2x^2 + 8x + 1 = 0$
$2x^2 + 8x = -1$
$x^2 + 4x = -\frac{1}{2}$
$x^2 + 4x + (2)^2 = -\frac{1}{2} + (2)^2$
$(x + 2)^2 = -\frac{1}{2} + 4$
$(x + 2)^2 = \frac{7}{2}$
$\sqrt{(x + 2)^2} = \sqrt{\frac{7}{2}}$
$x + 2 = \pm\frac{\sqrt{7}}{\sqrt{2}} \cdot \frac{\sqrt{2}}{\sqrt{2}}$
$x = -2 \pm \frac{\sqrt{14}}{2} = \frac{-4 \pm \sqrt{14}}{2}$

$3x^2 - 5x + 2 = 0$
$3x^2 - 5x = -2$
$x^2 - \frac{5}{3}x = -\frac{2}{3}$
$x^2 - \frac{5}{3}x + \left(\frac{5}{6}\right)^2 = -\frac{2}{3} + \left(\frac{5}{6}\right)^2$
$\left(x - \frac{5}{6}\right)^2 = -\frac{2}{3} + \frac{25}{36}$
$\left(x - \frac{5}{6}\right)^2 = \frac{1}{36}$
$\sqrt{\left(x - \frac{5}{6}\right)^2} = \sqrt{\frac{1}{36}}$
$x - \frac{5}{6} = \pm\frac{1}{6}$
$x = \frac{5}{6} \pm \frac{1}{6}$
$x = 1, \frac{2}{3}$

$4x^2 + 2x - 1 = 0$
$4x^2 + 2x = 1$
$x^2 + \frac{1}{2}x = \frac{1}{4}$
$x^2 + \frac{1}{2}x + \left(\frac{1}{4}\right)^2 = \frac{1}{4} + \left(\frac{1}{4}\right)^2$
$\left(x + \frac{1}{4}\right)^2 = \frac{1}{4} + \frac{1}{16}$
$\left(x + \frac{1}{4}\right)^2 = \frac{5}{16}$
$\sqrt{\left(x + \frac{1}{4}\right)^2} = \sqrt{\frac{5}{16}}$
$x + \frac{1}{4} = \pm\frac{\sqrt{5}}{4}$
$x = -\frac{1}{4} \pm \frac{\sqrt{5}}{4} = \frac{-1 \pm \sqrt{5}}{4}$

Sketching the Graph of Parabolas Worksheet 50

① Sketch the graph of each parabola.

$f(x) = -3x^2$

x	y
0	0
1	-3
2	-12
-1	-3
-2	-12

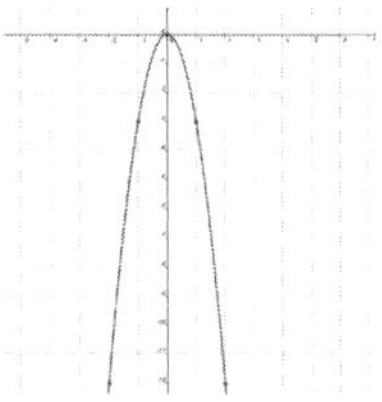

$f(x) = -\frac{1}{2}x^2$

x	y
0	0
2	-2
4	-8
-2	-2
-4	-8

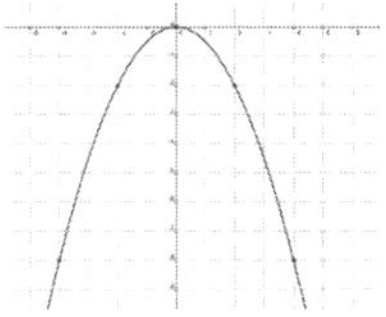

$f(x) = 2x^2$

x	y
0	0
1	2
2	8
-1	2
-2	8

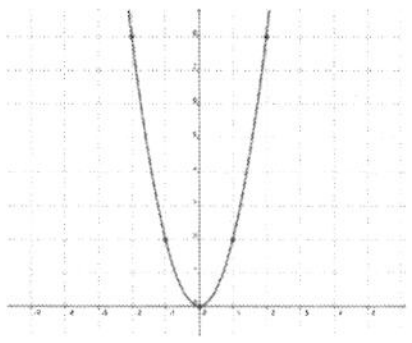

$f(x) = -x^2 - 1$

x	y
0	-1
1	-2
2	-5
-1	-2
-2	-5

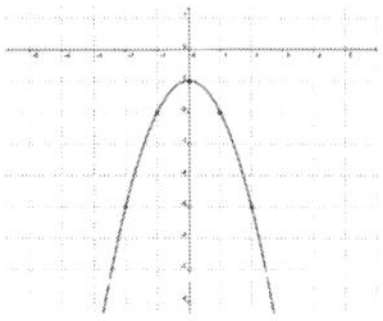

$f(x) = 2x^2 - 3$

x	y
0	-3
1	-1
2	5
-1	-1
-2	5

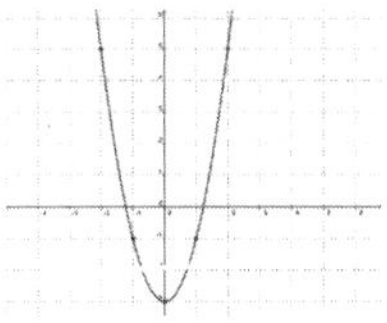

$f(x) = -x^2 + 2$

x	y
0	2
1	1
2	-2
-1	1
-2	-2

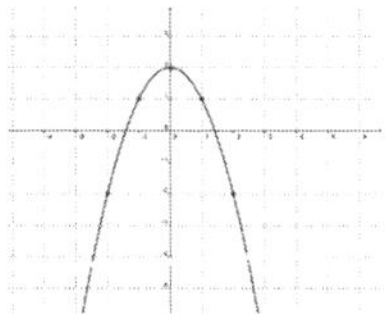

Teaching Tips, Cont.

- Remind the students to use both the positive and negative values of the radical when listing their answers.
- Complete the Classwork exercises. Have some students work the problems on the board for the class and explain their answers. All students should work the problems in their books.
- Review for Test 10 using worksheets 46-50. These worksheets were assigned in previous lessons.

Assignments

- Complete Lesson 100, Activity 2.
- Worksheet 50.
- Study for Test 10 (Lessons 88-97).

Test 10

Testing Objectives

The student will:

- Simplify complex rational expressions
- State exclusions
- Solve quadratic equations by factoring
- Solve quadratic equations by taking the roots
- Solve quadratic equations by completing the square
- Solve quadratic equations by using the quadratic formula
- Find the discriminant of a quadratic equation
- Tell how many roots a quadratic equation has

Materials Needed

- Test 10
- *It's College Test Prep Time!* from the Student Book
- Exploring Math through... Tennis from Student Book

Teaching Tips

- ➢ Administer Test 10, allowing the students 30-40 minutes to complete the test.
- ➢ When all students are finished taking the test, introduce *It's College Test Prep Time* from the student book. This page may be completed in class or assigned as homework.

① Simplify the complex rational expressions. Remember to state any exclusions. **13 points**

$\dfrac{\frac{3}{x-3}}{4}$ LCD = $x - 3$.

$\dfrac{(\cancel{x-3})\left(\frac{3}{\cancel{x-3}}\right)}{(x-3)(4)} = \dfrac{3}{4x-12}; x \neq 3$

$\dfrac{5}{\frac{8}{6x+1}}$ LCD = $6x + 1$.

$\dfrac{(6x+1)(5)}{(\cancel{6x+1})\left(\frac{8}{\cancel{6x+1}}\right)} = \dfrac{30x+5}{8}; x \neq -\frac{1}{6}$

$\dfrac{\frac{7}{3x} + \frac{5}{x+4}}{\frac{x-4}{x^2-16}}$

$\dfrac{\frac{7}{3x} + \frac{5}{x+4}}{\frac{\cancel{x-4}}{(x+4)(\cancel{x-4})}}$

The LCD is $3x(x+4)$.

$\dfrac{\cancel{3x}(x+4)\left(\frac{7}{\cancel{3x}}\right) + 3x(\cancel{x+4})\left(\frac{5}{\cancel{x+4}}\right)}{3x(\cancel{x+4})\left(\frac{1}{\cancel{x+4}}\right)} =$

$\dfrac{(x+4)(7) + 3x(5)}{3x(1)} =$

$\dfrac{7x + 28 + 15x}{3x} =$

$\dfrac{22x+28}{3x}; x \neq -4, 0, 4$

$\dfrac{\frac{2}{2x+1} + \frac{3}{x-2}}{\frac{x+1}{x^2-x-2} - \frac{2x+4}{x^2-4}}$

$\dfrac{\frac{2}{2x+1} + \frac{3}{x-2}}{\frac{\cancel{x+1}}{(\cancel{x+1})(x-2)} - \frac{2(\cancel{x+2})}{(\cancel{x+2})(x-2)}}$

The LCD is $(2x+1)(x-2)$.

$\dfrac{(\cancel{2x+1})(x-2)\left(\frac{2}{\cancel{2x+1}}\right) + (2x+1)(\cancel{x-2})\left(\frac{3}{\cancel{x-2}}\right)}{(2x+1)(\cancel{x-2})\left(\frac{1}{\cancel{x-2}}\right) - (2x+1)(\cancel{x-2})\left(\frac{2}{\cancel{x-2}}\right)} =$

$\dfrac{(x-2)(2) + (2x+1)(3)}{(2x+1)(1) - (2x+1)(2)} =$

$\dfrac{(2x-4) + (6x+3)}{2x+1-4x-2} =$

$\dfrac{8x-1}{-2x-1}; x \neq -2, -1, -\frac{1}{2}, 2$

② Solve each quadratic equation by factoring. **7 points**

$10x^2 - 27x = -18$
$10x^2 - 27x + 18 = 0$
$(5x-6)(2x-3) = 0$
$5x - 6 = 0; x = \frac{6}{5}$
$2x - 3 = 0; x = \frac{3}{2}$
The solution is $x = \frac{6}{5}$ and $\frac{3}{2}$.

$x^2 + 8x + 16 = 0$
$(x+4)(x+4) = 0$
$x + 4 = 0; x = -4$
$x + 4 = 0; x = -4$
The solution is $x = -4$.

$x^2 - 12x + 35 = 0$
$(x-7)(x-5) = 0$
$x - 7 = 0; x = 7$
$x - 5 = 0; x = 5$
The solution is $x = 7$ and 5.

$x^2 = 25$
$x^2 - 25 = 0$
$(x+5)(x-5) = 0$
$x + 5 = 0; x = -5$
$x - 5 = 0; x = 5$
The solution is $x = 5$ and -5.

③ Solve each quadratic equation by taking the roots. **4 points**

$x^2 - 32 = 0$
$x^2 = 32$
$\sqrt{x^2} = \sqrt{32}$
$\sqrt{x^2} = \sqrt{2 \cdot 4 \cdot 4}$
$x = \pm 4\sqrt{2}$

$x^2 - 49 = 0$
$x^2 = 49$
$\sqrt{x^2} = \sqrt{49}$
$x = \pm 7$

$x^2 - 97 = 0$
$x^2 = 97$
$\sqrt{x^2} = \sqrt{97}$
$x = \pm\sqrt{97}$

$x^2 - 50 = 0$
$x^2 = 50$
$\sqrt{x^2} = \sqrt{50}$
$\sqrt{x^2} = \sqrt{2 \cdot 5 \cdot 5}$
$x = \pm 5\sqrt{2}$

④ Solve each quadratic equation by completing the square. **3 points**

$x^2 - 7x + 4 = 0$
$x^2 - 7x = -4$
$x^2 - 7x + \left(-\frac{7}{2}\right)^2 = -4 + \left(-\frac{7}{2}\right)^2$
$x^2 - 7x + \frac{49}{4} = -\frac{16}{4} + \frac{49}{4}$
$x^2 - 7x + \frac{49}{4} = \frac{33}{4}$
$\left(x - \frac{7}{2}\right)^2 = \frac{33}{4}$
$\sqrt{\left(x - \frac{7}{2}\right)^2} = \sqrt{\frac{33}{4}}$
$x - \frac{7}{2} = \pm\frac{\sqrt{33}}{2}$
$x = \frac{7 \pm \sqrt{33}}{2}$

$x^2 + 10x - 3 = 0$
$x^2 + 10x = 3$
$x^2 + 10x + \left(\frac{10}{2}\right)^2 = 3 + \left(\frac{10}{2}\right)^2$
$x^2 + 10x + 25 = 3 + 25$
$x^2 + 10x + 25 = 28$
$(x+5)^2 = 28$
$\sqrt{(x+5)^2} = \sqrt{28}$
$x + 5 = \pm\sqrt{2 \cdot 2 \cdot 7}$
$x = -5 \pm 2\sqrt{7}$

$x^2 - 9x - 2 = 0$
$x^2 - 9x = 2$
$x^2 - 9x + \left(-\frac{9}{2}\right)^2 = 2 + \left(-\frac{9}{2}\right)^2$
$x^2 - 9x + \frac{81}{4} = \frac{8}{4} + \frac{81}{4}$
$x^2 - 9x + \frac{81}{4} = \frac{89}{4}$
$\left(x - \frac{9}{2}\right)^2 = \frac{89}{4}$
$\sqrt{\left(x - \frac{9}{2}\right)^2} = \sqrt{\frac{89}{4}}$
$x - \frac{9}{2} = \pm\frac{\sqrt{89}}{2}$
$x = \frac{9 \pm \sqrt{89}}{2}$

⑤ Use the quadratic formula to solve each equation. **3 points**

$2x^2 - 6x - 1 = 0$
$x = \dfrac{-(-6) \pm \sqrt{(-6)^2 - 4(2)(-1)}}{2(2)}$
$x = \dfrac{6 \pm \sqrt{36+8}}{4}$
$x = \dfrac{6 \pm \sqrt{44}}{4}$
$x = \dfrac{6 \pm 2\sqrt{11}}{4}$
$x = \dfrac{6}{4} \pm \dfrac{2\sqrt{11}}{4}$
$x = \dfrac{3 \pm \sqrt{11}}{2}$

$2x^2 + 4x - 3 = 0$
$x = \dfrac{-4 \pm \sqrt{4^2 - 4(2)(-3)}}{2(2)}$
$x = \dfrac{-4 \pm \sqrt{16+24}}{4}$
$x = \dfrac{-4 \pm \sqrt{40}}{4}$
$x = \dfrac{-4 \pm 2\sqrt{10}}{4}$
$x = \dfrac{-4}{4} \pm \dfrac{2\sqrt{10}}{4}$
$x = -1 \pm \dfrac{\sqrt{10}}{2}$

$5x^2 - 7x - 2 = 0$
$x = \dfrac{-(-7) \pm \sqrt{(-7)^2 - 4(5)(-2)}}{2(5)}$
$x = \dfrac{7 \pm \sqrt{49+40}}{10}$
$x = \dfrac{7 \pm \sqrt{89}}{10}$

⑥ Find the discriminant and tell the number of real roots in each quadratic equation. **6 points**

$3x^2 + 4x + 5 = 0$
$4^2 - 4(3)(5) =$
$16 - 60 =$
-44
The discriminant is less than zero, so there are no real roots.

$2x^2 - 8x + 3 = 0$
$(-8)^2 - 4(2)(3) =$
$64 - 24 =$
40
The discriminant is greater than zero, so there are 2 real roots.

$9x^2 - 6x + 1 = 0$
$(-6)^2 - 4(9)(1) =$
$36 - 36 =$
0
The discriminant is equal to zero, so there is one real root.

36 points total

It's College Test Prep Time!

1. Given $4x^2 - 25 = 0$ and $x > 0$, what is the value of x?
   A. $\frac{2}{5}$
   B. 1
   C. 2 — Factor to get $(2x+5)(2x-5)=0$ so $x = -\frac{5}{2}$ or $x = \frac{5}{2}$
   D. $\frac{5}{2}$ — Because x > 0, $x = \frac{5}{2}$.
   E. 5

2. A certain sequence has integers that are always increasing. The 5th term of the sequence is 32 and the 12th term of the sequence is 81. If the difference between consecutive terms is always the same, what is the first term in the sequence?
   A. 1 — It takes 12 - 5 = 7 terms to get from 32 to 81.
   B. 4 — There are 81 - 32 = 49 integers in that range.
   C. 7 — The difference between consecutive terms is 49 ÷ 7 = 7.
   D. 27 — The first term is 4 terms below the 5th term, or 4(7) = 28.
   E. 28 — Less than the 5 term. 32 - 28 = 4. This is the first term.

Alternate solution to #2 above.
Set up a system of equations. Let n = the first number in the sequence, and x = the difference between consecutive terms. The fifth term is 4 terms past the first term, and the twelfth term is 11 terms past the first term.

$n + 11x = 81$
$n + 4x = 32$
$7x = 49$
$x = 7$

The difference between consecutive terms is 7.

$n + 4(7) = 32$
$n + 28 = 32$
$n = 4$

The first term in the sequence is 4.

Exploring Math through... Tennis

Like other sports, tennis uses math in a variety of aspects. Detailed measurements are required in three dimensions for the court. Angles and trajectories must be considered each time the ball is hit. Force, distance, and spin affect every play of the game. Statistics are crucial when comparing and ranking players, and they are even used when planning the material for the surface of the tennis court.

The playing area of a tennis court is different for singles matches than it is for doubles matches. There are specific guidelines for the boundary lines and the net. The height of the net changes at certain positions along the court and the thickness of the cable used to attach the net is also important. There are even special measurements that apply to indoor tennis courts.

Players must constantly calculate angles and trajectories during all phases of play. A small adjustment in the angle a ball is hit can make the difference between that ball landing in bounds or out of bounds. It can also make the difference between a ball the opponent can easily return and a ball that will take a double bounce.

Tennis officials rely heavily on statistics in tennis. Players are seeded for tournaments based on statistical analysis of several factors. Individual player statistics are kept so players and coaches can monitor a player's progress as well as have a basis of comparison against an opponent. Officials even consider statistics related to the tennis court surface when planning tournaments.

Teaching Tips, Cont.

- Have students read the Exploring Math feature for Lessons 101-110.

Assignments

- Complete *It's College Test Prep Time!*
- Read Exploring Math through... Tennis

Lesson 101

Concepts

- Quadratic functions
- Parabolas
- Completing the square

Learning Objectives

The student will be able to:

- Find the vertex of a parabola from its quadratic function
- Sketch the graph of a parabola in the form $f(x) = a(x - h)^2 + k$

Materials Needed

- Student Book, Lesson 101

Teaching Tips

- Review parabolas. (See Lessons 98-99)
- Review completing the square. (See Lessons 93 and 100)
- Ask the students what the value of k does to the graph of a parabola. (It moves the graph to the right when k is positive and to the left when k is negative.)
- Tell the students that it is also possible to move the graph up and down on the coordinate plane.
- Introduce the quadratic form $f(x) = a(x - h)^2 + k$ from the teaching box. Explain that when h is positive (x minus a number) the graph moves to the right and when h is negative (x plus a number) the graph moves to the left.

Lesson 101

Quadratic Functions of the Form $f(x) = a(x-h)^2 + k$

So far you have learned how to sketch the graph of a parabola with the vertex at the origin and with the vertex on the y-axis. In this lesson, you will graph parabolas with vertices on any point on the graph.

Quadratic functions of the form $f(x) = a(x-h)^2 + k$ have the vertex at the point (h, k). Pay special attention to the signs of h and k in the general equation.

If the value of h is positive, the graph shifts to the right. If the value of h is negative, the graph shifts to the left.

Complete the square to write the function in proper parabolic form.
$f(x) = 2x^2 - 12x + 13$

Set the equation equal to zero.
$2x^2 - 12x + 13 = 0$
Isolate the constant term on one side of the equal sign.
$2x^2 - 12x = -13$
Factor out a 2 from the left side so the x^2 term has a coefficient of 1.
$2(x^2 - 6x) = -13$
Complete the square.
$2(x^2 - 6x + 9) = -13 + 2(9)$
Notice that the 9 is added inside the parentheses on the left side. The entire parentheses are multiplied by 2, including the 9. You must multiply the 9 by 2 when adding to the right side to keep the sides equal.
$2(x^2 - 6x + 9) = -13 + 18$
Factor the left side.
$2(x-3)^2 = 5$
Move the constant so the equation is equal to zero.
$2(x-3)^2 - 5 = 0$
Write the equation as a function.
$f(x) = 2(x-3)^2 - 5$
Vertex = (h, k) = (3, -5)

① **Classwork**
Give the vertex (h, k) and sketch the graph of the parabola.

$f(x) = 2(x+1)^2 - 2$
Vertex = (h, k) = (-1, -2)

x	y
1	6
0	0
-1	-2
-2	0
-3	6

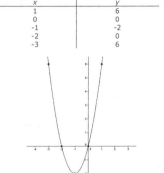

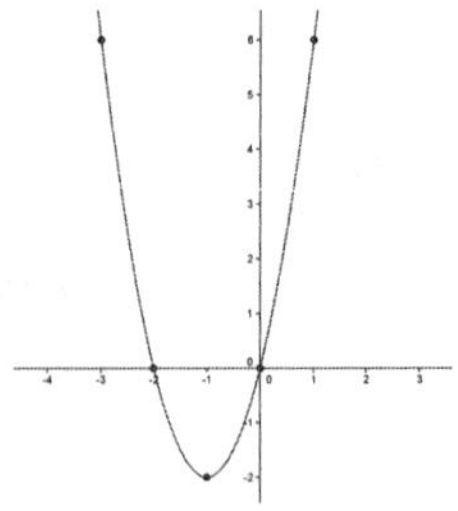

Complete the square to write the function in proper parabolic form and give the vertex (h, k).
$f(x) = 2x^2 - 8x + 5$
Set the equation equal to 0.
$2x^2 - 8x + 5 = 0$
$2x^2 - 8x = -5$
$2(x^2 - 4x) = -5$
$2(x^2 - 4x + 4) = -5 + 2(4)$
Because 4 was added inside theparentheses, the number outside the parentheses must be multipliedon both sides to keep the sides equal.
$2(x-2)^2 = -5 + 8$
$2(x-2)^2 - 3 = 0$
$f(x) = 2(x-2)^2 - 3$
Vertex = (h, k) = (2, -3)

Activities

② Complete the square to write each function in parabolic form. Give the vertex (h, k) of each parabola.

$f(x) = 3x^2 + 12x + 5$
$3x^2 + 12x + 5 = 0$
$3x^2 + 12x = -5$
$3(x^2 + 4x) = -5$
$3(x^2 + 4x + 4) = -5 + 3(4)$
$3(x + 2)^2 = -5 + 12$
$3(x + 2)^2 - 7 = 0$
$f(x) = 3(x + 2)^2 - 7$
The vertex is (-2, -7).

$f(x) = 2x^2 + 4x + 5$
$2x^2 + 4x + 5 = 0$
$2x^2 + 4x = -5$
$2(x^2 + 2x) = -5$
$2(x^2 + 2x + 1) = -5 + 2(1)$
$2(x + 1)^2 = -5 + 2$
$2(x + 1)^2 + 3 = 0$
$f(x) = 2(x + 1)^2 + 3$
The vertex is (-1, 3).

$f(x) = 3x^2 - 6x + 2$
$3x^2 - 6x + 2 = 0$
$3x^2 - 6x = -2$
$3(x^2 - 2x) = -2$
$3(x^2 - 2x + 1) = -2 + 3(1)$
$3(x - 1)^2 = -2 + 3$
$3(x - 1)^2 - 1 = 0$
$f(x) = 3(x - 1)^2 - 1$
The vertex is (1, -1).

$f(x) = 4x^2 - 8x + 9$
$4x^2 - 8x + 9 = 0$
$4x^2 - 8x = -9$
$4(x^2 - 2x) = -9$
$4(x^2 - 2x + 1) = -9 + 4(1)$
$4(x - 1)^2 = -9 + 4$
$4(x - 1)^2 + 5 = 0$
$f(x) = 4(x - 1)^2 + 5$
The vertex is (1, 5).

$f(x) = -x^2 - 2x - 5$
$-x^2 - 2x - 5 = 0$
$-x^2 - 2x = 5$
$-(x^2 + 2x) = 5$
$-(x^2 + 2x + 1) = 5 + (-1)(1)$
$-(x + 1)^2 = 5 - 1$
$-(x + 1)^2 - 4 = 0$
$f(x) = -(x + 1)^2 - 4$
The vertex is (-1, -4).

$f(x) = -2x^2 - 8x + 7$
$-2x^2 - 8x + 7 = 0$
$-2x^2 - 8x = -7$
$-2(x^2 + 4x) = -7$
$-2(x^2 + 4x + 4) = -7 + (-2)(4)$
$-2(x + 2)^2 = -7 - 8$
$-2(x + 2)^2 + 15 = 0$
$f(x) = -2(x + 2)^2 + 15$
The vertex is (-2, 15).

③ Sketch the graph of each parabola from the first row of Activity ②.

$f(x) = 3x^2 + 12x + 5$

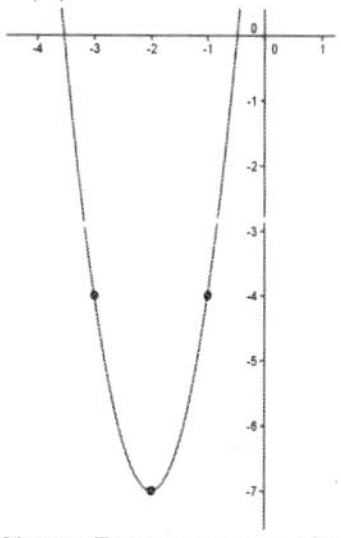

$f(x) = 2x^2 + 4x + 5$

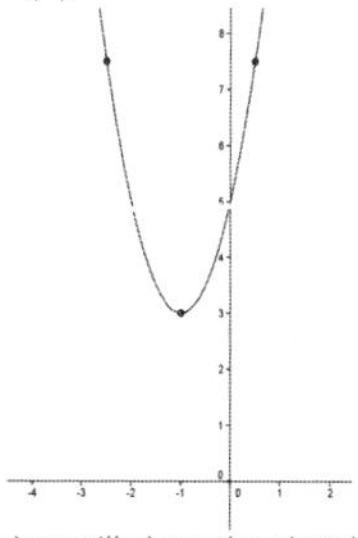

$f(x) = 3x^2 - 6x + 2$

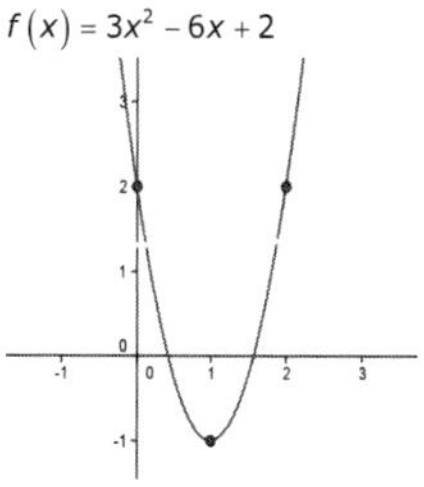

Note: From now on, the solution key will show the sketch of the graph with some points marked. The T-chart will not be included in the solution.

Teaching Tips, Cont.

- Tell the students that they can complete the square of an equation in standard form to obtain the parabolic form, making it easy to determine the vertex.
- Teach graphing parabolas of the form $f(x) = a(x - h)^2 + k$. Explain that the easiest way to determine the best points to use to sketch a graph is to start with the vertex. Then choose two values of x to the left and right of the vertex.
- Complete the Classwork exercises. Have some students work the problems on the board for the class and explain their answers. All students should work the problems in their books.

Assignment

- Complete Lesson 101, Activities 2-3.

Lesson 102

Concepts
- Quadratic functions
- Parabolas
- Zeros of a function
- Graphing parabolas
- Trends in graphs

Learning Objectives
The student will be able to:
- Sketch the graph of parabolas
- Identify the zeros of a quadratic function by looking at the graph
- Identify graphs with no zeros by looking at the graph

Materials Needed
- Student Book, Lesson 102
- Worksheet 51

Teaching Tips
- Have students complete Worksheet 51 in class. This may be for added practice of earlier topics, or graded as a quiz, if desired.
- Review parabolas. (See Lessons 98-99, and 101)
- Review zeros of quadratic functions. (See Lesson 91)
- Ask the students what value is equal to zero when giving the zeros of a function. (y)
- Ask the students where on a graph the value of y is equal to zero. (On the x-axis)

Zeros of a Function: Graphing

The zeros of a function are the points at which the graph of the function crosses the x-axis. In other words, the points at which $y = 0$.

Graph the parabola and identify any zeros.

$f(x) = 2(x-3)^2 - 2$

x	y
3	-2
4	0
5	6
2	0
1	6

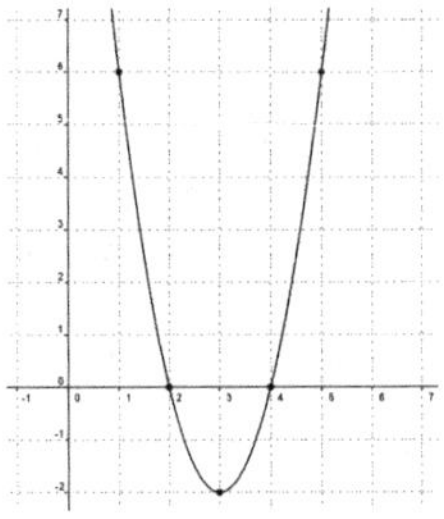

The graph crosses the x-axis at the points (2, 0) and (4, 0). The zeros are $x = 2$ and 4.

① Classwork
Graph the parabola and identify any zeros.

$f(x) = x^2 - 1$

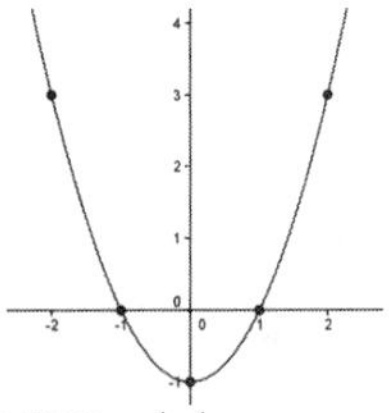

The zeros are $x = -1, 1$.

$f(x) = x^2 + 2$

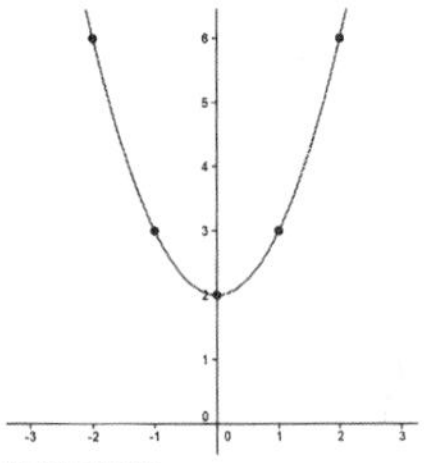

There are no zeros.

Activities

② Graph the parabola and identify any zeros.

$f(x) = -x^2 - 1$

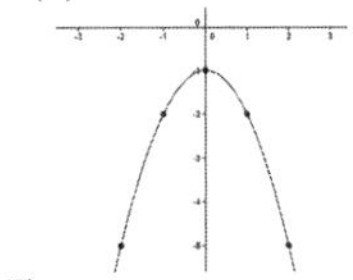

There are no zeros.

$f(x) = -x^2$

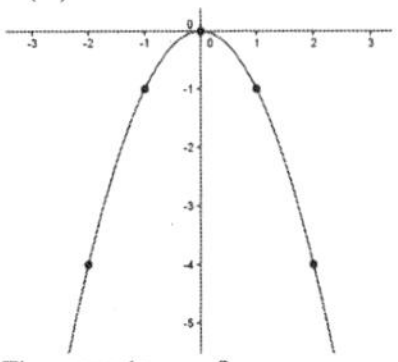

The zero is $x = 0$.

$f(x) = (x+1)^2 - 1$

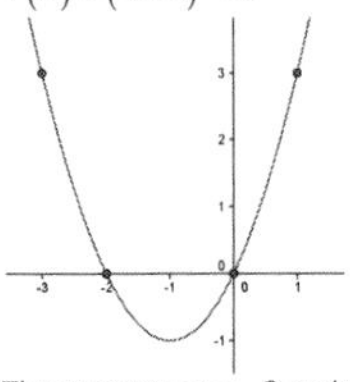

The zeros are $x = -2$ and 0.

③ Graph the parabola and identify any zeros.

$f(x) = x^2 - 4$

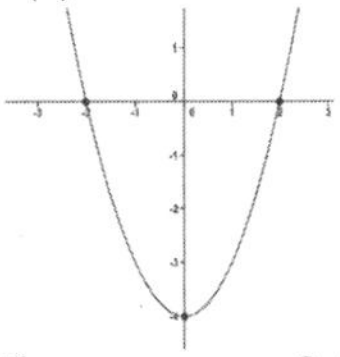

The zeros are $x = -2, 2$.

$f(x) = \frac{1}{2}x^2$

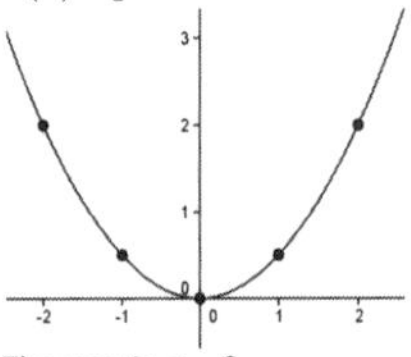

The zero is $x = 0$.

$f(x) = -x^2 + 1$

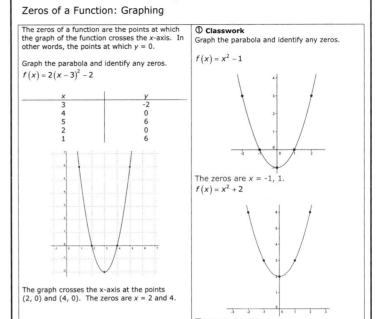

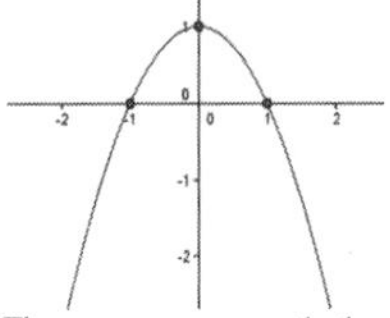

The zeros are $x = -1, 1$.

④ Answer the questions.

What happens to the parabola when the value of a is negative?
The graph opens downward.

What happens to the parabola as the absolute value of a gets larger?
The graph gets narrower.

What happens to the parabola as the absolute value of a gets smaller?
The graph gets wider.

What happens to the parabola when $k > 0$?
The vertex is higher on the y-axis.

What happens to the parabola when $k < 0$?
The vertex is lower on the y-axis.

How many zeros does the graph have when $k = 0$?
1 (The vertex is on the x-axis.)

How many zeros does the graph have when $a > 0$ and $k > 0$?
0 (The graph opens up and starts above the x-axis.)

How many zeros does the graph have when $a > 0$ and $k < 0$?
2 (The graph opens up and starts below the x-axis.)

How many zeros does the graph have when $a < 0$ and $k > 0$?
2 (The graph opens down and starts above the x-axis.)

How many zeros does the graph have when $a < 0$ and $k < 0$?
0 (The graph opens down and starts below the x-axis.)

Graphing Parabolas, Completing the Square Worksheet 51

① Sketch the graph of each parabola.

$f(x) = x^2 - 1$

x	y
0	-1
1	0
2	3
-1	0
-2	3

$f(x) = 2x^2 - 5$

x	y
0	-5
1	-3
2	3
-1	-3
-2	3

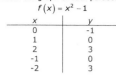

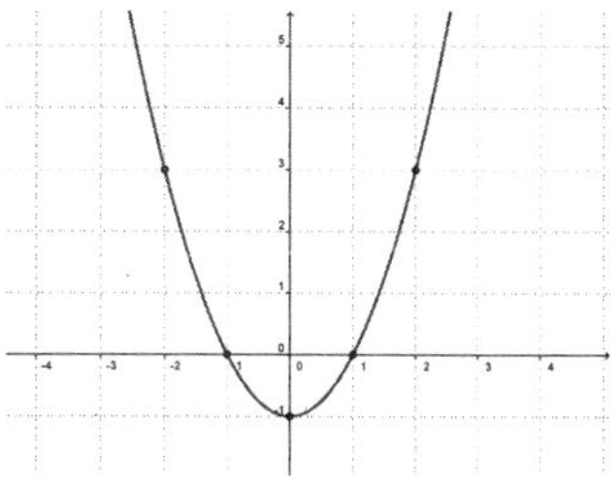

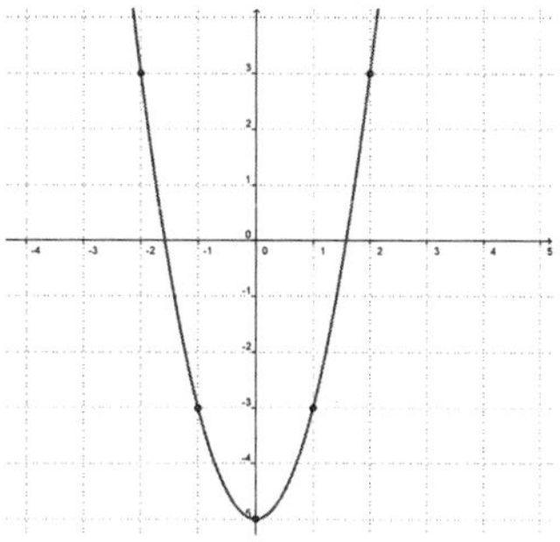

② Complete the square to solve each equation.

$4x^2 + 6x - 3 = 0$
$4x^2 + 6x = 3$
$x^2 + \frac{6}{4}x = \frac{3}{4}$
$x^2 + \frac{6}{4}x + \left(\frac{3}{4}\right)^2 = \frac{3}{4} + \left(\frac{3}{4}\right)^2$
$\left(x + \frac{3}{4}\right)^2 = \frac{3}{4} + \frac{9}{16}$
$\left(x + \frac{3}{4}\right)^2 = \frac{21}{16}$
$\sqrt{\left(x + \frac{3}{4}\right)^2} = \sqrt{\frac{21}{16}}$
$x + \frac{3}{4} = \pm\frac{\sqrt{21}}{4}$
$x = -\frac{3}{4} \pm \frac{\sqrt{21}}{4} = \frac{-3\pm\sqrt{21}}{4}$

$4x^2 - 8x - 9 = 0$
$4x^2 - 8x = 9$
$x^2 - 2x = \frac{9}{4}$
$x^2 - 2x + (1)^2 = \frac{9}{4} + (1)^2$
$(x - 1)^2 = \frac{9}{4} + 1$
$(x - 1)^2 = \frac{13}{4}$
$\sqrt{(x - 1)^2} = \sqrt{\frac{13}{4}}$
$x - 1 = \pm\frac{\sqrt{13}}{2}$
$x = 1 \pm \frac{\sqrt{13}}{2}$ or $\frac{2\pm\sqrt{13}}{2}$

$2x^2 + 7x + 1 = 0$
$2x^2 + 7x = -1$
$x^2 + \frac{7}{2}x = -\frac{1}{2}$
$x^2 + \frac{7}{2}x + \left(\frac{7}{4}\right)^2 = -\frac{1}{2} + \left(\frac{7}{4}\right)^2$
$\left(x + \frac{7}{4}\right)^2 = -\frac{1}{2} + \frac{49}{16}$
$\left(x + \frac{7}{4}\right)^2 = \frac{41}{16}$
$\sqrt{\left(x + \frac{7}{4}\right)^2} = \sqrt{\frac{41}{16}}$
$x + \frac{7}{4} = \pm\frac{\sqrt{41}}{4}$
$x = -\frac{7}{4} \pm \frac{\sqrt{41}}{4} = \frac{-7\pm\sqrt{41}}{4}$

Teaching Tips, Cont.

- Ask the student how they think they could find the zeros of a function by looking at the graph. (Elicit the idea that since the value of *y* is equal to zero at the *x*-axis, the zeros of a function are where the graph crosses or touches the *x*-axis.)
- Teach how to find the zeros of a function by graphing from the teaching box.
- Complete the Classwork exercises. Have some students work the problems on the board for the class and explain their answers. All students should work the problems in their books.

Assignment

- Complete Lesson 102, Activities 2-4.

Lesson 103

Concepts

- Zeros of a function
- Completing the square
- Math in the real world

Learning Objectives

The student will be able to:

- Complete the square of a quadratic function
- Use the resulting equation to find the roots of a quadratic function

Materials Needed

- Student Book, Lesson 103
- Worksheet 52

Teaching Tips

➢ Review completing the square. (See Lessons 93 and 100)

➢ Tell the students they can find the zeros of a function without having to draw a graph.

➢ Teach how to find the zeros of a function by completing the square from the teaching box. Explain that this is the exact same procedure they used to solve quadratic equations in Lesson 100.

Zeros of a Function: Completing the Square

Finding the zeros of a function by graphing works when the graph crosses the x-axis at an easily identifiable point. Unfortunately, most graphs of parabolas do not have easily identifiable zeros on a graph. In this situation, you can apply what you have already learned to find the zeros.

In Lesson 93 you learned to solve quadratic equations by completing the square. The same method is used to find the zeros of quadratic functions.

Remember that $f(x)$ is the same thing as y in an equation. Because the zeros of a function are where the graph crosses the x-axis and $y = 0$, simply substitute 0 for $f(x)$ and follow the same steps to complete the square.

Find the zeros of the function $f(x) = x^2 + 5x + 3$.

Substitute 0 for $f(x)$.
$0 = x^2 + 5x + 3$

Isolate the constant.
$x^2 + 5x = -3$

Add $\left(\frac{5}{2}\right)^2 = \frac{25}{4}$ to both sides.
$x^2 + 5x + \frac{25}{4} = -3 + \frac{25}{4}$

Factor the perfect square trinomial.
$\left(x + \frac{5}{2}\right)^2 = -\frac{12}{4} + \frac{25}{4} \Rightarrow \left(x + \frac{5}{2}\right)^2 = \frac{13}{4}$

Take the square root of each side.
$\sqrt{\left(x + \frac{5}{2}\right)^2} = \sqrt{\frac{13}{4}} \Rightarrow \left(x + \frac{5}{2}\right) = \pm\frac{\sqrt{13}}{2}$

Solve for x.
$x + \frac{5}{2} = \frac{\sqrt{13}}{2}$ and $x + \frac{5}{2} = -\frac{\sqrt{13}}{2}$
$x = -\frac{5}{2} + \frac{\sqrt{13}}{2}$ and $x = -\frac{5}{2} - \frac{\sqrt{13}}{2}$
$x = \frac{-5 \pm \sqrt{13}}{2}$

① **Classwork**
Find the zeros of each function.

$f(x) = x^2 + 4x + 2$
$0 = x^2 + 4x + 2$
$x^2 + 4x = -2$
$x^2 + 4x + \left(\frac{4}{2}\right)^2 = -2 + \left(\frac{4}{2}\right)^2$
$x^2 + 4x + 4 = -2 + 4$
$x^2 + 4x + 4 = 2$
$(x + 2)^2 = 2$
$\sqrt{(x + 2)^2} = \sqrt{2}$
$x + 2 = \pm\sqrt{2}$
$x = -2 \pm \sqrt{2}$

$f(x) = x^2 - 6x - 5$
$0 = x^2 - 6x - 5$
$x^2 - 6x = 5$
$x^2 - 6x + \left(-\frac{6}{2}\right)^2 = 5 + \left(-\frac{6}{2}\right)^2$
$x^2 - 6x + 9 = 5 + 9$
$x^2 - 6x + 9 = 14$
$(x - 3)^2 = 14$
$\sqrt{(x - 3)^2} = \sqrt{14}$
$x - 3 = \pm\sqrt{14}$
$x = 3 \pm \sqrt{14}$

Activities

② Find the zeros of each function.

$f(x) = x^2 + 8x + 5$
$0 = x^2 + 8x + 5$
$x^2 + 8x = -5$
$x^2 + 8x + \left(\frac{8}{2}\right)^2 = -5 + \left(\frac{8}{2}\right)^2$
$x^2 + 8x + 16 = -5 + 16$
$x^2 + 8x + 16 = 11$
$(x + 4)^2 = 11$
$\sqrt{(x + 4)^2} = \sqrt{11}$
$x + 4 = \pm\sqrt{11}$
$x = -4 \pm \sqrt{11}$

$f(x) = x^2 + 10x - 3$
$0 = x^2 + 10x - 3$
$x^2 + 10x = 3$
$x^2 + 10x + \left(\frac{10}{2}\right)^2 = 3 + \left(\frac{10}{2}\right)^2$
$x^2 + 10x + 25 = 3 + 25$
$x^2 + 10x + 25 = 28$
$(x + 5)^2 = 28$
$\sqrt{(x + 5)^2} = \sqrt{28}$
$x + 5 = \pm\sqrt{2 \cdot 2 \cdot 7}$
$x = -5 \pm 2\sqrt{7}$

$f(x) = x^2 - 2x - 4$
$0 = x^2 - 2x - 4$
$x^2 - 2x = 4$
$x^2 - 2x + \left(-\frac{2}{2}\right)^2 = 4 + \left(-\frac{2}{2}\right)^2$
$x^2 - 2x + 1 = 4 + 1$
$x^2 - 2x + 1 = 5$
$(x - 1)^2 = 5$
$\sqrt{(x - 1)^2} = \sqrt{5}$
$x - 1 = \pm\sqrt{5}$
$x = 1 \pm \sqrt{5}$

$f(x) = x^2 - 7x + 4$
$0 = x^2 - 7x + 4$
$x^2 - 7x = -4$
$x^2 - 7x + \left(-\frac{7}{2}\right)^2 = -4 + \left(-\frac{7}{2}\right)^2$
$x^2 - 7x + \frac{49}{4} = -\frac{16}{4} + \frac{49}{4}$
$x^2 - 7x + \frac{49}{4} = \frac{33}{4}$
$\left(x - \frac{7}{2}\right)^2 = \frac{33}{4}$
$\sqrt{\left(x - \frac{7}{2}\right)^2} = \sqrt{\frac{33}{4}}$
$x - \frac{7}{2} = \pm\frac{\sqrt{33}}{2}$
$x = \frac{7 \pm \sqrt{33}}{2}$

$f(x) = x^2 - 9x - 2$
$0 = x^2 - 9x - 2$
$x^2 - 9x = 2$
$x^2 - 9x + \left(-\frac{9}{2}\right)^2 = 2 + \left(-\frac{9}{2}\right)^2$
$x^2 - 9x + \frac{81}{4} = \frac{8}{4} + \frac{81}{4}$
$x^2 - 9x + \frac{81}{4} = \frac{89}{4}$
$\left(x - \frac{9}{2}\right)^2 = \frac{89}{4}$
$\sqrt{\left(x - \frac{9}{2}\right)^2} = \sqrt{\frac{89}{4}}$
$x - \frac{9}{2} = \pm\frac{\sqrt{89}}{2}$
$x = \frac{9 \pm \sqrt{89}}{2}$

$f(x) = x^2 + 3x - 8$
$0 = x^2 + 3x - 8$
$x^2 + 3x = 8$
$x^2 + 3x + \left(\frac{3}{2}\right)^2 = 8 + \left(\frac{3}{2}\right)^2$
$x^2 + 3x + \frac{9}{4} = \frac{32}{4} + \frac{9}{4}$
$x^2 + 3x + \frac{9}{4} = \frac{41}{4}$
$\left(x + \frac{3}{2}\right)^2 = \frac{41}{4}$
$\sqrt{\left(x + \frac{3}{2}\right)^2} = \sqrt{\frac{41}{4}}$
$x + \frac{3}{2} = \pm\frac{\sqrt{41}}{2}$
$x = \frac{-3 \pm \sqrt{41}}{2}$

③ Solve.
The maximum diameter of the cord securing a tennis net is $\frac{1}{3}$ inch. If you wrap a string around the cord to check its circumference and the string measures exactly 1 inch long, does the cord meet the specifications of a net cord? (Circumference of a circle = πd and $\pi = \frac{22}{7}$)

$d \le \frac{1}{3}$
$C \le \pi\left(\frac{1}{3}\right)$
$C \le \left(\frac{22}{7}\right)\left(\frac{1}{3}\right)$
$C \le \frac{22}{21}$ in.

Yes, the cord meets the specifications of a net cord.

Vertex of a Parabola, Zeros of a Function Worksheet 52

① Complete the square to write each function in parabolic form. Give the vertex (h, k) of each parabola.

$f(x) = 3x^2 + 18x + 5$
$3x^2 + 18x + 5 = 0$
$3x^2 + 18x = -5$
$3(x^2 + 6x) = -5$
$3(x^2 + 6x + 9) = -5 + 3(9)$
$3(x+3)^2 = -5 + 27$
$3(x+3)^2 - 22 = 0$
$f(x) = 3(x+3)^2 - 22$
The vertex is (-3, -22).

$f(x) = 4x^2 - 8x + 3$
$4x^2 - 8x + 3 = 0$
$4x^2 - 8x = -3$
$4(x^2 - 2x) = -3$
$4(x^2 - 2x + 1) = -3 + 4(1)$
$4(x-1)^2 = -3 + 4$
$4(x-1)^2 - 1 = 0$
$f(x) = 4(x-1)^2 - 1$
The vertex is (1, -1).

$f(x) = 2x^2 + 4x - 7$
$2x^2 + 4x - 7 = 0$
$2x^2 + 4x = 7$
$2(x^2 + 2x) = 7$
$2(x^2 + 2x + 1) = 7 + 2(1)$
$2(x+1)^2 = 9$
$2(x+1)^2 - 9 = 0$
$f(x) = 2(x+1)^2 - 9$
The vertex is (-1, -9).

② Complete the square to find the zeros of each function.

$f(x) = x^2 + 8x + 1$
$0 = x^2 + 8x + 1$
$x^2 + 8x = -1$
$x^2 + 8x + \left(\frac{8}{2}\right)^2 = -1 + \left(\frac{8}{2}\right)^2$
$x^2 + 8x + 16 = -1 + 16$
$x^2 + 8x + 16 = 15$
$(x+4)^2 = 15$
$\sqrt{(x+4)^2} = \sqrt{15}$
$x + 4 = \pm\sqrt{15}$
$x = -4 \pm \sqrt{15}$

$f(x) = x^2 - 7x + 3$
$0 = x^2 - 7x + 3$
$x^2 - 7x = -3$
$x^2 - 7x + \left(-\frac{7}{2}\right)^2 = -3 + \left(-\frac{7}{2}\right)^2$
$x^2 - 7x + \frac{49}{4} = -\frac{12}{4} + \frac{49}{4}$
$x^2 - 7x + \frac{49}{4} = \frac{37}{4}$
$\left(x - \frac{7}{2}\right)^2 = \frac{37}{4}$
$\sqrt{\left(x - \frac{7}{2}\right)^2} = \sqrt{\frac{37}{4}}$
$x - \frac{7}{2} = \pm\frac{\sqrt{37}}{2}$
$x = \frac{7 \pm \sqrt{37}}{2}$

$f(x) = x^2 + 10x - 6$
$0 = x^2 + 10x - 6$
$x^2 + 10x = 6$
$x^2 + 10x + \left(\frac{10}{2}\right)^2 = 6 + \left(\frac{10}{2}\right)^2$
$x^2 + 10x + 25 = 6 + 25$
$x^2 + 10x + 25 = 31$
$(x+5)^2 = 31$
$\sqrt{(x+5)^2} = \sqrt{31}$
$x + 5 = \pm\sqrt{31}$
$x = -5 \pm \sqrt{31}$

$f(x) = x^2 + 6x - 8$
$0 = x^2 + 6x - 8$
$x^2 + 6x = 8$
$x^2 + 6x + \left(\frac{6}{2}\right)^2 = 8 + \left(\frac{6}{2}\right)^2$
$x^2 + 6x + 9 = 8 + 9$
$x^2 + 6x + 9 = 17$
$(x+3)^2 = 17$
$\sqrt{(x+3)^2} = \sqrt{17}$
$x + 3 = \pm\sqrt{17}$
$x = -3 \pm \sqrt{17}$

$f(x) = x^2 + 12x + 5$
$0 = x^2 + 12x + 5$
$x^2 + 12x = -5$
$x^2 + 12x + \left(\frac{12}{2}\right)^2 = -5 + \left(\frac{12}{2}\right)^2$
$x^2 + 12x + 36 = -5 + 36$
$x^2 + 12x + 36 = 31$
$(x+6)^2 = 31$
$\sqrt{(x+6)^2} = \sqrt{31}$
$x + 6 = \pm\sqrt{31}$
$x = -6 \pm \sqrt{31}$

$f(x) = x^2 + 6x - 9$
$0 = x^2 + 6x - 9$
$x^2 + 6x = 9$
$x^2 + 6x + \left(\frac{6}{2}\right)^2 = 9 + \left(\frac{6}{2}\right)^2$
$x^2 + 6x + 9 = 9 + 9$
$x^2 + 6x + 9 = 18$
$(x+3)^2 = 18$
$\sqrt{(x+3)^2} = \sqrt{18}$
$x + 3 = \pm\sqrt{2 \cdot 3 \cdot 3}$
$x = -3 \pm 3\sqrt{2}$

Teaching Tips, Cont.

- Remind the students to include both the positive and negative values of the radical when taking a square root.
- Complete the Classwork exercises. Have some students work the problems on the board for the class and explain their answers. All students should work the problems in their books.

Assignments

- Complete Lesson 103, Activities 2-3.
- Worksheet 52.

Lesson 104

Concepts
- Quadratic functions
- Zeros of functions
- Math in the real world

Learning Objectives
The student will be able to:
- Recognize quadratic functions in factored form
- Find the zeros of quadratic functions in factored form

Materials Needed
- Student Book, Lesson 104

Teaching Tips
- Review solving quadratic equations by factoring. (See Lesson 91)
- Tell the students that quadratic functions can be solved by factoring just like quadratic equations.
- Teach how to find the zeros of quadratic functions by factoring.
- Point out that quadratic functions that are given in factored form do not have to be multiplied out. The factored form can be used to find the zeros without multiplying.

Solving Quadratic Functions in Factored Form

Think about the similarities between quadratic equations and quadratic functions. Both have a polynomial with an x^2 term. Both graph as a parabola. Both can be solved for their roots. So far you have learned to solve quadratic functions by graphing and by completing the square. You have also learned some additional methods for solving quadratic equations.

Any method of finding the roots of a quadratic equation will also work to find the zeros of a quadratic function.

When a quadratic function is written in factored form, do not multiply the factors to find the polynomial. Set the function equal to zero and solve for the zeros from the given factors.

Find the zeros of the quadratic function.
$f(x) = (2x+3)(x-2)$

This is already written in factored form, so set each factor equal to zero and solve.
$(2x+3) = 0$ and $(x-2) = 0$

$2x = -3$ and $x = 2$

$x = -\frac{3}{2}, 2$

① **Classwork**
Find the zeros of each quadratic function.

$f(x) = (3x+2)(x-1)$
$3x+2=0 \quad x-1=0$
$3x=-2 \quad x=1$
$x=-\frac{2}{3}, 1$

$f(x) = (x+4)(4x+3)$
$x+4=0 \quad 4x+3=0$
$x=-4 \quad 4x=-3$
$x=-4, -\frac{3}{4}$

$f(x) = (2x-1)(x-2)$
$2x-1=0 \quad x-2=0$
$2x=1 \quad x=2$
$x=\frac{1}{2}, 2$

Activities
② Find the zeros of each quadratic function.

$f(x) = (7x+2)(3x-1)$
$7x+2=0 \quad 3x-1=0$
$7x=-2 \quad 3x=1$
$x=-\frac{2}{7}, \frac{1}{3}$

$f(x) = (5x+2)(x-8)$
$5x+2=0 \quad x-8=0$
$5x=-2 \quad x=8$
$x=-\frac{2}{5}, 8$

$f(x) = (10x+3)(x-9)$
$10x+3=0 \quad x-9=0$
$10x=-3 \quad x=9$
$x=-\frac{3}{10}, 9$

$f(x) = (x+2)(2x+5)$
$x+2=0 \quad 2x+5=0$
$x=-2 \quad 2x=-5$
$x=-2, -\frac{5}{2}$

$f(x) = (x+11)(6x+13)$
$x+11=0 \quad 6x+13=0$
$x=-11 \quad 6x=-13$
$x=-11, -\frac{13}{6}$

$f(x) = (x+9)(x+9)$
$x+9=0 \quad x+9=0$
$x=-9 \quad x=-9$
$x=-9$

$f(x) = (4x-3)(9x-7)$
$4x-3=0 \quad 9x-7=0$
$4x=3 \quad 9x=7$
$x=\frac{3}{4}, \frac{7}{9}$

$f(x) = (2x-15)(x-4)$
$2x-15=0 \quad x-4=0$
$2x=15 \quad x=4$
$x=\frac{15}{2}, 4$

$f(x) = (2x-7)(x-12)$
$2x-7=0 \quad x-12=0$
$2x=7 \quad x=12$
$x=\frac{7}{2}, 12$

③ Solve.
A doubles tennis court is a rectangle whose length is 6 feet more than twice its width. A singles tennis court is a rectangle whose width is 1 foot more than one third its length. The lengths of the two courts are equal. Express the width of the singles court in terms of the width of the doubles court.
Let L = the length of the doubles court and the length of the singles court
Let d = the width of the doubles court
Let w = the width of the singles court

$L = 6 + 2d$

$w = 1 + \frac{1}{3}L$
$3w = 3 + L$
$3w - 3 = L$

$3w - 3 = 6 + 2d$
$3w = 9 + 2d$
$w = 3 + \frac{2}{3}d$ or $w = 3 + \frac{2d}{3}$ or $w = \frac{9+2d}{3}$

Find the dimensions of each court if the lengths are equal and the difference between the two areas is 702 square feet. (Area of a rectangle = length x width)
$Ld - Lw = 702$
$(6 + 2d)(d) - (6 + 2d)(3 + \frac{2}{3}d) = 702$
$(6d + 2d^2) - (18 + 10d + \frac{4}{3}d^2) = 702$
$6d + 2d^2 - 18 - 10d - \frac{4}{3}d^2 = 702$
$\frac{2}{3}d^2 - 4d - 18 = 702$
$\frac{2}{3}d^2 - 4d = 720$
$2d^2 - 12d = 2160$ Set up an equation and solve.
$d^2 - 6d = 1080$
$d^2 - 6d + 9 = 1080 + 9$
$(d - 3)^2 = 1089$
$d - 3 = \pm\sqrt{1089}$
$d = 3 \pm 33$
$d = 36$ or -30

The width of the doubles court cannot be negative, so it is 36 feet.
The length of each court is $L = 6 + 2d = 6 + 2(36) = 6 + 72 = 78$ feet.
The width of the singles court is $w = 3 + \frac{2}{3}d = 3 + \frac{2}{3}(36) = 3 + 24 = 27$ feet.

Teaching Tips, Cont.

- Complete the Classwork exercises. Have some students work the problems on the board for the class and explain their answers. All students should work the problems in their books.

Assignment

- Complete Lesson 104, Activities 2-3.

Lesson 105

Concepts

- Radicals in quadratic equations
- Quadratic formula
- Systems of equations

Learning Objectives

The student will be able to:

- Apply the quadratic formula to quadratic equations with radicals
- Find the roots of quadratic equations containing radicals
- Rationalize the denominator of the roots when necessary

Materials Needed

- Student Book, Lesson 105
- Worksheet 53

Teaching Tips

- Have students complete Worksheet 53 in class. This may be for added practice of earlier topics, or graded as a quiz, if desired.
- Review the quadratic formula. (See Lesson 94)
- Ask the students if radicals are allowed in the denominator of an answer. (No.) Ask the students what must be done to remove radicals from the denominator. (Rationalize the denominator.)
- Review rationalizing the denominator. (See Lesson 25)

Radicals in Quadratic Equations

When a quadratic equation has one or more radicals as coefficients, the easiest method of finding the roots is to use the quadratic formula. When rationalizing the denominator, remember to multiply the radical by each term in both the numerator and the denominator.

Find the roots of $\sqrt{2}x^2 + \sqrt{3}x - 4 = 0$.

Use the quadratic formula to find the roots.

$$x = \frac{-b \pm \sqrt{b^2 - 4ac}}{2a}$$

$a = \sqrt{2}; b = \sqrt{3}; c = -4$

$$x = \frac{-\sqrt{3} \pm \sqrt{(\sqrt{3})^2 - 4(\sqrt{2})(-4)}}{2(\sqrt{2})}$$

$$x = \frac{-\sqrt{3} \pm \sqrt{3 + 16\sqrt{2}}}{2\sqrt{2}} \cdot \frac{\sqrt{2}}{\sqrt{2}}$$

When $\sqrt{2}$ is moved inside the radical it becomes 2.

$$x = \frac{-\sqrt{3}\sqrt{2} \pm \sqrt{2(3 + 16\sqrt{2})}}{2\sqrt{2}\sqrt{2}} = \frac{-\sqrt{6} \pm \sqrt{6 + 32\sqrt{2}}}{4}$$

Remember to rationalize the denominator if a radical appears in the denominator after applying the quadratic formula.

① Classwork

Find the roots.

$\sqrt{3}x^2 + \sqrt{5}x - 2 = 0$

$$x = \frac{-\sqrt{5} \pm \sqrt{(\sqrt{5})^2 - 4(\sqrt{3})(-2)}}{2(\sqrt{3})}$$

$$x = \frac{-\sqrt{5} \pm \sqrt{5 + 8\sqrt{3}}}{2\sqrt{3}} \cdot \frac{\sqrt{3}}{\sqrt{3}} = \frac{-\sqrt{5}\sqrt{3} \pm \sqrt{3(5 + 8\sqrt{3})}}{2\sqrt{3}\sqrt{3}}$$

$$x = \frac{-\sqrt{15} \pm \sqrt{15 + 24\sqrt{3}}}{6}$$

$2\sqrt{2}x^2 + 4\sqrt{3}x - 1 = 0$

$$x = \frac{-4\sqrt{3} \pm \sqrt{(4\sqrt{3})^2 - 4(2\sqrt{2})(-1)}}{2(2\sqrt{2})}$$

$$x = \frac{-4\sqrt{3} \pm \sqrt{48 + 8\sqrt{2}}}{4\sqrt{2}} \cdot \frac{\sqrt{2}}{\sqrt{2}}$$

$$x = \frac{-4\sqrt{3}\sqrt{2} \pm \sqrt{2(48 + 8\sqrt{2})}}{4\sqrt{2}\sqrt{2}} = \frac{-4\sqrt{6} \pm \sqrt{96 + 16\sqrt{2}}}{8}$$

$$x = \frac{-4\sqrt{6} \pm \sqrt{16(6 + \sqrt{2})}}{8}$$

$$x = \frac{-4\sqrt{6} \pm 4\sqrt{6 + \sqrt{2}}}{8}$$

$$x = \frac{-\sqrt{6} \pm \sqrt{6 + \sqrt{2}}}{2}$$

Activities

② Find the roots.

$\sqrt{3}x^2 + \sqrt{7}x - 5 = 0$

$$x = \frac{-\sqrt{7} \pm \sqrt{(\sqrt{7})^2 - 4(\sqrt{3})(-5)}}{2(\sqrt{3})}$$

$$x = \frac{-\sqrt{7} \pm \sqrt{7 + 20\sqrt{3}}}{2\sqrt{3}} \cdot \frac{\sqrt{3}}{\sqrt{3}}$$

$$x = \frac{-\sqrt{7}\sqrt{3} \pm \sqrt{3(7 + 20\sqrt{3})}}{2\sqrt{3}\sqrt{3}}$$

$$x = \frac{-\sqrt{21} \pm \sqrt{21 + 60\sqrt{3}}}{6}$$

$\sqrt{11}x^2 + \sqrt{3}x - 10 = 0$

$$x = \frac{-\sqrt{3} \pm \sqrt{(\sqrt{3})^2 - 4(\sqrt{11})(-10)}}{2(\sqrt{11})}$$

$$x = \frac{-\sqrt{3} \pm \sqrt{3 + 40\sqrt{11}}}{2\sqrt{11}} \cdot \frac{\sqrt{11}}{\sqrt{11}} = \frac{-\sqrt{3}\sqrt{11} \pm \sqrt{11(3 + 40\sqrt{11})}}{2\sqrt{11}\sqrt{11}}$$

$$x = \frac{-\sqrt{33} \pm \sqrt{33 + 440\sqrt{11}}}{22}$$

③ Find the roots.

$\sqrt{10}x^2 + 5\sqrt{2}x - 4 = 0$

$$x = \frac{-5\sqrt{2} \pm \sqrt{(5\sqrt{2})^2 - 4(\sqrt{10})(-4)}}{2(\sqrt{10})}$$

$$x = \frac{-5\sqrt{2} \pm \sqrt{50 + 16\sqrt{10}}}{2\sqrt{10}} \cdot \frac{\sqrt{10}}{\sqrt{10}}$$

$$x = \frac{-5\sqrt{20} \pm \sqrt{10(50 + 16\sqrt{10})}}{20}$$

$$x = \frac{-5\sqrt{4 \cdot 5} \pm \sqrt{500 + 160\sqrt{10}}}{20}$$

$$x = \frac{-10\sqrt{5} \pm \sqrt{4(125 + 40\sqrt{10})}}{20} = \frac{-10\sqrt{5} \pm 2\sqrt{125 + 40\sqrt{10}}}{20}$$

$$x = \frac{-5\sqrt{5} \pm \sqrt{125 + 40\sqrt{10}}}{10}$$

$\sqrt{6}x^2 + 3\sqrt{2}x - 8 = 0$

$$x = \frac{-3\sqrt{2} \pm \sqrt{(3\sqrt{2})^2 - 4(\sqrt{6})(-8)}}{2(\sqrt{6})}$$

$$x = \frac{-3\sqrt{2} \pm \sqrt{18 + 32\sqrt{6}}}{2\sqrt{6}} \cdot \frac{\sqrt{6}}{\sqrt{6}}$$

$$x = \frac{-3\sqrt{12} \pm \sqrt{6(18 + 32\sqrt{6})}}{12}$$

$$x = \frac{-3\sqrt{4 \cdot 3} \pm \sqrt{108 + 192\sqrt{6}}}{12} = \frac{-6\sqrt{3} \pm \sqrt{4(27 + 48\sqrt{6})}}{12}$$

$$x = \frac{-6\sqrt{3} \pm 2\sqrt{27 + 48\sqrt{6}}}{12} = \frac{-3\sqrt{3} \pm \sqrt{27 + 48\sqrt{6}}}{6}$$

$3\sqrt{5}x^2 + \sqrt{7}x - 6 = 0$

$$x = \frac{-\sqrt{7} \pm \sqrt{(\sqrt{7})^2 - 4(3\sqrt{5})(-6)}}{2(3\sqrt{5})}$$

$$x = \frac{-\sqrt{7} \pm \sqrt{7 + 72\sqrt{5}}}{6\sqrt{5}} \cdot \frac{\sqrt{5}}{\sqrt{5}}$$

$$x = \frac{-\sqrt{35} \pm \sqrt{5(7 + 72\sqrt{5}}}{30} = \frac{-\sqrt{35} \pm \sqrt{35 + 360\sqrt{5}}}{30}$$

$3\sqrt{2}x^2 + 2\sqrt{3}x - 3 = 0$

$$x = \frac{-2\sqrt{3} \pm \sqrt{(2\sqrt{3})^2 - 4(3\sqrt{2})(-3)}}{2(3\sqrt{2})}$$

$$x = \frac{-2\sqrt{3} \pm \sqrt{12 + 36\sqrt{2}}}{6\sqrt{2}} \cdot \frac{\sqrt{2}}{\sqrt{2}}$$

$$x = \frac{-2\sqrt{6} \pm \sqrt{2(12 + 36\sqrt{2})}}{12}$$

$$x = \frac{-2\sqrt{6} \pm \sqrt{24 + 72\sqrt{2}}}{12}$$

$$x = \frac{-2\sqrt{6} \pm \sqrt{4(6 + 18\sqrt{2})}}{12} = \frac{-2\sqrt{6} \pm 2\sqrt{6 + 18\sqrt{2}}}{12}$$

$$x = \frac{-\sqrt{6} \pm \sqrt{6 + 18\sqrt{2}}}{6}$$

④ Solve each system of equations.

$x - y - 5 = 0$
$-2x + y + 9 = 0$
$x - y = 5$
$-2x + y = -9$
$-x = -4$
$x = 4$
$4 - y - 5 = 0$
$y = -1$
(4, -1)

$10x - 3y - 5 = 0$
$7x - 2y - 4 = 0$
$10x - 3y = 5$
$7x - 2y = 4$
$20x - 6y = 10$
$21x - 6y = 12$
$-x = -2$
$x = 2$
$10(2) - 3y - 5 = 0$
$20 - 3y = 5$
$-3y = -15$
$y = 5$
(2 5)

$11x + 22y - 22 = 0$
$-x - 4y + 10 = 0$
$11x + 22y = 22$
$-x - 4y = -10$
$x + 2y = 2$
$-x - 4y = -10$
$-2y = -8$
$y = 4$
$-x - 4(4) + 10 = 0$
$-x - 16 = -10$
$-x = 6$
$x = -6$
(-6, 4)

$4x - 12y - 8 = 0$
$6x - 18y - 12 = 0$
$4x - 12y = 8$
$6x - 18y = 12$
Divide the first equation by 4 and the second equation by 6.
$x - 3y = 2$
$x - 3y = 2$
$0 = 0$
All real numbers

Vertex of a Parabola, Zeros of a Function Worksheet 53

① Complete the square to write each function in parabolic form. Give the vertex (h, k) of each parabola.

$f(x)=4x^2+12x+5$	$f(x)=4x^2-8x-3$	$f(x)=2x^2+20x+5$
$4x^2+12x+5=0$	$4x^2-8x-3=0$	$2x^2+20x+5=0$
$4x^2+12x=-5$	$4x^2-8x=3$	$2x^2+20x=-5$
$4(x^2+3x)=-5$	$4(x^2-2x)=3$	$2(x^2+10x)=-5$
$4(x^2+3x+\frac{9}{4})=-5+4(\frac{9}{4})$	$4(x^2-2x+1)=3+4(1)$	$2(x^2+10x+25)=-5+2(25)$
$4(x+\frac{3}{2})^2=-5+9$	$4(x-1)^2=3+4$	$2(x+5)^2=-5+50$
$4(x+\frac{3}{2})^2-4=0$	$4(x-1)^2-7=0$	$2(x+5)^2-45=0$
$f(x)=4(x+\frac{3}{2})^2-4$	$f(x)=4(x-1)^2-7$	$f(x)=2(x+5)^2-45$
The vertex is $(-\frac{3}{2},-4)$	The vertex is (1, -7).	The vertex is (-5, -45).

② Complete the square to find the zeros of each function.

$f(x)=x^2+8x-2$	$f(x)=x^2-9x+4$	$f(x)=x^2+10x+3$
$0=x^2+8x-2$	$0=x^2-9x+4$	$0=x^2+10x+3$
$x^2+8x=2$	$x^2-9x=-4$	$x^2+10x=-3$
$x^2+8x+(\frac{8}{2})^2=2+(\frac{8}{2})^2$	$x^2-9x+(-\frac{9}{2})^2=-4+(-\frac{9}{2})^2$	$x^2+10x+(\frac{10}{2})^2=-3+(\frac{10}{2})^2$
$x^2+8x+16=2+16$	$x^2-9x+\frac{81}{4}=-\frac{16}{4}+\frac{81}{4}$	$x^2+10x+25=-3+25$
$x^2+8x+16=18$	$x^2-9x+\frac{81}{4}=\frac{65}{4}$	$x^2+10x+25=22$
$(x+4)^2=18$	$(x-\frac{9}{2})^2=\frac{65}{4}$	$(x+5)^2=22$
$\sqrt{(x+4)^2}=\sqrt{18}$	$\sqrt{(x-\frac{9}{2})^2}=\sqrt{\frac{65}{4}}$	$\sqrt{(x+5)^2}=\sqrt{22}$
$x+4=\pm\sqrt{2\cdot3\cdot3}$	$x-\frac{9}{2}=\pm\frac{\sqrt{65}}{2}$	$x+5=\pm\sqrt{22}$
$x=-4\pm3\sqrt{2}$	$x=\frac{9\pm\sqrt{65}}{2}$	$x=-5\pm\sqrt{22}$

Teaching Tips, Cont.

- Teach how to find the roots of quadratic functions with radicals from the teaching box. Remind the students to rationalize the denominator whenever a radical appears in the denominator of the answer.
- Complete the Classwork exercises. Have some students work the problems on the board for the class and explain their answers. All students should work the problems in their books.

Assignment

- Complete Lesson 105, Activities 2-4.

Lesson 106

Concepts

- Parabolas
- Directrix
- Focus
- Axis of symmetry
- Dividing polynomials

Learning Objectives

The student will be able to:

- Graph parabolas of the form $4p(y - k) = (x - h)^2$
- Give the coordinates of the vertex and focus of the parabola
- Give the equations for the directrix and axis of symmetry of the parabola

Materials Needed

- Student Book, Lesson 106

Teaching Tips

- Review parabolas. (See Lessons 98-99 and 101)
- Ask the students what happens when *k* is positive. (The graph shifts to the right.) Ask the students what happens when *k* is negative. (The graph shifts to the left.)
- Ask the students what happens when *h* is positive. (The graph shifts up.) Ask the students what happens when *h* is negative. (The graph shifts down.)

Parabolas

You have learned to recognize the graph of a quadratic equation as a parabola. However, not all U-shaped graphs are parabolas.

A **parabola** is the set of all points that are equidistant from a given line and a given point not on the line. The given line is called the **directrix**, and the given point not on the directrix is called the **focus**. Each parabola has an **axis of symmetry** that divides the parabola into two parts that are mirror images of each other.

When using quadratic equations of the form $y = a(x-h)^2 + k$, the vertex, focus, directrix, and axis of symmetry can all be found with a simple rearrangement of the equation.

$y - k = a(x-h)^2$

$\frac{y-k}{a} = (x-h)^2$ or $\frac{1}{a}(y-k) = (x-h)^2$

By definition (and to make the remaining formulas simpler) the value of $\frac{1}{a} = 4p$. This makes the formula for a parabola $4p(y-k) = (x-h)^2$.

The vertex of the parabola is the point (h, k), the axis of symmetry is the line $x = h$, the focus is the point $(h, k+p)$ and the directrix is the line $y = k - p$.

Give the coordinates for the vertex and focus, and the equations of the lines for the axis of symmetry and the directrix of the parabola.

$8(y-3) = (x+2)^2$

$4p = 8 \Rightarrow p = 2; k = 3; h = -2$

The vertex is (-2, 3).
The focus is (-2, 3 + 2) = (2, 5).
The axis of symmetry is the line $x = -2$.
The directrix is the line $y = 3 - 2 \Rightarrow y = 1$.

① Classwork

Rewrite each equation in the form $4p(y-k) = (x-h)^2$. Identify the value of the variables *p*, *k*, and *h*, and give the coordinates for the vertex and focus, and the equations of the lines for the axis of symmetry and the directrix of the parabola.

$y = 2(x-2)^2 - 3$

$y + 3 = 2(x-2)^2$

$\frac{y+3}{2} = (x-2)^2$

$\frac{1}{2}(y+3) = (x-2)^2$

$4p = \frac{1}{2} \Rightarrow p = \frac{1}{8}$

$k = -3$

$h = 2$

The vertex is (2, -3).
The focus is $(2, -3 + \frac{1}{8}) = \left(2, -\frac{23}{8}\right)$.
The axis of symmetry is the line $x = 2$.
The directrix is the line $y = -3 - \frac{1}{8} \Rightarrow y = -\frac{25}{8}$.

$y = \frac{1}{8}(x+3)^2 + 5$

$y - 5 = \frac{1}{8}(x+3)^2$

$\frac{y-5}{\frac{1}{8}} = (x+3)^2$

$8(y-5) = (x+3)^2$

$4p = 8 \Rightarrow p = 2$

$k = 5$

$h = -3$

The vertex is (-3, 5).
The focus is (-3, 5 + 2) = (-3, 7).
The axis of symmetry is the line $x = -3$.
The directrix is the line $y = 5 - 2 \Rightarrow y = 3$.

Activities

② Rewrite each equation in the form $4p(y-k)=(x-h)^2$. Identify the value of the variables p, k, and h, and give the coordinates for the vertex and focus, and the equations of the lines for the axis of symmetry and the directrix of the parabola.

$y=\frac{1}{4}(x-1)^2-2$

$y+2=\frac{1}{4}(x-1)^2$

$\frac{y+2}{\frac{1}{4}}=(x-1)^2$

$4(y+2)=(x-1)^2$

$4p=4\Rightarrow p=1$
$k=-2$
$h=1$

The vertex is (1, -2).
The focus is (1, -2 + 1) = (1, -1).
The axis of symmetry is the line $x=1$.
The directrix is the line $y=-2-1\Rightarrow y=-3$.

$y=\frac{1}{12}(x-2)^2+3$

$y-3=\frac{1}{12}(x-2)^2$

$\frac{y-3}{\frac{1}{12}}=(x-2)^2$

$12(y-3)=(x-2)^2$

$4p=12\Rightarrow p=3$
$k=3$
$h=2$

The vertex is (2, 3).
The focus is (2, 3 + 3) = (2, 6).
The axis of symmetry is the line $x=2$.
The directrix is the line $y=3-3\Rightarrow y=0$.

$y=3(x+2)^2+6$

$y-6=3(x+2)^2$

$\frac{y-6}{3}=(x+2)^2$

$\frac{1}{3}(y-6)=(x+2)^2$

$4p=\frac{1}{3}\Rightarrow p=\frac{1}{12}$
$k=6$
$h=-2$

The vertex is (-2, 6).
The focus is (-2, 6 + $\frac{1}{12}$) = (-2, $\frac{73}{12}$).
The axis of symmetry is the line $x=-2$.
The directrix is the line $y=6-\frac{1}{12}\Rightarrow y=\frac{71}{12}$.

$y=\frac{1}{2}(x+7)^2-4$

$y+4=\frac{1}{2}(x+7)^2$

$\frac{y+4}{\frac{1}{2}}=(x+7)^2$

$2(y+4)=(x+7)^2$

$4p=2\Rightarrow p=\frac{1}{2}$
$k=-4$
$h=-7$

The vertex is (-7, -4).
The focus is (-7, -4 + $\frac{1}{2}$) = (-7, $-\frac{7}{2}$).
The axis of symmetry is the line $x=-7$.
The directrix is the line $y=-4-\frac{1}{2}\Rightarrow y=-\frac{9}{2}$.

③ Divide.

$(15x^2+23x-28)\div(5x-4)$

$$\begin{array}{r} 3x+7 \\ 5x-4\overline{)15x^2+23x-28} \\ \underline{15x^2-12x} \\ 35x-28 \\ \underline{35x-28} \end{array}$$

$(8x^2+30x-27)\div(2x+9)$

$$\begin{array}{r} 4x-3 \\ 2x+9\overline{)8x^2+30x-27} \\ \underline{8x^2+36x} \\ -6x-27 \\ \underline{-6x-27} \end{array}$$

$(35x^2-31x+6)\div(7x-2)$

$$\begin{array}{r} 5x-3 \\ 7x-2\overline{)35x^2-31x+6} \\ \underline{35x^2-10x} \\ -21x+6 \\ \underline{-21x+6} \end{array}$$

Teaching Tips, Cont.

- Teach how to find the coordinates for the vertex and the focus from the teaching box. Explain that the vertex is always on the parabola at the point where the parabola turns around and the focus is always inside the parabola directly above the vertex.

- Teach how to find the equations for the directrix and the axis of symmetry from the teaching box. Explain that the axis of symmetry is a line that contains both the vertex and the focus and the directrix is a line perpendicular to the axis of symmetry located outside the parabola such that the vertex is the midpoint on the axis of symmetry between the focus and the directrix. An illustration of the parts of a parabola is included in the teaching box of Lesson 107.

- Complete the Classwork exercises. Have some students work the problems on the board for the class and explain their answers. All students should work the problems in their books.

Assignment

- Complete Lesson 106, Activities 2-3.

Lesson 107

Concepts

- Parabolas
- Vertex
- Focus
- Directrix
- Axis of symmetry
- Graphing
- Math in the real world

Learning Objectives

The student will be able to:

- Graph a parabola
- Graph the vertex and focus
- Graph the directrix and axis of symmetry

Materials Needed

- Student Book, Lesson 107

Teaching Tips

- Review parabolas (See Lessons 98-99, 101)
- Review finding the coordinates of the vertex and focus. (See Lesson 106)
- Review finding the equation of the directrix and axis of symmetry. (See Lesson 106)
- Tell the students they must memorize the formulas for the coordinates of the vertex and focus and the equations of the directrix and axis of symmetry.

Graphing Parabolas of the Form $4p(y-k)=(x-h)^2$

A complete graph of a parabola includes the U-shaped graph, as well as the vertex, focus, directrix, and axis of symmetry. These can be found from the form $4p(y-k)=(x-h)^2$.

Memorize these formulas for parts of a parabola.

Vertex: (h, k)
Focus: $(h, k+p)$
Directrix: $y = k - p$.
Axis of symmetry: $x = h$

Graph $\frac{1}{2}(y+2)=(x-3)^2$. Include the vertex, focus, directrix, and axis of symmetry.

Begin by identifying the values of h, k, and p.
$h=3; k=-2; 4p=\frac{1}{2}; p=\frac{1}{8}$

Make a chart that includes the vertex and at least 2 points on each side of the vertex.

x	y
3	2
4	0
5	6
2	0
1	6

Find the focus, directrix, and axis of symmetry.
Focus: $\left(3, -2+\frac{1}{8}\right) \Rightarrow \left(3, -\frac{15}{8}\right)$
Directrix: $y=-2-\frac{1}{8} \Rightarrow y=-\frac{17}{8}$
Axis of symmetry: $x = 3$

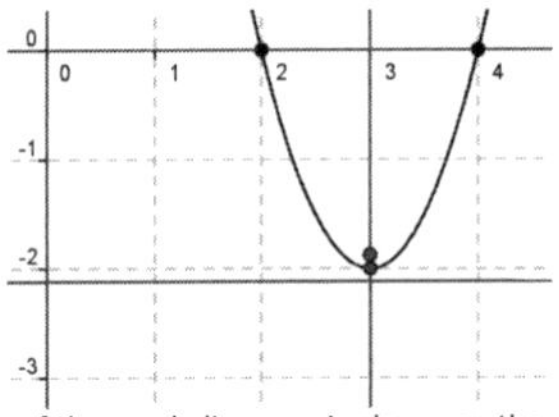

More of the parabolic curve is shown on the graph in Lesson 100. This graph is zoomed in so you can see the focus and directrix.

① **Classwork**
Graph each parabola. Include the vertex, focus, directrix, and axis of symmetry.

$y=2(x-2)^2-3$

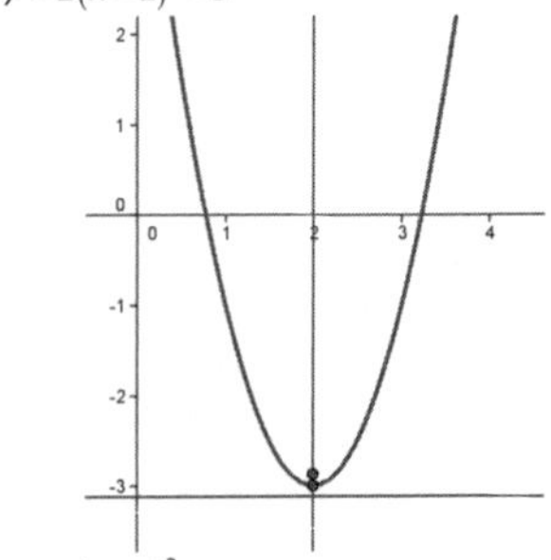

$y=\frac{1}{8}(x+3)^2+5$

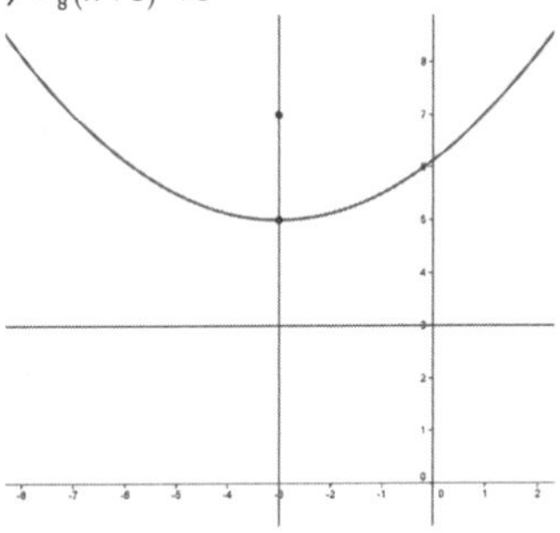

Note: The graphs in this Lesson are the same equations the students solved in Lesson 106. See the solution key from Lesson 106 for detailed solutions for the vertex, focus, directrix, and axis of symmetry.

Activities

② Graph each parabola. Include the vertex, focus, directrix, and axis of symmetry.

$y = \frac{1}{4}(x-1)^2 - 2$

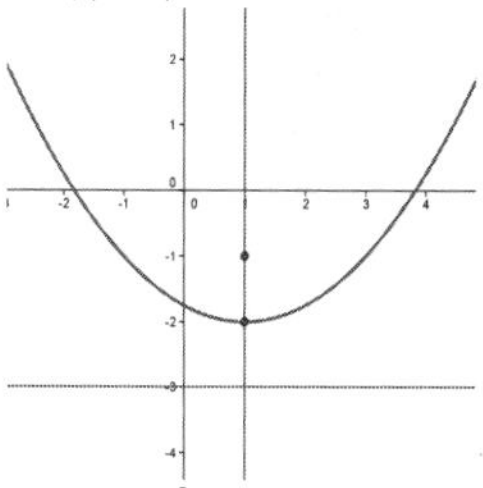

$y = \frac{1}{12}(x-2)^2 + 3$

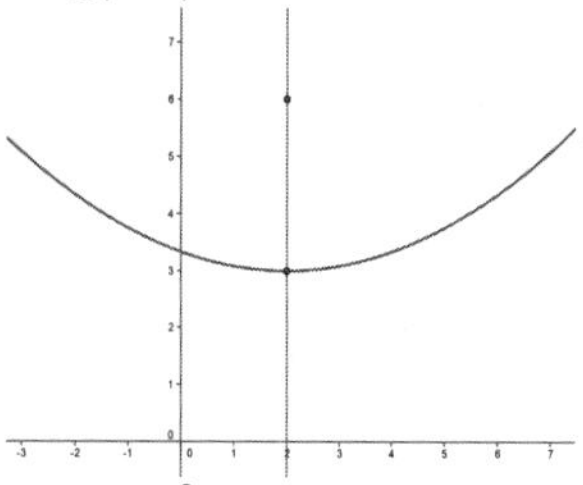

$y = 3(x+2)^2 + 6$

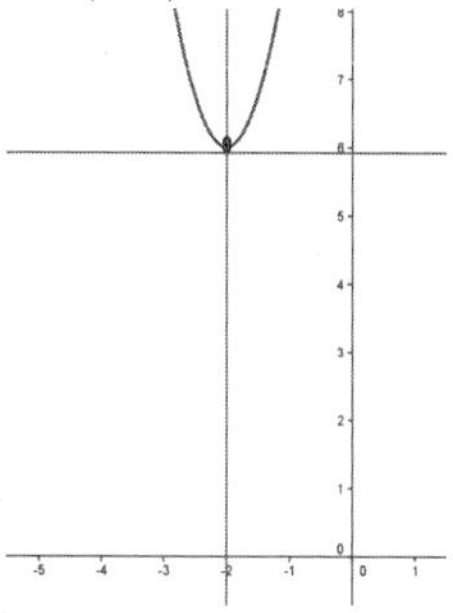

$y = \frac{1}{2}(x+7)^2 - 4$

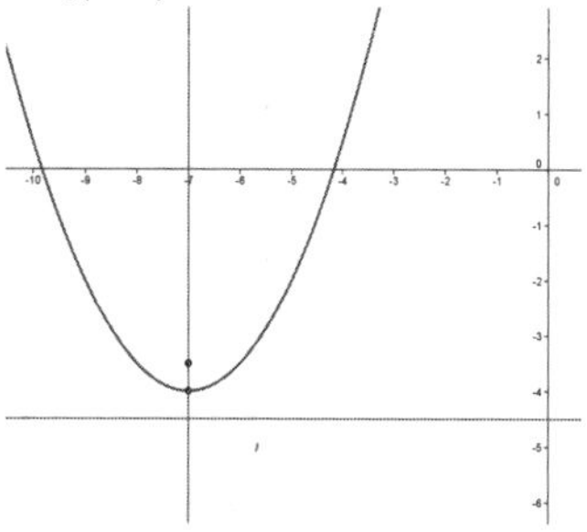

③ Solve.

The amount of drag on a tennis ball is given by the formula $F = \frac{1}{2}C_d \rho V^2 \pi r^2$, where F is the force of drag, C_d is the coefficient for drag, ρ is the density of the air, V is the velocity of the ball, and r is the radius of the ball. Find the force of drag on a tennis ball with a 2.5-inch diameter if the coefficient for drag is 0.7, the density of the air is 0.075 lb/ft^3, and the velocity of the ball is 88 ft/s. Express your answer in terms of ft.-lb./s^2.

The diameter is 2.5 inches, so the radius is 1.25 inches. Convert this to feet.

$\left(\frac{5}{4}\ \text{in.}\right)\left(\frac{1\ \text{ft.}}{12\ \text{in.}}\right) = \frac{5}{48}\ \text{ft.}$

$F = \frac{1}{2}(0.7)(0.075\ \text{lb./ft.}^3)(88\ \text{ft./s})^2\,\pi\left(\frac{5}{48}\ \text{ft.}\right)^2$

$F = \frac{0.7}{2}\left(\frac{0.075\ \text{lb.}}{1\ \text{ft.}^3}\right)\left(\frac{88\ \text{ft.}}{1\ \text{s}}\right)^2 \pi\left(\frac{5}{48}\ \text{ft.}\right)^2$

$F = \frac{10164}{4608}\pi = \frac{847}{384}\pi$ ft.-lb./s^2 or 2.21π ft.-lb./s^2

Teaching Tips, Cont.

- Teach graphing parabolas from the teaching box. The vertex, focus, directrix, and axis of symmetry are color-coded on the sample graph in the student book. You may refer students to the diagram in the teaching box of the student book as you teach this section. The vertex is shown in red, the focus in green, the directrix in blue, and the axis of symmetry in purple.
- Complete the Classwork exercises. Have some students work the problems on the board for the class and explain their answers. All students should work the problems in their books.

Assignment

- Complete Lesson 107, Activities 2-3.

Lesson 108

Concepts

- Discriminant
- Parabolas
- Roots of quadratic equations
- Factoring polynomials

Learning Objectives

The student will be able to:

- Use the discriminant to determine how many times the graph of a parabola will cross the x-axis
- Convert equations from parabolic form to standard form

Materials Needed

- Student Book, Lesson 108
- Worksheet 54

Teaching Tips

- Have students complete Worksheet 54 in class. This may be for added practice of earlier topics, or graded as a quiz, if desired.
- Review the discriminant. (See Lesson 95)
- Ask the students where the zeros of a graph are located. (On the x-axis)
- Explain that since the discriminant can be used to determine the number of roots a quadratic equation has, it can also be used to determine the number of times the graph of a parabola crosses the x-axis.

Using the Discriminant

In Lesson 95 you learned how to use the discriminant to find the number of roots in a quadratic equation. The discriminant can also be used to help determine what the graph of a parabola will look like.

To use the discriminant, you must first convert the equation to the format $y = ax^2 + bx + c$. Then find the discriminant, $b^2 - 4ac$.

If the discriminant is greater than zero, the graph of the parabola will cross the x-axis in 2 places.

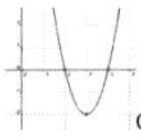 or 

If the discriminant equals zero, the vertex of the parabola will lie on the x-axis.

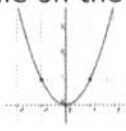 or 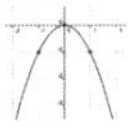

If the discriminant is less than zero, the parabola will not touch the x-axis.

 or 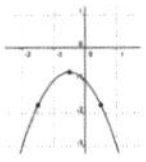

In how many places will the graph of $\frac{1}{2}(y+2) = (x-3)^2$ touch the x-axis?

Convert the equation to the $y = ax^2 + bx + c$ format.

$\frac{1}{2}(y+2) = x^2 - 6x + 9$

$y + 2 = 2(x^2 - 6x + 9)$

$y + 2 = 2x^2 - 12x + 18$

$y = 2x^2 - 12x + 16$

Find the discminінant.

$(-12)^2 - 4(2)(16) = 144 - 128 = 16$

The discriminant is positive, so the graph will touch the x-axis in 2 places.

① Classwork

Convert each equation to the form $y = ax^2 + bx + c$. Find the discriminant and give the number of roots in the equation.

$y = 2(x-2)^2 - 3$

$y = 2(x^2 - 4x + 4) - 3$

$y = 2x^2 - 8x + 8 - 3$

$y = 2x^2 - 8x + 5$

$b^2 - 4ac = (-8)^2 - 4(2)(5) =$

$64 - 40 = 24$

The discriminant is positive, so there are two roots.

$y = \frac{1}{8}(x+3)^2 + 5$

$y = \frac{1}{8}(x^2 + 6x + 9) + 5$

$y = \frac{1}{8}x^2 + \frac{6}{8}x + \frac{9}{8} + 5$

$y = \frac{1}{8}x^2 + \frac{6}{8}x + \frac{9}{8} + \frac{40}{8}$

$y = \frac{1}{8}x^2 + \frac{3}{4}x + \frac{49}{8}$

$b^2 - 4ac = \left(\frac{3}{4}\right)^2 - 4\left(\frac{1}{8}\right)\left(\frac{49}{8}\right) =$

$\frac{9}{16} - \frac{49}{16} = -\frac{40}{16} = -\frac{5}{2}$

The discriminant is negative, so there are no roots.

Note: The equations used in this Lesson are the same as the equations from Lesson 108. After students have completed this lesson, have them look back at the graphs of these parabolas in Lesson 108 and notice the number of times each graph touches the x-axis. If all work is completed correctly, the number of times the graph touches the x-axis will equal the number of roots.

Activities

② Convert each equation to the form $y = ax^2 + bx + c$. Find the discriminant and give the number of roots in the equation.

$y = \frac{1}{4}(x-1)^2 - 2$

$y = \frac{1}{4}(x^2 - 2x + 1) - 2$

$y = \frac{1}{4}x^2 - \frac{2}{4}x + \frac{1}{4} - 2$

$y = \frac{1}{4}x^2 - \frac{1}{2}x + \frac{1}{4} - \frac{8}{4}$

$y = \frac{1}{4}x^2 - \frac{1}{2}x - \frac{7}{4}$

$b^2 - 4ac = \left(-\frac{1}{2}\right)^2 - 4\left(\frac{1}{4}\right)\left(-\frac{7}{4}\right) =$

$\frac{1}{4} + \frac{7}{4} = \frac{8}{4} = 2$

The discriminant is positive, so there are two roots.

$y = 3(x+2)^2 + 6$

$y = 3(x^2 + 4x + 4) + 6$

$y = 3x^2 + 12x + 12 + 6$

$y = 3x^2 + 12x + 18$

$b^2 - 4ac = (12)^2 - 4(3)(18) =$

$144 - 216 = -72$

The discriminant is negative, so there are no roots.

$y = \frac{1}{12}(x-2)^2 + 3$

$y = \frac{1}{12}(x^2 - 4x + 4) + 3$

$y = \frac{1}{12}x^2 - \frac{4}{12}x + \frac{4}{12} + 3$

$y = \frac{1}{12}x^2 - \frac{1}{3}x + \frac{1}{3} + \frac{9}{3}$

$y = \frac{1}{12}x^2 - \frac{1}{3}x + \frac{10}{3}$

$b^2 - 4ac = \left(-\frac{1}{3}\right)^2 - 4\left(\frac{1}{12}\right)\left(\frac{10}{3}\right) =$

$\frac{1}{9} - \frac{10}{9} = -\frac{9}{9} = -1$

The discriminant is negative, so there are no roots.

$y = \frac{1}{2}(x+7)^2 - 4$

$y = \frac{1}{2}(x^2 + 14x + 49) - 4$

$y = \frac{1}{2}x^2 + 7x + \frac{49}{2} - 4$

$y = \frac{1}{2}x^2 + 7x + \frac{49}{2} - \frac{8}{2}$

$y = \frac{1}{2}x^2 + 7x + \frac{41}{2}$

$b^2 - 4ac = (7)^2 - 4\left(\frac{1}{2}\right)\left(\frac{41}{2}\right) =$

$49 - 41 = 8$

The discriminant is positive, so there are two roots.

③ Factor each polynomial completely.

$x^4 - 625$

$(x^2 + 25)(x^2 - 25) =$

$(x^2 + 25)(x + 5)(x - 5)$

$2x^3 - 162x$

$2x(x^2 - 81) =$

$2x(x + 9)(x - 9)$

$5x^4 - 245$

$5(x^4 - 49) =$

$5(x^2 + 7)(x^2 - 7) =$

$5(x^2 + 7)(x + \sqrt{7})(x - \sqrt{7})$

$x^3 - 16x$

$x(x^2 - 16) =$

$x(x + 4)(x - 4)$

$x^5 - 15x^3$

$x^3(x^2 - 15) =$

$x^3(x + \sqrt{15})(x - \sqrt{15})$

$3x^5 - 768x$

$3x(x^4 - 256) =$

$3x(x^2 + 16)(x^2 - 16) =$

$3x(x^2 + 16)(x + 4)(x - 4)$

Finding Zeros of Quadratic Functions Worksheet 54

① Find the zeros of each quadratic function.

$f(x) = x^2 + 8x - 6$

$0 = x^2 + 8x - 6$

$x^2 + 8x = 6$

$x^2 + 8x + \left(\frac{8}{2}\right)^2 = 6 + \left(\frac{8}{2}\right)^2$

$x^2 + 8x + 16 = 6 + 16$

$x^2 + 8x + 16 = 22$

$(x + 4)^2 = 22$

$\sqrt{(x + 4)^2} = \sqrt{22}$

$x + 4 = \pm\sqrt{22}$

$x = -4 \pm \sqrt{22}$

$f(x) = x^2 - 7x + 9$

$0 = x^2 - 7x + 9$

$x^2 - 7x = -9$

$x^2 - 7x + \left(-\frac{7}{2}\right)^2 = -9 + \left(-\frac{7}{2}\right)^2$

$x^2 - 7x + \frac{49}{4} = -\frac{36}{4} + \frac{49}{4}$

$x^2 - 7x + \frac{49}{4} = \frac{13}{4}$

$\left(x - \frac{7}{2}\right)^2 = \frac{13}{4}$

$\sqrt{\left(x - \frac{7}{2}\right)^2} = \sqrt{\frac{13}{4}}$

$x - \frac{7}{2} = \pm\frac{\sqrt{13}}{2}$

$x = \frac{7 \pm \sqrt{13}}{2}$

$f(x) = x^2 - 7x - 10$

$0 = x^2 - 7x - 10$

$x^2 - 7x = 10$

$x^2 - 7x + \left(-\frac{7}{2}\right)^2 = 10 + \left(-\frac{7}{2}\right)^2$

$x^2 - 7x + \frac{49}{4} = \frac{40}{4} + \frac{49}{4}$

$x^2 - 7x + \frac{49}{4} = \frac{89}{4}$

$\left(x - \frac{7}{2}\right)^2 = \frac{89}{4}$

$\sqrt{\left(x - \frac{7}{2}\right)^2} = \sqrt{\frac{89}{4}}$

$x - \frac{7}{2} = \pm\frac{\sqrt{89}}{2}$

$x = \frac{7 \pm \sqrt{89}}{2}$

② Find the roots.

$\sqrt{10}x^2 + 5\sqrt{2}x - 1 = 0$

$$x = \frac{-5\sqrt{2} \pm \sqrt{\left(5\sqrt{2}\right)^2 - 4\left(\sqrt{10}\right)(-1)}}{2\left(\sqrt{10}\right)}$$

$$x = \frac{-5\sqrt{2} \pm \sqrt{50 + 4\sqrt{10}}}{2\sqrt{10}} \cdot \frac{\sqrt{10}}{\sqrt{10}}$$

$$x = \frac{-5\sqrt{20} \pm \sqrt{10(50 + 4\sqrt{10})}}{20}$$

$$x = \frac{-5\sqrt{4 \cdot 5} \pm \sqrt{500 + 40\sqrt{10}}}{20}$$

$$x = \frac{-10\sqrt{5} \pm \sqrt{4(125 + 10\sqrt{10})}}{20}$$

$$x = \frac{-10\sqrt{5} \pm 2\sqrt{125 + 10\sqrt{10}}}{20}$$

$$x = \frac{-5\sqrt{5} \pm \sqrt{125 + 10\sqrt{10}}}{10}$$

$\sqrt{6}x^2 + 3\sqrt{2}x - 9 = 0$

$$x = \frac{-3\sqrt{2} \pm \sqrt{\left(3\sqrt{2}\right)^2 - 4\left(\sqrt{6}\right)(-9)}}{2\left(\sqrt{6}\right)}$$

$$x = \frac{-3\sqrt{2} \pm \sqrt{18 + 36\sqrt{6}}}{2\sqrt{6}} \cdot \frac{\sqrt{6}}{\sqrt{6}}$$

$$x = \frac{-3\sqrt{12} \pm \sqrt{6(18 + 36\sqrt{6})}}{12}$$

$$x = \frac{-3\sqrt{4 \cdot 3} \pm \sqrt{108 + 216\sqrt{6}}}{12}$$

$$x = \frac{-3\sqrt{4 \cdot 3} \pm \sqrt{36(3 + 6\sqrt{6})}}{12}$$

$$x = \frac{-6\sqrt{3} \pm 6\sqrt{3 + 6\sqrt{6}}}{12}$$

$$x = \frac{-\sqrt{3} \pm \sqrt{3 + 6\sqrt{6}}}{2}$$

Teaching Tips, Cont.

- Teach how to use the discriminant to find the number of zeros in the graph of a parabola.
- Review as necessary the process for converting equations from one form to another. This is a matter of following order of operations to solve for *y* in this case, just like solving literal equations.
- Complete the Classwork exercises. Have some students work the problems on the board for the class and explain their answers. All students should work the problems in their books.

Assignment

- Complete Lesson 108, Activities 2-3.

Lesson 109

Concepts

- Quadratic functions
- Parts of a parabola
- Discriminant
- Roots of equations

Learning Objectives

The student will be able to:

- Use the discriminant to determine the number of roots of a quadratic function
- Complete the square of a quadratic function
- Give the coordinates of the vertex and focus of a parabola
- Give the equation for the directrix and axis of symmetry of a parabola

Materials Needed

- Student Book, Lesson 109

Teaching Tips

➢ Review the parts of a parabola. (See Lessons 106-107)

➢ Review using the directrix to find the number of roots of a quadratic function. (See Lesson 108)

➢ Review completing the square. (See Lessons 93 and 100-101)

➢ This lesson is a summary review of parabolas, to include solving for the vertex, focus, directrix, and axis of symmetry. There is no new material presented in this lesson.

Lesson 109

Review of Quadratic Functions

Quadratic functions will always graph as a parabola. The number of zeros on the graph can be determined by using the discriminant.

The values of the zeros, if any, can be found by graphing, completing the square, factoring, or using the quadratic formula.

A complete graph of a parabola includes the U-shaped graph, as well as the vertex, focus, directrix, and axis of symmetry. These can be found from the form $4p(y-k)=(x-h)^2$.

Memorize these formulas for parts of a parabola.

Vertex: (h, k)
Focus: $(h, k+p)$
Directrix: $y = k - p$.
Axis of symmetry: $x = h$

Give the vertex, focus, directrix, axis of symmetry, and the zeros (if any) for the quadratic function $f(x)=\frac{1}{4}x^2+x+2$.

The discriminant is $1^2-4\left(\frac{1}{4}\right)(2)=1-2=-1$ so there are no roots to find.

Substitute y for $f(x)$ and complete the square to get the form $4p(y-k)=(x-h)^2$.

$y=\frac{1}{4}x^2+x+2$

$4y=x^2+4x+8$

$4y-8=x^2+4x$

$4y-8+4=x^2+4x+4$

$4y-4=(x+2)^2$

$4(y-1)=(x+2)^2$

Now find the values of h, k, and p.
$h = -2$; $k = 1$; $p = 1$

Use these values to find the vertex, focus, directrix, and axis of symmetry.
Vertex: (-2, 1)
Focus: (-2, 2)
Directrix: $y = 0$
Axis of symmetry: $x = -2$

① **Classwork.**
Use the discriminant to determine the number of roots for the quadratic function. Then complete the square and give the coordinates of the vertex and focus, and the equation for the directrix and axis of symmetry.

$f(x)=\frac{1}{8}x^2+2x+4$

$b^2-4ac=(2)^2-4\left(\frac{1}{8}\right)(4)=$

$4-2=2$

The discriminant is positive, so there are two roots.

$y=\frac{1}{8}x^2+2x+4$

$8y=x^2+16x+32$

$8y-32=x^2+16x$

$8y-32+64=x^2+16x+64$

$8y+32=(x+8)^2$

$8(y+4)=(x+8)^2$

$h = -8$; $k = -4$; $p = 2$

Vertex: (-8, -4)
Focus: (-8, -2)
Directrix: $y=-4-2 \Rightarrow y=-6$
Axis of symmetry: $x=-8$

Activities

② Use the discriminant to determine the number of roots for the quadratic function. Then complete the square and give the coordinates of the vertex and focus, and the equation for the directrix and axis of symmetry.

$f(x) = \frac{1}{4}x^2 + 4x + 2$

$b^2 - 4ac = (4)^2 - 4(\frac{1}{4})(2) =$

$16 - 2 = 14$

The discriminant is positive, so there are two roots.

$y = \frac{1}{4}x^2 + 4x + 2$

$4y = x^2 + 16x + 8$

$4y - 8 = x^2 + 16x$

$4y - 8 + 64 = x^2 + 16x + 64$

$4y + 56 = (x + 8)^2$

$4(y + 14) = (x + 8)^2$

h = -8; k = -14; p = 1

Vertex: (-8, -14)

Focus: (-8, -13)

Directrix: $y = -14 - 1 \Rightarrow y = -15$

Axis of symmertry: $x = -8$

$f(x) = \frac{1}{4}x^2 - x + 1$

$b^2 - 4ac = (-1)^2 - 4(\frac{1}{4})(1) =$

$1 - 1 = 0$

The discriminant is zero, so there is one root.

$y = \frac{1}{4}x^2 - x + 1$

$4y = x^2 - 4x + 4$

$4y - 4 = x^2 - 4x$

$4y - 4 + 4 = x^2 - 4x + 4$

$4y = (x - 2)^2$

$4(y + 0) = (x - 2)^2$

h = 2; k = 0; p = 1

Vertex: (2, 0)

Focus: (2, 1)

Directrix: $y = 0 - 1 \Rightarrow y = -1$

Axis of symmertry: $x = 2$

Note: The last problem on this page is a challenge problem. Some students may require assistance.

$f(x) = \frac{1}{2}x^2 + 3x + 6$

$b^2 - 4ac = (3)^2 - 4(\frac{1}{2})(6) =$

$9 - 12 = -3$

The discriminant is negative, so there are no roots.

$y = \frac{1}{2}x^2 + 3x + 6$

$2y = x^2 + 6x + 12$

$2y - 12 = x^2 + 6x$

$2y - 12 + 9 = x^2 + 6x + 9$

$2y - 3 = (x + 3)^2$

$2(y - \frac{3}{2}) = (x + 3)^2$

h = -3; $k = \frac{3}{2}$; $p = \frac{1}{2}$

Vertex: $(-3, \frac{3}{2})$

Focus: (-3, 2)

Directrix: $y = \frac{3}{2} - \frac{1}{2} \Rightarrow y = 1$

Axis of symmertry: $x = -3$

$f(x) = \frac{1}{3}x^2 - \frac{1}{6}x - 6$

$b^2 - 4ac = (-\frac{1}{6})^2 - 4(\frac{1}{3})(-6) =$

$\frac{1}{36} + 8 = \frac{289}{36}$

The discriminant is positive, so there are two roots.

$y = \frac{1}{3}x^2 - \frac{1}{6}x - 6$

$3y = x^2 - \frac{1}{2}x - 18$

$3y + 18 = x^2 - \frac{1}{2}x$

$3y + 18 + \frac{1}{16} = x^2 - \frac{1}{2}x + \frac{1}{16}$

$3y + \frac{289}{16} = (x - \frac{1}{4})^2$

$3(y + \frac{289}{48}) = (x - \frac{1}{4})^2$

$h = \frac{1}{4}$; $k = -\frac{289}{48}$; $p = \frac{3}{4}$

Vertex: $(\frac{1}{4}, -\frac{289}{48})$

Focus: $(\frac{1}{4}, -\frac{253}{48})$

Directrix: $y = -\frac{289}{48} - \frac{3}{4} \Rightarrow y = -\frac{325}{48}$

Axis of symmertry: $x = \frac{1}{4}$

Teaching Tips, Cont.

- Remind the students that they must have the formulas in the box memorized for the test.
- Complete the Classwork exercise. Have one student work the problem on the board for the class and explain the answer. All students should work the problem in their books.

Assignment

- Complete Lesson 109, Activity 2.

Lesson 110

Concepts
- Graphing quadratic inequalities
- Order of operations
- Radicals
- Math in the real world

Learning Objectives
The student will be able to:
- Graph quadratic inequalities
- Determine whether to shade inside or outside the parabola

Materials Needed
- Student Book, Lesson 110
- Worksheet 55

Teaching Tips
- Review graphing linear inequalities. (See Lesson 50)
- Review graphing parabolas. (See Lessons 98-99, and 101)
- Ask the students how an inequality with < or > is graphed. (With a dotted line) Tell the students the same rule applies for graphing quadratic inequalities. The difference is that quadratic inequalities will graph as a parabola rather than a straight line.
- Teach how to graph quadratic inequalities from the teaching box. Remind the students to plot at least 5 points, including the vertex and two points on either side of the vertex.

Graphing Quadratic Inequalities

In Lesson 50 you learned to graph linear inequalities. Recall that inequalities containing < or > are graphed with a dashed line. Inequalities containing ≤ or ≥ are graphed with a solid line. The same holds true for graphing quadratic inequalities.

The other major difference between graphing equations and inequalities is that inequalities will always have a portion of the graph shaded.

To determine which portion of the graph should be shaded, choose a point not on the parabola curve and substitute the coordinate values into the original inequality. If the coordinates make a true mathematical statement, shade that part of the graph (either inside the parabola or outside the parabola). Otherwise shade the opposite part.

This table provides a summary of the shading patterns for quadratic inequalities.

symbol	a	shade
> or ≥	+	inside
> or ≥	–	outside
< or ≤	+	outside
< or ≤	–	inside

Sketch the graph of $y > x^2 + 2x + 1$.
The graph is shaded inside the parabola because the equation is in the format $y > ax^2 + bx + c$ (the symbol is >) and *a* is positive ($a = 1$).

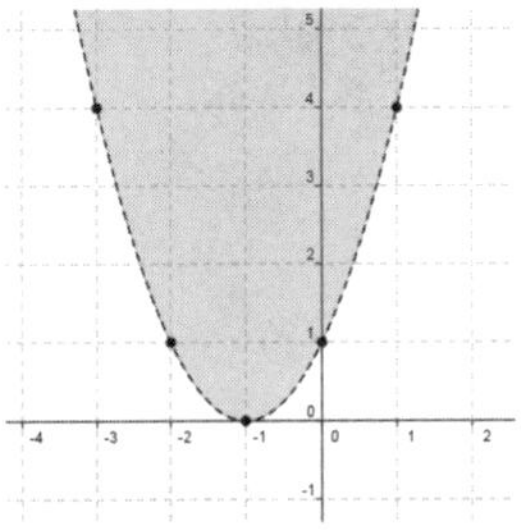

① **Classwork**
Sketch the graph of each inequality.

$y > -x^2 + 2x - 1$
The symbol is > and *a* is negative, so the graph will be shaded outside the parabola.

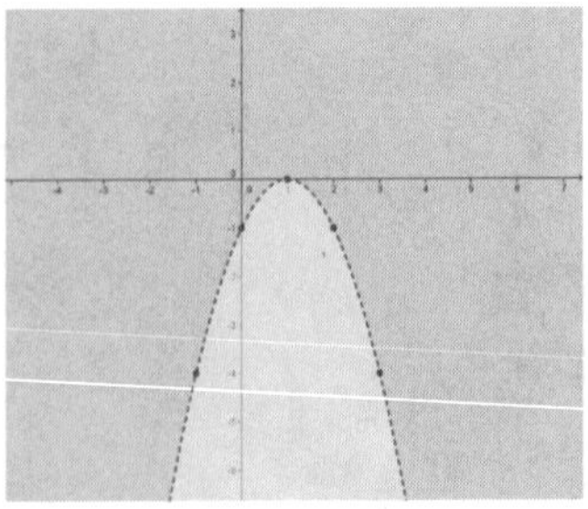

$y < -x^2 - 2x + 1$
The symbol is < and *a* is negative, so the graph will be shaded inside the parabola.

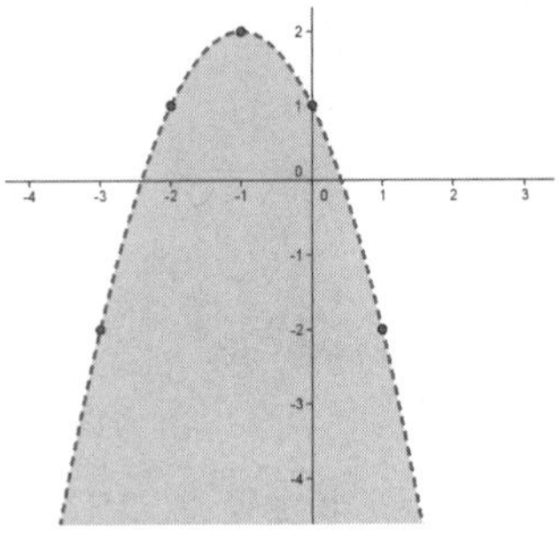

Activities
② Sketch the graph of each inequality.

$y < x^2 - 2x + 1$
The symbol is < and *a* is positive, so the graph will be shaded outside the parabola.

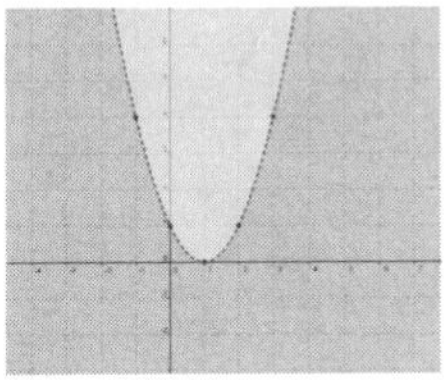

$y \geq x^2 + 2x - 4$
The symbol is ≥ and *a* is positive, so the graph will be shaded inside the parabola.

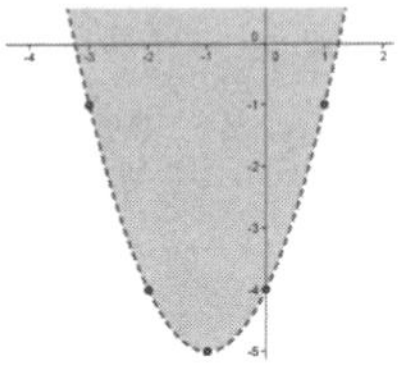

$y \leq -x^2 + 4x + 4$
The symbol is ≤ and *a* is negative, so the graph will be shaded inside the parabola.

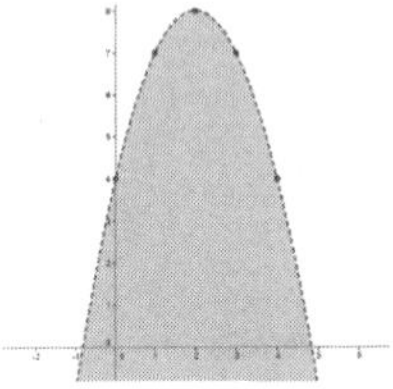

③ Solve.
The amount of drag on a tennis ball is given by the formula $F = \frac{1}{2}C_d\rho V^2\pi r^2$, where *F* is the force of drag, C_d is the coefficient for drag, ρ is the density of the air, *V* is the velocity of the ball, and *r* is the radius of the ball. Rewrite the equation to solve for each of the variables C_d, ρ, V, and r. You may leave fractions under the radical for this exercise.

$C_d = \frac{2F}{\rho V^2\pi r^2}$ $\quad \rho = \frac{2F}{C_d V^2\pi r^2}$

$V^2 = \frac{2F}{C_d\rho\pi r^2} \Rightarrow V = \sqrt{\frac{2F}{C_d\rho\pi r^2}}$ $\quad r^2 = \frac{2F}{C_d\rho V^2\pi} \Rightarrow r = \sqrt{\frac{2F}{C_d\rho V^2\pi}}$

④ Solve.

$6x - (2-9)^2 = -5(7-x)$
$6x - 7^2 = -35 + 5x$
$6x - 49 = -35 + 5x$
$x = 14$

$8x - 3(5-2x) - 2 = 5x - (2^3 - 3^3)$
$8x - 15 + 6x - 2 = 5x - (8 - 27)$
$14x - 17 = 5x + 19$
$9x = 36$
$x = 4$

$4(3-2x) + \sqrt{2(3^3+5)} = 3x - 2$
$12 - 8x + \sqrt{2(27+5)} = 3x - 2$
$12 - 8x + \sqrt{2(32)} = 3x - 2$
$12 - 8x + \sqrt{64} = 3x - 2$
$12 - 8x + 8 = 3x - 2$
$20 = 11x - 2$
$22 = 11x$
$x = 2$

Using the Discriminant, Finding Parts of a Parabola Worksheet 55

① Use the discriminant to determine the number of roots for the quadratic function. Then complete the square and give the coordinates of the vertex and focus, and the equation for the directrix and axis of symmetry.

$f(x) = \frac{1}{4}x^2 + 4x + 4$

$b^2 - 4ac = (4)^2 - 4(\frac{1}{4})(4) =$

$16 - 4 = 12$

The discriminant is positive, so there are two roots.

$y = \frac{1}{4}x^2 + 4x + 4$

$4y = x^2 + 16x + 16$

$4y - 16 = x^2 + 16x$

$4y - 16 + 64 = x^2 + 16x + 64$

$4y + 48 = (x + 8)^2$

$4(y + 12) = (x + 8)^2$

$h = -8$; $k = -12$; $p = 1$

Vertex: (-8, -12)

Focus: (-8, -11)

Directrix: $y = -12 - 1 \Rightarrow y = -13$

Axis of symmetry: $x = -8$

$f(x) = \frac{1}{4}x^2 - x + 6$

$b^2 - 4ac = (-1)^2 - 4(\frac{1}{4})(6) =$

$1 - 6 = -5$

The discriminant is negative, so there are no roots.

$y = \frac{1}{4}x^2 - x + 6$

$4y = x^2 - 4x + 24$

$4y - 24 = x^2 - 4x$

$4y - 24 + 4 = x^2 - 4x + 4$

$4y - 20 = (x - 2)^2$

$4(y - 5) = (x - 2)^2$

$h = 2$; $k = 5$; $p = 1$

Vertex: (2, 5)

Focus: (2, 6)

Directrix: $y = 5 - 1 \Rightarrow y = 4$

Axis of symmetry: $x = 2$

$f(x) = \frac{1}{2}x^2 + 4x + 8$

$b^2 - 4ac = (4)^2 - 4(\frac{1}{2})(8) =$

$16 - 16 = 0$

The discriminant is zero, so there is one root.

$y = \frac{1}{2}x^2 + 4x + 8$

$2y = x^2 + 8x + 16$

$2y - 16 = x^2 + 8x$

$2y - 16 + 16 = x^2 + 8x + 16$

$2y = (x + 4)^2$

$2(y - 0) = (x + 4)^2$

$h = -4$; $k = 0$; $p = \frac{1}{2}$

Vertex: $(-4, 0)$

Focus: $(-4, \frac{1}{2})$

Directrix: $y = 0 - \frac{1}{2} \Rightarrow y = -\frac{1}{2}$

Axis of symmetry: $x = -4$

$f(x) = \frac{1}{4}x^2 - x - 6$

$b^2 - 4ac = (-1)^2 - 4(\frac{1}{4})(-6) =$

$1 + 6 = 7$

The discriminant is positive, so there are two roots.

$y = \frac{1}{4}x^2 - x - 6$

$4y = x^2 - 4x - 24$

$4y + 24 = x^2 - 4x$

$4y + 24 + 4 = x^2 - 4x + 4$

$4y + 28 = (x - 2)^2$

$4(y + 7) = (x - 2)^2$

$h = 2$; $k = -7$; $p = 1$

Vertex: (2, -7)

Focus: (2, -6)

Directrix: $y = -7 - 1 \Rightarrow y = -8$

Axis of symmetry: $x = 2$

Teaching Tips, Cont.

- Tell the students that they do not have to graph the focus, directrix, or axis of symmetry when graphing quadratic inequalities.
- Refer students to the chart in the teaching box of this lesson. The chart summarizes which part of the graph should be shaded based on the symbol and whether or not the value of *a* is positive or negative. Students may select any point not on the parabola and test to determine where to shade just like they did with linear inequalities. This chart provides additional reinforcement of the correct shading. The chart is not supplied on quizzes or tests, so students must know how to determine the correct shading if they do not memorize the chart.
- Complete the Classwork exercises. Have some students work the problems on the board for the class and explain their answers. All students should work the problems in their books.
- Review for Test 11 using worksheets 51-55. These worksheets were assigned in previous lessons.

Assignments

- Complete Lesson 110, Activities 2-4.
- Worksheet 55.
- Study for Test 11 (Lessons 98-107).

Test 11

Testing Objectives

The student will:

- Sketch the graph of parabolas
- Complete the square to write functions in parabolic form
- Find the roots of equations with radicals
- Find the zeros of functions
- Find the vertex, focus, directrix, and axis of symmetry from the equation of a parabola

Materials Needed

- Test 11
- *It's College Test Prep Time!* from the Student Book
- Exploring Math through... Baseball from Student Book

Teaching Tips

- Administer Test 11, allowing the students 30-40 minutes to complete the test.
- When all students are finished taking the test, introduce *It's College Test Prep Time* from the student book. This page may be completed in class or assigned as homework.

Test 11

① Sketch the graph of each parabola. **3 points**

$f(x) = -2x^2$

x	y
0	0
1	-2
2	-8
-1	-2
-2	-8

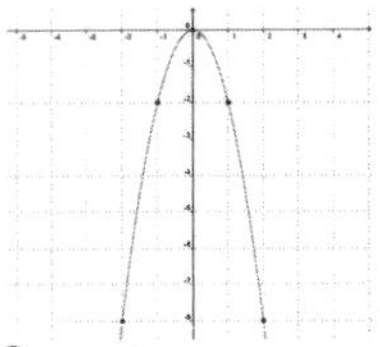

$f(x) = x^2 - 3$

x	y
0	-3
1	-2
2	1
-1	-2
-2	1

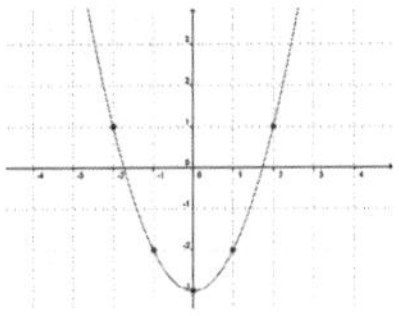

$y = 3(x+1)^2 - 4$

x	y
0	-1
1	8
-1	-4
-2	-1
-3	8

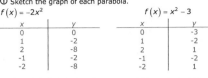

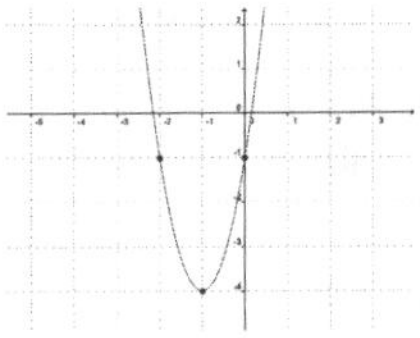

② Complete the square to write each function in parabolic form. Give the vertex (h, k) of each parabola. **6 points**

$f(x) = 3x^2 + 6x - 1$
$3x^2 + 6x - 1 = 0$
$3x^2 + 6x = 1$
$3(x^2 + 2x) = 1$
$3(x^2 + 2x + 1) = 1 + 3(1)$
$3(x+1)^2 = 1 + 3$
$3(x+1)^2 - 4 = 0$
$f(x) = 3(x+1)^2 - 4$
The vertex is (-1, -4).

$f(x) = 4x^2 - 8x + 3$
$4x^2 - 8x + 3 = 0$
$4x^2 - 8x = -3$
$4(x^2 - 2x) = -3$
$4(x^2 - 2x + 1) = -3 + 4(1)$
$4(x-1)^2 = -3 + 4$
$4(x-1)^2 - 1 = 0$
$f(x) = 4(x-1)^2 - 1$
The vertex is (1, -1).

$f(x) = 2x^2 + 16x + 13$
$2x^2 + 16x + 13 = 0$
$2x^2 + 16x = -13$
$2(x^2 + 8x) = -13$
$2(x^2 + 8x + 16) = -13 + 2(16)$
$2(x+4)^2 = -13 + 32$
$2(x+4)^2 - 19 = 0$
$f(x) = 2(x+4)^2 - 19$
The vertex is (-4, -19).

③ Find the roots. **2 points**

$\sqrt{3}x^2 + \sqrt{5}x - 6 = 0$

$x = \dfrac{-\sqrt{5} \pm \sqrt{(\sqrt{5})^2 - 4(\sqrt{3})(-6)}}{2(\sqrt{3})}$

$x = \dfrac{-\sqrt{5} \pm \sqrt{5 + 24\sqrt{3}}}{2\sqrt{3}} \cdot \dfrac{\sqrt{3}}{\sqrt{3}}$

$x = \dfrac{-\sqrt{15} \pm \sqrt{3(5 + 24\sqrt{3})}}{6} = \dfrac{-\sqrt{15} \pm \sqrt{15 + 72\sqrt{3}}}{6}$

$\sqrt{6}x^2 + \sqrt{2}x - 3 = 0$

$x = \dfrac{-\sqrt{2} \pm \sqrt{(\sqrt{2})^2 - 4(\sqrt{6})(-3)}}{2(\sqrt{6})}$

$x = \dfrac{-\sqrt{2} \pm \sqrt{2 + 12\sqrt{6}}}{2\sqrt{6}} \cdot \dfrac{\sqrt{6}}{\sqrt{6}} = \dfrac{-\sqrt{12} \pm \sqrt{6(2 + 12\sqrt{6})}}{12}$

$x = \dfrac{-2\sqrt{3} \pm \sqrt{12 + 72\sqrt{6}}}{12} = \dfrac{-2\sqrt{3} \pm \sqrt{4(3 + 18\sqrt{6})}}{12}$

$x = \dfrac{-2\sqrt{3} \pm 2\sqrt{3 + 18\sqrt{6}}}{12} = \dfrac{-\sqrt{3} \pm \sqrt{3 + 18\sqrt{6}}}{6}$

Test 11

④ Find the zeros of each function. **9 points**

$f(x) = x^2 - 5x - 2$
$0 = x^2 - 5x - 2$
$x^2 - 5x = 2$
$x^2 - 5x + \left(-\frac{5}{2}\right)^2 = 2 + \left(-\frac{5}{2}\right)^2$
$x^2 - 5x + \frac{25}{4} = \frac{8}{4} + \frac{25}{4}$
$x^2 - 5x + \frac{25}{4} = \frac{33}{4}$
$\left(x - \frac{5}{2}\right)^2 = \frac{33}{4}$
$\sqrt{\left(x - \frac{5}{2}\right)^2} = \sqrt{\frac{33}{4}}$
$x - \frac{5}{2} = \pm\frac{\sqrt{33}}{2}$
$x = \frac{5 \pm \sqrt{33}}{2}$
$f(x) = (5x+2)(3x-4)$
$5x + 2 = 0 \quad 3x - 4 = 0$
$5x = -2 \quad 3x = 4$
$x = -\frac{2}{5}, \frac{4}{3}$

$f(x) = x^2 - 2x - 7$
$0 = x^2 - 2x - 7$
$x^2 - 2x = 7$
$x^2 - 2x + \left(-\frac{2}{2}\right)^2 = 7 + \left(-\frac{2}{2}\right)^2$
$x^2 - 2x + 1 = 7 + 1$
$x^2 - 2x + 1 = 8$
$(x-1)^2 = 8$
$\sqrt{(x-1)^2} = \sqrt{8}$
$x - 1 = \pm 2\sqrt{2}$
$x = 1 \pm 2\sqrt{2}$
$f(x) = (x+13)(6x+7)$
$x + 13 = 0 \quad 6x + 7 = 0$
$x = -13 \quad 6x = -7$
$x = -13, -\frac{7}{6}$

$f(x) = x^2 + 3x - 2$
$0 = x^2 + 3x - 2$
$x^2 + 3x = 2$
$x^2 + 3x + \left(\frac{3}{2}\right)^2 = 2 + \left(\frac{3}{2}\right)^2$
$x^2 + 3x + \frac{9}{4} = \frac{8}{4} + \frac{9}{4}$
$x^2 + 3x + \frac{9}{4} = \frac{17}{4}$
$\left(x + \frac{3}{2}\right)^2 = \frac{17}{4}$
$\sqrt{\left(x + \frac{3}{2}\right)^2} = \sqrt{\frac{17}{4}}$
$x + \frac{3}{2} = \pm\frac{\sqrt{17}}{2}$
$x = \frac{-3 \pm \sqrt{17}}{2}$
$f(x) = (3x-7)(5x-12)$
$3x - 7 = 0 \quad 5x - 12 = 0$
$3x = 7 \quad 5x = 12$
$x = \frac{7}{3}, \frac{12}{5}$

⑥ Rewrite each equation in the form $4p(y-k) = (x-h)^2$. Identify the value of the variables p, k, and h, and give the coordinates for the vertex and focus, and the equations of the lines for the axis of symmetry and the directrix of the parabola. **16 points**

$y = \frac{1}{4}(x-1)^2 - 2$
$y + 2 = \frac{1}{4}(x-1)^2$
$\frac{y+2}{\frac{1}{4}} = (x-1)^2$
$4(y+2) = (x-1)^2$

$4p = 4 \Rightarrow p = 1$
$k = -2$
$h = 1$

The vertex is (1, -2).
The focus is (1, -2 + 1) = (1, -1).
The axis of symmetry is the line $x = 1$.
The directrix is the line $y = -2 - 1 \Rightarrow y = -3$.

$y = 3(x+2)^2 + 6$
$y - 6 = 3(x+2)^2$
$\frac{y-6}{3} = (x+2)^2$
$\frac{1}{3}(y-6) = (x+2)^2$

$4p = \frac{1}{3} \Rightarrow p = \frac{1}{12}$
$k = 6$
$h = -2$

The vertex is (-2, 6).
The focus is (-2, 6 + $\frac{1}{12}$) = (-2, $\frac{73}{12}$).
The axis of symmetry is the line $x = -2$.
The directrix is the line $y = 6 - \frac{1}{12} \Rightarrow y = \frac{71}{12}$.

36 points total

It's College Test Prep Time!

1. The figure below shows the graph of a quadratic function. Considering all points (x, y) on the graph, for what value of x is the value of y the least?

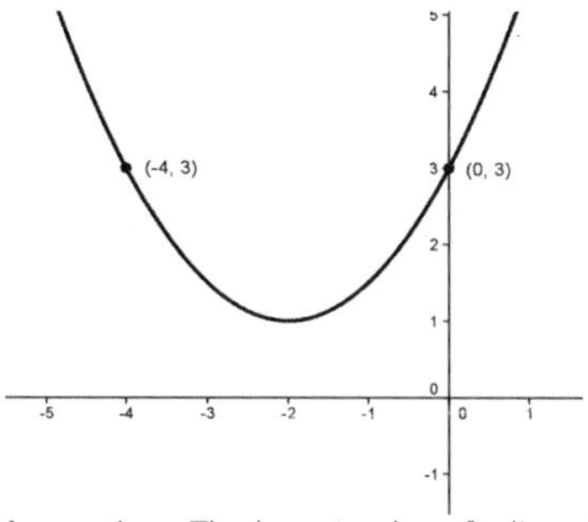

A.	-4	The lowest value of y lies at the bottom of the U, between
B.	-2	$x = -4$ and $x = 0$. The value of x halfway between these
C.	0	two is $x = -2$.
D.	1	
E.	3	

2. Given positive odd integers x and y, such that $\sqrt{x} - \sqrt{y} = 2$, which of the following is NOT a possible value of $x - y$?

A.	16	Make a list of possibilities that will equal 2: 3 – 1, 5 – 3,
B.	24	7 – 5, 9 – 7, 11 – 9, etc. Square these to find the values
C.	32	of x and y and then find the difference. 9 – 1 = 8,
D.	36	25 – 9 = 16, 49 – 25 = 24, 81 – 49 = 32, 121 – 81 = 40
E.	40	The only number that is missing is 36.

Exploring Math through... Baseball

Baseball is a game of numbers. Watch any major league game and you will see statistics for every player. Batters are concerned about their batting averages, slugging percentages, and on base percentages. Pitchers are judged based on their earned run averages. Fielders are evaluated based on their fielding percentages. All of these statistics influence strategy – from where fielders stand to which pitch a pitcher will throw to a particular batter.

Individual players are not the only part of baseball affected by math. Teams are ranked based on their winning percentage. Math is used to determine which teams play in the Division Championship Series, and ultimately in the World Series.

Even the playing field itself is a mathematical masterpiece – from the angles of home plate to the configuration of the infield. Specific dimensions must be adhered to when lining the field, placing the bases, and forming the pitching mound.

A final aspect of baseball that involves math is the equipment. Players look for a specific length-to-weight ratio when selecting a bat. Even gloves have different measurements and ratios depending on the purpose of the glove. Outfielders' gloves are longer than infielders' gloves, and catchers' gloves have more padding than fielding gloves.

Whether you are a seasoned player or the occasional fan, an understanding of the mathematics of baseball can make the game more enjoyable and understandable.

Teaching Tips, Cont.

- Have students read the Exploring Math feature for Lessons 111-120.

Assignments

- Complete *It's College Test Prep Time!*
- Read Exploring Math through... Baseball

Lesson 111

Concepts

- Money word problems
- Systems of equations
- Graphing inequalities
- Math in the real world

Learning Objectives

The student will be able to:

- Solve two-variable word problems involving money
- Apply systems of equations to real-world scenarios

Materials Needed

- Student Book, Lesson 111

Teaching Tips

- Review systems of equations. (See Lessons 51-58)
- Teach how to solve word problems involving money by setting up a chart and making a system of equations. A detailed example is provided in the teaching box.
- Tell the students that when working with all coins, the number of cents can be expressed as whole numbers. For example, the value of a dime is expressed as 10, not 0.010.
- Tell the students that if all the money in the problem is bills, they may use the value of the bill as the value in the problem. If there are bills and coins, then all values should be written in terms of the number of cents. For example, a $1 bill would be expressed as 100.

Word Problems: Money

The easiest way to tackle word problems involving money is to make a chart listing the number of each type of coin or bill, the value each type of coin or bill, and the total value of the coins and bill. Use the information in the chart to set up a system of equations and solve.

You emptied out your change jar and found a total of 123 nickels and pennies with a total value of $2.87. How many of each coin was in the jar?

Make a chart showing the information in the problem. List coin values in cents

Type of coin	Number	Total Value
Nickel	n	$5(n)$
Penny	p	$1(p)$
Total	123	287

Set up a system of equations and solve.

$$n + p = 123$$
$$-(5n + p = 287)$$
$$-4n = -164$$
$$n = 41$$

$$n + p = 123$$
$$41 + p = 123$$
$$p = 82$$

There were 41 nickels and 82 pennies.

① **Classwork**

Solve.

At the end of a bake sale, your class has a money box with $27.75. $11 is in paper bills and the remaining amount is 141 coins. Determine the number of quarters, dimes, nickels, and pennies in the cash box if there are twice as many quarters as dimes, four times as many quarters as nickels, and the remaining coins are pennies.

$27.75 - $11 = $16.75 in coins.

Let q = the number of quarters, d = the number of dimes, n = the number of nickels, and p = the number of pennies.

Type of coin	Number	Total Value
Quarter	$q = 2d = 4n$	$25(4n)$
Dime	$d = 2n$	$10(2n)$
Nickel	n	$5(n)$
Penny	p	$1(p)$
Total	141	1675

Set up a system of equations and solve.

$$25(4n) + 10(2n) + 5(n) + 1(p) = 1675$$
$$-(4n + 2n + n + p = 141)$$

$$125n + p = 1675$$
$$-(7n + p = 141)$$
$$118n = 1534 \Rightarrow n = 13$$

There are 13 nickels, 13(2) = 26 dimes, 13(4) = 52 quarters and 141 - 13 - 26 - 52 = 50 pennies.

Activities

② Solve.

You have saved a jar full of loose change to use on your next family vacation. There are 953 coins in the jar. If the mixture of pennies, nickels, dimes, and quarters totals $68.75, how many of each coin are in the jar if there are twice times as many pennies as nickels, three times as many dimes as nickels, and the remaining coins are quarters?

Type of coin	Number	Total Value
Quarter	q	$25(q)$
Dime	$d = 3n$	$10(3n)$
Nickel	n	$5(n)$
Penny	$p = 2n$	$1(2n)$
Total	953	6875

Set up a system of equations and solve.

$$25(q) + 10(3n) + 5(n) + 1(2n) = 6875$$
$$-(q + 3n + n + 2n = 953)$$

$$q + 6n = 953$$
$$-(25q + 37n = 6875) \Rightarrow$$

$$25q + 150n = 23825$$
$$-(25q + 37n = 6875)$$
$$113n = 16950$$
$$n = 150$$

There are 150 nickels, 150(3) = 450 dimes, 150(2) = 300 pennies and 953 - 150 - 450 - 300 = 53 quarters.

③ Solve.
A youth baseball tournament charges \$5 for adults and \$2 for students to watch the games. At the end of one day, the ticket booth had collected 345 bills for a total of \$1500. The number of \$20 bills was equal to the number of \$5 bills and was twice the number of \$10 bills. The remaining bills were \$1 bills. How many of each type of bill did the ticket booth have?
Let w = the number of \$20 bills, t = the number of \$10 bills, f = the number of \$5 bills, and n = the number of \$1 bills.

Type of bill	Number	Total Value
\$20	$w = f = 2t$	$20(2t)$
\$10	t	$10(t)$
\$5	$f = 2t$	$5(2t)$
\$1	n	$1(n)$
Total	345	1500

Set up a system of equations and solve.

$$20(2t)+10(t)+5(2t)+1(n)=1500$$
$$-\ (2t + t + 2t + n = 345)$$

$$60t+n=1500$$
$$-(5t+n=345)$$
$$55t=1155$$
$$t=21$$

There are 21 tens, 21(2) = 42 twenties, 21(2) = 42 fives and 345 - 21 - 42 - 42 = 240 ones.
If there were 450 fans at the game, how many were adults?

Let a = the number of adults and s = the number of students.

$$5a+2s=1500$$
$$a+s=450$$

$$5a+2s=1500$$
$$2a+2s=900$$
$$3a=600$$
$$a=200$$

There were 200 adults and 450 - 200 = 250 students.
④ Graph the inequalities.

$y > -5x^2 + 2$
The symbol is > and a is negative, so the graph will be shaded outside the parabola.

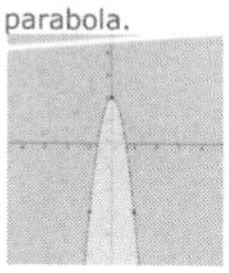

$y \le 5x^2 - 1$
The symbol is ≤ and a is positive, so the graph will be shaded outside the parabola.

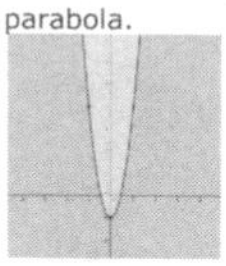

$y > 5x^2 - 2$
The symbol is > and a is positive, so the graph will be shaded inside the parabola.

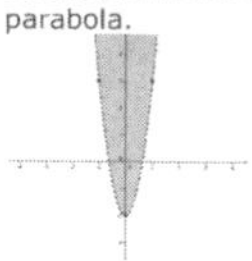

Teaching Tips, Cont.

- Emphasize the importance of converting to the same unit — either all dollars or all cents. The problems will be easier to work if dollars are converted to cents rather than coins converted to dollars and expressed as a decimal.
- Complete the Classwork exercise. Have one student work the problem on the board for the class and explain the answer. All students should work the problem in their books.

Assignment

- Complete Lesson 111, Activities 2-4.

Lesson 112

Concepts

- Interest word problems
- Simple interest
- Math in the real world

Learning Objectives

The student will be able to:

- Calculate the amount of simple interest earned when given the initial principle, the interest rate, and the amount of time invested
- Calculate the interest rate when given the initial principle, the amount of interest earned, and the amount of time invested
- Calculate the initial principle required to obtain a given amount of interest at a given rate over a given amount of time
- Calculate the amount of time it will take for a given amount of money to earn a given amount of interest in a given amount of time

Materials Needed

- Student Book, Lesson 112
- Worksheet 56

Teaching Tips

➢ Have students complete Worksheet 56 in class. This may be for added practice of earlier topics or graded as a quiz, if desired.

➢ Introduce the concept of earning interest. This should appeal to students, especially those who are starting to think about saving for college.

➢ Tell the students there are two types of interest: simple interest and compound interest. This lesson will focus on simple interest.

Word Problems: Interest

There are two different ways that interest can be calculated: simple interest and compound interest. Simple interest is calculated based on the principle (amount of money invested or borrowed) only. Compound interest is calculated based on the accrued value of principle and interest over time. This lesson will focus on simple interest.

The amount of interest (i) depends on three things: the amount of the principle (p), the interest rate (r), and the amount of time (t) the principle is invested or borrowed, in years.

The easiest way to solve interest problems is to make a chart showing the value of each. Then use the formula for simple interest, $i = prt$ to solve for the missing variable.

It is important to note that the interest rate is given as a percent. You must convert the percent to a decimal by dividing by 100 before inserting the value in the formula.

How much money must you invest at 4% if you want to earn $35 interest at the end of 1 year?

i	*p*	*r*	*t*
$35	*p*	0.04	1

Substitute the values into the formula.

$$i = prt$$
$$\$35 = p(0.04)(1)$$
$$\$875 = p$$

You must invest $875 at 4% to earn $35 interest.

① Classwork

Solve.

How much money must you invest at 3% if you want to earn $60 at the end of 2 years?

i	*p*	*r*	*t*
$60	*p*	0.03	2

Substitute the values into the formula.

$$i = prt$$
$$\$60 = p(0.03)(2)$$
$$\$1000 = p$$

You must invest $1000 at 3% to earn $60 interest.

What is the minimum interest rate you must have for $5000 invested for 4 years to be worth at least $6000?

The minimum amount of interest you must earn is $6000 – $5000 = $1000

i	*p*	*r*	*t*
$1000	$5000	*r*	4

Substitute the values into the formula.

$$i \le prt$$
$$\$1000 \le \$5000(r)(4)$$
$$0.05 \le r$$

You must invest $5000 at 5% to earn $1000 interest in 4 years.

Activities

② Solve.

How long will it take $500 invested at 2.5% to earn $75?

i	*p*	*r*	*t*
$75	500	0.025	*t*

Substitute the values into the formula.

$$i = prt$$
$$\$75 = \$500(0.025)(t)$$
$$6 = t$$

You must invest $500 at 2.5% for 6 years to earn $75 interest.

③ Solve.

How much money must you invest at 1.75% if you want to earn $350 at the end of 10 years?

i	*p*	*r*	*t*
$350	*p*	0.0175	10

Substitute the values into the formula.

$$i = prt$$
$$\$350 = p(0.0175)(10)$$
$$\$2000 = p$$

You must invest $2000 at 1.75% to earn $350 interest.

What is the minimum interest rate you must have for $25,000 invested for 25 years to be worth at least $100,000?

The minimum amount of interest you must earn is $100,000 – $25,000 = $75,000

i	*p*	*r*	*t*
$75,000	$25,000	*r*	25

Substitute the values into the formula.

$$i \le prt$$
$$\$75{,}000 \le \$25{,}000(r)(25)$$
$$0.12 \le r$$

You must invest $25,000 at 12% to earn $75,000 interest in 25 years.

④ Solve.

The bases on a little league field are 60 feet apart. The four bases form a square with each side 60 feet long. The pitching rubber is located on the diagonal of the square between home plate and second base, 46 feet from home plate. How far is the pitching rubber from second base? (Hint: Draw a diagram and use the Pythagorean Theorem.)

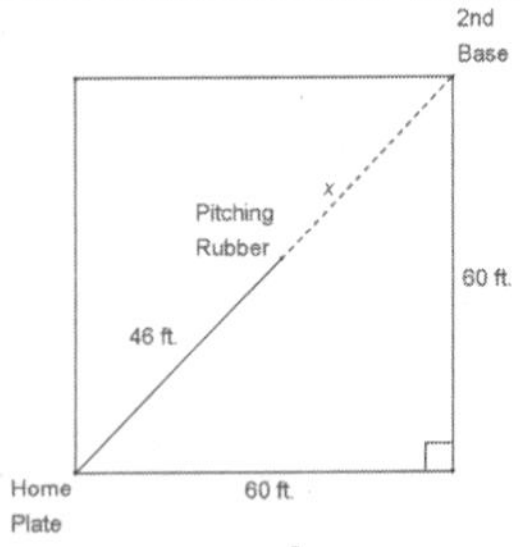

$$60^2 + 60^2 = (46 + x)^2$$
$$3600 + 3600 = 2116 + 92x + x^2$$
$$x^2 + 92x - 5084 = 0$$

Use the quadratic formula.

$$x = \frac{-92 \pm \sqrt{92^2 - 4(1)(-5084)}}{2(1)}$$
$$x = \frac{-92 \pm \sqrt{8464 + 20336}}{2}$$
$$x = \frac{-92 \pm \sqrt{28800}}{2}$$
$$x = \frac{-92 \pm \sqrt{120(120)(2)}}{2}$$
$$x = \frac{-92 \pm 120\sqrt{2}}{2}$$
$$x = -46 \pm 60\sqrt{2}$$

The distance cannot be negative, so the answer is $x = -46 + 60\sqrt{2}$ feet.

If students express their answer as a decimal, it is 38.85 feet.

Parts of a Parabola, Graphing Inequalities Worksheet 56

① Complete the square and give the coordinates of the vertex and focus, and the equation for the directrix and axis of symmetry.

$f(x) = \frac{1}{4}x^2 + 4x - 1$

$y = \frac{1}{4}x^2 + 4x - 1$

$4y = x^2 + 16x - 4$

$4y + +4 = x^2 + 16x$

$4y + 4 + 64 = x^2 + 16x + 64$

$4y + 68 = (x + 8)^2$

$4(y + 17) = (x + 8)^2$

$h = -8$; $k = -17$; $p = 1$
Vertex: (-8, -17)
Focus: (-8, -16)
Directrix: $y = -17 - 1 \Rightarrow y = -18$
Axis of symmertry: $x = -8$

$f(x) = \frac{1}{4}x^2 - x + 3$

$y = \frac{1}{4}x^2 - x + 3$

$4y = x^2 - 4x + 12$

$4y - 12 = x^2 - 4x$

$4y - 12 + 4 = x^2 - 4x + 4$

$4y - 8 = (x - 2)^2$

$4(y - 2) = (x - 2)^2$

$h = 2$; $k = 2$; $p = 1$
Vertex: (2, 2)
Focus: (2, 3)
Directrix: $y = 2 - 1 \Rightarrow y = 1$
Axis of symmertry: $x = 2$

② Sketch the graph of each inequality.

$y \geq -x^2 + 2x - 2$

The symbol is $\geq$ and a is negative, so the graph will be shaded outside the parabola.

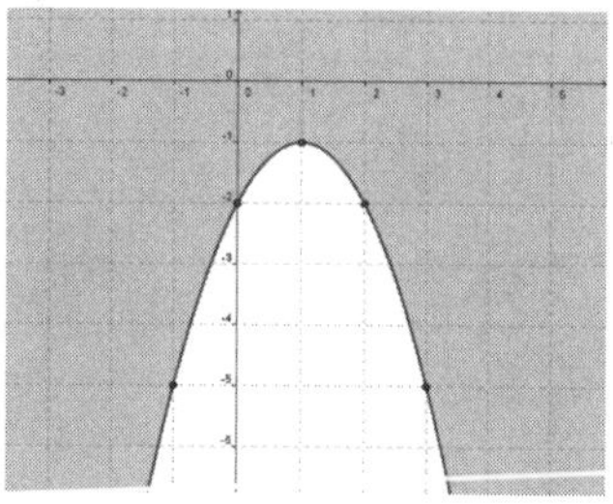

$y < -x^2 + 2x - 1$

The symbol is < and a is negative, so the graph will be shaded inside the parabola.

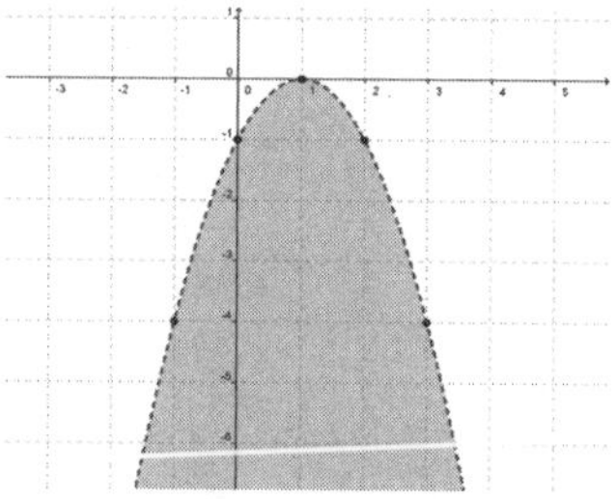

Teaching Tips, Cont.

- Tell the students there are three things that influence the amount of interest that is earned: the amount of principle (the money invested), the interest rate, and the amount of time the money is invested.
- Teach how to calculate simple interest from the teaching box. For students who took the Horizons Pre-Algebra course, this information is review material.
- Complete the Classwork exercises. Have some students work the problems on the board for the class and explain their answers. All students should work the problems in their books.

Assignment

- Complete Lesson 112, Activities 2-4.

Lesson 113

Concepts

- Motion word problems
- Quadratic formula
- Math in the real world

Learning Objectives

The student will be able to:

- Solve real-world problems involving different rates of motion
- Apply the distance formula to solve word problems involving rates of motion

Materials Needed

- Student Book, Lesson 113
- Worksheet 57

Teaching Tips

➢ Introduce the distance formula from the teaching box. The students should memorize this formula. It will be used during this course, and is a standard formula in basic physics courses.

➢ Teach how to solve word problems involving motion from the teaching box.

➢ Tell the students they must make sure the same units are used consistently throughout the problem.

Word Problems: Motion

Motion problems involve a distance traveled (d), a rate of travel (r), and time (t) it takes to travel the given distance. The formula used for motion problems is $d = rt$.

When working with motion problems, it is often helpful to draw a diagram to illustrate the problem before you set up a chart to solve it.

Two runners leave the starting line at the same time. One runner has an average speed of 11 feet per second. The other runner has an average speed of 10 feet per second. If the race is 1 mile long, how far will the second runner have gone when the first runner crosses the finish line? (1 mile = 5280 feet)

Draw a diagram.

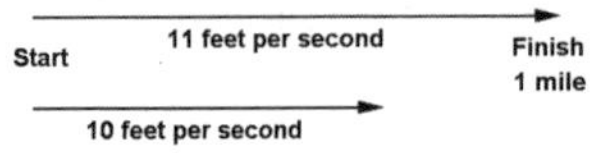

Make a chart of the known information.

Runner	d	r	t
First	5280 ft	11 ft/s	t
Second	10t	10 ft/s	t

Solve for t using the information from the first runner.

$d = rt$

$5280 \text{ ft.} = (11 \text{ ft./s})(t)$

$\frac{5280 \text{ ft.}}{11 \text{ ft./s}} = t$

$480 \text{ s} = t$

It took the first runner 480 seconds to run the race. Substitute this for t in the second runner's distance to find out how far the second runner ran in this time.

$d = rt$

$d = (10 \text{ ft./s})(480 \text{ s})$

$d = 4800 \text{ ft.}$

The second runner had finished 4800 feet of the race when the first runner crossed the finish line.

① Classwork

Solve.

Two baseball players are positioned 100 feet apart in the outfield. Player A can sprint 25 feet per second, and player B can sprint 24 feet per second. If the two players start running for a fly ball at the same time and collide on the field, how far, to the nearest hundredth of a foot, did player B run? (Assume all running was in a straight line.)

Let a = the distance player A ran and b = the distance player B ran.

$a + b = 100 \text{ ft.}$

$a = 100 \text{ ft.} - b$

$a = 25t$ $\qquad$ $b = 24t$

$100 - b = 25t$ $\qquad$ $t = \frac{b}{24}$

$t = \frac{100-b}{25}$

$\frac{100-b}{25} = \frac{b}{24}$

$24(100 - b) = 25b$

$2400 - 24b = 25b$

$2400 = 49b$

$b = 48.98 \text{ ft.}$

How long, to the nearest hundredth of a second, did the players run before the collision?

$b = 24t$

$48.98 \text{ ft.} = (24 \text{ ft./s.})t$

$t = 2.04 \text{ s.}$

Activities

② Solve.

A baseball player runs 25 feet per second when trying to steal second base. If he has a 10-ft. lead off first base, how long will it take him to run the remaining 80 feet to second base? (Assume the time for sliding is included in the run speed.)

$80 \text{ ft.} = 25 \text{ ft./s.}(t) \Rightarrow t = 3.2 \text{ s.}$

If the catcher throws the ball from home plate to second base at 85 miles per hour when the runner is 20 feet away from second base, will the ball arrive in time to get the runner out? (1 mile = 5280 feet; 1 hour = 3600 seconds)

Let x = the distance from home to second base.

$90^2 + 90^2 = x^2$

$8100 + 8100 = x^2$

$16200 = x^2$

$x = \sqrt{16200} = \sqrt{(100)(81)(2)}$

$x = 90\sqrt{2}$

Time for the ball to get to second base:

$90\sqrt{2} \text{ ft.} = \frac{85 \text{ mi.}}{1 \text{ hr.}}\left(\frac{5280 \text{ ft.}}{1 \text{ mi.}}\right)\left(\frac{1 \text{ hr.}}{3600 \text{ s.}}\right)(t) \Rightarrow t = 1.02 \text{ s.}$

Time for the runner to run 20 feet.

$20 \text{ ft.} = \frac{25 \text{ ft.}}{1 \text{ s.}}(t) \Rightarrow t = 0.8 \text{ s.}$

The ball will not arrive in time.

③ Solve.

The distance from the pitcher's mound to home plate on a major league field is 60.5 feet. If a pitcher throws a 95-mile-per-hour fast ball, how long, to the nearest hundredth of a second, will it take the ball to reach home plate once it leaves the pitcher's hand? (1 mile = 5280 feet; 1 hour = 3600 seconds)

Convert the ball's speed to feet per second.

$\frac{95 \text{ mi.}}{1 \text{ hr.}} \cdot \frac{5280 \text{ ft.}}{1 \text{ mi.}} \cdot \frac{1 \text{ hr.}}{3600 \text{ s.}} = \frac{501{,}600 \text{ ft.}}{3600 \text{ s.}}$

$= \frac{418}{3}$ feet per second

$d = rt$

$60.5 \text{ ft.} = \frac{418}{3} \text{ ft./s.}(t)$

$\frac{121}{2} \text{ ft.} = \frac{418}{3} \text{ ft./s.}(t)$

$0.43 = t$

The ball will reach home plate in 0.43 seconds.

The bases on a major league field are 90 feet apart. The four bases form a square with each side 90 feet long. The pitcher's mound is located on the diagonal of the square between home plate and second base, 60.5 feet from home plate. How far is the pitcher's mound from second base?

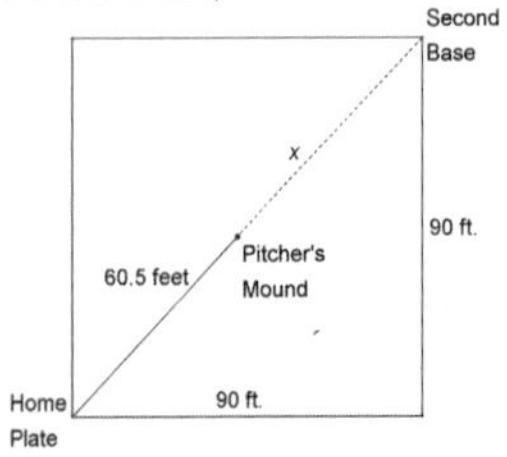

$90^2 + 90^2 = (60.5 + x)^2$

$8100 + 8100 = 3660.25 + 121x + x^2$

$x^2 + 121x - 12539.75 = 0$

Use the quadratic formula.

$x = \frac{-121 \pm \sqrt{121^2 - 4(1)(-12539.75)}}{2(1)}$

$x = \frac{-121 \pm \sqrt{14641 + 50159}}{2}$

$x = \frac{-121 \pm \sqrt{64800}}{2}$

$x = \frac{-121 \pm \sqrt{32400(2)}}{2} = \frac{-121 \pm 180\sqrt{2}}{2}$

The distance cannot be negative, so the answer is $x = \frac{-121 + 180\sqrt{2}}{2}$ feet.

If students express their answer as a decimal, it is 66.78 feet.

Money, Investment, and Motion Problems Worksheet 57

① Solve.

You have saved a jar full of loose change to use on your next family vacation. There are 1379 coins in the jar. If the mixture of pennies, nickels, dimes, and quarters totals $90.50, how many of each coin are in the jar if there are twice as many pennies as nickels, three times as many dimes as nickels, and the remaining coins are quarters?

Type of coin	Number	Total Value
Quarter	q	$25(q)$
Dime	$d = 3n$	$10(3n)$
Nickel	n	$5(n)$
Penny	$p = 2n$	$1(2n)$
Total	1379	9050

$$q + 6n = 1379 \qquad 25q + 150n = 34475$$
$$-(25q + 37n = 9050) \Rightarrow -(25q + 37n = 9050)$$
$$113n = 25425$$
$$n = 225$$

There are 225 nickels, 225(3) = 675 dimes, 225(2) = 450 pennies and 1379 - 225 - 675 - 450 = 29 quarters.

How long will it take $7500 invested at 5% to earn $750?

i	p	r	t
$750	$7500	0.05	t

Substitute the values into the formula.

$$i = prt$$
$$\$750 = \$7500(0.05)(t)$$
$$2 = t$$

You must invest $7500 at 5% for 2 years to earn $750 interest.

If the catcher throws the ball from home plate to second base at 90 miles per hour when the runner is 25 feet away from second base, will the ball arrive in time to get the runner out if the runner has an average speed of 23 feet per second? The bases on the field are 90 feet apart and the four bases form a square. Round to the nearest hundredths.

Let x = the distance from home to second base.

$$90^2 + 90^2 = x^2$$
$$8100 + 8100 = x^2$$
$$16200 = x^2$$
$$x = \sqrt{16200} = \sqrt{(100)(81)(2)}$$
$$x = 90\sqrt{2}$$

Time for the ball to get to second base:

$$90\sqrt{2}\text{ ft.} = \frac{90\text{ mi.}}{1\text{ hr.}}\left(\frac{5280\text{ ft.}}{1\text{ mi.}}\right)\left(\frac{1\text{ hr.}}{3600\text{ s.}}\right)(t) \Rightarrow t = 0.96\text{ s.}$$

Time for the runner to run 25 feet.

$$25\text{ ft.} = \frac{23\text{ ft.}}{1\text{ s.}}(t) \Rightarrow t = 1.09\text{ s.}$$

The ball will arrive in time.

Teaching Tips, Cont.

- Ask the students what will happen if time is expressed in minutes for one part of the problem and seconds in a different part of the problem. (They will get the wrong answer!)
- Complete the Classwork exercises. Have some students work the problems on the board for the class and explain their answers. All students should work the problems in their books.

Assignments

- Complete Lesson 113, Activities 2-3.
- Worksheet 57.

Lesson 114

Concepts
- Mixture problems
- Math in the real world

Learning Objectives
The student will be able to:
- Solve real-world problems involving mixtures
- Write algebraic equations to represent adding and removing mixtures

Materials Needed
- Student Book, Lesson 114

Teaching Tips
- Review converting percents to decimals as necessary. Students in Algebra 1 are expected to know how to do this already and it is not taught past the Pre-Algebra book. For those who need the review, remind them that the word percent means hundredth. For example, 25% is 25 hundredths, or 0.25, of the whole. To convert a percent to a decimal, divide the number by 100. To convert a decimal to a percent, multiply the decimal by 100.
- Teach solving mixture problems from the teaching box. Tell the students to convert all percents to decimals before doing the calculations.

Word Problems: Adding and Removing Mixtures

The concentration of a mixture changes whenever you add something to it or remove something from it. The easiest way to solve mixture problems is to make a chart with all the information you have.

You have mixed up 50 ounces of a solution that is 15% salt. You then realized that your science project needs a solution that is 20% salt. How many ounces of salt do you need to add to your solution to make it the proper concentration?

Make a chart with everything you know from the problem. The concentration of the salt you are adding is expressed as 1 because you are adding 100% salt. Change the percent to a decimal to get 1 as the concentration.

	Concen.	Amount	Totals
Start	0.15	50 oz.	0.15(50)
Add	1	x	x
Final	0.20	50 + x	0.2(50 + x)

Multiply the concentration (percent expressed as a decimal) by the amount in each row to get the row totals. The *totals* column forms the algebraic equation.

$0.15(50) + x = 0.2(50 + x)$

$7.5 + x = 10 + 0.2x$

$75 + 10x = 100 + 2x$

$8x = 25$

$x = \frac{25}{8}$ or $3\frac{1}{8}$ oz.

When you are removing part of a solution, you set the chart up the same way, except you would subtract instead of add.

① Classwork

Solve.

A 54-gram serving of cereal is 24% sugar. If you add 125 grams of milk that is 5% sugar and sprinkle 6 grams of sugar on top, what is the resulting concentration of sugar? Express your answer to the nearest tenth of a percent.

	Concen.	Amount	Totals
Start	0.24	54 g	0.24(54)
Add	.05	125 g	0.05(125)
Add	1.00	6 g	1.00(6)
Final	x	185	x(185)

$0.24(54) + 0.05(125) + 1.00(6) = 185x$

$12.96 + 6.25 + 6 = 185x$

$25.21 = 185x$

$x = 0.136 = 13.6\%$.

A 40-ounce canister of mixed nuts is 40% peanuts. If you remove 10 ounces of peanuts from the mix, what percent of the remaining mix is peanuts?

	Concen.	Amount	Totals
Start	0.40	40 oz.	0.40(40)
Remove	1.00	10 oz.	1.00(10)
Final	x	30 oz.	30x

$0.40(40) - 1.00(10) = 30x$

$16 - 10 = 30x$

$6 = 30x$

$x = 0.2 = 20\%$

Activities

② Solve.

A baseball team of 25 players is 40% pitchers. After the team added 15 players, 37.5% of the team were pitchers. What percent of the 15 added players were pitchers? Express your answer to the nearest tenth of a percent.

	Percent	Players	Total pitchers
Start	0.40	25	0.40(25)
Add	x	15	15x
Final	0.375	40	0.375(40)

$0.40(25) + 15x = 0.375(40)$

$10 + 15x = 15$

$15x = 5$

$x = 0.333 = 33.3\%$

③ Solve.

You have mixed up 40 ounces of a solution that is 20% salt. You then realized that your science project needs a solution that is 15% salt. How many ounces of water do you need to add to your solution to make it the proper concentration? Hint: Water is a 0% concentration of salt.

	Concen.	Amount	Totals
Start	0.20	40 oz.	0.20(40)
Add	0	x	0
Final	0.15	40 + x	0.15(40 + x)

$0.20(40) + 0 = 0.15(40 + x)$

$8 = 6 + 0.15x$

$2 = .15x$

$200 = 15x$

$x = \frac{200}{15} = \frac{40}{.3}$ or $13\frac{1}{3}$ oz.

A 1-ounce box of caramel-coated popcorn and peanuts is 30% peanuts by weight. If the ballparks want a package that is 50% peanuts by weight with the same amount of popcorn, how many ounces of peanuts, to the nearest hundredth of an ounce, must be added to the mix to make it 50% peanuts by weight? What will be the new weight of the ballpark mixture?

	Concen.	Amount	Totals
Start	0.30	1 oz.	0.30(1)
Add	1.00	x	x
Final	0.50	1 + x	0.50(1 + x)

$0.30(1) + x = 0.50(1 + x)$

$0.30 + x = 0.50 + 0.50x$

$0.50x = .20$

$x = 0.4$

The ballpark mix will have 0.4 ounces of peanuts added, making the mixture 1.4 ounces.

④ Solve.

Find the values of x, y, and z in the diagram of a major league baseball field below to find the distance from the pitcher's mound to first base. Round the value of each variable to the nearest hundredth. Which is a shorter throw – from the pitcher's mound to home plate or from the pitcher's mound to first base?

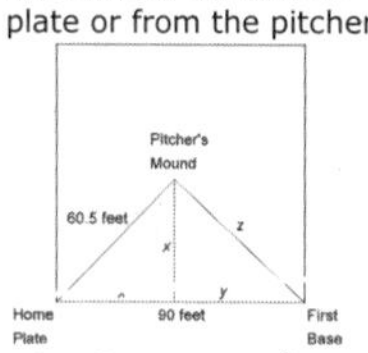

$x^2 + x^2 = (60.5 \text{ ft.})^2$

$2x^2 = 3660.25$ sq. ft.

$x^2 = 1830.125$ sq. ft.

$x = 42.78$ ft.

$y = 90 \text{ ft.} - x$

$y = 90 \text{ ft.} - 42.78 \text{ ft.}$

$y = 47.22$ ft.

$x^2 + y^2 - z^2$

$(42.78 \text{ ft.})^2 + (47.22 \text{ ft.})^2 = z^2$

$1830.1284 \text{ sq. ft.} + 2229.7284 \text{ sq. ft.} = z^2$

$4059.8568 \text{ sq. ft.} = z^2$

$z = 63.72$ ft.

The distance from the pitcher's mound to home is shorter.

Teaching Tips, Cont.

- Use the sample problem to show the students how to set up a chart with the information given and the information requested. If the chart is set up correctly, it will automatically provide the correct equation to solve.
- Complete the Classwork exercises. Have some students work the problems on the board for the class and explain their answers. All students should work the problems in their books.

Assignment

- Complete Lesson 114, Activities 2-4.

Lesson 115

Concepts

- Mixture problems
- Completing the square
- Parabolic form
- Math in the real world

Learning Objectives

The student will be able to:

- Solve real-world problems involving mixtures
- Write algebraic equations to represent substituting and combining mixtures

Materials Needed

- Student Book, Lesson 115
- Worksheet 58

Teaching Tips

- Have students complete Worksheet 58 in class. This may be for added practice of earlier topics, or graded as a quiz, if desired.
- Review adding and subtracting mixtures. (See Lesson 114)
- Tell the students that so far they have learned to add a substance to an existing mixture and remove a substance from an existing mixture. In this lesson they will learn to combine two different mixtures to obtain a different concentration, and to substitute a portion of a mixture with an equal amount of a different mixture to obtain a desired concentration.

Word Problems: Substituting and Combining Mixtures

When solving problems that involve mixing two different substances, or removing part of one substance to make room for another, make a chart to summarize what you are looking for.

You have a 56-ounce container full of mixed nuts that costs 22 cents per ounce. You want to add chocolate candies that cost 17 cents per ounce to make a snack mix that costs 20 cents per ounce. If your snack mix must fit in the 56-ounce container, how many ounces of nuts must be replaced with chocolate?

Make a chart with all the information you know.

	Start	Remove	Add	Finish
Cost	22	22	17	20
Amount	56	x	x	56
Total	22(56)	$22x$	$17x$	20(56)

The Total boxes are the products of the boxes above them. This line becomes the formula for solving the problem.

$22(56) - 22x + 17x = 20(56)$

$1232 - 5x = 1120$

$5x = 112$

$x = 22.4$

You must replace 22.4 ounces of mixed nuts with chocolate pieces to make a snack mix that costs 20 cents per ounce.

① **Classwork**

Solve.

The instructions for your science experiment say to use 500mL of a 20% solution of an acid, but you only have a 10% solution and a 30% solution on hand. How much of each solution should you mix to make 500mL of a 20% solution?

mL	% acid	Total
x	0.10	$0.1x$
$500 - x$	0.30	$0.3(500 - x)$
500 mL	0.20	500(0.2)

$0.1x + 0.3(500 - x) = 500(0.2)$

$0.1x + 150 - 0.3x = 100$

$-0.2x = -50$

$x = 250$

Your solution should contain 250mL of the 10% solution and 500 - 250 = 250mL of the 30% solution.

Activities

② Solve.

Granola costs $4 per pound and chocolate candies cost $5.50 per pound. How many pounds of each must be mixed to obtain 10 pounds of a mixture that costs $4.50 per pound? Round your answers to the nearest tenth of a pound.

Pounds	Cost	Total
x	4	$4x$
$10 - x$	5.50	$5.50(10 - x)$
10	4.50	10(4.50)

$4x + 5.50(10 - x) = 10(4.50)$

$4x + 55 - 5.5x = 45$

$-1.5x = -10$

$x = 6\frac{2}{3}$

Your solution should contain $6\frac{2}{3}$ pounds of granola and $10 - 6\frac{2}{3} = 3\frac{1}{3}$ pounds of chocolate candies.

③ Solve.

A 50-pound bag of fertilizer is 15% phosphorus. How much must be substituted with fertilizer that is 60% phosphorus to obtain 50 pounds of fertilizer that is 25% phosphorus? Round your answer to the nearest tenth of a pound.

	Start	Remove	Add	Finish
Concentration	0.15	0.15	0.60	0.25
Amount	50	x	x	50
Total	0.15(50)	$0.15x$	$0.60x$	0.25(50)

$0.15(50) - 0.15x + 0.60x = 0.25(50)$

$7.5 + 0.45x = 12.5$

$0.45x = 5$

$x = 11.1$

You must substitute 11.1 pounds of fertilizer.

How many pounds of fertilizer that is 60% phosphorus must be added to 50 pounds of a fertilizer mixture that is 15% phosphorus to obtain a mixture that is 25% phosphorus without removing any of the original fertilizer mixture? Round your answer to the nearest tenth of a pound.

	Concen.	Amount	Totals
Start	0.15	50 lb.	0.15(50)
Add	0.60	x	$0.60x$
Final	0.25	$50 + x$	$0.25(50 + x)$

$0.15(50) + 0.60x = 0.25(50 + x)$

$7.5 + 0.60x = 12.5 + 0.25x$

$0.35x = 5$

$x = 14.3$

You must add 14.3 pounds of fertilizer that is 60% phosphorus to 50 pounds of fertilizer that is 15% phosphorus to make a mixture that is 25% phosphorus.

④ Complete the square to write each function in parabolic form.

$f(x) = 4x^2 + 12x + 7$

$4x^2 + 12x + 7 = 0$

$4x^2 + 12x = -7$

$4(x^2 + 3x) = -7$

$4(x^2 + 3x + \frac{9}{4}) = -7 + 4(\frac{9}{4})$

$4(x + \frac{3}{2})^2 = -7 + 9$

$4(x + \frac{3}{2})^2 - 2 = 0$

$f(x) = 4(x + \frac{3}{2})^2 - 2$

$f(x) = 3x^2 - 18x + 5$

$3x^2 - 18x + 5 = 0$

$3x^2 - 18x = -5$

$3(x^2 - 6x) = -5$

$3(x^2 - 6x + 9) = -5 + 3(9)$

$3(x - 3)^2 = -5 + 27$

$3(x - 3)^2 - 22 = 0$

$f(x) = 3(x - 3)^2 - 22$

$f(x) = 2x^2 + 6x + 15$

$2x^2 + 6x + 15 = 0$

$2x^2 + 6x = -15$

$2(x^2 + 3x) = -15$

$2(x^2 + 3x + \frac{9}{4}) = -15 + 2(\frac{9}{4})$

$2(x + \frac{3}{2})^2 = -15 + \frac{9}{2}$

$2(x + \frac{3}{2})^2 + \frac{21}{2} = 0$

$f(x) = 2(x + \frac{3}{2})^2 + \frac{21}{2}$

Money, Investment, and Motion Problems Worksheet 58

① Solve.

You have saved a jar full of loose change to use on your next family vacation. There are 839 coins in the jar. If the mixture of pennies, nickels, dimes, and quarters totals $60.59, how many of each coin are in the jar if there are twice as many pennies as nickels, three times as many dimes as nickels, and the remaining coins are quarters?

Type of coin	Number	Total Value
Quarter	q	$25(q)$
Dime	$d = 3n$	$10(3n)$
Nickel	n	$5(n)$
Penny	$p = 2n$	$1(2n)$
Total	839	6059

$$q + 6n = 839 \qquad 25q + 150n = 20975$$
$$-(25q + 37n = 6059) \Rightarrow -(25q + 37n = 6059)$$
$$113n = 14916$$
$$n = 132$$

There are 132 nickels, 132(3) = 396 dimes, 132(2) = 264 pennies and 847 - 132 - 396 - 272 = 47 quarters.

How long will it take $1500 invested at 2.5% to earn $1500?

i	p	r	t
$1500	$1500	0.025	t

Substitute the values into the formula.

$$i = prt$$
$$\$1500 = \$1500(0.025)(t)$$
$$40 = t$$

You must invest $1500 at 2.5% for 40 years to earn $1500 interest.

If the catcher throws the ball from home plate to second base at 95 miles per hour when the runner is 30 feet away from second base, will the ball arrive in time to get the runner out if the runner has an average speed of 25 feet per second? The bases on the field are 90 feet apart and the four bases form a square. Round to the nearest hundredths.

Let x = the distance from home to second base.

$$90^2 + 90^2 = x^2$$
$$8100 + 8100 = x^2$$
$$16200 = x^2$$
$$x = \sqrt{16200} = \sqrt{(100)(81)(2)}$$
$$x = 90\sqrt{2}$$

Time for the ball to get to second base:

$$90\sqrt{2}\text{ ft.} = \frac{95\text{ mi.}}{1\text{ hr.}}\left(\frac{5280\text{ ft.}}{1\text{ mi.}}\right)\left(\frac{1\text{ hr.}}{3600\text{ s.}}\right)(t) \Rightarrow t = 0.91\text{ s.}$$

Time for the runner to run 20 feet.

$$30\text{ ft.} = \frac{25\text{ ft.}}{1\text{ s.}}(t) \Rightarrow t = 1.2\text{ s.}$$

The ball will arrive in time.

Teaching Tips, Cont.

- Teach solving mixture problems from the teaching box. Tell the students to convert all percents to decimals before doing the calculations.
- Use the sample problem to show the students how to set up a chart with the information given and the information requested. If the chart is set up correctly, it will automatically provide the correct equation to solve.
- Complete the Classwork exercise. Have one student work the problem on the board for the class and explain the answer. All students should work the problem in their books.

Assignment

- Complete Lesson 115, Activities 2-4.

Lesson 116

Concepts
- Ratios
- Zeros of functions
- Equations with radicals
- Math in the real world

Learning Objectives
The student will be able to:
- Solve real-world problems involving ratios
- Set up a proportion and write an equation to solve ratio problems

Materials Needed
- Student Book, Lesson 116

Teaching Tips
- Review ratios and proportions as necessary. Students in Algebra 1 are expected to know how to do this already and it is not taught past the Pre-Algebra book. For those who need the review, remind them that a ratio is a fraction and a proportion is two fractions that are set equal to each other. The important thing to remember is that the units of the numerators must be the same and the units of the denominators must be the same.

- Teach how to solve word problems involving ratios from the teaching box. Make sure all students understand and follow the five steps given in the lesson.

Word Problems: Ratios

Some word problems use ratios to show the relationship between two or more things. When solving problems involving ratios, follow these steps.

- Assign a variable to each thing.
- Write all ratios in the form of a fraction.
- Label all units in all numerators and denominators. Make sure the same things appear consistently throughout the problem in the numerators and denominators.
- Make sure all units are the same. Convert as necessary.
- Cross multiply and solve for the variable.

A game has 252 pegs that are either red or white. If the ratio of red pegs to white pegs is 1:2, how many white pegs does the game have?

Assign variables.
Let w = the number of white pegs.
Then $252 - w$ = the number of red pegs.

Set up a ratio, labeling the numerator and denominator.
$\frac{\text{red pegs}}{\text{white pegs}} = \frac{1}{2} = \frac{252-w}{w}$

Cross multiply and solve for w.
$w = 2(252 - w)$
$w = 504 - 2w$
$3w = 504$
$w = 168$
There are 168 white pegs.

① **Classwork**
Solve.

A baseball team drafted 50 players. If the ratio of pitchers to non-pitchers was 2:3, how many pitchers were drafted?

Let p = the number of pitchers drafted.
Then $50 - p$ = the number of non-pitchers.

$\frac{\text{pitchers}}{\text{non-pitchers}} = \frac{2}{3} = \frac{p}{50-p}$
$2(50 - p) = 3p$
$100 - 2p = 3p$
$100 = 5p$
$p = 20$
There were 20 pitchers drafted.

The ratio of coaches to non-pitchers on the team is 3:7. If there are a total of 30 coaches and non-pitchers, how many coaches does the team have?
Let c = the number of coaches.
Then $30 - c$ = the number of non-pitchers.

$\frac{\text{coaches}}{\text{non-pitchers}} = \frac{3}{7} = \frac{c}{30-c}$
$3(30 - c) = 7c$
$90 - 3c = 7c$
$90 = 10c$
$c = 9$
There are 9 coaches.

Activities
② Solve.
There are 30 major league baseball teams. The ratio of American League teams to National League teams is 7:8. How many teams are in each league?
Let a = the number of American League teams.
Then $30 - a$ = the number of National League teams.
$\frac{\text{American League}}{\text{National League}} = \frac{7}{8} = \frac{a}{30-a}$
$7(30 - a) = 8a$
$210 - 7a = 8a$
$210 = 15a$
$a = 14$
There are 14 American League teams and 30 - 14 = 16 National League teams.

③ Solve.
A baseball player's batting average is the ratio of his number of hits to his number of times at bat. (This ratio is expressed as a decimal rounded to the nearest thousandth when giving baseball statistics.) If a player's batting average is 0.375 and he had 296 at bats during the season, how many hits did he have?

Let h = the number of hits.

$\frac{\text{hits}}{\text{at bats}} = \frac{375}{1000} = \frac{3}{8} = \frac{h}{296}$

$8h = 3(296)$

$8h = 888$

$h = 111$

The player had 111 hits.

④ Find the zeros of each function.

$f(x) = 2x^2 + 8x + 7$

$0 = 2x^2 + 8x + 7$

$0 = x^2 + 4x + \frac{7}{2}$

$x^2 + 4x = -\frac{7}{2}$

$x^2 + 4x + \left(\frac{4}{2}\right)^2 = -\frac{7}{2} + \left(\frac{4}{2}\right)^2$

$x^2 + 4x + 4 = -\frac{7}{2} + 4$

$x^2 + 4x + 4 = \frac{1}{2}$

$(x+2)^2 = \frac{1}{2}$

$\sqrt{(x+2)^2} = \sqrt{\frac{1}{2}}$

$x + 2 = \pm\sqrt{\frac{1}{2}} \cdot \frac{\sqrt{2}}{\sqrt{2}}$

$x = -2 \pm \frac{\sqrt{2}}{2}$

$f(x) = x^2 - 5x + 3$

$0 = x^2 - 5x + 3$

$x^2 - 5x = -3$

$x^2 - 5x + \left(-\frac{5}{2}\right)^2 = -3 + \left(-\frac{5}{2}\right)^2$

$x^2 - 5x + \frac{25}{4} = -\frac{12}{4} + \frac{25}{4}$

$x^2 - 5x + \frac{25}{4} = \frac{13}{4}$

$\left(x - \frac{5}{2}\right)^2 = \frac{13}{4}$

$\sqrt{\left(x - \frac{5}{2}\right)^2} = \sqrt{\frac{13}{4}}$

$x - \frac{5}{2} = \pm\frac{\sqrt{13}}{2}$

$x = \frac{5 \pm \sqrt{13}}{2}$

$f(x) = x^2 + 12x - 10$

$0 = x^2 + 12x - 10$

$x^2 + 12x = 10$

$x^2 + 12x + \left(\frac{12}{2}\right)^2 = 10 + \left(\frac{12}{2}\right)^2$

$x^2 + 12x + 36 = 10 + 36$

$x^2 + 12x + 36 = 46$

$(x+6)^2 = 46$

$\sqrt{(x+6)^2} = \sqrt{46}$

$x + 6 = \pm\sqrt{46}$

$x = -6 \pm \sqrt{46}$

⑤ Find the roots.

$\sqrt{2}x^2 + 2\sqrt{3}x - 5 = 0$

$x = \frac{-2\sqrt{3} \pm \sqrt{\left(2\sqrt{3}\right)^2 - 4\left(\sqrt{2}\right)(-5)}}{2\left(\sqrt{2}\right)}$

$x = \frac{-2\sqrt{3} \pm \sqrt{12 + 20\sqrt{2}}}{2\sqrt{2}} \cdot \frac{\sqrt{2}}{\sqrt{2}}$

$x = \frac{-2\sqrt{6} \pm \sqrt{24 + 40\sqrt{2}}}{4}$

$x = \frac{-2\sqrt{6} \pm \sqrt{4\left(6 + 10\sqrt{2}\right)}}{4}$

$x = \frac{-2\sqrt{6} \pm 2\sqrt{6 + 10\sqrt{2}}}{4} = \frac{-\sqrt{6} \pm \sqrt{6 + 10\sqrt{2}}}{2}$

$\sqrt{5}x^2 + 3\sqrt{2}x + 7 = 0$

$x = \frac{-3\sqrt{2} \pm \sqrt{\left(3\sqrt{2}\right)^2 - 4\left(\sqrt{5}\right)(7)}}{2\left(\sqrt{5}\right)}$

$x = \frac{-3\sqrt{2} \pm \sqrt{18 - 28\sqrt{5}}}{2\sqrt{5}}$

The argument (portion under the radical) is negative, so there are no real roots.

Teaching Tips, Cont.

- Emphasize the importance of consistency in the units. If the units in the numerators are not consistent throughout the problem, or of the units in the denominators are not consistent throughout the problem, it is nearly impossible to obtain the correct answer.
- Complete the Classwork exercises. Have some students work the problems on the board for the class and explain their answers. All students should work the problems in their books.

Assignment

- Complete Lesson 116, Activities 2-5.

Lesson 117

Concepts
- Consecutive integers
- Math in the real world

Learning Objectives
The student will be able to:
- Write an algebraic equation to solve for consecutive integers
- Write an algebraic equation to solve for consecutive odd integers
- Write an algebraic equation to solve for consecutive even integers

Materials Needed
- Student Book, Lesson 117

Teaching Tips
➢ Ask the students what *consecutive* means. (Coming one after another in order, without skipping.)

➢ Ask the students to give an example of consecutive integers. (1, 2, 3, 4, 5, ... or 13, 14, 15, ... etc. The integers do not have to start with 1, but must come in order without skipping any integers.)

➢ Ask the students how they could express consecutive integers if the first integer in the sequence is represented by x. (x, $x + 1$, $x + 2$, $x + 3$, ...)

➢ Ask the students to give an example of consecutive odd integers. (1, 3, 5, 7, 9, ... or 13, 15, 17, ... etc. The integers do not have to start with 1, but must come in order without skipping any odd integers.)

Word Problems: Consecutive Integers

Consecutive integers are integers in a sequence in which each integer is exactly one more than the previous integer, x. Consecutive integers are represented as x, $x + 1$, $x + 2$, $x + 3$, ..., where x is any integer.

Consecutive odd integers are integers in a sequence, beginning with an odd integer, in which each integer is exactly two more than the previous integer, x. Consecutive odd integers are represented as x, $x + 2$, $x + 4$, $x + 6$, ..., where x is any odd integer.

Consecutive even integers are integers in a sequence, beginning with an even integer, in which each integer is exactly two more than the previous integer, x. Consecutive even integers are represented as x, $x + 2$, $x + 4$, $x + 6$, ..., where x is any even integer.

The heights of the four levels on a set of choral risers are represented by consecutive integers. If the sum of the heights is 10 feet, what is the height of each riser?

The heights are represented by x, $x + 1$, $x + 2$, and $x + 3$. Set up an equation and solve.

$x + (x + 1) + (x + 2) + (x + 3) = 10$

$4x + 6 = 10$

$4x = 4$

$x = 1$

The first level is one foot high. This makes the four levels 1 foot, 2 feet, 3 feet, and 4 feet high.

① **Classwork**

Solve.

The number of seats in each row of a section in a ballpark is represented by consecutive integers. If there are total of 135 seats in the first six rows, how many seats does the shortest row have?

The numbers of seats are represented by x, $x + 1$, $x + 2$, $x + 3$, $x + 4$, and $x + 5$.

$x + (x + 1) + (x + 2) + (x + 3) + (x + 4) + (x + 5) = 135$

$6x + 15 = 135$

$6x = 120$

$x = 20$

The shortest row has 20 seats.

The number of peanuts found in three boxes of a ballpark mixture of caramel-coated popcorn and peanuts is represented by consecutive odd integers. If there were 51 total peanuts, how many peanuts were in the box with the most peanuts?

The numbers of peanuts are represented by x, $x + 2$, and $x + 4$.

$x + (x + 2) + (x + 4) = 51$

$3x + 6 = 51$

$3x = 45$

$x = 15$

The box with the most peanuts had 15 + 4 = 19 peanuts.

Activities

② Solve.

A ballpark concession stand sells soft drinks in three different sized cups. The prices of the drinks are consecutive even integers. Purchasing one drink of each size would cost you $18. How much does the least expensive drink cost?

The drink costs are represented by x, $x + 2$, and $x + 4$.

$x + (x + 2) + (x + 4) = 18$

$3x + 6 = 18$

$3x = 12$

$x = 4$

The least expensive drink costs $4.

③ Solve.

Four consecutive odd integers have a sum of 96. What are the integers?

The integers are represented by x, $x + 2$, $x + 4$, and $x + 6$.

$x+(x+2)+(x+4)+(x+6)=96$

$4x+12=96$

$4x=84$

$x=21$

The integers are 21, 23, 25, and 27.

Six consecutive integers have a sum of 285. What are the integers?

The integers are represented by x, $x + 1$, $x + 2$, $x + 3$, $x + 4$, and $x + 5$.

$x+(x+1)+(x+2)+(x+3)+(x+4)+(x+5)=285$

$6x+15=285$

$6x=270$

$x=45$

The integers are 45, 46, 47, 48, 49, and 50.

Nine consecutive even integers have a sum of 144. What are the integers?

The integers are represented by x, $x + 2$, $x + 4$, $x + 6$, $x + 8$, $x + 10$, $x + 12$, $x + 14$, and $x + 16$.

$x+(x+2)+(x+4)+(x+6)+(x+8)+(x+10)+(x+12)+(x+14)+(x+16)=144$

$9x+72=144$

$9x=72$

$x=8$

The integers are 8, 10, 12, 14, 16, 18, 20, 22, and 24.

④ Solve.

A baseball player's on base percentage (also called the on base average) is given by the formula $a=\frac{h+w+p}{b+w+p+f}$, where a is the on base percentage (average), h is the number of hits, w is the number of walks, p is the number of time hit by a pitch, b is the number of at bats, and f is the number of sacrifice flies. Rewrite the formula to solve for each of the variables h, w, p, b, and f.

$a(b+w+p+f)=h+w+p$

$h=a(b+w+p+f)-w-p$

$ab+aw+ap+af=h+w+p$

$ab=-aw-ap-af+h+w+p$

$b=\frac{-aw-ap-af+h+w+p}{a}$

$ab+aw+ap+af=h+w+p$

$aw-w=-ab-ap-af+h+p$

$w=\frac{-ab-ap-af+h+p}{a-1}$

$ab+aw+ap+af=h+w+p$

$ap-p=-ab-aw-af+h+w$

$p=\frac{-ab-aw-af+h+w}{a-1}$

$ab+aw+ap+af=h+w+p$

$af=-ab-aw-ap+h+w+p$

$f=\frac{-ab-aw-ap+h+w+p}{a}$

Teaching Tips, Cont.

- Ask the students how they could express consecutive odd integers if the first integer in the sequence is represented by x. (x, $x + 2$, $x + 4$, $x + 6$, ...)
- Ask the students to give an example of consecutive even integers. (2, 4, 6, 8, 10, ... or 14, 16, 18, ... etc. The integers do not have to start with 2, but must come in order without skipping any even integers.)
- Ask the students how they could express consecutive even integers if the first integer in the sequence is represented by x. (x, $x + 2$, $x + 4$, $x + 6$, ...)
- Teach how to solve for consecutive integers from the teaching box.
- Complete the Classwork exercises. Have some students work the problems on the board for the class and explain their answers. All students should work the problems in their books.

Assignment

- Complete Lesson 117, Activities 2-4.

Lesson 118

Concepts

- Functions and relations
- Math in the real world

Learning Objectives

The student will be able to:

- Define *function*
- Define *relation*
- Identify whether or not an equation is a function
- Give a relation that proves an equation is not a function

Materials Needed

- Student Book, Lesson 118
- Worksheet 59

Teaching Tips

➢ Have students complete Worksheet 59 in class. This may be for added practice of earlier topics, or graded as a quiz, if desired.

➢ Review functions. (See Lesson 97)

➢ Teach the definitions of *relation*, *domain*, and *range* from the teaching box.

➢ Teach how to evaluate equations to determine whether or not they are functions from the teaching box. The example in the teaching box suggests substituting 0 for x to determine the relation. This will work in all instances except the formats $y^2 = kx$ and $y^2 = kx - c$. In these instances, choose a larger value of x that will yield a positive number in the argument.

Functions and Relations

In Lesson 97 you learned that a **function** is an equation in which each value of the independent variable has exactly one corresponding value of the dependent variable. You also learned to recognize functions by looking at the graph of the equation.

But how can you tell if an equation is a function without seeing a graph? This can easily be done by checking its relation. A **relation** is a set of ordered pairs, such as coordinate points. If an equation is a function, each x-value (domain) will have exactly one y-value (range). In cases where you do not have values labeled x and y, each independent variable – the value you begin with – will have exactly one corresponding dependent variable – the value you end with.

Consider a list of 8th-grade students and their ages. Each student will have exactly one age at any one time. Therefore the relation (student, age) is a function. However, a given age, such as 14 years old, may have several students that fit the category. Therefore the relation (age, student) is not a function. In other words, all functions are relations, but not all relations are functions.

Evaluate the equation to determine whether or not it is a function. If it is not a function, give an example from the relation to show why it is not a function.

$y^2 + 2x - 9 = 0$

Because a function must have one value of y for each value of x, solve for y.

$y^2 = -2x + 9$

$y = \sqrt{-2x + 9}$

Remember that square roots may be positive or negative, so the answer must be written $y = \pm\sqrt{-2x + 9}$.

Substituting 0 in for x, we get the relation (0, 3) and (0, -3). The equation is not a function because each value of x does not have one unique value of y.

① Classwork

Evaluate each equation to determine whether or not it is a function. If it is not a function, give an example from the relation to show why it is not a function.

$y - x^2 + 9 = 0$
$y = x^2 - 9$
Substitute 0 for x.
$y = 0 - 9$
$y = -9$
This equation is a function.

$y - 81x^2 + 16 = 0$
$y = 81x^2 - 16$
Substitute 0 for x.
$y = 0 - 16$
$y = -16$
This equation is a function.

$y^2 + x - 9 = 0$
$y^2 = -x + 9$
Substitute 0 for x.
$y^2 = 0 + 9$
$y^2 = 9$
$y = \pm 3$
This equation is not a function.
(0, 3) and (0, -3)

$y^2 + 81x^2 - 16 = 0$
$y^2 = -81x + 16$
Substitute 0 for x.
$y^2 = 0 + 16$
$y^2 = 16$
$y = \pm 4$
This equation is not a function.
(0, 4) and (0, -4)

Point out that any time there is a y^2 term, the equation is not a function.

Activities

② Evaluate each equation to determine whether or not it is a function. If it is not a function, give an example from the relation to show why it is not a function.

$y - 25x^2 + 17 = 0$
$y = 25x^2 - 17$
Substitute 0 for x.
$y = 0 - 17$
$y = -17$
This equation is a function.

$y + 3x + 7 = 0$
$y = -3x - 7$
Substitute 0 for x.
$y = 0 - 7$
$y = -7$
This equation is a function.

$y^2 + 6x - 13 = 0$
$y^2 = -6x + 13$
Substitute 0 for x.
$y^2 = 0 + 13$
$y^2 = 13$
$y = \pm\sqrt{13}$
This equation is not a function.
$(0, \sqrt{13})$ and $(0, -\sqrt{13})$

$y^2 + 14x^2 - 1 = 0$
$y^2 = -14x + 1$
Substitute 0 for x.
$y^2 = 0 + 1$
$y^2 = 1$
$y = \pm 1$
This equation is not a function.
(0, 1) and (0, -1)

$y - 11x^2 + 4 = 0$
$y = 11x^2 - 4$
Substitute 0 for x.
$y = 0 - 4$
$y = -4$
This equation is a function.

$y + 21x^2 - 25 = 0$
$y = -21x^2 + 25$
Substitute 0 for x.
$y = 0 + 25$
$y = 25$
This equation is a function.

$y - 6x^2 + 29 = 0$
$y = 6x^2 - 29$
Substitute 0 for x.
$y = 0 - 29$
$y = -29$
This equation is a function.

$y^2 + \sqrt{5}x^2 - 4 = 0$
$y^2 = -\sqrt{5}x + 4$
Substitute 0 for x.
$y^2 = 0 + 4$
$y^2 = 4$
$y = \pm 2$
This equation is not a function.
(0, 2) and (0, -2)

$y - 3x^2 + \sqrt{2} = 0$
$y = 3x^2 - \sqrt{2}$
Substitute 0 for x.
$y = 0 - \sqrt{2}$
$y = -\sqrt{2}$
This equation is a function.

③ Solve.

A baseball player's on base percentage (also called the on base average) is given by the formula $a = \frac{h+w+p}{b+w+p+f}$, where a is the on base percentage (average), h is the number of hits, w is the number of walks, p is the number of time hit by a pitch, b is the number of at bats, and f is the number of sacrifice flies. Find the on base percentage of a player who had 173 hits, 92 walks, 5 sacrifice flies, 513 at bats, and was not hit by a pitch. Round your answer to the nearest thousandth.

$a = \dfrac{173 + 92 + 0}{513 + 92 + 0 + 5}$

$a = \dfrac{265}{610}$

$a = 0.434$

Mixture Problems Worksheet 59

① Solve.

A 1-ounce box of caramel-coated popcorn and peanuts is 40% peanuts by weight. If the ballparks want a package that is 60% peanuts by weight with the same amount of popcorn, how many ounces of peanuts, to the nearest hundredth of an ounce, must be added to the mix to make it 60% peanuts by weight? What will be the new weight of the ballpark mixture?

	Concen.	Amount	Totals
Start	0.40	1 oz.	0.40(1)
Add	1.00	x	x
Final	0.60	$1 + x$	$0.60(1 + x)$

$0.40(1) + x = 0.60(1 + x)$

$0.40 + x = 0.60 + 0.60x$

$0.40x = .20$

$x = 0.5$

The ballpark mix will have 0.5 ounces of peanuts added, making the mixture 1.5 ounces.

Granola costs $4 per pound and chocolate candies cost $5.50 per pound. How many pounds of each must be mixed to obtain 10 pounds of a mixture that costs $5 per pound? Round your answers to the nearest tenth of a pound.

Pounds	Cost	Total
x	4	$4x$
$10 - x$	5.50	$5.50(10 - x)$
10	5	10(5)

$4x + 5.50(10 - x) = 10(5)$

$4x + 55 - 5.5x = 50$

$-1.5x = -5$

$x = 3.3$

Your solution should contain 3.3 pounds of granola and $10 - 3.3 = 6.7$ pounds of chocolate candies.

A 50-pound bag of fertilizer is 15% phosphorus. How much must be substituted with fertilizer that is 60% phosphorus to obtain 50 pounds of fertilizer that is 30% phosphorus? Round your answer to the nearest tenth of a pound.

	Start	Remove	Add	Finish
Concentration	0.15	0.15	0.60	0.30
Amount	50	x	x	50
Total	0.15(50)	$0.15x$	$0.60x$	0.30(50)

$0.15(50) - 0.15x + 0.60x = 0.30(50)$

$7.5 + 0.45x = 15$

$0.45x = 7.5$

$x = 16.7$

You must substitute 16.7 pounds of fertilizer.

Teaching Tips, Cont.

- Complete the Classwork exercises. Have some students work the problems on the board for the class and explain their answers. All students should work the problems in their books.

Assignment

- Complete Lesson 118, Activities 2-3.

Lesson 119

Concepts

- Direct variation
- Quadratic equations
- Parabolas
- Dividing polynomials

Learning Objectives

The student will be able to:

- Define *direct variation*
- Define *constant of variation*
- State the constant of variation for a given linear equation
- Write an equation to show direct variation

Materials Needed

- Student Book, Lesson 119

Teaching Tips

- Teach the definition of *direct variation* from the teaching box.
- Ask the students to give examples of direct variation from real-life experiences. (If one hamburger costs *d* dollars, then *h* hamburgers cost *hd* dollars. If students are having difficulty thinking of an example, elicit the idea that shopping is direct variation.)
- Have the students write an equation showing the total cost, *c*, of *h* hamburgers that cost *d* dollars each. ($c = hd$)
- Tell the students that in the equation they just wrote, the variable *h* is known as the constant of variation.

Direct Variation

A linear equation in which one variable is a multiple of another variable is known as a **direct variation**. One variable varies directly as the other variable. In other words, as one variable gets larger (or smaller), the other variable gets larger (or smaller) at the same rate.

A direct variation can be written as either $\frac{y}{x} = k$ or $y = kx$. In either case, *k* is called the **constant of variation**. A direct variation will always graph through the point (0, 0) with the slope equal to *k*.

If *y* varies directly as *x* and $y = 27$ when $x = 9$, what is value of *k*? State the value of *k* and write an equation to show the direct variation.

$y = kx$

$27 = k(9)$

$\frac{27}{9} = 3 = k$

$y = 3x$

① **Classwork.**
Solve.

If *y* varies directly as *x* and $y = 4$ when $x = 10$, what is value of *k*? State the value of *k* and write an equation to show the direct variation.

$y = kx$

$4 = k(10)$

$\frac{4}{10} = \frac{2}{5} = k$

$y = \frac{2}{5}x$

If *y* varies directly as *x* and $y = 15$ when $k = 3$, what is value of *x*? State the value of *x* and write an equation to show the direct variation.

$y = kx$

$15 = 3(x)$

$\frac{15}{3} = 5 = x$

$y = 3x$

Activities

② Solve.

If *y* varies directly as *x* and $y = 20$ when $x = 12$, what is value of *k*? State the value of *k* and write an equation to show the direct variation.

$y = kx$

$20 = k(12)$ $\quad y = \frac{5}{3}x$

$\frac{20}{12} = \frac{5}{3} = k$

If *y* varies directly as *x* and $y = 15$ when $k = 6$, what is value of *x*? State the value of *x* and write an equation to show the direct variation.

$y = kx$

$15 = 6(x)$ $\quad y = 6x$

$\frac{15}{6} = \frac{5}{2} = x$

If *y* varies directly as *x* and $x = 7$ when $k = 4$, what is value of *y*? State the value of *y* and write an equation to show the direct variation.

$y = kx$

$y = 4(7)$ $\quad y = 4x$

$y = 28$

③ Rewrite each equation in the form $4p(y-k)=(x-h)^2$. Identify the value of the variables p, k, and h, and give the coordinates for the vertex and focus, and the equations of the lines for the axis of symmetry and the directrix of the parabola.

$y=\frac{1}{8}(x-2)^2-5$

$y+5=\frac{1}{8}(x-2)^2$

$\frac{y+5}{\frac{1}{8}}=(x-2)^2$

$8(y+5)=(x-2)^2$

$4p=8 \Rightarrow p=2$

$k=-5$

$h=2$

The vertex is (2, -5).
The focus is (2, -5 + 2) = (2, -3).
The axis of symmetry is the line $x=2$.
The directrix is the line $y=-5-2 \Rightarrow y=-7$.

$y=\frac{1}{4}(x-3)^2+6$

$y-6=\frac{1}{4}(x-3)^2$

$\frac{y-6}{\frac{1}{4}}=(x-3)^2$

$4(y-6)=(x-3)^2$

$4p=4 \Rightarrow p=1$

$k=6$

$h=3$

The vertex is (3, 6).
The focus is (3, 6 + 1) = (3, 7).
The axis of symmetry is the line $x=3$.
The directrix is the line $y=6-1 \Rightarrow y=5$.

$y=3(x+4)^2+9$

$y-9=3(x+4)^2$

$\frac{y-9}{3}=(x+4)^2$

$\frac{1}{3}(y-9)=(x+4)^2$

$4p=\frac{1}{3} \Rightarrow p=\frac{1}{12}$

$k=9$

$h=-4$

The vertex is (-4, 9).
The focus is $(-4, 9+\frac{1}{12})=(-4, \frac{109}{12})$.
The axis of symmetry is the line $x=-4$.
The directrix is the line $y=9-\frac{1}{12} \Rightarrow y=\frac{107}{12}$.

$y=\frac{1}{4}(x+5)^2-8$

$y+8=\frac{1}{4}(x+5)^2$

$\frac{y+8}{\frac{1}{4}}=(x+5)^2$

$4(y+8)=(x+5)^2$

$4p=4 \Rightarrow p=1$

$k=-8$

$h=-5$

The vertex is (-5, -8).
The focus is (-5, -8 +1) = (-5,-7).
The axis of symmetry is the line $x=-5$.
The directrix is the line $y=-8-1 \Rightarrow y=-9$.

④ Divide.

$(24x^2+10x-99)\div(6x-11)$

$$\begin{array}{r} 4x+9 \\ 6x-11\overline{)24x^2+10x-99} \\ \underline{24x^2-44x} \\ 54x-99 \\ \underline{54x-99} \end{array}$$

$(56x^2-27x-18)\div(8x+3)$

$$\begin{array}{r} 7x-6 \\ 8x+3\overline{)56x^2-27x-18} \\ \underline{56x^2+21x} \\ -48x-18 \\ \underline{-48x-18} \end{array}$$

$(5x^2-69x+108)\div(x-12)$

$$\begin{array}{r} 5x-9 \\ x-12\overline{)5x^2-69x+108} \\ \underline{5x^2-60x} \\ -\ 9x+108 \\ \underline{-\ 9x+108} \end{array}$$

Teaching Tips, Cont.

- Teach direct variation from the teaching box. Refer students to the example about the costs of hamburgers as necessary for clarification.
- Complete the Classwork exercises. Have some students work the problems on the board for the class and explain their answers. All students should work the problems in their books.

Assignment

- Complete Lesson 119, Activities 2-4.

Lesson 120

Concepts

- Inverse variation
- Discriminant
- Quadratic functions
- Completing the square
- Parabolas

Learning Objectives

The student will be able to:

- Define *inverse variation*
- Describe a hyperbola
- State the constant of variation for a given linear equation
- Write an equation to show inverse variation

Materials Needed

- Student Book, Lesson 120
- Worksheet 60

Teaching Tips

➢ Review direct variation. (See Lesson 119)

➢ Tell the students that while direct variation has one variable increasing as another variable increases, inverse variation has one variable increasing as another variable decreases.

➢ Ask the students to give examples of inverse variation from real-life experiences. (The faster you drive, the less time it takes to go a certain distance, or the higher your altitude, the lower the air pressure.)

Inverse Variation

An equation in which one variable increases at the same rate another variable decreases is known as an **inverse variation**. One variable varies inversely as the other variable. In other words, as one variable gets larger (or smaller), the other variable gets smaller (or larger) at the same rate.

A direct variation can be written as either $y = \frac{k}{x}$ or $xy = k$. In either case, k is called the **constant of variation**. An inverse variation will never graph as a straight line. It always forms as special type of curved graph called a **hyperbola**. A hyperbola is a conic section, much like a parabola, but with two broad U-shaped curves in opposite directions.

If y varies inversely as x and $y = 4$ when $x = 3$, what is value of k? State the value of k and write an equation to show the inverse variation.

$xy = k$
$3(4) = k$ $\quad y = \frac{12}{x}$
$12 = k$

① Classwork
Solve.

If y varies inversely as x and $y = 7$ when $x = 2$, what is value of k? State the value of k and write an equation to show the inverse variation.
$xy = k$
$2(7) = k$ $\quad y = \frac{14}{x}$
$14 = k$

If y varies inversely as x and $y = 6$ when $k = 5$, what is value of x? State the value of x and write an equation to show the inverse variation.
$xy = k$
$x(6) = 5$ $\quad y = \frac{5}{x}$
$x = \frac{5}{6}$

Activities
② Solve.
If y varies inversely as x and $y = 8$ when $x = 9$, what is value of k? State the value of k and write an equation to show the inverse variation.
$xy = k$
$9(8) = k$ $\quad y = \frac{72}{x}$
$72 = k$

If y varies inversely as x and $y = 10$ when $k = 6$, what is value of x? State the value of x and write an equation to show the inverse variation.
$xy = k$
$x(10) = 6$ $\quad y = \frac{6}{x}$
$x = \frac{6}{10} = \frac{3}{5}$

If y varies inversely as x and $x = 3$ when $k = 11$, what is value of y? State the value of y and write an equation to show the inverse variation.
$xy = k$
$3y = 11$ $\quad y = \frac{11}{x}$
$y = \frac{11}{3}$

③ Use the discriminant to determine the number of roots for the quadratic function. Then complete the square and give the coordinates of the vertex and focus, and the equation for the directrix and axis of symmetry.

$f(x) = \frac{1}{16}x^2 + 8x + 20$
$b^2 - 4ac = (8)^2 - 4\left(\frac{1}{16}\right)(20) =$
$64 - 5 = 59$
The discriminant is positive, so there are two roots.
$y = \frac{1}{16}x^2 + 8x + 20$
$16y = x^2 + 128x + 320$
$16y - 320 = x^2 + 128x$
$16y - 320 + 64^2 = x^2 + 128x + 64^2$
$16y + 3776 = (x + 64)^2$
$16(y + 236) = (x + 64)^2$
$h = -64;\ k = -236;\ p = 4$
Vertex: (-64, -236)
Focus: (-64, -232)
Directrix: $y = -236 - 4 \Rightarrow y = -240$
Axis of symmertry: $x = -64$

$f(x) = \frac{1}{4}x^2 - 2x + 4$
$b^2 - 4ac = (-2)^2 - 4\left(\frac{1}{4}\right)(4) =$
$4 - 4 = 0$
The discriminant is zero, so there is one root.
$y = \frac{1}{4}x^2 - 2x + 4$
$4y = x^2 - 8x + 16$
$4y - 16 = x^2 - 8x$
$4y - 16 + 16 = x^2 - 8x + 16$
$4y = (x - 4)^2$
$4(y + 0) = (x - 4)^2$
$h = 4;\ k = 0;\ p = 1$
Vertex: (4, 0)
Focus: (4, 1)
Directrix: $y = 0 - 1 \Rightarrow y = -1$
Axis of symmertry: $x = 4$

$f(x) = \frac{1}{2}x^2 + 4x + 15$
$b^2 - 4ac = (4)^2 - 4\left(\frac{1}{2}\right)(15) =$
$16 - 30 = -14$
The discriminant is negative, so there are no roots.
$y = \frac{1}{2}x^2 + 4x + 15$
$2y = x^2 + 8x + 30$
$2y - 30 = x^2 + 8x$
$2y - 30 + 16 = x^2 + 8x + 16$
$2y - 14 = (x + 4)^2$
$2(y - 7) = (x + 4)^2$
$h = -4;\ k = 7;\ p = \frac{1}{2}$
Vertex: $(-4, 7)$
Focus: (-4, $\frac{15}{2}$)
Directrix: $y = 7 - \frac{1}{2} \Rightarrow y = \frac{13}{2}$
Axis of symmertry: $x = -4$

$f(x) = \frac{1}{3}x^2 - \frac{1}{4}x - 3$
$b^2 - 4ac = \left(-\frac{1}{4}\right)^2 - 4\left(\frac{1}{3}\right)(-3) =$
$\frac{1}{16} + 4 = \frac{65}{16}$
The discriminant is positive, so there are two roots.
$y = \frac{1}{3}x^2 - \frac{1}{4}x - 3$
$3y = x^2 - \frac{3}{4}x - 9$
$3y + 9 = x^2 - \frac{3}{4}x$
$3y + 9 + \frac{9}{64} = x^2 - \frac{3}{4}x + \frac{9}{64}$
$3y + \frac{585}{64} = \left(x - \frac{3}{8}\right)^2$
$3\left(y + \frac{195}{64}\right) = \left(x - \frac{3}{8}\right)^2$
$h = \frac{3}{8};\ k = -\frac{195}{64};\ p = \frac{3}{4}$
Vertex: ($\frac{3}{8}, -\frac{195}{64}$)
Focus: ($\frac{3}{8}, -\frac{147}{64}$)
Directrix: $y = -\frac{195}{64} - \frac{3}{4} \Rightarrow y = -\frac{243}{64}$
Axis of symmertry: $x = \frac{3}{8}$

Consecutive Integers, Direct and Inverse Variation Worksheet 60

① Solve.

Four consecutive odd integers have a sum of 408. What are the integers?

The integers are represented by x, $x + 2$, $x + 4$, and $x + 6$.

$x + (x + 2) + (x + 4) + (x + 6) = 408$

$4x + 12 = 408$

$4x = 396$

$x = 99$

The integers are 99, 101, 103, and 105.

Six consecutive integers have a sum of 345. What are the integers?

The integers are represented by x, $x + 1$, $x + 2$, $x + 3$, $x + 4$, and $x + 5$.

$x + (x + 1) + (x + 2) + (x + 3) + (x + 4) + (x + 5) = 345$

$6x + 15 = 345$

$6x = 330$

$x = 55$

The integers are 55, 56, 57, 58, 59, and 60.

② Solve.

If y varies directly as x and $y = 24$ when $x = 15$, what is value of k? State the value of k and write an equation to show the direct variation.

$y = kx$

$24 = k(15)$ $\quad y = \frac{8}{5}x$

$\frac{24}{15} = \frac{8}{5} = k$

If y varies directly as x and $y = 9$ when $k = 12$, what is value of x? State the value of x and write an equation to show the direct variation.

$y = kx$

$9 = 12(x)$ $\quad y = 12x$

$\frac{9}{12} = \frac{3}{4} = x$

If y varies directly as x and $x = 6$ when $k = 3$, what is value of y? State the value of y and write an equation to show the direct variation.

$y = kx$

$y = 3(6)$ $\quad y = 3x$

$y = 18$

If y varies inversely as x and $y = 11$ when $x = 2$, what is value of k? State the value of k and write an equation to show the inverse variation.

$xy = k$

$2(11) = k$ $\quad y = \frac{22}{x}$

$22 = k$

If y varies inversely as x and $y = 20$ when $k = 8$, what is value of x? State the value of x and write an equation to show the inverse variation.

$xy = k$

$x(20) = 8$ $\quad y = \frac{8}{x}$

$x = \frac{8}{20} = \frac{2}{5}$

Teaching Tips, Cont.

- Have the students write an equation showing that the distance traveled, d, is equal to the rate of travel, r, times the amount of time traveled, t. ($d = rt$)
- Tell the students that in the equation they just wrote, the variable r is known as the constant of variation.
- Teach inverse variation from the teaching box. Refer students to the example about distance, rate, and time, if necessary, for clarification.
- Complete the Classwork exercises. Have some students work the problems on the board for the class and explain their answers. All students should work the problems in their books.
- Review for Test 12 using worksheets 56-60. These worksheets were assigned in previous lessons.
- Review for Exam 3 using worksheets 41-60.

Assignments

- Complete Lesson 120, Activities 2-3.
- Worksheet 60.
- Study for Test 12 (Lessons 108-117).
- Study for Exam 3 (Lessons 81-117), if Exam 3 is being administered.

Test 12

Testing Objectives

The student will:

- Find the discriminant of quadratic equations
- Determine the number of roots in a quadratic equation
- Sketch the graph of quadratic inequalities
- Solve money problems
- Solve investment problems
- Solve mixture problems
- Solve consecutive integer problems

Materials Needed

- Test 12
- *It's College Test Prep Time!* from the Student Book
- Exploring Math through... Fundraising from Student Book

Teaching Tips

- ➢ Administer Test 12, allowing the students 30-40 minutes to complete the test.
- ➢ When all students are finished taking the test, introduce *It's College Test Prep Time* from the student book. This page may be completed in class or assigned as homework.

① Convert each equation to the form $y = ax^2 + bx + c$. Find the discriminant and give the number of roots in the equation. **4 points**

$y = \frac{1}{4}(x-1)^2 - 4$

$y = \frac{1}{4}(x^2 - 2x + 1) - 4$

$y = \frac{1}{4}x^2 - \frac{2}{4}x + \frac{1}{4} - 4$

$y = \frac{1}{4}x^2 - \frac{1}{2}x + \frac{1}{4} - \frac{16}{4}$

$y = \frac{1}{4}x^2 - \frac{1}{2}x - \frac{15}{4}$

$b^2 - 4ac = \left(-\frac{1}{2}\right)^2 - 4\left(\frac{1}{4}\right)\left(-\frac{15}{4}\right) =$

$\frac{1}{4} + \frac{15}{4} = \frac{16}{4} = 4$

The discriminant is positive, so there are two roots.

$y = 3(x+2)^2 + 1$

$y = 3(x^2 + 4x + 4) + 1$

$y = 3x^2 + 12x + 12 + 1$

$y = 3x^2 + 12x + 13$

$b^2 - 4ac = (12)^2 - 4(3)(13) =$

$144 - 156 = -12$

The discriminant is negative, so there are no roots.

② Sketch the graph of each inequality. **8 points**

$y < x^2 - 2x + 3$

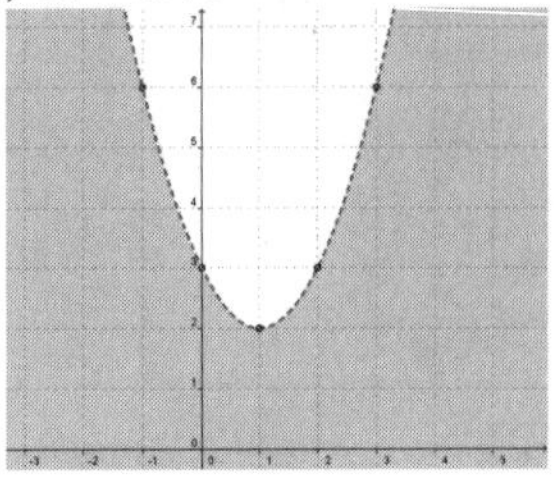

$y \geq -x^2 + 2x - 4$

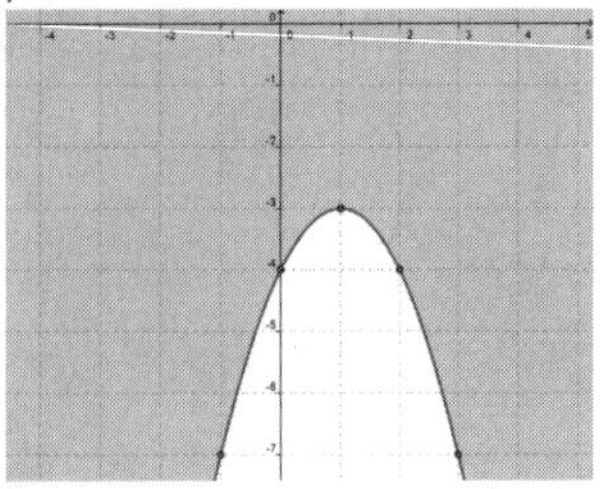

$y > x^2 + 2x - 2$

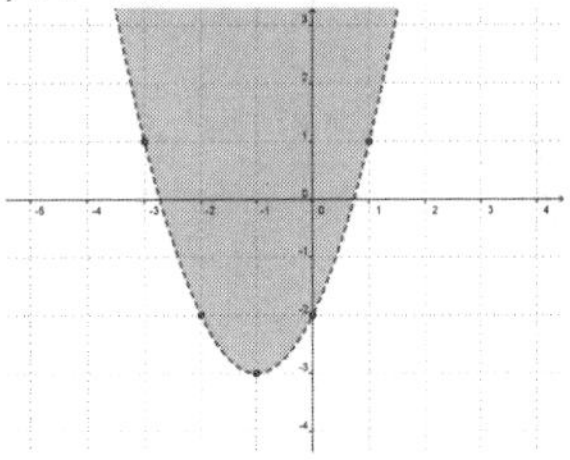

$y \leq -x^2 + 2x + 1$

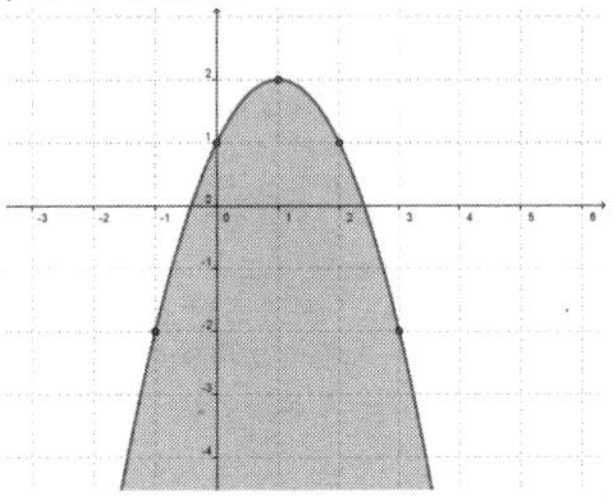

③ Solve. **18 points**

There are 527 coins in a jar. If the mixture of pennies, nickels, dimes, and quarters totals $47, how many of each coin are in the jar if there are two times as many pennies as nickels, three times as many dimes as nickels, and the remaining coins are quarters?

Type of coin	Number	Total Value
Quarter	q	$25(q)$
Dime	$d = 3n$	$10(3n)$
Nickel	n	$5(n)$
Penny	$p = 2n$	$1(2n)$
Total	527	4700

$25(q) + 10(3n) + 5(n) + 1(2n) = 4700$

$-(q + 3n + n + 2n = 527)$

$q + 6n = 527$ $\quad 25q + 150n = 13175$

$-(25q + 37n = 4700) \Rightarrow -(25q + 37n = 4700)$

$113n = 8475$

$n = 75$

There are 75 nickels, 75(3) = 225 dimes, 75(2) = 150 pennies and 527 - 75 - 225 - 150 = 77 quarters.

How long will it take $750 invested at 3.5% to earn $183.75?

i	p	r	t
$183.75	$750	0.035	t

$i = prt$

$\$183.75 = \$750(0.035)(t)$

$7 = t$

You must invest $750 at 3.5% for 7 years to earn $173.75 interest.

You need 50mL of a 25% solution of an acid, but you only have a 10% solution and a 30% solution on hand. How much of each solution should you mix to make 50mL of a 25% solution?

mL	% acid	Total
x	0.10	$0.1x$
$50 - x$	0.30	$0.3(50 - x)$
50 mL	0.25	50(0.25)

$0.1x + 0.3(50 - x) = 50(0.25)$

$0.1x + 15 - 0.3x = 12.5$

$-0.2x = -2.5$

$x = 12.5$

You need 12.5mL of the 10% solution and 50 - 12.5 = 37.5mL of the 30% solution.

Six consecutive integers have a sum of 273. What are the integers?

The integers are represented by x, $x + 1$, $x + 2$, $x + 3$, $x + 4$, and $x + 5$.

$x + (x+1) + (x+2) + (x+3) + (x+4) + (x+5) = 273$

$6x + 15 = 273$

$6x = 258$

$x = 43$

The integers are 43, 44, 45, 46, 47, and 48.

Five consecutive even integers have a sum of 130. What are the integers?

The integers are represented by x, $x + 2$, $x + 4$, $x + 6$, $x + 8$.

$x + (x+2) + (x+4) + (x+6) + (x+8) = 144$

$5x + 20 = 130$

$5x = 110$

$x = 22$

The integers are 22, 24, 26, 28, and 30.

30 points total

It's College Test Prep Time!

1. A restaurant serves peanuts for its guests to snack on while waiting for their meal to arrive. The price the restaurant pays for the peanuts is directly proportional to the number of pounds of peanuts the restaurant buys. If the peanuts cost d dollars per pound and the restaurant orders p pounds of peanuts, what is the total price of the peanuts in terms of d and p?

   A. dp Multiply the cost per pound by the number of pounds.
   B. $\frac{d}{p}$
   C. $\frac{p}{d}$
   D. $d + p$
   E. $d - p$

2. An amusement park ride can accommodate 305 riders in 15 minutes. At this rate, how many riders can it accommodate in $3\frac{1}{2}$ hours?

   A. 560 $\frac{305 \text{ riders}}{15 \text{ min.}} = \frac{r \text{ riders}}{210 \text{ min.}}$
   B. 1068 $305 \text{ riders}(210 \text{ min.}) = r \text{ riders}(15 \text{ min.})$
   C. 4270 $r = 4270$
   D. 7116
   E. 64,050

3. In the equations below, what is the value of c in terms of y if $y \neq 0$?
   $x = 3y$
   $5y = 12z$
   $(2x)(12z) = cy$

   A. $10y$ $2x = 6y;\ 12z = 5y$
   B. $15y$ $(6y)(5y) = cy$
   C. $24y$ $30y^2 = cy$
   D. $30y$ $c = 30y$
   E. $36y$

Exploring Math through... Fundraising

While fundraising itself is not necessarily a hobby or sport, it has become an integral part of nearly every organized sport. School teams as well as city and county leagues raise money to pay for uniforms, tournaments, and other game-related expenses.

Before a fundraiser can be started, someone must decide how much money needs to be raised. This impacts the decisions about what product or products to sell, how much to charge, and how many must be sold. Other options include service-type fundraisers such as washing cars or doing other types of manual labor. Some teams solicit donations without selling anything or giving anything to the donor.

During a fundraiser someone must record the number of each item sold and track the gross profit earned. Sometimes a fundraiser may have to be extended to meet a goal. Other times a fundraiser may be stopped early if the profit is high enough.

Sometimes the biggest amount of work comes at the end of a fundraiser. When the shipment of products arrives, someone must take inventory to ensure the order is accurate. Then the products must be sorted so each individual player can make deliveries to his customers. Accounting must be done to make sure that all the money is collected and distributed to the proper funds.

Most sports teams could not survive without some form of fundraising. Whether it is in the form of a concession stand, selling and delivering products to individuals, running a car wash, or collecting donations on a street corner or store front, math is involved in every aspect.

Teaching Tips, Cont.

- Have students read the Exploring Math feature for Lessons 121-130.
- Review for Exam 3 using worksheets 41-60.

Assignments

- Complete *It's College Test Prep Time!*
- Read Exploring Math through... Fundraising
- Study for Exam 3 (Lessons 81-117), if Exam 3 is being administered.

Exam 3

Testing Objectives

The student will:

- Add rational equations
- Subtract rational equations
- Multiply rational equations
- Divide rational equations
- Simplify complex fractions
- Simplify complex rational expressions
- State exclusions
- Solve quadratic equations
- Complete the square
- Find zeros of functions
- Write equations in parabolic form
- Find the vertex, focus, directrix, and axis of symmetry from a quadratic equation in parabolic form
- Solve mixture problems
- Find consecutive integers

Materials Needed

- Exam 3

Teaching Tips

➢ Administer Exam 3, allowing the students 45-50 minutes to complete the test.

① Solve. Remember to state any exclusions. **16 points**

$\frac{4x}{x+3}+\frac{7x}{x-1}=$

$\frac{4x(x-1)}{(x+3)(x-1)}+\frac{7x(x+3)}{(x+3)(x-1)}=$

$\frac{4x^2-4x}{x^2+2x-3}+\frac{7x^2+21x}{x^2+2x-3}=$

$\frac{11x^2+17x}{x^2+2x-3}; x\neq -3,1$

$\frac{9x}{x+2}-\frac{3x}{x-5}=$

$\frac{9x(x-5)}{(x+2)(x-5)}-\frac{3x(x+2)}{(x+2)(x-5)}=$

$\frac{9x^2-45x}{x^2-3x-10}-\frac{3x^2+6x}{x^2-3x-10}=$

$\frac{6x^2-51x}{x^2-3x-10}; x\neq -2,5$

$\frac{24x+42}{56x^2+16x}\cdot\frac{28x^2+8x}{4x^2-9x-28}=$

$\frac{{}_3\cancel{6}\cancel{(4x+7)}}{{}_2\cancel{8x}\cancel{(7x+2)}}\cdot\frac{\cancel{4x}\cancel{(7x+2)}}{\cancel{(4x+7)}(x-4)}=$

$\frac{3}{x-4}; x\neq -\frac{7}{4},-\frac{2}{7},0,4$

$\frac{3x+9}{x^2+5x}\div\frac{x^2-4x-21}{x^2-7x}=$

$\frac{3x+9}{x^2+5x}\cdot\frac{x^2-7x}{x^2-4x-21}=$

$\frac{3\cancel{(x+3)}}{\cancel{x}(x+5)}\cdot\frac{\cancel{x}\cancel{(x-7)}}{\cancel{(x+3)}\cancel{(x-7)}}=$

$\frac{3}{x+5}; x\neq -5,-3,0,7$

② Simplify the complex fractions. Remember to state any exclusions. **12 points**

$\frac{\frac{2}{3}}{5}$ LCD = 3.

$\frac{\cancel{3}\left(\frac{2}{\cancel{3}}\right)}{3(5)}=\frac{2}{15}$

$\frac{\frac{7}{3x}+\frac{5}{x+4}}{\frac{2x-8}{x^2-16}}$

$\frac{\frac{7}{3x}+\frac{5}{x+4}}{\frac{2\cancel{(x-4)}}{(x+4)\cancel{(x-4)}}}$

The LCD is $3x(x+4)$.

$\frac{\cancel{3x}(x+4)\left(\frac{7}{\cancel{3x}}\right)+3x\cancel{(x+4)}\left(\frac{5}{\cancel{x+4}}\right)}{3x\cancel{(x+4)}\left(\frac{2}{\cancel{x+4}}\right)}=$

$\frac{(x+4)(7)+3x(5)}{3x(2)}=$

$\frac{7x+28+15x}{6x}=$

$\frac{22x+28}{6x}=\frac{11x+14}{3x}; x\neq -4,0,4$

$\frac{4}{\frac{3}{6x+1}}$ LCD = 6x + 1.

$\frac{(6x+1)(4)}{\cancel{(6x+1)}\left(\frac{3}{\cancel{6x+1}}\right)}=\frac{24x+4}{3}; x\neq -\frac{1}{6}$

$\frac{\frac{4}{2x+1}+\frac{7}{x-2}}{\frac{x+1}{x^2-x-2}-\frac{2x+4}{x^2-4}}$

$\frac{\frac{4}{2x+1}+\frac{7}{x-2}}{\frac{\cancel{x+1}}{\cancel{(x+1)}(x-2)}-\frac{2\cancel{(x+2)}}{\cancel{(x+2)}(x-2)}}$

The LCD is $(2x+1)(x-2)$.

$\frac{\cancel{(2x+1)}(x-2)\left(\frac{4}{\cancel{2x+1}}\right)+(2x+1)\cancel{(x-2)}\left(\frac{7}{\cancel{x-2}}\right)}{(2x+1)\cancel{(x-2)}\left(\frac{1}{\cancel{x-2}}\right)-(2x+1)\cancel{(x-2)}\left(\frac{2}{\cancel{x-2}}\right)}=$

$\frac{(x-2)(4)+(2x+1)(7)}{(2x+1)(1)-(2x+1)(2)}=$

$\frac{(4x-8)+(14x+7)}{2x+1-4x-2}=$

$\frac{18x-1}{-2x-1}=x\neq -2,-1,-\frac{1}{2},2$

③ Solve each quadratic equation. **4 points**

$x^2-6x-27=0$

$(x-9)(x+3)=0$

$x-9=0; x=9$

$x+3=0; x=-3$

The solution is $x=9$ and -3.

$x^2+6x-8=0$

$x^2+6x=8$

$x^2+6x+\left(\frac{6}{2}\right)^2=8+\left(\frac{6}{2}\right)^2$

$x^2+6x+9=8+9$

$x^2+6x+9=17$

$(x+3)^2=17$

$\sqrt{(x+3)^2}=\sqrt{17}$

$x+3=\pm\sqrt{17}$

$x=-3\pm\sqrt{17}$

$x^2-121=0$

$x^2=121$

$\sqrt{x^2}=\sqrt{121}$

$x=\pm 11$

$2x^2-6x+3=0$

$x=\frac{-(-6)\pm\sqrt{(-6)^2-4(2)(3)}}{2(2)}$

$x=\frac{6\pm\sqrt{36-24}}{4}$

$x=\frac{6\pm\sqrt{12}}{4}$

$x=\frac{6\pm 2\sqrt{3}}{4}$

$x=\frac{6}{4}\pm\frac{2\sqrt{3}}{4}$

$x=\frac{3\pm\sqrt{3}}{2}$

④ Complete the square to write each function in parabolic form. **3 points**

$f(x)=3x^2+6x-2$

$3x^2+6x-2=0$

$3x^2+6x=2$

$3(x^2+2x)=2$

$3(x^2+2x+1)=2+3(1)$

$3(x+1)^2=2+3$

$3(x+1)^2-5=0$

$f(x)=3(x+1)^2-5$

$f(x)=4x^2-8x+7$

$4x^2-8x+7=0$

$4x^2-8x=-7$

$4(x^2-2x)=-7$

$4(x^2-2x+1)=-7+4(1)$

$4(x-1)^2=-7+4$

$4(x-1)^2+3=0$

$f(x)=4(x-1)^2+3$

$f(x)=2x^2+16x+5$

$2x^2+16x+5=0$

$2x^2+16x=-5$

$2(x^2+8x)=-5$

$2(x^2+8x+16)=-5+2(16)$

$2(x+4)^2=-5+32$

$2(x+4)^2-27=0$

$f(x)=2(x+4)^2-27$

⑤ Find the zeros. **3 points**

$\sqrt{2}x^2+\sqrt{10}x-6=0$

$x=\frac{-\sqrt{10}\pm\sqrt{(\sqrt{10})^2-4(\sqrt{2})(-6)}}{2(\sqrt{2})}$

$x=\frac{-\sqrt{10}\pm\sqrt{10+24\sqrt{2}}}{2\sqrt{2}}\cdot\frac{\sqrt{2}}{\sqrt{2}}$

$x=\frac{-\sqrt{20}\pm\sqrt{2(10+24\sqrt{2})}}{4}$

$x=\frac{-\sqrt{20}\pm\sqrt{20+48\sqrt{2})}}{4}$

$x=\frac{-2\sqrt{5}\pm\sqrt{4(5+12\sqrt{2})}}{4}$

$x=\frac{-\sqrt{5}\pm\sqrt{5+12\sqrt{2}}}{2}$

$f(x)=x^2-5x-2$

$0=x^2-5x-2$

$x^2-5x=2$

$x^2-5x+\left(-\frac{5}{2}\right)^2=2+\left(-\frac{5}{2}\right)^2$

$x^2-5x+\frac{25}{4}=\frac{8}{4}+\frac{25}{4}$

$x^2-5x+\frac{25}{4}=\frac{33}{4}$

$\left(x-\frac{5}{2}\right)^2=\frac{33}{4}$

$\sqrt{\left(x-\frac{5}{2}\right)^2}=\sqrt{\frac{33}{4}}$

$x-\frac{5}{2}=\pm\frac{\sqrt{33}}{2}$

$x=\frac{5\pm\sqrt{33}}{2}$

$f(x)=(5x+2)(3x-4)$

$5x+2=0$ $\quad 3x-4=0$

$5x=-2$ $\quad 3x=4$

$x=-\frac{2}{5},\frac{4}{3}$

Exam 3

⑥ Rewrite each equation in the form $4p(y-k)=(x-h)^2$. Identify the value of the variables *p*, *k*, and *h*, and give the coordinates for the vertex and focus, and the equations of the lines for the axis of symmetry and the directrix of the parabola. **16 points**

$y=\frac{1}{4}(x-2)^2-5$

$y+5=\frac{1}{4}(x-2)^2$

$\frac{y+5}{\frac{1}{4}}=(x-2)^2$

$4(y+5)=(x-2)^2$

$4p=4\Rightarrow p=1$

$k=-5$

$h=2$

The vertex is (2, -5).
The focus is (2, -5 + 1) = (2, -4).
The axis of symmetry is the line $x = 2$.
The directrix is the line $y=-5-1\Rightarrow y=-6$.

$y=3(x+2)^2+1$

$y-1=3(x+2)^2$

$\frac{y-1}{3}=(x+2)^2$

$\frac{1}{3}(y-1)=(x+2)^2$

$4p=\frac{1}{3}\Rightarrow p=\frac{1}{12}$

$k=1$

$h=-2$

The vertex is (-2, 1).
The focus is (-2, 1 + $\frac{1}{12}$) = (-2, $\frac{13}{12}$).
The axis of symmetry is the line $x = -2$.
The directrix is the line $y=1-\frac{1}{12}\Rightarrow y=\frac{11}{12}$.

⑦ Solve. **8 points**

You need 100mL of a 15% solution of an acid, but you only have a 10% solution and a 30% solution on hand. How much of each solution should you mix to make 100mL of a 15% solution?

mL	% acid	Total
x	0.10	$0.1x$
$100-x$	0.30	$0.3(100-x)$
100 mL	0.15	100(0.15)

$0.1x+0.3(100-x)=100(0.15)$

$0.1x+30-0.3x=15$

$-0.2x=-15$

$x=75$

You need 75mL of the 10% solution and 100 - 75 = 25mL of the 30% solution.

Five consecutive integers have a sum of 125. What are the integers?

The integers are represented by x, $x+1$, $x+2$, $x+3$, and $x+4$.

$x+(x+1)+(x+2)+(x+3)+(x+4)=125$

$5x+10=125$

$5x=115$

$x=23$

The integers are 23, 24, 25, 26, and 27.

62 points total

Assignment

- There is no assignment for this lesson.

Lesson 121

Concepts

- Inequalities on a number line
- Math in the real world

Learning Objectives

The student will be able to:

- Express inequalities on a number line
- Use the closed circle and open circle correctly to indicate whether or not inequalities can also be equal to a number

Materials Needed

- Student Book, Lesson 121

Teaching Tips

- ➢ Ask the students where on the *x*-axis they would find positive values. (To the right of the origin)
- ➢ Ask the students where on the *x*-axis they would find negative values. (To the left of the origin)
- ➢ Tell the students that it is possible to use just the *x*-axis to express inequalities.
- ➢ Teach graphing inequalities from the teaching box. Make sure the students understand that any time the symbol is < or > they use an open circle rather than a closed circle to represent the starting point of the ray.

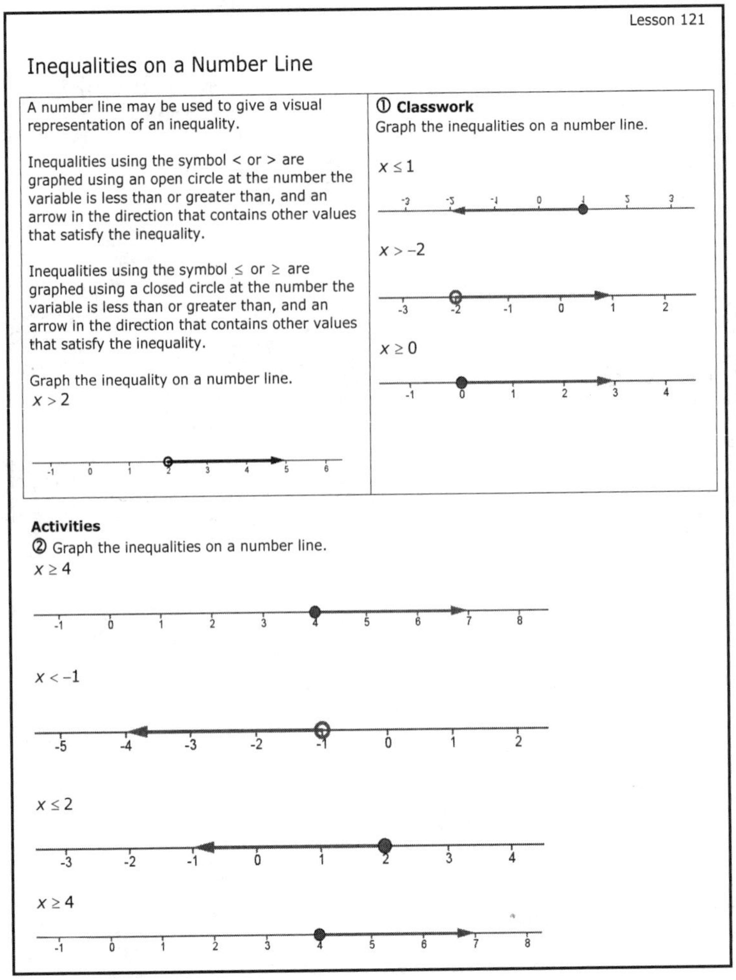

Lesson 121

Inequalities on a Number Line

A number line may be used to give a visual representation of an inequality.

Inequalities using the symbol < or > are graphed using an open circle at the number the variable is less than or greater than, and an arrow in the direction that contains other values that satisfy the inequality.

Inequalities using the symbol ≤ or ≥ are graphed using a closed circle at the number the variable is less than or greater than, and an arrow in the direction that contains other values that satisfy the inequality.

Graph the inequality on a number line.
$x > 2$

① **Classwork**
Graph the inequalities on a number line.

$x \le 1$

$x > -2$

$x \ge 0$

Activities
② Graph the inequalities on a number line.

$x \ge 4$

$x < -1$

$x \le 2$

$x \ge 4$

③ Solve.

At the end of a car wash fundraiser, a team had collected 66 bills worth a total of $304. There were twice as many $5 bills as there were $10 bills, and the rest were $1 bills. How many of each bill did the team have at the end of the fundraiser?

Let t = the number of $10 bills, f = the number of $5 bills, and n = the number of $1 bills.

Type of bill	Number	Total Value
$10	t	$10(t)$
$5	$f = 2t$	$5(2t)$
$1	n	$1(n)$
Total	66	304

Set up a system of equations and solve.

$10(t)+5(2t)+1(n)=304$

$-(t + 2t + n = 66)$

$20t + n = 304$

$-(3t + n = 66)$

$17t = 238$

$t = 14$

There are 14 tens, 14(2) = 28 fives and 66 - 14 - 28 = 24 ones.

The team washed 12 cars in the first 90 minutes. At this rate, how many cars did they wash in 6 hours?

6 hours = 6(60) = 360 minutes.

Let c = the number of cars washed in 6 hours.

$\frac{12 \text{ cars}}{90 \text{ min.}} = \frac{c \text{ cars}}{360 \text{ min.}}$

$12 \text{ cars}(360 \text{ min.}) = c \text{ cars}(90 \text{ min.})$

$4320 = 90c$

$48 = c$

The team washed 48 cars in 6 hours.

The team received either a $10 bill, a $5 bill, or some $1 bills for each car they washed. If each car that paid with $1 bills gave the same amount, how much did each of these cars give?

From the information above, we know that 14 cars gave a $10 bill and 28 cars gave a $5 bill. This leaves 48 - 14 - 28 = 6 cars paying with $1 bills.

If there were 24 $1 bills, then each of those cars gave 24 ÷ 6 = $4.

Teaching Tips, Cont.

- Complete the Classwork exercises. Have some students work the problems on the board for the class and explain their answers. All students should work the problems in their books.

Assignment

- Complete Lesson 121, Activities 2-3.

Lesson 122

Concepts
- Compound inequalities
- Inequalities on a number line

Learning Objectives
The student will be able to:
- Define *compound inequality*
- Write a compound inequality from two inequalities joined by the word *and*
- Graph a compound inequality formed from two inequalities joined by the word *and*
- Use open and closed circles correctly in the graph of a compound inequality

Materials Needed
- Student Book, Lesson 122
- Worksheet 61

Teaching Tips
- Have students complete Worksheet 61 in class. This may be for added practice of earlier topics, or graded as a quiz, if desired.
- Review graphing inequalities on a number line. (See Lesson 121)
- Teach the definition of *compound inequality* from the teaching box.
- Tell the students that this lesson will focus exclusively on compound inequalities joined by the word *and*.
- Tell the students that the rules about open and closed circles in graphing inequalities apply to graphing compound inequalities with the word *and*.

Compound Inequalities: And

A **compound inequality** is two inequalities joined by a conjunction – either *and* or *or*. This lesson will focus on compound inequalities that use the word *and*.

When two inequalities are joined by the word *and*, they may be combined into a single inequality. This single inequality may then be graphed on a number line as two endpoints joined by a line segment.

The solution of a compound inequality joined by the word *and* must satisfy both individual inequalities. If a number is part of the solution of one inequality but not the other, then it is not part of the solution of the compound inequality.

Using the given inequalities, write a compound inequality and draw its graph on a number line.
$-1 < x$ and $x \le 3$

Because the inequalities are already written such that x is greater than one number and less than another number, form a compound inequality with x in the center and the two extremes on either side. Make sure the symbols are identical to the original inequalities.
$-1 < x \le 3$

To graph the compound inequality, mark the numbers using the appropriate circle symbol and join the two points with a line segment.

If a compound inequality must be solved, separate it into two separate inequalities and solve them individually. Then rejoin them to make a new compound inequality.

Solve $1 < x + 3 < 5$.

Separate the compound inequality. Solve each part and then rejoin.
$1 < x + 3$ and $x + 3 < 5$
$-2 < x$ and $x < 2$
$-2 < x < 2$

① **Classwork**
Using the given inequalities, write a compound inequality and draw its graph on a number line.

$-2 < x$ and $x < 1$
$-2 < x < 1$

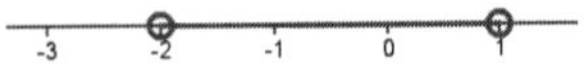

$1 \ge x$ and $x > -3$
$-3 < x \le 1$

Solve each compound inequality and draw its graph on a number line.

$-1 < x + 2 < 4$
$-1 < x + 2$ and $x + 2 < 4$
$-3 < x$ and $x < 2$
$-3 < x < 2$

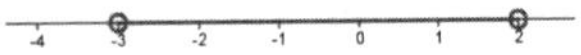

$-2 < x + 3 \le 6$
$-2 < x + 3$ and $x + 3 \le 6$
$-5 < x$ and $x \le 3$
$-5 < x \le 3$

$2 \le x + 1 \le 3$
$2 \le x + 1$ and $x + 1 \le 3$
$1 \le x$ and $x \le 2$
$1 \le x \le 2$

Activities
② Using the given inequalities, write a compound inequality and draw its graph on a number line.

$-5 < x$ and $x < -3$
$-5 < x < -3$

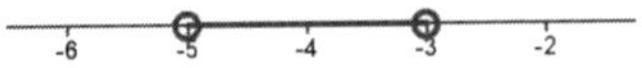

$-3 < x$ and $x < 2$
$-3 < x < 2$

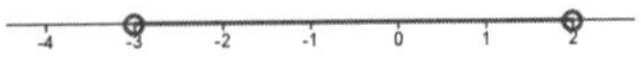

$1 \ge x$ and $x > -4$
$-4 < x \le 1$

$5 \ge x$ and $x > 0$
$0 < x \le 5$

③ Solve each compound inequality and draw its graph on a number line.

$-1 < x - 2 < 4$
$-1 < x - 2$ and $x - 2 < 4$
$1 < x$ and $x < 6$
$1 < x < 6$

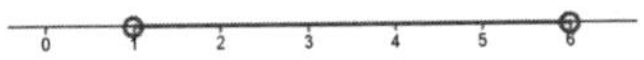

$-6 < x - 4 < -3$
$-6 < x - 4$ and $x - 4 < -3$
$-2 < x$ and $x < 1$
$-2 < x < 1$

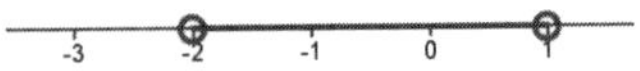

$3 \le x + 5 \le 7$
$3 \le x + 5$ and $x + 5 \le 7$
$-2 \le x$ and $x \le 2$
$-2 \le x \le 2$

$-8 < x - 3 \le -4$
$-8 < x - 3$ and $x - 3 \le -4$
$-5 < x$ and $x \le -1$
$-5 < x \le -1$

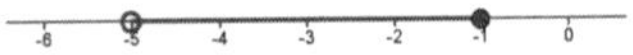

$3 \le x + 4 \le 9$
$3 \le x + 4$ and $x + 4 \le 9$
$-1 \le x$ and $x \le 5$
$-1 \le x \le 5$

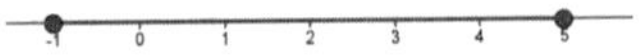

$-5 \le x - 3 \le -1$
$-5 \le x - 3$ and $x - 3 \le -1$
$-2 \le x$ and $x \le 2$
$-2 \le x \le 2$

$-1 < 2x + 3 \le 5$
$-1 < 2x + 3$ and $2x + 3 \le 5$
$-4 < 2x$ and $2x \le 2$
$-2 < x$ and $x \le 1$
$-2 < x \le 1$

$2 \le 3x - 1 \le 5$
$2 \le 3x - 1$ and $3x - 1 \le 5$
$3 \le 3x$ and $3x \le 6$
$1 \le x \le 2$

Consecutive Integers, Direct and Inverse Variation Worksheet 61

① Solve.

Four consecutive odd integers have a sum of 120. What are the integers?

The integers are represented by x, $x + 2$, $x + 4$, and $x + 6$.

$x + (x + 2) + (x + 4) + (x + 6) = 120$

$4x + 12 = 120$

$4x = 108$

$x = 27$

The integers are 27, 29, 31, and 33.

Six consecutive integers have a sum of 207. What are the integers?

The integers are represented by x, $x + 1$, $x + 2$, $x + 3$, $x + 4$, and $x + 5$.

$x + (x + 1) + (x + 2) + (x + 3) + (x + 4) + (x + 5) = 207$

$6x + 15 = 207$

$6x = 192$

$x = 32$

The integers are 32, 33, 34, 35, 36, and 37.

② Solve.

If y varies directly as x and $y = 36$ when $x = 27$, what is value of k? State the value of k and write an equation to show the direct variation.

$y = kx$

$36 = k(27)$ $\qquad y = \frac{4}{3}x$

$\frac{36}{27} = \frac{4}{3} = k$

If y varies directly as x and $y = 8$ when $k = 12$, what is value of x? State the value of x and write an equation to show the direct variation.

$y = kx$

$8 = 12(x)$ $\qquad y = 12x$

$\frac{8}{12} = \frac{2}{3} = x$

If y varies directly as x and $x = 3$ when $k = 5$, what is value of y? State the value of y and write an equation to show the direct variation.

$y = kx$

$y = 5(3)$ $\qquad y = 5x$

$y = 15$

If y varies inversely as x and $y = 10$ when $x = 3$, what is value of k? State the value of k and write an equation to show the inverse variation.

$xy = k$

$3(10) = k$ $\qquad y = \frac{30}{x}$

$30 = k$

If y varies inversely as x and $y = 14$ when $k = 7$, what is value of x? State the value of x and write an equation to show the inverse variation.

$xy = k$

$x(14) = 7$ $\qquad y = \frac{7}{x}$

$x = \frac{7}{14} = \frac{1}{2}$

Teaching Tips, Cont.

- Teach how to join two inequalities into a single compound inequality from the teaching box. Make sure the students understand that this will only work when the two inequalities are joined by the word *and*.
- Teach how to graph a compound inequality on a number line. Remind the students when to use an open circle rather than a closed circle on the graphs. Point out that it is possible for the graph to have two open circles, two closed circles, or one of each. It all depends on the symbols used in the compound inequality.
- Complete the Classwork exercises. Have some students work the problems on the board for the class and explain their answers. All students should work the problems in their books.

Assignment

- Complete Lesson 122, Activities 2-3.

Lesson 123

Concepts
- Compound inequalities
- Inequalities on a number line
- Functions

Learning Objectives
The student will be able to:
- Graph a compound inequality formed from two inequalities joined by the word *or*
- Use open and closed circles correctly in the graph of a compound inequality

Materials Needed
- Student Book, Lesson 123
- Worksheet 62

Teaching Tips
- Review graphing inequalities on a number line. (See Lesson 121)
- Review compound inequalities joined by the word *and*. (See Lesson 122)
- Tell the students that the rules about open and closed circles in graphing inequalities apply to graphing compound inequalities with the word *or*.
- Teach compound inequalities joined by the word *or* from the teaching box. Make sure the students understand that in this case, the value of x can satisfy one inequality at a time. Because both inequalities cannot be met at the same time, it is impossible to combine the inequalities into a single statement.

Compound Inequalities: Or

In the previous lesson you learned to solve compound inequalities that used the word *and*. In this lesson, you will solve compound inequalities that use the word *or*. While compound inequalities that use the word *and* are graphed as a single line segment, compound inequalities that use the word *or* are graphed as two separate rays.

Graph the compound inequality on a number line.

$x \le 1$ or $x > 3$

The inequality is joined by the word *or*, so there will be two separate rays on the graph. Begin by drawing the appropriate circles for each number and add the arrow in the appropriate direction for each inequality.

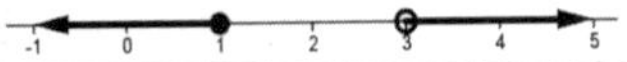

① **Classwork**

Graph the compound inequality on a number line.

$x \le -1$ or $x > 1$

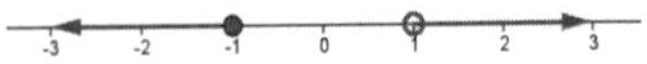

$x < 0$ or $x > 3$

$x \le -2$ or $x \ge 0$

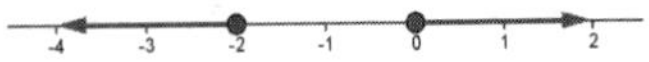

Activities

② Graph the compound inequality on a number line.

$x \le 2$ or $x > 4$

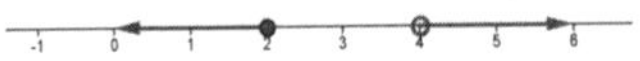

$x \le -3$ or $x > 0$

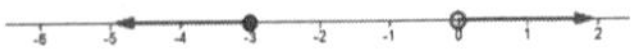

$x < -3$ or $x > -1$

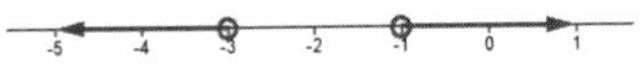

$x < 0$ or $x > 4$

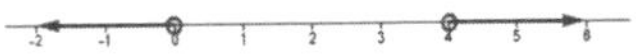

$x \le -4$ or $x \ge -1$

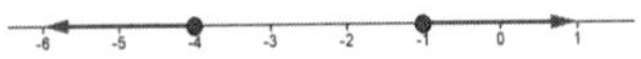

$x \le 1$ or $x \ge 5$

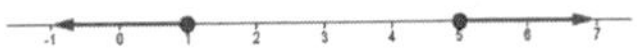

$x < 3$ or $x \ge 4$

$x < -5$ or $x \ge -2$

③ Solve each compound inequality and draw its graph on a number line.

$1 < 3x + 4 < 10$
$1 < 3x + 4$ and $3x + 4 < 10$
$-3 < 3x$ and $3x < 6$
$-1 < x$ and $x < 2$
$-1 < x < 2$

$-9 \le 2x - 5 \le -3$
$-9 \le 2x - 5$ and $2x - 5 \le -3$
$-9 \le 2x - 5$ and $2x - 5 \le -3$
$-4 \le 2x$ and $2x \le 2$
$-2 \le x \le 1$

$-7 < 4x - 3 \le 1$
$-7 < 4x - 3$ and $4x - 3 \le 1$
$-4 < 4x$ and $4x \le 4$
$-1 < x$ and $x \le 1$
$-1 < x \le 1$

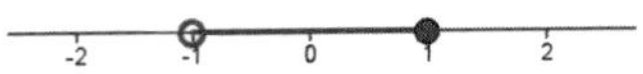

$-9 \le 5x + 1 \le 16$
$-9 \le 5x + 1$ and $5x + 1 \le 16$
$-10 \le 5x$ and $5x \le 15$
$-2 \le x$ and $x \le 3$
$-2 \le x \le 3$

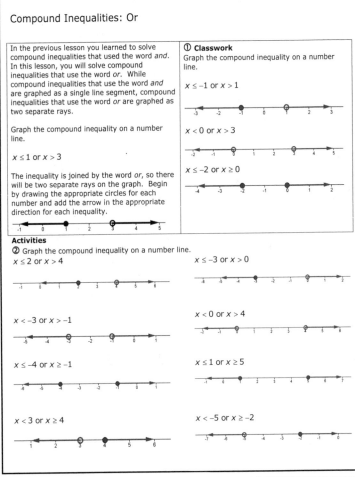

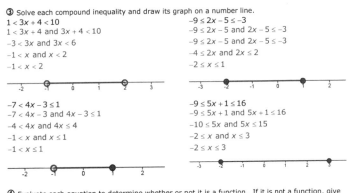

④ Evaluate each equation to determine whether or not it is a function. If it is not a function, give an example from the relation to show why it is not a function.

$y - 13x^2 + 27 = 0$
$y = 13x^2 - 27$
Substitute 0 for x.
$y = 0 - 27$
$y = -27$
This is a function.

$y + 5x + 2 = 0$
$y = -5x - 2$
Substitute 0 for x.
$y = 0 - 2$
$y = -2$
This is a function.

$y^2 + 12x - 25 = 0$
$y^2 = -12x + 25$
Substitute 0 for x.
$y^2 = 0 + 25$
$y^2 = 25$
$y = \pm 5$
This is not a function.
$(0,5)$ and $(0,-5)$

$y^2 + 11x^2 - 1 = 0$
$y^2 = -11x + 1$
Substitute 0 for x.
$y^2 = 0 + 1$
$y^2 = 1$
$y = \pm 1$
This is not a function.
(0, 1) and (0, -1)

$y - 32x^2 + 9 = 0$
$y = 32x^2 - 9$
Substitute 0 for x.
$y = 0 - 9$
$y = -9$
This is a function.

$y + 63x^2 - 16 = 0$
$y = -63x^2 + 16$
Substitute 0 for x.
$y = 0 + 16$
$y = 16$
This is a function.

$y - 81x^2 + 9 = 0$
$y = 81x^2 - 9$
Substitute 0 for x.
$y = 0 - 9$
$y = -9$
This is a function.

$y^2 + \sqrt{7}x^2 - 3 = 0$
$y^2 = -\sqrt{7}x + 3$
Substitute 0 for x.
$y^2 = 0 + 3$
$y^2 = 3$
$y = \pm\sqrt{3}$
This is not a function.
$(0, \sqrt{3})$ and $(0, -\sqrt{3})$

$y - 2x^2 + \sqrt{5} = 0$
$y = 2x^2 - \sqrt{5}$
Substitute 0 for x.
$y = 0 - \sqrt{5}$
$y = -\sqrt{5}$
This is a function.

Graphing Inequalities on a Number Line Worksheet 62

① Graph the inequalities on a number line.

$x \geq -2$

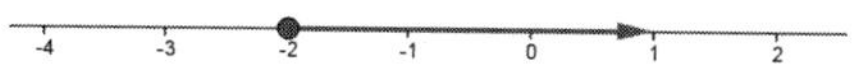

$x < 3$

$-2 < x - 1 < 5$
$-2 < x - 1$ and $x - 1 < 5$
$-1 < x$ and $x < 6$
$-1 < x < 6$

$3 \leq x + 2 \leq 7$
$3 \leq x + 2$ and $x + 2 \leq 7$
$1 \leq x$ and $x \leq 5$
$1 \leq x \leq 5$

$x \leq 1$ or $x > 3$

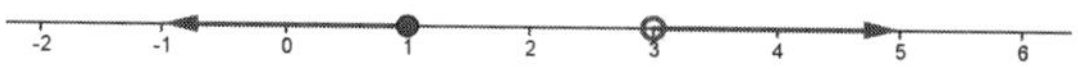

$x < -4$ or $x > -1$

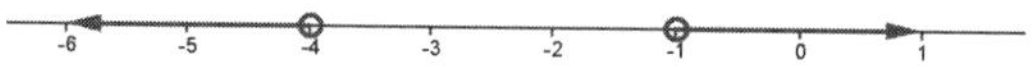

$x \leq -3$ or $x \geq 1$

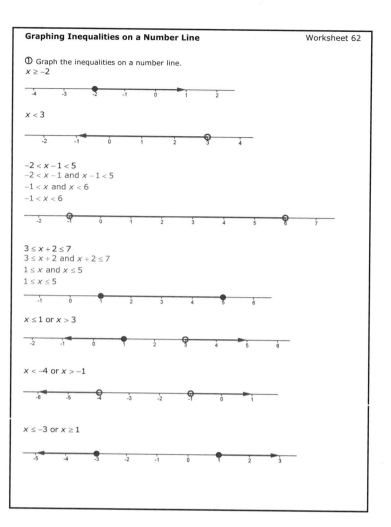

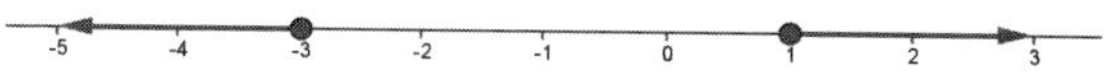

Teaching Tips, Cont.

- Teach how to graph a compound inequality on a number line. Remind the students when to use an open circle rather than a closed circle on the graphs. Point out that it is possible for the graph to have two open circles, two closed circles, or one of each. It all depends on the symbols used in the compound inequality.
- Complete the Classwork exercises. Have some students work the problems on the board for the class and explain their answers. All students should work the problems in their books.

Assignments

- Complete Lesson 123, Activities 2-4.
- Worksheet 62.

Lesson 124

Concepts

- Conjunctions
- Compound inequalities
- Inequalities on a number line
- Math in the real world

Learning Objectives

The student will be able to:

- Define *conjunction*
- Identify whether or not a conjunction is true or false

Materials Needed

- Student Book, Lesson 124

Teaching Tips

- ➢ Review compound inequalities joined with the word *and*. (See Lesson 122)
- ➢ Teach the definition of *conjunction* from the teaching box.
- ➢ Refer the students to Lesson 122. Show them that all of the problems in Activity 2 are conjunctions because they can be expressed as two separate inequalities joined by the word *and*.
- ➢ Teach how to determine whether or not a conjunction is true from the teaching box.

Conjunctions

A **conjunction** is two mathematical sentences joined by the word *and*. Rather than using the word *and*, you may alternately use the symbol $\cap$. For a conjunction to be true, both mathematical sentences must be true. If either sentence is false, the entire conjunction is false.

Tell whether or not the conjunction is true.
$(8 > 5) \cap (7 - 2 < 6)$

Analyze each part separately.
$8 > 5$ true
$7 - 2 < 6$
$5 < 6$ true

Because both parts are true, the conjunction is true. If either part had been false, the entire conjunction would have been false.

① **Classwork**

Tell whether or not the conjunction is true.

$(9 > 3) \cap (3 - 2 < 8)$
$9 > 3$ true
$3 - 2 < 8$
$1 < 8$ true
The conjunction is true.

$(x > 5) \cap (7 - 2 > x)$
$(x > 5) \cap (5 > x)$
They can't both be true at the same time, so the conjunction is false.

$(8 > x) \cap (7 - 2 = x)$
$(8 > x) \cap (5 = x)$
$8 > 5$ true
The conjunction is true.

Activities

② Tell whether or not the conjunction is true.

$(-7 > 8) \cap (-2 < 1)$
$-7 > 8$ false $-2 < 1$ true
The conjunction is false.

$(x < 3) \cap (1 + 4 < x)$
$(x < 3) \cap (5 < x)$
They can't both be true at the same time, so the conjunction is false.

$(-1 > x) \cap (2 - 5 = x)$
$(-1 > x) \cap (-3 = x)$
$-1 > -3$ true
The conjunction is true.

$(3 + 5 > 9 - 4) \cap (3 \cdot 2 < 14 \div 2)$
$8 > 5$ true $6 < 7$ true
The conjunction is true.

$(x < 2) \cap (-2 + 5 = x)$
$(x < 2) \cap (3 = x)$
$3 < 2$ false
The conjunction is false.

$(2 + 3 < x - 1) \cap (5 + 8 = x + 2)$
$(6 < x) \cap (11 = x)$
$6 < 11$ true
The conjunction is true.

$(2 > 5) \cap (3 - 4 < -3)$
$2 > 5$ false $-1 < -3$ false
The conjunction is false.

$(2x > 8) \cap (7 - 1 = 3x)$
$(x > 4) \cap (2 = x)$
$2 > 4$ false
The conjunction is false.

$(2 \cdot 6 < 3x) \cap (16 - 1 = 3x)$
$(4 < x) \cap (5 = x)$
$4 < 5$ true
The conjunction is true.

$(10 - 8 > 3 + 4) \cap (12 \div 2 > \sqrt{25})$
$2 > 7$ false $6 > 5$ true
The conjunction is false.

$(2x > 3 + 7) \cap (3 - 2 > x)$
$(x > 5) \cap (1 > x)$
They can't both be true at the same time, so the conjunction is false.

$(3x < x + 4) \cap (1 = x)$
$(x < 2) \cap (1 = x)$
$1 < 2$ true
The conjunction is true.

③ Graph each compound inequality on a number line.

$x \le -6$ or $x > -4$

$x \le 0$ or $x > 1$

$2x < -8$ or $3x > -6$
$x < -4$ or $x > -2$

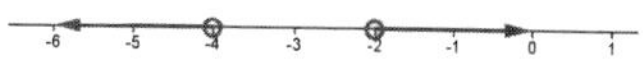

$x + 3 < -5$ or $x - 2 > -6$
$x < -8$ or $x > -4$

$2 < 3x + 2 < 14$
$2 < 3x + 2$ and $3x + 2 < 14$
$0 < 3x$ and $3x < 12$
$0 < x$ and $x < 4$
$0 < x < 4$

$-13 < 5x - 3 \le -8$
$-13 < 5x - 3$ and $5x - 3 \le -8$
$-10 < 5x$ and $5x \le -5$
$-2 < x$ and $x \le -1$
$-2 < x \le -1$

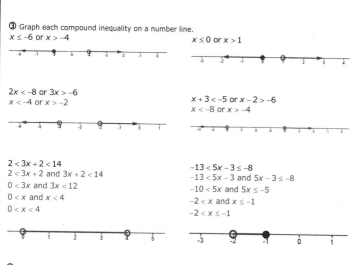

④ Solve.

A team is selling gift wrap and bows to raise money for shoes. They earn $4.40 for each roll of wrapping paper sold and $2 for each pack of bows sold. If one team member sold a total of 46 items and earned $159.20, how many of each item was sold?

Let p = the number of rolls of wrapping paper sold.
Let b = the number of packs of bows sold.

$p + b = 46$
$4.4p + 2b = 159.2$

$4.4p + 2b = 159.2$
$2p + 2b = 92$
$2.4p = 67.2$
$p = 28$

$28 + b = 46$; $b = 18$

The team member sold 28 rolls of wrapping paper and 18 packs of bows.

If each team member is expected to raise a minimum of $100, what is the minimum number of rolls of wrapping paper that must be sold if no packs of ribbon are sold?

$4.4p \ge 100$
$p \ge 22.7$

Because a partial roll of paper cannot be sold, the team member must sell a minimum of 23 rolls of wrapping paper to raise a minimum of $100.

Teaching Tips, Cont.

- Refer the students to Activity 2 in Lesson 123. Ask them if the word *or* was replaced with the word *and*, would the conjunctions be true? (No.) Why not? (Because x cannot satisfy both conditions at the same time.)
- Emphasize that *both* conditions must be true for a conjunction to be true. If either condition is false, then the conjunction is false.
- Complete the Classwork exercises. Have some students work the problems on the board for the class and explain their answers. All students should work the problems in their books.

Assignment

- Complete Lesson 124, Activities 2-4.

Lesson 125

Concepts
- Disjunctions
- Conjunctions
- Compound inequalities
- Inequalities on a number line

Learning Objectives
The student will be able to:
- Define *disjunction*
- Identify whether or not a disjunction is true or false

Materials Needed
- Student Book, Lesson 125
- Worksheet 63

Teaching Tips
- Have students complete Worksheet 63 in class. This may be for added practice of earlier topics, or graded as a quiz, if desired.
- Review conjunctions. (See Lesson 124)
- Review compound inequalities joined by the word *or*. (See Lesson 123)
- Review graphing inequalities on a number line. (See Lesson 121)
- Teach the definition of disjunction from the teaching box.

Disjunctions

A **disjunction** is two mathematical sentences joined by the word *or*. Rather than using the word *or*, you may alternately use the symbol $\cup$. For a disjunction to be true, at least one of the mathematical sentences must be true. A disjunction is false only if both mathematical sentences are false.

Tell whether or not the disjunction is true.
$(8 < 5) \cup (7 - 2 < 6)$

Analyze each part separately.
$8 < 5$ false
$7 - 2 < 6$
$5 < 6$ true

Because at least one part is true, the disjunction is true. If both parts had been false, the entire disjunction would have been false.

① Classwork
Tell whether or not the disjunction is true.

$(9 > 3) \cup (3 - 2 < 8)$
$9 > 3$ true
$3 - 2 < 8$
$1 < 8$ true
The disjunction is true.

$(x > 5) \cup (7 - 2 \geq x)$
$(x > 5) \cup (5 \geq x)$
One of them has to be true, so the disjunction is true.

$(8 > 9) \cup (7 - 2 < 4)$
$(8 > 9) \cup (5 < 4)$
false false
The disjunction is false.

Activities
② Tell whether or not the disjunction is true.

$(-7 > 8) \cup (-2 < 1)$
$-7 > 8$ false $-2 < 1$ true
The disjunction is true.

$(x \leq 3) \cup (-1 + 4 < x)$
$(x \leq 3) \cup (3 < x)$
One of them has to be true, so the disjunction is true.

$(x - 1 > x + 3) \cup (2 - 5 < 1 - 7)$
$(-1 > 3) \cup (-3 < -6)$
false false
The disjunction is false.

$(3 + 5 < 9 - 4) \cup (3 \cdot 2 < 14 \div 2)$
$8 < 5$ false $6 < 7$ true
The disjunction is true.

$(x < 2) \cup (-3 + 5 \leq x)$
$(x < 2) \cup (2 \leq x)$
One of them has to be true, so the disjunction is true.

$(2 + 3 < 4 - 1) \cup (5 + 8 \leq 9 + 2)$
$(5 < 3) \cup (13 \leq 11)$
false false
The disjunction is false.

$(2 > 5) \cup (3 - 4 < -3)$
$2 > 5$ false $-1 < -3$ false
The disjunction is false.

$(2x > 8) \cup (7 + 5 \geq 3x)$
$(x > 4) \cup (4 \geq x)$
One of them has to be true, so the disjunction is true.

$(2 \cdot 6 < 4x) \cup (16 - 1 \geq 5x)$
$(3 < x) \cup (3 \geq x)$
One of them has to be true, so the disjunction is true.

$(10 - 8 > 3 + 4) \cup (12 \div 2 > \sqrt{25})$
$2 > 7$ false $6 > 5$ true
The disjunction is true.

$(2x > 2x + 7) \cup (x - 2 > x)$
$(0 > 7) \cup (-2 > 0)$
false false
The disjunction is false.

$(2 + 9 < 6 - 4) \cup (3 \cdot 2 < 21 \div 3)$
$11 < 2$ false $6 < 7$ true
The disjunction is true.

③ Tell whether or not the conjunction is true.

$(-9 > 2) \cap (-3 < 4)$
$-9 > 2$ false $-3 < 4$ true
The conjunction is false.

$(-3 > 1) \cap (8 - 1 > 4 + 6)$
$-3 > 1$ false $7 > 10$ false
The conjunction is false.

$(3x > 12) \cap (7 + 3 = 5x)$
$(x > 4) \cap (2 = x)$
$2 > 4$ false
The conjunction is false.

$(4x > 13 + 7) \cap (5 - 4 > x)$
$(x > 5) \cap (1 > x)$
They can't both be true at the same time, so the conjunction is false.

$(7x < -x + 4) \cap (-1 = x)$
$(x < 2) \cap (-1 = x)$
$-1 < 2$ true
The conjunction is true.

$(x < -1) \cap (-3 + 7 = x)$
$(x < -1) \cap (4 = x)$
$4 < -1$ false
The conjunction is false.

$(x < 2) \cap (-1 + 4 < x)$
$(x < 2) \cap (3 < x)$
They can't both be true at the same time, so the conjunction is false.

$(0 > x) \cap (3 - 5 = x)$
$(0 > x) \cap (-2 = x)$
$0 > -2$ true
The conjunction is true.

$(2 + 5 < x - 3) \cap (6 + 9 = x + 3)$
$(10 < x) \cap (12 = x)$
$10 < 12$ true
The conjunction is true.

$(2 \cdot 9 < 6x) \cap (23 - 5 = 2x)$
$(3 < x) \cap (9 = x)$
$3 < 9$ true
The conjunction is true.

$(5 + 4 > 11 - 4) \cap (3 \cdot 2 - 1 < 16 \div 2)$
$9 > 7$ true $5 < 8$ true
The conjunction is true.

$(11 - 9 > 2 + 5) \cap (18 \div 2 > \sqrt{49})$
$2 > 7$ false $9 > 7$ true
The conjunction is false.

④ Graph each compound inequality on a number line.

$x \leq -5$ or $x > -2$

$x \leq 1$ or $x > 5$

$4x < -12$ or $5x > 10$
$x < -3$ or $x > 2$

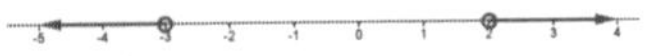

$x + 4 < -2$ or $x - 3 > -5$
$x < -6$ or $x > -2$

$2 < 3x + 5 < 17$
$2 < 3x + 5$ and $3x + 5 < 17$
$-3 < 3x$ and $3x < 12$
$-1 < x$ and $x < 4$
$-1 < x < 4$

$-3 \leq x - 1 \leq 2$
$-3 \leq x - 1$ and $x - 1 \leq 2$
$-2 \leq x$ and $x \leq 3$
$-2 \leq x \leq 3$

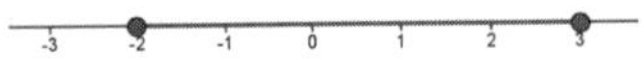

Graphing Inequalities on a Number Line Worksheet 63

① Graph the inequalities on a number line.

$x \leq 4$

$x > -1$

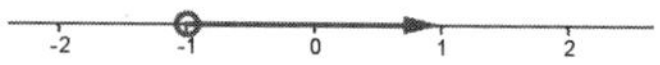

$1 < x - 2 \leq 7$
$1 < x - 2$ and $x - 2 \leq 7$
$3 < x$ and $x \leq 9$
$3 < x \leq 9$

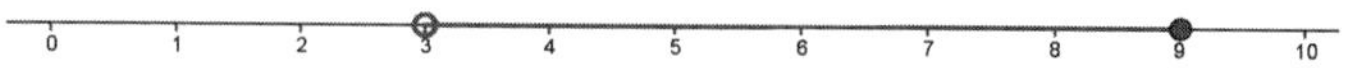

$-2 \leq x - 3 \leq 1$
$-2 \leq x - 3$ and $x - 3 \leq 1$
$1 \leq x$ and $x \leq 4$
$1 \leq x \leq 4$

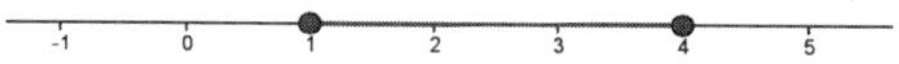

$x \leq -1$ or $x > 3$

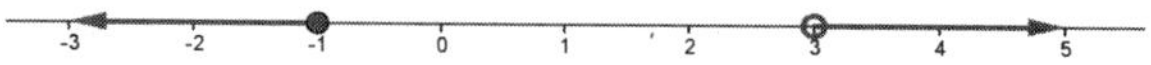

$x < 3$ or $x > 4$

$x \leq -4$ or $x \geq -2$

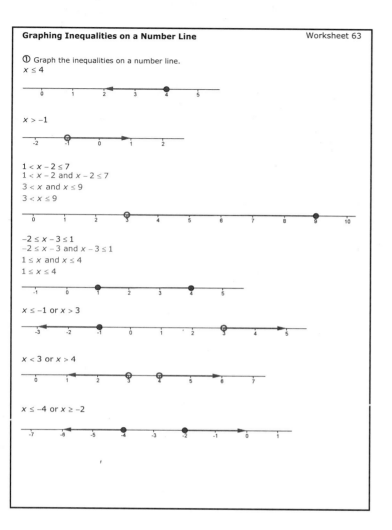

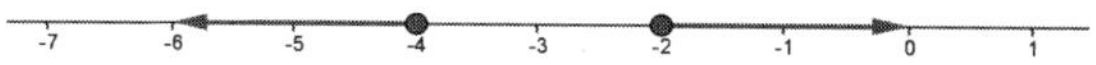

Teaching Tips, Cont.

- Refer the students to Lesson 123. Show them that all of the problems in Activity 2 are disjunctions because they are expressed as two separate inequalities joined by the word *or*.
- Emphasize that *both* conditions must be false for a disjunction to be false. If either condition is true, then the disjunction is true.
- Complete the Classwork exercises. Have some students work the problems on the board for the class and explain their answers. All students should work the problems in their books.

Assignment

- Complete Lesson 125, Activities 2-4.

Lesson 126

Concepts
- Inequalities
- Absolute value
- Inequalities on a number line

Learning Objectives
The student will be able to:
- Rewrite inequalities containing an absolute value symbol as compound inequalities with no absolute value symbol
- Correctly use the words *and* and *or* in compound inequalities
- Graph inequalities containing an absolute value symbol on a number line

Materials Needed
- Student Book, Lesson 126

Teaching Tips
- Review absolute value as the distance from zero. (See Lesson 5)
- Review compound inequalities (See Lessons 122-123)
- Teach how to solve inequalities with absolute value symbols from the teaching box.
- Tell the students to place the absolute value symbol with the variable on the left side and the constant terms on the right side of the inequality. If the inequality has a less than symbol, use the word *and* to form the compound inequality. If the inequality has a greater than symbol, use the word *or* to form the compound inequality.

Inequalities with Absolute Value

Remember from Lesson 5 that the absolute value of a number is its distance from zero on a number line. This distance may be in either direction, positive or negative.

When solving inequalities that have absolute values, isolate the absolute value expression and rewrite the inequality as a compound inequality.

If the inequality symbol is < or ≤ the compound inequality will have the word *and*. If the inequality symbol is > or ≥ the compound inequality will have the word *or*.

There are two exceptions to the above rules. If the absolute value symbol is isolated on the left side of the inequality symbol < or ≤ and a negative number is on the right side, then the answer is *no solution*. If the absolute value symbol is isolated on the left side of the inequality symbol > or ≥ and a negative number is on the right side, then the answer is *all real numbers*. The absolute value will always be positive, and therefore greater than any negative number.

Solve the inequality and draw the graph on a number line.

$|x-2|+1<2$

Isolate the absolute value.

$|x-2|<1$

Write the inequality as a compound inequality using the word *and*.

$x-2<1$ and $x-2>-1$

Notice that the direction of the symbol changed when the right side was multiplied by -1. Solve the compound inequality.

$x<3$ and $x>1$

$1<x<3$

① **Classwork**

Solve each inequality and draw the graph on a number line.

$|x-3|+2<5$

$|x-3|<3$

$x-3<3$ and $x-3>-3$

$x<6$ and $x>0$

$0<x<6$

$|x+2|-5\le -1$

$|x+2|\le 4$

$x+2\le 4$ and $x+2\ge -4$

$x\le 2$ and $x\ge -6$

$-6\le x\le 2$

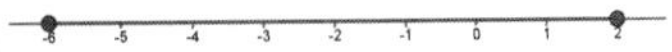

$|x-1|+7\ge -3$

$|x-1|\ge -10$

All real numbers.

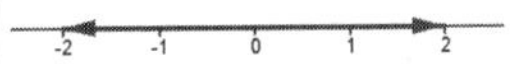

$|x+4|+3>8$

$|x+4|>5$

$x+4>5$ or $x+4<-5$

$x>1$ or $x<-9$

Activities

② Solve each inequality and draw the graph on a number line.

$|x-1|+3<6$
$|x-1|<3$
$x-1<3$ and $x-1>-3$
$x<4$ and $x>-2$
$-2<x<4$

$|x+3|-4\le -2$
$|x+3|\le 2$
$x+3\le 2$ and $x+3\ge -2$
$x\le -1$ and $x\ge -5$
$-5\le x\le -1$

$|x+3|+7<2$
$|x+3|<-5$
No solution.

$|2x+7|-5>2$
$|2x+7|>7$
$2x+7>7$ or $2x+7<-7$
$2x>0$ or $2x<-14$
$x>0$ or $x<-7$

$|4x-5|-1\ge -5$
$|4x-5|\ge -4$
All real numbers.

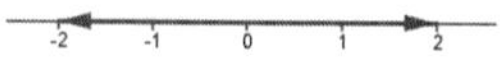

$|x-4|+3\le -5$
$|x-4|\le -8$
No solution.

$|x-5|+4<8$
$|x-5|<4$
$x-5<4$ and $x-5>-4$
$x<9$ and $x>1$
$1<x<9$

$|x+4|-6\le -3$
$|x+4|\le 3$
$x+4\le 3$ and $x+4\ge -3$
$x\le -1$ and $x\ge -7$
$-7\le x\le -1$

$|3x-2|+6\ge 1$
$|3x-2|\ge -5$
All real numbers.

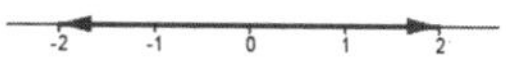

$|2x+1|+2>9$
$|2x+1|>7$
$2x+1>7$ or $2x+1<-7$
$2x>6$ or $2x<-8$
$x>3$ or $x<-4$

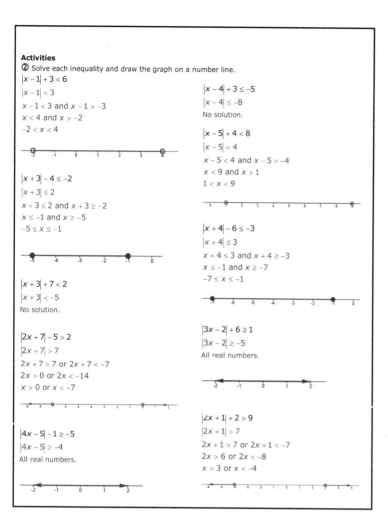

Teaching Tips, Cont.

- A mnemonic device that may help students remember whether to use *and* or *or* is to place them in alphabetical order with the symbol in between. Whichever word the symbol is pointing to is the word they should use. *(and < > or)*
- Ask the students if the absolute value of a number can ever be negative. (No.)
- Tell the students there is a special rule that applies when the constant on the right side is a negative number. If the problem states that the absolute value is less than a negative number, this is impossible, so the answer is *no solution*. If the problem states that the absolute value is greater than a negative number, then all positive numbers apply, so the answer is *all real numbers*.
- Complete the Classwork exercises. Have some students work the problems on the board for the class and explain their answers. All students should work the problems in their books.

Assignment

- Complete Lesson 126, Activity 2.

Lesson 127

Concepts

- Compound inequalities
- Inequalities on a number line
- Conjunctions
- Disjunctions

Learning Objectives

The student will be able to:

- Graph compound inequalities on a number line
- Identify compound inequalities having no solution

Materials Needed

- Student Book, Lesson 127

Teaching Tips

➢ Review graphing inequalities on a number line. (See Lesson 121)

➢ Review compound inequalities (See Lessons 122-123)

➢ Review conjunctions. (See Lesson 124)

➢ Review disjunctions. (See Lesson 125)

➢ Review inequalities with absolute value. (See Lesson 126)

Lesson 127

Inequalities: Review

When single-variable inequalities are graphed on a number line, the symbols < and > use an open circle, and the symbols ≤ and ≥ use a solid dot.

Compound inequalities may be joined by the word *and* (conjunctions) or the word *or* (disjunctions).

Compound inequalities with absolute value signs have their own set of rules. You should remember the following rules from Lesson 126.

If the inequality symbol is < or ≤ the compound inequality will have the word *and*. If the inequality symbol is > or ≥ the compound inequality will have the word *or*.

There are two exceptions to the above rules. If the absolute value symbol is isolated on the left side of the inequality symbol < or ≤ and a negative number is on the right side, then the answer is *no solution*. If the absolute value symbol is isolated on the left side of the inequality symbol > or ≥ and a negative number is on the right side, then the answer is *all real numbers*. The absolute value will always be positive, and therefore greater than any negative number.

① Classwork

Graph each compound inequality on a number line.

$3 \ge x$ and $x > -2$

$-2 < x \le 3$

$x < 1$ or $x > 3$

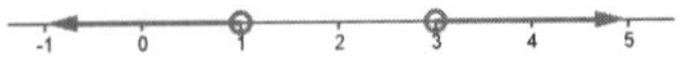

$|x-1| + 4 < 5$

$|x-1| < 1$

$x-1 < 1$ and $x-1 > -1$

$x < 2$ and $x > 0$

$0 < x < 2$

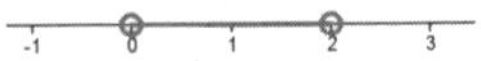

Activities

② Graph each compound inequality on a number line.

$-5 < 2x - 3 \le -1$

$-5 < 2x - 3$ and $2x - 3 \le -1$

$-2 < 2x$ and $2x \le 2$

$-1 < x$ and $x \le 1$

$-1 < x \le 1$

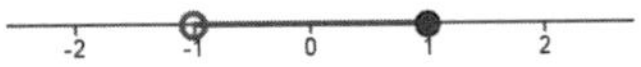

$4x < -12$ or $3x > -6$

$x < -3$ or $x > -2$

$|x+5| - 7 \le -3$

$|x+5| \le 4$

$x+5 \le 4$ and $x+5 \ge -4$

$x \le -1$ and $x \ge -9$

$-9 \le x \le -1$

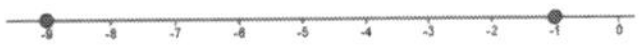

$|5x-2| + 3 \ge -2$

$|5x-2| \ge -5$

All real numbers.

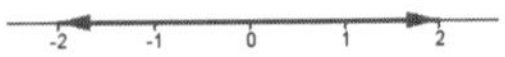

③ Tell whether or not each conjunction or disjunction is true.

$(-7 > 3) \cap (-4 < 2)$
false true
The conjunction is false.

$(x \le 5) \cap (-3 + 8 < x)$
$(x \le 5) \cap (5 < x)$
They can't both be true at the same time, so the conjunction is false.

$(x - 2 > x + 5) \cap (3 - 5 < 4 - 9)$
$-2 > 5$ $-2 < -5$
false false
The conjunction is false.

$(3 \cdot 5 < 13 - 4) \cap (14 \div 7 < 5 \cdot 3)$
$15 < 9$ $2 < 15$
false true
The conjunction is false.

$(2x < 6) \cap (-3 + 9 \le 2x)$
$(x < 3) \cap (3 \le x)$
They can't both be true at the same time, so the conjunction is false.

$(7 - 2 < 2 + 1) \cap (3 + 8 \ge 9 + 4)$
$(5 < 3) \cap (11 \ge 13)$
false false
The conjunction is false.

$(x < -1) \cap (-4 + 3 \le x)$
$(x < -) \cap (-1 \le x)$
They can't both be true at the same time, so the conjunction is false.

$(2 \cdot 3 < 1^7) \cap (6^2 \le 3^3)$
$(6 < 1) \cap (36 \le 27)$
false false
The conjunction is false.

$(-7 > 3) \cup (-4 < 2)$
false true
The disjunction is true.

$(x \le 5) \cup (-3 + 8 < x)$
$(x \le 5) \cup (5 < x)$
One of them has to be true, so the disjunction is true.

$(x - 2 > x + 5) \cup (3 - 5 < 4 - 9)$
$(-2 > 5) \cup (-2 < -5)$
false false
The disjunction is false.

$(3 \cdot 5 < 13 - 4) \cup (14 \div 7 < 5 \cdot 3)$
$15 < 9$ $2 < 15$
false true
The disjunction is true.

$(2x < 6) \cup (-3 + 9 \le 2x)$
$(x < 3) \cup (3 \le x)$
One of them has to be true, so the disjunction is true.

$(7 - 2 < 2 + 1) \cup (3 + 8 \ge 9 + 4)$
$(5 < 3) \cup (11 \ge 13)$
false false
The disjunction is false.

$(x < -1) \cup (-4 + 3 \le x)$
$(x < -) \cup (-1 \le x)$
One of them has to be true, so the disjunction is true.

$(2 \cdot 3 < 1^7) \cup (6^2 \le 3^3)$
$(6 < 1) \cup (36 \le 27)$
false false
The disjunction is false.

Teaching Tips, Cont.

- Ask the students what condition would have no solution. (An absolute value less than a negative number)
- Ask the students what condition would have all real numbers as the solution. (An absolute value greater than a negative number)
- Complete the Classwork exercises. Have some students work the problems on the board for the class and explain their answers. All students should work the problems in their books.

Assignment

- Complete Lesson 127, Activities 2-3.

Lesson 128

Concepts
- Systems of linear inequalities
- Bounded solutions
- Unbounded solutions
- Inequalities

Learning Objectives
The student will be able to:
- Solve a system of linear inequalities by graphing
- State whether the solution of a system of linear inequalities is bounded or unbounded

Materials Needed
- Student Book, Lesson 128
- Worksheet 64

Teaching Tips
➢ Have students complete Worksheet 64 in class. This may be for added practice of earlier topics, or graded as a quiz, if desired.

➢ Review inequalities. (See Lessons 45-46)

➢ Review graphing inequalities. (See Lesson 50)

➢ Ask the students what methods they could use to solve a system of linear equations. (Adding, subtracting, setting the equations equal, linear combinations, graphing, etc.)

➢ Tell the students that the easiest method of solving a system of linear inequalities is by graphing.

Systems of Linear Inequalities

You have already learned how to solve systems of linear equations. You had several options available to you to find these solutions. Only one of these methods, however, will work to solve a system of linear inequalities.

To solve a system of linear inequalities, graph each of the inequalities on the same coordinate plane and shade the appropriate side of the line. The portion of the graph with the overlapping shading is the solution of the system of linear inequalities.

A system of linear inequalities that has two separate inequalities with an overlapping shaded portion has an unbounded solution. The graph starts off looking like it will form a triangle, but the third side is missing, allowing the graph to continue on infinitely in that direction.

A system on linear inequalities that has three separate inequalities with a portion of all three graphs overlapping has a bounded solution because the overlapping shaded area is bounded on all sides, forming a triangle.

Graph the solution of the system of linear inequalities and state whether the solution is bounded or unbounded.

$x - y > 3$
$x + y < 4$
$x + 2y > 1$

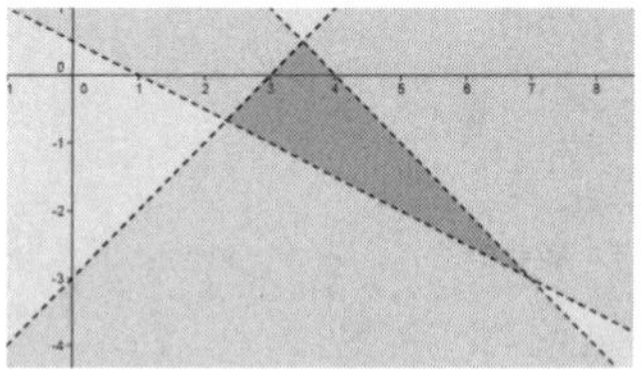

The solution is the triangular shape formed by the intersection of the shaded areas of the three individual graphs of the inequalities. This graph is bounded because it is closed on all sides.

① Classwork
Graph the solution of the system of linear inequalities and state whether the solution is bounded or unbounded.

$x - y > 0$
$x < 4$
$y > -1$

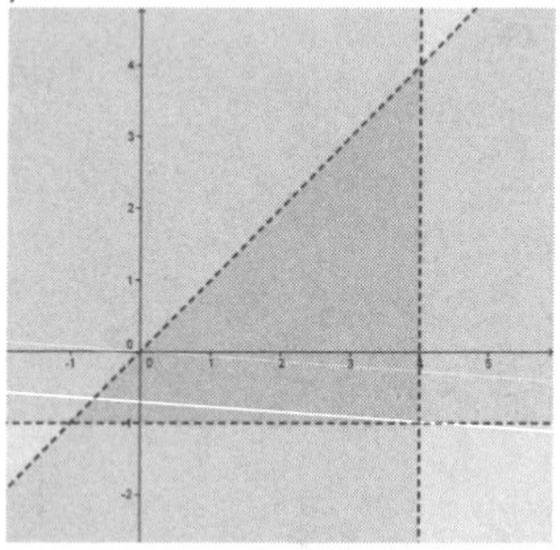

The graph is bounded.

$x - y < 0$
$x > 4$
$y > -1$

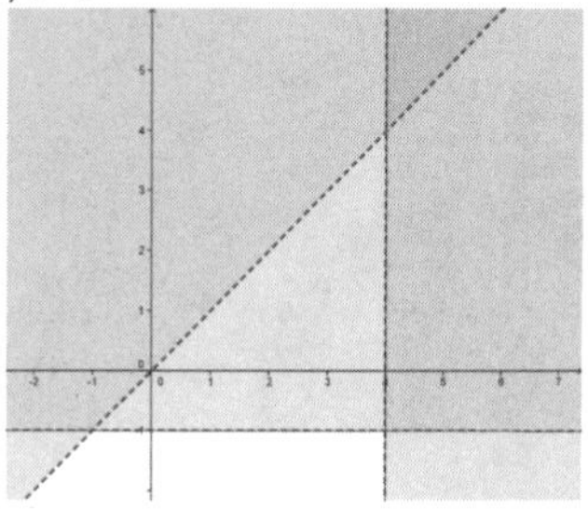

The graph is unbounded.

Activities
② Graph the solution of the system of linear inequalities and state whether the solution is bounded or unbounded.

$x - y < 0$
$x + y > 0$
$x < 3$

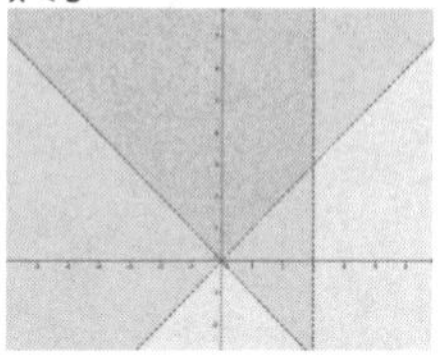

The graph is unbounded.

$x - y < 0$
$x + y > 0$
$x > 3$

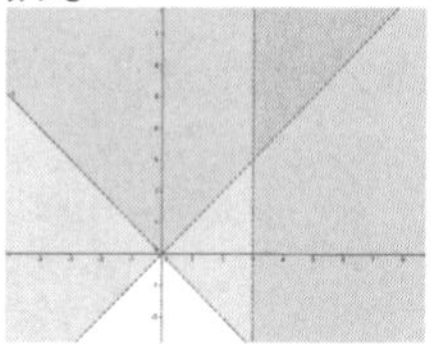

The graph is unbounded.

$x - y < 0$
$x + y > 0$
$y < 3$

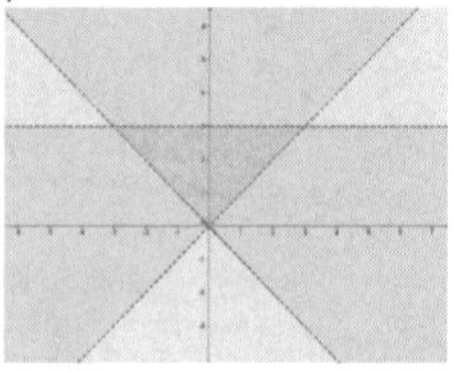

The graph is bounded.

$x - y < 0$
$x + y > 0$
$y > 3$

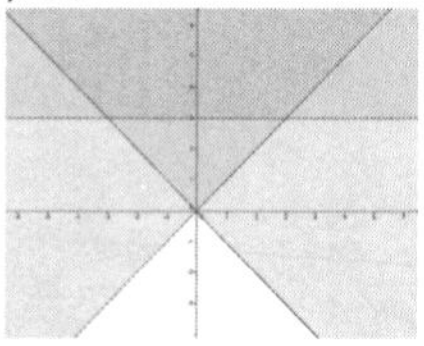

The graph is unbounded.

③ Write an inequality for each situation. You do not have to solve.

A baseball team, t, has no more than 25 players.
$t \le 25$

A penalty, p, is at least 5 yards in a football game.
$p \ge 5$

A football team on its own 1-yard line must move the ball, b, at least 10 yards but less than 99 yards to get a first down.
$10 \le b < 99$

The number of dollars, d, a softball team must earn in their fundraiser is at least 125 times the number of players, p.
$d \ge 125p$

Conjunctions, Disjunctions Worksheet 64

① Tell whether or not the conjunction is true.

$(-9 > 3) \cap (-4 < 2)$
$-9 > 3$ false $-4 < 2$ true
The conjunction is false.

$(7 < 11) \cap (-4 < 2)$
$7 < 11$ true $-4 < 2$ true
The conjunction is true.

$(x < -2) \cap (3 - 5 \leq x)$
$(x < -2) \cap (-2 \leq x)$
They can't both be true at the same time, so the conjunction is false.

$(4 < -1) \cap (-3 + 7 = x)$
$(4 < -1) \cap (3 = x)$
$4 < -1$ false
The conjunction is false.

$(-2 > x) \cap (1 - 5 = x)$
$(-2 > x) \cap (-4 = x)$
$-2 > -4$ true
The conjunction is true.

$(3 + 4 < x - 2) \cap (6 + 8 = x + 3)$
$(9 < x) \cap (11 = x)$
$9 < 11$ true
The conjunction is true.

② Tell whether or not the disjunction is true.

$(-9 > 3) \cup (-4 < 2)$
$-9 > 3$ false $-4 < 2$ true
The disjunction is true.

$(7 < 11) \cup (-4 < 2)$
$7 < 11$ true $-4 < 2$ true
The disjunction is true.

$(x < -2) \cup (3 - 5 \leq x)$
$(x < -2) \cup (-2 \leq x)$
One of them has to be true, so the disjunction is true.

$(x < 3) \cup (-2 + 5 \leq x)$
$(x < 3) \cup (3 \leq x)$
One of them has to be true, so the disjunction is true.

$(x - 4 > x + 2) \cup (2 - 5 < 2 - 7)$
$(-4 > 2) \cup (-3 < -5)$
false false
The disjunction is false.

$(2 + 6 < 11 - 8) \cup (3 + 8 \leq 9 - 2)$
$(8 < 3) \cup (11 \leq 7)$
false false
The disjunction is false.

Teaching Tips, Cont.

- Ask the students how they could find the solution to a system of linear equations by graphing. (Find the point where the lines intersect.)
- Teach solving systems of linear inequalities by graphing from the teaching box. Explain that rather than a single point in common, there will be a shaded region in common.
- Explain that the solution is bounded if the overlapping shaded areas form a closed figure, such as a triangle, and the solution is unbounded is one or more sides of the figure are missing. The sides of the shaded figure *must* be the inequality lines that were originally graphed.
- Complete the Classwork exercises. Have some students work the problems on the board for the class and explain their answers. All students should work the problems in their books.

Assignment

- Complete Lesson 128, Activities 2-3.

Lesson 129

Concepts

- Systems of linear inequalities
- Math in the real world

Learning Objectives

The student will be able to:

- Use a system of linear inequalities to find possible solutions to real-world scenarios
- Identify specific possible solutions by finding coordinate points in the shaded region on a graph

Materials Needed

- Student Book, Lesson 129

Teaching Tips

➢ Review systems of linear inequalities. (See Lesson 128)

➢ Ask the students how they know what the solution is to a system of linear inequalities. (Look for the overlapping shaded region.)

➢ Tell the students that the coordinate points in this region can be used to find specific potential solutions to a problem.

Solving Word Problems with Systems of Linear Inequalities

When using a system of linear inequalities to solve a word problem, each point in the combined shaded area is a solution to the problem. Generally, only integers are used in stating possible solutions.

To solve a word problem using a system of linear inequalities, label what each variable stands for and write an inequality for each condition stated in the problem. Graph all inequalities for a given problem on a single Cartesian plane, shading the appropriate side of each line. Make a list of coordinate points that lie in the combined shaded area as the possible solution combinations.

A volleyball team is selling popcorn and candles to raise at least $500 to offset expenses for the season. They earn $2.80 for each container of popcorn sold and $4.50 for each candle sold. From past experience, they expect to sell at least 100 containers of popcorn. Make a graph of the information and list at least 3 combinations of popcorn and candles sold that will satisfy the minimum fundraising requirements.
Let x = popcorn sold
Let y = candles sold

Set up a system of equations with the given information.

$2.8x + 4.5y \geq 500$

$x \geq 100$

Graph the system of equations.

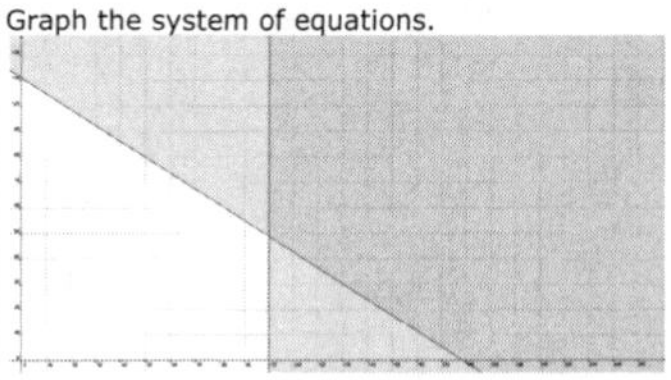

Anything in the dark shaded region is a solution. Pick any three points in this region.
100 popcorn and 60 candles, 110 popcorn and 50 candles, and 120 popcorn and 40 candles all lie in this region and are possible solutions.

① **Classwork.**
Use a graph to find at least three combinations that satisfy the requirements.

A soccer team is selling donuts and washing cars to raise at least $750 to offset expenses for the season. They earn $6 for each box of donuts sold and $10 for each car they wash. From past experience, they expect to sell at least 50 boxes of donuts. Make a graph of the information and list at least 3 combinations of donuts and cars that will satisfy the minimum fundraising requirements.

Let x = donuts sold
Let y = cars washed

$6x + 10y \geq 750$

$x \geq 50$

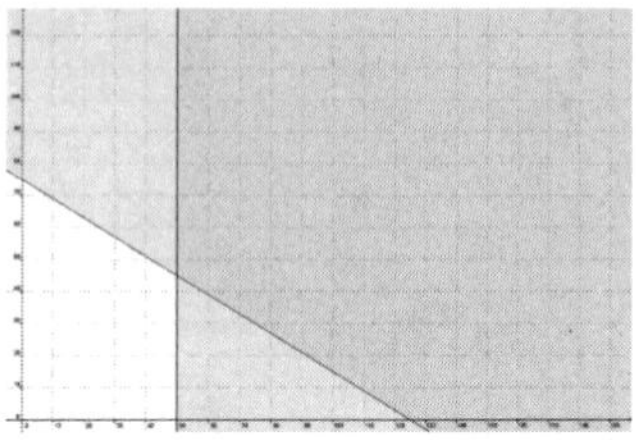

There are numerous possible combinations acceptable, which include 50 boxes of donuts and 50 cars, 70 boxes of donuts and 40 cars, and 90 boxes of donuts and 30 cars.

Any three points in the dark shaded area are acceptable. All numbers given must be integers since you cannot sell a partial box of donuts or wash a partial car in a fundraiser.

Activities

② Use a graph to find at least three combinations that satisfy the requirements.
The athletic club wants to raise at least $8500 to purchase bleachers. They are selling 150 season passes valid for all home games for an entire school year for $50 for an adult pass and $10 for a student pass. If they need to raise at least 50% of the funds through the sale of season passes, how many of each pass must they sell? Give three possible combinations of pass sales that will meet the requirements. Hint: Let each square on your graph paper represent 10 rather than 1.)

Let x = the number of adult passes.
Let y = the number of student passes.
50% of $8500 is $4250.

$x + y \leq 150$

$50x + 10y \geq 4250$

Possible solutions lie in the dark shaded triangle and include 90 adults and 10 students, 100 adults and 20 students, and 110 adults and 30 students.

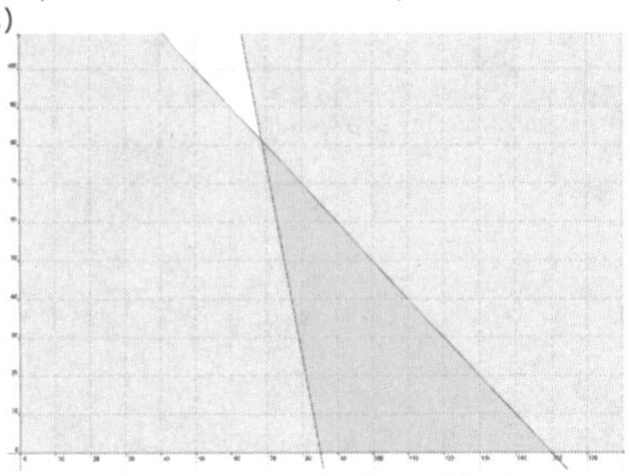

③ Solve. (Challenge question! You may use any method of your choice to solve this problem.)
A basketball team wants to save 82.25GB worth of footage from the season onto disk. A blu-ray disk costs $2.30 and holds 25GB of data. A DVD costs $0.39 and holds 4.7GB of data. If the team has room to store no more than 10 disks, and wants to spend no more than $7.50 on disks, how many of each type of disk should they use to store the footage?

Let x = the number of blu-ray disks.
Let y = the number of DVDs.

$x + y \leq 10$

$2.3x + .39y \leq 7.50$

$25x + 4.7y \geq 82.25$

The only integer point that falls in the shaded triangle is 2 blu-rays and 7 DVDs.

Note: This is a challenge problem due to the nature of the graph. You may wish to do this exercise as a class using a graphing calculator, or allow the students to use an alternate method, such as making a chart, to solve. This is a type of question that may appear on standardized tests, so the students should know how to solve it.

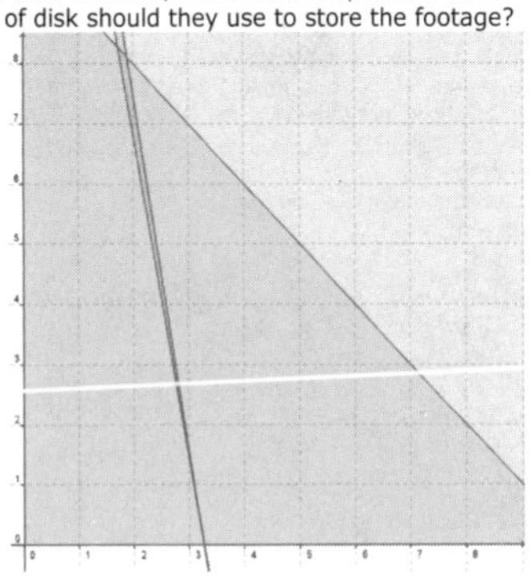

Teaching Tips, Cont.

- Teach solving word problems with systems of linear inequalities from the teaching box.
- Explain that any point in the overlapping shaded region is an acceptable solution to the system of linear inequalities. When the problem asks for an answer, any point in the region is a correct answer. Some problems may have several possible correct answers.
- Make sure the students understand that most problems will require integers for the solution point. Any time it is not possible to have a fraction of something, such as people, the only correct solutions are those that are integers. In other words, (2, 5) would be an acceptable solution, but (2.5, 5) would not.
- Complete the Classwork exercise. Have one student work the problem on the board for the class and explain the answer. All students should work the problem in their books.

Assignment

- Complete Lesson 129, Activities 2-3.

Lesson 130

Concepts

- Systems of linear inequalities
- Direct variation
- Inverse variation

Learning Objectives

The student will be able to:

- Graph the solution of a system of linear inequalities
- Identify systems of linear inequalities that have no solution

Materials Needed

- Student Book, Lesson 130

Teaching Tips

- Review systems of linear inequalities. (See Lessons 128-129)

- Tell the students that so far they have learned to solve systems of linear inequalities by graphing, identify whether the solution is bounded or unbounded, and give specific solutions for the system.

- Ask the students if all systems of linear equations have a solution. (No. A system of equations that are parallel lines does not have a solution because they never intersect.)

Systems of Linear Inequalities: No Solution

So far you have learned to solve systems of linear inequalities by graphing and looking for the region that lies in the shaded portion of each individual inequality. Sometimes, however, you will have a system of equations that does not have a shaded region that overlaps every individual inequality. In this case, there is no solution.

Graph the system of inequalities and tell whether or not it has a solution.

$x - y \le 3$

$x + y \ge 4$

$x + 2y \le 1$

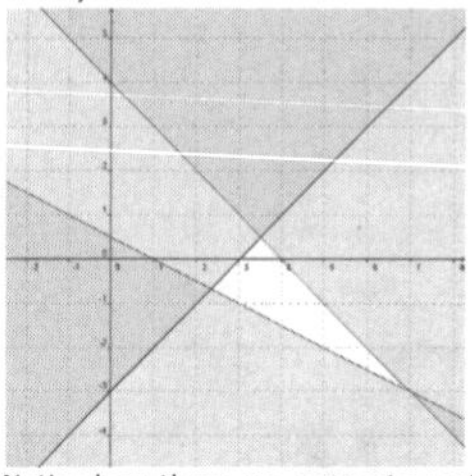

Notice how there are separate regions of overlapping shading, but no single region that is part of all three inequalities. This system of inequalities has no solution.

① Classwork

Graph the system of inequalities and tell whether or not it has a solution.

$x - y < 0$

$x > 4$

$y < -1$

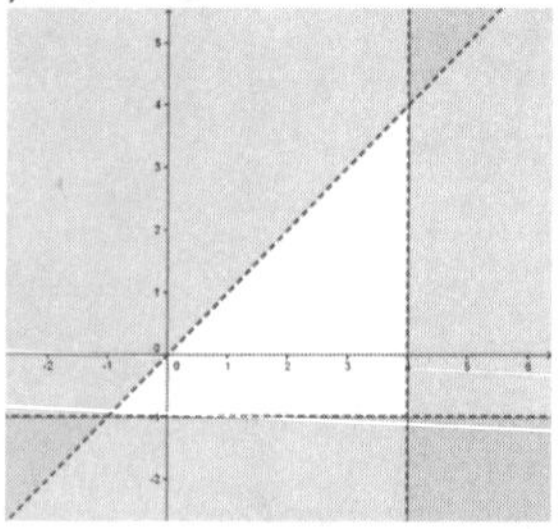

There is no area of shading that overlaps all three inequalities, so this system of inequalities has no solution.

Activities

② Graph the system of inequalities and tell whether or not it has a solution. You do not have to solve them.

$x - y \le 3$

$x + y \le 4$

$x + 2y \le 1$

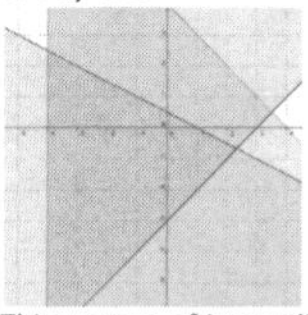

This system of inequalities does have a solution.

$x - y > 0$

$x + y < 0$

$y > 3$

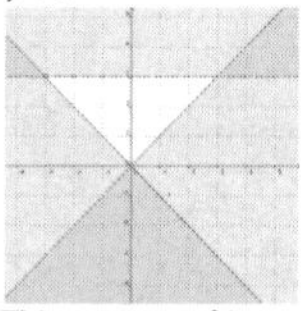

This system of inequalities has no solution.

③ Solve.

If y varies directly as x and $y = 25$ when $x = 15$, what is value of k? State the value of k and write an equation to show the direct variation.

$y = kx$

$25 = k(15)$ $\quad y = \frac{5}{3}x$

$\frac{25}{15} = \frac{5}{3} = k$

If y varies directly as x and $y = 24$ when $k = 3$, what is value of x? State the value of x and write an equation to show the direct variation.

$y = kx$

$24 = 3(x)$ $\quad y = 3x$

$\frac{24}{3} = 8 = x$

If y varies directly as x and $x = 10$ when $k = 7$, what is value of y? State the value of y and write an equation to show the direct variation.

$y = kx$

$y = 7(10)$ $\quad y = 7x$

$y = 70$

If y varies inversely as x and $y = 12$ when $x = 8$, what is value of k? State the value of k and write an equation to show the inverse variation.

$xy = k$

$8(12) = k$ $\quad y = \frac{96}{x}$

$96 = k$

If y varies inversely as x and $y = 4$ when $k = 18$, what is value of x? State the value of x and write an equation to show the inverse variation.

$xy = k$

$x(4) = 18$ $\quad y = \frac{18}{x}$

$x = \frac{18}{4} = \frac{9}{2}$

If y varies inversely as x and $x = 7$ when $k = 21$, what is value of y? State the value of y and write an equation to show the inverse variation.

$xy = k$

$7y = 21$ $\quad y = \frac{21}{x}$

$y = \frac{21}{7} = 3$

Teaching Tips, Cont.

- Tell the students that it is also possible for a system of linear inequalities to have no solution.
- Teach systems of linear inequalities with no solution from the teaching box. Make sure the students understand that the shaded regions of every inequality in the system must overlap for there to be a system. If there are three inequalities and only two of them have overlapping shaded areas, there is no solution because there is no point common to the shaded area of all three inequalities.
- Complete the Classwork exercise. Have one student work the problem on the board for the class and explain the answer. All students should work the problem in their books.
- Review for Test 13 using worksheets 61-64. These worksheets were assigned in previous lessons.

Assignments

- Complete Lesson 130, Activities 2-3.
- Study for Test 13 (Lessons 118-127).

Test 13

Testing Objectives

The student will:

- Solve direct variation problems
- Solve inverse variation problems
- Graph inequalities on a number line
- Graph inequalities with absolute value on a number line
- Tell whether or not conjunctions are true
- Tell whether or not disjunctions are true

Materials Needed

- Test 13
- *It's College Test Prep Time!* from Student Book
- Exploring Math through... Winter Olympics from Student Book

Teaching Tips

- ➢ Administer Test 13, allowing the students 30-40 minutes to complete the test.
- ➢ When all students are finished taking the test, introduce *It's College Test Prep Time* from the student book. This page may be completed in class or assigned as homework.

① Solve. **8 points**

If y varies directly as x and $y = 25$ when $x = 15$, what is value of k? State the value of k and write an equation to show the direct variation.

$y = kx$

$25 = k(15)$ $\quad y = \frac{5}{3}x$

$\frac{25}{15} = \frac{5}{3} = k$

If y varies directly as x and $y = 36$ when $k = 12$, what is value of x? State the value of x and write an equation to show the direct variation.

$y = kx$

$36 = 12(x)$ $\quad y = 12x$

$\frac{36}{12} = 3 = x$

If y varies inversely as x and $y = 4$ when $x = 9$, what is value of k? State the value of k and write an equation to show the inverse variation.

$xy = k$

$9(4) = k$ $\quad y = \frac{36}{x}$

$36 = k$

If y varies inversely as x and $y = 16$ when $k = 6$, what is value of x? State the value of x and write an equation to show the inverse variation.

$xy = k$

$x(16) = 6$ $\quad y = \frac{6}{x}$

$x = \frac{6}{16} = \frac{3}{8}$

② Graph the inequalities on a number line. **16 points**

$x \ge 4$

$x < -1$

$-6 < x - 4 < -3$

$-6 < x - 4$ and $x - 4 < -3$

$-2 < x$ and $x < 1$

$-2 < x < 1$

$|x - 1| + 3 < 6$

$|x - 1| < 3$

$x - 1 < 3$ and $x - 1 > -3$

$x < 4$ and $x > -2$

$-2 < x < 4$

$-8 < x - 3 \le -4$

$-8 < x - 3$ and $x - 3 \le -4$

$-5 < x$ and $x \le -1$

$-5 < x \le -1$

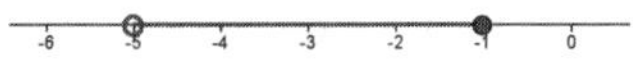

$x \le 2$ or $x > 4$

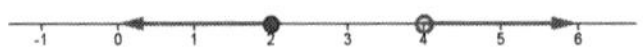

$x < -3$ or $x > -1$

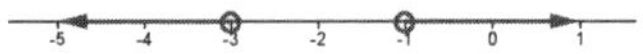

$|3x - 2| + 6 \ge 1$

$|3x - 2| \ge -5$

All real numbers.

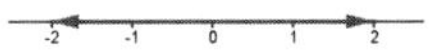

③ Tell whether or not each conjunction or disjunction is true. **16 points**

$(-17 > 13) \cap (-14 < 12)$

false true

The conjunction is false.

$(-17 > 13) \cup (-14 < 12)$

false true

The disjunction is true.

$(x \le 8) \cap (-2 + 10 < x)$

$(x \le 8) \cap (8 < x)$

They can't both be true at the same time, so the conjunction is false.

$(x \le 15) \cup (-2 + 10 < x)$

$(x \le 8) \cup (8 < x)$

One of them has to be true, so the disjunction is true.

$(x - 2 > x + 5) \cap (3 - 5 < 4 - 9)$

$-2 > 5$ $\quad -2 < -5$

false false

The conjunction is false.

$(x - 2 > x + 5) \cup (3 - 5 < 4 - 9)$

$(-2 > 5) \cup (-2 < -5)$

false false

The disjunction is false.

$(3 \cdot 5 < 13 - 4) \cap (14 \div 7 < 5 \cdot 3)$

$15 < 9$ $\quad 2 < 15$

false true

The conjunction is false.

$(3 \cdot 5 < 13 - 4) \cup (14 \div 7 < 5 \cdot 3)$

$15 < 9$ $\quad 2 < 15$

false true

The disjunction is true.

$(3x < 9) \cap (-3 + 9 \le 2x)$

$(x < 3) \cap (3 \le x)$

They can't both be true at the same time, so the conjunction is false.

$(3x < 9) \cup (-3 + 9 \le 2x)$

$(x < 3) \cup (3 \le x)$

One of them has to be true, so the disjunction is true.

$(11 - 6 < 5 - 2) \cap (3 + 8 \ge 9 + 4)$

$(5 < 3) \cap (11 \ge 13)$

false false

The conjunction is false.

$(11 - 6 < 5 - 2) \cup (3 + 8 \ge 9 + 4)$

$(5 < 3) \cup (11 \ge 13)$

false false

The disjunction is false.

$(x < -1) \cap (-7 + 6 \le x)$

$(x < -1) \cap (-1 \le x)$

They can't both be true at the same time, so the conjunction is false.

$(x < -1) \cup (-7 + 6 \le x)$

$(x < -1) \cup (-1 \le x)$

One of them has to be true, so the disjunction is true.

$(2 \cdot 3 < 1^7) \cap (6^2 \le 3^3)$

$(6 < 1) \cap (36 \le 27)$

false false

The conjunction is false.

$(2 \cdot 3 < 1^7) \cup (6^2 \le 3^3)$

$(6 < 1) \cup (36 \le 27)$

false false

The disjunction is false.

40 points total

It's College Test Prep Time!

1. Given $-1 < x < 0$, which of the following statements is FALSE?
   Pick a value for x, substitute, and solve. The examples use $x = -\frac{1}{2}$.

   A. $x < x^2$ $\quad -\frac{1}{2} < \frac{1}{4}$ true
   B. $2x < 2$ $\quad -1 < -\frac{1}{2}$ true
   C. $\frac{1}{x} < x$ $\quad -2 < -\frac{1}{2}$ true
   D. $\frac{x}{2} < x$ $\quad -\frac{1}{4} < -\frac{1}{2}$ false
   E. $3x < x$ $\quad -\frac{3}{2} < -\frac{1}{2}$ true

2. Given $x > 0$ and $0 < x^2 < \frac{1}{16}$, which of the following is a possible value of x?

   A. $-\frac{1}{16}$ $\quad x$ must be positive, so this cannot be correct.
   B. 0 $\quad x$ is *greater than* zero, so this cannot be correct.
   C. $\frac{1}{8}$ $\quad$ Taking the square root gives $0 < x < \frac{1}{4}$.
   D. $\frac{1}{4}$ $\quad$ x must be *less than* $\frac{1}{4}$ so this cannot be correct.
   E. $\frac{1}{2}$ $\quad$ must be *less than* $\frac{1}{4}$ so this cannot be correct.

3. Given $x < 3$ and $y = 2x - 4$, which of the following represents all possible values of y?

   A. $y < 2$ $\quad$ Substitute 3 for x to get $y = 2(3) - 4 = 6 - 4 = 2$.
   B. $0 < y < 2$ $\quad x$ must be less that 3, so $y < 2$.
   C. $y < 0$
   D. $-4 < y < 2$
   E. $y > -4$

Exploring Math through... Winter Olympics

The Winter Olympic Games use math on every level – from simple arithmetic to complex calculus-level operations. Speed races are timed to the hundredth of a second to determine the winner, and oftentimes the time separating the gold-medalist from a non-medalist is a fraction of a second.

Some Olympic events, such as the bobsled, luge, and skeleton, are affected by forces of gravity and friction. The athletes must gain as much momentum as possible at the start of the race and carefully steer their sleds to minimize the effects of friction without allowing gravity to accelerate the sled to an unsafe speed.

Other Olympic events, such as hockey and curling, rely on angles and principles of physics. Hockey players must strike the puck with the proper force at the correct angle to score a goal or to pass the puck to a teammate. Curling players must factor in spin and friction on the ice when planning the proper angle and velocity at which to release their stones.

Events on the snow have their own mathematical complications. The density of the snow, slope of the course, angle of the banks, and even the air temperature can all affect the performance of the athlete. These factors affect friction on the course, the momentum of the athlete, and the ultimate speed an athlete travels along the course. This, in turn, affects reaction times. To complicate matters further, the conditions of a ski slope are directly affected by the weather and can be different each time an athlete completes a run.

No matter what aspect of the Winter Olympic Games you are considering, competing, scoring, or preparing a track, math is highly involved and affects the outcome of the Games.

Teaching Tips, Cont.

- Have students read the Exploring Math feature for Lessons 131-140.

Assignments

- Complete *It's College Test Prep Time!*
- Read Exploring Math through... Winter Olympics

Lesson 131

Concepts

- Exponential growth
- Compound interest
- Math in the real world

Learning Objectives

The student will be able to:

- Solve exponential growth problems
- Calculate compound interest
- Apply principles of exponential growth to real-world scenarios

Materials Needed

- Student Book, Lesson 131
- Worksheet 65

Teaching Tips

- Review simple interest. (See Lesson 112)
- Tell the students that simple interest is calculated on the principle only, while compound interest is also paid on previously earned interest. Ask the students what effect that has on the amount of interest earned. (More interest is earned with compound interest.)
- Explain that compound interest is an example of exponential growth.
- Teach exponential growth from the teaching box. Students should familiarize themselves with the general formula for exponential growth and notice the similarities between it and the formula for compound interest. For students who used Horizons Pre-Algebra, the concept of compound interest should be familiar.

Exponential Growth Functions

By now you should be very familiar with linear functions that increase (or decrease) steadily by a given factor, the slope.

Not all functions, however, follow a linear increase or decrease. Consider the formula for compound interest, $A = P(1+r)^t$, where P is the principal (beginning amount), r is the interest rate expressed as a decimal, and t is the number of years. The amount of interest added each year increases because interest is paid on previously earned interest.

When a variable appears in the exponent, the equation is exponential rather than linear. When the equation is a function and the value of the exponent is increasing, the function is called an exponential growth function.

The general formula for exponential growth is $y = a(1+b)^x$, where y is the final amount, a is the original amount, b is the growth percentage rate expressed as a decimal, and x is time.

Compare this formula with the formula for compound interest. The A corresponds to y, P corresponds to a, r corresponds to b, and t corresponds to x.

If you want to have $25,000 saved for college 4 years from now, how much of an initial investment must you make at 4% interest compounded annually to reach your goal with no additional contributions?

Assign your variables and substitute in the formula.

$y = 25000$; $b = 0.04$; $x = 4$

$25000 = a(1+0.04)^4$

Follow the order of operations to solve.

$25,000 = a(1.04)^4$

$\frac{25,000}{(1.04)^4} = a(1.04)^4$

$\frac{25,000}{1.16985856} = a$

$21,370.10 = a$

You should invest $21,370.10 to reach the goal.

① Classwork

Solve.

If your grandparents invested $10,000 in a college savings plan for you on your 5th birthday at 6% interest compounded annually, how much will be in your college saving account when you turn 18? (Round to the nearest hundredth after calculating the exponent.)

$P = 10,000$; $b = 0.06$; $x = 18 - 5 = 13$

$y = \$10,000(1+0.06)^{13}$

$y = \$10,000(1.06)^{13}$

$y = \$10,000(2.13)$

$y = \$21,300$

If your parents invested an additional $5,000 in a college savings plan for you on your 13th birthday at 6% interest compounded annually, how much additional money will be in your college saving account when you turn 18? (Round to the nearest hundredth after calculating the exponent.)

$P = 5,000$; $b = 0.06$; $x = 18 - 13 = 5$

$y = \$5,000(1+0.06)^5$

$y = \$5,000(1.06)^5$

$y = \$5,000(1.34)$

$y = \$6700$

Activities

② Solve.

In each of the first 25 Olympic Games following their debut in Athens, Greece, in 1896, the Olympics saw an average increase in participation of 16.25%. If there were 241 participants in Athens in 1896, approximately how many participants were there in Atlanta, Georgia, in 1996? Hint: Time is 25 since this is 25 games later. Round to the nearest ten thousandth after calculating the exponent. $a = 241$, $b = 0.1625$, $x = 25$

$y = 241(1+0.1625)^{25}$

$y = 241(1.1625)^{25}$

$y = 241(43.1344)$

$y = 10395$

There were approximately 10,394 participants in the Atlanta games in 1996.

Note: The actual number of participants in Atlanta in 1996 was 10,318.

③ Complete the chart.

If your parents deposited $1000 into a college savings plan earning 7% interest the day you were born, and added $1000 at the same 7% interest rate each year on your birthday, how much money would you have saved for college on your 18th birthday before they added the money for your 18th birthday? Complete the chart to do your calculations.

Birthday	$ Deposited	Interest rate	Years	Final value
Birth	$1000	7%	18	$y = \$1,000(1+0.07)^{18} = \$3379.93$
1	$1000	7%	17	$y = \$1,000(1+0.07)^{17} = \$3158.82$
2	$1000	7%	16	$y = \$1,000(1+0.07)^{16} = \$2952.16$
3	$1000	7%	15	$y = \$1,000(1+0.07)^{15} = \$2759.03$
4	$1000	7%	14	$y = \$1,000(1+0.07)^{14} = \$2578.53$
5	$1000	7%	13	$y = \$1,000(1+0.07)^{13} = \$2409.85$
6	$1000	7%	12	$y = \$1,000(1+0.07)^{12} = \$2252.19$
7	$1000	7%	11	$y = \$1,000(1+0.07)^{11} = \$2104.85$
8	$1000	7%	10	$y = \$1,000(1+0.07)^{10} = \$1967.15$
9	$1000	7%	9	$y = \$1,000(1+0.07)^{9} = \$1838.46$
10	$1000	7%	8	$y = \$1,000(1+0.07)^{8} = \$1718.19$
11	$1000	7%	7	$y = \$1,000(1+0.07)^{7} = \$1605.78$
12	$1000	7%	6	$y = \$1,000(1+0.07)^{6} = \$1500.73$
13	$1000	7%	5	$y = \$1,000(1+0.07)^{5} = \$1402.55$
14	$1000	7%	4	$y = \$1,000(1+0.07)^{4} = \$1310.80$
15	$1000	7%	3	$y = \$1,000(1+0.07)^{3} = \$1225.04$
16	$1000	7%	2	$y = \$1,000(1+0.07)^{2} = \$1144.90$
17	$1000	7%	1	$y = \$1,000(1+0.07)^{1} = \$1070.00$
Totals	$18,000	7%	18	$36,378.96

Systems of Inequalities Worksheet 65

① Use a graph to find at least three combinations that satisfy the requirements.
The band needs to raise at least $15,525 to purchase new uniforms. They are selling regular candy bars that bring $104 profit per case, and premium candy bars that bring $30 profit per case. If the fundraising company requires a minimum of 11 cases of regular candy bars sold and a minimum of 42 cases of premium candy bars sold, how many cases of each candy bar must they sell? Give three possible combinations of candy bar sales that will meet the requirements.
Let x = the number of cases of regular candy bars.
Let y = the number of cases of premium candy bars.

$x \geq 11$

$y \geq 42$

$104x + 30y \geq 15{,}525$

Possible solutions lie in the dark shaded triangle and include 100 cases of regular candy bars and 200 cases of premium candy bars, 200 cases of regular candy bars and 200 cases of premium candy bars, and 300 cases of regular candy bars and 100 cases of premium candy bars.

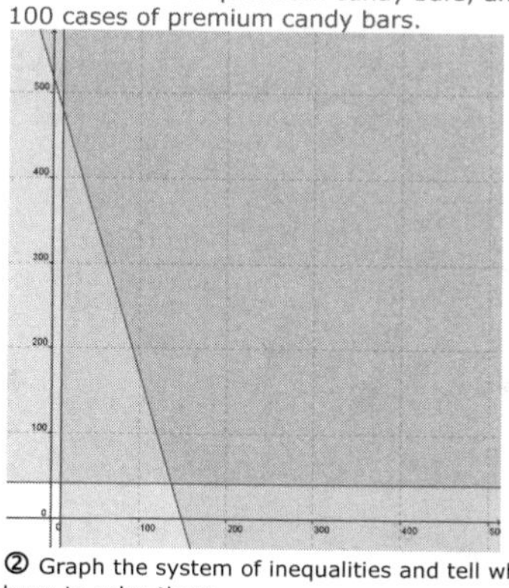

② Graph the system of inequalities and tell whether or not it has a solution. You do not have to solve them.

$x - y \leq 4$

$x + y \leq 3$

$x + 2y \leq 2$

This system of inequalities does have a solution.

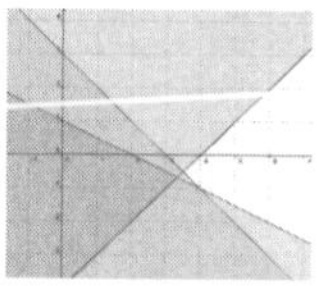

$x \geq 4$

$x + y \leq 2$

$y \geq 4$

This system of inequalities has no solution.

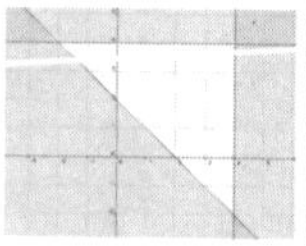

Teaching Tips, Cont.

- Complete the Classwork exercises. Have some students work the problems on the board for the class and explain their answers. All students should work the problems in their books.

Assignments

- Complete Lesson 131, Activities 2-3.
- Worksheet 65.

Lesson 132

Concepts

- Exponential decay
- Quadratic equations
- Factoring
- Math in the real world

Learning Objectives

The student will be able to:

- Solve exponential decay problems
- Apply principles of exponential decay to real-world scenarios

Materials Needed

- Student Book, Lesson 132
- Worksheet 66

Teaching Tips

- Have students complete Worksheet 66 in class. This may be for added practice of earlier topics or graded as a quiz, if desired.
- Review exponential growth. (See Lesson 131)
- Ask the students what they think exponential decay is if exponential growth is something getting larger. (Something getting smaller)
- Teach exponential decay from the teaching box.

Exponential Decay Functions

In Lesson 131 you learned about exponential growth functions, where the values get continuously larger.

In this lesson, the same concept is applied, but the values get continuously smaller. The formula for exponential decay has one sign different from the formula for exponential growth. The formula for exponential decay is $y = a(1-b)^x$, where y is the final amount, a is the initial amount, b is the rate of decay expressed as a decimal, and x is the time.

Suppose you have $25,000 saved for college. You spend 10% of your saved amount the first month of college. Each month of the first semester you spend 10% of the balance. If no interest is earned and no deposits are made, how much money will be left in the account at the end of 4 months?

Assign variables and substitute in the formula.
a = 25,000; b = 0.10; x = 4

$y = 25{,}000(1-0.10)^4$

Follow the order of operations to solve.

$y = 25{,}000(0.90)^4$

$y = 25{,}000(0.6561)$

$y = 16{,}402.5$

At the end of 4 months you will have $16,402.50 remaining in the account.

① **Classwork**

Solve.

During a recent depression, housing values in one neighborhood dropped exponentially by an average rate of 11% per year for 4 years. If a house was worth $175,000 at the beginning of the depression, what was the value of the house after 4 years? Round to the nearest ten thousandth after calculating the exponent.

$y = \$175{,}000(1-0.11)^4$

$y = \$175{,}000(0.89)^4$

$y = \$175{,}000(0.6274)$

$y = \$109{,}795$

If the same house declined in value at a rate of 9% each year for 5 years, what would the $175,000 house be worth after 5 years? Round to the nearest ten thousandth after calculating the exponent.

$y = \$175{,}000(1-0.09)^5$

$y = \$175{,}000(0.91)^5$

$y = \$175{,}000(0.6240)$

$y = \$109{,}200$

Activities

② Solve.

The population of Detroit, MI, has declined exponentially since 1950 at an average rate of 14.67% every 10 years. The 2010 census for Detroit was 713,777. Approximately how many people were living in Detroit 6 decades earlier, in 1950?

$713{,}777 = a(1-0.1467)^6$

$713{,}777 = a(0.8533)^6$

$713{,}777 = a(0.3860)$

$a = 1{,}849{,}163$

Note: The actual population in 1950 was 1,849,568.

③ Solve.

In 1976, the record time for the men's 1000-meter speed skating was 1 minute, 19.32 seconds. A new Olympic record was set in 5 of the next 6 Winter Olympic Games (1980, 1984, 1988, 1994, 1998, and 2002), with each new record averaging 3.27% faster than the previous record. What was new Olympic record set for the men's 1000-meter speed skating in 2002 Winter Olympics? (Note: Both Summer and Winter Olympics were held every four years up to 1988. In 1992 only the Summer Olympic Games were held, moving the Winter Games to 1994. Now the Olympic Games are held every two years, alternating Summer and Winter.) Hint: Convert all times to seconds. Give your answer to the nearest hundredth of a second.

$y = 79.32(1-0.0327)^5$

$y = 79.32(0.9673)^5$

$y = 79.32(0.8468)$

$y = 67.17$

The current record is 67.17 seconds, or 1 minute, 7.17 seconds.

④ Solve each quadratic equation by factoring.

$6x^2 + x - 12 = 0$
$(3x-4)(2x+3) = 0$
$3x - 4 = 0; x = \frac{4}{3}$
$2x + 3 = 0; x = -\frac{3}{2}$
The solution is $x = \frac{4}{3}$ and $-\frac{3}{2}$.

$2x^2 + x - 6 = 0$
$(x+2)(2x-3) = 0$
$x + 2 = 0; x = -2$
$2x - 3 = 0; x = \frac{3}{2}$
The solution is $x = -2$ and $\frac{3}{2}$.

$6x^2 - 3x - 3 = 0$
$3(x-1)(2x+1) = 0$
$x - 1 = 0; x = 1$
$2x + 1 = 0; x = -\frac{1}{2}$
The solution is $x = 1$ and $-\frac{1}{2}$.

$x^2 - 11x + 18 = 0$
$(x-9)(x-2) = 0$
$x - 9 = 0; x = 9$
$x - 2 = 0; x = 2$
The solution is $x = 9$ and 2.

$4x^2 - 9 = 0$
$(2x-3)(2x+3) = 0$
$2x - 3 = 0; x = \frac{3}{2}$
$2x + 3 = 0; x = -\frac{3}{2}$
The solution is $x = \frac{3}{2}$ and $-\frac{3}{2}$.

$6x^2 + 5x - 25 = 0$
$(2x+5)(3x-5) = 0$
$2x + 5 = 0; x = -\frac{5}{2}$
$3x - 5 = 0; x = \frac{5}{3}$
The solution is $x = -\frac{5}{2}$ and $\frac{5}{3}$.

$4x^2 = 1$
$4x^2 - 1 = 0$
$(2x-1)(2x+1) = 0$
$2x - 1 = 0; x = \frac{1}{2}$
$2x + 1 = 0; x = -\frac{1}{2}$
The solution is $x = \frac{1}{2}$ and $-\frac{1}{2}$.

$12x^2 - 5x = 2$
$12x^2 - 5x - 2 = 0$
$(3x-2)(4x+1) = 0$
$3x - 2 = 0; x = \frac{2}{3}$
$4x + 1 = 0; x = -\frac{1}{4}$
The solution is $x = \frac{2}{3}$ and $-\frac{1}{4}$.

$20x^2 - 39x = -18$
$20x^2 - 39x + 18 = 0$
$(5x-6)(4x-3) = 0$
$5x - 6 = 0; x = \frac{6}{5}$
$4x - 3 = 0; x = \frac{3}{4}$
The solution is $x = \frac{6}{5}$ and $\frac{3}{4}$.

Systems of Inequalities Worksheet 66

① Use a graph to find at least three combinations that satisfy the requirements.
A ten-person team of 7th and 8th graders must have at least 4 students from each grade. Give three combinations of students that satisfy the requirements of the team.
Let x = the number of 7th graders.
Let y = the number of 8th graders.

$x \geq 4$

$y \geq 4$

$x + y = 10$

There are exactly three possible solutions. These lie where the line $x + y = 10$ borders the dark shaded triangle and are 4 7th graders and 6 8th graders, 5 7th graders and 5 8th graders, and 6 7th graders and 4 8th graders.

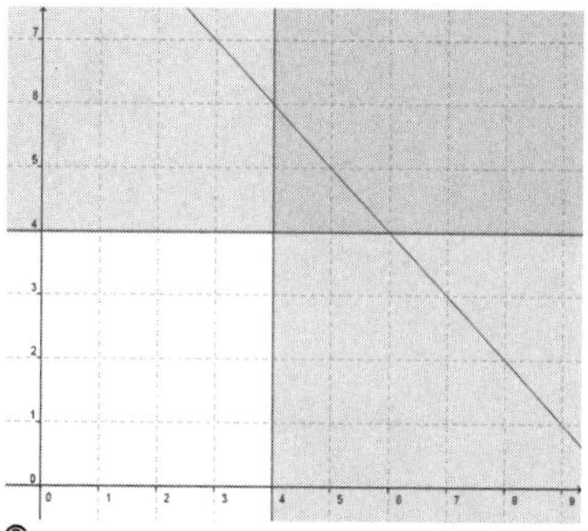

② Graph the system of inequalities and tell whether or not it has a solution. You do not have to solve them.

$x - y \leq 5$

$x + y \geq 1$

$x + 2y < 3$

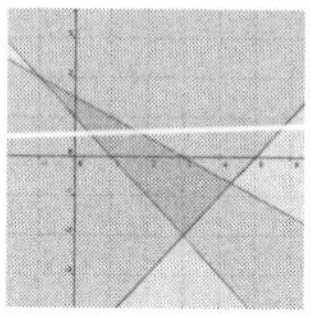

This system of inequalities does have a solution.

$x - y > 1$

$x + y < 1$

$y > 2$

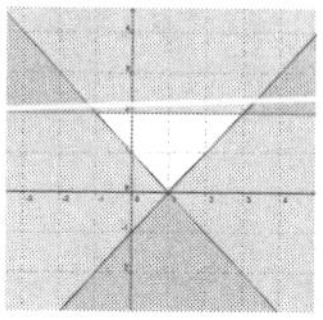

This system of inequalities has no solution.

Teaching Tips, Cont.

- Have the students compare the formula for exponential decay from the teaching box of Lesson 132 with the formula for exponential growth from the teaching box of Lesson 131 and ask them what the difference is. (Exponential decay has a minus sign where exponential growth has a plus sign.)
- Complete the Classwork exercises. Have some students work the problems on the board for the class and explain their answers. All students should work the problems in their books.

Assignment

- Complete Lesson 132, Activities 2-4.

Lesson 133

Concepts

- Graphs of exponential functions
- Adding polynomials
- Subtracting polynomials
- Math in the real world

Learning Objectives

The student will be able to:

- Graph exponential growth functions
- Graph exponential decay functions

Materials Needed

- Student Book, Lesson 133
- Worksheet 67

Teaching Tips

➢ Review exponential growth. (See Lesson 131)

➢ Review exponential decay. (See Lesson 132)

➢ Tell the students that exponential functions are graphed following the same procedure used for quadratic functions, except at least 7 points should be plotted before drawing the curve.

➢ Teach graphing exponential functions from the teaching box.

Graphs of Exponential Functions

Exponential functions do not graph as straight lines. Instead, they are curved lines that have one end approaching a specific number and the other end approaching infinity.

To graph an exponential function, follow the same procedure for graphing a linear function.

Graph $y = 2^x$.

Make a T-chart with values of x and y. For exponential functions you should have more coordinate pairs than you would for linear functions. You should have at least 7 points to graph unless otherwise instructed.

x	y
0	$2^0 = 1$
1	$2^1 = 2$
2	$2^2 = 4$
3	$2^3 = 8$
-1	$2^{-1} = \frac{1}{2}$
-2	$2^{-2} = \frac{1}{4}$
-3	$2^{-3} = \frac{1}{8}$

Plot the points on a Cartesian plane and join them with a smooth curve.

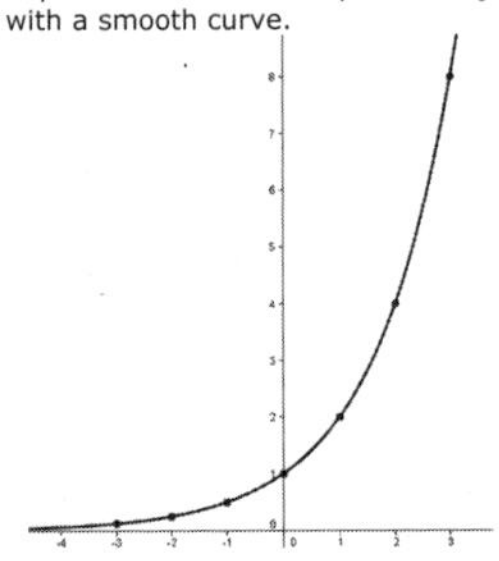

Notice that as the value of x gets smaller, the value of y approaches 0. As the value of x gets larger, the value of y approaches infinity.

① **Classwork**

Draw the graph of each exponential function.

$y = 3^x$ (You may graph 5 points for this graph.)

x	y
0	$3^0 = 1$
1	$3^1 = 3$
2	$3^2 = 9$
-1	$3^{-1} = \frac{1}{3}$
-2	$3^{-2} = \frac{1}{9}$

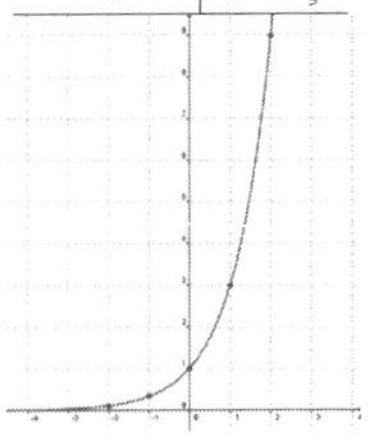

$y = 2^{-x}$

x	y
0	$2^0 = 1$
1	$2^{-1} = \frac{1}{2}$
2	$2^{-2} = \frac{1}{4}$
3	$2^{-3} = \frac{1}{8}$
-1	$2^1 = 2$
-2	$2^2 = 4$
-3	$2^3 = 8$

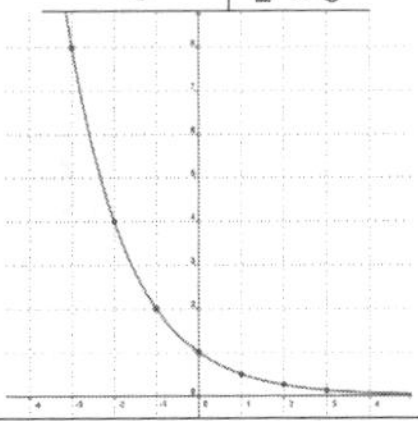

Activities

② Graph.

Consider cell division. When a single cell divides, there are 2 cells. When those cells divide, there are 4 cells, then 8 cells, then 16 cells, etc. The amount added each time increases exponentially. Study the chart below.

Number of divisions	Number of cells
0	1
1	2
2	4
3	8

An equation can be formed to show the relation between the number of divisions, d, and the number of cells, c. $c = 2^d$ Draw a graph to show the number of cells, c, there are after d divisions.

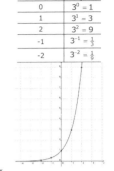

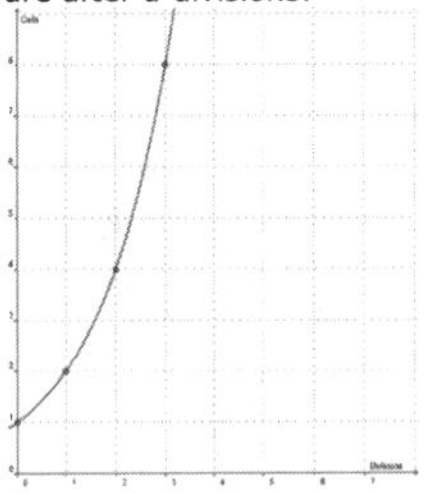

The coordinate points for this graph are obtained from the chart above, where the number of divisions corresponds to the x-axis and the number of cells corresponds to the y-axis. Only the values of $x \geq 0$ are shown because you cannot have fewer than zero divisions.

③ Add.

$$\begin{array}{r} 3x^2 + 2x - 4 \\ +\ \underline{4x^2 + 3x + 1} \\ 7x^2 + 5x - 3 \end{array} \qquad \begin{array}{r} 3x^2 + 4x + 2 \\ \underline{+2x^2 - 2x - 5} \\ 5x^2 + 2x - 3 \end{array} \qquad \begin{array}{r} 2x^2 - 5x - 2 \\ \underline{+3x^2 + 2x - 3} \\ 5x^2 - 3x - 5 \end{array}$$

$$\begin{array}{r} 2x^2 + 3x + 2 \\ +\ \underline{4x^2 + 5x - 3} \\ 6x^2 + 8x - 1 \end{array} \qquad \begin{array}{r} 4x^2 + 3x + 2 \\ \underline{+3x^2 - 7x - 5} \\ 7x^2 - 4x - 3 \end{array} \qquad \begin{array}{r} 2x^2 - 3x + 2 \\ \underline{+5x^2 - 2x - 3} \\ 7x^2 - 5x - 1 \end{array}$$

④ Subtract.

$$\begin{array}{r} (5x^2 + 4x + 3) \\ \underline{-(2x^2 + 2x - 1)} \\ 3x^2 + 2x + 4 \end{array} \qquad \begin{array}{r} (4x^2 - 5x + 2) \\ \underline{-(x^2 - 2x - 1)} \\ 3x^2 - 3x + 3 \end{array} \qquad \begin{array}{r} (6x^2 - 5x - 2) \\ \underline{-(3x^2 + 3x - 3)} \\ 3x^2 - 8x + 1 \end{array}$$

$$\begin{array}{r} (5x^2 + 3x + 2) \\ \underline{-(3x^2 - 2x + 1)} \\ 2x^2 + 5x + 1 \end{array} \qquad \begin{array}{r} (6x^2 + 3x - 5) \\ \underline{-(2x^2 - 7x - 2)} \\ 4x^2 + 10x - 3 \end{array} \qquad \begin{array}{r} (7x^2 - 3x - 3) \\ \underline{-(2x^2 - 5x - 5)} \\ 5x^2 + 2x + 2 \end{array}$$

Graphs of Exponential Functions Worksheet 67

① Draw the graph of each exponential function.

$y = 4^x$ (You may graph 5 points for this graph.)

x	y
0	$4^0 = 1$
1	$4^1 = 4$
2	$4^2 = 16$
-1	$4^{-1} = \frac{1}{4}$
-2	$4^{-2} = \frac{1}{16}$

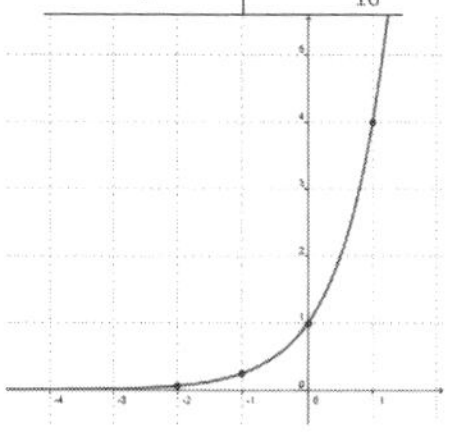

$y = -2^x$ (You may graph 5 points for this graph.)

x	y
0	$-2^0 = -1$
1	$-2^1 = -2$
2	$-2^2 = -4$
-1	$-2^{-1} = -\frac{1}{2}$
-2	$-2^{-2} = -\frac{1}{4}$

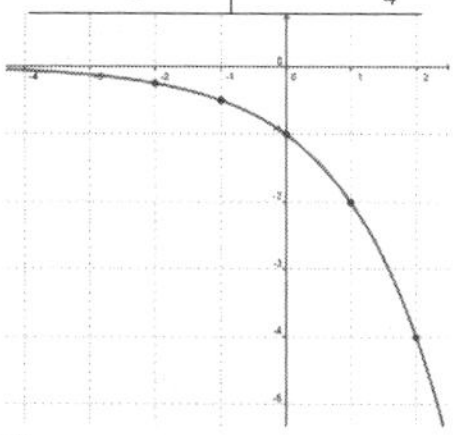

$y = 3^{-x}$

x	y
0	$3^0 = 1$
1	$3^{-1} = \frac{1}{3}$
2	$3^{-2} = \frac{1}{9}$
3	$3^{-3} = \frac{1}{27}$
-1	$3^1 = 3$
-2	$3^2 = 9$
-3	$3^3 = 27$

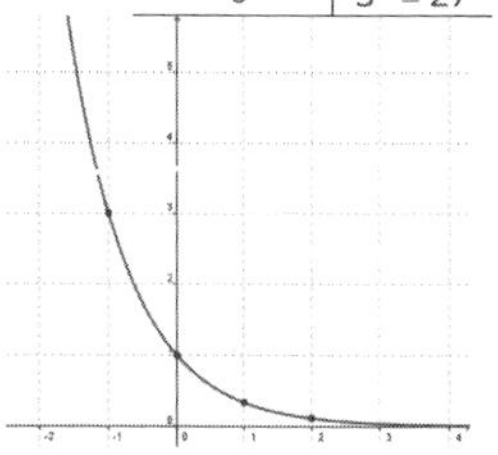

$y = 2^{-x}$

x	y
0	$2^0 = 1$
1	$2^{-1} = \frac{1}{2}$
2	$2^{-2} = \frac{1}{4}$
3	$2^{-3} = \frac{1}{8}$
-1	$2^1 = 2$
-2	$2^2 = 4$
-3	$2^3 = 8$

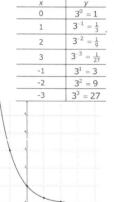

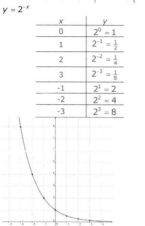

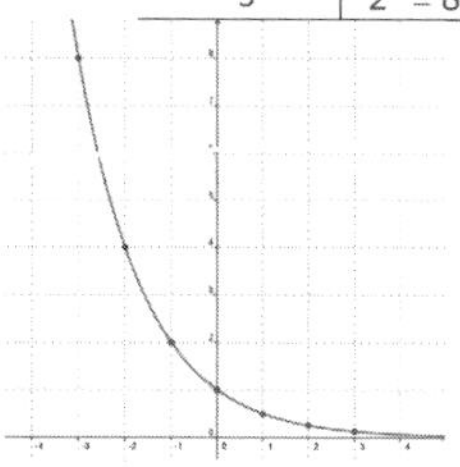

Teaching Tips, Cont.

- Ask the students what happens to the graph of an exponential growth function as the value of x increases. (It gets higher.)
- Ask the students what happens to the graph of an exponential decay function as the value of x increases. (It gets lower and approaches the x-axis.)
- Complete the Classwork exercises. Have some students work the problems on the board for the class and explain their answers. All students should work the problems in their books.

Assignments

- Complete Lesson 133, Activities 2-4.
- Worksheet 67.

Lesson 134

Concepts
- Ratios
- Proportions
- Math in the real world

Learning Objectives
The student will be able to:
- Define *proportion*
- Solve proportions
- Apply ratios and proportions to real-world scenarios

Materials Needed
- Student Book, Lesson 134

Teaching Tips
- Teach the definition of *proportion* from the teaching box.
- Teach proportions from the teaching box.
- Emphasize the importance of having consistent units throughout the numerators and denominators of the problem.
- Encourage the students to write a ratio using just the units before setting up a proportion, and to convert units as necessary from the information in the problem so all units match the ratio initially set up.

Ratios and Proportions

A **proportion** is two ratios (fractions) set equal to each other. This forms an equation that can then be solved for an unknown.

When using proportions to solve word problems, it is often helpful to first write the proportion using words and then substitute values and variables. It is essential that the numerators have identical units and the denominators have identical units.

The ratio of thrill rides to total attractions at an amusement park is 2:5. If the amusement park has 14 thrill rides, how many attractions are at the park?

Set up a proportion using words.

$$\frac{\text{thrill rides}}{\text{attractions}} = \frac{\text{thrill rides}}{\text{attractions}}$$

Assign a variable to the part you must solve to find. Substitute values for the words, keeping separate ratios in separate fractions.

Let a = the total number of attractions.

$\frac{2}{5} = \frac{14}{a}$

Solve the proportion by multiplying each fraction by the lowest common denominator.

$\cancel{5}a\left(\frac{2}{\cancel{5}}\right) = 5\cancel{a}\left(\frac{14}{\cancel{a}}\right)$

$2a = 70$

$a = 35$

There are 35 total attractions in the park.

① **Classwork**

Solve.

The ratio of male athletes to female athletes in the 1976 Montreal Olympic Games was 134:35. If there were 1260 female athletes, how many male athletes were there?

$$\frac{\text{Male athletes}}{\text{Female athletes}} = \frac{\text{Male athletes}}{\text{Female athletes}}$$

Let m = the number of male athletes.

$\frac{134}{35} = \frac{m}{1260}$

$\cancel{35}(1260)\frac{134}{\cancel{35}} = 35(\cancel{1260})\frac{m}{\cancel{1260}}$

$168{,}840 = 35m$

$m = 4824$

The ratio of Winter Olympic sports to Summer Olympic sports is 1:4. If there are a total of 35 different Olympic sports, how many winter sports are there? (Hint: Rewrite the ratio to represent Winter Olympic sports to all Olympic sports.)

The new ratio is 1:1 + 4 = 1:5.

$$\frac{\text{Winter Olympic sports}}{\text{Total Olympic sports}} = \frac{\text{Winter Olympic sports}}{\text{Total Olympic sports}}$$

$\frac{1}{5} = \frac{w}{35}$

$\cancel{5}(35)\frac{1}{\cancel{5}} = 5(\cancel{35})\frac{w}{\cancel{35}}$

$35 = 5w$

$w = 7$

There are 7 different Winter Olympic sports. (Biathlon, skating, skiing, luge, ice hockey, curling, bobsleigh)

Activities

② Solve.

The ratio of the number of events at the Winter Olympic Games that have men and women competing together to the number of events at the Winter Olympics that are only men competing is 1:15. If ice dancing, ice skating pairs mixed, and luge doubles mixed are the only Winter Olympic events that have men and women competing together, how many events are only men?

$\frac{\text{Mixed}}{\text{Male athletes}} = \frac{\text{Mixed}}{\text{Male athletes}}$ Let m = the number of male athletes.

$\frac{1}{15} = \frac{3}{m}$

$\cancel{15}m\frac{1}{\cancel{15}} = 15\cancel{m}\left(\frac{3}{\cancel{m}}\right)$

$m = 45$

③ Solve.
An object's stopping distance is affected by its speed and the coefficient of friction between the object and the surface it is traveling on. The formula for determining stopping distance is $d = \frac{v^2}{2g\mu}$, where d is the stopping distance, v is the object's speed, g is the force of gravity, and μ is the coefficient of friction.

The track record at Whistler Sliding Center, home of the 2010 Winter Olympics, is 153.98 km/h. What is the record speed in meters/second? Give your answer to the nearest hundredth of a meter.

$$\frac{153.98\ \cancel{km}}{\cancel{hr.}} = \frac{1000\ m}{1\ \cancel{km}} = \frac{1\ \cancel{hr.}}{60\ \cancel{min.}} = \frac{1\ \cancel{min.}}{60\ s} = 42.77\ m/s$$

At this speed, how long would it take a bobsled stop on the ice if the force of gravity is 9.8 m/s^2 and the coefficient of friction of metal on ice is 0.02? Give your answer to the nearest hundredth of a meter.

$$d = \frac{(42.77\ m/s)^2}{2(9.8\ m/s^2)(0.02)} = 4666.51\ m$$

④ Solve.
There are 6 different event categories for Winter Olympic skiing. There are 6 more men's events than there are women's events. If there are a total of 40 skiing events, how many events do the women compete in?
Let w = the number of women's events. Then $w + 6$ = the number of men's events.

$w + w + 6 = 40$

$2w + 6 = 40$

$2w = 34$

$w = 17$

There are 17 women's skiing events in the Winter Olympics.
There are 24 different ice skating events in the Winter Olympics. The number of events that the women compete in is two more than the number of events the women do not compete in. Because there are some events that have men and women competing together, the men and women have an equal number of ice skating events. How many ice skating events are men only? Women only? Men and women together?
Let w = the number of events that are women only = the number of events that are men only.
Let m = the number of mixed events.

$w + w + m = 24$

$(w + m) - 2 = w$ | $2w + m = 24$

$w + m = w + 2$ | $2w + 2 = 24$

$m = 2$ | $2w = 22$

$w = 11$

The men and women each have 11 events. There are an additional 2 mixed events.

Teaching Tips, Cont.

- Tell the students that they may cross multiply or multiply each ratio by the lowest common denominator when solving the proportion.
- Complete the Classwork exercises. Have some students work the problems on the board for the class and explain their answers. All students should work the problems in their books.

Assignment

- Complete Lesson 134, Activities 2-4.

Lesson 135

Concepts

- Literal equations
- Pythagorean Theorem
- Quadratic equations
- Completing the square
- Math in the real world

Learning Objectives

The student will be able to:

- Define *literal equation*
- Solve a formula for any variable in the formula

Materials Needed

- Student Book, Lesson 135
- Worksheet 68

Teaching Tips

- Have students complete Worksheet 68 in class. This may be for added practice of earlier topics or graded as a quiz, if desired.
- Teach literal equations from the teaching box. Explain that some variables are more difficult to solve for than others, such as the variable x in the sample problem in the teaching box.
- Note: The students will never be asked to solve for a variable that appears as an exponent in this book. Solving for an exponent requires the use of logarithms, which are not introduced until Algebra 2.

Literal Equations

Literal equations are equations that contain multiple variables. You have been working with numerous literal equations so far this year. Solving literal equations involves rewriting the equation so you can find a different variable than the one it is written to find. For example, the formula for exponential growth is $y = a(1+b)^x$. If you know the value of y and are looking for the value of a, you can solve the equation for a by applying the order of operations.

$y = a(1+b)^x$

$\frac{y}{(1+b)^x} = \frac{a\cancel{(1+b)^x}}{\cancel{(1+b)^x}}$

$a = \frac{y}{(1+b)^x}$

Any literal equation can be solved for any of its variables, although some variables will be more difficult to solve for than others. Although it is possible to solve for variables that appear as exponents, that concept is more complex and will be saved for a later time.

① **Classwork**

Solve.

The formula for the area of a trapezoid is $A = \frac{1}{2}(a+b)h$, where A is the area, a and b are the lengths of the bases, and h is the height. Rewrite the formula to solve for a, b, and h.

$2A = (a+b)h$
$\frac{2A}{h} = a + b$
$\frac{2A}{h} - b = a$

$2A = (a+b)h$
$\frac{2A}{h} = a + b$
$\frac{2A}{h} - a = b$

$2A = (a+b)h$
$\frac{2A}{a+b} = h$

Activities

② Solve.

An object's stopping distance is affected by its speed and the coefficient of friction between the object and the surface it is traveling on. The formula for determining stopping distance is $d = \frac{v^2}{2g\mu}$, where d is the stopping distance, v is the object's speed, g is the force of gravity, and μ is the coefficient of friction. Solve the formula $d = \frac{v^2}{2g\mu}$ for v, g, and μ.

$v^2 = 2dg\mu$
$v = \sqrt{2dg\mu}$

$g = \frac{v^2}{2d\mu}$

$\mu = \frac{v^2}{2dg}$

③ Solve.

The Pythagorean Theorem is used to find the lengths of the sides of a right triangle. Solve the formula $a^2 + b^2 = c^2$ for a, b, and c.

$a^2 = c^2 - b^2$
$a = \sqrt{c^2 - b^2}$

$b^2 = c^2 - a^2$
$b = \sqrt{c^2 - a^2}$

$c^2 = a^2 + b^2$
$c = \sqrt{a^2 + b^2}$

④ Solve each quadratic equation by completing the square.

$x^2 + 10x + 7 = 0$
$x^2 + 10x = -7$
$x^2 + 10x + \left(\frac{10}{2}\right)^2 = -7 + \left(\frac{10}{2}\right)^2$
$x^2 + 10x + 25 = -7 + 25$
$x^2 + 10x + 25 = 18$
$(x+5)^2 = 18$
$\sqrt{(x+5)^2} = \sqrt{18}$
$x + 5 = \pm\sqrt{9 \cdot 2}$
$x = -5 \pm 3\sqrt{2}$

$x^2 + 12x - 2 = 0$
$x^2 + 12x = 2$
$x^2 + 12x + \left(\frac{12}{2}\right)^2 = 2 + \left(\frac{12}{2}\right)^2$
$x^2 + 12x + 36 = 2 + 36$
$x^2 + 12x + 36 = 38$
$(x+6)^2 = 38$
$\sqrt{(x+6)^2} = \sqrt{38}$
$x + 6 = \pm\sqrt{38}$
$x = -6 \pm \sqrt{38}$

$x^2 - 8x - 11 = 0$
$x^2 - 8x = 11$
$x^2 - 8x + \left(-\frac{8}{2}\right)^2 = 11 + \left(-\frac{8}{2}\right)^2$
$x^2 - 8x + 16 = 11 + 16$
$x^2 - 8x + 16 = 27$
$(x-4)^2 = 27$
$\sqrt{(x-4)^2} = \sqrt{27}$
$x - 4 = \pm\sqrt{9 \cdot 3}$
$x = 4 \pm 3\sqrt{3}$

$x^2 - 11x + 6 = 0$
$x^2 - 11x = -6$
$x^2 - 11x + \left(-\frac{11}{2}\right)^2 = -6 + \left(-\frac{11}{2}\right)^2$
$x^2 - 11x + \frac{121}{4} = -\frac{24}{4} + \frac{121}{4}$
$x^2 - 11x + \frac{121}{4} = \frac{97}{4}$
$\left(x - \frac{11}{2}\right)^2 = \frac{97}{4}$
$\sqrt{\left(x - \frac{11}{2}\right)^2} = \sqrt{\frac{97}{4}}$
$x - \frac{11}{2} = \pm\frac{\sqrt{97}}{2}$
$x = \frac{11 \pm \sqrt{97}}{2}$

$x^2 - 5x - 3 = 0$
$x^2 - 5x = 3$
$x^2 - 5x + \left(-\frac{5}{2}\right)^2 = 3 + \left(-\frac{5}{2}\right)^2$
$x^2 - 5x + \frac{25}{4} = \frac{12}{4} + \frac{25}{4}$
$x^2 - 5x + \frac{25}{4} = \frac{37}{4}$
$\left(x - \frac{5}{2}\right)^2 = \frac{37}{4}$
$\sqrt{\left(x - \frac{5}{2}\right)^2} = \sqrt{\frac{37}{4}}$
$x - \frac{5}{2} = \pm\frac{\sqrt{37}}{2}$
$x = \frac{5 \pm \sqrt{37}}{2}$

$x^2 + x - 4 = 0$
$x^2 + x = 4$
$x^2 + x + \left(\frac{1}{2}\right)^2 = 4 + \left(\frac{1}{2}\right)^2$
$x^2 + x + \frac{1}{4} = \frac{16}{4} + \frac{1}{4}$
$x^2 + x + \frac{1}{4} = \frac{17}{4}$
$\left(x + \frac{1}{2}\right)^2 = \frac{17}{4}$
$\sqrt{\left(x + \frac{1}{2}\right)^2} = \sqrt{\frac{17}{4}}$
$x + \frac{1}{2} = \pm\frac{\sqrt{17}}{2}$
$x = \frac{-1 \pm \sqrt{17}}{2}$

Exponential Growth and Decay Worksheet 68

① Solve.

If your parents invested \$5,000 in a college savings plan for you on your 5th birthday at 7% interest compounded annually, how much will be in your college saving account when you turn 18? (Round to the nearest hundredth after calculating the exponent.)

$P = 5000;\ b = 0.07;\ x = 18 - 5 = 13$

$y = \$5000(1+0.07)^{13}$

$y = \$5000(1.07)^{13}$

$y = \$5000(2.41)$

$y = \$12{,}050$

If your parents invested an additional \$5,000 in a college savings plan for you on your 13th birthday at 7% interest compounded annually, how much additional money will be in your college saving account when you turn 18? (Round to the nearest hundredth after calculating the exponent.)

$P = 5000;\ b = 0.07;\ x = 18 - 13 = 5$

$y = \$5{,}000(1+0.07)^{5}$

$y = \$5{,}000(1.07)^{5}$

$y = \$5{,}000(1.40)$

$y = \$7000$

During a recent depression, housing values in one neighborhood dropped exponentially by an average rate of 8% per year for 4 years. If a house was worth \$100,000 at the beginning of the depression, what was the value of the house after 4 years? Round to the nearest ten thousandth after calculating the exponent.

$y = \$100{,}000(1-0.08)^{4}$

$y = \$100{,}000(0.92)^{4}$

$y = \$100{,}000(0.7164)$

$y = \$71{,}640$

If the same house declined in value at a rate of 9% each year for 5 years, what would the \$100,000 house be worth after 5 years? Round to the nearest ten thousandth after calculating the exponent.

$y = \$100{,}000(1-0.09)^{5}$

$y = \$100{,}000(0.91)^{5}$

$y = \$100{,}000(0.6240)$

$y = \$62{,}400$

Teaching Tips, Cont.

- Complete the Classwork exercises. Have some students work the problems on the board for the class and explain their answers. All students should work the problems in their books.

Assignment

- Complete Lesson 135, Activities 2-4.

Lesson 136

Concepts
- Work problems
- Fractions
- Quadratic formula
- Solving quadratic equations
- Math in the real world

Learning Objectives
The student will be able to:
- Use fractions to represent the amount of work done in a given amount of time
- Calculate the amount of time it takes to accomplish a job at different combined rates

Materials Needed
- Student Book, Lesson 136

Teaching Tips
➢ Review ratios and proportions. (See Lesson 134)

➢ Teach work problems from the teaching box. Explain that the equation must contain one fraction for each person or machine involved, as well as a fraction representing the combined effort.

➢ Tell the students to be sure to convert all measurements to the same unit. If one rate is given in minutes and another rate in hours, both rates must be expressed in the same unit — either minutes or hours.

Work Problems

Work problems involve two or more people or machines working together to accomplish a single task. To solve work problems, set up an equation using fractions that show what part of the job each individual can accomplish in a given unit of time. The sum of the individual fractions is equal to the part that can be accomplished in the given unit of time together.

If Mike works on a landscaping project alone, he can finish the job in 4 hours. Dave can finish the same landscaping job in 5 hours. How long will it take to finish the job if Mike and Dave work together?

Start by identifying the fractions.

Let j = the time to complete the job together.
Mike can complete $\frac{1}{4}$ of the job in an hour.
Dave can complete $\frac{1}{5}$ of the job in an hour.
Together they can complete $\frac{1}{j}$ of the job in an hour.

Make an equation and solve for j.

$\frac{1}{4}+\frac{1}{5}=\frac{1}{j}$

${}_{5}\cancel{20}j\left(\frac{1}{\cancel{4}}\right)+{}_{4}\cancel{20}j\left(\frac{1}{\cancel{5}}\right)=20\cancel{j}\left(\frac{1}{\cancel{j}}\right)$

$5j+4j=20$

$9j=20$

$j=\frac{20}{9}$

It will take Mike and Dave $\frac{20}{9}=2\frac{2}{9}$ hours to complete the job together.

To express the answer in hours and minutes, set up a proportion.

$\frac{2}{9}=\frac{x}{60\text{ minutes}}$

$9x=120$ minutes

$x=13\frac{1}{3}$ minutes

It will take Mike and Dave 2 hours $13\frac{1}{3}$ minutes to complete the job together.

① **Classwork**

Solve.

It takes one Zamboni operator 6 minutes to resurface an ice rink. It takes another Zamboni operator 8 minutes to resurface the same rink. How long would it take the two Zamboni operators working together to resurface the ice rink?

Let j = the time to complete the job together.
The first operator can complete $\frac{1}{6}$ of the job in a minute. The second operator can complete $\frac{1}{8}$ of the job in a minute. Together they can complete $\frac{1}{j}$ of the job in a minute.

$\frac{1}{6}+\frac{1}{8}=\frac{1}{j}$

${}_{4}\cancel{24}j\left(\frac{1}{\cancel{6}}\right)+{}_{3}\cancel{24}j\left(\frac{1}{\cancel{8}}\right)=24\cancel{j}\left(\frac{1}{\cancel{j}}\right)$

$4j+3j=24$

$7j=24$

$j=\frac{24}{7}$

It will take the two operators $\frac{24}{7}=3\frac{3}{7}$ minutes to complete the job together.

John can build a snowman in 30 minutes. Levi can build a snowman the same size in 20 minutes. How long will it take John and Levi to build the snowman if they work together?

Let j = the time to complete the job together.
John can complete $\frac{1}{30}$ of the snowman in a minute. Levi can complete $\frac{1}{20}$ of the snowman in a minute. Together they can complete $\frac{1}{j}$ of the snowman in a minute.

$\frac{1}{30}+\frac{1}{20}=\frac{1}{j}$

${}_{2}\cancel{60}j\left(\frac{1}{\cancel{30}}\right)+{}_{3}\cancel{60}j\left(\frac{1}{\cancel{20}}\right)=60\cancel{j}\left(\frac{1}{\cancel{j}}\right)$

$2j+3j=60$

$5j=60$

$j=\frac{60}{5}=12$

It will take John and Levi 12 minutes to build the snowman together.

Activities

② Solve.

Joe can wax a snowboard in 15 minutes. Frank can wax a snowboard in 20 minutes. How long would it take to wax 7 snowboards if Joe and Frank work together?

Let j = the time to complete one snowboard together.

Joe can complete $\frac{1}{15}$ of one snowboard in a minute. Frank can complete $\frac{1}{20}$ of one snowboard in a minute. Together they can complete $\frac{1}{j}$ of one snowboard in a minute.

$$\frac{1}{15} + \frac{1}{20} = \frac{1}{j}$$

$$_4\cancel{60}\,j\left(\frac{1}{\cancel{15}}\right) + _3\cancel{60}\,j\left(\frac{1}{\cancel{20}}\right) = 60\,\cancel{j}\left(\frac{1}{\cancel{j}}\right)$$

$$4j + 3j = 60$$

$$7j = 60$$

$$j = \frac{60}{7}$$

This is not the final answer. This is the time for 1 snowboard. Multiply by 7 to get the amount of time it takes to wax 7 snowboards.

$$\frac{60}{7}(7) = 60 \text{ minutes} = 1 \text{ hour}$$

③ Use the quadratic formula to solve each equation.

$x^2 + 10x + 7 = 0$	$x^2 + 12x - 2 = 0$	$x^2 - 8x - 11 = 0$
$x = \frac{-10 \pm \sqrt{10^2 - 4(1)(7)}}{2(1)}$	$x = \frac{-12 \pm \sqrt{12^2 - 4(1)(-2)}}{2(1)}$	$x = \frac{8 \pm \sqrt{(-8)^2 - 4(1)(-11)}}{2(1)}$
$x = \frac{-10 \pm \sqrt{100 - 28}}{2}$	$x = \frac{-12 \pm \sqrt{144 + 8}}{2}$	$x = \frac{8 \pm \sqrt{64 + 44}}{2}$
$x = \frac{-10 \pm \sqrt{72}}{2}$	$x = \frac{-12 \pm \sqrt{152}}{2}$	$x = \frac{8 \pm \sqrt{108}}{2}$
$x = \frac{-10 \pm \sqrt{36 \cdot 2}}{2}$	$x = \frac{-12 \pm \sqrt{4 \cdot 38}}{2}$	$x = \frac{8 \pm \sqrt{36 \cdot 3}}{2}$
$x = \frac{-10 \pm 6\sqrt{2}}{2}$	$x = \frac{-12 \pm 2\sqrt{38}}{2}$	$x = \frac{8 \pm 6\sqrt{3}}{2}$
$x = -5 \pm 3\sqrt{2}$	$x = -6 \pm \sqrt{38}$	$x = -4 \pm 3\sqrt{3}$

$x^2 - 11x + 6 = 0$	$x^2 - 5x - 3 = 0$	$x^2 + x - 4 = 0$
$x = \frac{-11 \pm \sqrt{(-11)^2 - 4(1)(6)}}{2(1)}$	$x = \frac{5 \pm \sqrt{(-5)^2 - 4(1)(-3)}}{2(1)}$	$x = \frac{-1 \pm \sqrt{1^2 - 4(1)(-4)}}{2(1)}$
$x = \frac{-11 \pm \sqrt{121 - 24}}{2}$	$x = \frac{5 \pm \sqrt{25 + 12}}{2}$	$x = \frac{-1 \pm \sqrt{1 + 16}}{2}$
$x = \frac{-11 \pm \sqrt{97}}{2}$	$x = \frac{5 \pm \sqrt{37}}{2}$	$x = \frac{-1 \pm \sqrt{17}}{2}$

Note: These are the same problems from Lesson 135, but solved using a different method. All answers will be the same regardless of which method is used. Use this opportunity to reinforce this concept.

Teaching Tips, Cont.

➢ Remind the students to find the lowest common denominator of the fractions before solving. Students should not need review on this concept at this point, but you may refer them to Lesson 6 for review if necessary.

➢ Complete the Classwork exercises. Have some students work the problems on the board for the class and explain their answers. All students should work the problems in their books.

Assignment

• Complete Lesson 136, Activities 2-3.

Lesson 137

Concepts

- Investment problems
- Literal equations
- Simple interest
- Subtracting polynomials
- Math in the real world

Learning Objectives

The student will be able to:

- Solve the simple interest formula in terms of principle, rate, and time
- Use the simple interest formula to find the amount of principle, the interest rate, or the amount of time invested

Materials Needed

- Student Book, Lesson 137

Teaching Tips

➢ Review simple interest. (See Lesson 112)

➢ Review literal equations. (See Lesson 135)

➢ Show the students that the formula for simple interest is a literal equation that can be rearranged to solve for any of the variables.

➢ Teach investment problems from the teaching box.

Investment Problems

Investment problems use a literal equation to show the relationship of simple interest, principal, interest rate, and time. The literal equation can be rearranged to solve for any variable. The formula $i = prt$ shows the relationship of interest (i), principal (p), the interest rate (r), and time (t). It is important to note that the interest rate is a percent expressed as a decimal, and the unit of time must match the unit of time used in the interest rate. For example, if interest is paid at a rate of 5 percent per year, time must be expressed in years. If the interest rate is 2% per month, time must be expressed in months.

If you invest $300 at 2% annual interest, how long will it take to earn $54 interest?

Identify the variables.
$i = \$54$, $p = \$30$, $r = 2\% = 0.02$, $t =$ years

Write the literal equation and rearrange to solve for the unknown variable.

$\frac{i}{pr} = \frac{prt}{pr}$

$t = \frac{i}{pr}$

Substitute and solve.

$t = \frac{\$54}{(\$300)(0.02)} = \frac{54}{6} = 9$

The unit of time must match the time shown in the interest rate. The interest rate was stated as an annual rate, so time must be in years.

It will take 9 years to earn $54 interest.

① **Classwork**

Solve.

If your grandparents invested $10,000 in a college savings plan for you on your 5th birthday at 6% simple interest, how much interest will you earn by the time you turn 18?

$p = \$10,000$, $r = 6\% = 0.06$, $t = 13$ years

$P = 10,000$; $r = 0.06$; $t = 18 - 5 = 13$

$i = \$10,000(.06)(13)$

$i = \$7800$

What will be the total balance in your account?

$10,000 + $7800 = $17,800

If your parents invested an additional $5,000 in a college savings plan for you on your 13th birthday at 6% simple interest, how much additional interest will you earn by the time you turn 18?

$p = \$5000$, $r = 6\% = 0.06$, $t = 5$ years

$P = 10,000$; $r = 0.06$; $t = 18 - 13 = 5$

$i = \$5000(.06)(5)$

$i = \$1500$

What will be the total balance in your account?

$17,800 + $5000 + $1500 = $24,300

Activities

② Solve.

If you invest $1000 at 3% annual interest, how long will it take to earn $90 interest?

$i = \$90$, $p = \$1000$, $r = 3\% = 0.03$, $t =$ years

$\frac{i}{pr} = \frac{prt}{pr}$

$t = \frac{i}{pr}$

$t = \frac{\$90}{(\$1000)(0.03)} = \frac{90}{30} = 3$

It will take 3 years to earn $90 interest.

If you invest $2500 for 11 years, what interest rate do you need to earn $1100 interest?

$i = \$1100$, $p = \$2500$, $r =$ rate, $t = 11$ years

$\frac{i}{pt} = \frac{prt}{pt}$

$r = \frac{i}{pt}$

$r = \frac{\$1100}{(\$2500)(11)} = \frac{1100}{27,500} = 0.04 = 4\%$

You need a 4% interest rate.

③ Solve.
If your parents deposited $1000 into a college savings plan earning 7% simple interest the day you were born, and added $1000 at the same 7% simple interest rate each year on your birthday, how much money would you have saved for college on your 18th birthday before they added the money for your 18th birthday? Complete the chart to do your calculations.

Birthday	$ Deposited	Interest rate	Years	Interest earned
Birth	$1000	7%	18	$i = \$1,000(0.07)(18) = \$1260$
1	$1000	7%	17	$i = \$1,000(0.07)(17) = \$1190$
2	$1000	7%	16	$i = \$1,000(0.07)(16) = \$1120$
3	$1000	7%	15	$i = \$1,000(0.07)(15) = \$1050$
4	$1000	7%	14	$i = \$1,000(0.07)(14) = \$980$
5	$1000	7%	13	$i = \$1,000(0.07)(13) = \$910$
6	$1000	7%	12	$i = \$1,000(0.07)(12) = \$840$
7	$1000	7%	11	$i = \$1,000(0.07)(11) = \$770$
8	$1000	7%	10	$i = \$1,000(0.07)(10) = \$700$
9	$1000	7%	9	$i = \$1,000(0.07)(9) = \$630$
10	$1000	7%	8	$i = \$1,000(0.07)(8) = \$560$
11	$1000	7%	7	$i = \$1,000(0.07)(7) = \$490$
12	$1000	7%	6	$i = \$1,000(0.07)(6) = \$420$
13	$1000	7%	5	$i = \$1,000(0.07)(5) = \$350$
14	$1000	7%	4	$i = \$1,000(0.07)(4) = \$280$
15	$1000	7%	3	$i = \$1,000(0.07)(3) = \$210$
16	$1000	7%	2	$i = \$1,000(0.07)(2) = \$140$
17	$1000	7%	1	$i = \$1,000(0.07)(1) = \$70$
Totals	$18,000	7%	18	$11,970

The total amount in the account will be $18,000 + $11,970 = $29,970.

④ Subtract.

$$\begin{array}{r}(7x^2+4x+5)\\-(4x^2+3x-3)\\\hline 3x^2+\ \ x+8\end{array}\qquad\begin{array}{r}(6x^2-2x+3)\\-(3x^2-5x-8)\\\hline 3x^2+3x+11\end{array}\qquad\begin{array}{r}(6x^2-7x-4)\\-(5x^2+2x-3)\\\hline x^2-9x-1\end{array}$$

$$\begin{array}{r}(3x^2+2x+1)\\-(4x^2-7x+4)\\\hline -x^2+9x-3\end{array}\qquad\begin{array}{r}(2x^2+4x-2)\\-(8x^2-7x-6)\\\hline -6x^2+11x+4\end{array}\qquad\begin{array}{r}(8x^2-7x-5)\\-(5x^2-6x-8)\\\hline 3x^2-\ \ x+3\end{array}$$

Teaching Tips, Cont.

- Remind the students to double check the units before solving. If the interest rate is given as a percent per year, then the time must be expressed in years. If the interest rate is given as a percent per month, then the time must be expressed in months.
- Complete the Classwork exercises. Have some students work the problems on the board for the class and explain their answers. All students should work the problems in their books.

Assignment

- Complete Lesson 137, Activities 2-4.

Lesson 138

Concepts

- Motion problems
- Distance formula
- Literal equations
- Adding polynomials
- Multiplying a polynomial by a monomial
- Math in the real world

Learning Objectives

The student will be able to:

- Write an equation to represent motion problems
- Apply the distance formula to real-world scenarios

Materials Needed

- Student Book, Lesson 138
- Worksheet 69

Teaching Tips

- Have students complete Worksheet 69 in class. This may be for added practice of earlier topics, or graded as a quiz, if desired.
- Review literal equations. (See Lesson 135)
- Introduce the distance formula form the teaching box. Students should memorize this formula. It will be used in both math and science classes in years to come.
- Teach how to solve motion problems from the teaching box. Encourage the students to set up a chart similar to the one shown to facilitate writing the equation.

Motion Problems

Most motion problems use the formula $d = rt$, where d is distance, r is the rate of motion, and t is time. The unit of time in the rate must match the unit of time in the amount of time.

This formula is a literal formula and may be rearranged to solve for any of the three variables.

When solving motion problems, identify the value of each variable in the problem. Convert the time units if necessary so that all the units match. Some problems may have multiple values for two of the variables. In this case, you would have to set up a proportion to solve.

One car took 9 hours to travel a certain distance. A second car took 10 hours to travel the same distance. If the first car traveled at a rate of 7 miles per hour faster than the second car, what was the rate of each car and how many miles did each car drive?

Set up a chart with the values of the variables.

	Car 1	Car 2
d	d	d
r	$r + 7$	r
t	9	10

Because the variable d is the same for both cars, the equation can be written as follows.

$d_1 = d_2$

$r_1t_1 = r_2t_2$

Substitute the values from the chart and solve.

$(r+7)(9) = 10r$

$9r + 63 = 10r$

$r = 63$

Car 2 was traveling at 63 miles/hour.
Car 1 was traveling at 63 + 7 = 70 miles/hour.

The cars each drove the same distance.

$d = rt$

$d_1 = (70 \text{ miles/hour})(9 \text{ hours}) = 630 \text{ miles}$

$d_2 = (63 \text{ miles/hour})(10 \text{ hours}) = 630 \text{ miles}$

① Classwork

Solve.

One luge sled took 46.817 seconds to travel a certain distance. A second luge sled took 46.293 seconds to travel the same distance. If the first sled traveled at a rate of 0.298 meters per second slower than the second sled, what was the rate of each sled? Round your answer to the nearest thousandth.

	Sled 1	Sled 2
d	d	d
r	$r - 0.298$	r
t	46.817	46.293

$d_1 = d_2$

$r_1t_1 = r_2t_2$

$(r - 0.298)(46.817) = 46.293r$

$46.817r - 13.951466 = 46.293r$

$0.524r = 13.951466$

$r = 26.625$

Sled 2 was traveling at 26.625 meters/second.
Sled 1 was traveling at 26.625 - 0.298 = 26.327 meters/second.

How many meters did each sled travel? Round your answer to the nearest hundredth.

$d = rt$

$d_1 = (26.625 \text{ m/s})(46.293) = 1232.55 \text{ m}$

$d_2 = (26.327 \text{ m/s})(46.817) = 1232.55 \text{ m}$

Activities

② Solve.

One speed skater took 12 minutes, 41.69 seconds to travel a certain distance. A second speed skater took 13 minutes, 22.93 seconds to travel the same distance. If the first skater traveled at a rate of 0.6743 meters per second faster than the second skater, what was the rate of each skater? Round your answer to the nearest ten thousandth.

	Skater 1	Skater 2
d	d	d
r	$r + 0.6743$	r
t	761.69 s	802.93 s

$d_1 = d_2$

$r_1t_1 = r_2t_2$

$(r + 0.6743)(761.69) = 802.93r$

$761.69r + 513.607567 = 802.93r$

$41.24r = 513.607567$

$r = 12.4541$

Skater 2 was traveling at 12.4541 meters/second.
Sled 1 was traveling at 12.4541 +0.6743 = 13.1284 meters/second.

How many meters did each speed skater travel? Round your answer to the nearest meter.

$d = rt$

$d_1 = (13.1284 \text{ m/s})(761.69) = 10{,}000 \text{ m}$

$d_2 = (12.4541 \text{ m/s})(802.93) = 10{,}000 \text{ m}$

③ Add.

$$\begin{array}{r} 4x^2 + 3x - 5 \\ +\ 7x^2 + \ \ x + 3 \\ \hline 11x^2 + 4x - 2 \end{array} \qquad \begin{array}{r} 6x^2 + 2x + 3 \\ +3x^2 - 5x - 8 \\ \hline 9x^2 - 3x - 5 \end{array} \qquad \begin{array}{r} 6x^2 - 7x - 4 \\ +5x^2 + 2x - 3 \\ \hline 11x^2 - 5x - 7 \end{array}$$

$$\begin{array}{r} 3x^2 + 2x + 1 \\ +\ 4x^2 + 7x - 4 \\ \hline 7x^2 + 9x - 3 \end{array} \qquad \begin{array}{r} 2x^2 + 4x + 2 \\ +8x^2 - 7x - 6 \\ \hline 10x^2 - 3x - 4 \end{array} \qquad \begin{array}{r} 8x^2 - 7x + 5 \\ +5x^2 - 6x - 8 \\ \hline 13x^2 - 13x - 3 \end{array}$$

④ Multiply.

$4x(3x^2 + 2x - 5)$

$4x(3x^2) + 4x(2x) + 4x(-5) =$

$12x^3 + 8x^2 - 20x$

$2x(5x^2 - 3x + 3)$

$2x(5x^2) + 2x(-3x) + 2x(3) =$

$10x^3 - 6x^2 + 6x$

$2x^2(3x^2 - 2x + 5)$

$2x^2(3x^2) + 2x^2(-2x) + 2x^2(5) =$

$6x^4 - 4x^3 + 10x^2$

$3x^2(7x^2 + 4x - 6)$

$3x^2(7x^2) + 3x^2(4x) + 3x^2(-6) =$

$21x^4 + 12x^3 - 18x^2$

Ratios and Proportions, Literal Equations Worksheet 69

① Solve.

The ratio of boys to girls in one 8th grade class was 4:5. If there were 15 girls in the class, how many boys were there?

$\frac{\text{Boys}}{\text{Girls}} = \frac{\text{Boys}}{\text{Girls}}$

Let b = the number of boys.

$\frac{4}{5} = \frac{b}{15}$

$\cancel{5}(15)\frac{4}{\cancel{5}} = 5(\cancel{15})\frac{b}{\cancel{15}}$

$60 = 5b$

$b = 12$

The ratio of basketball players to all students in the 8th grade is 2:5. If there are a total of 35 students in the 8th grade, how many students play basketball?

Let b = the number of basketball players.

$\frac{\text{Basketball players}}{8^{th}\text{ grade students}} = \frac{\text{Basketball players}}{8^{th}\text{ grade students}}$

$\frac{2}{5} = \frac{b}{35}$

$\cancel{5}(35)\frac{2}{\cancel{5}} = 5(\cancel{35})\frac{b}{\cancel{35}}$

$70 = 5b$

$b = 14$

There are 14 basketball players.

② Solve.

The formula for universal gravitation is $F = G\left(\frac{m_1m_2}{r^2}\right)$, where F is force of attraction between two objects, m_1 and m_2 are the masses of two objects, and r is the distance between the two objects. Rewrite the formula to solve for G, r, m_1 and m_2.

$F = G\left(\frac{m_1m_2}{r^2}\right)$

$Fr^2 = G(m_1m_2)$

$\frac{Fr^2}{m_1m_2} = G$

$F = G\left(\frac{m_1m_2}{r^2}\right)$

$Fr^2 = G(m_1m_2)$

$r^2 = \frac{G(m_1m_2)}{F}$

$r = \sqrt{\frac{G(m_1m_2)}{F}} \cdot \frac{\sqrt{F}}{\sqrt{F}} = \frac{\sqrt{FG(m_1m_2)}}{F}$

$F = G\left(\frac{m_1m_2}{r^2}\right)$

$Fr^2 = G(m_1m_2)$

$\frac{Fr^2}{Gm_2} = m_1$

$F = G\left(\frac{m_1m_2}{r^2}\right)$

$Fr^2 = G(m_1m_2)$

$\frac{Fr^2}{Gm_1} = m_2$

Teaching Tips, Cont.

- Remind the students to make sure all units match. If one object is moving in miles per hour, the other one cannot be measured in feet per second. One rate would have to be converted to the other. It does not matter which one you choose as long as both are in the same units.
- Complete the Classwork exercises. Have some students work the problems on the board for the class and explain their answers. All students should work the problems in their books.

Assignment

- Complete Lesson 138, Activities 2-4.

Lesson 139

Concepts

- Square roots without a calculator
- Radicals

Learning Objectives

The student will be able to:

- Calculate the square root of a number to the nearest hundredth without using a calculator

Materials Needed

- Student Book, Lesson 139

Teaching Tips

- ➢ Ask the students how they could find the square root of a number that is not a perfect square, such as 156. (Use a calculator)

- ➢ Suggest that another method they could use is a guess-and-check method, such as knowing it is more than 12 ($12^2 = 144$) but less than 13 ($13^2 = 169$), and then multiplying by hand to figure it out. Students may comment that this method is time consuming. Tell them they are right!

- ➢ Tell the students there is a faster method of finding the square root of a number without using a calculator.

- ➢ Teach how to find the square root of a number without using a calculator. The method is presented in the teaching box, but more detailed information is provided in the space to the right.

Square Roots without a Calculator

There are many methods of estimating square roots. Two of them can easily be done with the math skills you already have. The first is essentially guess and check. You guess a number, square it, and see if it is too high or too low and adjust accordingly, repeating the process as many times as necessary until you get the correct answer. This method will provide the correct answer, but will also provide a lot of frustration in the process.

A better, more reliable method of estimating square roots is by using algorithm. An **algorithm** is a step-by-step method of solving a problem.

Find $\sqrt{156}$ to the nearest hundredth.

There should be two more than twice as many digits after the decimal point in the problem as the answer requires. Because the answer asks for hundredths, there should be 2 x 2 + 2 = 6 zeros after the decimal point in the problem.

$\sqrt{156.000000}$

Beginning on the right side of the radicand, underline the digits in groups of 2. If there is an odd number of digits to the left of the decimal point, add a leading zero.

$\sqrt{\underline{01}\underline{56}.\underline{00}\underline{00}\underline{00}}$

Estimate the first digit of the answer by taking the square root of the left-most underlined numbers. In this case, $\sqrt{1} = 1$. This is the first number in the answer.

If the left-most underlined pair of numbers is not a perfect square, take the square root of the largest perfect square that is less than the number pair in the problem. For example, if the first underlined number pair was 07, the largest perfect square less than 7 is 4. The square root of 4 is 2, so 2 is the first digit in the answer.

The remainder of the solution to this problem is shown step-by-step with instructions below.

	1 2. 4 8 9	
	$\sqrt{\underline{0156}.\underline{000000}}$	
	<u>01</u>	square the first digit in the answer; subtract
2	0056	bring down next 2 numbers; double 1st digit of answer to the left
22	<u>44</u>	(20+what)(what) is ≤ 56? This is 2nd digit; multiply
	1200	subtract; bring down next 2; double 1st 2 digits of answer
244	<u>976</u>	(240+what)(what) ≤ 1200? This is 3rd digit; multiply
	22400	subtract; bring down next 2; double 1st 3 digits of answer
2488	<u>19904</u>	(2480+what)(what) ≤ 22400? This is 4th digit; multiply
	249600	subtract; bring down next 2; double 1st 4 digits of answer
24969	<u>224721</u>	(24960+what)(what) ≤ 249600? This is 5th digit; multiply

Calculating square roots without a calculator

1. Determine to which place value you wish to round. The exercises in this Lesson state to round to the hundredths, or two places after the decimal.

2. Double the desired number of digits after the decimal and add 2. For this lesson, this means 2(2) + 2 = 4 + 2 = 6. Place this number of zeros after the decimal in the problem. This means 156 becomes 156.000000 for calculating the square root.

3. Beginning on the right-hand side of the radicand, underline the digits in groups of two. There are three groups of two after the decimal, one group of two immediately to the left of the decimal, and a 1 left over. Whenever there is a single digit left over, place a zero to the left so that there is a group of two. See the sample problem in the teaching box for the proper notation.

① **Classwork.**
Find the square roots to the nearest hundredth without using a calculator.

$\sqrt{37} = 6.08$

```
         6. 0 8 2
       √37.000000
        36
12      0100
120      00
        10000
1208     9664
          33600
12162     24324
           9276
```

$\sqrt{213} = 14.59$

```
          1 4. 5 9 4
        √0213.000000
         01
2        0113
24        96
          1700
285       1425
           27500
2909       26181
            131900
29184       116736
             15164
```

Activities

② Find the square roots to the nearest hundredth without using a calculator.

$\sqrt{7} = 2.65$

```
        2. 6 4 5
      √7.000000
       4
4      300
46     276
        2400
524     2096
         30400
5285     26425
          3975
```

$\sqrt{61} = 7.81$

```
         7. 8 1 0
      √61.000000
        49
14      1200
148      1184
           1600
1561       1561
             3900
15620           0
             3900
```

$\sqrt{458} = 21.40$

```
          2 1. 4 0 0
       √0458.000000
         04
4        0058
41         41
          1700
424       1696
            400
4280          0
           40000
42800          0
           40000
```

$\sqrt{9455} = 97.24$

```
          9 7. 2 3 6
       √9455.000000
         81
18       1355
187      1309
          4600
1942      3884
           71600
19443      58329
           1327100
194466     1166796
            160304
```

$\sqrt{10} = 3.16$

```
         3. 1 6 2
      √10.000000
        9
6       100
61       61
         3900
626      3756
          14400
6322      12644
           1756
```

$\sqrt{2} = 1.41$

```
        1. 4 1 4
      √2.000000
       1
2      100
24      96
        400
281     281
        11900
2824    11296
          604
```

Teaching Tips, Cont.

- Complete the Classwork exercises. Have some students work the problems on the board for the class and explain their answers. All students should work the problems in their books.

Assignment

- Complete Lesson 139, Activity 2.

Calculating square roots without a calculator, continued

4. Take the square root of the first set of underlined numbers. This will be a single-digit number. Write the answer above the radical, over the underlined pair.

5. Square this number and subtract the square from the underlined pair. Bring down the next underlined pair and write it on the right side of the difference you just found.

6. Double the number(s) in the answer at this point and write the doubled number to the left, leaving space between these numbers and the subtraction.

7. Find a single-digit number that, when written to the right of the doubled number and then multiplied by the newly-formed number, is less than or equal to the number you formed by bringing down the underlined pair at the end of step 4.

8. Write this answer to the right of the doubled number from step 6 and above the radical, over the underlined pair you just brought down.

9. Repeat steps 5 – 8 until you have used all of the underlined pairs.

Lesson 140

Concepts

- Functions
- Square roots
- Domain
- Range
- Graphing functions

Learning Objectives

The student will be able to:

- Sketch the graph of a function containing a radical
- Determine the limits of the domain

Materials Needed

- Student Book, Lesson 140
- Worksheet 70

Teaching Tips

- ➢ Write the equation $y = -x^2 + 2$ on the board and ask the students what the graph will look like. (It is a parabola that opens down with the vertex at the point (0, 2).)
- ➢ Now rewrite the equation, switching the x and y so it reads $x = -y^2 + 2$ and ask the students what they think will happen to the parabola. (If the students are having difficulty, point out that the *x*- and *y*-coordinates are just swapped. This is a parabola that opens left with the vertex at the point (2, 0).)
- ➢ Ask the students if this equation is a function. (No. A sideways parabola will have two values of *y* for most values of *x*.)

Functions Involving Square Roots

The domain (values of *x*) and range (values of *y*) have special rules when there is a square root of a variable in a function. Because the radicand (the portion under the square root symbol) must be positive, you must set the radicand greater than or equal to zero and solve for the variable to determine the limitations on the domain and range.

When graphing functions involving square roots, *always* start by finding the limitations of the domain. Then make a T-chart, using valid values for the variables.

Sketch the graph of $y = \sqrt{2-x}$.

Determine the limitations of the domain.

$2 - x \ge 0$

$2 \ge x$

$x \le 2$

Make a T-chart to find point to plot. If you are careful, you can choose values of *x* that will produce whole numbers for *y*. Be careful not to choose a value for *x* that will have the square root of a negative number, which does not exist.

x	y
2	$\sqrt{2-2} = \sqrt{0} = 0$
1	$\sqrt{2-1} = \sqrt{1} = 1$
-2	$\sqrt{2-(-2)} = \sqrt{4} = 2$
-7	$\sqrt{2-(-7)} = \sqrt{9} = 3$
-14	$\sqrt{2-(-14)} = \sqrt{16} = 4$

Plot theses points on a coordinate plane and join them with a smooth curve.

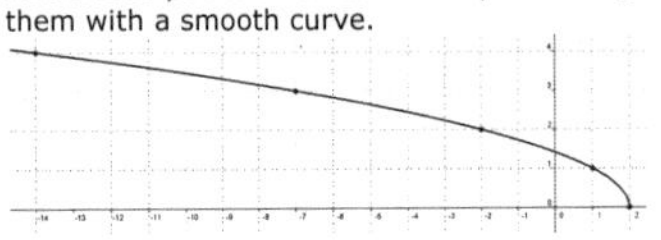

Notice that the graph stays above the x-axis and does not extend past $x = 2$ in the positive direction.

① **Classwork**

Determine the limits of the domain and graph each function.

$y = \sqrt{3-x}$

$3 - x \ge 0$

$3 \ge x$

$x \le 3$

x	y
3	$\sqrt{3-3} = \sqrt{0} = 0$
2	$\sqrt{3-2} = \sqrt{1} = 1$
-1	$\sqrt{3-(-1)} = \sqrt{4} = 2$
-6	$\sqrt{3-(-6)} = \sqrt{9} = 3$

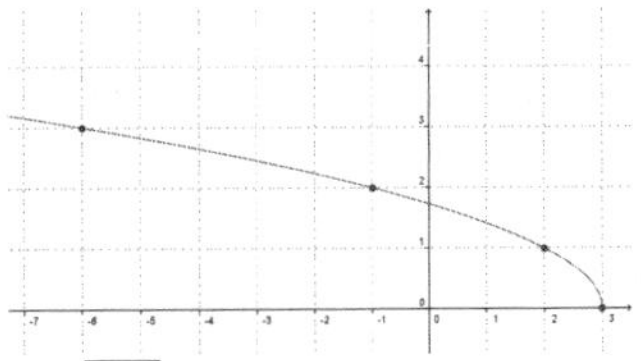

$y = \sqrt{x+2}$

$x + 2 \ge 0$

$x \ge -2$

x	y
-2	$\sqrt{-2+2} = \sqrt{0} = 0$
-1	$\sqrt{-1+2} = \sqrt{1} = 1$
2	$\sqrt{2+2} = \sqrt{4} = 2$
7	$\sqrt{7+2} = \sqrt{9} = 3$

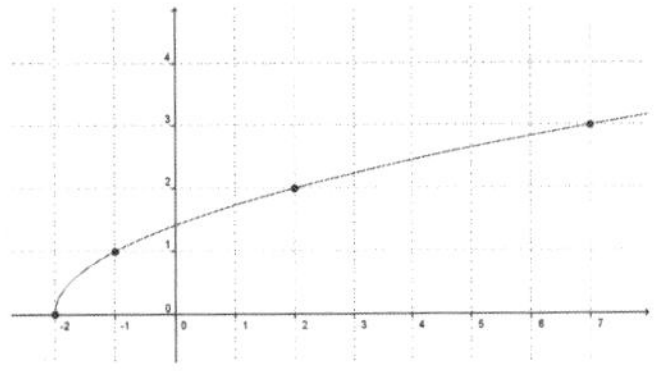

Activities

② Determine the limits of the domain and graph each function.

$y = \sqrt{5-x}$

$5 - x \ge 0$

$5 \ge x$

$x \le 5$

x	y
5	$\sqrt{5-5} = \sqrt{0} = 0$
4	$\sqrt{5-4} = \sqrt{1} = 1$
1	$\sqrt{5-1} = \sqrt{4} = 2$
-4	$\sqrt{5-(-4)} = \sqrt{9} = 3$

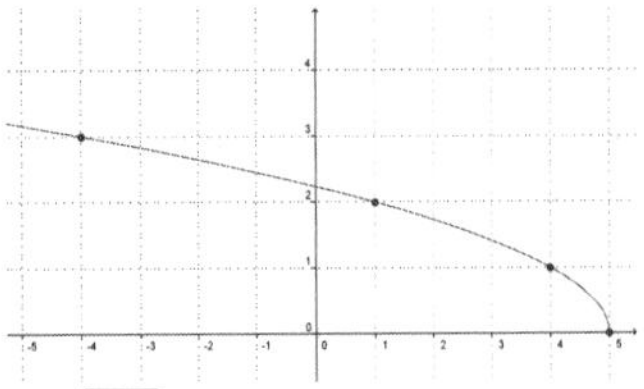

$y = \sqrt{-1-x}$

$-1 - x \ge 0$

$-1 \ge x$

$x \le -1$

x	y
-1	$\sqrt{-1-(-1)} = \sqrt{0} = 0$
-2	$\sqrt{-1-(-2)} = \sqrt{1} = 1$
-5	$\sqrt{-1-(-5)} = \sqrt{4} = 2$
-10	$\sqrt{-1-(-10)} = \sqrt{9} = 3$

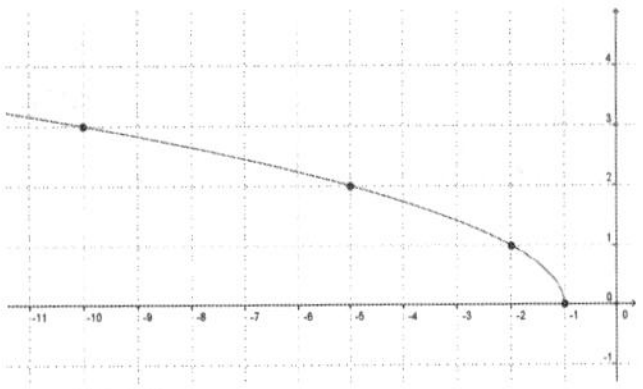

$y = \sqrt{x-2}$

$x - 2 \ge 0$

$x \ge 2$

x	y
2	$\sqrt{2-2} = \sqrt{0} = 0$
3	$\sqrt{3-2} = \sqrt{1} = 1$
6	$\sqrt{6-2} = \sqrt{4} = 2$
11	$\sqrt{11-2} = \sqrt{9} = 3$

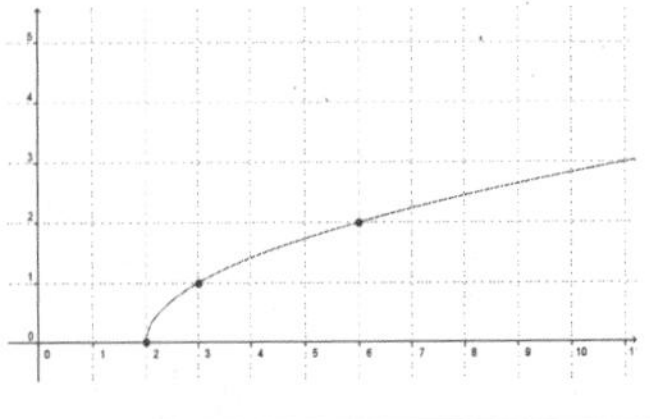

$y = \sqrt{x+3}$

$x + 3 \ge 0$

$x \ge -3$

x	y
-3	$\sqrt{-3+3} = \sqrt{0} = 0$
-2	$\sqrt{-2+3} = \sqrt{1} = 1$
1	$\sqrt{1+3} = \sqrt{4} = 2$
6	$\sqrt{6+3} = \sqrt{9} = 3$

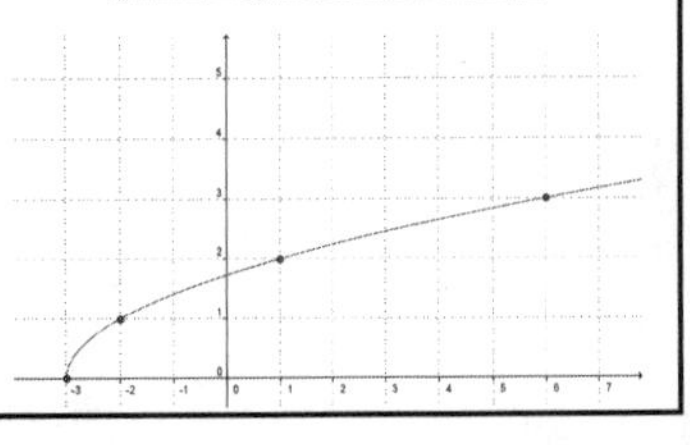

Factoring Polynomials, Solving Rational Expressions Worksheet 70

① Factor.

$9x^2 - 8$

$(3x + 2\sqrt{2})(3x - 2\sqrt{2})$

$x^2 - 71$

$(x + \sqrt{71})(x - \sqrt{71})$

$16x^2 - 18$

$(4x + 3\sqrt{2})(4x - 3\sqrt{2})$

$25x^2 - 17$

$(5x + \sqrt{17})(5x - \sqrt{17})$

$100x^2 - 49$

$(10x + 7)(10x - 7)$

$81x^2 - 198x + 121$

$(9x - 11)^2$

② Solve. List any exclusions.

$\frac{7x}{2x+5} + \frac{4x}{2x+5} =$

$\frac{7x+4x}{2x+5} =$

$\frac{11x}{2x+5}; x \neq -\frac{5}{2}$

$\frac{8x-7}{x-6} - \frac{4x+3}{x-6} =$

$\frac{(8x-7)-(4x+3)}{x-6} =$

$\frac{4x-10}{x-6}; x \neq 6$

$\frac{27x+36}{2x^2+6x} \cdot \frac{4x^2-6x}{6x^2-x-12} =$

$\frac{9(3x+4)}{2x(x+3)} \cdot \frac{2x(2x-3)}{(3x+4)(2x-3)} =$

$\frac{9}{x+3}; x \neq -3, -\frac{4}{3}, 0, \frac{3}{2}$

$\frac{20x^2-7x-6}{4x^2+16x+7} \cdot \frac{8x^2+2x-1}{20x^2+3x-2} =$

$\frac{(4x-3)(5x+2)}{(2x+1)(2x+7)} \cdot \frac{(2x+1)(4x-1)}{(5x+2)(4x-1)} =$

$\frac{4x-3}{2x+7}; x \neq -\frac{7}{2}, -\frac{1}{2}, -\frac{2}{5}, \frac{1}{4}$

Teaching Tips, Cont.

- Have the students solve the equation $x = -y^2 + 2$ for y. $(y = \sqrt{2-x})$
- Tell the students that this equation would graph only those points that have a positive *y*-coordinate, thus resulting in half of a parabola.
- Ask the students if this equation is a function. (Yes.)
- Teach functions involving square roots from the teaching box. Tell the students to choose their values of *x* carefully when plotting points to make sure they get perfect squares in the radicand. This will make graphing the function easier.
- Complete the Classwork exercises. Have some students work the problems on the board for the class and explain their answers. All students should work the problems in their books.
- Review for Test 14 using worksheets 65-70. These worksheets were assigned in previous lessons.

Assignments

- Complete Lesson 140, Activity 2.
- Worksheet 70.
- Study for Test 14 (Lessons 128-137).

Test 14

Testing Objectives

The student will:

- Graph the solution of systems of linear inequalities
- Identify the graphs as bounded, unbounded, or no solution
- Solve exponential growth problems
- Solve exponential decay problems
- Solve ratio problems
- Solve literal equations
- Solve work problems

Materials Needed

- Test 14
- *It's College Test Prep Time!* from Student Book
- Exploring Math through... Geocaching from Student Book

Teaching Tips

➢ Administer Test 14, allowing the students 30-40 minutes to complete the test.

➢ When all students are finished taking the test, introduce *It's College Test Prep Time* from the student book. This page may be completed in class or assigned as homework.

① Graph the solution of the system of linear inequalities and state whether the solution is bounded, unbounded, or no solution. **12 points**

$x - y < 0$
$x + y > 0$
$x < 3$

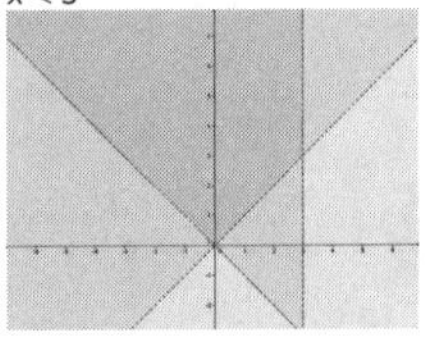

The graph is unbounded.

$x - y < 0$
$x + y > 0$
$y < 3$

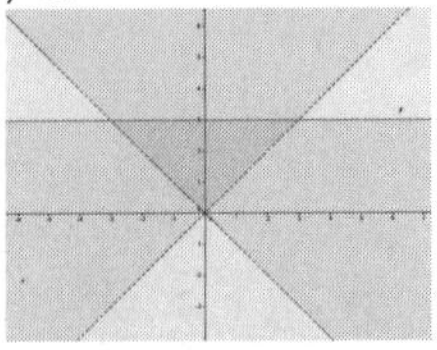

The graph is bounded.

$x - y < 0$
$x + y > 0$
$x > 3$

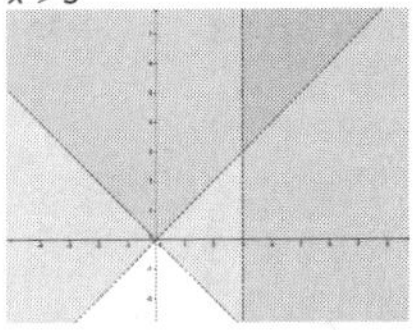

The graph is unbounded.

$x - y < 0$
$x + y < 0$
$x > 3$

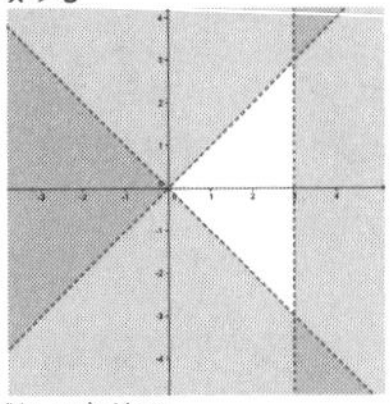

No solution.

$x - y < 0$
$x + y > 0$
$y > 3$

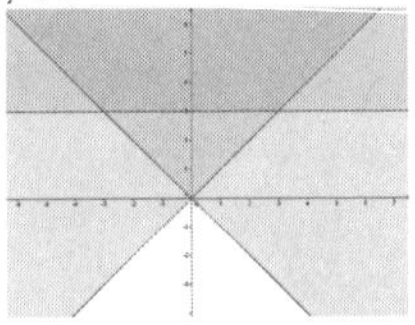

The graph is unbounded.

$x - y > 0$
$x + y < 0$
$y > 3$

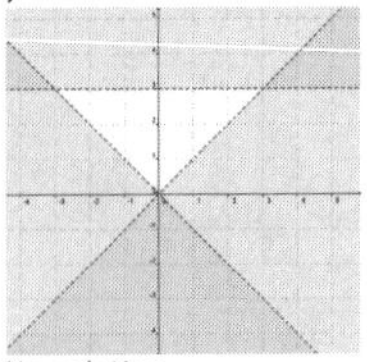

No solution.

② Complete the chart **8 points**

If your parents deposited \$5000 into a college savings plan earning 6% interest on your 10th birthday and added \$2000 at the same 6% interest rate each year on your birthday, how much money would you have saved for college on your 16th birthday before they added the money for your 16th birthday? Complete the chart to do your calculations.

Birthday	\$ Deposited	Interest rate	Years	Final value
10	\$5000	6%	6	$y = \$5,000(1+0.06)^6 = \$7092.60$
11	\$2000	6%	5	$y = \$2,000(1+0.06)^5 = \$2676.45$
12	\$2000	6%	4	$y = \$2,000(1+0.06)^4 = \$2524.95$
13	\$2000	6%	3	$y = \$2,000(1+0.06)^3 = \$2382.03$
14	\$2000	6%	2	$y = \$2,000(1+0.06)^2 = \$2247.20$
15	\$2000	6%	1	$y = \$2,000(1+0.06)^1 = \$2120$
Totals	\$15,000	6%	6	\$19,043.23

③ Solve. **5 points**

During a recent depression, housing values in one neighborhood dropped exponentially by an average rate of 10% per year for 4 years. If a house was worth \$200,000 at the beginning of the depression, what was the value of the house after 4 years? Round to the nearest ten thousandth after calculating the exponent.

$y = \$200,000(1-0.10)^4$
$y = \$200,000(0.90)^4$
$y = \$200,000(0.6561)$
$y = \$131,220$

If the same house declined in value at a rate of 11% each year for 5 years, what would the \$200,000 house be worth after 5 years? Round to the nearest ten thousandth after calculating the exponent.

$y = \$200,000(1-0.11)^5$
$y = \$200,000(0.89)^5$
$y = \$200,000(0.5584)$
$y = \$111,680$

The ratio of male athletes to female athletes in the 1976 Montreal Olympic Games was 134:35. If there were 4824 male athletes, how many female athletes were there?

$\frac{\text{Male athletes}}{\text{Female athletes}} = \frac{\text{Male athletes}}{\text{Female athletes}}$

Let f = the number of female athletes.

$\frac{134}{35} = \frac{4824}{f}$

$\cancel{35}(f)\frac{134}{\cancel{35}} = 35(\cancel{f})\frac{4824}{\cancel{f}}$

$134f = 168,840$

$f = 1260$

The formula for exponential growth is $y = a(1+b)^x$. Solve this formula for the variable a.

$y = a(1+b)^x$

$\frac{y}{(1+b)^x} = \frac{a\cancel{(1+b)^x}}{\cancel{(1+b)^x}}$

$a = \frac{y}{(1+b)^x}$

Danielle can paint a room in 4 hours. Alyssa can paint the same room in 5 hours. How long will it take Danielle and Alyssa to paint the room if they work together?

Let j = the time to complete the job together.
Danielle can complete $\frac{1}{4}$ of the job in an hour.
Alyssa can complete $\frac{1}{5}$ of the job in an hour.
Together they can complete $\frac{1}{j}$ of the job in an hour.

$\frac{1}{4} + \frac{1}{5} = \frac{1}{j}$

${}_5\cancel{20}j\left(\frac{1}{\cancel{4}}\right) + {}_4\cancel{20}j\left(\frac{1}{\cancel{5}}\right) = 20\cancel{j}\left(\frac{1}{\cancel{j}}\right)$

$5j + 4j = 20$

$9j = 20$

$j = \frac{20}{9}$

25 points total

It's College Test Prep Time!

1. Left unchecked and with an unlimited food source, a rabbit population can grow at a rate of 19% per month. If there are 137 rabbits now, how many rabbits were there a year ago?

   A. 7
   B. 11 $137 = a(1.19)^{12}$
   C. 15 $137 = a(8.06)$
   D. 17 $a = 17$
   E. 1104

2. For all real numbers x and y, let $x\zeta y$ be defined as $x\zeta y = x^2 - 2xy$. Find the value of $2\zeta(3\zeta4)$.

   A. -68
   B. -56 $2\zeta(3^2 - 2(3)4) = 2\zeta(9 - 24) = 2\zeta(-15)$
   C. 64 $2\zeta(-15) = 2^2 - 2(2)(-15) = 4 + 60 = 64$
   D. 76
   E. 128

3. If x is an integer and $4 < \sqrt{x-1} < 6$, how many unique values of x are possible?

   A. 1 $4 < \sqrt{x-1}$ and $\sqrt{x-1} < 6$
   B. 3 $16 < x - 1$ and $x - 1 < 36$
   C. 19 $17 < x$ and $x < 37$
   D. 20 There are 19 integers between 17 and 37.
   E. 21

Exploring Math through... Geocaching

Geocaching was started May 3, 2000, the day after the government removed selective availability from 24 satellites. The high-tech treasure hunt, which started in Oregon, has gone international, with caches hidden on every continent including Antarctica. Physical caches can range in size from the micro, which can be as small as the tip of your little finger, to a large cache the size of a 5-gallon bucket or a suitcase.

Different geocaches have different requirements, but the tools of the trade are the same for nearly all of them. The most important item is the GPS itself. This is used to mark locations using latitude and longitude coordinates, as well as track altitude, speed, direction, and distance. Other necessities include a pen to sign the log book, and swag if you wish to trade items in a cache. Some caches also require the use of a compass.

Nearly every aspect of geocaching involves math. It all starts with the cache owner selecting a place to hide a cache. Geocaching rules state that caches must be at least 528 feet apart. The cache owner, who designs and hides the cache, must document the GPS coordinates of the cache location. Some cache owners supply other GPS coordinates, known as waypoints, in the cache listing to aid those seeking the cache.

Some caches require the seeker to do a lot of math to find the cache. Some caches are puzzle caches that require numerous calculations. Other caches require the seeker to take altitude measurements or calculate angles and distances.

Some of the most challenging caches available are not necessarily difficult to find once you are at the location. Rather finding the coordinates for the location itself is difficult. Some cache owners enjoy challenging the cache seekers with mathematical or logical puzzles to solve to get the GPS coordinates for the cache container.

Whether you are an avid geocacher who hunts caches at every opportunity, or a curious beginner still waiting for your first find, you cannot escape using math when geocaching.

Teaching Tips, Cont.

- Have students read the Exploring Math feature for Lessons 141-150.

Assignments

- Complete *It's College Test Prep Time!*
- Read Exploring Math through... Geocaching

Lesson 141

Concepts

- Pythagorean Theorem
- Hypotenuse
- Square roots
- Math in the real world

Learning Objectives

The student will be able to:

- Define *hypotenuse*
- Apply the Pythagorean Theorem to find the length of the hypotenuse of a right triangle

Materials Needed

- Student Book, Lesson 141
- Graph paper (optional)
- Scissors (optional)

Teaching Tips

- Introduce the Pythagorean Theorem from the teaching box. Tell the students that a Theorem is a mathematical statement that has either been proven true or is assumed to be true based on known facts. The Pythagorean Theorem is the only theorem that will be discussed in this course. A high school geometry course covers many different theorems.

- Tell the students that in a right triangle (a triangle that has one right angle) the two sides that form the right angle are called the legs and the third side, which is opposite the right angle, is called the hypotenuse. The hypotenuse is always the longest side in a right triangle.

The Pythagorean Theorem

The **Pythagorean Theorem** is used to find the lengths of the sides of right triangles.

In a right triangle, the legs are the sides that make the right angle, and the **hypotenuse** is the side opposite the right angle.

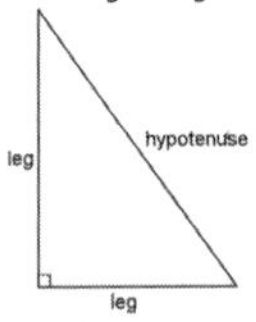

In any right triangle, the sum of the squares of the lengths of the legs is equal to the square of the length of the hypotenuse.

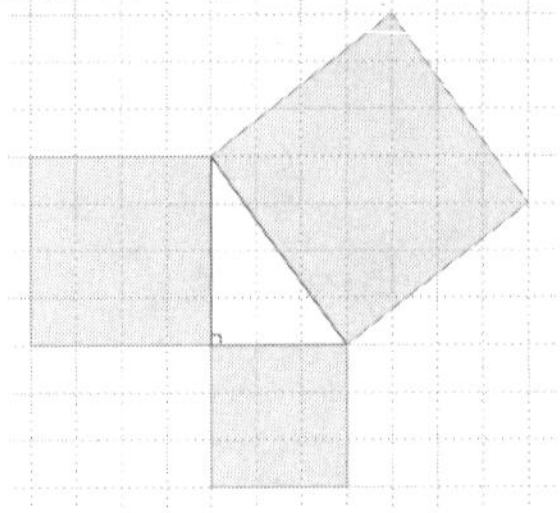

Written as a formula, the Pythagorean Theorem is $a^2 + b^2 = c^2$, where a and b are the lengths of the sides, and c is the length of the hypotenuse.

Find the length of the hypotenuse in the figure above.

$a^2 + b^2 = c^2$

$3^2 + 4^2 = c^2$

$9 + 16 = c^2$

$25 = c^2$

$\sqrt{25} = \sqrt{c^2}$

$5 = c$

① **Classwork**

Find the length of the missing sides.

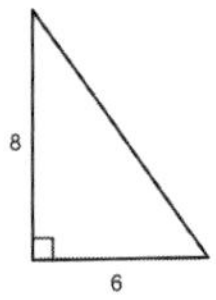

$a^2 + b^2 = c^2$

$6^2 + 8^2 = c^2$

$36 + 64 = c^2$

$100 = c^2$

$\sqrt{100} = \sqrt{c^2}$

$10 = c$

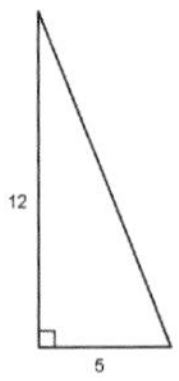

$a^2 + b^2 = c^2$

$5^2 + 12^2 = c^2$

$25 + 144 = c^2$

$169 = c^2$

$\sqrt{169} = \sqrt{c^2}$

$13 = c$

Activities

② Use the Pythagorean Theorem to find the length of the hypotenuse, c.

a	b	c
3	4	$c=\sqrt{3^2+4^2} \to c=5$
5	12	$c=\sqrt{5^2+12^2} \to c=13$
6	8	$c=\sqrt{6^2+8^2} \to c=10$
7	24	$c=\sqrt{7^2+24^2} \to c=25$
8	15	$c=\sqrt{8^2+15^2} \to c=17$
9	40	$c=\sqrt{9^2+40^2} \to c=41$

What do you notice about the length of the hypotenuse, c, compared to the lengths of the legs, a and b?

The hypotenuse is always longer than either of the two legs, but always shorter than than sum of the two legs. Note: The longest leg of any triangle is always shorter than the sum of the other two legs.

③ Solve.

A multi-cache is a geocache that requires the seeker to visit multiple locations before arriving at the actual cache location. A particular multi-cache in Marietta, Georgia, requires the seeker to gather information at the starting location, walk 282 feet east, then 10 feet north to get to the second location. To get to the third location, the seeker must then walk 177 feet north and 528 feet east. To get to the location of the actual cache, the seeker must then walk 476 feet, either north, south, east, or west. If the seeker parked at the starting location, what are the four possible straight-line distances from the cache location to the car? Round your answers to the nearest foot. A diagram (not drawn to scale) has been provided to get you started.

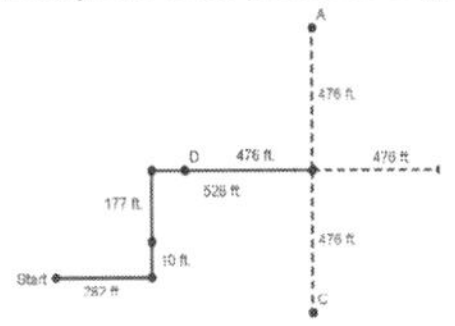

From start to A:
282 + 528 = 810 ft. east
10 + 177 + 476 = 663 ft. north
$810^2+663^2=c^2$
$656{,}100+439{,}569=c^2$
$1047\text{ ft.}=c$

From start to B:
282 + 528 + 476 = 1286 ft. east
10 + 177 = 187 ft. north
$1286^2+187^2=c^2$
$1{,}653{,}796+34{,}969=c^2$
$1300\text{ ft.}=c$

From start to C:
282 + 528 = 810 ft. east
476 − 10 − 177 = 289 ft. south
$810^2+289^2=c^2$
$656{,}100+83{,}521=c^2$
$860\text{ ft.}=c$

From start to D:
282 + 528 − 476 = 334 ft. east
10 + 177 = 187 ft. north
$334^2+187^2=c^2$
$111{,}556+34{,}969=c^2$
$383\text{ ft.}=c$

Teaching Tips, Cont.

- Teach the formula for the Pythagorean Theorem from the teaching box.
- If students are having a difficult time "seeing" this concept, you may have them use graph paper to illustrate the concept. Have the students draw a right triangle with one leg 3 squares long and the other leg 4 squares long. To prove the hypotenuse is really 5 squares long, have them cut a strip of graph paper that is 5 squares long and lay it against the hypotenuse. They will see that the corners line up perfectly.
- Complete the Classwork exercises. Have some students work the problems on the board for the class and explain their answers. All students should work the problems in their books.

Assignment

- Complete Lesson 141, Activities 2-3.

Lesson 142

Concepts
- Pythagorean Theorem
- Literal equations
- Systems of equations
- Parabolas

Learning Objectives
The student will be able to:
- Apply the principles of literal equations to the Pythagorean Theorem to solve for *a*, *b*, and *c*
- Calculate the length of a leg of a right triangle when the length of the other leg and the hypotenuse are known

Materials Needed
- Student Book, Lesson 142
- Worksheet 71

Teaching Tips
- Have students complete Worksheet 71 in class. This may be for added practice of earlier topics or graded as a quiz, if desired.
- Review the Pythagorean Theorem. (See Lesson 141)
- Review literal equations. (See Lesson 135)
- Teach how to use the Pythagorean Theorem to solve for the length of a missing side of a right triangle.

The Pythagorean Theorem

The formula for the Pythagorean Theorem is a literal equation that can be rearranged to solve for any of the three variables. This allows you to solve for the third side of a right triangle when any two sides are known.

The hypotenuse of a right triangle is10 inches and one of the legs is 8 inches. Find the length of the other leg.

Assign the variables.
The hypotenuse is always represented by *c*, so $c = 10$.
The legs are represented by *a* and *b*, so you may assign either variable to the known leg.
$a = 8$

Rearrange the formula to solve for the correct variable. In this case, we are solving for *b*.

$a^2 + b^2 = c^2$

$b^2 = c^2 - a^2$

Substitute the known values in the formula.

$b^2 = 10^2 - 8^2$

$b^2 = 100 - 64$

$b^2 = 36$

$\sqrt{b^2} = \sqrt{36}$

$b = 6$

The third side is 6 inches.

① **Classwork**
Find the length of the missing sides.

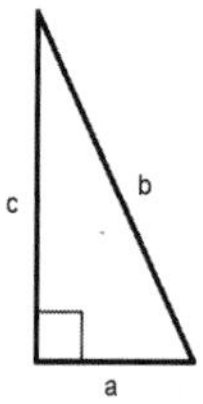

$b = 21;\ c = 29$

$a = \sqrt{29^2 - 21^2}$

$a = \sqrt{841 - 441}$

$a = \sqrt{400}$

$a = 20$

$a = 12;\ c = 37$

$a = \sqrt{37^2 - 12^2}$

$a = \sqrt{1369 - 144}$

$a = \sqrt{1225}$

$a = 35$

Activities

② Find the length of the missing side.

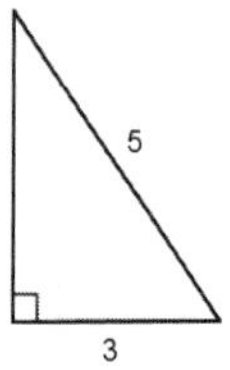

$a^2 + b^2 = c^2$

$a^2 + 3^2 = 5^2$

$a^2 + 9 = 25$

$a^2 = 16$

$\sqrt{a^2} = \sqrt{16}$

$a = 4$

③ A Pythagorean triple is a set of three positive integers that satisfy the formula $a^2 + b^2 = c^2$. Complete the chart to find the Pythagorean triples.

a	*b*	*c*
3	4	$c = \sqrt{3^2 + 4^2} \rightarrow c = 5$
$a = \sqrt{13^2 - 12^2} \rightarrow a = 5$	12	13
8	$b = \sqrt{17^2 - 8^2} \rightarrow b = 15$	17
7	24	$c = \sqrt{7^2 + 24^2} \rightarrow c = 25$
6	$b = \sqrt{10^2 - 6^2} \rightarrow b = 8$	10
$a = \sqrt{41^2 - 40^2} \rightarrow a = 9$	40	41

④ Solve the systems of equations.

$x - y - 9 = 0$
$-2x + y + 11 = 0$
$x - y = 9$
$-2x + y = -11$
$-x = -2$
$x = 2$
$2 - y - 9 = 0$
$y = -7$
(2, -7)

$10x + 7y + 22 = 0$
$5x + 2y + 17 = 0$
$10x + 7y = -22$
$5x + 2y = -17$
$10x + 7y = -22$
$10x + 4y = -34$
$3y = 12$
$y = 4$
$10x + 7(4) + 22 = 0$
$10x + 28 = -22$
$10x = -50$
$x = -5$
(-5, 4)

$16x - 20y - 32 = 0$
$12x - 15y - 24 = 0$
$16x - 20y = 32$
$12x - 15y = 24$
Divide the top equation by 4 and the bottom equation by 3.
$4x - 5y = 8$
$4x - 5y = 8$
$0 = 0$
All real numbers

$11x + 22y + 22 = 0$
$-x - 4y + 2 = 0$
$11x + 22y = -22$
$-x - 4y = -2$
$x + 2y = -2$
$-x - 4y = -2$
$-2y = -4$
$y = 2$
$-x - 4(2) + 2 = 0$
$-x - 8 = -2$
$-x = 6$
$x = -6$
(-6, 2)

⑤ Sketch the graph of each parabola.

$f(x) = -3x^2$

x	*y*
0	0
1	-3
2	-12
-1	-3
-2	-12

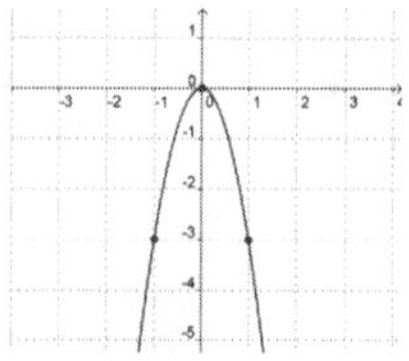

$f(x) = \frac{1}{3}x^2$

x	*y*
0	0
1	$\frac{1}{3}$
2	$\frac{4}{3}$
-1	$\frac{1}{3}$
-2	$\frac{4}{3}$

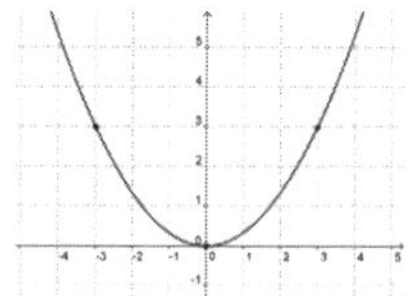

$f(x) = 3x^2$

x	*y*
0	0
1	3
2	12
-1	3
-2	12

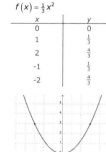

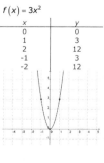

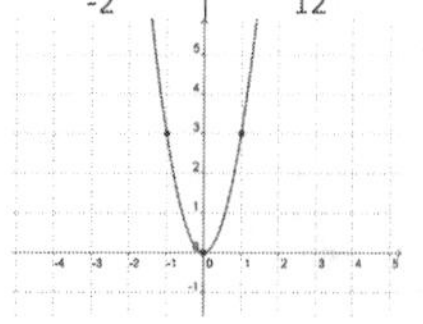

Motion and Investment Problems Worksheet 71

① Solve.

Rick can clean his room in 20 minutes. Joe can clean the same room in 30 minutes. How long would it take to clean the room if Rick and Joe work together?

Let j = the time to clean the room together.

Rick can complete $\frac{1}{20}$ of the room in a minute. Frank can complete $\frac{1}{30}$ of the room in a minute. Together they can complete $\frac{1}{j}$ of the room in a minute.

$\frac{1}{20} + \frac{1}{30} = \frac{1}{j}$

${}_3\cancel{60}j\left(\frac{1}{\cancel{20}}\right) + {}_2\cancel{60}j\left(\frac{1}{\cancel{30}}\right) = 60\cancel{j}\left(\frac{1}{\cancel{j}}\right)$

$3j + 2j = 60$

$5j = 60$

$j = \frac{60}{5} = 12$

Rick and Joe can clean the room together in 12 minutes.

② Solve.

If your grandparents invested \$10,000 in a college savings plan for you on your 1st birthday at 5% simple interest, how much interest will you earn by the time you turn 18?

$p = \$10{,}000$, $r = 6\% = 0.05$, $t = 17$ years

$P = 10{,}000$; $b = 0.05$; $x = 18 - 1 = 17$

$i = \$10{,}000(.05)(17)$

$i = \$8500$

What will be the total balance in your account?

\$10,000 + \$8500 = \$18,500

Teaching Tips, Cont.

- Complete the Classwork exercises. Have some students work the problems on the board for the class and explain their answers. All students should work the problems in their books.

Assignment

- Complete Lesson 142, Activities 2-5.

Lesson 143

Concepts
- Length of a segment
- Pythagorean Theorem
- Math in the real world

Learning Objectives
The student will be able to:
- Apply the Pythagorean Theorem to find the length of a segment on a graph

Materials Needed
- Student Book, Lesson 143
- Worksheet 72
- Graph paper

Teaching Tips
- ➢ Review the Pythagorean Theorem. (See Lesson 141)
- ➢ Draw a horizontal line on a piece of graph paper and ask the students to tell how many units long the line is.
- ➢ Draw a vertical line on a piece of graph paper and ask the students to tell how many units long the line is.
- ➢ Draw a diagonal line on a piece of graph paper. Ask the students how they could determine the length of the line in graph paper units. (Draw a right triangle with the diagonal line as the hypotenuse. Then use the Pythagorean Theorem.)

Geometry: Length of a Segment

It is easy to look at a graph and tell the length of a horizontal or vertical line segment.

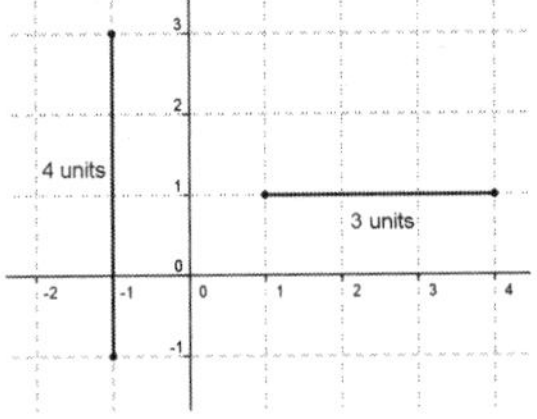

How can you determine the length of a diagonal segment?

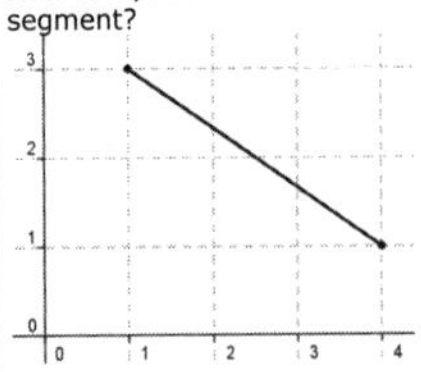

Use the Pythagorean Theorem. Imagine the segment is the hypotenuse of a right triangle.

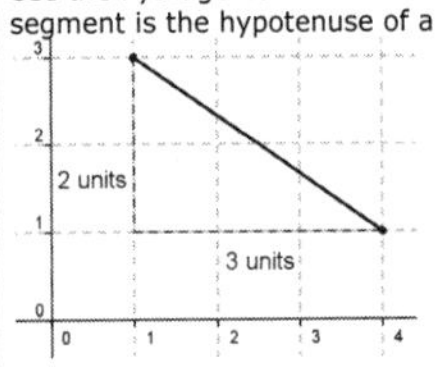

The lengths of the legs are 2 units and 3 units. These correspond to *a* and *b* in the formula.

$2^2 + 3^2 = c^2$

$4 + 9 = c^2$

$13 = c^2$

$\sqrt{13} = c$

The diagonal line is $\sqrt{13}$ units long.

① **Classwork**

Find the length of each segment.

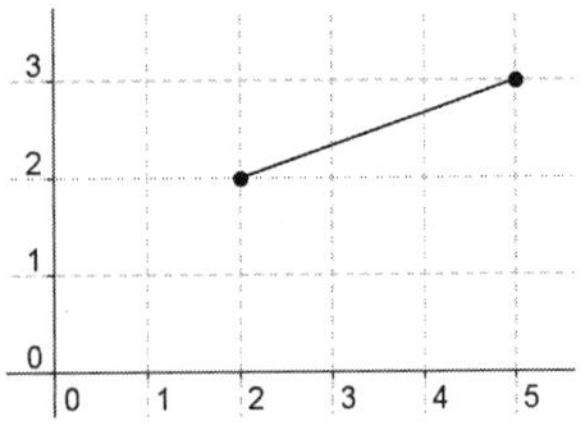

$1^2 + 3^2 = c^2$

$1 + 9 = c^2$

$10 = c^2$

$\sqrt{10} = c$

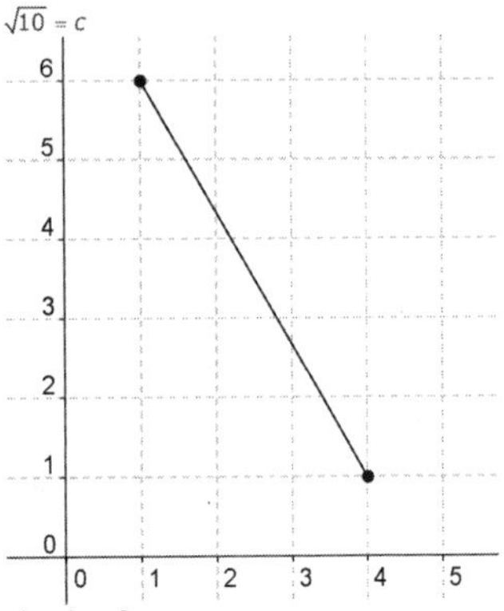

$5^2 + 3^2 = c^2$

$25 + 9 = c^2$

$34 = c^2$

$\sqrt{34} = c$

Activities

② Find the length of each segment.

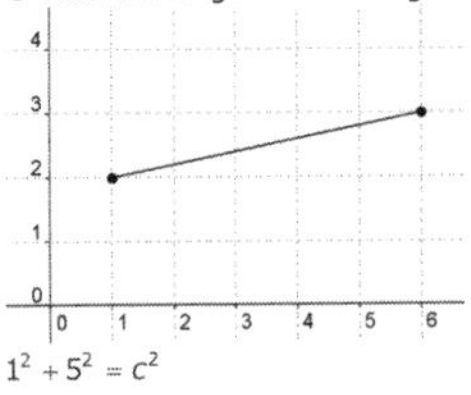

$1^2 + 5^2 = c^2$

$1 + 25 = c^2$

$26 = c^2$

$\sqrt{26} = c$

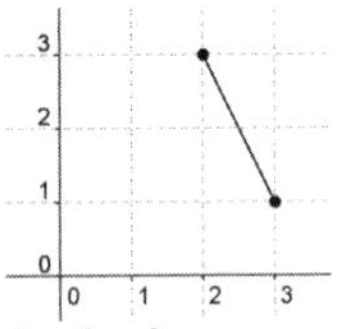

$1^2 + 2^2 = c^2$

$1 + 4 = c^2$

$5 = c^2$

$\sqrt{5} = c$

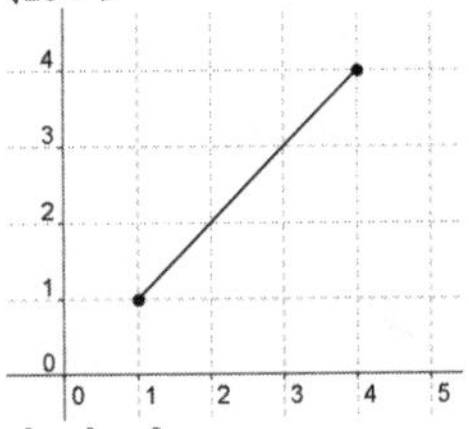

$3^2 + 3^2 = c^2$

$9 + 9 = c^2$

$18 = c^2$

$\sqrt{18} = c$

$3\sqrt{2} = c$

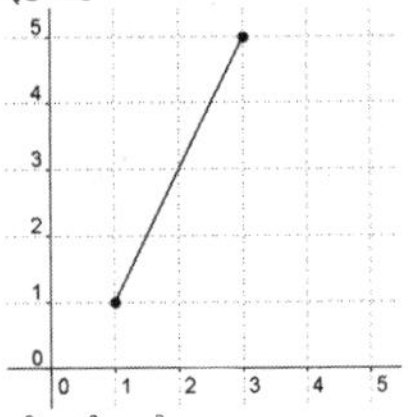

$2^2 + 4^2 = c^2$

$4 + 16 = c^2$

$20 = c^2$

$\sqrt{20} = c$

$2\sqrt{5} = c$

③ Solve.

A geocache is located 80 feet due north of where a geocacher parked his car, but the trailhead is a certain distance west of his car. If the cache is 100 feet straight down the trail, how far is the trailhead from the geocacher's car?

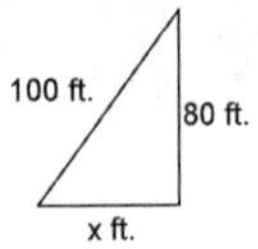

$x = \sqrt{100^2 - 80^2}$

$x = \sqrt{10{,}000 - 6400}$

$x = \sqrt{3600}$

$x = 60$

The trailhead is 60 feet west of the geocacher's car.

Pythagorean Theorem, Length of a Segment Worksheet 72

① Find the length of the missing sides.

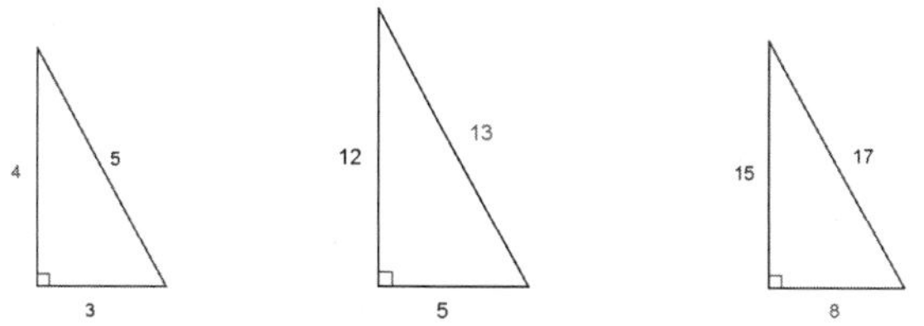

$a^2 + 3^2 = 5^2$
$a^2 + 9 = 25$
$a^2 = 16$
$a = 4$

$12^2 + 5^2 = c^2$
$144 + 25 = c^2$
$169 = c^2$
$c = 13$

$15^2 + b^2 = 17^2$
$225 + b^2 = 289$
$b^2 = 64$
$b = 8$

② Find the length of each segment.

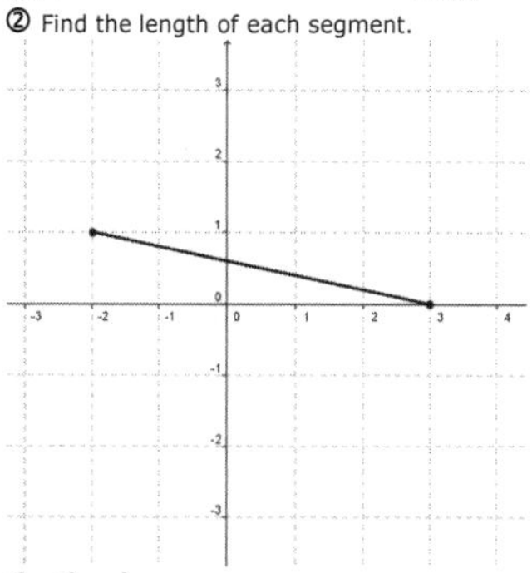

$1^2 + 5^2 = c^2$
$1 + 25 = c^2$
$26 = c^2$
$\sqrt{26} = c$

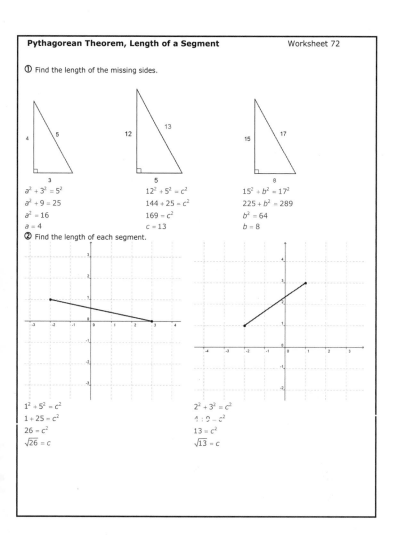

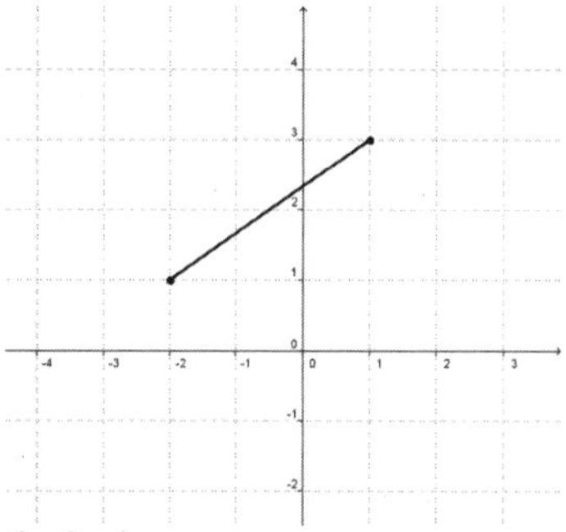

$2^2 + 3^2 = c^2$
$4 + 9 = c^2$
$13 = c^2$
$\sqrt{13} = c$

Teaching Tips, Cont.

- Teach how to use the Pythagorean Theorem to find the length of diagonal lines from the teaching box.
- Complete the Classwork exercises. Have some students work the problems on the board for the class and explain their answers. All students should work the problems in their books.

Assignments

- Complete Lesson 143, Activities 2-3.
- Worksheet 72.

Lesson 144

Concepts
- Distance formula
- Length of a segment
- Adding polynomials

Learning Objectives
The student will be able to:
- State the distance formula for segments on a graph
- Apply the distance formula to find the lengths of segments on a graph

Materials Needed
- Student Book, Lesson 144

Teaching Tips
➢ Review the Pythagorean Theorem. (See Lesson 141)

➢ Review how to use the Pythagorean Theorem to find the length of a segment on a graph. (See Lesson 143)

➢ Teach the distance formula for segments on a graph from the teaching box. Show the students how this formula is obtained by using the Pythagorean Theorem.

Geometry: The Distance Formula

You have learned to apply the Pythagorean Theorem to segments on a graph by forming a right triangle. Sometimes, however, it is not practical to draw a graph to find the distance between two points. There is a formula based on the Pythagorean Theorem for finding the distance between two points without graphing.

Consider the graph from Lesson 143.

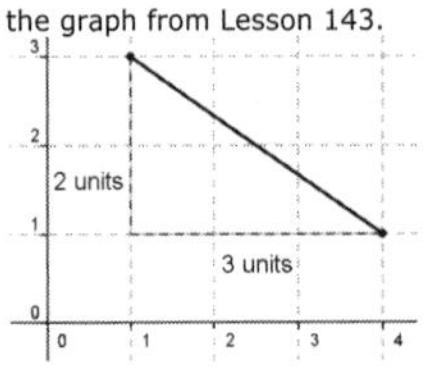

The endpoints are (1, 3) and (4, 1). The distance across the bottom of the triangle (the side parallel to the x-axis) is 3. Notice the difference between the x-coordinates for each point. $4 - 1 = 3$ The length of the side parallel to the y-axis is 2. Notice the difference between the y-coordinates for each point. $3 - 1 = 2$

This information can be used to make a general formula that can be used to find the distance between any two points (x_1, y_1) and (x_2, y_2).

$$d = \sqrt{(x_2 - x_1)^2 + (y_2 - y_1)^2}$$

Using the points in the above graph, we get

$$d = \sqrt{(4-1)^2 + (1-3)^2}$$
$$d = \sqrt{(3)^2 + (-2)^2}$$
$$d = \sqrt{9+4}$$
$$d = \sqrt{13}$$

The diagonal line is $\sqrt{13}$ units long. Notice that this is the same answer we got using the Pythagorean Theorem in Lesson 143.

① **Classwork**
Use the distance formula to find the length of each segment.

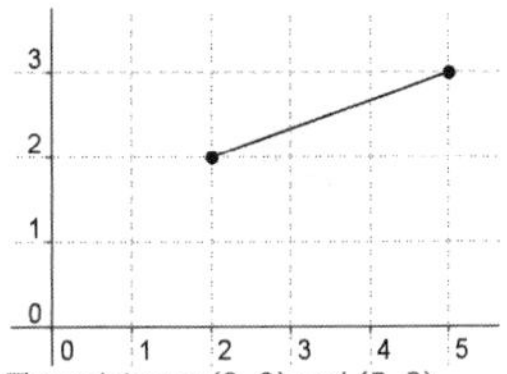

The points are (2, 2) and (5, 3).

$$d = \sqrt{(5-2)^2 + (3-2)^2}$$
$$d = \sqrt{(3)^2 + (1)^2}$$
$$d = \sqrt{9+1}$$
$$d = \sqrt{10}$$

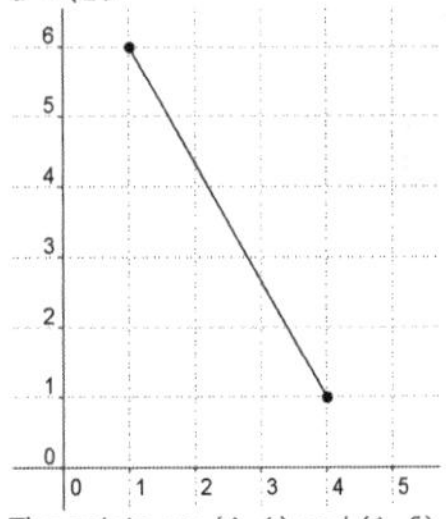

The points are (4, 1) and (1, 6).

$$d = \sqrt{(1-4)^2 + (6-1)^2}$$
$$d = \sqrt{(-3)^2 + (5)^2}$$
$$d = \sqrt{9+25}$$
$$d = \sqrt{34}$$

Students should notice these are the same segments as in Lesson 144 and should get the same answers.

Activities

② Use the distance formula to find the length of each segment.

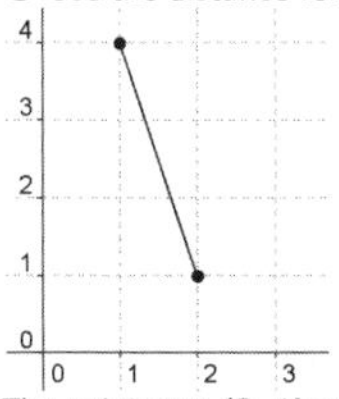

The points are (2, 1) and (1, 4).

$d = \sqrt{(1-2)^2 + (4-1)^2}$

$d = \sqrt{(-1)^2 + (3)^2}$

$d = \sqrt{1+9}$

$d = \sqrt{10}$

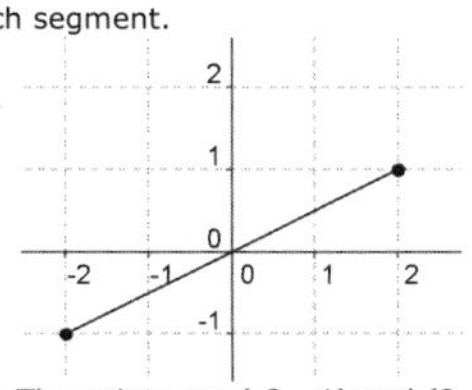

The points are (-2, -1) and (2, 1).

$d = \sqrt{(2-(-2))^2 + (1-(-1))^2}$

$d = \sqrt{(4)^2 + (2)^2}$

$d = \sqrt{16+4}$

$d = \sqrt{20} = 2\sqrt{5}$

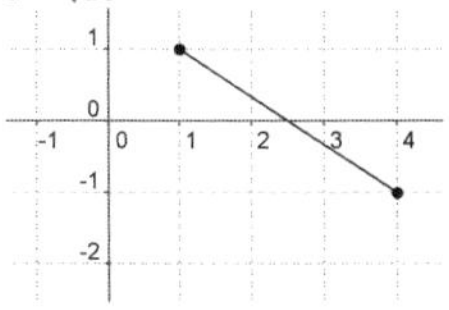

The points are (1, 1) and (4, -1).

$d = \sqrt{(4-1)^2 + (-1-1)^2}$

$d = \sqrt{(3)^2 + (-2)^2}$

$d = \sqrt{9+4}$

$d = \sqrt{13}$

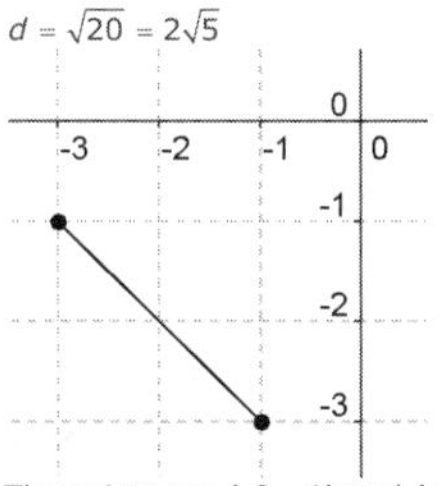

The points are (-3, -1) and (-1, -3).

$d = \sqrt{(-1-(-3))^2 + (-3-(-1))^2}$

$d = \sqrt{(2)^2 + (-2)^2}$

$d = \sqrt{4+4}$

$d = \sqrt{8} = 2\sqrt{2}$

③ Add.

$$\begin{array}{r} 6x^2 + 2x - 7 \\ +\ 5x^2 + 5x + 3 \\ \hline 11x^2 + 7x - 4 \end{array} \qquad \begin{array}{r} 8x^2 + 3x + 4 \\ +7x^2 - 8x - 9 \\ \hline 15x^2 - 5x - 5 \end{array} \qquad \begin{array}{r} 7x^2 - 3x - 5 \\ +9x^2 + 8x - 9 \\ \hline 16x^2 + 5x - 14 \end{array}$$

$$\begin{array}{r} 4x^2 + 6x + 8 \\ +\ 5x^2 + 7x - 9 \\ \hline 9x^2 + 13x - 1 \end{array} \qquad \begin{array}{r} 3x^2 + 2x + 6 \\ +9x^2 - 7x - 8 \\ \hline 12x^2 - 5x - 2 \end{array} \qquad \begin{array}{r} 9x^2 - 2x + 4 \\ +9x^2 - 7x - 8 \\ \hline 18x^2 - 9x - 4 \end{array}$$

Teaching Tips, Cont.

- Complete the Classwork exercises. Have some students work the problems on the board for the class and explain their answers. All students should work the problems in their books.

Assignment

- Complete Lesson 144, Activities 2-3.

Lesson 145

Concepts
- Middle of a segment
- Subtracting polynomials
- Multiplying a polynomial by a monomial
- Dividing a polynomial by a monomial
- Math in the real world

Learning Objectives
The student will be able to:
- Use averages to find the coordinate of the midpoint of a segment on a graph

Materials Needed
- Student Book, Lesson 145
- Worksheet 73
- Graph paper

Teaching Tips
➢ Have students complete Worksheet 73 in class. This may be for added practice of earlier topics or graded as a quiz, if desired.

➢ Draw a line 4 units long on a piece of graph paper. Ask the students to find the center of the line. (It is the point two squares in from each end.)

➢ Draw a line 5 units long on a piece of graph paper. Ask the students to find the center of the line. (It is the point two and one-half squares in from each end. Most students should be able to eyeball this.)

Geometry: The Middle of a Segment

Sometimes it is easy to look at a graph and find the exact center of a line.

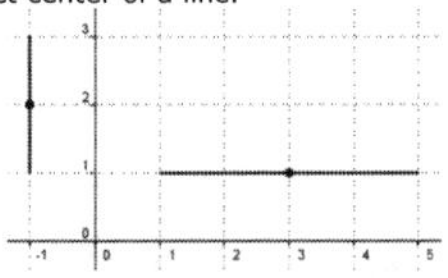

Other times the exact middle of a line is not as obvious. So how can you find the coordinates of the point in the middle?

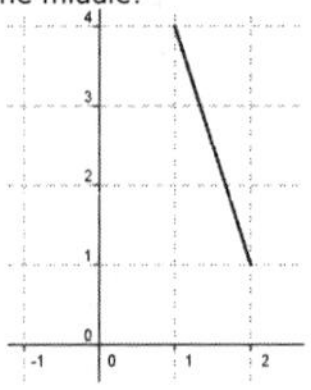

The x-coordinate of the middle point is exactly halfway between the x-coordinates of the endpoints. In this case, it is halfway between 1 and 2, which is $\frac{1+2}{2} = \frac{3}{2}$. The y-coordinate of the middle point is exactly halfway between the y-coordinates of the endpoints. In this case, it is halfway between 1 and 4, or $\frac{1+4}{2} = \frac{5}{2}$.

The coordinates of the middle of the segment are $\left(\frac{3}{2}, \frac{5}{2}\right)$.

① Classwork
Give the coordinate of the middle of each segment.

The x-coordinate is halfway between 2 and 5, which is $\frac{2+5}{2} = \frac{7}{2}$. The y-coordinate is halfway between 2 and 3, which is $\frac{2+3}{2} = \frac{5}{2}$. The coordinate of the middle of the segment is $\left(\frac{7}{2}, \frac{5}{2}\right)$.

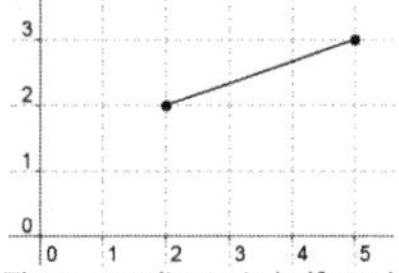

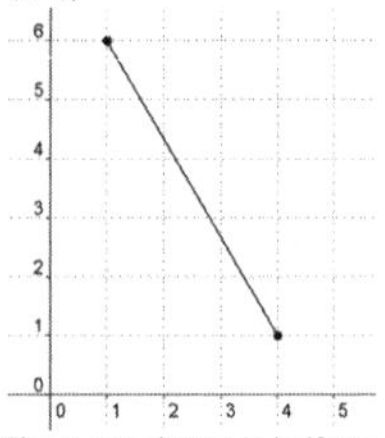

The x-coordinate is halfway between 1 and 4, which is $\frac{1+4}{2} = \frac{5}{2}$. The y-coordinate is halfway between 1 and 6, which is $\frac{1+6}{2} = \frac{7}{2}$. The coordinate of the middle of the segment is $\left(\frac{5}{2}, \frac{7}{2}\right)$.

Activities

② Give the coordinate of the middle of each segment.

The x-coordinate is halfway between 1 and 2, $\frac{1+2}{2} = \frac{3}{2}$.
The y-coordinate is halfway between 1 and 4, $\frac{1+4}{2} = \frac{5}{2}$.
The coordinate of the middle of the segment is $\left(\frac{3}{2}, \frac{5}{2}\right)$.

The x-coordinate is halfway between 1 and 4, $\frac{1+4}{2} = \frac{5}{2}$.

The y-coordinate is halfway between 1 and -1, $\frac{1+(-1)}{2} = \frac{0}{2} = 0$. The coordinate of the middle of the segment is $\left(\frac{5}{2}, 0\right)$.

---

③ Solve.
Your GPS tells you that a geocache is 410 feet away from your current location on the trail, but angles off the trail. After you walk 400 feet down the trail, your GPS indicates that the straight path to the cache forms a right angle with the trail. How many feet are you from the cache?

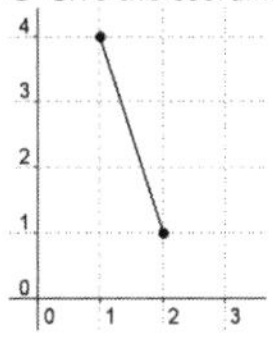

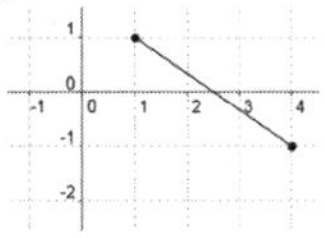

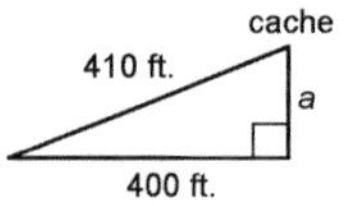

$a = \sqrt{410^2 - 400^2}$
$a = \sqrt{168,100 - 160,000}$
$a = \sqrt{8100}$
$a = 90$
You are 90 feet from the cache.

④ Subtract.

$$\begin{array}{r}(6x^2 + 3x + 9) \\ -(3x^2 + 5x - 7) \\ \hline 3x^2 - 2x + 16\end{array} \qquad \begin{array}{r}(5x^2 - 7x + 6) \\ -(2x^2 - 4x - 5) \\ \hline 3x^2 - 3x + 11\end{array} \qquad \begin{array}{r}(7x^2 - 9x - 9) \\ -(4x^2 + 5x - 2) \\ \hline 3x^2 - 14x - 7\end{array}$$

$$\begin{array}{r}(3x^2 + 6x + 5) \\ -(7x^2 - 8x + 3) \\ \hline -4x^2 + 14x + 2\end{array} \qquad \begin{array}{r}(4x^2 + 2x - 5) \\ -(9x^2 - 5x - 6) \\ \hline -5x^2 + 7x + 1\end{array} \qquad \begin{array}{r}(2x^2 - 4x - 3) \\ -(8x^2 - 9x - 7) \\ \hline -6x^2 + 5x + 4\end{array}$$

⑤ Multiply.

$$3x(5x^2 + 3x - 4)$$
$$3x(5x^2) + 3x(3x) + 3x(-4) =$$
$$15x^3 + 9x^2 - 12x$$

$$5x^2(2x^2 - 6x + 4)$$
$$5x^2(2x^2) + 5x^2(-6x) + 5x^2(4) =$$
$$10x^4 - 30x^3 + 20x^2$$

$$6x(7x^2 - 4x + 8)$$
$$6x(7x^2) + 6x(-4x) + 6x(8) =$$
$$42x^3 - 24x^2 + 48x$$

$$7x^2(7x^2 + 5x - 9)$$
$$7x^2(7x^2) + 7x^2(5x) + 7x^2(-9) =$$
$$49x^4 + 35x^3 - 63x^2$$

⑥ Divide.

$(10x + 15) \div 5$

$$\begin{array}{r} 2x + 3 \\ 5\overline{)10x + 15} \\ \underline{10x} \\ 15 \\ \underline{15} \end{array}$$

$(18x - 27) \div 9$

$$\begin{array}{r} 2x - 3 \\ 9\overline{)18x - 27} \\ \underline{18x} \\ -27 \\ \underline{-27} \end{array}$$

$(16x - 32) \div 4$

$$\begin{array}{r} 4x - 8 \\ 4\overline{)16x - 32} \\ \underline{16x} \\ -32 \\ \underline{-32} \end{array}$$

$(14x^2 - 7x + 21) \div 7$

$$\begin{array}{r} 2x^2 - x + 3 \\ 7\overline{)14x^2 - 7x + 21} \\ \underline{14x^2} \\ -7x \\ \underline{-7x} \\ 21 \\ \underline{21} \end{array}$$

$(10x^4 + 6x^3 - 8x^2) \div 2x^2$

$$\begin{array}{r} 5x^2 + 3x - 4 \\ 2x^2\overline{)10x^4 + 6x^3 - 8x^2} \\ \underline{10x^4} \\ 6x^3 \\ \underline{6x^3} \\ -8x^2 \\ \underline{-8x^2} \end{array}$$

$(12x^5 + 8x^4 - 20x^3) \div 4x$

$$\begin{array}{r} 3x^4 + 2x^3 - 5x^2 \\ 4x\overline{)12x^5 + 8x^4 - 20x^3} \\ \underline{12x^5} \\ 8x^4 \\ \underline{8x^4} \\ -20x^3 \\ \underline{-20x^3} \end{array}$$

Pythagorean Theorem, Length of a Segment Worksheet 73

① Find the length of the missing sides.

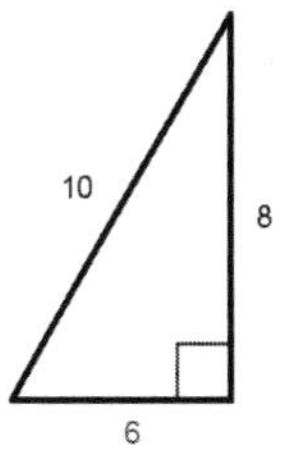

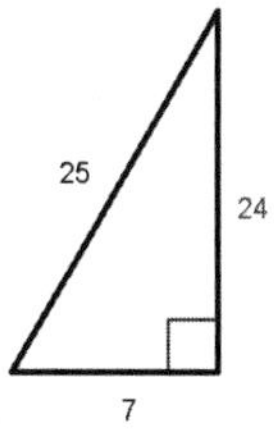

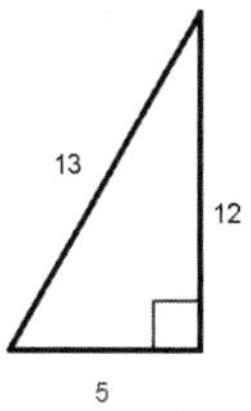

$a^2 + 8^2 = 10^2$
$a^2 + 64 = 100$
$a^2 = 36$
$a = 6$

$7^2 + b^2 = 25^2$
$49 + b^2 = 625$
$b^2 = 576$
$b = 24$

$a^2 + 12^2 = 13^2$
$a^2 + 144 = 169$
$a^2 = 25$
$a = 5$

② Find the length of each segment.

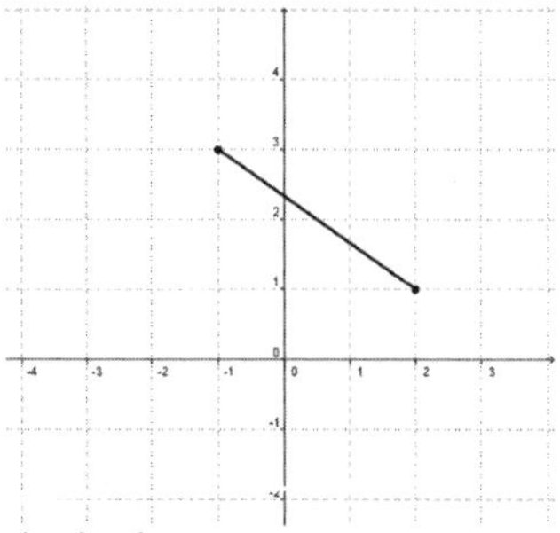

$2^2 + 3^2 = c^2$
$4 + 9 = c^2$
$13 = c^2$
$\sqrt{13} = c$

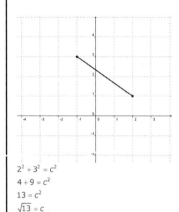

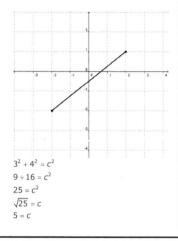

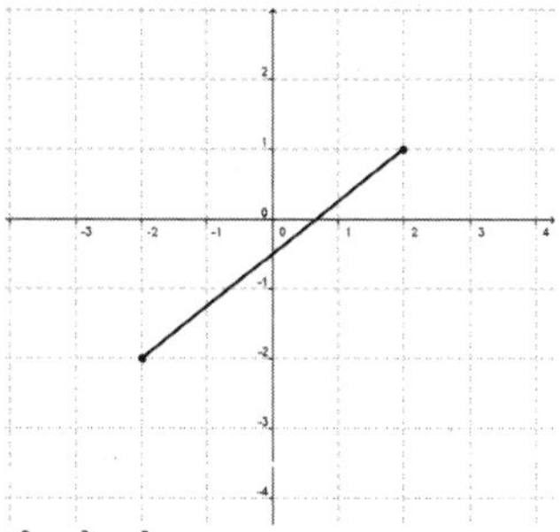

$3^2 + 4^2 = c^2$
$9 + 16 = c^2$
$25 = c^2$
$\sqrt{25} = c$
$5 = c$

Teaching Tips, Cont.

- Draw a long diagonal line that does not have an obvious center point. Ask the students how they could find the center of this line. (They may suggest drawing the right triangle that has this line as its hypotenuse. Draw a line perpendicular to each leg through its center. Where these lines meet the hypotenuse is the center of the hypotenuse.)
- Tell the students that the quick way to find the coordinate of the center of the line is to average the *x*-coordinates of the horizontal leg to get the *x*-coordinate, and average the *y*-coordinates of the vertical leg to get the *y*-coordinate.
- Teach how to find the middle of a segment from the teaching box.
- Complete the Classwork exercises. Have some students work the problems on the board for the class and explain their answers. All students should work the problems in their books.

Assignment

- Complete Lesson 145, Activities 2-6.

Lesson 146

Concepts

- Midpoint formula
- Systems of equations
- Slope
- *y*-intercept
- Graphing linear equations

Learning Objectives

The student will be able to:

- Apply the midpoint formula to find the center of a segment on a graph

Materials Needed

- Student Book, Lesson 146

Teaching Tips

- Review finding the middle of a segment. (See Lesson 145)
- Teach the formula for finding the midpoint of a segment from the teaching box.
- Show the students that this formula is really just averaging the *x*- and *y*-coordinates like they did in Lesson 145.

Lesson 146

Geometry: The Midpoint Formula

In Lesson 145 you learned to use averages to find the middle of a segment. There is a formula that will work to find the **midpoint** (the point in the exact middle of a segment) of the segment formed by any two points, (x_1, y_1) and (x_2, y_2).

The midpoint formula is $\left(\frac{x_1+x_2}{2}, \frac{y_1+y_2}{2}\right)$.

Using the graph from Lesson 146, find the midpoint using the formula.

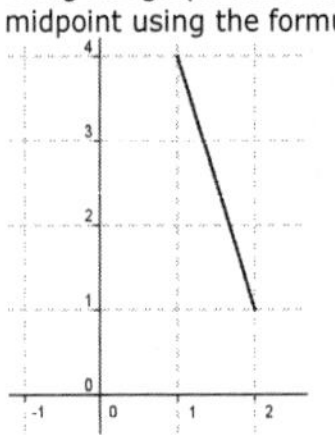

The points are (2, 1) and (1, 4).

$\left(\frac{2+1}{2}, \frac{1+4}{2}\right) = \left(\frac{3}{2}, \frac{5}{2}\right)$

Notice that this is the same point we found in Lesson 145.

① **Classwork**

Find the midpoint of each segment using the formula.

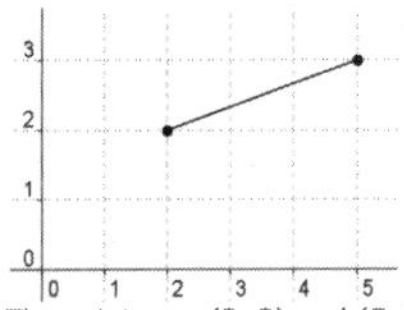

The points are (2, 2) and (5, 3).

$\left(\frac{2+5}{2}, \frac{2+3}{2}\right) = \left(\frac{7}{2}, \frac{5}{2}\right)$.

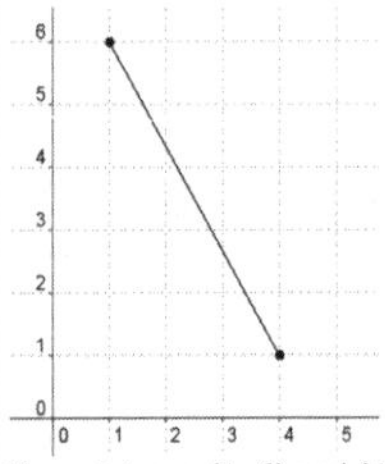

The points are (1, 6) and (4, 1).

$\left(\frac{1+4}{2}, \frac{6+1}{2}\right) = \left(\frac{5}{2}, \frac{7}{2}\right)$.

Activities

② Find the midpoint of each segment using the formula.

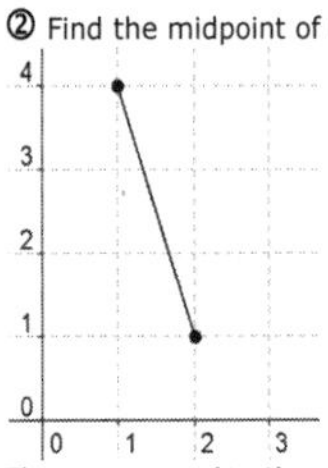

The points are (1, 4) and (2, 1).

$\left(\frac{1+2}{2}, \frac{4+1}{2}\right) = \left(\frac{3}{2}, \frac{5}{2}\right)$

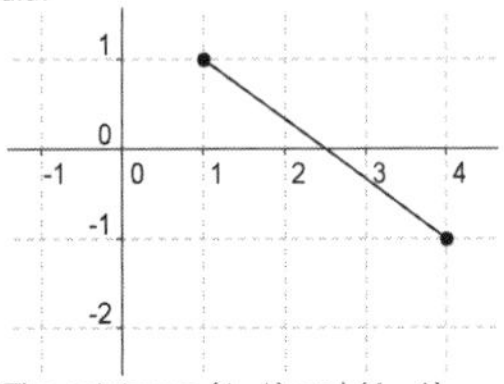

The points are (1, 1) and (4, -1).

$\left(\frac{1+4}{2}, \frac{1+(-1)}{2}\right) = \left(\frac{5}{2}, \frac{0}{2}\right) = \left(\frac{5}{2}, 0\right)$.

③ For each equation, identify the slope and y-intercept. Solve each system of equations. Write the solution as a coordinate point.

$y = 3x - 3$
$y = -4x + 11$
slope $= 3$; y-intercept $= -3$
slope $= -4$; y-intercept $= 11$
$3x - 3 = -4x + 11$
$7x = 14$
$x = 2$
$y = 3(2) - 3$
$y = 6 - 3 = 3$
$(2,3)$

$-3x + y - 7 = 0$
$4x + y + 7 = 0$
$y = 3x + 7$ slope $= 3$; y-intercept $= 7$
$y = -4x - 7$ slope $= -4$; y-intercept $= -7$
$3x + 7 = -4x - 7$
$7x = -14$; $x = -2$
$-3(-2) + y - 7 = 0$
$6 + y - 7 = 0$
$y = 1$
$(-2,1)$

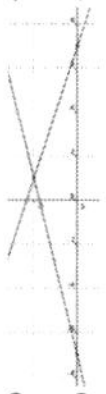

$y = \frac{2}{3}x - 5$
$y = -\frac{1}{3}x - 2$
slope $= \frac{2}{3}$; y-intercept $= -5$
slope $= -\frac{1}{3}$; y-intercept $= -2$
$\frac{2}{3}x - 5 = -\frac{1}{3}x - 2$
$2x - 15 = -x - 6$
$3x = 9$
$x = 3$
$y = \frac{2}{3}(3) - 5$
$y = 2 - 5 = -3$
$(3,-3)$

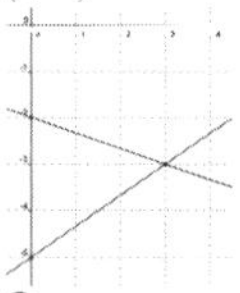

$3x - 2y - 10 = 0$
$x + 2y - 2 = 0$
$y = \frac{3}{2}x - 5$ slope $= \frac{3}{2}$; y-intercept $= -5$
$y = -\frac{1}{2}x + 1$ slope $= -\frac{1}{2}$; y-intercept $= 1$
$\frac{3}{2}x - 5 = -\frac{1}{2}x + 1$
$3x - 10 = -x + 2$
$4x = 12$; $x = 3$
$3 + 2y - 2 = 0$
$2y = -1$
$y = -\frac{1}{2}$
$(3,-\frac{1}{2})$

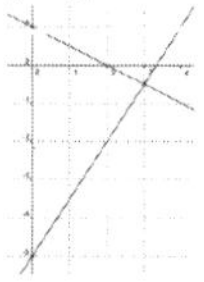

④ Graph each system of equations above on your own graph paper and identify the coordinates of the point of intersection.
(See above for the graphs of each system of equations.)

Teaching Tips, Cont.

- Complete the Classwork exercises. Have some students work the problems on the board for the class and explain their answers. All students should work the problems in their books.

Assignment

- Complete Lesson 146, Activities 2-4.

Lesson 147

Concepts
- Literal equations
- Pythagorean Theorem
- Distance formula
- Midpoint formula
- Math in the real world

Learning Objectives
The student will be able to:
- Use literal equations to solve right triangles
- Apply the Pythagorean Theorem to solve for the lengths of the sides of a right triangle
- Apply the distance formula to find the lengths of segments on a graph
- Apply the midpoint formula to find the center of a segment on a graph

Materials Needed
- Student Book, Lesson 147

Teaching Tips
- ➢ Review Pythagorean Theorem. (See Lessons 141-142)
- ➢ Review finding the length of a segment. (See Lessons 143-144)
- ➢ Review finding the middle of a segment. (See Lessons 145-146)
- ➢ There is no new material presented in this lesson. Rather, this lesson should be used to make sure all students fully grasp these concepts. The Pythagorean Theorem, distance formula, and midpoint formula will be used extensively in high school geometry and students should memorize these formulas now.

Review of Geometric Concepts

There are three literal equations that are useful for solving geometry-related problems.

The Pythagorean Theorem allows you to solve for the lengths of the sides of a right triangle.

$a^2 + b^2 = c^2$

The distance formula gives the distance between two points on a coordinate plane.

$d = \sqrt{(x_2 - x_1)^2 + (y_2 - y_1)^2}$

The midpoint formula gives the coordinates of the point in the exact center of a segment on a coordinate plane.

$\left(\frac{x_1+x_2}{2}, \frac{y_1+y_2}{2}\right)$

Calculate the length of the hypotenuse using both the Pythagorean Theorem and the distance formula. Then find the midpoint of the hypotenuse.

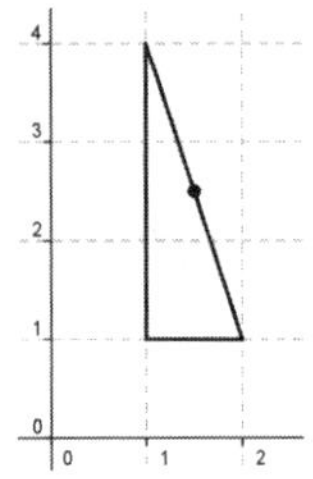

Pythagorean Theorem

$a = 1; b = 3$

$1^2 + 3^2 = c^2$

$1 + 9 = c^2$

$10 = c^2$

$c = \sqrt{10}$

Distance Formula

$x_1 = 2; y_1 = 1; x_2 = 1; y_2 = 4$

$d = \sqrt{(1-2)^2 + (4-1)^2}$

$d = \sqrt{(-1)^2 + (3)^2}$

$d = \sqrt{1+9}$

$d = \sqrt{10}$

midpoint $= \left(\frac{2+1}{2}, \frac{1+4}{2}\right) = \left(\frac{3}{2}, \frac{5}{2}\right)$

① **Classwork**

Calculate the length of the hypotenuse using both the Pythagorean Theorem and the distance formula. Then find the midpoint of the hypotenuse.

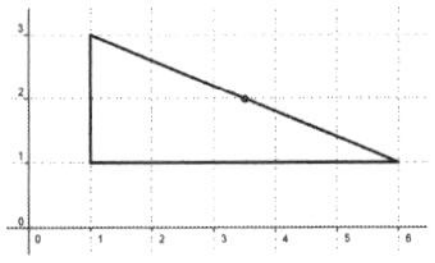

Pythagorean Theorem

$a = 2; b = 5$

$2^2 + 5^2 = c^2$

$4 + 25 = c^2$

$29 = c^2$

$c = \sqrt{29}$

Distance Formula

$x_1 = 1; y_1 = 3; x_2 = 6; y_2 = 1$

$d = \sqrt{(6-1)^2 + (1-3)^2}$

$d = \sqrt{(5)^2 + (-2)^2}$

$d = \sqrt{25+4}$

$d = \sqrt{29}$

midpoint $= \left(\frac{1+6}{2}, \frac{1+3}{2}\right) = \left(\frac{7}{2}, \frac{4}{2}\right) = \left(\frac{7}{2}, 2\right)$

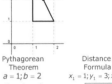

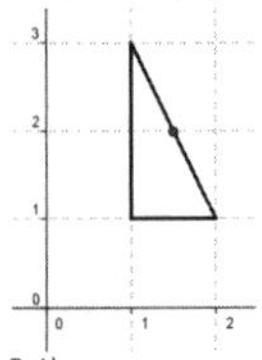

Pythagorean Theorem

$a = 1; b = 2$

$1^2 + 2^2 = c^2$

$1 + 4 = c^2$

$5 = c^2$

$c = \sqrt{5}$

Distance Formula

$x_1 = 1; y_1 = 3; x_2 = 2; y_2 = 1$

$d = \sqrt{(2-1)^2 + (1-3)^2}$

$d = \sqrt{(1)^2 + (-2)^2}$

$d = \sqrt{1+4}$

$d = \sqrt{5}$

midpoint $= \left(\frac{1+2}{2}, \frac{1+3}{2}\right) = \left(\frac{3}{2}, \frac{4}{2}\right) = \left(\frac{3}{2}, 2\right)$

Activities

② Calculate the length of the hypotenuse using both the Pythagorean Theorem and the distance formula. Then find the midpoint of the hypotenuse.

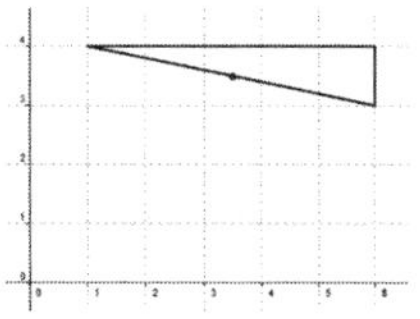

Pythagorean Theorem

$a = 5; b = 1$

$5^2 + 1^2 = c^2$

$25 + 1 = c^2$

$26 = c^2$

$c = \sqrt{26}$

Distance Formula

$x_1 = 1; y_1 = 4; x_2 = 6; y_2 = 3$

$d = \sqrt{(6-1)^2 + (3-4)^2}$

$d = \sqrt{(5)^2 + (-1)^2}$

$d = \sqrt{25+1}$

$d = \sqrt{26}$

midpoint = $\left(\frac{1+6}{2}, \frac{4+3}{2}\right) = \left(\frac{7}{2}, \frac{7}{2}\right)$

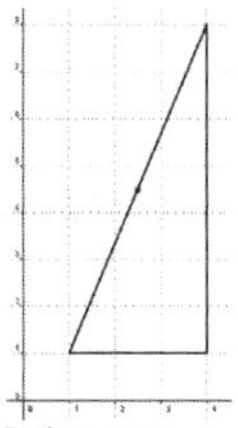

Pythagorean Theorem

$a = 3; b = 7$

$3^2 + 7^2 = c^2$

$9 + 49 = c^2$

$58 = c^2$

$c = \sqrt{58}$

Distance Formula

$x_1 = 1; y_1 = 1; x_2 = 4; y_2 = 8$

$d = \sqrt{(4-1)^2 + (8-1)^2}$

$d = \sqrt{(3)^2 + (7)^2}$

$d = \sqrt{9+49}$

$d = \sqrt{58}$

midpoint = $\left(\frac{1+4}{2}, \frac{1+8}{2}\right) = \left(\frac{5}{2}, \frac{9}{2}\right)$

③ Solve.

A virtual geocache does not have a physical container, but rather requires the seeker to answer questions or submit a photo to prove he was at the cache location. The virtual cache at Clingmans Dome in the Great Smoky Mountain National Park requires visitors to hike to the highest point on the Appalachian Trail. The elevation of Clingmans Dome is 6643 feet. The elevation at the beginning of the Clingmans Dome Trail is 6308 feet. If the trail is a half mile long, what is the slope of the trail? Express your answer as a percent rounded to the nearest whole. (1 mile = 5280 feet)

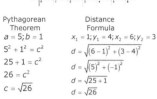

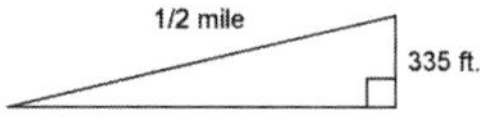

$\frac{1}{2}$ mile $= \frac{1}{2}(5280 \text{ ft.}) = 2640$ ft.

$a = \sqrt{2640^2 - 335^2}$

$a = \sqrt{6969600 - 112225}$

$a = \sqrt{6857375}$

$a \approx 2619$

Slope $= \frac{335 \text{ ft.}}{2619 \text{ ft.}} = 0.128 = 13\%$

Teaching Tips, Cont.

- Complete the Classwork exercises. Have some students work the problems on the board for the class and explain their answers. All students should work the problems in their books.

Assignment

- Complete Lesson 147, Activities 2-3.

Lesson 148

Concepts

- Absolute value
- Extraneous solutions
- Radicals
- Adding polynomials
- Subtracting polynomials
- Multiplying monomials
- Dividing monomials
- Multiplying polynomials

Learning Objectives

The student will be able to:

- Find all possible solutions of equations containing absolute value or radicals and identify exclusions
- Apply mathematical operations to monomials and polynomials

Materials Needed

- Student Book, Lesson 148
- Worksheet 74

Teaching Tips

➢ Have students complete Worksheet 74 in class. This may be for added practice of earlier topics or graded as a quiz, if desired.

➢ Note: This lesson begins an intensive review for the final exam. The final test of the year (Exam 4) allows the teacher two options. You may administer the entire test as a final comprehensive exam or you may administer the first two pages as a fourth quarter exam.

Review: Algebraic Expressions

Activities

① Find all possible solutions. Identify any extraneous solutions.

$|5x+2|-8=4x-19$

$|5x+2|=4x-11$

$5x+2=4x-11$ or $5x+2=-(4x-11)$

$x=-13$ $\quad 5x+2=-4x+11$

$9x=9 \Rightarrow x=1$

check:

$|5(-13)+2|-8=4(-13)-19$

$|-65+2|-8=-52-19$

$|-63|-8=-71$

$63-8\neq-71$ extraneous

$|5(1)+2|-8=4(1)-19$

$|5+2|-8=4-19$

$|7|-8=-15$

$7-8\neq-15$ extraneous

$|5x-2|-11=-4x+23$

$|5x-2|=-4x+34$

$5x-2=-4x+34$ or $5x-2=-(-4x+34)$

$9x=36$ $\quad 5x-2=4x-34$

$x=4$ $\quad x=-32$

check:

$|5(4)-2|-11=-4(4)+23$

$|20-2|-11=-16+23$

$18-11=7$

$|5(-32)-2|-11=-4(-32)+23$

$|-160-2|-11=128+23$

$162-11=151$

$\sqrt{-3x+4}-3=2$

$\sqrt{-3x+4}=5$

$\left(\sqrt{-3x+4}\right)^2=5^2$

$-3x+4=25$

$-3x=21$

$x=-7$

check:

$\sqrt{-3(-7)+4}-3=2$

$\sqrt{21+4}-3=2$

$\sqrt{25}-3=2$

$5-3=2$

$\sqrt{7x-5}+9=13$

$\sqrt{7x-5}=4$

$\left(\sqrt{7x-5}\right)^2=4^2$

$7x-5=16$

$7x=21$

$x=3$

check:

$\sqrt{7(3)-5}+9=13$

$\sqrt{21-5}+9=13$

$\sqrt{16}+9=13$

$4+9=13$

② Multiply, using the formulas for special products.

$(3x+8)^2$

$(3x)^2+2(24x)+8^2=$

$9x^2+48x+64$

$(x-9)^2$

$x^2-2(9x)+9^2=$

$x^2-18x+81$

$(4x-3)^2$

$(4x)^2-2(12x)+3^2=$

$16x^2-24x+9$

$(5x+4)(5x-4)$

$(5x)^2-4^2=25x^2-16$

③ Solve.

$$\begin{array}{r} 76a^2+53a+49 \\ \underline{+17a^2-38a+26} \\ 93a^2+15a+75 \end{array} \qquad \begin{array}{r} 46b^2+52b+17 \\ \underline{+36b^2-73b-51} \\ 82b^2-21b-34 \end{array} \qquad \begin{array}{r} 43c^2-18c+21 \\ \underline{+38c^2+37c-13} \\ 81c^2+19c+8 \end{array}$$

$$\begin{array}{r} (36d^2+72d+19) \\ \underline{-(25d^2+23d+51)} \\ 11d^2+49d-32 \end{array} \qquad \begin{array}{r} (58e^2+38e+65) \\ \underline{-(28e^2-44e+15)} \\ 30e^2+82e+50 \end{array} \qquad \begin{array}{r} (78f^2-44f-37) \\ \underline{-(71f^2+43f-56)} \\ 7f^2-87f+19 \end{array}$$

$4g^4(-5g^{-5}h^8)(3g^4h^{-7})$

$(4\cdot-5\cdot3)(g^{4-5+4})(h^{8-7})=$

$-60g^3h$

$-3j^5(5jk^3)(6j^{-6}k^{-3})$

$(-3\cdot5\cdot6)(j^{5+1-6})(k^{3-3})=$

-90

$-4m^4(5m^{-7}n^9)(-9m^{-3}n^{-4})$

$(-4\cdot5\cdot-9)(m^{4-7-3})(n^{9-4})=$

$180m^{-6}n^5$

$63p^5\div7p^2$

$\frac{63p^5}{7p^2}=9p^{5-2}=9p^3$

$48r^2\div16r^5$

$\frac{48r^2}{16r^5}=3r^{2-5}=3r^{-3}$ or $\frac{3}{r^3}$

$88t^4\div8t^{-9}$

$\frac{88t^4}{8t^{-9}}=11t^{4-(-9)}=11t^{13}$

④ Multiply.

$(x+3)(x+5)$

$x^2+5x+3x+15=$

$x^2+8x+15$

$(x-6)(x-7)$

$x^2-7x-6x+42=$

$x^2-13x+42$

$(x+3)(x^2+x+2)$

$x^3+x^2+2x+3x^2+3x+6=$

x^3+4x^2+5x+6

$(x-5)(x^2-2x-7)$

$x^3-2x^2-7x-5x^2+10x+35=$

$x^3-7x^2+3x+35$

$(3x+5)(x-4)$

$3x^2-12x+5x-20=$

$3x^2-7x-20$

$(5x+2)(3x-4)$

$15x^2-20x+6x-8=$

$15x^2-14x-8$

$(2x+5)(4x^2-2x-3)$

$8x^3-4x^2-6x+20x^2-10x-15=$

$8x^3+16x^2-16x-15$

$(x^2+3x+1)(2x^2-4x-3)$

$2x^4-4x^3-3x^2+6x^3-12x^2-9x+2x^2-4x-3=$

$2x^4+2x^3-13x^2-13x-3$

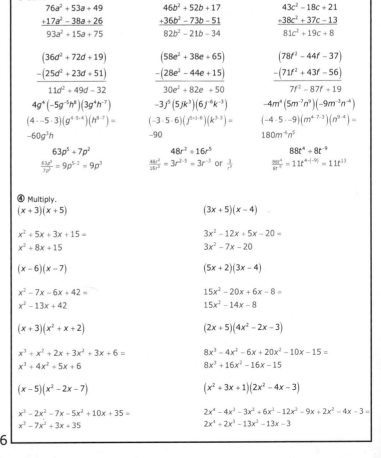

Distance Formula, Midpoint Formula Worksheet 74

① Use the distance formula to find the length of each segment.

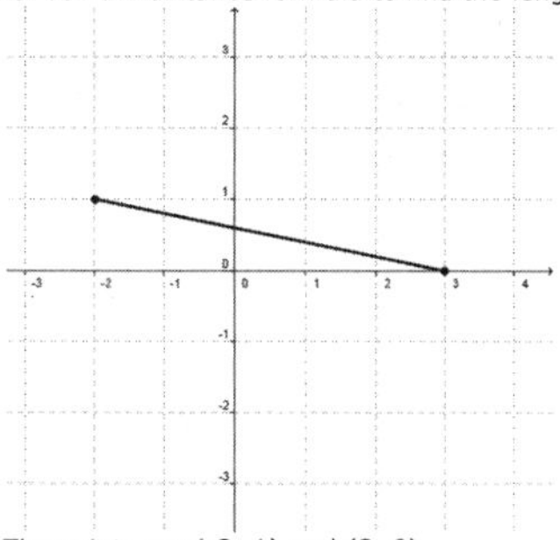

The points are (-2, 1) and (3, 0).

$d = \sqrt{(-2-3)^2 + (1-0)^2}$

$d = \sqrt{(-5)^2 + (1)^2}$

$d = \sqrt{25+1}$

$d = \sqrt{26}$

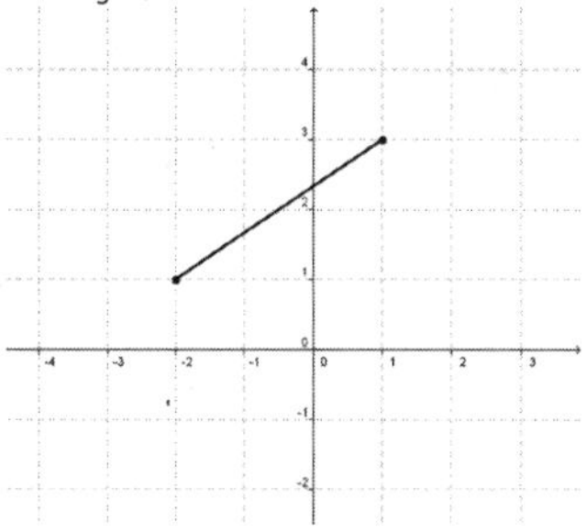

The points are (-2, 1) and (1, 3).

$d = \sqrt{(-2-1)^2 + (1-3)^2}$

$d = \sqrt{(-3)^2 + (-2)^2}$

$d = \sqrt{9+4}$

$d = \sqrt{13}$

② Find the midpoint of each segment using the formula.

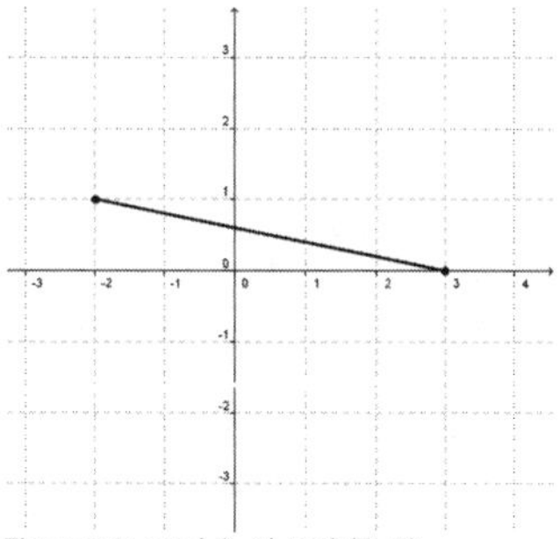

The points are (-2, 1) and (3, 0).

$\left(\frac{-2+3}{2}, \frac{1+0}{2}\right) = \left(\frac{1}{2}, \frac{1}{2}\right)$

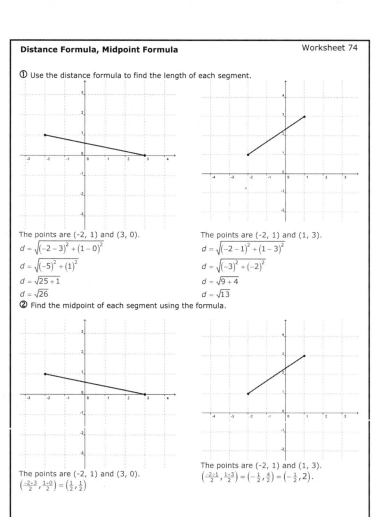

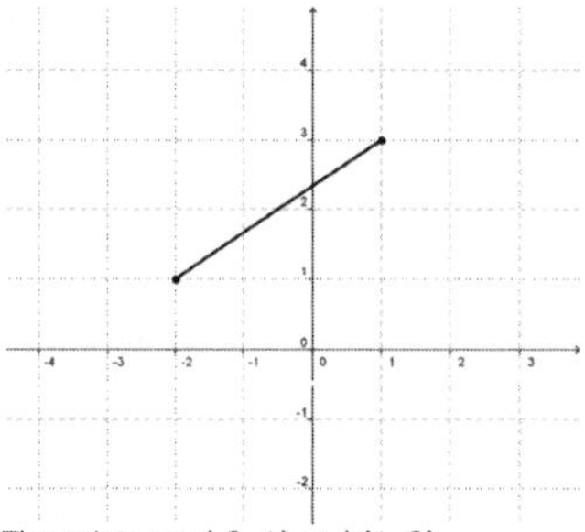

The points are (-2, 1) and (1, 3).

$\left(\frac{-2+1}{2}, \frac{1+3}{2}\right) = \left(-\frac{1}{2}, \frac{4}{2}\right) = \left(-\frac{1}{2}, 2\right)$.

Teaching Tips, Cont.

- Review adding and subtracting polynomials. (See Lessons 12-13)
- Review multiplying and dividing monomials. (See Lessons 14-15)
- Review linear equations with absolute value. (See Lesson 20)
- Review linear equations with radicals. (See Lesson 26)
- Review multiplying binomials. (See Lessons 61-62, 64)
- Review multiplying polynomials. (See Lesson 63)
- Allow students to begin working on the review exercises in class as time permits. Assist individual students as needed.

Assignment

- Complete Lesson 148, Activities 1-4.

Lesson 149

Concepts

- Linear equations
- Slope-intercept form
- Point-slope form
- Intercepts
- Parallel lines
- Perpendicular lines

Learning Objectives

The student will be able to:

- Write equations in slope-intercept form, point-slope form, and standard form
- Find the intercepts of a line
- Write equations for horizontal, vertical, parallel, and perpendicular lines

Materials Needed

- Student Book, Lesson 149

Teaching Tips

- Review finding the slope and intercepts.
  (See Lessons 31-32 and 35)
- Review slope-intercept form.
  (See Lessons 32 and 39)
- Review point-slope form.
  (See Lessons 33 and 40)

Review: Linear Equations

Activities

① Rewrite each equation in slope-intercept form. Give the slope and y-intercept of each equation.

$6x+y+3=0$	$4x+y-7=0$	$x-2y+8=0$	$4x+3y-9=0$
$y=-6x-3$	$y=-4x+7$	$2y=x+8$	$3y=-4x+9$
$m=-6$	$m=-4$	$y=\frac{x+8}{2}$	$y=\frac{-4x+9}{3}$
$b=-3$	$b=7$	$y=\frac{1}{2}x+4$	$y=\frac{-4}{3}x+3$
		$m=\frac{1}{2}$	$m=\frac{-4}{3}$
		$b=4$	$b=3$

② Write the point-slope form of the equation of a line. Rewrite each equation in slope-intercept form.

$m=5$	$m=-3$	$m=2$
(3, 4)	(4, -1)	(-6, -7)
$y-4=5(x-3)$	$y-(-1)=-3(x-4)$	$y-(-7)=2(x-(-6))$
$y-4=5x-15$	$y+1=-3x+12$	$y+7=2(x+6)$
$y=5x-11$	$y=-3x+11$	$y+7=2x+12$
		$y=2x+5$

③ Write an equation for each line using the information provided. Convert each equation to standard form.

Slope = -9	Slope = $\frac{1}{4}$	Points (-2, 4) and (3, -7)
y-intercept = $\frac{2}{3}$	Point: (3, -6)	Slope = $\frac{-7-4}{3-(-2)}=\frac{-11}{5}$
$y=-9x+\frac{2}{3}$	$y+6=\frac{1}{4}(x-3)$	$y+7=-\frac{11}{5}(x-3)$
$3y=3(-9x)+3\left(\frac{2}{3}\right)$	$4(y)+4(6)=4\left(\frac{1}{4}x\right)-4\left(\frac{3}{4}\right)$	$5(y)+5(7)=5\left(-\frac{11}{5}\right)(x-3)$
$3y=-27x+2$	$4y+24=x-3$	$5y+35=-11x+33$
$27x+3y=2$	$x-4y=27$	$11x+5y=-2$

Slope = $\frac{4}{5}$	Slope = $-\frac{2}{5}$	Points (-3, -1) and (2, 0)
y-intercept = $\frac{1}{3}$	Point: (-1, -1)	Slope = $\frac{0-(-1)}{2-(-3)}=\frac{1}{5}$
$y=\frac{4}{5}x+\frac{1}{3}$	$y+1=-\frac{2}{5}(x+1)$	$y-0=\frac{1}{5}(x-2)$
$15(y)=15\left(\frac{4}{5}x\right)+15\left(\frac{1}{3}\right)$	$5(y)+5(1)=5\left(-\frac{2}{5}\right)(x+1)$	$5y-5(0)=5\left(\frac{1}{5}\right)(x-2)$
$15y=12x+5$	$5y+5=-2x-2$	$5y=x-2$
$12x-15y=-5$	$2x+5y=-7$	$x-5y=2$

④ Find the x- and y-intercepts of each line.

$4x + 5y = 12$	$2x + 3y = 8$	$3x + 7y = -6$
$4x + 5(0) = 12$	$2x + 3(0) = 8$	$3x + 7(0) = -6$
$4x = 12$	$2x = 8$	$3x = -6$
$x = 3$	$x = 4$	$x = -2$
$(3,0)$ is the x-intercept	$(4,0)$ is the x-intercept	$(-2,0)$ is the x-intercept
$4(0) + 5y = 12$	$2(0) + 3y = 8$	$3(0) + 7y = -6$
$y = \frac{12}{5}$	$y = \frac{8}{3}$	$y = -\frac{6}{7}$
$(0, \frac{12}{5})$ is the y-intercept	$(0, \frac{8}{3})$ is the y-intercept	$(0, -\frac{6}{7})$ is the y-intercept

⑤ Write an equation of the line in the graph. Then write an equation of a parallel line, a horizontal line through point A, a vertical line through point B, and a perpendicular line through point C.

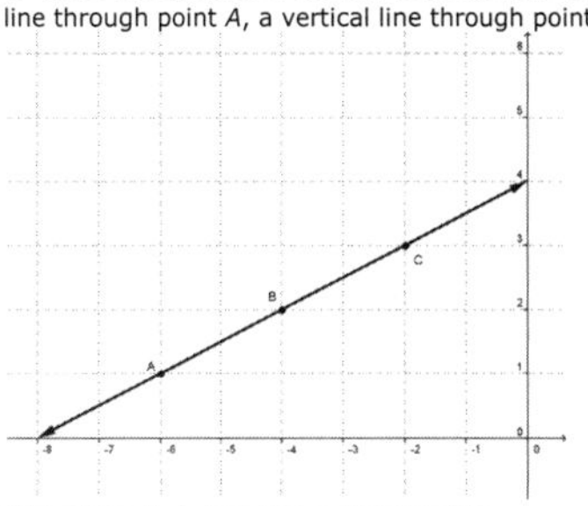

The slope is $\frac{1}{2}$ and the y-intercept is (0, 4) so $b = 4$. The equation of the line is $y = \frac{1}{2}x + 4$ or $x - 2y = -8$ (standard form).
A parallel line has the same slope as the given line and any y-intercept except that of the given line. For example, $x - 2y = 2$.
Point A is (-6, 1) so a horizontal line is $y = 1$.
Point B is (-4, 2) so a vertical line is $x = -4$.
The negative reciprocal of the slope is -2, so a perpendicular line through point C is
$y - 3 = -2(x + 2) \Rightarrow y - 3 = -2x - 4 \Rightarrow$
$2x + y = -1$

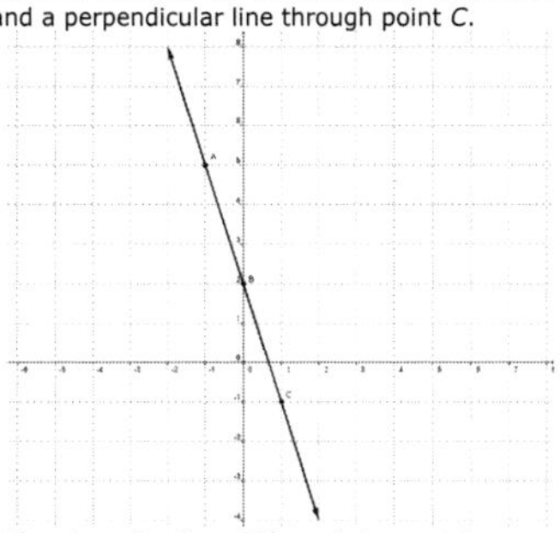

The slope is -3 and the y-intercept is (0, 2) so $b = 2$. The equation of the line is $y = -3x + 2$ or $3x + y = 2$ (standard form).
A parallel line has the same slope as the given line and any y-intercept except that of the given line. For example, $3x + y = 1$.
Point A is (-1, 5) so a horizontal line is $y = 5$.
Point B is (0, 2) so a vertical line is $x = 0$.
The negative reciprocal of the slope is $\frac{1}{3}$, so a perpendicular line through point C is
$y + 1 = \frac{1}{3}(x - 1) \Rightarrow 3y + 3 = x - 1 \Rightarrow$
$x - 3y = 4$

Teaching Tips, Cont.

- Review horizontal and vertical lines. (See Lesson 34)
- Review parallel and perpendicular lines.
(See Lessons 36-37 and 42-43)
- Review standard form.
(See Lessons 38 and 41)
- Allow students to begin working on the review exercises in class as time permits. Assist individual students as needed.

Assignment

- Complete Lesson 149, Activities 1-5.

Lesson 150

Concepts

- Linear inequalities
- Absolute value
- Graphing inequalities

Learning Objectives

The student will be able to:

- Solve inequalities with absolute value
- Graph inequalities
- Solve inequalities with fractions

Materials Needed

- Student Book, Lesson 150
- Worksheet 75

Teaching Tips

- Review inequalities. (See Lessons 45-47) Pay special attention to multiplying and dividing by signed numbers. Make sure the students remember to change the direction of the inequality sign when multiplying or dividing by a negative number.
- Review inequalities with absolute value. (See Lessons 48-49) Pay special attention to situations in which the absolute value is greater than or less than a negative number.
- Review graphing inequalities. (See Lesson 50)

Review: Linear Inequalities

Activities

① Solve the inequalities.

$|5x| < x + 24$

$-(x+24) < 5x < x + 24$

$-x - 24 < 5x < x + 24$

$-x - 24 < 5x$ and $5x < x + 24$

$-24 < 6x \qquad 4x < 24$

$-4 < x \qquad x < 6$

$-4 < x < 6$

$|9x + 5| + 4 < 1$

$|9x + 5| < -3$ NO SOLUTION

Stop working here. The absolute value of anything can never be negative, so the answer is no solution.

$|3x + 4| - 5 < x + 7$

$|3x + 4| < x + 12$

$-(x + 12) < 3x + 4 < x + 12$

$-x - 12 < 3x + 4$ and $3x + 4 < x + 12$

$-16 < 4x \qquad 2x < 8$

$-4 < x \qquad x < 4$

$-4 < x < 4$

$|5x + 3| < x + 9$

$-(x + 9) < 5x + 3 < x + 9$

$-x - 9 < 5x + 3 < x + 9$

$-x - 9 < 5x + 3$ and $5x + 3 < x + 9$

$-12 < 6x \qquad 4x < 6$

$-2 < x \qquad x < \frac{6}{4} \Rightarrow x < \frac{3}{2}$

$-2 < x < \frac{3}{2}$

$|9x - 4| + 6 > 1$

$|9x - 4| > -5$ ALL REAL NUMBERS

Stop working here. The absolute value of anything can never be negative, so the answer is all real numbers.

$|7x + 4| - 9 < 30$

$|7x + 4| < 39$

$-39 < 7x + 4 < 39$

$-39 < 7x + 4$ and $7x + 4 < 39$

$-43 < 7x \qquad 7x < 35$

$-\frac{43}{7} < x \qquad x < 5$

$-\frac{43}{7} < x < 5$

$|2x - 5| - 26 > -23$

$|2x - 5| > 3$

$2x - 5 > 3$ or $2x - 5 < -3$

$2x > 8 \qquad 2x < 2$

$x > 4 \qquad x < 1$

$x > 4$ or $x < 1$

$|3x - 7| + 4 < 2$

$|3x - 7| < -2$ NO SOLUTION

Stop working here. The absolute value of anything can never be negative, so the answer is no solution.

$|3x + 2| + 5 < 19$

$|3x + 2| < 14$

$-14 < 3x + 2 < 14$

$-14 < 3x + 2$ and $3x + 2 < 14$

$-16 < 3x \qquad 3x < 12$

$-\frac{16}{3} < x \qquad x < 4$

$-\frac{16}{3} < x < 4$

$|4x - 1| - 3 > -3x + 17$

$|4x - 1| > -3x + 20$

$4x - 1 > -3x + 20$ or $4x - 1 < 3x - 20$

$7x > 21 \qquad x < -19$

$x > 3 \qquad x < -19$

$x > 3$ or $x < -19$

② Graph the inequalities on your own graph paper.

$y < -4x$

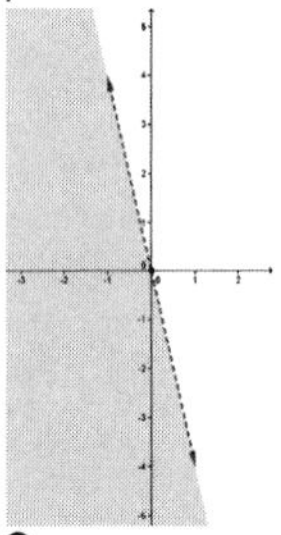

$y > 2x + 3$

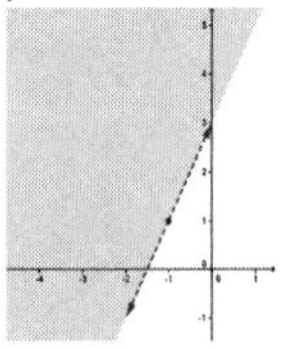

$y \le 2x - 1$

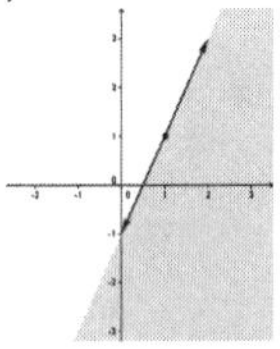

$y \ge 2(x + 1)$

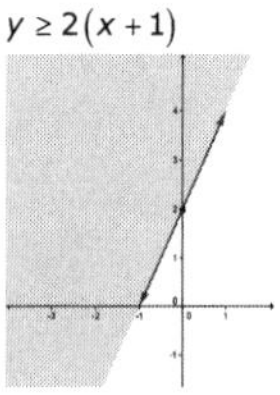

③ Solve the inequalities.

$\frac{4x}{5} + 1 < -7$

$\frac{4x}{5} < -8$

$\not{5}\left(\frac{4x}{\not{5}}\right) < 5(-8)$

$4x < -40$

$x < -10$

$\frac{7x}{9} + 4 < -3$

$\frac{7x}{9} < -7$

$\not{9}\left(\frac{7x}{\not{9}}\right) < 9(-7)$

$7x < -63$

$x < -9$

$\frac{5x - 2}{2} - 9 > 4x - 1$

$\frac{5x - 2}{2} > 4x + 8$

$\not{2}\left(\frac{5x - 2}{\not{2}}\right) > 2(4x + 8)$

$5x - 2 > 8x + 16$

$-3x > 18$

$-x > 6$

$x < -6$

$\frac{x}{3} + 1 < 2x - 9$

$\frac{x}{3} < 2x - 10$

$\not{3}\left(\frac{x}{\not{3}}\right) < 3(2x - 10)$

$x < 6x - 30$

$-5x < -30$

$-x < -\frac{30}{5}$

$x > 6$

$\frac{3x}{4} + 8 < 4x + 9$

$\frac{3x}{4} < 4x + 1$

$\not{4}\left(\frac{3x}{\not{4}}\right) < 4(4x + 1)$

$3x < 16x + 4$

$-13x < 4$

$-x < \frac{4}{13}$

$x > -\frac{4}{13}$

$\frac{6x - 11}{2} - 2 > 2x - 5$

$\frac{6x - 11}{2} > 2x - 3$

$\not{2}\left(\frac{6x - 11}{\not{2}}\right) > 2(2x - 3)$

$6x - 11 > 4x - 6$

$2x > 5$

$x > \frac{5}{2}$

Equations of Parallel, Perpendicular, Horizontal, Vertical Lines Worksheet 75

① Write an equation of the line in the graph. Then write an equation of a parallel line, a horizontal line through point *A*, a vertical line through point *B*, and a perpendicular line through point *C*. Write the equations in standard form.

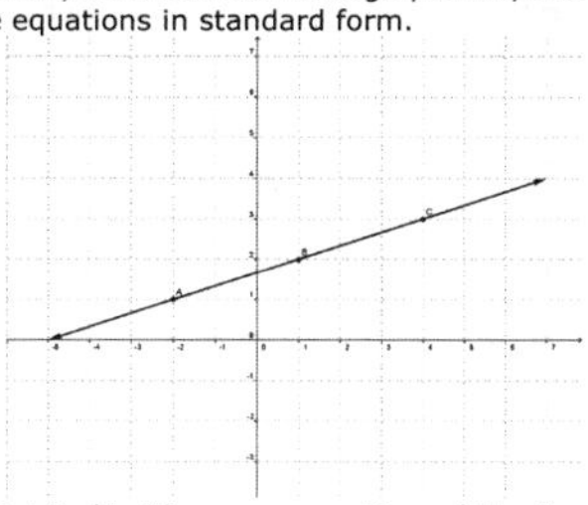

The slope is $\frac{1}{3}$ and a point is (1, 2) so an equation of the line is $y - 2 = \frac{1}{3}(x - 1)$ or $x - 3y = -5$ (standard form).
A parallel line has the same slope as the given line and any *y*-intercept except that of the given line. For example, $x - 3y = -12$.
Point *A* is (-2, 1) so a horizontal line is $y = 1$.
Point *B* is (1, 2) so a vertical line is $x = 1$.
The negative reciprocal of the slope is -3, so a perpendicular line through point *C* is $y - 3 = -3(x - 4) \Rightarrow y - 3 = -3x + 12 \Rightarrow 3x + y = 15$

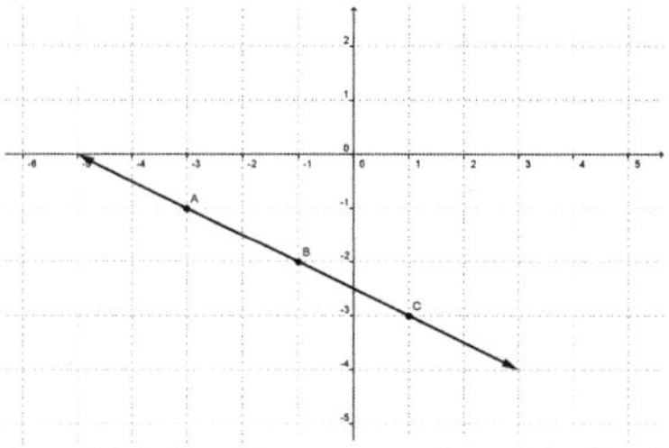

The slope is $-\frac{1}{2}$ and a point is (1, -3) so an equation of the line is $y + 3 = -\frac{1}{2}(x - 1)$ or $x + 2y = -5$ (standard form).
A parallel line has the same slope as the given line and any *y*-intercept except that of the given line. For example, $x + 2y = 1$.
Point *A* is (-3, -1) so a horizontal line is $y = -1$.
Point *B* is (-1, -2) so a vertical line is $x = -1$.
The negative reciprocal of the slope is 2, so a perpendicular line through point *C* is $y + 3 = 2(x - 1) \Rightarrow y + 3 = 2x - 2 \Rightarrow 2x - y = 5$

Teaching Tips, Cont.

- Allow students to begin working on the review exercises in class as time permits. Assist individual students as needed.
- Review for Test 15 using worksheets 71-75. These worksheets were assigned in previous lessons.

Assignments

- Complete Lesson 150, Activities 1-3.
- Worksheet 75.
- Study for Test 15 (Lessons 138-147).

Test 15

Testing Objectives

The student will:

- Solve distance problems
- Calculate square roots without using a calculator
- Determine the limits of a domain
- Graph functions involving square roots
- Use the Pythagorean Theorem to find Pythagorean triples
- Calculate the length of a segment
- Give the coordinates of the midpoint of a segment

Materials Needed

- Test 15
- *It's College Test Prep Time!* from Student Book
- Exploring Math through... Your Hobbies and Interests from Student Book

Teaching Tips

- ➢ Administer Test 15, allowing the students 30-40 minutes to complete the test.
- ➢ When all students are finished taking the test, introduce *It's College Test Prep Time* from the student book. This page may be completed in class or assigned as homework.

① Solve. **4 points**

One car took 9 hours to travel a certain distance. A second car took 10 hours to travel the same distance. If the first car traveled at a rate of 7 miles per hour faster than the second car, what was the rate of each car and how many miles did each car drive?

	Car 1	Car 2
d	d	d
r	$r+7$	r
t	9	10

$(r+7)(9) = 10r$

$9r + 63 = 10r$

$r = 63$

Car 2 was traveling at 63 miles/hour.
Car 1 was traveling at 63 + 7 = 70 miles/hour.
The cars each drove the same distance.

$d = rt$

$d_1 = (70 \text{ miles/hour})(9 \text{ hours}) = 630 \text{ miles}$

$d_2 = (63 \text{ miles/hour})(10 \text{ hours}) = 630 \text{ miles}$

② Find the square roots to the nearest hundredth without using a calculator. **3 points**

$\sqrt{5} = 2.24$

	2. 2 3 6
	$\sqrt{5.000000}$
	4
4	100
42	84
	1600
443	1329
	27100
4466	26796
	304

$\sqrt{63} = 7.94$

	7. 9 3 7
	$\sqrt{63.000000}$
	49
14	1400
149	1341
	5900
1583	4749
	115100
15867	111069
	4031

$\sqrt{243} = 15.59$

	1 5. 5 8 8
	$\sqrt{0243.000000}$
	1
2	0143
25	125
	1800
305	1525
	27500
3108	24864
	263600
31168	249344
	14256

③ Determine the limits of the domain and graph the function. **2 points**

$y = \sqrt{5-x}$

$5 - x \geq 0$

$5 \geq x$

$x \leq 5$

x	y
5	$\sqrt{5-5} = \sqrt{0} = 0$
4	$\sqrt{5-4} = \sqrt{1} = 1$
1	$\sqrt{5-1} = \sqrt{4} = 2$
-4	$\sqrt{5-(-4)} = \sqrt{9} = 3$

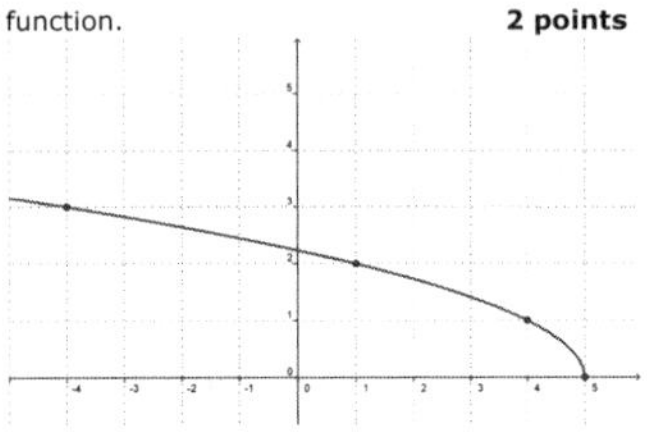

④ Complete the chart to find the Pythagorean triples. **6 points**

a	b	c
$a = \sqrt{5^2 - 4^2} \rightarrow a = 3$	4	5
5	$b = \sqrt{13^2 - 5^2} \rightarrow b = 12$	13
8	15	$c = \sqrt{8^2 + 15^2} \rightarrow c = 17$
7	24	$c = \sqrt{7^2 + 24^2} \rightarrow c = 25$
6	$b = \sqrt{10^2 - 6^2} \rightarrow b = 8$	10
$a = \sqrt{41^2 - 40^2} \rightarrow a = 9$	40	41

⑤ Find the length and midpoint of each segment. **8 points**

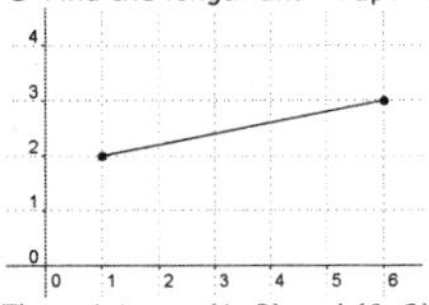

The points are (1, 2) and (6, 3).

$d = \sqrt{(6-1)^2 + (3-2)^2}$

$d = \sqrt{(5)^2 + (1)^2}$

$d = \sqrt{25+1}$

$d = \sqrt{26}$

$\left(\frac{1+6}{2}, \frac{2+3}{2}\right) = \left(\frac{7}{2}, \frac{5}{2}\right)$

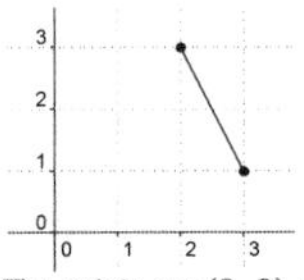

The points are (2, 3) and (3, 1).

$d = \sqrt{(3-2)^2 + (1-3)^2}$

$d = \sqrt{(1)^2 + (-2)^2}$

$d = \sqrt{1+4}$

$d = \sqrt{5}$

$\left(\frac{2+3}{2}, \frac{3+1}{2}\right) = \left(\frac{5}{2}, 2\right)$

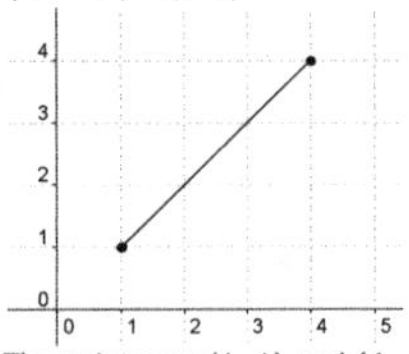

The points are (1, 1) and (4, 4).

$d = \sqrt{(4-1)^2 + (4-1)^2}$

$d = \sqrt{(3)^2 + (3)^2}$

$d = \sqrt{9+9}$

$d = \sqrt{18} = 3\sqrt{2}$

$\left(\frac{1+4}{2}, \frac{1+4}{2}\right) = \left(\frac{5}{2}, \frac{5}{2}\right)$

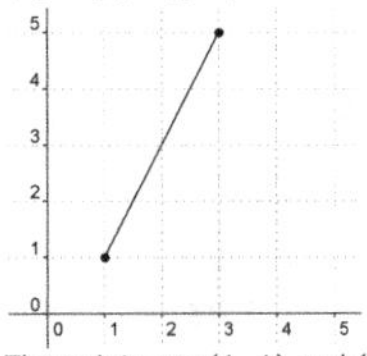

The points are (1, 1) and (3, 5).

$d = \sqrt{(3-1)^2 + (5-1)^2}$

$d = \sqrt{(2)^2 + (4)^2}$

$d = \sqrt{4+16}$

$d = \sqrt{20} = 2\sqrt{5}$

$\left(\frac{1+3}{2}, \frac{1+5}{2}\right) = (2, 3)$

23 points total

It's College Test Prep Time!

1. Given the sequence 8, 12, 20, 36, 68, ..., where 8 is the first number in the sequence, what is a rule for finding each successive number in the sequence?

   A. Add 4 to the preceding number.
   B. Divide the preceding number by 2 and add 8 to the result.
   C. Double the preceding number and subtract 4 from the result.
   D. Divide the preceding number by 4 and add 10 to the result.
   E. Triple the preceding number and divide the result by 2.

2. Given x is an integer and $\frac{x}{15} < \frac{7}{15} < \frac{x+2}{15}$, what is the value of x?

   A. 5 — The denominators are equal, so set up inequalities
   B. 6 — with the numerators and solve.
   C. 7 — $x < 7$ and $7 < x + 2$
   D. 8 — $x < 7$ and $5 < x$
   E. 9 — The only integer less than 7 and greater than 5 is 6.

3. Given $4 < \sqrt{x+3} < 6$, how many different values of x are possible if x is an integer?

   A. 3 — $4 < \sqrt{x+3}$ and $\sqrt{x+3} < 6$
   B. 10 — $16 < x+3$ and $x+3 < 36$
   C. 19 — $13 < x < 33$
   D. 20 — The possible value of x are 14, 15, 16, 17, 18, 19,
   E. 21 — 20, 21, 22, 23, 24, 25, 26, 27, 28, 29, 30, 31, 32.

Exploring Math through... Your Hobbies and Interests

This year, you have read about how math is used in fifteen different sports and hobbies. Think of a sport or hobby that interests you and research how math is used in that sport or hobby. You may use the internet, as well as books, periodicals, and other printed media. You may also include information you have learned from personal experience. If you know any adults who have the same hobby or interest, you may interview them as well. Write a one-page paper about how math is used in your chosen sport or hobby. Some areas to look for math in your chosen sport or hobby are listed below.

If it is a sport, how is the scoring done? Is everything worth the same number of points, or are there different point values for different things?

Are precise measurements required?

Are any angles used?

Are there any ratios or proportions that must be maintained?

Are there any formulas used for statistical analysis?

Teaching Tips, Cont.

- Have students complete the Exploring Math feature for Lessons 151-160. Allow students at least one week to complete this assignment.

Assignments

- Complete *It's College Test Prep Time!*
- Complete Exploring Math through... Your Hobbies and Interests. Set the due date at least one week away.

Lesson 151

Concepts

- Systems of equations
- Multiplying a polynomial by a monomial
- Multiplying binomials
- Multiplying polynomials
- Dividing polynomials

Learning Objectives

The student will be able to:

- Solve systems of equations
- Multiply polynomials by monomials and binomials
- Multiply binomials
- Divide polynomials

Materials Needed

- Student Book, Lesson 151

Teaching Tips

- ➢ Review various methods of solving systems of equations. (See Lessons 51 and 53-59) On the exam, students will be allowed to use the method of their choice. However, they should be familiar with all methods because some methods are easier than others depending on the nature of the problem.
- ➢ Review adding and subtracting polynomials. (See Lesson 52)
- ➢ Review subtracting fractions and mixed numbers. (See Lessons 35 and 39)
- ➢ Review multiplying by a monomial. (See Lesson 60)

Review

Activities

① Solve the systems of equations.

$x - y + 11 = 0$
$-2x + y - 15 = 0$

$x - y = -11$
$-2x + y = 15$
$-x = 4$
$x = -4$

$-4 - y + 11 = 0$
$y = 7$

(-4, 7)

$x - y + 13 = 0$
$-2x + y - 18 = 0$

$x - y = -13$
$-2x + y = 18$
$-x = 5$
$x = -5$

$-5 - y + 13 = 0$
$-y = -8$
$y = 8$

(-5, 8)

$10x - 3y - 2 = 0$
$7x + 2y - 26 = 0$
$10x - 3y = 2$
$7x + 2y = 26$

$20x - 6y = 4$
$21x + 6y = 78$
$41x = 82$
$x = 2$
$10(2) - 3y - 2 = 0$
$20 - 3y - 2 = 0$
$-3y = -18$
$y = 6$
(2, 6)

$x - y + 7 = 0$
$-2x + y - 10 = 0$

$x - y = -7$
$-2x + y = 10$
$-x = 3$
$x = -3$

$-3 - y + 7 = 0$
$-y = -4$
$y = 4$

(-3, 4)

$11x + 22y + 88 = 0$
$-x - 4y - 18 = 0$
$11x + 22y = -88$
$-x - 4y = 18$

$x + 2y = -8$
$-x - 4y = 18$
$-2y = 10$
$y = -5$

$-x - 4(-5) - 18 = 0$
$-x + 20 - 18 = 0$
$-x = -2$
$x = 2$
(2, -5)

$x - y + 3 = 0$
$-2x + y - 9 = 0$

$x - y = -3$
$-2x + y = 9$
$-x = 6$
$x = -6$

$-6 - y + 3 = 0$
$-y = 3$
$y = -3$

(-6, -3)

$7x - 3y - 2 = 0$
$21x - 9y - 6 = 0$
$7x - 3y = 2$
$21x - 9y = 6$

$7x - 3y = 2$
$7x - 3y = 2$
$0 = 0$

All real numbers

$x + y + 7 = 0$
$-2x + y + 13 = 0$

$x + y = -7$
$-2x + y = -13$
$3x = 6$
$x = 2$

$2 + y + 7 = 0$
$y = -9$

(2, -9)

② Multiply.

$4x(3x^2 - 2x + 6)$
$4x(3x^2) + 4x(-2x) + 4x(6) =$
$12x^3 - 8x^2 + 24x$

$6x(4x^2 - 2x + 9)$
$6x(4x^2) + 6x(-2x) + 6x(9) =$
$24x^3 - 12x^2 + 54x$

$5x(3x^2 + 8x - 4)$
$5x(3x^2) + 5x(8x) + 5x(-4) =$
$15x^3 + 40x^2 - 20x$

$9x(7x^2 + 8x - 5)$
$9x(7x^2) + 9x(8x) + 9x(-5) =$
$63x^3 + 72x^2 - 45x$

③ Multiply.

$(x+12)^2$

$x^2+24x+144$

$(3x+5)(3x-5)$

$(3x)^2-5^2=9x^2-25$

$(x-4)(x^2-2x-7)$

$x(x^2)+x(-2x)+x(-7)-4(x^2)-4(-2x)-4(-7)=$

$x^3-2x^2-7x-4x^2+8x+28=$

x^3-6x^2+x+28

$(x+8)(2x^2-7x-4)$

$x(2x^2)+x(-7x)+x(-4)+8(2x^2)+8(-7x)+8(-4)=$

$2x^3-7x^2-4x+16x^2-56x-32=$

$2x^3+9x^2-60x-32$

$(5x^2-3x-6)(3x^2+2x+10)$

$5x^2(3x^2)+5x^2(2x)+5x^2(10)-3x(3x^2)-3x(2x)-$

$3x(10)-6(3x^2)-6(2x)-6(10)=$

$15x^4+10x^3+50x^2-9x^3-6x^2-30x-18x^2-12x-60=$

$15x^4+x^3+26x^2-42x-60$

$2x(12x^2+5x-8)$

$2x(12x^2)+2x(5x)+2x(-8)=$

$24x^3+10x^2-16x$

$(4x+9)(x^2+3x-2)$

$4x(x^2)+4x(3x)+4x(-2)+9(x^2)+9(3x)+9(-2)=$

$4x^3+12x^2-8x+9x^2+27x-18=$

$4x^3+21x^2+19x-18$

$(7x-4)^2$

$49x^2-56x+16$

$(3x+7)(4x^2+3x-2)$

$3x(4x^2)+3x(3x)+3x(-2)+7(4x^2)+7(3x)+7(-2)=$

$12x^3+9x^2-6x+28x^2+21x-14=$

$12x^3+37x^2+15x-14$

$(6x-5)(3x^2+7x-4)$

$6x(3x^2)+6x(7x)+6x(-4)-5(3x^2)-5(7x)-5(-4)=$

$18x^3+42x^2-24x-15x^2-35x+20=$

$18x^3+27x^2-59x+20$

④ Divide.

$(x^2+14x+45)\div(x+5)$

$x+9$

$x+5\overline{)x^2+14x+45}$

$\underline{x^2+5x}$

$9x+45$

$\underline{9x+45}$

$(3x^2-19x+28)\div(x-4)$

$3x-7$

$x-4\overline{)3x^2-19x+28}$

$\underline{3x^2-12x}$

$-7x+28$

$\underline{-7x+28}$

$(12x^2+25x-22)\div(3x-2)$

$4x+11$

$3x-2\overline{)12x^2+25x-22}$

$\underline{12x^2-8x}$

$33x-22$

$\underline{33x-22}$

$(4x^2-7x-36)\div(4x+9)$

$x-4$

$4x+9\overline{)4x^2-7x-36}$

$\underline{4x^2+9x}$

$-16x-36$

$\underline{-16x-36}$

$(5x^2-37x-24)\div(x-8)$

$5x+3$

$x-8\overline{)5x^2-37x-24}$

$\underline{5x^2-40x}$

$3x-24$

$\underline{3x-24}$

$(42x^2-13x-42)\div(6x-7)$

$7x+6$

$6x-7\overline{)42x^2-13x-42}$

$\underline{42x^2-49x}$

$36x-42$

$\underline{36x-42}$

Teaching Tips, Cont.

- Review multiplying binomials. (See Lessons 61-62 and 64)
- Review multiplying polynomials. (See Lesson 63)
- Review dividing polynomials. (See Lessons 65-67)
- Allow students to begin working on the review exercises in class as time permits. Assist individual students as needed.

Assignment

- Complete Lesson 151, Activities 1-4.

Lesson 152

Concepts
- Factoring polynomials
- Rational expressions

Learning Objectives
The student will be able to:
- Factor polynomials
- Simplify rational expressions
- Add rational expressions
- Subtract rational expressions
- Multiply rational expressions
- Divide rational expressions

Materials Needed
- Student book, Lesson 152
- Worksheet 76

Teaching Tips
- Review factoring polynomials. (See Lessons 68-77)
- Review simplifying rational expressions. (See Lesson 78)
- Review adding and subtracting rational expressions. (See Lessons 79, 82-84)
- Review multiplying rational expressions. (See Lessons 80 and 85)

Review

Activities

① Factor each polynomial completely.

$21x^2 - 27x$

$3x(7x - 9)$

$12x^3 + 6x^2 - 18x$

$6x(2x^2 + x - 3) = 6x(2x + 3)(x - 1)$

$15x^3 + 30x^2 - 5x$

$5x(3x^2 + 6x - 1)$

$49x^2 - 64$

$(7x + 8)(7x - 8)$

$9x^2 + 30x + 25$

$(3x + 5)^2$

$4x^3 - 4x^2 - 24x$

Factor out 4x. $4x(x^2 - x - 6)$

$4x(x - 3)(x + 2)$

$6x^2 - 12xy - 48y^2$

Factor out a 6. $6(x^2 - 2xy - 8y^2)$

$6(x + 2y)(x - 4y)$

$9x^2 - 48x + 64$

$(3x - 8)^2$

$4x^4 - 484$

$4(x^4 - 121) =$

$4(x^2 + 11)(x^2 - 11) =$

$4(x^2 + 11)(x + \sqrt{11})(x - \sqrt{11})$

$64x^3 + 27$

$(4x + 3)(16x^2 - 12x + 9)$

$-7x + xy - 3y + 21$

$(-7x + xy) + (-3y + 21)$

$x(-7 + y) - 3(y - 7)$

$(x - 3)(y - 7)$

$28x^3 - 56x^2 + 35x$

$7x(4x^2 - 8x + 5)$

$24x^3 + 56x^2 - 32x$

$8x(3x^2 + 7x - 4)$

$49x^2 - 18$

$(7x + 3\sqrt{2})(7x - 3\sqrt{2})$

$64x^2 - 80\sqrt{3}x + 75$

$(8x - 5\sqrt{3})^2$

$x^2 - 13x + 36$

$(x - 9)(x - 4)$

$20x^2 + 43x + 21$

$(4x + 3)(5x + 7)$

$60x^3 + 159x^2y + 54xy^2$

Factor out 3x. $3x(20x^2 + 53xy + 18y^2)$

$3x(4x + 9y)(5x + 2y)$

$64x^2 + 112x + 49$

$(8x + 7)^2$

$7x^5 - 567x$

$7x(x^4 - 81) =$

$7x(x^2 + 9)(x^2 - 9) =$

$7x(x^2 + 9)(x + 3)(x - 3)$

$27x^3 - 8$

$(3x - 2)(9x^2 + 6x + 4)$

$32x + 20xy + 45y + 72$

$(32x + 20xy) + (45y + 72)$

$4x(8 + 5y) + 9(5y + 8)$

$(4x + 9)(5y + 8)$

② Simplify. Remember to state any exclusions.

$\frac{18x^2 - 30x}{3x - 5}$

$\frac{6x\cancel{(3x - 5)}}{\cancel{3x - 5}} = 6x; x \neq \frac{5}{3}$

$\frac{x^2 - 6x - 27}{x^2 - 81}$

$\frac{(x + 3)\cancel{(x - 9)}}{(x + 9)\cancel{(x - 9)}} = \frac{x + 3}{x + 9}; x \neq -9, 9$

$\frac{2x^2 + 19x + 35}{2x^2 + 3x - 5}$

$\frac{\cancel{(2x + 5)}(x + 7)}{\cancel{(2x + 5)}(x - 1)} = \frac{x + 7}{x - 1}; x \neq -\frac{5}{2}, 1$

③ Solve. Remember to state any exclusions.

$\frac{7x}{x - 3} - \frac{2x}{x - 3} =$

$\frac{7x - 2x}{x - 3} = \frac{5x}{x - 3}; x \neq 3$

$\frac{x + 4}{5x + 6} + \frac{2x - 7}{5x + 6} =$

$\frac{(x + 4) + (2x - 7)}{5x + 6} =$

$\frac{3x - 3}{5x + 6}; x \neq -\frac{6}{5}$

$\frac{11x + 55}{x^2 + 8x} \cdot \frac{x^2 - 9x}{x^2 - 4x - 45} =$

$\frac{11\cancel{(x + 5)}}{\cancel{x}(x + 8)} \cdot \frac{\cancel{x}\cancel{(x - 9)}}{\cancel{(x + 5)}\cancel{(x - 9)}} =$

$\frac{11}{x + 8}; x \neq -8, -5, 0, 9$

$\frac{24x^2 + 60x}{30x^3 - 40x^2} \div \frac{6x^2 + 15x}{15x^2 - 20x} =$

$\frac{24x^2 + 60x}{30x^3 - 40x^2} \cdot \frac{15x^2 - 20x}{6x^2 + 15x} =$

$\frac{{}_{2}\cancel{4}\cancel{12x}\cancel{(2x + 5)}}{{}_{x}\cancel{2x}\cancel{10x^2}\cancel{(3x - 4)}} \cdot \frac{\cancel{5x}\cancel{(3x - 4)}}{\cancel{3x}\cancel{(2x + 5)}} =$

$\frac{2}{x}; x \neq -\frac{5}{2}, 0, \frac{4}{3}$

$\frac{5x}{4x + 1} - \frac{3x}{5} =$

$\frac{(5x)(5)}{(4x + 1)(5)} - \frac{(3x)(4x + 1)}{(5)(4x + 1)} =$

$\frac{25x - 12x^2 - 3x}{20x + 5} =$

$\frac{-12x^2 + 22x}{20x + 5}; x \neq -\frac{1}{4}$

$\frac{12}{5x + 8} + \frac{4x}{5x + 8} =$

$\frac{4x + 12}{5x + 8}; x \neq -\frac{8}{5}$

$\frac{5x - 8}{x - 6} - \frac{3x + 4}{x - 6} =$

$\frac{(5x - 8) - (3x + 4)}{x - 6} = \frac{2x - 12}{x - 6} =$

$\frac{2\cancel{(x - 6)}}{\cancel{x - 6}} = 2; x \neq 6$

$\frac{2x^2 - 5x - 42}{4x^2 + 5x - 6} \cdot \frac{x^2 - 2x - 8}{x^2 - 10x + 24} =$

$\frac{(2x + 7)\cancel{(x - 6)}}{(4x - 3)\cancel{(x + 2)}} \cdot \frac{\cancel{(x + 2)}\cancel{(x - 4)}}{\cancel{(x - 6)}\cancel{(x - 4)}} =$

$\frac{2x + 7}{4x - 3}; x \neq -2, \frac{3}{4}, 4, 6$

$\frac{6x^2 - 17x - 3}{7x^2 + 48x - 64} \div \frac{x^2 - 7x + 12}{x^2 + 4x - 32} =$

$\frac{6x^2 - 17x - 3}{7x^2 + 48x - 64} \cdot \frac{x^2 + 4x - 32}{x^2 - 7x + 12} =$

$\frac{(6x + 1)\cancel{(x - 3)}}{(7x - 8)\cancel{(x + 8)}} \cdot \frac{\cancel{(x + 8)}\cancel{(x - 4)}}{\cancel{(x - 3)}\cancel{(x - 4)}} =$

$\frac{6x + 1}{7x - 8}; x \neq -8, \frac{8}{7}, 3, 4$

$\frac{8}{5x + 12} - \frac{x}{9} =$

$\frac{(8)(9)}{(5x + 12)(9)} - \frac{(x)(5x + 12)}{(9)(5x + 12)} =$

$\frac{72 - 5x^2 - 12x}{45x + 108} =$

$\frac{-5x^2 - 12x + 72}{45x + 108}; x \neq -\frac{12}{5}$

Systems of Equations Worksheet 76

① Solve the systems of equations.

$x - y + 8 = 0$
$-2x + y - 11 = 0$

$x - y = -8$
$-2x + y = 11$
$-x = 3$
$x = -3$

$-3 - y + 8 = 0$
$y = 5$

(-3, 5)

$x - y - 6 = 0$
$-2x + y + 4 = 0$

$x - y = 6$
$-2x + y = -4$
$-x = 2$
$x = -2$

$-2 - y - 6 = 0$
$-y = 8$
$y = -8$

(-2, -8)

$10x - 3y - 65 = 0$
$7x + 2y - 25 = 0$
$10x - 3y = 65$
$7x + 2y = 25$

$20x - 6y = 130$
$21x + 6y = 75$
$41x = 205$
$x = 5$
$10(5) - 3y - 65 = 0$
$50 - 3y - 65 = 0$
$-3y = 15$
$y = -5$
(5, -5)

$x - y - 9 = 0$
$2x - y - 12 = 0$

$x - y = 9$
$2x - y = 12$
$-x = -3$
$x = 3$

$3 - y - 9 = 0$
$-y = 6$
$y = -6$

(3, -6)

$11x - 22y + 44 = 0$
$-x + 4y - 6 = 0$
$11x - 22y = -44$
$-x + 4y = 6$

$x - 2y = -4$
$-x + 4y = 6$
$2y = 2$
$y = 1$

$-x + 4(1) - 6 = 0$
$-x + 4 - 6 = 0$
$-x = 2$
$x = -2$
(-2, 1)

$x - y + 1 = 0$
$-2x + y + 1 = 0$

$x - y = -1$
$-2x + y = -1$
$-x = -2$
$x = 2$

$2 - y + 1 = 0$
$-y = -3$
$y = 3$

(2, 3)

$6x - 9y - 15 = 0$
$8x - 12y - 20 = 0$
$6x - 9y = 15$
$8x - 12y = 20$

$2x - 3y = 5$
$2x - 3y = 5$
$0 = 0$

All real numbers

$x + y - 12 = 0$
$-2x + y + 15 = 0$

$x + y = 12$
$-2x + y = -15$
$3x = 27$
$x = 9$

$9 + y - 12 = 0$
$y = 3$

(9, 3)

$x + y - 4 = 0$
$-2x + y - 7 = 0$

$x + y = 4$
$-2x + y = 7$
$3x = -3$
$x = -1$

$-1 + y - 4 = 0$
$y = 5$

(-1, 5)

Teaching Tips, Cont.

- Review dividing rational expressions. (See Lessons 81 and 86)
- Have students complete Worksheet 76 in class as a review exercise. Provide assistance as needed.
- Allow students to begin working on the review exercises in class as time permits. Assist individual students as needed.

Assignment

- Complete Lesson 152, Activities 1-3.

Lesson 153

Concepts

- Rational expressions
- Complex fractions
- Quadratic equations

Learning Objectives

The student will be able to:

- Add, subtract, multiply, and divide rational expressions
- Simplify complex fractions
- Simplify complex rational expressions
- Solve quadratic equations

Materials Needed

- Student book, Lesson 153
- Worksheet 77

Teaching Tips

- Review rational expressions as needed. (See Lessons 78-86)
- Review complex fractions. (See Lesson 87)
- Review complex rational expressions. (See Lessons 88-89)
- Review quadratic equations. (See Lesson 90)

Review

Activities

① Solve. Remember to state any exclusions.

$\frac{5x}{4x+3}+\frac{2}{3x-1}=$

$\frac{5x(3x-1)}{(4x+3)(3x-1)}+\frac{2(4x+3)}{(4x+3)(3x-1)}=$

$\frac{15x^2-5x}{12x^2+5x-3}+\frac{8x+6}{12x^2+5x-3}=$

$\frac{15x^2+3x+6}{12x^2+5x-3};x\neq-\frac{3}{4},\frac{1}{3}$

$\frac{2}{3x+1}+\frac{1}{2x-1}=$

$\frac{2(2x-1)}{(3x+1)(2x-1)}+\frac{1(3x+1)}{(3x+1)(2x-1)}=$

$\frac{4x-2}{6x^2-x-1}+\frac{3x+1}{6x^2-x-1}=$

$\frac{7x-1}{6x^2-x-1};x\neq-\frac{1}{3},\frac{1}{2}$

$\frac{4x}{x-3}-\frac{5x}{3x-5}=$

$\frac{4x(3x-5)}{(x-3)(3x-5)}-\frac{5x(x-3)}{(3x-5)(x-3)}=$

$\frac{12x^2-20x}{3x^2-14x+15}-\frac{5x^2-15x}{3x^2-14x+15}=$

$\frac{7x^2-5x}{3x^2-14x+15};x\neq\frac{5}{3},3$

$\frac{5}{2x-3}-\frac{2}{x-4}=$

$\frac{5(x-4)}{(2x-3)(x-4)}-\frac{2(2x-3)}{(2x-3)(x-4)}=$

$\frac{5x-20}{2x^2-11x+12}-\frac{4x-6}{2x^2-11x+12}=$

$\frac{x-14}{2x^2-11x+12};x\neq\frac{3}{2},4$

$\frac{36x^3+96x^2-105x}{80x^2+152x-448}\cdot\frac{8x^2-68x+32}{6x^3-53x^2+40x}=$

$\frac{3\cancel{x}\cancel{(2x+7)}\cancel{(6x-5)}}{{}_2\cancel{8}(5x-8)\cancel{(2x+7)}}\cdot\frac{\cancel{4}\cancel{(x-8)}(2x-1)}{\cancel{x}\cancel{(6x-5)}\cancel{(x-8)}}=$

$\frac{3}{2(5x-8)}\cdot\frac{2x-1}{1}=\frac{6x-3}{10x-16};x\neq-\frac{7}{2},0,\frac{5}{6},\frac{8}{5},8$

$\frac{x^2-8x+16}{6x^2+13x+6}\cdot\frac{9x^2+12x+4}{3x^2-10x-8}=$

$\frac{\cancel{(x-4)}(x-4)}{\cancel{(3x+2)}(2x+3)}\cdot\frac{\cancel{(3x+2)}\cancel{(3x+2)}}{\cancel{(3x+2)}\cancel{(x-4)}}=$

$\frac{x-4}{2x+3};x\neq-\frac{3}{2},-\frac{2}{3},4$

$\frac{15x^2-4x-3}{12x^2-31x+7}\div\frac{15x^2-4x-3}{9x^2-49}=$

$\frac{15x^2-4x-3}{12x^2-31x+7}\cdot\frac{9x^2-49}{15x^2-4x-3}=$

$\frac{\cancel{(3x+1)}\cancel{(5x-3)}}{(4x-1)\cancel{(3x-7)}}\cdot\frac{(3x+7)\cancel{(3x-7)}}{\cancel{(5x-3)}\cancel{(3x+1)}}=$

$\frac{3x+7}{4x-1};x\neq-\frac{1}{3},\frac{1}{4},\frac{3}{5},\frac{7}{3},-\frac{7}{3}$

$\frac{40x^2+2x-3}{49x^2-36}\div\frac{12x^2-11x+2}{21x^2+4x-12}=$

$\frac{40x^2+2x-3}{49x^2-36}\cdot\frac{21x^2+4x-12}{12x^2-11x+2}=$

$\frac{(10x+3)\cancel{(4x-1)}}{(7x-6)\cancel{(7x+6)}}\cdot\frac{\cancel{(7x+6)}\cancel{(3x-2)}}{\cancel{(3x-2)}\cancel{(4x-1)}}=$

$\frac{10x+3}{7x-6};x\neq-\frac{6}{7},\frac{1}{4},\frac{2}{3},\frac{6}{7}$

② Simplify the complex fractions.

$\frac{\frac{5}{6}}{3}$ LCD = 6.

$\frac{\cancel{6}\left(\frac{5}{\cancel{6}}\right)}{6(3)}=\frac{5}{18}$

$\frac{5}{\frac{8}{13}}$ LCD = 13.

$\frac{13(5)}{\cancel{13}\left(\frac{8}{\cancel{13}}\right)}=\frac{65}{8}$

$\frac{\frac{5}{8}}{\frac{2}{3}}$ LCD = 8(3) = 24.

$\frac{{}_3\cancel{24}\left(\frac{5}{\cancel{8}}\right)}{{}_8\cancel{24}\left(\frac{2}{\cancel{3}}\right)}=\frac{15}{16}$

③ Simplify the complex rational expressions.

$\frac{\frac{1}{x-6}}{\frac{4}{x+2}}$ LCD = $(x-6)(x+2)$.

$\frac{\cancel{(x-6)}(x+2)\left(\frac{1}{\cancel{x-6}}\right)}{(x-6)\cancel{(x+2)}\left(\frac{4}{\cancel{x+2}}\right)}=\frac{x+2}{4x-24}$

$\frac{\frac{2}{3x-7}}{5}$ LCD = $3x-7$.

$\frac{\cancel{(3x-7)}\left(\frac{2}{\cancel{3x-7}}\right)}{5(3x-7)}=\frac{2}{15x-35}$

$\frac{10}{\frac{3}{2x+9}}$ LCD = $2x+9$.

$\frac{(2x+9)(10)}{\cancel{(2x+9)}\left(\frac{3}{\cancel{2x+9}}\right)}=\frac{20x+90}{3}$

$\frac{\frac{2}{4x-5}}{\frac{6}{7x+2}}$ LCD = $(4x-5)(7x+2)$.

$\frac{\cancel{(4x-5)}(7x+2)\left(\frac{\cancel{2}}{\cancel{4x-5}}\right)}{(4x-5)\cancel{(7x+2)}\left(\frac{\cancel{6}_3}{\cancel{7x+2}}\right)}=\frac{7x+2}{12x-15}$

④ Solve each quadratic equation.

$x^2+13x+40=0$
$(x+8)(x+5)=0$
$x+8=0;x=-8$
$x+5=0;x=-5$
$x=-8$ and -5.

$x^2-144=0$
$x^2=144$
$\sqrt{x^2}=\sqrt{144}$
$x=\pm12$

$x^2+12x+5=0$
$x^2+12x=-5$
$x^2+12x+\left(\frac{12}{2}\right)^2=-5+\left(\frac{12}{2}\right)^2$
$x^2+12x+36=-5+36$
$x^2+12x+36=31$
$(x+6)^2=31$
$\sqrt{(x+6)^2}=\sqrt{31}$
$x+6=\pm\sqrt{31}$
$x=-6\pm\sqrt{31}$

$3x^2+5x-9=0$
$x=\frac{-5\pm\sqrt{5^2-4(3)(-9)}}{2(3)}$
$x=\frac{-5\pm\sqrt{25+108}}{6}$
$x=\frac{-5\pm\sqrt{133}}{6}$

$x^2-5x-36=0$
$(x+4)(x-9)=0$
$x+4=0;x=-4$
$x-9=0;x=9$
$x=-4$ and 9.

$x^2-71=0$
$x^2=71$
$\sqrt{x^2}=\sqrt{71}$
$x=\pm\sqrt{71}$

$x^2+6x-13=0$
$x^2+6x=13$
$x^2+6x+\left(\frac{6}{2}\right)^2=13+\left(\frac{6}{2}\right)^2$
$x^2+6x+9=13+9$
$x^2+6x+9=22$
$(x+3)^2=22$
$\sqrt{(x+3)^2}=\sqrt{22}$
$x+3=\pm\sqrt{22}$
$x=-3\pm\sqrt{22}$

$5x^2+11x+4=0$
$x=\frac{-11\pm\sqrt{11^2-4(5)(4)}}{2(5)}$
$x=\frac{-11\pm\sqrt{121-80}}{10}$
$x=\frac{-11\pm\sqrt{41}}{10}=-$

$x^2-14x+33=0$
$(x-3)(x-11)=0$
$x-3=0;x=3$
$x-11=0;x=11$
$x=3$ and 11.

$x^2-75=0$
$x^2=75$
$\sqrt{x^2}=\sqrt{75}$
$\sqrt{x^2}=\sqrt{3\cdot5\cdot5}$
$x=\pm5\sqrt{3}$

$x^2+10x-25=0$
$x^2+10x=25$
$x^2+10x+\left(\frac{10}{2}\right)^2=25+\left(\frac{10}{2}\right)^2$
$x^2+10x+25=25+25$
$x^2+10x+25=50$
$(x+5)^2=50$
$\sqrt{(x+5)^2}=\sqrt{50}$
$x+5=\pm\sqrt{2\cdot5\cdot5}$
$x=-5\pm5\sqrt{2}$

$2x^2-3x-8=0$
$x=\frac{-(-3)\pm\sqrt{(-3)^2-4(2)(-8)}}{2(2)}$
$x=\frac{3\pm\sqrt{9+64}}{4}$
$x=\frac{3\pm\sqrt{73}}{4}$

Solving Quadratic Equations Worksheet 77

① Solve each quadratic equation.

$x^2 + 9x + 18 = 0$
$(x+3)(x+6) = 0$
$x + 3 = 0; x = -3$
$x + 6 = 0; x = -6$
x = -3 and -6.

$x^2 - 9x - 10 = 0$
$(x+1)(x-10) = 0$
$x + 1 = 0; x = -1$
$x - 10 = 0; x = 10$
x = -1 and 10.

$x^2 - 12x + 27 = 0$
$(x-9)(x-3) = 0$
$x - 9 = 0; x = 9$
$x - 3 = 0; x = 3$
x = 9 and 3.

$x^2 - 64 = 0$
$x^2 = 144$
$\sqrt{x^2} = \sqrt{64}$
$x = \pm 8$

$x^2 - 39 = 0$
$x^2 = 39$
$\sqrt{x^2} = \sqrt{39}$
$x = \pm\sqrt{39}$

$x^2 - 125 = 0$
$x^2 = 125$
$\sqrt{x^2} = \sqrt{125}$
$\sqrt{x^2} = \sqrt{5 \cdot 5 \cdot 5}$
$x = \pm 5\sqrt{5}$

$x^2 + 8x + 9 = 0$
$x^2 + 8x = -9$
$x^2 + 8x + \left(\frac{8}{2}\right)^2 = -9 + \left(\frac{8}{2}\right)^2$
$x^2 + 8x + 16 = -9 + 16$
$x^2 + 8x + 16 = 7$
$(x+4)^2 = 7$
$\sqrt{(x+4)^2} = \sqrt{7}$
$x + 4 = \pm\sqrt{7}$
$x = -4 \pm \sqrt{7}$

$x^2 + 4x - 13 = 0$
$x^2 + 4x = 13$
$x^2 + 4x + \left(\frac{4}{2}\right)^2 = 13 + \left(\frac{4}{2}\right)^2$
$x^2 + 4x + 4 = 13 + 4$
$x^2 + 4x + 4 = 17$
$(x+2)^2 = 17$
$\sqrt{(x+2)^2} = \sqrt{17}$
$x + 2 = \pm\sqrt{17}$
$x = -2 \pm \sqrt{17}$

$x^2 + 14x - 21 = 0$
$x^2 + 14x = 21$
$x^2 + 14x + \left(\frac{14}{2}\right)^2 = 21 + \left(\frac{14}{2}\right)^2$
$x^2 + 14x + 49 = 21 + 49$
$x^2 + 14x + 49 = 70$
$(x+7)^2 = 70$
$\sqrt{(x+7)^2} = \sqrt{70}$
$x + 7 = \pm\sqrt{70}$
$x = -7 \pm \sqrt{70}$

$3x^2 + 4x - 5 = 0$
$x = \frac{-4 \pm \sqrt{4^2 - 4(3)(-5)}}{2(3)}$
$x = \frac{-4 \pm \sqrt{16 + 60}}{6}$
$x = \frac{-4 \pm \sqrt{76}}{6}$
$x = \frac{-4 \pm \sqrt{4 \cdot 19}}{6}$
$x = \frac{-4 \pm 2\sqrt{19}}{6} = \frac{-2 \pm \sqrt{19}}{3}$

$3x^2 + 9x + 2 = 0$
$x = \frac{-9 \pm \sqrt{9^2 - 4(3)(2)}}{2(3)}$
$x = \frac{-9 \pm \sqrt{81 - 24}}{6}$
$x = \frac{-9 \pm \sqrt{57}}{6}$

$2x^2 - 3x - 7 = 0$
$x = \frac{-(-3) \pm \sqrt{(-3)^2 - 4(2)(-7)}}{2(2)}$
$x = \frac{3 \pm \sqrt{9 + 56}}{4}$
$x = \frac{3 \pm \sqrt{65}}{4}$

Teaching Tips, Cont.

- Review various methods of solving quadratic equations. (See Lessons 91-96) Students will be allowed to use the method of their choice when solving quadratic equations on the exam. Students should be familiar with all methods because some methods are easier than others depending on the problem.
- Allow students to begin working on the review exercises in class as time permits. Assist individual students as needed.

Assignments

- Complete Lesson 153, Activities 1-4.
- Worksheet 77.

Lesson 154

Concepts

- Parabolas
- Vertex
- Focus
- Axis of symmetry
- Directrix
- Graphing parabolas

Learning Objectives

The student will be able to:

- Write equations in parabolic form
- Give the coordinates for the vertex and focus of a parabola
- Give the equations for the axis of symmetry and directrix of a parabola
- Graph a parabola

Materials Needed

- Student book, Lesson 154

Teaching Tips

➢ Review parabolas. (See Lessons 98-99, 101, 106, and 109) Pay special attention to the parts of a parabola in Lessons 106 and 109.

➢ Review completing the square. (See Lesson 100)

➢ Review graphing parabolas. (See Lessons 102 and 107)

Review

Activities

① Rewrite each equation in the form $4p(y-k)=(x-h)^2$. Give the coordinates for the vertex and focus, and the equations of the lines for the axis of symmetry and the directrix of the parabola.

$y=\frac{1}{12}(x-3)^2+2$
$y-2=\frac{1}{12}(x-3)^2$
$\frac{y-2}{\frac{1}{12}}=(x-3)^2$
$12(y-2)=(x-3)^2$
$4p=12 \Rightarrow p=3$
$k=2$
$h=3$
The vertex is (3, 2).
The focus is (3, 2 + 3) = (3, 5).
The axis of symmetry is the line x = 3.
The directrix is the line $y=2-3 \Rightarrow y=-1$.

$y=\frac{1}{8}(x-2)^2+3$
$y-3=\frac{1}{8}(x-2)^2$
$\frac{y-3}{\frac{1}{8}}=(x-2)^2$
$8(y-3)=(x-2)^2$
$4p=8 \Rightarrow p=2$
$k=3$
$h=2$
The vertex is (2, 3).
The focus is (2, 3 + 2) = (2, 5).
The axis of symmetry is the line x = 2.
The directrix is the line $y=3-2 \Rightarrow y=1$.

$y=\frac{1}{4}(x-3)^2+2$
$y-2=\frac{1}{4}(x-3)^2$
$\frac{y-2}{\frac{1}{4}}=(x-3)^2$
$4(y-2)=(x-3)^2$
$4p=4 \Rightarrow p=1$
$k=2$
$h=3$
The vertex is (3, 2).
The focus is (3, 2 + 1) = (3, 3).
The axis of symmetry is the line x = 3.
The directrix is the line $y=2-1 \Rightarrow y=1$.

$y=\frac{1}{12}(x-1)^2+4$
$y-4=\frac{1}{12}(x-1)^2$
$\frac{y-4}{\frac{1}{12}}=(x-1)^2$
$12(y-4)=(x-1)^2$
$4p=12 \Rightarrow p=3$
$k=4$
$h=1$
The vertex is (1, 4).
The focus is (1, 4 + 3) = (1, 7).
The axis of symmetry is the line x = 1.
The directrix is the line $y=4-3 \Rightarrow y=1$.

$y=\frac{1}{8}(x+2)^2-3$
$y+3=\frac{1}{8}(x+2)^2$
$\frac{y+3}{\frac{1}{8}}=(x+2)^2$
$8(y+3)=(x+2)^2$
$4p=8 \Rightarrow p=2$
$k=-3$
$h=-2$
The vertex is (-2, -3).
The focus is (-2, -3 + 2) = (-2, -1).
The axis of symmetry is the line x = -2.
The directrix is the line $y=-3-2 \Rightarrow y=-5$.

$y=\frac{1}{4}(x+1)^2-4$
$y+4=\frac{1}{4}(x+1)^2$
$\frac{y+4}{\frac{1}{4}}=(x+1)^2$
$4(y+4)=(x+1)^2$
$4p=4 \Rightarrow p=1$
$k=-4$
$h=-1$
The vertex is (-1, -4).
The focus is (-1, -4 + 1) = (-1, -3).
The axis of symmetry is the line x = -1.
The directrix is the line $y=-4-1 \Rightarrow y=-5$.

② Draw the graph of each equation from Activity ①. Include the parabola, vertex, focus, axis of symmetry, and directrix.

$y = \frac{1}{12}(x-3)^2 + 2$

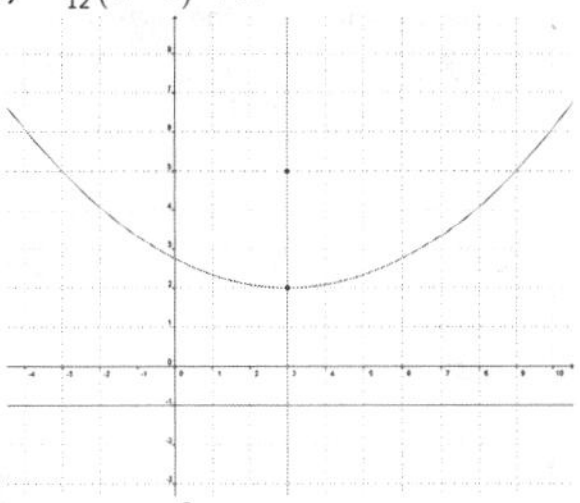

$y = \frac{1}{8}(x-2)^2 + 3$

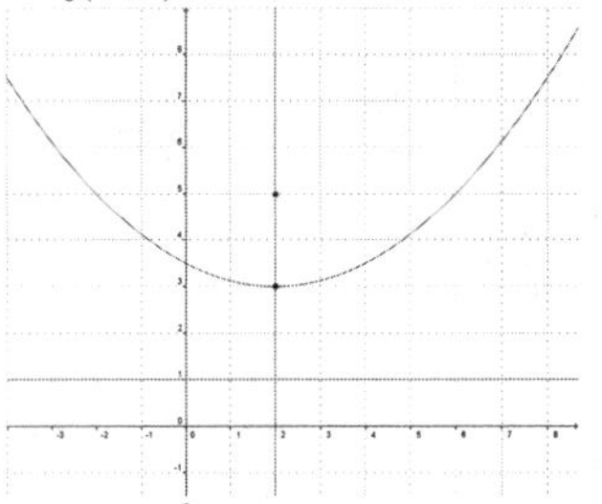

$y = \frac{1}{4}(x-3)^2 + 2$

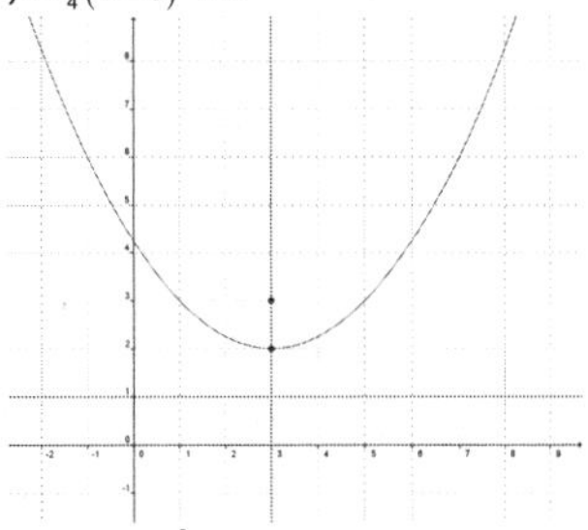

$y = \frac{1}{12}(x-1)^2 + 4$

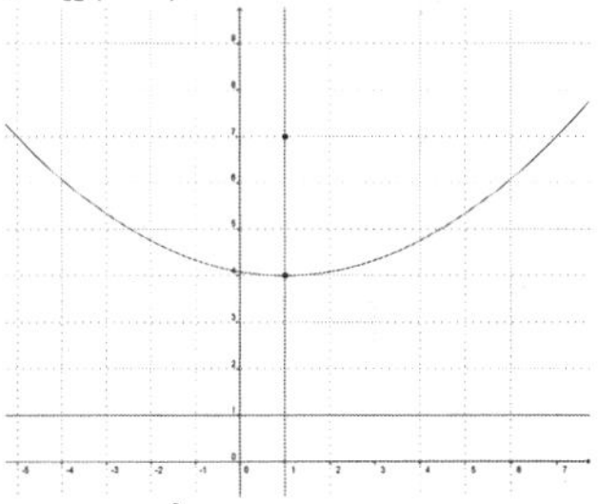

$y = \frac{1}{8}(x+2)^2 - 3$

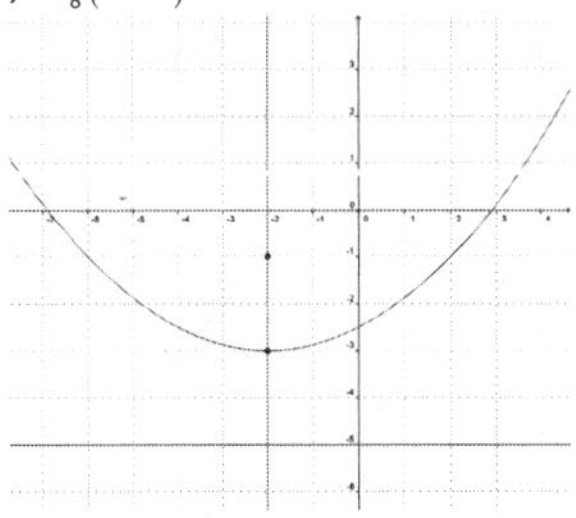

$y = \frac{1}{4}(x+1)^2 - 4$

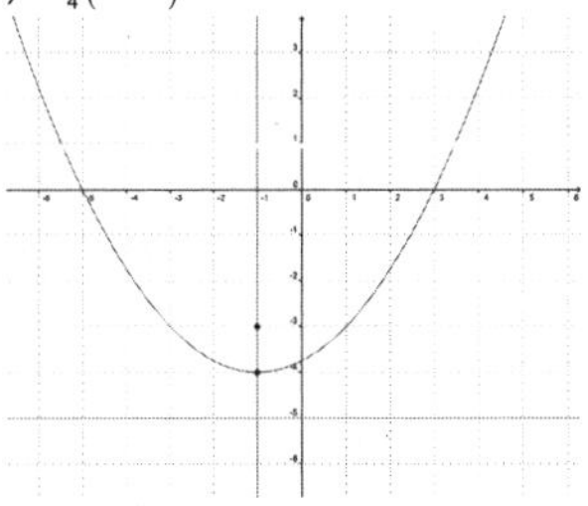

Teaching Tips, Cont.

- Allow students to begin working on the review exercises in class as time permits. Assist individual students as needed.

Assignment

- Complete Lesson 154, Activities 1-2.

Lesson 155

Concepts

- Graphing quadratic inequalities
- Quadratic equations with radicals
- Roots of quadratic equations
- Square roots without calculators

Learning Objectives

The student will be able to:

- Sketch the graph of quadratic inequalities
- Find the roots of quadratic equations with radicals
- Calculate the square root of numbers without using a calculator

Materials Needed

- Student book, Lesson 155
- Worksheet 78

Teaching Tips

- ➢ Review quadratic equations with radicals. (See Lesson 105)
- ➢ Review graphing quadratic inequalities. (See Lesson 110)
- ➢ Review finding square roots without using a calculator. (See Lesson 139)

Review

Activities

① Sketch the graph of each inequality.

$y < x^2 + 2x - 4$

The symbol is < and a is positive, so the graph will be shaded outside the parabola.

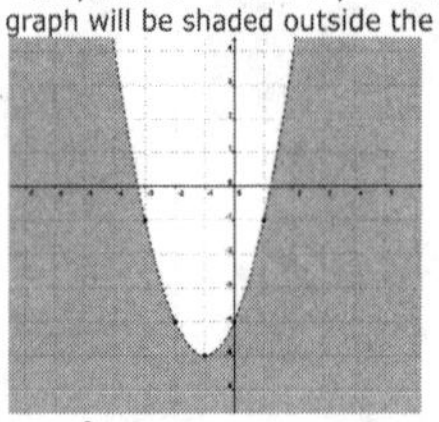

$y \ge x^2 + 4x - 1$

The symbol is ≥ and a is positive, so the graph will be shaded inside the parabola.

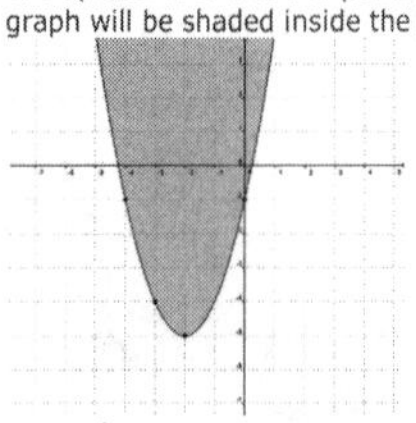

$y > x^2 + 2x - 1$

The symbol is > and a is positive, so the graph will be shaded inside the parabola.

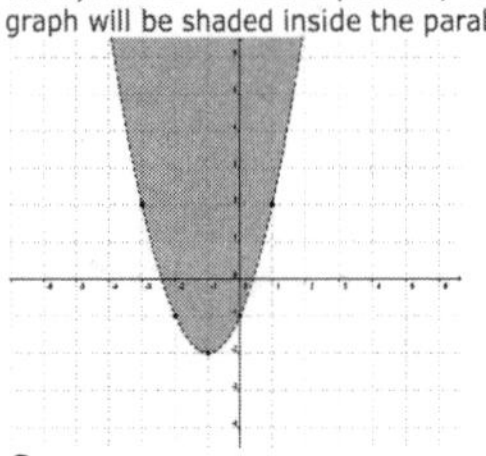

$y \ge -x^2 + 4x + 4$

The symbol is ≥ and a is negative, so the graph will be shaded outside the parabola.

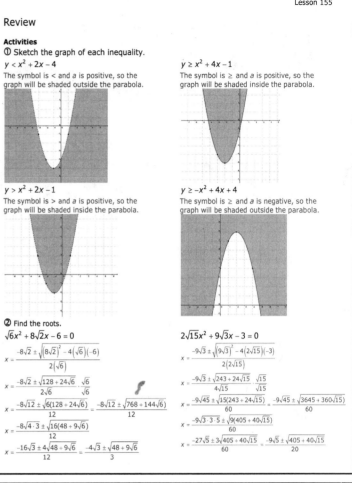

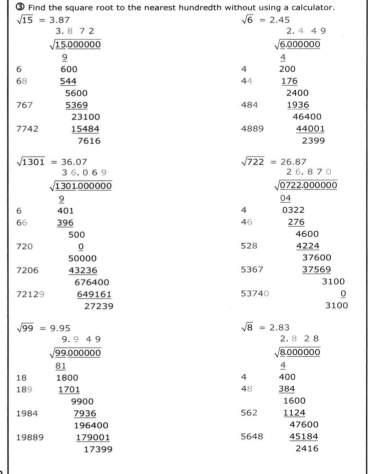

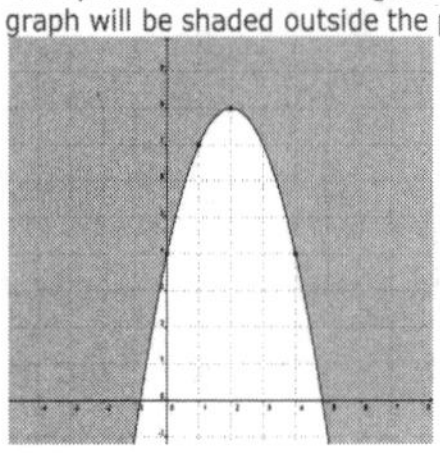

② Find the roots.

$\sqrt{6}x^2 + 8\sqrt{2}x - 6 = 0$

$$x = \frac{-8\sqrt{2} \pm \sqrt{(8\sqrt{2})^2 - 4(\sqrt{6})(-6)}}{2(\sqrt{6})}$$

$$x = \frac{-8\sqrt{2} \pm \sqrt{128 + 24\sqrt{6}}}{2\sqrt{6}} \cdot \frac{\sqrt{6}}{\sqrt{6}}$$

$$x = \frac{-8\sqrt{12} \pm \sqrt{6(128 + 24\sqrt{6})}}{12} = \frac{-8\sqrt{12} \pm \sqrt{768 + 144\sqrt{6})}}{12}$$

$$x = \frac{-8\sqrt{4 \cdot 3} \pm \sqrt{16(48 + 9\sqrt{6})}}{12}$$

$$x = \frac{-16\sqrt{3} \pm 4\sqrt{48 + 9\sqrt{6}}}{12} = \frac{-4\sqrt{3} \pm \sqrt{48 + 9\sqrt{6}}}{3}$$

$2\sqrt{15}x^2 + 9\sqrt{3}x - 3 = 0$

$$x = \frac{-9\sqrt{3} \pm \sqrt{(9\sqrt{3})^2 - 4(2\sqrt{15})(-3)}}{2(2\sqrt{15})}$$

$$x = \frac{-9\sqrt{3} \pm \sqrt{243 + 24\sqrt{15}}}{4\sqrt{15}} \cdot \frac{\sqrt{15}}{\sqrt{15}}$$

$$x = \frac{-9\sqrt{45} \pm \sqrt{15(243 + 24\sqrt{15})}}{60} = \frac{-9\sqrt{45} \pm \sqrt{3645 + 360\sqrt{15})}}{60}$$

$$x = \frac{-9\sqrt{3 \cdot 3 \cdot 5} \pm \sqrt{9(405 + 40\sqrt{15})}}{60}$$

$$x = \frac{-27\sqrt{5} \pm 3\sqrt{405 + 40\sqrt{15}}}{60} = \frac{-9\sqrt{5} \pm \sqrt{405 + 40\sqrt{15}}}{20}$$

③ Find the square root to the nearest hundredth without using a calculator.

$\sqrt{15} = 3.87$

	3. 8 7 2
	$\sqrt{15.000000}$
	9
6	600
68	544
	5600
767	5369
	23100
7742	15484
	7616

$\sqrt{6} = 2.45$

	2. 4 4 9
	$\sqrt{6.000000}$
	4
4	200
44	176
	2400
484	1936
	46400
4889	44001
	2399

$\sqrt{1301} = 36.07$

	3 6. 0 6 9
	$\sqrt{1301.000000}$
	9
6	401
66	396
	500
720	0
	50000
7206	43236
	676400
72129	649161
	27239

$\sqrt{722} = 26.87$

	2 6. 8 7 0
	$\sqrt{0722.000000}$
	04
4	0322
46	276
	4600
528	4224
	37600
5367	37569
	3100
53740	0
	3100

$\sqrt{99} = 9.95$

	9. 9 4 9
	$\sqrt{99.000000}$
	81
18	1800
189	1701
	9900
1984	7936
	196400
19889	179001
	17399

$\sqrt{8} = 2.83$

	2. 8 2 8
	$\sqrt{8.000000}$
	4
4	400
48	384
	1600
562	1124
	47600
5648	45184
	2416

Quadratic Equations with Radicals Worksheet 78

① Find the roots

$\sqrt{6}x^2 + 3\sqrt{2}x - 4 = 0$

$$x = \frac{-3\sqrt{2} \pm \sqrt{\left(3\sqrt{2}\right)^2 - 4\left(\sqrt{6}\right)(-4)}}{2\left(\sqrt{6}\right)}$$

$$x = \frac{-3\sqrt{2} \pm \sqrt{18 + 16\sqrt{6}}}{2\sqrt{6}} \cdot \frac{\sqrt{6}}{\sqrt{6}}$$

$$x = \frac{-3\sqrt{12} \pm \sqrt{18\sqrt{6} + 96}}{12}$$

$$x = \frac{-3\sqrt{2 \cdot 2 \cdot 3} \pm \sqrt{18\sqrt{6} + 96}}{12}$$

$$x = \frac{-6\sqrt{3} \pm \sqrt{18\sqrt{6} + 96}}{12}$$

$\sqrt{3}x^2 + 4\sqrt{2}x - 5 = 0$

$$x = \frac{-4\sqrt{2} \pm \sqrt{\left(4\sqrt{2}\right)^2 - 4\left(\sqrt{3}\right)(-5)}}{2\left(\sqrt{3}\right)}$$

$$x = \frac{-4\sqrt{2} \pm \sqrt{32 + 20\sqrt{3}}}{2\sqrt{3}} \cdot \frac{\sqrt{3}}{\sqrt{3}}$$

$$x = \frac{-4\sqrt{6} \pm \sqrt{32\sqrt{3} + 60}}{6}$$

$$x = \frac{-4\sqrt{6} \pm \sqrt{4\left(8\sqrt{3} + 15\right)}}{6}$$

$$x = \frac{-4\sqrt{6} \pm 2\sqrt{8\sqrt{3} + 15}}{6} = \frac{-2\sqrt{6} \pm \sqrt{8\sqrt{3} + 15}}{3}$$

$4\sqrt{15}x^2 + 2\sqrt{3}x - 6 = 0$

$$x = \frac{-2\sqrt{3} \pm \sqrt{\left(2\sqrt{3}\right)^2 - 4\left(4\sqrt{15}\right)(-6)}}{2\left(4\sqrt{15}\right)}$$

$$x = \frac{-2\sqrt{3} \pm \sqrt{12 + 96\sqrt{15}}}{8\sqrt{15}} \cdot \frac{\sqrt{15}}{\sqrt{15}}$$

$$x = \frac{-2\sqrt{45} \pm \sqrt{12\sqrt{15} + 1440}}{120}$$

$$x = \frac{-2\sqrt{3 \cdot 3 \cdot 5} \pm \sqrt{4\left(3\sqrt{15} + 360\right)}}{120}$$

$$x = \frac{-6\sqrt{5} \pm 2\sqrt{3\sqrt{15} + 360}}{120} = \frac{-3\sqrt{5} \pm \sqrt{3\sqrt{15} + 360}}{60}$$

$2\sqrt{10}x^2 + 3\sqrt{5}x - 7 = 0$

$$x = \frac{-3\sqrt{5} \pm \sqrt{\left(3\sqrt{5}\right)^2 - 4\left(2\sqrt{10}\right)(-7)}}{2\left(2\sqrt{10}\right)}$$

$$x = \frac{-3\sqrt{5} \pm \sqrt{45 + 56\sqrt{10}}}{4\sqrt{10}} \cdot \frac{\sqrt{10}}{\sqrt{10}}$$

$$x = \frac{-3\sqrt{50} \pm \sqrt{45\sqrt{10} + 560}}{40}$$

$$x = \frac{-3\sqrt{2 \cdot 5 \cdot 5} \pm \sqrt{45\sqrt{10} + 560}}{40}$$

$$x = \frac{-15\sqrt{2} \pm \sqrt{45\sqrt{10} + 560}}{40}$$

Teaching Tips, Cont.

- Allow students to begin working on the review exercises in class as time permits. Assist individual students as needed.

Assignments

- Complete Lesson 155, Activities 1-3.
- Worksheet 78.

Lesson 156

Concepts

- Investment problems
- Motion problems
- Mixture problems
- Ratios and proportions
- Consecutive integers
- Math in the real world

Learning Objectives

The student will be able to:

- Apply the simple interest formula
- Calculate distance and time
- Calculate mixtures and concentrations
- Use ratios and proportions to solve real-world problems
- Find consecutive integers

Materials Needed

- Student book, Lesson 156

Teaching Tips

- Review money and interest problems. (See Lessons 111-112)
- Review motion problems. (See Lessons 113)
- Review mixture problems. (See Lessons 114-115)

Word Problems

Activities

① Solve.

How long will it take $1500 invested at 4% to earn $240?

i	p	r	t
$240	$1500	0.04	t

Substitute the values into the formula.

$i = prt$

$\$240 = \$1500(0.04)(t)$

$4 = t$

You must invest $1500 at 4% for 4 years to earn $240 interest.

Two baseball players are positioned 75 feet apart in the outfield. Player A can sprint 23 feet per second, and player B can spring 22 feet per second. If the two players start running for a fly ball at the same time and collide on the field, how far, to the nearest hundredth of a foot, did player B run? (Assume all running was in a straight line.)

Let a = the distance player A ran and b = the distance player B ran.

$a + b = 75$ ft.

$a = 75$ ft. $- b$

$a = 23t$

$75 - b = 23t$

$t = \frac{75-b}{23}$

$b = 22t$

$t = \frac{b}{22}$

$\frac{75-b}{23} = \frac{b}{22}$

$22(75 - b) = 23b$

$1650 - 22b = 23b$

$1650 = 45b$

$b = 36.67$ ft.

How long, to the nearest hundredth of a second, did the players run before the collision?

$b = 24t$

$36.67 \text{ ft.} = (22 \text{ ft./s.})t$

$t = 1.67$ s.

A 96-ounce canister of mixed nuts is 35% peanuts. If you remove 16 ounces of peanuts from the mix, what percent of the remaining mix is peanuts?

	Concen.	Amount	Totals
Start	0.35	96 oz.	0.35(96)
Remove	1.00	16 oz.	1.00(16)
Final	x	80 oz.	$80x$

$0.35(96) - 1.00(16) = 80x$

$33.6 - 16 = 80x$

$17.6 = 80x$

$x = 0.22 = 22\%$

② Solve.

A 20-pound bag of fertilizer is 15% phosphorus. How much must be substituted with fertilizer that is 60% phosphorus to obtain 20 pounds of fertilizer that is 25% phosphorus? Round your answer to the nearest tenth of a pound.

	Start	Remove	Add	Finish
Concentration	0.15	0.15	0.60	0.25
Amount	20	x	x	20
Total	0.15(20)	$0.15x$	$0.60x$	0.25(20)

$0.15(20) - 0.15x + 0.60x = 0.25(20)$

$3 + 0.45x = 5$

$0.45x = 2$

$x = 4.4$

You must substitute 4.4 pounds of fertilizer.

A baseball player's batting average is the ratio of his number of hits to his number of times at bat. (This ratio is expressed as a decimal rounded to the nearest thousandth when giving baseball statistics.) If a player's batting average is 0.290 and he had 300 at bats during the season, how many hits did he have?

Let h = the number of hits.

$\frac{\text{hits}}{\text{at bats}} = \frac{290}{1000} = \frac{29}{100} = \frac{h}{300}$

$100h = 29(300)$

$100h = 8700$

$h = 87$

The player had 87 hits.

Four consecutive odd integers have a sum of 136. What are the integers?

The integers are represented by x, $x + 2$, $x + 4$, and $x + 6$.

$x + (x + 2) + (x + 4) + (x + 6) = 136$

$4x + 12 = 136$

$4x = 124$

$x = 31$

The integers are 31, 33, 35, and 37.

Six consecutive integers have a sum of 465. What are the integers?

The integers are represented by x, $x + 1$, $x + 2$, $x + 3$, $x + 4$, and $x + 5$.

$x + (x + 1) + (x + 2) + (x + 3) + (x + 4) + (x + 5) = 465$

$6x + 15 = 465$

$6x = 450$

$x = 75$

The integers are 75, 76, 77, 78, 79, and 80.

Teaching Tips, Cont.

- Review ratios and proportions. (See Lesson 116)
- Review consecutive integers. (See Lesson 117)
- Allow students to begin working on the review exercises in class as time permits. Assist individual students as needed.

Assignment

- Complete Lesson 156, Activities 1-2.

Lesson 157

Concepts

- Exponential growth and decay
- Ratios and proportions
- Investment problems
- Work problems
- Distance problems
- Math in the real world

Learning Objectives

The student will be able to:

- Solve real-world exponential growth and decay problems
- Apply ratios and proportions
- Solve problems involving rates of work
- Calculate distance and speed

Materials Needed

- Student book, Lesson 157

Teaching Tips

- Review exponential growth. (See Lesson 131)
- Review exponential decay. (See Lesson 132)
- Review ratios and proportions. (See Lesson 134)
- Review work problems. (See Lesson 136)

Lesson 157

Word Problems

Activities

① Solve.

During a recent depression, housing values in one neighborhood dropped exponentially by an average rate of 12% per year for 4 years. If a house was worth $190,000 at the beginning of the depression, what was the value of the house after 4 years? Round to the nearest ten thousandth after calculating the exponent.

$y = \$190,000(1-0.12)^4$

$y = \$190,000(0.88)^4$

$y = \$190,000(0.5997)$

$y = \$113,943$

If the same house declined in value at a rate of 8% each year for 6 years, what would the $190,000 house be worth after 6 years? Round to the nearest ten thousandth after calculating the exponent.

$y = \$190,000(1-0.08)^6$

$y = \$190,000(0.92)^6$

$y = \$190,000(0.6064)$

$y = \$115,216$

The ratio of male athletes to female athletes from the United States in the 2010 Vancouver Olympic Games was 22:15. If there were 90 female athletes, how many male athletes were there?

$\frac{\text{Male athletes}}{\text{Female athletes}} = \frac{\text{Male athletes}}{\text{Female athletes}}$

Let m = the number of male athletes.

$\frac{22}{15} = \frac{m}{90}$

$\cancel{15}(90)\frac{22}{\cancel{15}} = 15(\cancel{90})\frac{m}{\cancel{90}}$

$1980 = 15m$

$m = 132$

If your grandparents invested $7500 in a college savings plan for you on your 1st birthday at 5% simple interest, how much interest will you earn by the time you turn 18?

$p = \$7500$, $r = 5\% = 0.05$, $t = 17$ years

$P = 7500$; $b = 0.05$; $x = 18 - 1 = 17$

$i = \$7500(.05)(17)$

$i = \$6375$

What will be to total balance in your account?

$7500 + $6375 = $13,875

② Solve.

Ethan can rake leaves in 2 hours. Bryson can rake the same amount of leaves in $2\frac{1}{2}$ hours. How long will it take Ethan and Bryson to rake the leaves if they work together? Round your answer to the nearest tenth of an hour.

Let j = the time to complete the job together.

Ethan can complete $\frac{1}{2}$ of the job in an hour. Bryson can complete $\frac{1}{2\frac{1}{2}}$ of the job in an hour. Together they can complete $\frac{1}{j}$ of the job in an hour.

$\frac{1}{2}+\frac{1}{2\frac{1}{2}}=\frac{1}{j}$

${}_5\cancel{10}j\left(\frac{1}{\cancel{2}}\right)+{}_2\cancel{10}j\left(\frac{2}{\cancel{5}}\right)=10\cancel{j}\left(\frac{1}{\cancel{j}}\right)$

$5j+4j=10$

$9j=10$

$j=\frac{10}{9}=1.1$

It will take Ethan and Bryson 1.1 hours to rake the leaves together.

One bobsleigh took 51.720 seconds to travel a certain distance. A second bobsleigh took 51.800 seconds to travel the same distance. If the first sled traveled at a rate of 0.038 meters per second faster than the second sled, what was the rate of each sled? Round your answer to the nearest thousandth.

	Sled 1	Sled 2
d	d	d
r	$r + 0.038$	r
t	51.720	51.800

$d_1=d_2$

$r_1t_1=r_2t_2$

$(r+0.038)(51.720)=51.800r$

$51.720r+1.96536=51.800r$

$1.96536=0.08r$

$r=24.567$

Sled 2 was traveling at 24.567 meters/second.
Sled 1 was traveling at 24.567 + 0.038 = 24.605 meters/second.

How many meters did each sled travel? Round your answer to the nearest hundredth.

$d=rt$

$d_1=(24.605\text{ m/s})(51.720)=1272.57\text{ m}$

$d_2=(24.567\text{ m/s})(51.800)=1272.57\text{ m}$

Teaching Tips, Cont.

- Review investment problems. (See Lesson 137)
- Review motion problems. (See Lesson 138)
- Allow students to begin working on the review exercises in class as time permits. Assist individual students as needed.

Assignment

- Complete Lesson 157, Activities 1-2.

Lesson 158

Concepts

- Slope
- y-intercept
- Graphing linear equations
- Systems of equations
- Direct variation
- Inverse variation

Learning Objectives

The student will be able to:

- Find the slope of a line when two points are given
- Find the slope of a linear equation
- Write a linear equation when the slope and y-intercept are given
- Graph linear equations
- Solve systems of equations
- Use coordinate points to express the solution of a system of equations
- Write an equation to show direct variation
- Write an equation to show inverse variation

Materials Needed

- Student book, Lesson 158
- Worksheet 79

Teaching Tips

- Review direct variation. (See Lesson 119)
- Review inverse variation. (See Lesson 120)

Review

Activities

① Find the slope of the line joining the points.

(4, -5) and (-1, 3)

$m = \frac{3-(-5)}{-1-4} = \frac{8}{-5} = -\frac{8}{5}$

(-2, 1) and (4, -4)

$m = \frac{-4-1}{4-(-2)} = \frac{-5}{6} = -\frac{5}{6}$

(5, 3) and (-7, -3)

$m = \frac{-3-3}{-7-5} = \frac{-6}{-12} = \frac{1}{2}$

(-2, -7) and (-2, -2)

$m = \frac{-2-(-7)}{-2-(-2)} = \frac{5}{0} =$ no slope

② Find the slope of each line.

$2x + y - 4 = 0$
$y = -2x + 4$
$m = -2$

$x + y - 5 = 0$
$y = -x + 5$
$m = -1$

$-3x + y - 4 = 0$
$y = 3x + 4$
$m = 3$

$-4x + 2y - 3 = 0$
$2y = 4x + 3$
$y = 2x + \frac{3}{2}$
$m = 2$

$-5x + y + 3 = 0$
$y = 5x - 3$
$m = 5$

$3x + 3y - 4 = 0$
$3y = -3x + 4$
$y = -x + \frac{4}{3}$
$m = -1$

$3x + 2y + 6 = 0$
$2y = -3x - 6$
$y = -\frac{3}{2}x - 3$
$m = -\frac{3}{2}$

$2x + 3y + 3 = 0$
$3y = -2x - 3$
$y = -\frac{2}{3}x - 1$
$m = -\frac{2}{3}$

$4x + 5y + 3 = 0$
$5y = -4x - 3$
$y = -\frac{4}{5}x - \frac{3}{5}$
$m = -\frac{4}{5}$

③ Write an equation having the given slope and y-intercept and sketch the graph.

$m = \frac{5}{2}$
$b = -2$
$y = \frac{5}{2}x - 2$

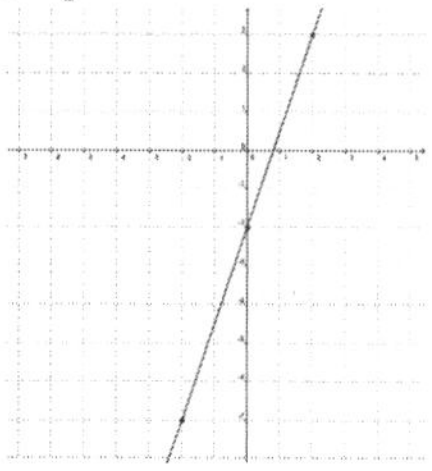

$m = -\frac{1}{2}$
$b = 3$
$y = -\frac{1}{2}x + 3$

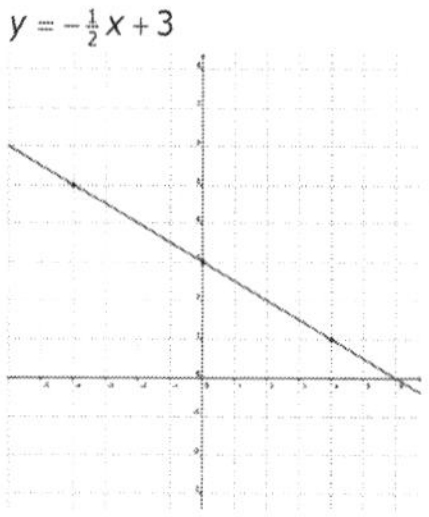

$m = -1$
$b = -1$
$y = -x - 1$

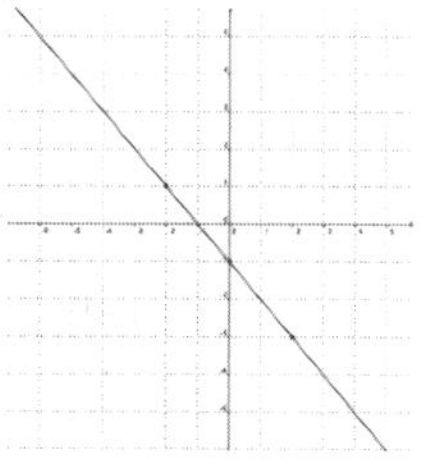

④ Solve. Express the answer as a coordinate point.

$-x - 2y + 10 = 0$
$3x + 2y - 2 = 0$
$2y = -x + 10$
$2y = -3x + 2$
$-x + 10 = -3x + 2$
$2x = -8$
$x = -4$
$-(-4) - 2y + 10 = 0$
$4 - 2y + 10 = 0$
$2y = 14$
$y = 7$
$(-4, 7)$

$4x - y + 3 = 0$
$-2x + y - 3 = 0$
$y = 4x + 3$
$y = 2x + 3$
$4x + 3 = 2x + 3$
$2x = 0$
$x = 0$
$4(0) - y + 3 = 0$
$y = 0 + 3$
$y = 3$
$(0, 3)$

$-3x + y - 1 = 0$
$3x - 2y + 5 = 0$
$-3x + y = 1$
$3x - 2y = -5$
$-y = -4$
$y = 4$
$-3x + 4 - 1 = 0$
$-3x = -3$
$x = 1$
$(1, 4)$

$x + y - 1 = 0$
$2x + y - 3 = 0$
$y = -x + 1$
$y = -2x + 3$
$-x + 1 = -2x + 3$
$x = 2$
$2 + y - 1 = 0$
$y = -1$
$(2, -1)$

$-x + 2y - 1 = 0$
$3x - 2y + 7 = 0$
$-x + 2y = 1$
$3x - 2y = -7$
$2x = -6$
$x = -3$
$-(-3) + 2y - 1 = 0$
$2y = -2$
$y = -1$
$(-3, -1)$

$x - 2y - 7 = 0$
$3x - 2y - 17 = 0$
$x - 2y = 7$
$3x - 2y = 17$
$-2x = -10$
$x = 5$
$5 - 2y - 7 = 0$
$-2y = 2$
$y = -1$
$(5, -1)$

⑤ Solve.

If y varies directly as x and $y = 40$ when $x = 16$, what is value of k? State the value of k and write an equation to show the direct variation.

$y = kx$
$40 = k(16)$ $\quad y = \frac{5}{2}x$
$\frac{40}{16} = \frac{5}{2} = k$

If y varies directly as x and $y = 35$ when $k = 10$, what is value of x? State the value of x and write an equation to show the direct variation.

$y = kx$
$35 = 10(x)$ $\quad y = 10x$
$\frac{35}{10} = \frac{7}{2} = x$

If y varies inversely as x and $y = 3$ when $x = 5$, what is value of k? State the value of k and write an equation to show the inverse variation.

$xy = k$
$5(3) = k$ $\quad y = \frac{15}{x}$
$15 = k$

If y varies inversely as x and $y = 20$ when $k = 12$, what is value of x? State the value of x and write an equation to show the inverse variation.

$xy = k$
$x(20) = 12$ $\quad y = \frac{12}{x}$
$x = \frac{12}{20} = \frac{3}{5}$

Slope, y-intercept, Standard Form Equations, Graphing Worksheet 79

① Write an equation in slope-intercept form of the line having the given slope and y-intercept and sketch the graph.

$m = \frac{3}{2}$
$b = -1$
$y = \frac{3}{2}x - 1$

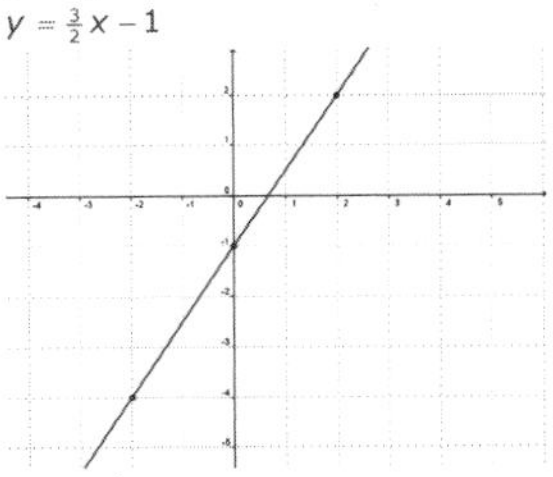

$m = 2$
$b = -2$
$y = 2x - 2$

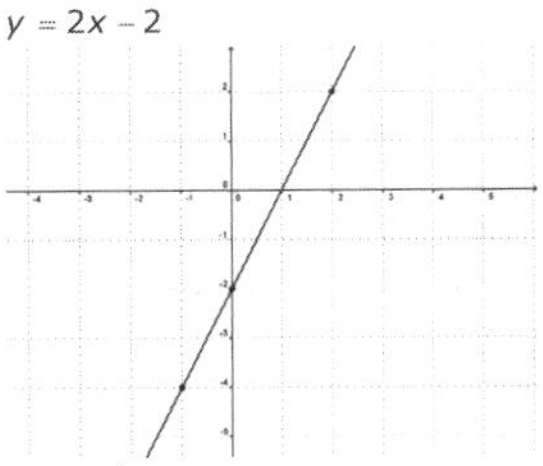

$m = -\frac{1}{4}$
$b = 3$
$y = -\frac{1}{4}x + 3$

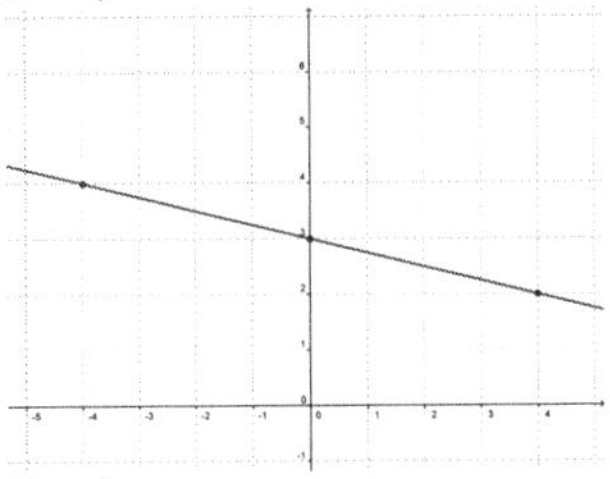

$m = -\frac{1}{2}$
$b = 1$
$y = -\frac{1}{2}x + 1$

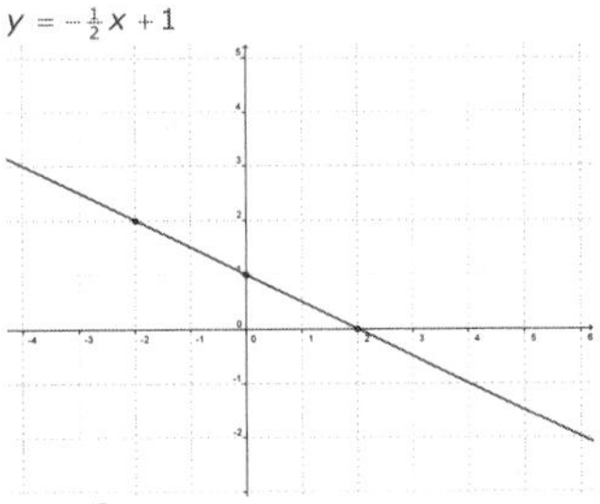

$m = -1$
$b = 2$
$y = -x + 2$

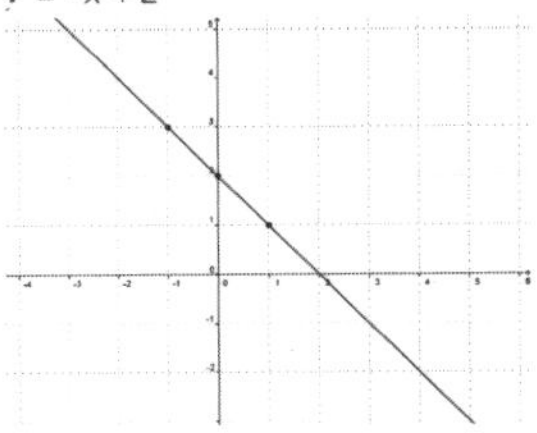

$m = -2$
$b = -1$
$y = -2x - 1$

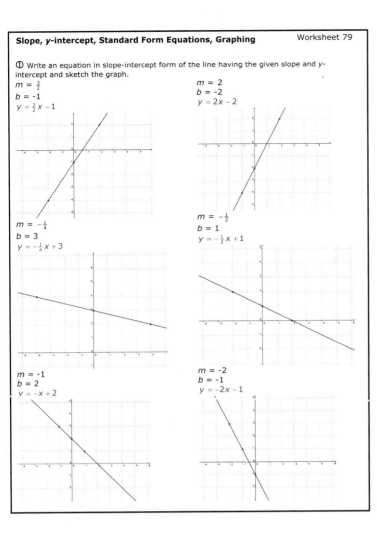

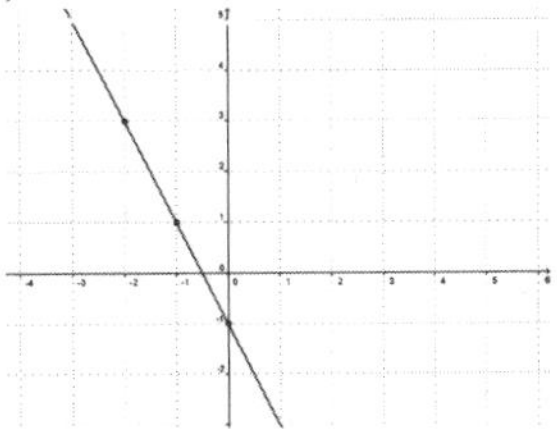

Teaching Tips, Cont.

- ➢ The remaining concepts in this lesson have already been reviewed. Additional practice from this lesson may be assigned at the teacher's discretion.
- ➢ Have students complete Worksheet 79 in class.
- ➢ Allow students to begin working on the review exercises in class as time permits. Assist individual students as needed.

Assignment

- Complete Lesson 158, Activities 1-5.
- Worksheet 79.

Lesson 159

Concepts

- Inequalities on a number line
- Conjunctions
- Disjunctions
- Inequalities with absolute value
- Systems of linear inequalities

Learning Objectives

The student will be able to:

- Graph inequalities on a number line
- Tell whether or not conjunctions and disjunctions are true
- Solve inequalities with absolute value
- Graph systems of linear inequalities and identify the solution as bounded, unbounded, or no solution.

Materials Needed

- Student book, Lesson 159

Teaching Tips

- ➢ Review graphing inequalities on a number line. (See Lessons 121-123)
- ➢ Review conjunctions. (See Lesson 124)
- ➢ Review disjunctions. (See Lesson 125)
- ➢ Review inequalities with absolute value. (See Lesson 126)

Review

Activities

① Graph the inequalities on a number line.

$x < -2$

$x \geq 3$

$-5 < x - 2 \leq 1$

$-5 < x - 2$ and $x - 2 \leq 1$

$-3 < x$ and $x \leq 3$

$-3 < x \leq 3$

$x < -2$ or $x \geq 1$

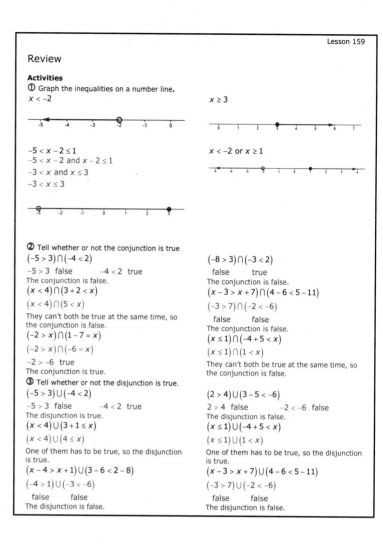

② Tell whether or not the conjunction is true

$(-5 > 3) \cap (-4 < 2)$

$-5 > 3$ false $\quad -4 < 2$ true

The conjunction is false.

$(x < 4) \cap (3 + 2 < x)$

$(x < 4) \cap (5 < x)$

They can't both be true at the same time, so the conjunction is false.

$(-2 > x) \cap (1 - 7 = x)$

$(-2 > x) \cap (-6 = x)$

$-2 > -6$ true

The conjunction is true.

$(-8 > 3) \cap (-3 < 2)$

false $\quad$ true

The conjunction is false.

$(x - 3 > x + 7) \cap (4 - 6 < 5 - 11)$

$(-3 > 7) \cap (-2 < -6)$

false $\quad$ false

The conjunction is false.

$(x \leq 1) \cap (-4 + 5 < x)$

$(x \leq 1) \cap (1 < x)$

They can't both be true at the same time, so the conjunction is false.

③ Tell whether or not the disjunction is true.

$(-5 > 3) \cup (-4 < 2)$

$-5 > 3$ false $\quad -4 < 2$ true

The disjunction is true.

$(x < 4) \cup (3 + 1 \leq x)$

$(x < 4) \cup (4 \leq x)$

One of them has to be true, so the disjunction is true.

$(x - 4 > x + 1) \cup (3 - 6 < 2 - 8)$

$(-4 > 1) \cup (-3 < -6)$

false $\quad$ false

The disjunction is false.

$(2 > 4) \cup (3 - 5 < -6)$

$2 > 4$ false $\quad -2 < -6$ false

The disjunction is false.

$(x \leq 1) \cup (-4 + 5 < x)$

$(x \leq 1) \cup (1 < x)$

One of them has to be true, so the disjunction is true.

$(x - 3 > x + 7) \cup (4 - 6 < 5 - 11)$

$(-3 > 7) \cup (-2 < -6)$

false $\quad$ false

The disjunction is false.

④ Solve each inequality and draw the graph on a number line.

$|x+3|-7 \le -5$
$|x+3| \le 2$
$x+3 \le 2$ and $x+3 \ge -2$
$x \le -1$ and $x \ge -5$
$-5 \le x \le -1$

$|2x+7|-9 > -2$
$|2x+7| > 7$
$2x+7 > 7$ or $2x+7 < -7$
$2x > 0$ or $2x < -14$
$x > 0$ or $x < -7$

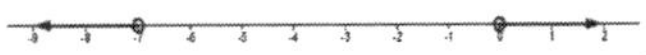

$|x+4|+6 < 3$
$|x+4| < -3$
No solution.

$|5x-2|+8 \ge 3$
$|5x-2| \ge -5$
All real numbers.

⑤ Graph the solution of the system of linear inequalities and state whether the solution is bounded, unbounded, or no solution.

$x-y<0$
$x+y>0$
$x<5$

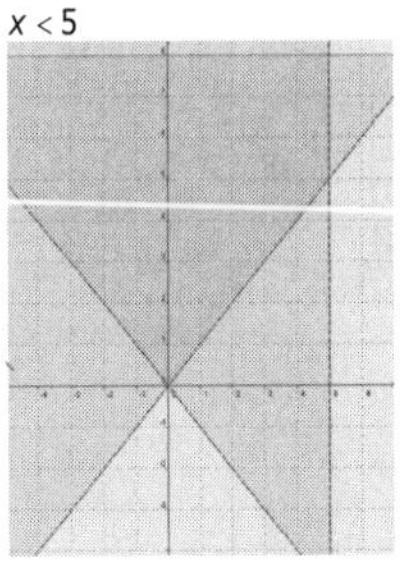

The graph is unbounded.

$x-y<0$
$x+y>0$
$y<4$

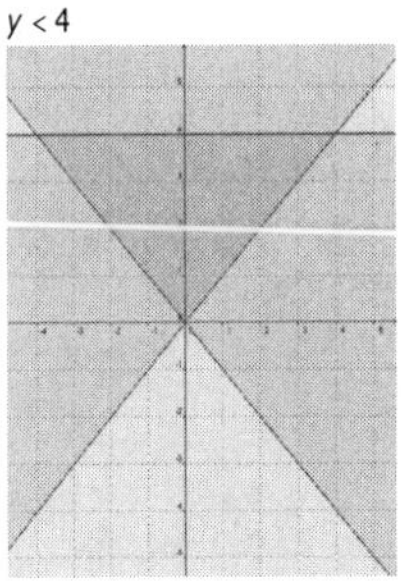

The graph is bounded.

$x-y>0$
$x+y<0$
$y>4$

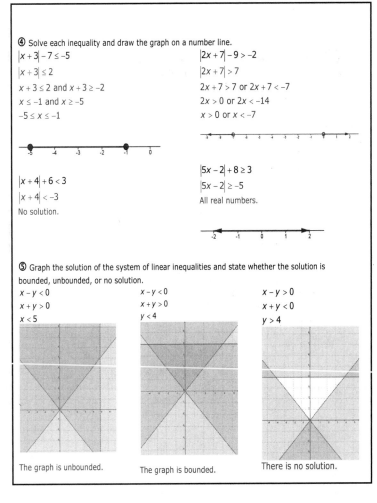

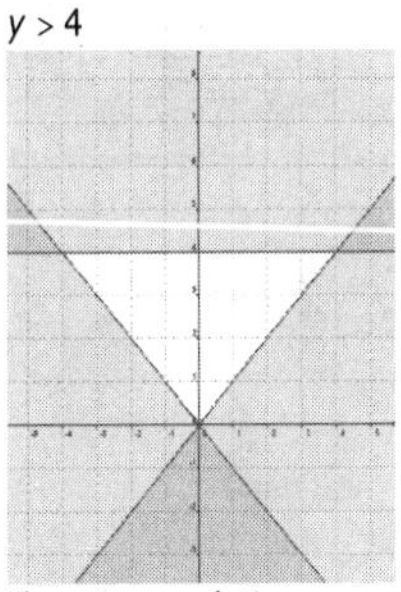

There is no solution.

Teaching Tips, Cont.

- Review systems of linear inequalities. (See Lessons 128-130)
- Allow students to begin working on the review exercises in class as time permits. Assist individual students as needed.

Assignment

- Complete Lesson 159, Activities 1-5.

Lesson 160

Concepts

- Functions with square roots
- Graphs of exponential functions
- Pythagorean Theorem
- Distance formula
- Midpoint formula

Learning Objectives

The student will be able to:

- Determine the limits of the domain of functions with square roots
- Sketch the graph of functions with square roots
- Graph exponential functions
- Use the Pythagorean Theorem to find Pythagorean triples
- Calculate the length of a segment on a graph
- Find the coordinates of the midpoint of a segment on a graph

Materials Needed

- Student book, Lesson 160
- Worksheet 80

Teaching Tips

➢ Review functions with square roots. (See Lesson 140)

➢ Review the Pythagorean Theorem. (See Lessons 141-142)

➢ Review lengths of segments. (See Lessons 143-144)

➢ Review midpoints of segments. (See Lessons 145-146)

Review

Activities

① Determine the limits of the domain and graph each function.

$y = \sqrt{x-5}$

$x - 5 \geq 0$

$x \geq 5$

x	y
5	$\sqrt{5-5} = \sqrt{0} = 0$
6	$\sqrt{6-5} = \sqrt{1} = 1$
9	$\sqrt{9-5} = \sqrt{4} = 2$
14	$\sqrt{14-5} = \sqrt{9} = 3$

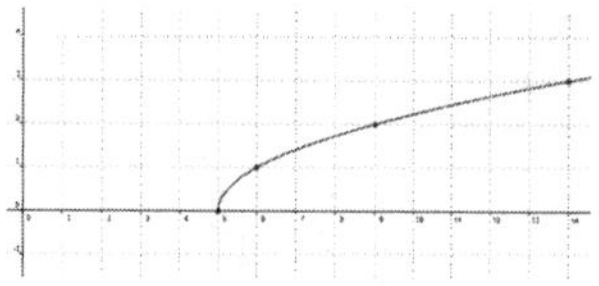

$y = \sqrt{-2-x}$

$-2 - x \geq 0$

$-2 \geq x$

$x \leq -2$

x	y
-2	$\sqrt{-2-(-2)} = \sqrt{0} = 0$
-3	$\sqrt{-2-(-3)} = \sqrt{1} = 1$
-6	$\sqrt{-2-(-6)} = \sqrt{4} = 2$
-11	$\sqrt{-2-(-11)} = \sqrt{9} = 3$

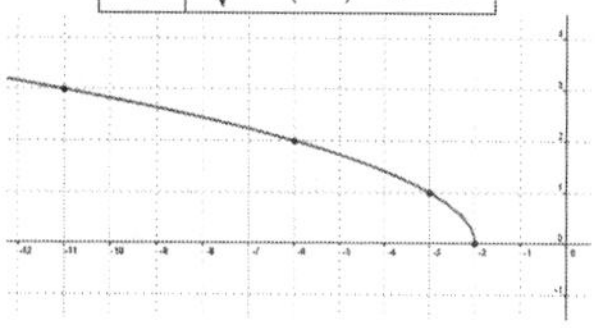

② Draw the graph of each exponential function.

$y = 2^x$ (You may use 5 points for this graph.)

x	y
0	$2^0 = 1$
1	$2^1 = 2$
2	$2^2 = 4$
-1	$2^{-1} = \frac{1}{2}$
-2	$2^{-2} = \frac{1}{4}$

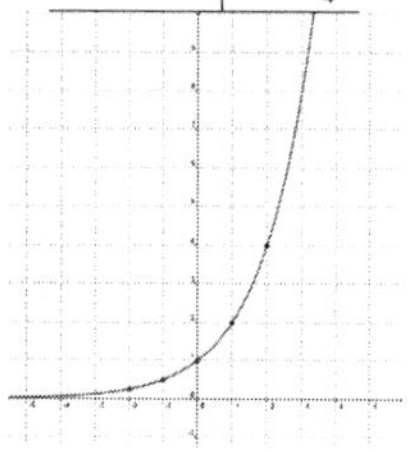

$y = 3^{-x}$

x	y
0	$3^0 = 1$
1	$3^{-1} = \frac{1}{3}$
2	$3^{-2} = \frac{1}{9}$
-1	$3^1 = 3$
-2	$3^2 = 9$

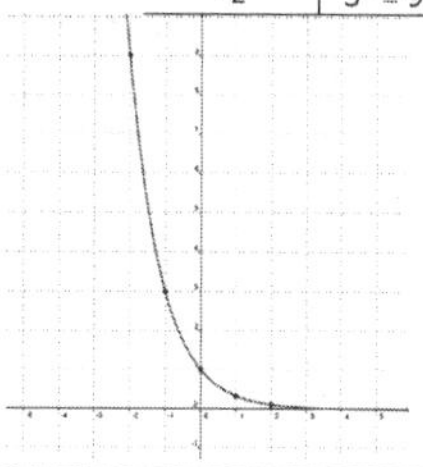

③ Complete the chart to find the Pythagorean triples.

a	b	c
3	$b = \sqrt{5^2 - 3^2} \to b = 4$	5
5	12	$c = \sqrt{5^2 + 12^2} \to c = 13$
$a = \sqrt{17^2 - 15^2} \to a = 8$	15	17
7	$b = \sqrt{25^2 - 7^2} \to b = 24$	25
6	8	$c = \sqrt{6^2 + 8^2} \to c = 10$
$a = \sqrt{41^2 - 40^2} \to a = 9$	40	41

④ Use the distance formula to find the length of each segment.

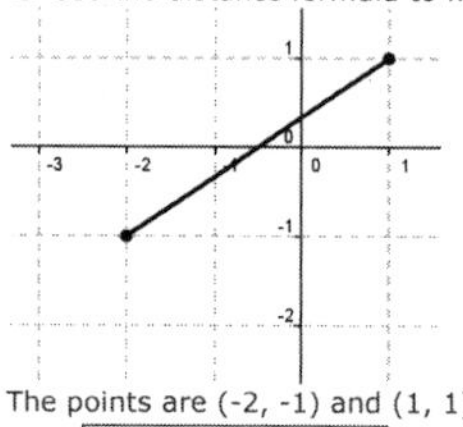

The points are (-2, -1) and (1, 1).

$d = \sqrt{(1-(-2))^2 + (1-(-1))^2}$

$d = \sqrt{(3)^2 + (2)^2}$

$d = \sqrt{9+4}$

$d = \sqrt{13}$

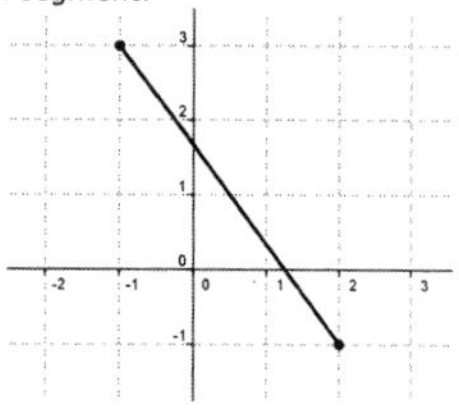

The points are (-1, 3) and (2, -1).

$d = \sqrt{(2-(-1))^2 + (-1-3)^2}$

$d = \sqrt{(3)^2 + (-4)^2}$

$d = \sqrt{9+16}$

$d = \sqrt{25} = 5$

⑤ Find the midpoint of each segment using the formula.

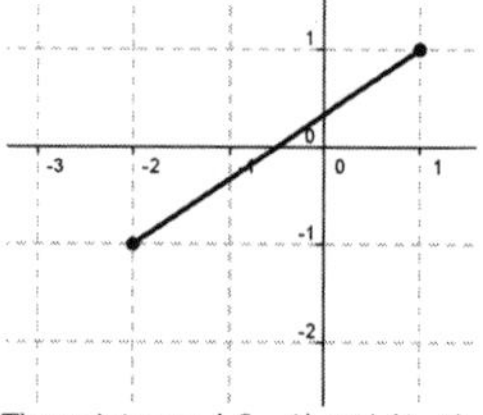

The points are (-2, -1) and (1, 1).

$\left(\frac{-2+1}{2}, \frac{-1+1}{2}\right) = \left(\frac{-1}{2}, \frac{0}{2}\right) = \left(-\frac{1}{2}, 0\right)$

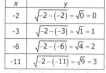

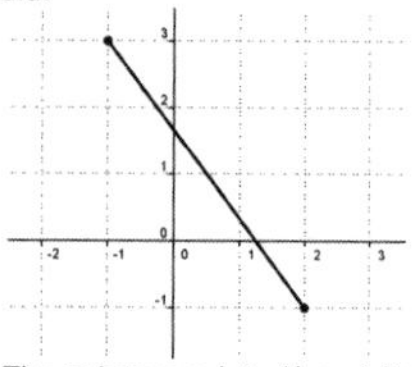

The points are (-1, 3) and (2, -1).

$\left(\frac{-1+2}{2}, \frac{3+(-1)}{2}\right) = \left(\frac{1}{2}, \frac{2}{2}\right) = \left(\frac{1}{2}, 1\right).$

Limits of the Domain, Graphing Exponential Functions Worksheet 80

① Determine the limits of the domain and graph each function.

$y=\sqrt{x-3}$

$x-3\ge 0$

$x\ge 3$

x	y
3	$\sqrt{3-3}=\sqrt{0}=0$
4	$\sqrt{4-3}=\sqrt{1}=1$
7	$\sqrt{7-3}=\sqrt{4}=2$
12	$\sqrt{12-3}=\sqrt{9}=3$

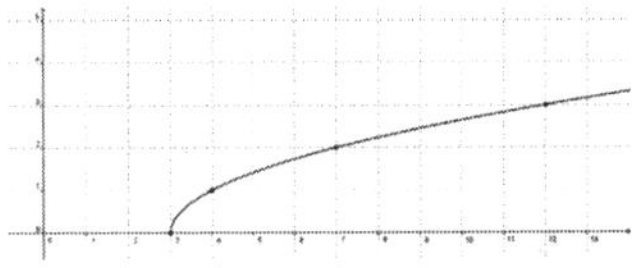

$y=\sqrt{-1-x}$

$-1-x\ge 0$

$-1\ge x$

$x\le -1$

x	y
-1	$\sqrt{-1-(-1)}=\sqrt{0}=0$
-2	$\sqrt{-1-(-2)}=\sqrt{1}=1$
-5	$\sqrt{-1-(-5)}=\sqrt{4}=2$
-10	$\sqrt{-1-(-10)}=\sqrt{9}=3$

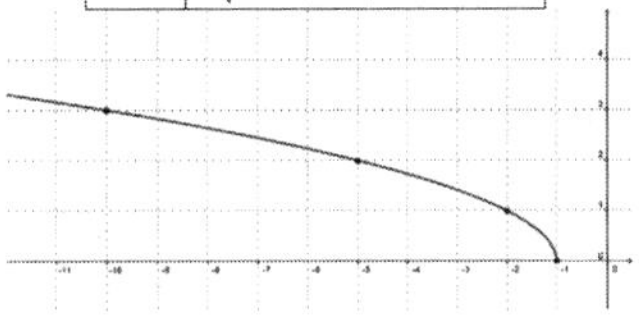

② Draw the graph of each exponential function.

$y=2^{-x}$ (You may use 5 points for this graph.)

x	y
0	$2^0=1$
1	$2^{-1}=\frac{1}{2}$
2	$2^{-2}=\frac{1}{4}$
-1	$2^1=2$
-2	$2^2=4$

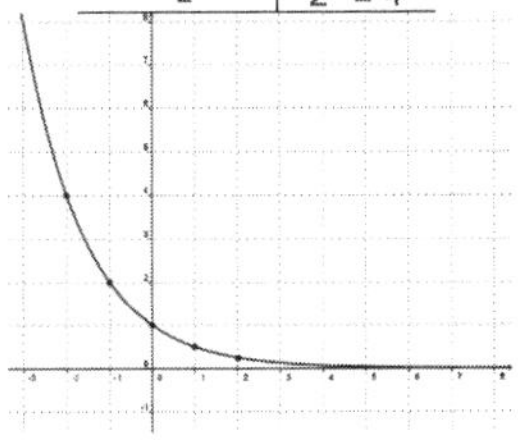

$y=3^{-x}$

x	y
0	$3^0=1$
1	$3^{-1}=\frac{1}{3}$
2	$3^{-2}=\frac{1}{9}$
-1	$3^1=3$
-2	$3^2=9$

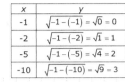

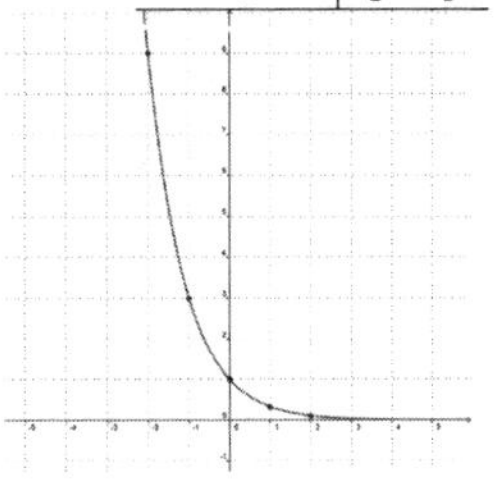

Teaching Tips, Cont.

- Allow students to begin working on the review exercises in class as time permits. Assist individual students as needed.
- Review for Test 16 using worksheets 76-80. These worksheets were assigned in previous lessons.
- Review for Exam 4 using worksheets 41-80.

Assignments

- Complete Lesson 160, Activities 1-5.
- Worksheet 80.
- Study for Test 16 (Lessons 141-146, and 160).

Test 16

Testing Objectives

The student will:

- Use the Pythagorean Theorem to calculate the lengths of sides in a right triangle
- Calculate the distance between two points
- Calculate the coordinates of the midpoint between two points

Materials Needed

- Test 16

Teaching Tips

- Administer Test 16, allowing the students 20-30 minutes to complete the test.
- If you plan to administer Exam 4, review as time permits when all students have finished Test 16.
- Allow the students to ask questions as a final review for Exam 4.
- Review for Exam 4 using worksheets 41-80.

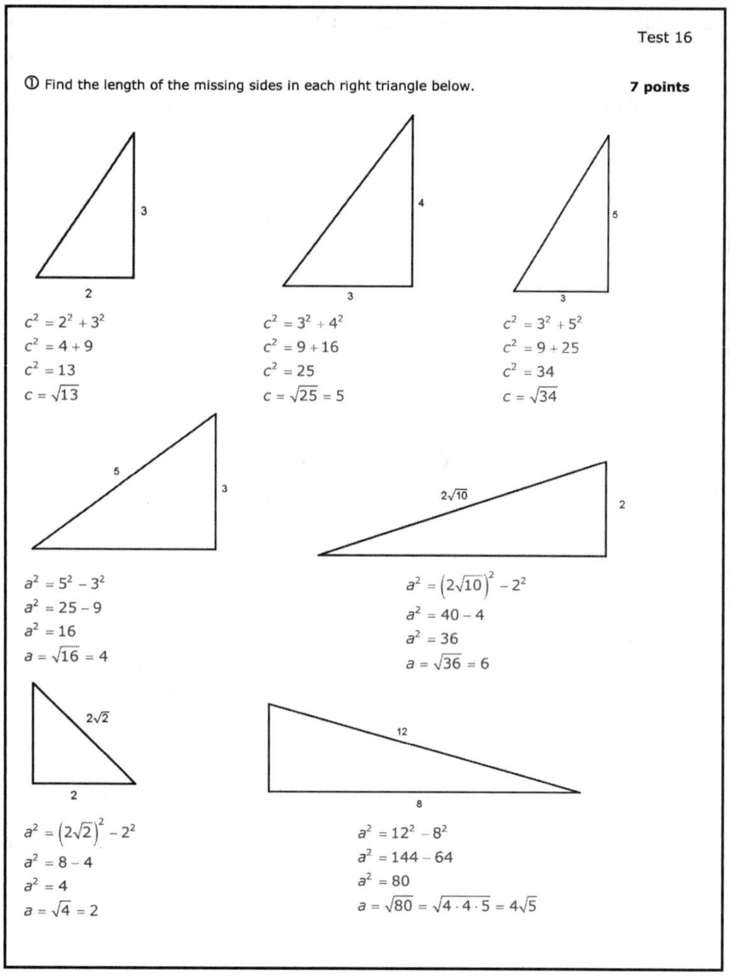

Test 16

① Find the length of the missing sides in each right triangle below. **7 points**

$c^2 = 2^2 + 3^2$
$c^2 = 4 + 9$
$c^2 = 13$
$c = \sqrt{13}$

$c^2 = 3^2 + 4^2$
$c^2 = 9 + 16$
$c^2 = 25$
$c = \sqrt{25} = 5$

$c^2 = 3^2 + 5^2$
$c^2 = 9 + 25$
$c^2 = 34$
$c = \sqrt{34}$

$a^2 = 5^2 - 3^2$
$a^2 = 25 - 9$
$a^2 = 16$
$a = \sqrt{16} = 4$

$a^2 = \left(2\sqrt{10}\right)^2 - 2^2$
$a^2 = 40 - 4$
$a^2 = 36$
$a = \sqrt{36} = 6$

$a^2 = \left(2\sqrt{2}\right)^2 - 2^2$
$a^2 = 8 - 4$
$a^2 = 4$
$a = \sqrt{4} = 2$

$a^2 = 12^2 - 8^2$
$a^2 = 144 - 64$
$a^2 = 80$
$a = \sqrt{80} = \sqrt{4 \cdot 4 \cdot 5} = 4\sqrt{5}$

Test 16

② Find the distance between each set of points. **9 points**

(1, 1) and (5, 3)
$d = \sqrt{(5-1)^2 + (3-1)^2}$
$d = \sqrt{4^2 + 2^2}$
$d = \sqrt{16 + 4}$
$d = \sqrt{20} = \sqrt{2 \cdot 2 \cdot 5} = 2\sqrt{5}$

(4, -3) and (6, 2)
$d = \sqrt{(6-4)^2 + (2-(-3))^2}$
$d = \sqrt{2^2 + 5^2}$
$d = \sqrt{4 + 25}$
$d = \sqrt{29}$

(-2, 7) and (1, 5)
$d = \sqrt{(1-(-2))^2 + (5-7)^2}$
$d = \sqrt{3^2 + (-2)^2}$
$d = \sqrt{9 + 4}$
$d = \sqrt{13}$

(6, 2) and (-2, 8)
$d = \sqrt{(-2-6)^2 + (8-2)^2}$
$d = \sqrt{(-8)^2 + 6^2}$
$d = \sqrt{64 + 36}$
$d = \sqrt{100} = 10$

(9, 4) and (7, -3)
$d = \sqrt{(7-9)^2 + (-3-4)^2}$
$d = \sqrt{(-2)^2 + (-7)^2}$
$d = \sqrt{4 + 49}$
$d = \sqrt{53}$

(-6, -1) and (4, 2)
$d = \sqrt{(4-(-6))^2 + (2-(-1))^2}$
$d = \sqrt{10^2 + 3^2}$
$d = \sqrt{100 + 9}$
$d = \sqrt{109}$

(1, -5) and (-8, 4)
$d = \sqrt{(-8-1)^2 + (4-(-5))^2}$
$d = \sqrt{(-9)^2 + 9^2}$
$d = \sqrt{81 + 81}$
$d = \sqrt{162} = \sqrt{2 \cdot 9 \cdot 9} = 9\sqrt{2}$

(-1, -1) and (-3, 3)
$d = \sqrt{(-3-(-1))^2 + (3-(-1))^2}$
$d = \sqrt{(-2)^2 + 4^2}$
$d = \sqrt{4 + 16}$
$d = \sqrt{20} = \sqrt{2 \cdot 2 \cdot 5} = 2\sqrt{5}$

(-6, -9) and (-5, -1)
$d = \sqrt{(-5-(-6))^2 + (-1-(-9))^2}$
$d = \sqrt{1^2 + (-8)^2}$
$d = \sqrt{1 + 64}$
$d = \sqrt{65}$

③ Find the coordinates of the midpoint between each set of points. **9 points**

(1, 1) and (5, 3)
midpoint $= \left(\frac{1+5}{2}, \frac{1+3}{2}\right)$
midpoint $= (3, 2)$

(4, -3) and (6, 2)
midpoint $= \left(\frac{4+6}{2}, \frac{-3+2}{2}\right)$
midpoint $= \left(5, -\frac{1}{2}\right)$

(-2, 7) and (1, 5)
midpoint $= \left(\frac{-2+1}{2}, \frac{7+5}{2}\right)$
midpoint $= \left(-\frac{1}{2}, 6\right)$

(6, 2) and (-2, 8)
midpoint $= \left(\frac{6-2}{2}, \frac{2+8}{2}\right)$
midpoint $= (2, 5)$

(9, 4) and (7, -3)
midpoint $= \left(\frac{9+7}{2}, \frac{4-3}{2}\right)$
midpoint $= \left(8, \frac{1}{2}\right)$

(-6, -1) and (4, 2)
midpoint $= \left(\frac{-6+4}{2}, \frac{-1+2}{2}\right)$
midpoint $= \left(-1, \frac{1}{2}\right)$

(1, -5) and (-8, 4)
midpoint $= \left(\frac{1-8}{2}, \frac{-5+4}{2}\right)$
midpoint $= \left(-\frac{7}{2}, -\frac{1}{2}\right)$

(-1, -1) and (-3, 3)
midpoint $= \left(\frac{-1-3}{2}, \frac{-1+3}{2}\right)$
midpoint $= (-2, 1)$

(-6, -9) and (-5, -1)
midpoint $= \left(\frac{-6-5}{2}, \frac{-9-1}{2}\right)$
midpoint $= \left(-\frac{11}{2}, -5\right)$

25 points total

Teaching Tips, Cont.

Assignment

- Study for Exam 4. (Lessons 118-160 if you are giving the entire test as a final cumulative exam; Lessons 118-147 if you are giving just the first two pages as a fourth-quarter exam.)

Exam 4/Final Exam

Testing Objectives (first two pages)

The student will:

- Write an equation for direct variation
- Write an equation for inverse variation
- Graph inequalities on a number line
- Tell whether conjunctions and disjunctions are true or false
- Find the midpoint and distance between the coordinates of two points
- Draw the graphs of transformations
- Solve word problems involving exponential decay, rates of work, and motion
- Find square roots without the use of a calculator

Testing Objectives (last four pages)

The student will:

- Solve rational equations
- Solve complex equations
- Solve quadratic equations
- Solve word problems involving mixtures and consecutive numbers
- Write equations in parabolic form
- Find the vertex, focus, directrix, and axis of symmetry of a parabola
- Add polynomials
- Subtract polynomials
- Multiply monomials
- Multiply binomials
- Solve problems with fractions as exponents
- Write equations in point-slope form and slope-intercept form
- Solve systems of equations
- Find the slope of a line
- Factor polynomials
- Multiply polynomials
- Divide polynomials
- Solve systems of equations

① Solve. **4 points**

If y varies directly as x and $y = 12$ when $k = 3$, what is value of x? State the value of x and write an equation to show the direct variation.

$y = kx$

$12 = 3(x)$ $\quad y = 3x$

$\frac{12}{3} = 4 = x$

If y varies inversely as x and $y = 12$ when $x = 3$, what is value of k? State the value of k and write an equation to show the inverse variation.

$xy = k$

$3(12) = k$ $\quad y = \frac{36}{x}$

$36 = k$

② Graph the inequalities on a number line. **8 points**

$x < -5$

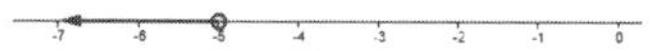

$|x-2| + 3 < 4$

$|x-2| < 1$

$x-2 < 1$ and $x-2 > -1$

$x < 3$ and $x > 1$

$1 < x < 3$

$-5 < x-2 < -1$

$-5 < x-2$ and $x-2 < -1$

$-3 < x$ and $x < 1$

$-3 < x < 1$

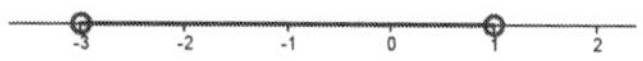

$|2x-3| + 4 \geq -1$

$|2x-3| \geq -5$

All real numbers.

③ Tell whether or not each conjunction or disjunction is true **6 points**

$(-37 > 24) \cap (-16 < 13)$

false true

The conjunction is false.

$(x \leq 10) \cap (-12 + 22 < x)$

$(x \leq 10) \cap (10 < x)$

They can't both be true at the same time, so the conjunction is false.

$(x - 4 > x + 3) \cap (2 - 5 < 3 - 9)$

$(-4 > 3) \cap (-3 < -6)$

false false

The conjunction is false.

$(-37 > 24) \cup (-16 < 13)$

false true

The disjunction is true.

$(x \leq 10) \cup (-12 + 22 < x)$

$(x \leq 10) \cup (10 < x)$

One of them is true, so the disjunction is true.

$(x - 4 > x + 3) \cup (2 - 5 < 3 - 9)$

$(-4 > 3) \cup (-3 < -6)$

false false

The disjunction is false.

④ Find the midpoint and distance for each set of points. **4 points**

(2, -1) and (6, 5)

midpoint $= \left(\frac{2+6}{2}, \frac{-1+5}{2}\right)$ $\quad d = \sqrt{(6-2)^2 + (5-(-1))^2}$

midpoint $= (4, 2)$ $\quad d = \sqrt{4^2 + 6^2}$

$d = \sqrt{16 + 36}$

$d = \sqrt{52} = \sqrt{2 \cdot 2 \cdot 13} = 2\sqrt{13}$

(-1, 1) and (3, -1)

midpoint $= \left(\frac{-1+3}{2}, \frac{1+(-1)}{2}\right)$ $\quad d = \sqrt{(3-(-1))^2 + (-1-1)^2}$

midpoint $= (1, 0)$ $\quad d = \sqrt{4^2 + (-2)^2}$

$d = \sqrt{16 + 4}$

$d = \sqrt{20} = \sqrt{2 \cdot 2 \cdot 5} = 2\sqrt{5}$

⑤ Solve. **6 points**

Recently, housing values in one neighborhood dropped exponentially by an average rate of 11% per year for 4 years. If a house was worth \$225,000 at the beginning of the depression, what was the value of the house after 4 years? Round to the nearest ten thousandth after calculating the exponent.

$y = \$225{,}000(1 - 0.11)^4$

$y = \$225{,}000(0.89)^4$

$y = \$225{,}000(0.6274) = \$141{,}165$

Mary can decorate a cake in 3 hours. Heather can decorate the same cake in 4 hours. How long will it take Mary and Heather to decorate the cake if they work together?

Let j = the time to complete the job together. Mary can complete $\frac{1}{3}$ of the job in an hour. Heather can complete $\frac{1}{4}$ of the job in an hour. Together they can complete $\frac{1}{j}$ of the job in an hour.

$\frac{1}{3} + \frac{1}{4} = \frac{1}{j}$

${}_4\cancel{12}j\left(\frac{1}{\cancel{3}}\right) + {}_3\cancel{12}j\left(\frac{1}{\cancel{4}}\right) = 12\cancel{j}\left(\frac{1}{\cancel{j}}\right)$

$4j + 3j = 12$

$7j = 12$

$j = \frac{12}{7}$

One car took 8 hours to travel a certain distance. A second car took 10 hours to travel the same distance. If the first car traveled at a rate of 14 miles per hour faster than the second car, what was the rate of each car and how many miles did each car drive?

	Car 1	Car 2
d	d	d
r	$r + 14$	r
t	8	10

$(r + 14)(8) = 10r$

$8r + 112 = 10r$

$r = 56$

Car 2 was traveling at 56 miles/hour.

Car 1 was traveling at 56 + 14 = 70 miles/hour.

The cars each drove the same distance.

$d = rt$

$d_1 = (70 \text{ miles/hour})(8 \text{ hours}) = 560 \text{ miles}$

$d_2 = (56 \text{ miles/hour})(10 \text{ hours}) = 560 \text{ miles}$

⑥ Find the square roots to the nearest hundredth without using a calculator. **2 points**

$\sqrt{6} = 2.45$

```
         2. 4  4 9
        √6.000000
         4
4        200
44       176
         2400
484      1936
          46400
4889      44001
           2399
```

$\sqrt{75} = 8.66$

```
         8. 6  6 0
        √75.000000
         64
16       1100
166      996
         10400
1726     10356
            4400
17320          0
            4400
```

⑦ Solve. Remember to state any exclusions. **15 points**

$\frac{3x}{x+5}+\frac{4x}{x-4}=$

$\frac{3x(x-4)}{(x+5)(x-4)}+\frac{4x(x+5)}{(x+5)(x-4)}=$

$\frac{3x^2-12x}{x^2+x-20}+\frac{4x^2+20x}{x^2+x-20}=$

$\frac{7x^2+8x}{x^2+x-20};x\neq -5,4$

$\frac{\frac{3}{4x}+\frac{1}{x+3}}{\frac{10x-2}{5x^2+14x-3}}=$

$\frac{\frac{3}{4x}+\frac{1}{x+3}}{\frac{2(\cancel{5x-1})}{(x+3)(\cancel{5x-1})}}$

The LCD is $4x(x+3)$.

$\frac{\cancel{4x}(x+3)\left(\frac{3}{\cancel{4x}}\right)+4x(\cancel{x+3})\left(\frac{1}{\cancel{x+3}}\right)}{4x(\cancel{x+3})\left(\frac{2}{\cancel{x+3}}\right)}=$

$\frac{(x+3)(3)+4x(1)}{4x(2)}=$

$\frac{3x+9+4x}{8x}=$

$\frac{7x+9}{8x};x\neq -3,0,\frac{1}{5}$

$\frac{5x}{x+3}-\frac{2x}{4x-7}=$

$\frac{5x(4x-7)}{(x+3)(4x-7)}-\frac{2x(x+3)}{(x+3)(4x-7)}=$

$\frac{20x^2-35x}{4x^2+5x-21}-\frac{2x^2+6x}{4x^2+5x-21}=$

$\frac{18x^2-41x}{4x^2+5x-21};x\neq -3,\frac{7}{4}$

$\frac{\frac{4x}{2x+3}+\frac{7x}{3x-2}}{\frac{2x+1}{6x^2-x-2}-\frac{15x+6}{15x^2-4x-4}}=$

$\frac{\frac{4x}{2x+3}+\frac{7x}{3x-2}}{\frac{\cancel{2x+1}}{(\cancel{2x+1})(3x-2)}-\frac{3(\cancel{5x+2})}{(\cancel{5x+2})(3x-2)}}=\frac{\frac{4x}{2x+3}+\frac{7x}{3x-2}}{\frac{1-3}{3x-2}}$

The LCD is $(2x+3)(3x-2)$.

$\frac{(\cancel{2x+3})(3x-2)\left(\frac{4x}{\cancel{2x+3}}\right)+(2x+3)(\cancel{3x-2})\left(\frac{7x}{\cancel{3x-2}}\right)}{(2x+3)(\cancel{3x-2})\left(\frac{-2}{\cancel{3x-2}}\right)}=$

$\frac{(3x-2)(4x)+(2x+3)(7x)}{(2x+3)(-2)}=$

$\frac{(12x^2-8x)+(14x^2+21x)}{-4x-6}=$

$\frac{26x^2+13x}{-4x-6}=x\neq -\frac{3}{2},-\frac{1}{2},-\frac{2}{5},\frac{2}{3}$

⑧ Solve each quadratic equation. **4 points**

$x^2-3x-28=0$

$(x-7)(x+4)=0$

$x-7=0;x=7$

$x+4=0;x=-4$

The solution is $x = 7$ and -4.

$x^2+8x-10=0$

$x^2+8x=10$

$x^2+8x+\left(\frac{8}{2}\right)^2=10+\left(\frac{8}{2}\right)^2$

$x^2+8x+16=10+16$

$x^2+8x+16=26$

$(x+4)^2=26$

$\sqrt{(x+4)^2}=\sqrt{26}$

$x+4=\pm\sqrt{26}$

$x=-4\pm\sqrt{26}$

Note: Any method may be used to solve these equations. Factoring is shown in the first problem, and completing the square is shown in the second problem.

⑨ Complete the square to write each function in parabolic form. **3 points**

$f(x)=5x^2+10x-4$

$5x^2+10x-4=0$

$5x^2+10x=4$

$5(x^2+2x)=4$

$5(x^2+2x+1)=4+5(1)$

$5(x+1)^2=4+5$

$5(x+1)^2-9=0$

$f(x)=5(x+1)^2-9$

$f(x)=4x^2-8x+15$

$4x^2-8x+15=0$

$4x^2-8x=-15$

$4(x^2-2x)=-15$

$4(x^2-2x+1)=-15+4(1)$

$4(x-1)^2=-15+4$

$4(x-1)^2+11=0$

$f(x)=4(x-1)^2+11$

$f(x)=3x^2+18x+4$

$3x^2+18x+4=0$

$3x^2+18x=-4$

$3(x^2+6x)=-4$

$3(x^2+6x+9)=-4+3(9)$

$3(x+3)^2=-4+27$

$3(x+3)^2-23=0$

$f(x)=3(x+3)^2-23$

⑩ Solve. **3 points**

You need 100mL of a 25% solution of an acid, but you only have a 10% solution and a 30% solution on hand. How much of each solution should you mix to make 100mL of a 25% solution?

mL	% acid	Total
x	0.10	$0.1x$
$100-x$	0.30	$0.3(100-x)$
100 mL	0.25	100(0.25)

$0.1x+0.3(100-x)=100(0.25)$

$0.1x+30-0.3x=25$

$-0.2x=-5$

$x=25$

You need 25mL of the 10% solution and 100 − 25 = 75mL of the 30% solution.

Seven consecutive integers have a sum of 280. What are the integers?

The integers are represented by x, $x + 1$, $x + 2$, $x + 3$, $x + 4$, $x + 5$ and $x + 6$.

$x+(x+1)+(x+2)+(x+3)+(x+4)+(x+5)+(x+6)=280$

$7x+21=280$

$7x=259$

$x=37$

The integers are 37, 38, 39, 40, 41, 42, and 43.

⑪ Rewrite each equation in the form $4p(y-k)=(x-h)^2$. Identify the value of the variables p, k, and h, and give the coordinates for the vertex and focus, and the equations of the lines for the axis of symmetry and the directrix of the parabola. **16 points**

$y=\frac{1}{4}(x-4)^2-7$

$y+7=\frac{1}{4}(x-4)^2$

$\frac{y+7}{\frac{1}{4}}=(x-4)^2$

$4(y+7)=(x-4)^2$

$4p=4\Rightarrow p=1$

$k=-7$

$h=4$

The vertex is (4, -7).

The focus is (4, -7 + 1) = (4, -6).

The axis of symmetry is the line $x = 4$.

The directrix is the line $y=-7-1\Rightarrow y=-8$.

$y=\frac{1}{12}(x+2)^2+1$

$y-1=\frac{1}{12}(x+2)^2$

$\frac{y-1}{\frac{1}{12}}=(x+2)^2$

$12(y-1)=(x+2)^2$

$4p=12\Rightarrow p=3$

$k=1$

$h=-2$

The vertex is (-2, 1).

The focus is (-2, 1 + 3) = (-2, 4).

The axis of symmetry is the line $x = -2$.

The directrix is the line $y=1-3\Rightarrow y=-2$.

Exam 4/Final Exam, Cont.

Materials Needed

- Exam 4/Final Exam

Teaching Tips

- If you wish to test only material from the last quarter, administer the first two pages of Exam 4/Final Exam. For a cumulative exam covering the entire school year, administer all 6 pages.
- Administer Exam 4/Final Exam, allowing 30-40 minutes if you are administering just the first two pages, and 80-90 minutes if you are administering the entire exam.
- If you are administering just the first two pages, there are 30 total possible points.

Exam 4/Final Exam, Cont.

Assignment

- There is no assignment.

⑫ Add or subtract as indicated. **6 points**

$5x^2+8x+2$
$+\ 6x^2+4x+9$
$11x^2+12x+11$

$3x^2+9x+5$
$+x^2-7x-8$
$4x^2+2x-3$

$15x^2-13x+19$
$+14x^2+12x-17$
$29x^2-\ x+\ 2$

$(7x^2+2x+11)$
$-(4x^2+8x+6)$
$3x^2-6x+\ 5$

$(2x^2-7x+6)$
$-(6x^2-2x-8)$
$-4x^2-5x+14$

$(15x^2-12x-17)$
$-(12x^2+13x-19)$
$3x^2-25x+2$

⑬ Solve. **9 points**

$4x(11xy^2)=$
$(4\cdot 11)(x^{1+1})(y^2)=44x^2y^2$

$8x(2x^2+5x-9)=$
$8x(2x^2)+8x(5x)+8x(-9)=$
$16x^3+40x^2-72x$

$4x(5x^2-7x+8)=$
$4x(5x^2)+4x(-7x)+4x(8)=$
$20x^3-28x^2+32x$

$250^{\frac{1}{3}}=$
$\sqrt[3]{250}=\sqrt[3]{2\cdot 125}=\sqrt[3]{2\cdot 5^3}=5\sqrt[3]{2}$

$150^{\frac{1}{2}}=$
$\sqrt{150}=\sqrt{6\cdot 5^2}=5\sqrt{6}$

$63^{\frac{1}{2}}=\sqrt{63}=\sqrt{7\cdot 3^2}=3\sqrt{7}$

$(x+5)(x+3)$
$x(x)+x(3)+5(x)+5(3)=$
$x^2+3x+5x+15=x^2+8x+15$

$(x+2)(x-7)$
$x(x)+x(-7)+2(x)+2(-7)=$
$x^2-7x+2x-14=x^2-5x-14$

$(x-4)(x-9)$
$x(x)+x(-9)-4(x)-4(-9)=$
$x^2-9x-4x+36=x^2-13x+36$

⑭ Write the point-slope form and the slope-intercept form of the equation of a line. **4 points**

m = 6; (3, 8)
$y-8=6(x-3)$
$y-8=6x-18$
$y=6x-10$

m = -5; (5, -9)
$y-(-9)=-5(x-5)$
$y+9=-5x+25$
$y=-5x+16$

⑮ Solve. Express the answer as a coordinate point. **3 points**

$-3x-y-7=0$
$3x+2y+5=0$
$-3x-y=7$
$3x+2y=-5$
$y=2$
$-3x-2-7=0$
$-3x=9$
$x=-3$
$(-3, 2)$

$-3x-y-4=0$
$2x+y-2=0$
$-3x-y=4$
$2x+y=2$
$-x\ =6$
$x\ =-6$
$-3(-6)-y-4=0$
$18-y-4=0$
$y=14$
$(-6, 14)$

$-3x+y+7=0$
$4x+y-7=0$
$-3x+y=-7$
$4x+y=7$
$-7x\ =-14$
$x\ =2$
$-3(2)+y+7=0$
$-6+y+7=0$
$y=-1$
$(2, -1)$

⑯ Find the slope of the line joining the points. **3 points**

(6, 5) and (6, -3)
$m=\frac{-3-5}{6-6}=\frac{-8}{0}=$ no slope

(3, -4) and (-8, -4)
$m=\frac{-4-(-4)}{-8-3}=\frac{0}{-11}=0$

(9, -4) and (-6, 1)
$m=\frac{1-(-4)}{-6-9}=\frac{5}{-15}=-\frac{1}{3}$

⑰ Factor completely. **6 points**

$12x^2-28x+8$
$4(3x^2-7x+2)=$
$4(3x-1)(x-2)$

$2x^3-50x$
$2x(x^2-25)=$
$2x(x+5)(x-5)$

x^3+8
$a^3=x^3$ so $a=x$. $b^3=8$
so b = 2.
$(x+2)(x^2-2x+4)$

$25x^2-80x+64$
$(5x-8)^2$

$3x+12xy+20y+5$
$(3x+12xy)+(20y+5)$
$3x(1+4y)+5(4y+1)$
$(3x+5)(4y+1)$

$36x^2-5$
$(6x+\sqrt{5})(6x-\sqrt{5})$

⑱ Solve. **8 points**

$(4x-5)^2$
$16x^2-40x+25$

$(2x-5)^2$
$4x^2-20x+25$

$(15x^2-53x+42)\div(3x-7)$
$3x-7\overline{)15x^2-53x+42}$ quotient $5x-6$
$\underline{15x^2-35x}$
$-18x+42$
$\underline{-18x+42}$

$(6x^2-23x+20)\div(3x-4)$
$3x-4\overline{)6x^2-23x+20}$ quotient $2x-5$
$\underline{6x^2-8x}$
$-15x+20$
$\underline{-15x+20}$

$(3x+4)(2x^2-4x-1)$
$3x(2x^2)+3x(-4x)+3x(-1)+4(2x^2)+4(-4x)+4(-1)=$
$6x^3-12x^2-3x+8x^2-16x-4=$
$6x^3-4x^2-19x-4$

$(7x+2)(3x^2-4x-1)$
$7x(3x^2)+7x(-4x)+7x(-1)+2(3x^2)+2(-4x)+2(-1)=$
$21x^3-28x^2-7x+6x^2-8x-2=$
$21x^3-22x^2-15x-2$

$(32x-40)\div 8$
$8\overline{)32x-40}$ quotient $4x-5$
$\underline{32x}$
-40
$\underline{-40}$

$(15x^2-18x)\div 3x$
$3x\overline{)15x^2-18x}$ quotient $5x-6$
$\underline{15x^2}$
$-18x$
$\underline{-18x}$

110 points total